Mathematics for Business

TENTH EDITION

Stanley A. Salzman
American River College

Gary Clendenen
Siena College

PEARSON

Boston Columbus Indianapolis New York San Francisco Upper Saddle River
Amsterdam Cape Town Dubai London Madrid Milan Munich Paris Montreal Toronto
Delhi Mexico City Sao Paulo Sydney Hong Kong Seoul Singapore Taipei Tokyo

Editorial Director: Vernon R. Anthony
Acquisitions Editor: Sara Eilert
Development Editor: Laura Weaver
Editorial Assistant: Doug Greive
Director of Marketing: David Gesell
Senior Marketing Manager: Stacey Martinez
Senior Marketing Coordinator: Alicia Wozniak
Marketing Assistant: Les Roberts
Senior Managing Editor: JoEllen Gohr
Senior Project Manager: Steve Robb
Senior Operations Supervisor: Pat Tonneman

Creative Director: Andrea Nix
Senior Art Director: Diane Y. Ernsberger
Cover Designer: Jason Moore
Cover Image: iStockphoto©
Full Service Project Management: Haylee Schwenk, PreMediaGlobal
Composition: PreMediaGlobal
Printer/Binder: Edwards Brothers
Cover Printer: Lehigh/Phoenix Color Hagerstown
Text Font: Times LT Std 10/12

Credits and acknowledgments for content borrowed from other sources and reproduced, with permission, in this textbook appear on the appropriate page within the text.

Copyright © 2014 by Pearson Education, Inc. All rights reserved. Manufactured in the United States of America. This publication is protected by Copyright, and permission should be obtained from the publisher prior to any prohibited reproduction, storage in a retrieval system, or transmission in any form or by any means, electronic, mechanical, photocopying, recording, or likewise. To obtain permission(s) to use material from this work, please submit a written request to Pearson Education, Inc., Permissions Department, One Lake Street, Upper Saddle River, New Jersey 07458, or you may fax your request to 201-236-3290.

Many of the designations by manufacturers and sellers to distinguish their products are claimed as trademarks. Where those designations appear in this book, and the publisher was aware of a trademark claim, the designations have been printed in initial caps or all caps.

Library of Congress Cataloging-in-Publication Data

Salzman, Stanley A.
 Mathematics for business / Stanley A. Salzman, Gary Clendenen.—10th ed.
  p. cm.
 Includes index.
 ISBN 978-0-13-289835-5 (alk. paper)
 1. Business mathematics. I. Clendenen, Gary. II. Title.
 HF5691.S26 2014
 650.01'513—dc23

                    2012034677

10 9 8 7 6 5 4 3 2 1

NOTICE: This work is protected by U.S. copyright laws and is provided solely for the use of college instructors in reviewing course materials for classroom use. Dissemination or sale of this work, or any part (including on the World Wide Web), will destroy the integrity of the work and is not permitted. The work and materials from it should never be made available to students except by instructors using the accompanying text in their classes. All recipients of this work are expected to abide by these restrictions and to honor the intended pedagogical purposes and the needs of other instructors who rely on these materials.

ISBN 10: 0-13-307834-5
ISBN 13: 978-0-13-307834-3

Contents

PART 1   **Basic Mathematics**

PART 5	**Accounting and Other Applications**

Preface

New to This Edition

- Two new sections were added: Section 2.5, "Exponents and Order of Operations," and Section 4.2, "Graphing Equations Using Line Graphs."
- More emphasis was placed on the Global Financial Crisis throughout the book (in Chapter 11, for example).
- The introductory application (found on the first page of each chapter) was either rewritten or updated for almost all the chapters.
- Figures in Chapters 3, 11, 14, and 18 were modified for greater clarity.
- Sections 5.1, "Checking Accounts and Check Registers," and 5.3, "Bank Statement Reconciliation," were rewritten.
- Section 6.5, "Income Tax Withholding," was revised, and all exercises were updated.
- Section 7.3, "Personal Income Tax," was modified, and most of the exercises were updated.
- The focus company in Chapter 18 has been changed to Apple Inc., and all financial statements were changed accordingly.
- Sections 19.2 and 19.3 were updated, and many of the examples and exercises were changed.
- More than 150 examples and exercises were either updated or completely replaced.

The tenth edition of *Mathematics for Business* continues to provide solid, practical, and up-to-date coverage of those topics students must master to attain success in business today. The aim of this edition has been to put more focus on graphs, data, and analysis throughout the book. To accomplish this, the chapter on business statistics has been moved towards the front of the book and is now Chapter 4. This chapter shows students numerous graphs/tables and asks them to read/interpret that data. These skills are then reinforced throughout the rest of the chapters with numerous charts, graphs, and tables of relevant data.

The combination of increased use of graphs and tables throughout the book with the new Stop and Think feature has made the text more focused and integrated. This will give the students a better concept of how business math relates to the economic and business world around them, as well as their personal finances.

Unique to this text is coverage on topics such as payroll records and quarterly returns, inflation and the time value of money, distribution of profits in a corporation, range and standard deviation, and index numbers. It also covers retirement plans including regular and Roth IRAs.

Stop and Think features include data and related open-ended thought questions about issues relevant to students' financial lives and world. The globalization of our society is emphasized through examples and exercises that highlight foreign countries and international topics. The text also includes two Business Application Cases at the end of each chapter.

The new edition reflects the extensive business and teaching experience of the authors, as well as the suggestions of many reviewers nationwide. Providing solid, practical, and up-to-date coverage of business mathematics topics, the text begins with a brief review of basic mathematics and introduces the basic concepts in statistics. It then goes on to introduce key business topics, such as bank services, payroll, taxes, insurance, business discounts and markups, stocks and bonds, consumer loans, depreciation, and financial statements. The text is accompanied by a greatly enhanced supplements package that provides many avenues—both print and media—for students to practice and further explore the concepts discussed in the chapters. (Please see pages x to xii of this preface for full descriptions of the student and instructor supplements available.)

Features

Stop and Think   Each chapter opens with a graphic or table with data that relates to business, followed by a thought-provoking question. Applications have been chosen that will increase both student and faculty interest. For example, Chapter 4, "Business Statistics," opens with a graph showing forecasts of world population and world oil production. It demonstrates a belief held by many experts that world oil production will reach a peak and then begin to fall a few decades before world population is forecast to peak. The Stop and Think questions that follow ask students to describe possible major issues if world oil production is falling as world population continues to grow.

Enhanced Treatment of Real-World Applications   The tenth edition places a greater emphasis on real-world applications. The application problems have been updated throughout the text to be as relevant as possible to today's students. Financial statements from the giant retailer Apple Inc. are used throughout Chapter 18.

Art Program   The art program of the tenth edition includes graphs and charts that utilize actual data from a variety of recognized sources. Rendered to draw student attention while emphasizing the data itself, the graphs and charts help students see that the mathematics of business is inherent to the world around them. See pages 1, 119, and 681.

Business Application Cases   Two business application cases are found at the end of each chapter. These are slightly more involved, realistic scenarios that integrate concepts from that chapter. For example, one of the business cases at the end of Chapter 14, "Compound Interest," illustrates how a global bank makes profit based on the spread or difference in interest rates between funds borrowed and funds loaned to businesses.

Cumulative Reviews   Five Cumulative Reviews, found after Chapters 4, 8, 11, 16, and 19, help students review groups of related chapter topics and reinforce their understanding of the material. See pages 183, 352, 448, 639, and 761.

Metric System   The metric system of measurement, found in Appendix B, gives students the information needed to understand and use the metric system. See page 783.

Financial Calculator Solutions   Several financial calculator solution boxes demonstrate to the student how this tool can be used to solve problems. Financial calculators are also illustrated in section A.2 of Appendix A, which includes exercises that students may solve using the financial calculator of their choice. See pages 529, 565, and 569.

Quick Review with Chapter Terms   The end-of-chapter Quick Review feature begins with a list of key terms from the chapter and the pages on which they first appear. The Quick Review uses a two-column format (Concepts and Examples) to help students review all the main points presented in the chapter. See pages 218, 269, and 711.

Additional Features

Numerous Exercises   Mastering business mathematics requires working many exercises, so we have included more than 3,850 in the tenth edition. They range from simple drill problems to real-life application exercises that require several steps to solve. All problems have been independently checked to ensure accuracy. See pages 205, 304, and 746.

Graded Application Exercises   The application exercises in each section of this text increase in difficulty level. Each even-numbered application exercise is the same type of problem as the preceding odd-numbered exercise. This allows the student to solve an odd-numbered exercise, check the answer in the answer section of the text, and then solve the following even-numbered exercise with confidence. See pages 44, 89, and 321.

Scientific Calculator Solutions   Scientific calculators are covered in depth in section A.1 of Appendix A, and scientific calculator solution boxes are shown throughout the text. See pages 500, 541, and 547.

Supplementary Exercises   Three sets of supplementary exercises, in Chapter 3 and in Chapter 10, are designed to help students review and synthesize difficult concepts. Answers to the odd-numbered supplementary exercises are located in the back of the text. See pages 95, 102, and 413.

Writing Exercises   Designed to help students better understand and relate to the concepts within a section, these exercises, marked with ✎, require a short written answer. They often include references to specific learning objectives to help students formulate their answer. See pages 94, 233, and 496.

Pretest   A pretest for business mathematics is included in the text's introduction. This tool helps students and instructors identify individual and class strengths and weaknesses. See pages xx–xxii.

Notes   These notes provide helpful suggestions to the students and are located throughout the text. See pages 105, 124, and 168.

Glossary   A glossary of key words, located at the back of the book, provides a quick reference for the main ideas of the course.

Summary of Formulas   Appendix D provides a handy summary of commonly used information and business formulas from the book.

Student Supplements

MyMathLab®

MyMathLab® Online Course (access code required)   MyMathLab® is a text-specific, easily customizable online course that integrates interactive multimedia instruction with textbook content. MyMathLab gives instructors the tools they need to deliver all or a portion of the course online, whether students are in a lab setting or working from home.

- **Interactive homework exercises**, correlated to your textbook at the objective level, are algorithmically generated for unlimited practice and mastery. Most exercises are free-response and provide guided solutions, sample problems, and learning aids for extra help.
- **Personalized Study Plan**, generated when students complete a test or quiz, indicates which topics have been mastered and links to tutorial exercises for topics students have not mastered. Instructors can customize the available topics in the study plan to match their course concepts.
- **Multimedia learning aids**, such as video lectures, animations, and a complete multimedia textbook, help students independently improve their understanding and performance.
- **Assessment Manager** lets you assign media resources (such as a video segment or a textbook passage), homework, quizzes, and tests. If you prefer, you can create your own online homework, quizzes, and tests that are automatically graded. Select just the right mix of questions from the MyMathLab exercise bank, instructor-created custom exercises, and/or TestGen® test items.
- **Gradebook**, designed specifically for mathematics and statistics, automatically tracks students' results, lets you stay on top of student performance, and gives you control over how to calculate final grades. You can also add off-line (paper-and-pencil) grades to the gradebook.
- **MathXL® Exercise Builder** allows you to create static and algorithmic exercises for your online assignments. You can use the library of sample exercises as an easy starting point, or you can edit any course-related exercise.

■ **Pearson Tutor Center** (**www.pearsontutorservices.com**) access is available with MyMathLab. The Tutor Center is staffed by qualified math instructors who provide textbook-specific tutoring for students via toll-free phone, fax, email, and interactive Web sessions.

The new, Flash®-based MathXL Player is compatible with almost any browser (Firefox®, Safari™, or Internet Explorer®) on almost any platform (Macintosh® or Windows®). MyMathLab is powered by CourseCompass™, Pearson Education's online teaching and learning environment, and by MathXL®, our online homework, tutorial, and assessment system. MyMathLab is available to qualified adopters. For more information, visit **www.mymathlab.com** or contact your Pearson representative.

MathXL® Online Course (access code required)   MathXL® is a powerful online homework, tutorial, and assessment system that accompanies Pearson Education's textbooks in mathematics or statistics. With MathXL, instructors can:

■ Create, edit, and assign online homework and tests using algorithmically generated exercises correlated at the objective level to the textbook.
■ Create and assign their own online exercises and import TestGen tests for added flexibility.
■ Maintain records of all student work tracked in MathXL's online gradebook.

With MathXL, students can:

■ Take chapter tests in MathXL and receive personalized study plans based on their test results.
■ Use the study plan to link directly to tutorial exercises for the objectives they need to study and retest.
■ Access supplemental animations and video clips directly from selected exercises.

MathXL is available to qualified adopters. For information, visit our website at **www.mathxl.com**, or contact your Pearson representative.

MathXL® Tutorials on CD   This interactive tutorial CD-ROM provides algorithmically generated practice exercises that are correlated at the objective level to the exercises in the textbook. Every practice exercise is accompanied by an example and a guided solution designed to involve students in the solution process. Selected exercises may also include a video clip to help students visualize concepts. The software provides helpful feedback for incorrect answers and can generate printed summaries of students' progress.

Instructor Supplements

Supplements Available in Print

Annotated Instructor's Edition (AIE)   A printed AIE consists of the student edition with answers for all exercises printed directly on the pages. ISBN: 0-13-307834-5

Supplements Available for Download

Instructor's Solutions Manual (ISM)   The ISM contains worked solutions to all exercises in the student edition.

Test Generator (TestGen)   TestGen enables instructors to build, edit, print, and administer tests from a bank of questions developed to cover all test objectives. The test questions are algorithmically generated, making it easy to generate multiple versions of the same test with different numbers in the questions.

To access supplementary materials online, instructors need to request an instructor access code. Go to **www.pearsonhighered.com/irc**, where you can register for a code. Within 48 hours of registering, you will receive a confirming e-mail including an instructor access code. Once you have received your code, locate your text in the online catalog and click on the Instructor Resources button on the left side of the catalog product page. Select a supplement and a log-in page will appear. Once you have logged in, you can access instructor material for all Pearson textbooks.

Acknowledgments

We would like to thank the many users of previous editions for their insightful observations and suggestions for improving this book. We also wish to express our appreciation and thanks to the following reviewers for their contributions to this edition: James S. Cleveland, Sage College of Albany; Ken Newton, Cleveland State Community College; and Christy L. Peterson, College of DuPage.

Our appreciation also goes to Ellen Sawyer and Sandra Cottle for their careful accuracy checking of all the exercises and examples in the book and for the preparation of the Instructor's Solution Manual. We also would like to express our gratitude to our colleagues at American River College and Siena College who have helped us immeasurably with their support and encouragement.

The following individuals at Pearson had a large impact on this edition, and we are grateful for their work and professionalism: Sara Eilert, Laura Weaver, Doug Greive, and Steve Robb. Thanks are due as well to Haylee Schwenk at PreMediaGlobal for adeptly managing the production of this edition.

Stanley A. Salzman
Gary Clendenen

Index of Applications

Introduction for Students

Success in Business Mathematics

With our growing need for record keeping, establishing budgets, and understanding finance, taxation, and investment opportunities, mathematics has become a greater part of our daily lives. This text applies mathematics to daily business experience. Your success in future business courses and pursuits will be enhanced by the knowledge and skills you will learn in this course.

Studying business mathematics is different from studying subjects such as English or history. The key to success is regular practice. This should not be surprising. After all, can you learn to ski or to play a musical instrument without a lot of regular practice? The same is true for learning mathematics. Working problems nearly every day is the key to becoming successful. Here are some suggestions to help you succeed in business mathematics:

1. **Attend class regularly. Pay attention to what your instructor says, and take careful notes.** Note the problems the instructor works on the board and copy the complete solutions. Keep these notes separate from your homework to avoid confusion.

2. **Don't hesitate to ask questions in class.** Asking questions is not a sign of weakness, but of strength. There are always other students with the same question who are too shy to ask.

3. **Read your text carefully.** Many students read only enough to get by, usually only the examples. Reading the complete section will help you to be successful with the homework problems. As you read the text, work the example problems and check the answers. This will test your understanding of what you have read. Pay special attention to highlighted statements and those labeled "Note."

4. **Before you start on your homework assignment, rework the problems the instructor worked in class.** This will reinforce what you have learned. Many students say, "I understand it perfectly when you do it, but I get stuck when I try to work the problem myself."

5. **Do your homework assignment only after reading the text and reviewing your notes from class.** Estimate the answer before you begin working the problem in the text. Check your work before looking at the answers in the back of the book. If you get a problem wrong and are unable to see why, mark that problem and ask your instructor.

6. **Work as neatly as you can using a *pencil*, and organize your work carefully.** Write your symbols clearly, and make sure the problems are clearly separated from each other.

7. **After you have completed a homework assignment, look over the text again.** Try to decide what the main ideas are in the lesson. Often they are clearly highlighted or boxed in the text.

8. **Determine whether tutoring is available and know how to get help when needed.** Use the instructor's office hours to contact the instructor for suggestions and direction and call the Pearson Tutor Center (see page xi for details).

9. **Keep any quizzes and tests that are returned to you for studying for future tests and the final exam.** These quizzes and tests indicate what your instructor considers most important. Be sure to correct any test problems that you missed. Write all quiz and test scores on the front page of your notebook.

10. **Don't worry if you do not understand a new topic right away.** As you read more about it and work through the problems, you will gain understanding. No one understands each topic completely right from the start.

Pretest in Business Mathematics

This pretest measures your business mathematics skills at the beginning of the course. The solutions to each of these problems are found as examples throughout the book. The answers are on page xxii.

(page 9) 1. Convert to an improper fraction: $25\frac{3}{4}$

(page 10) 2. Convert to a mixed number: $\frac{23}{3}$

(page 12) 3. Find the least common denominator of the fractions $\frac{5}{12}$, $\frac{7}{18}$, and $\frac{11}{20}$.

(page 14) 4. Mixed numbers—add: $34\frac{1}{2} + 23\frac{3}{4} + 34\frac{1}{2} + 23\frac{3}{4}$

(page 15) 5. Common fractions—subtract: $\frac{17}{18} - \frac{20}{27}$

(page 15) 6. Mixed numbers—subtract: $36\frac{2}{9}$
$$-27\frac{5}{6}$$

(page 21) 7. Mixed numbers—multiply: $5\frac{5}{8} \times 4\frac{1}{6}$

(page 22) 8. Common fractions—divide: $\frac{25}{36} \div \frac{15}{18}$

(page 24) 9. Convert the decimal 0.028 to a fraction.

(page 39) 10. Solve $y + 12.3 = 20.5$ for y.

(page 42) 11. Solve $5r - 2 = 2(r + 5)$ for r.

(page 54) 12. Solve for T in the formula $M = P(1 + RT)$

(page 60) 13. Find x in the proportion: $\frac{4}{9} = \frac{36}{x}$

(page 78) 14. Express as a percent: 0.7

(page 80) 15. Express as a decimal: 142%

(page 85) 16. Solve for part: 1.2% of 180 is _____.

(page 91) 17. Solve for base: 135 is 15% of _____.

(page 92) 18. The 5% sales tax collected by Famous Footwear was $780. What was the amount of total sales?

(page 105) 19. The price of a home sold by real estate agent Tricia Marinaro this year is $187,000, which is 10% more than last year's value. Find the value of the home last year.

(page 105) 20. After Fleetfeet deducted 10% from the price of a pair of running shoes, Craig Bleyer paid $135. What was the original price of the shoes?

(page 146) 21. The diameter of a part coming out of a machining process is measured regularly. The diameters vary some, as shown in the frequency table. Find the (a) mean, (b) median, and (c) mode.

Diameter (inches)	Frequency
0.720–0.729	3
0.730–0.739	12
0.740–0.749	8
0.750–0.759	9
0.760–0.769	2

(page 266) 22. Suppose that during a certain quarter Leslie's Pool Supplies has collected $2765.42 from its employees for FICA tax, $638.17 for Medicare tax, and $3572.86 in federal withholding tax. Compute the total amount due to the Internal Revenue Service from Leslie's Pool Supplies.

(page 284) 23. Find the taxes on each of the following pieces of property. Assessed valuations and tax rates are given.
   a $58,975; 8.4%
   b $875,400; $7.82 per $100
   c $129,600; $64.21 per $1000
   d $221,750; 94 mills

(page 292) 24. Chris Kelly is single and has no dependents. He had an adjusted gross income of $26,735 last year, with deductions of $1352 for other taxes, $4118 for mortgage interest, and $317 for charity. Find his taxable income and his income tax.

(page 318) 25. Jo O'Neill owns an industrial building valued at $760,000. Her fire insurance policy (with an 80% coinsurance clause) has a face value of $570,000. The building suffers a fire loss of $144,000. Find the amount of the loss that the insurance company will pay and the amount that O'Neill must pay.

(page 359) 26. Oaks Hardware is offered a series discount of 20/10 on a Porter-Cable cordless drill with a list price of $150. Find the net cost after the series discount.

(page 371) 27. An invoice received by Bass Bait Shop for $840 is dated July 1 and offers terms of 2/10, n/30. If the invoice is paid on July 8 and the shipping and insurance charges, which were "FOB shipping point," are $18.70, find the total amount due.

(page 393) 28. The owner of Rose Fine Wines buys several cases of a popular wine bottled in Spain at a wholesale cost of $15 per bottle. In order to bring new customers into the store, the manager widely advertises a special promotion on this particular wine for $18.75 per bottle, or for considerably less than it can be purchased at competing stores. Find the percent of markup based on cost.

(page 408) 29. An athletic shoe manufacturer makes a walking shoe at a cost of $33.60 per pair. Based on past experience, 10% of the shoes will be defective and must be sold as irregulars for $48 per pair. If the manufacturer produces 1000 pairs of the shoes and desires a markup of 100% on cost, find the selling price per pair.

(page 434) 30. Olympic Sports and Leisure made the following purchases of the Explorer External Frame backpack during the year.

Beginning inventory	20 backpacks at $70
January	50 backpacks at $80
March	100 backpacks at $90
July	60 backpacks at $85
October	40 backpacks at $75

At the end of the year there are 75 backpacks in inventory. Use the weighted average method to find the inventory value.

(page 455) 31. After a large down payment, Jessica Warren borrowed $9000 from her credit union to purchase a previously owned Toyota Camry. Find the interest rate given that the loan was for 9 months and the interest was $540.

(page 498) 32. On February 27, the Andrews Kia dealership receives a 150-day simple interest note with a face value of $3500 at 8% interest per year. On March 27, the firm discounts the note at the bank. Find the proceeds if the discount rate is 12%. (Use ordinary or banker's interest.)

(page 528) 33. Jonathan Simons invests $2500 in an investment paying 4% compounded semiannually for 5 years. (a) Estimate the future value using simple interest. Then find (b) the compound amount, (c) the compound interest, and (d) the amount by which simple interest calculations underestimate the compound interest that is earned.

(page 581) 34. Arctic Drilling Inc. borrowed money by selling bonds with a maturity value in 15 years totaling $10,000,000. Find the amount of each payment into a sinking fund needed to build the required amount in 15 years to pay off the bonds. Assume 9% compounded annually.

(page 622) 35. Bob Jones used a $75,000 loan for 25 years at 8% to purchase a summer cabin. Annual insurance and taxes on the property are $654 and $1329, respectively. Find the monthly payment.

(page 656) 36. City Saturn purchased an electronic smog analyzer for $9000. Using the sum-of-the-years'-digits method of depreciation, find the first and second years' depreciation if the analyzer has an estimated life of 4 years and no salvage value.

(page 648) 37. A boat dock with a life of 10 years is installed on April 12 at a cost of $72,000. If the double-declining-balance method is used, find the depreciation for the first partial year and the next full year.

(page 689) 38. Write each of the following items as a percent of net sales.

Gross sales	$209,000	Salaries and wages	$11,000
Returns	$9000	Rent	$6000
Cost of goods sold	$145,000	Advertising	$11,000

(page 722) 39. Due to excessive debt, Alamo Energy paid no dividend last year. The company has done much better this year and the board of directors has set aside $175,000 for the payment of dividends. The company has outstanding 12,500 shares of cumulative preferred stock having par value of $50, with an 8% dividend. The company also has 40,000 shares of common stock. What dividend will be paid to the owners of each type of stock?

(page 722) 40. Laura Cameron, Jay Davis, and Donna Friedman opened a tool rental business. Cameron contributed $250,000 to the opening of the business, which will be operated by Davis and Friedman. The partners agree that Cameron will first receive a 10% return on her investment before any further division of profits. Additional profits will be divided in the ratio 1:2:2. Find the amount that each partner would receive from a profit of $75,000.

Answers: 1. $\frac{103}{4}$ **2.** $7\frac{2}{3}$ **3.** 180 **4.** $116\frac{1}{2}$ **5.** $\frac{11}{54}$ **6.** $8\frac{7}{18}$ **7.** $23\frac{7}{16}$ **8.** $\frac{5}{6}$ **9.** $\frac{7}{250}$ **10.** 8.2 **11.** 4 **12.** $T = \frac{M - P}{PR}$ **13.** 81 **14.** 70% **15.** 1.42 **16.** 2.160 **17.** 900 **18.** $15,600 **19.** $170,000 **20.** $150 **21. (a)** 0.743 **(b)** 0.7445 **(c)** 0.7345 **22.** $10,380.04 **23. (a)** $4953.90 **(b)** $68,456.28 **(c)** $8321.62 **(d)** $20,844.50 **24.** $17,898; $2334.70 **25.** $135,000; $9000 **26.** $108 **27.** $841.90 **28.** 25% **29.** $69.33 **30.** $6249.75 **31.** 8% **32.** $3469.59 **33. (a)** $3000 **(b)** $3047.49 **(c)** $547.49 **(d)** $47.49 **34.** $340,588.80 **35.** $744.25 **36.** $3600; $2700 **37.** $10,800; $12,240 **38.** 104.5%; 4.5%; 72.5%; 5.5%; 3%; 5.5% **39.** $8; $1.88 **40.** $35,000; $20,000; $20,000

javier brosch / Fotolia.com

Problem Solving and Operations with Fractions

Businesses use mathematics every day to prepare payrolls, find interest due on loans, determine markups, or calculate the amount of taxes owed. Mathematics is so important that every high school and college requires students to take one or more math courses. Math is an important part of your education.

In turn, education is extremely important today. For example, Figure 1.1 shows both the unemployment rate[1] and the median income by level of education for 2010, a year with high unemployment. The figure shows that those with higher levels of education are far less likely to be unemployed and also that they earn considerably more than those with less education. This has been true for many years now—education pays!

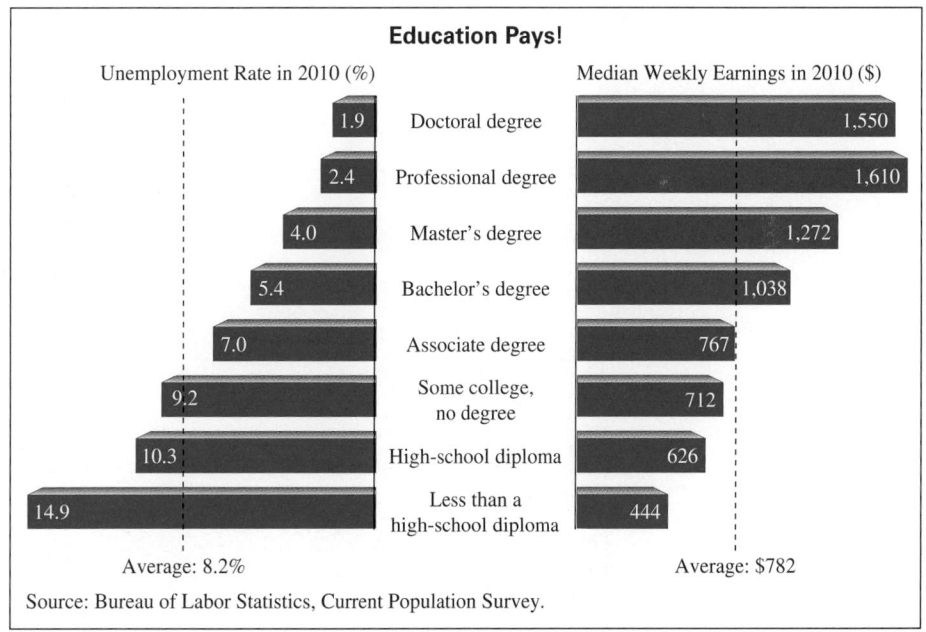

Figure 1.1 Unemployment rate and median income by level of education.

▶ STOP&THINK

Look carefully at Figure 1.1. Use the data in the figure to estimate the total earnings over 10 years for someone with a bachelor's degree as compared to someone with some college, no degree. Also, compare the difference in the unemployment rate between someone with a master's degree versus someone with less than a high-school diploma. What level of education should you work toward?

[1]Unemployment rate refers to the percent of people who do not have a job.

It is important for you to understand the fundamentals of mathematics so that you can solve more advanced problems in business mathematics. This chapter reviews problem solving and fractions. **Chapter 2** looks briefly at basic equations and formulas, **Chapter 3** discusses the very important topic of percents, and **Chapter 4** introduces basic concepts of statistics. The remaining chapters apply these math skills to various problems in business.

1.1   Problem Solving

OBJECTIVES

1 *Identify indicator words in application problems.*

2 *List the four steps for solving application problems.*

3 *Learn to estimate answers.*

It is important to carefully read and fully understand a problem or situation before doing any math. The suggestions given in this section will help you work the many word problems you will encounter both in this course and when working for an employer.

Objective

1 *Identify Indicator Words in Application Problems.* Look for **indicators** in the application problem—words that indicate the necessary operations—addition, subtraction, multiplication, or division. Some of these words appear below.

Addition	Subtraction	Multiplication	Division	Equals
plus	less	product	divided by	is
more	subtract	double	divided into	the same as
more than	subtracted from	triple	quotient	equals
added to	difference	times	goes into	equal to
increased by	less than	of	divide	yields
sum	fewer	twice	divided equally	results in
total	decreased by	twice as much	per	are
sum of	loss of			was
increase of	minus			were
gain of	take away			will be

NOTE   The word *and* does not indicate addition and does not appear as an indicator word above. Notice how the *and* shows the *location* of an operation sign.

The sum of 6 *and* 2 is 6 + 2.
The difference of 6 *and* 2 is 6 − 2.
The product of 6 *and* 2 is 6 × 2.
The quotient of 6 *and* 2 is 6 ÷ 2.

Objective

2 *List the Four Steps for Solving Application Problems.* Students sometimes make the mistake of trying to solve a problem before understanding it. Believe it or not, this actually wastes your time and often results in more mistakes. The first step in solving a problem is to try to **fully understand**. Look carefully at the following steps and try to use them on every problem you do.

Solving Application Problems

> **Step 1** Read the problem carefully. You may need to read it more than once to fully understand. Know what the problem is asking before you try to solve it. Clearly identify the unknown and keep it in mind.
> **Step 2** Develop a plan to work the problem. Indicator words may help.
> **Step 3** Estimate a reasonable answer using rounding.
> **Step 4** Solve the problem.
> **Step 5** Check to see if the answer is reasonable.

Each of these steps is very important. We suggest you do not take shortcuts—go through all of the steps every time. Getting in the habit of going through all of the steps will be a benefit to you later in life since employers will pay you more if you can solve more complex problems.

Objective

3   *Learn to Estimate Answers.* It is particularly important to estimate a reasonable answer and then check to see if the final answer is, in fact, reasonable. Doing so will allow you to catch your own mistakes before going on to something else.

What is a *reasonable answer*? Read the problem and try to determine the approximate size of the answer. Should the answer be part of a dollar, a few dollars, hundreds, thousands, or even millions of dollars? For example, if a problem asks for the cost of a man's shirt, would an answer of $30 be reasonable? $1000? $0.65? $65?

EXAMPLE **1**   **Applying Division**

At a group yard sale the total sales were $3584.20. The money was divided equally among the boys soccer club, the girls soccer club, the boys softball team, and the girls softball team. How much did each group receive?

Solution

STEP 1 Total sales of $3584.20 are to be divided equally among four different groups. The unknown is the amount that goes to each of the four groups.
STEP 2 Plan: Divide $3584.20 by 4.
STEP 3 Estimate by rounding $3584.20 to $3600. Dividing $3600 by 4 suggests that each group will receive about $900.
STEP 4 Find the answer by dividing.

$$
\begin{array}{r}
896.05 \\
4\overline{)3584.20} \\
\underline{32} \\
38 \\
\underline{36} \\
24 \\
\underline{24} \\
2 \\
0 \\
\underline{}20 \\
20 \\
\underline{}0
\end{array}
$$

STEP 5 The answer of $896.05 is close to $900, so our answer seems reasonable. Check it as follows.

$$
\begin{array}{r}
\$896.05 \quad \text{Amount received} \\
\times 4 \quad \text{Number of groups} \\
\hline
\$3584.20 \quad \text{Answer checks}
\end{array}
$$

EXAMPLE 2 **Applying Addition**

Mandy Crandall works part-time at Starbucks, where her hours vary by day. Her daily earnings for the 5 days of one week were $62.35, $75.40, $88.50, $48.30, and $55.80. Find her total earnings.

Solution

STEP 1 The problem gives daily earnings for 5 days and asks for total earnings for the week.

STEP 2 Plan: Add the five daily earnings.

STEP 3 Glancing at the daily earnings shows an average daily earnings of about $70 per day. Multiply $70 per day $\times$ 5 days to get an estimate of $350 for the week.

STEP 4 Solve by adding exact numbers.

$$
\begin{array}{r}
\$\ 62.35 \\
75.40 \\
88.50 \\
48.30 \\
\underline{55.80} \\
\$330.35
\end{array}
$$
   Total earnings for the week

STEP 5 The answer of $330.35 is relatively close to the estimate of $350. It is also a reasonable answer. An answer of, say, $1303.50 for the week would not be reasonable for one week's earnings by a part-time worker at a Starbucks.

EXAMPLE 3 **Applying Subtraction**

The number of students enrolled in Chabot College this year is 1012 fewer than the number enrolled last year. Enrollment last year was 21,382. Find the enrollment this year.

Solution

STEP 1 Last year's enrollment of 21,382 decreased by 1012 this year. The unknown is this year's enrollment.

STEP 2 Plan: The indicator word *fewer* suggests that subtraction should be used to find the number of students enrolled this year. Subtract the decrease in enrollment from last year's enrollment.

STEP 3 Estimate as follows.

$$
\begin{array}{r}
21,000 \\
-\ \ 1,000 \\
\hline
20,000
\end{array}
$$
   21,000   Estimate of last year's enrollment
   − 1,000   Estimate of decrease in enrollment
   20,000   Estimate of number enrolled this year

STEP 4 Find exact answer.

$$
\begin{array}{r}
21,382 \\
-\ \ 1,012 \\
\hline
20,370
\end{array}
$$
   20,370   Current enrollment

STEP 5 The exact number of 20,370 students is close to the estimate of 20,000. Check by adding.

$$
\begin{array}{r}
20,370 \\
\underline{1,012} \\
21,382
\end{array}
$$
   20,370   Current enrollment
   1,012   Decrease in enrollment compared to last year
   21,382   Enrollment last year

EXAMPLE **4** **Solving a Problem Needing Two Steps**

The owner of a small apartment house rents the seven apartments for $975 each. After paying $5920 in expenses, including a mortgage payment, in one month, find the amount that remains.

Solution

STEP 1 The unknown is the amount remaining after expenses for the month.
STEP 2 Plan: First find total rents for the month. Then subtract the expenses.
STEP 3 Estimate by assuming that each renter pays $1000 per month and that total expenses for the month are $6000.

$$7 \text{ apartments} \times \$1000 = \$7000 \text{ total rent}$$
$$\$7000 \text{ total rent} - \$6000 \text{ in expenses} = \$1000 \text{ remaining}$$

STEP 4 Solve for exact answer.

$975		$6825	Total rent
× 7		− 5920	Expenses
$6825	Total rent	$ 905	Remaining after paying expenses

STEP 5 The exact answer of $905 is close to the estimate of $1000. An answer, for example, of $4200 would not have been reasonable since total rents are only $6825.

We suggest that you try to use all five problem-solving steps every time you work a problem. It will make you a much better problem solver in the long run. Firms want individuals who are able to think and solve problems.

NOTE Recall the Order of Operations. Operations must be done in the following order.

1. Contents of parentheses
2. Exponents and square roots
3. Multiplication and division from left to right
4. Addition and subtraction from left to right

1.1	**Exercises**

Solve the following application problems.

1. **COMPETITIVE CYCLIST TRAINING**   During a week of training, Beth Andrews rode her bike 80 miles on Monday, 75 miles on Tuesday, 135 miles on Wednesday, 40 miles on Thursday, and 52 miles on Friday. What is the total number of miles she rode in the 5-day period?   382 miles

2. **COFFEE SALES**   During a recent week, Starbucks Coffee sold 325 pounds of Estate Java coffee, 75 pounds of Encanta Blend coffee, 137 pounds of Ethiopia Sidamo coffee, 495 pounds of Starbucks House-Blend Decaf coffee and 105 pounds of New Guinea Peaberry coffee. Find the total number of pounds of these coffees sold.   1137 pounds

3. **CRUISE SHIP TRAVEL**   A cruise ship has 1815 passengers. When in port at Grand Cayman, 1348 passengers go ashore for the day while the others remain on the ship. How many passengers remain on the ship?   467 passengers

4. **ATM CASH**   The amount of cash in an ATM ranges from $15,000 in small machines to $250,000 in large bank machines. How much more money is there in the large machines than in the small machines? $235,000

5. **GREENHOUSE GASES**   Estimates indicate that about 2.5 billion tons of the greenhouse gas carbon dioxide are emitted each year in the United States by utility companies

that generate electricity. If scientists estimate that no more than 0.8 billion tons can be emitted in the United States annually to keep global warming at bay, find the required reduction in carbon dioxide emissions.   1.7 billion tons

6. **WORLD POPULATION**   One scientist estimated that the rate at which world population was growing had fallen from 397,012 people per day to 364,383 people per day in 10 years. Find the decrease in the rate at which world population is growing. 32,629 people per day

7. **AUTOMOBILE WEIGHT**   A car weighs 2425 pounds. If its 582-pound engine is removed and replaced with a 634-pound engine, how much will the car weigh after the engine change?   2477 pounds

8. **PRESCHOOL MANAGER**   Tiffany Connolly has $2324 in her preschool operating account. After spending $734 from this account, the class parents raise $568 in a rummage sale. Find the balance in the account after depositing the money from the rummage sale. $2158

9. **BUSINESS ENTERPRISES**   There are 24 million business enterprises in the United States. Only 7000 of these businesses are large businesses having 500 or more employees, while the rest are small and midsize businesses. Find the number of small and midsize businesses.   23,993,000 small and midsize businesses

10. **WEIGHING FREIGHT**   A truck weighs 9250 pounds when empty. After being loaded with firewood, the truck weighs 21,375 pounds. What is the weight of the firewood?   12,125 pounds

11. **WORLD WAR II VETERANS**   World War II veterans, part of what is now called "the greatest generation," are dying at the rate of 900 each day. How many World War II veterans are projected to die in the next year of 365 days?   328,500 veterans

12. **FINANCIAL CRISIS**   To avoid bankruptcy during a recent financial crisis, a global bank offered a $30,000 bonus to each of 12,600 employees if they would take an early retirement. Of course, few of the employees are likely to take early retirement, but what would be the cost if everyone did take early retirement? $378,000,000

13. **HOTEL ROOM COSTS**   In a recent study of hotel/casinos, the cost per night at Harrah's Reno was $89, while the cost at Harrah's Lake Tahoe was $239 per night. Find the amount saved on a 5-night stay at Harrah's Reno instead of staying at Harrah's Lake Tahoe. $750

14. **LUXURY HOTELS**   The most expensive hotel room in a recent study was the Ritz-Carlton at $625 per night, while the least expensive was Motel 6 at $75 per night. Find the amount saved on a 4-night stay at Motel 6 over the cost of staying at the Ritz-Carlton. $2200

15. **PHYSICALLY IMPAIRED**   The Enabling Supply House purchases 6 wheelchairs at $1256 each and 15 speech compression recorder-players at $895 each. Find the total cost of the equipment. $20,961

16. **OFFICE COMPUTERS**   A regional office of Krispy Kreme Doughnuts purchased 23 laptop computers at a special price of $479 each and 8 printers costing $247 each. Find the total cost. $12,993

17. **THEATER RENOVATION**   A theater owner is remodeling and wants to provide enough seating for 1250 people. The main floor has 30 rows of 25 seats in each row. If the balcony has 25 rows, how many seats must be in each row of the balcony to satisfy the owner's seating requirements?   20 seats

18. **PACKING AND SHIPPING**   Nancy Hart makes 24 grapevine wreaths per week to sell to gift shops. She works 30 weeks a year and packages 6 wreaths per box. If she ships equal quantities to each of five shops, find the number of boxes each shop will receive.   24 boxes

19. **MALL-SHOPPING FACTS**   A recent study showed that the average trip to the mall lasts 4.4 hours, which is longer than a football game. How many hours would be needed for eight of these trips to the mall?   35.2 hours

20. **VENDING MACHINE**   The Selective End cold-drink vending machine is priced at $2679.99 at Costco. Find the cost of 14 of these machines. $37,519.86

21. **STOCKHOLDER LOSSES**   Bagoda Imports announced a $38 million loss, or $0.58 a share. Find the number of shares of stock in the company. Round to the nearest tenth of a million.   65.5 million shares

22. **SHARES OF STOCK**   Money Store officials said that they expect to post a loss of $42 million, or $0.65 a share. Find the number of shares of stock in the company. Round to the nearest million.   65 million shares (rounded)

23. **OLYMPIC GOLD COINS**   If a 5-dollar Olympic gold coin weighs 8.359 grams, find the number of coins that can be produced from 221 grams of gold, assuming no waste. Round down to the nearest whole number.   26 coins

24. **MEDICINE DOSAGE**   Each dosage of a medication contains 1.62 units of a certain ingredient. Find the number of dosages that can be made from 57.13 units of the ingredient. Round down to the nearest whole number.   35 dosages

25. **U.S. PAPER MONEY**   The thickness of one piece of paper money is 0.0043 inch.

    (a) If you had a pile of 100 bills, how high would it be?   0.43 inch

    (b) How high would a pile of 1000 bills be?   4.3 inches

26. Use the information from Exercise 25.

    (a) Find the number of bills in a pile that is 43 inches high.   10,000 bills

    (b) How much money would you have if the pile was all $20 bills? $200,000

27. **MANAGERIAL EARNINGS**   A parts department manager earns $3250 each month working a 42-hour week. Assume 1 month is 4.3 weeks and find

    (a) the number of hours worked each month, and   180.6 hours

    (b) the manager's hourly earnings. Round to the nearest cent. $18.00

28. **MANAGER AT TARGET**   An assistant manager at Target earns $3539.76 after taxes each month for working a 48-hour week. Assume 1 month is 4.3 weeks and find

    (a) the number of hours worked each month, and   206.4 hours

    (b) the manager's hourly after-tax earnings. $17.15

29. **REAL ESTATE FEES**   Robert Gonzalez recently sold his home for $246,500. He paid a real estate commission of 0.06 times the price of the house. What was the amount of the commission? $14,790

30. **BASEBOARD TRIM**   Kathy West bought 6.5 yards of baseboard trim to complete her kitchen remodeling. If she paid $8.70 per yard for the trim, what was her total cost? $56.55

1.2   Addition and Subtraction of Fractions

OBJECTIVES

1 *Recognize types of fractions.*

2 *Convert mixed numbers to improper fractions.*

3 *Write fractions in lowest terms.*

4 *Use the rules for divisibility.*

5 *Add or subtract like fractions.*

6 *Find the least common denominator.*

7 *Add unlike fractions.*

8 *Add mixed numbers.*

9 *Subtract unlike fractions.*

10 *Subtract mixed numbers.*

This section looks at **fractions**—numbers, like decimals, that can be used to represent parts of a whole. Fractions and decimals are two ways of representing the same quantity. Fractions are used in business and in our personal lives. For example, one restaurant uses the following recipe to make a cake that is a favorite of many of its customers. Notice that the recipe contains several fractions.

Chocolate Decadence Cake

2 cups unsalted butter, room temperature
$1\frac{1}{4}$ pounds bittersweet chocolate, chopped
10 eggs, separated and room temperature
2 tablespoons pure vanilla extract
$1\frac{3}{4}$ cups granulated sugar
$\frac{1}{4}$ teaspoon salt
$\frac{1}{4}$ cup cocoa powder

© Pete Saloutos/fotolia

A **fraction** represents parts of a whole. Fractions are written as one number over another, with a line between the two numbers, as in the following.

$$\frac{5}{8} \quad \frac{1}{4} \quad \frac{9}{7} \quad \frac{13}{10} \quad \begin{array}{l} \rightarrow \text{ Numerator} \\ \rightarrow \text{ Denominator} \end{array}$$

The number above the line is called the **numerator**, and the number below the line is called the **denominator**. In the fraction $\frac{2}{3}$, for example, the numerator is 2 and the denominator is 3. The denominator tells the number of equal parts into which the whole is divided, and the numerator tells how many of these parts we are talking about. For example, $\frac{2}{3}$ of an apple is "2 parts out of an apple cut into 3 equal parts," as shown in Figure 1.2.

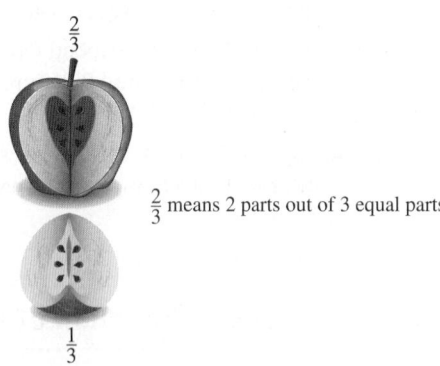

$\frac{2}{3}$ means 2 parts out of 3 equal parts

Figure 1.2

Objective

1 *Recognize Types of Fractions.* A **proper fraction**, or common fraction, is one in which the numerator is *smaller than* the denominator. An **improper fraction** is one in which the numerator is *greater than or equal to* the denonimator.

Examples						
Proper fractions	$\frac{1}{4}$	$\frac{3}{5}$	$\frac{5}{8}$	$\frac{1}{15}$	$\frac{19}{20}$	$\frac{71}{100}$
Improper fractions	$\frac{5}{2}$	$\frac{7}{3}$	$\frac{5}{5}$	$\frac{9}{5}$	$\frac{53}{45}$	$\frac{80}{62}$

A proper fraction has a value that is less than 1. An improper fraction has a value that is greater than or equal to 1. To write a whole number as a fraction, place the whole number over 1, as in the following examples.

$$7 = \frac{7}{1} \qquad 12 = \frac{12}{1} \qquad 55 = \frac{55}{1}$$

Objective

2 *Convert Mixed Numbers to Improper Fractions.* The sum of a whole number and a fraction is called a **mixed number**. Example of mixed numbers include $2\frac{1}{4}$, $5\frac{3}{4}$, and $12\frac{3}{8}$. The mixed number $2\frac{1}{4}$ is read as "two and one-fourth." It is a shortcut way of writing $2 + \frac{1}{4}$. Similarly, $5\frac{3}{4}$ is the same as $5 + \frac{3}{4}$, etc.

To Convert a Mixed Number to an Improper Fraction

Step 1 To find the numerator of the improper fraction, multiply the whole number by the denominator of the fraction and add to the numerator.

Step 2 Keep the same denominator.

$$\text{For example: } 4\frac{5}{8} = \frac{(4 \times 8) + 5}{8} = \frac{37}{8}$$

EXAMPLE 1 **Converting Mixed Numbers to Improper Fractions**

An opening in the kitchen cabinet is for a microwave oven that is $25\frac{3}{4}$ inches wide and $16\frac{1}{2}$ inches high. Convert both mixed numbers to improper fractions.

(a) $25\frac{3}{4}$ (b) $16\frac{1}{2}$

Solution

(a) First multiply the whole number (25) by the denominator (4), and then add the numerator (3). This gives $(25 \times 4) + 3 = 100 + 3 = 103$. The parentheses are used to show that 25 and 4 are multiplied first, before adding.

$$25\frac{3}{4} = \frac{(25 \times 4) + 3}{4} = \frac{103}{4}$$

(b) $16\frac{1}{2} = \frac{(16 \times 2) + 1}{2} = \frac{33}{2}$

Convert an improper fraction to a mixed number by dividing the numerator of the improper fraction by the denominator. The quotient is the whole number part of the mixed number, and the remainder is used as the numerator of the fraction part. The denominator stays the same.

EXAMPLE **2**   **Converting Improper Fractions to Mixed Numbers**

Convert $\frac{23}{3}$ to a mixed number.

Solution

Divide 23 by 3.

$$
\begin{array}{r}
7 \\
3\overline{)23} \\
\underline{21} \\
2
\end{array}
$$

The whole-number part is the quotient 7. The remainder 2 is used as the numerator of the fraction part. Keep 3 as the denominator.

$$\frac{23}{3} = 7\frac{4}{5}$$

NOTE   A proper fraction has a value that is smaller than 1. An improper fraction has a value that is 1 or greater.

Objective

3   *Write Fractions in Lowest Terms.* A fraction is said to be in **lowest terms** if no number other than 1 divides evenly (with no remainder) into both the numerator and denominator. Effectively, a fraction in lowest terms has been written in the simplest form possible for a fraction. For example, the fractions $\frac{1}{4}$, $\frac{1}{2}$, and $\frac{5}{6}$ are in lowest terms. However, the fraction $\frac{15}{25}$ is not in lowest terms since both 15 and 25 can be divided by 5. Write $\frac{15}{25}$ in lowest terms by dividing both the numerator and denominator by 5.

$$\frac{15}{25} = \frac{15 \div 5}{25 \div 5} = \frac{3}{5}$$
$$\underset{\text{Divide by 5.}}{\uparrow}$$

EXAMPLE **3**   **Writing Fractions in Lowest Terms**

Write the following fractions in lowest terms.

(a) $\frac{15}{40}$ **(b)** $\frac{33}{39}$

Solution   Look for the largest number that divides both numerator and denominator without remainder.

(a) Both 15 and 40 can be divided by 5.

$$\frac{15}{40} = \frac{15 \div 5}{40 \div 5} = \frac{3}{8}$$

(b) Divide both numerator and denominator by 3.

$$\frac{33}{39} = \frac{33 \div 3}{39 \div 3} = \frac{11}{13}$$

Objective

4   *Use the Rules for Divisibility.* Deciding which numbers will divide into another number without remainder is sometimes difficult. The following **rules for divisibility** may help.

Rules for Divisibility

A number can be divided evenly by:

2	if the last digit is 0, 2, 4, 6, or 8
3	if the sum of the digits is divisible by 3
4	if the last two digits form a number divisible by 4
5	if the last digit is 0 or 5
6	if the number is even and the sum of the digits is divisible by 3
8	if the last three digits form a number divisible by 8
9	if the sum of the digits is divisible by 9
10	if the last digit is 0

EXAMPLE **4** **Using the Divisibility Rules**

Determine whether the following statements are true.

(a) 3,746,892 is divisible by 4.   **(b)** 15,974,802 is divisible by 9.

Solution

(a) The number 3,746,892 is divisible by 4, since the last two digits form a number divisible by 4.

$$3, 746, 892$$

           — **92** is divisible by 4.

(b) See if 15,974,802 is divisible by 9 by adding the digits of the number.

$$1 + 5 + 9 + 7 + 4 + 8 + 0 + 2 = 36$$

           — **36** is divisible by 9.

Since 36 is divisible by 9, the given number is divisible by 9.

NOTE The rules for divisibility only help to identify which single-digit numbers divide evenly into a larger number. The division must actually be done in order to find the number of times one number divides into another.

Objective

5 *Add or Subtract Like Fractions.* Fractions with the same denominator are called **like fractions**. Such fractions have a **common denominator**. For example, $\frac{3}{4}$ and $\frac{1}{4}$ are like fractions and 4 is the common denominator, but $\frac{4}{7}$ and $\frac{4}{9}$ are not like fractions. Add or subtract like fractions by adding or subtracting the numerators and then placing the result over the common denominator. The answer can then be written in lowest terms, if necessary.

EXAMPLE **5** **Adding and Subtracting Like Fractions**

Add or subtract the following fractions.

(a) $\dfrac{3}{4} + \dfrac{1}{4} + \dfrac{5}{4}$ **(b)** $\dfrac{13}{25} - \dfrac{7}{25}$

Solution The fractions in both parts of this example are like fractions. Add or subtract the numerators and place the result over the common denominator. Write as a mixed number in lowest terms, as necessary.

Add numerators.

(a) $\dfrac{3}{4} + \dfrac{1}{4} + \dfrac{5}{4} = \dfrac{3 + 1 + 5}{4} = \dfrac{9}{4} = 2\dfrac{1}{4}$ Write the answer as a mixed number.

Use the common denominator.

(b) $\dfrac{13}{25} - \dfrac{7}{25} = \dfrac{13 - 7}{25} = \dfrac{6}{25}$

Objective

6 *Find the Least Common Denominator.* Fractions with different denominators are called **unlike fractions**. Add or subtract unlike fractions by first converting them to like fractions with a common denominator.

The **least common denominator (LCD)** for two or more fractions is the smallest whole number that can be divided, without remainder, by all the denominators of the fractions. For example, the least common denominator of the fractions $\frac{3}{4}$, $\frac{5}{6}$, and $\frac{1}{2}$ is 12, since 12 is the smallest number that can be divided without remainder by 4, 6, and 2.

In the cabinet specifications from American Landmark Cabinetry (shown below), the fractions in the Shelf-End Base drawing are **like fractions**, $23\frac{3}{16}$, $10\frac{9}{16}$, and $11\frac{3}{16}$, since 16 is the denominator of each fraction. However, in the drawing of the Shelf-End Peninsula Base, the fractions are **unlike fractions**, $22\frac{7}{16}$, $11\frac{3}{32}$, and $11\frac{5}{8}$, since the denominators differ.

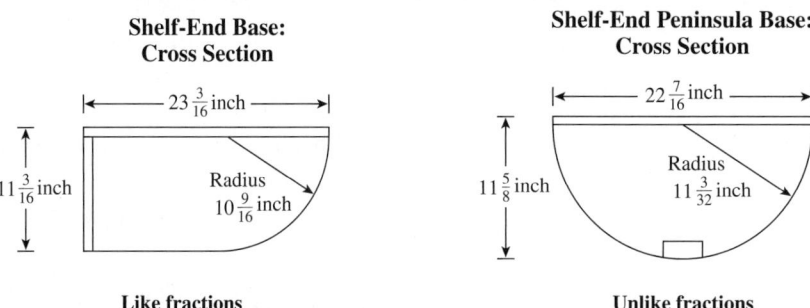

There are two methods of finding the least common denominator: the *inspection method* and the *method of prime numbers.*

Inspection. Check to see if the least common denominator can be found by inspection. For example, the least common denominator of $\frac{1}{3}$ and $\frac{1}{4}$ is 12, since 12 is the smallest number which 3 and 4 both divide into with remainder zero. This method works best when the denominators involved are small.

Method of prime numbers. If you cannot find the least common denominator by inspection, use the method of prime numbers, as shown in the next example.

A **prime number** is a number that can be divided without remainder only by itself and by 1. Prime numbers are 2, 3, 5, 7, 11, 13, 17, and so on.

NOTE All prime numbers other than 2 are odd numbers. However, not all odd numbers are prime numbers. For example, 27 is the product of 3 and 9, and it is not a prime number.

EXAMPLE **6** **Finding the Least Common Denominator**

Use the method of prime numbers to find the least common denominator of the fractions $\frac{5}{12}$, $\frac{7}{18}$, and $\frac{11}{20}$.

Solution

First write down the three denominators.

$$12 \quad 18 \quad 20$$

Begin by trying to divide the three denominators by the smallest prime number, 2. Write each quotient directly above the given denominator. (This way of writing the division process is just a handy way of writing the separate problems $2\overline{)12}$, $2\overline{)18}$, and $2\overline{)20}$.)

$$\begin{array}{r} 6 \quad\; 9 \quad 10 \\ \hline 2\overline{)12 \quad 18 \quad 20} \end{array}$$

Two of the new quotients, 6 and 10, can still be divided by 2, so perform the division again. Since 9 cannot be divided by 2, just bring up the 9.

$$
\begin{array}{c}
\qquad\qquad\downarrow \\
\begin{array}{r r r}
3 & 9 & 5 \\
\end{array} \quad \text{Just bring 9 up.} \\
2\overline{)\;6 \quad\; 9 \quad 10\;} \\
2\overline{)12 \quad 18 \quad 20\;}
\end{array}
$$

None of the new quotients in the top row can be divided by 2, so try the next prime number, 3. The number 9 can be divided twice by 3, as shown below on the left.

$$
\begin{array}{cc}
\begin{array}{r r r}
 & & \\
1 & 1 & 5 \\
\end{array} &
\begin{array}{r r r}
1 & 1 & 1 \\
\end{array} \\
\begin{array}{r}
3\overline{)\;1 \quad 3 \quad 5\;} \\
3\overline{)\;3 \quad 9 \quad 5\;} \\
2\overline{)\;6 \quad 9 \quad 10\;} \\
2\overline{)12 \quad 18 \quad 20\;}
\end{array} &
\begin{array}{r}
5\overline{)\;1 \quad 1 \quad 5\;} \\
3\overline{)\;1 \quad 3 \quad 5\;} \\
3\overline{)\;3 \quad 9 \quad 5\;} \\
2\overline{)\;6 \quad 9 \quad 10\;} \\
2\overline{)12 \quad 18 \quad 20\;}
\end{array}
\end{array}
$$

Since none of the new quotients in the top row can be divided by 3, try the next prime number, 5. The number 5 can be used only once. Now that the top row contains only 1s, find the least common denominator by multiplying the prime numbers in the left column.

$$2 \times 2 \times 3 \times 3 \times 5 = 180$$

The least common denominator for $\frac{5}{12}$, $\frac{7}{18}$, and $\frac{11}{20}$ is 180. ∎

NOTE It is **not necessary** to start dividing by the smallest prime number, as shown in Example 6. In fact, no matter which prime number you start with, you still get the same least common denominator.

Objective

7   *Add Unlike Fractions.* Add unlike fractions by rewriting the fractions with a common denominator. Since Example 6 shows that 180 is the least common denominator for $\frac{5}{12}$, $\frac{7}{18}$, and $\frac{11}{20}$, these three fractions can be added if each fraction is first written with a denominator of 180.

STEP 1 $\dfrac{5}{12} = \dfrac{}{180} \qquad \dfrac{7}{18} = \dfrac{}{180} \qquad \dfrac{11}{20} = \dfrac{}{180}$

Rewrite these fractions with a common denominator by first dividing the common denominator by the denominator of the original fractions.

$$180 \div 12 = 15 \qquad 180 \div 18 = 10 \qquad 180 \div 20 = 9$$

STEP 2   Next, multiply each quotient by the original numerator.

$$15 \times 5 = 75 \qquad 10 \times 7 = 70 \qquad 9 \times 11 = 99$$

STEP 3   Now, rewrite the fractions.

$$\dfrac{5}{12} = \dfrac{75}{180} \qquad \dfrac{7}{18} = \dfrac{70}{180} \qquad \dfrac{11}{20} = \dfrac{99}{180}$$

STEP 4   Add the fractions.

$$\frac{5}{12} + \frac{7}{18} + \frac{11}{20} = \frac{75}{180} + \frac{70}{180} + \frac{99}{180} = \frac{75 + 70 + 99}{180}$$

$$= \frac{244}{180} = 1\frac{64}{180} = 1\frac{16}{45} \quad \begin{array}{l}\text{Write the answer as a mixed number}\\ \text{with the fraction in lowest terms.}\end{array}$$

EXAMPLE **7** **Adding Unlike Fractions**

Add the following fractions.

(a) $\dfrac{3}{4} + \dfrac{1}{2} + \dfrac{5}{8}$ **(b)** $\dfrac{9}{10} + \dfrac{4}{5} + \dfrac{3}{8}$

Solution

(a) Inspection shows that the least common denominator is 8. Rewrite the fractions so they each have a denominator of 8. Then add.

$$\frac{3}{4} + \frac{1}{2} + \frac{5}{8} = \frac{6}{8} + \frac{4}{8} + \frac{5}{8} = \frac{6 + 4 + 5}{8} = \frac{15}{8} = 1\frac{7}{8}$$

(b) The method of prime numbers shows that the least common denominator is 40. Rewrite the fractions so they each have a denominator of 40. Then add.

$$\frac{9}{10} + \frac{4}{5} + \frac{3}{8} = \frac{36}{40} + \frac{32}{40} + \frac{15}{40} = \frac{36 + 32 + 15}{40} = \frac{83}{40} = 2\frac{3}{40}$$

 Scientific Calculator Approach

All calculator solutions are shown using a scientific calculator. The calculator solution to Example 7(b) uses the fraction key on the scientific calculator.

$$9\ \boxed{a\%c}\ 10\ \boxed{+}\ 4\ \boxed{a\%c}\ 5\ \boxed{+}\ 3\ \boxed{a\%c}\ 8\ \boxed{=}\ 2\frac{3}{40}$$

Objective

8   *Add Mixed Numbers.* Add two mixed numbers by first adding the fraction parts. Then add the whole number parts and combine the two sums.

EXAMPLE **8** **Adding Mixed Numbers**

A rubber gasket must extend around all four edges (perimeter) of the dishwasher panel shown below before it is installed. Find the length of gasket material needed.

Dishwasher door panel $\frac{3}{4}$ inch d $23\frac{3}{4}$ inch h $34\frac{1}{2}$ inch w

Add $34\frac{1}{2}$ inches and $23\frac{3}{4}$ inches and $34\frac{1}{2}$ inches and $23\frac{3}{4}$ inches.

Solution

$$34\frac{1}{2} = 34\frac{2}{4}$$

$$23\frac{3}{4} = 23\frac{3}{4}$$

$$34\frac{1}{2} = 34\frac{2}{4}$$

$$+\ 23\frac{3}{4} = 23\frac{3}{4} \qquad \nearrow\ \frac{10}{4} = 2\frac{2}{4}$$

$$114\frac{10}{4} = 114 + 2\frac{2}{4} = 116\frac{2}{4} = 116\frac{1}{2}\ \text{inches}$$

> **NOTE** When adding mixed numbers, first add the fraction parts and then add the whole number parts. Then combine the two answers.

Objective

9 *Subtract Unlike Fractions.* If the fractions to be subtracted have different denominators, first find the least common denominator. For example, to subtract $\frac{1}{3}$ from $\frac{5}{8}$, first find the least common denominator, 24. Now write each fraction with a denominator of 24 and subtract.

$$\frac{5}{8} - \frac{1}{3} = \frac{15}{24} - \frac{8}{24} = \frac{15 - 8}{24} = \frac{7}{24}$$

EXAMPLE 9 Subtracting Fractions

Subtract the following fractions.

(a) $\dfrac{3}{4} - \dfrac{5}{9}$ **(b)** $\dfrac{17}{18} - \dfrac{20}{27}$

Solution

Find the common denominator and then subtract.

(a) $\dfrac{3}{4} - \dfrac{5}{9} = \dfrac{27}{36} - \dfrac{20}{36} = \dfrac{7}{36}$ **(b)** $\dfrac{17}{18} - \dfrac{20}{27} = \dfrac{51}{54} - \dfrac{40}{54} = \dfrac{11}{54}$

Objective

10 *Subtract Mixed Numbers.* To subtract two mixed numbers, first, change the mixed numbers, if necessary, so that the fraction parts have a common denominator. Then subtract the fraction parts and the whole number parts separately. For example, subtract $3\frac{1}{12}$ from $8\frac{5}{8}$ by first finding that the least common denominator of the two fractions is 24. Then rewrite the problem as shown.

$$8\frac{5}{8} - 3\frac{1}{12}$$

Use 24 as a common denominator.

$$8\frac{15}{24} - 3\frac{2}{24}$$

Now subtract the fraction parts, and subtract the whole number parts.

$$\begin{array}{r} 8\frac{15}{24} \\ -\,3\frac{2}{24} \\ \hline 5\frac{13}{24} \end{array}$$

Subtract fractions.
Subtract whole numbers.

The following example shows how to subtract when **borrowing** is needed.

EXAMPLE 10 Subtracting with Borrowing

Subtract $27\frac{5}{6}$ from $36\frac{2}{9}$.

Solution

Start by rewriting the problem with a common denominator.

$$\begin{array}{r} 36\frac{2}{9} = 36\frac{4}{18} \\ -\,27\frac{5}{6} = 27\frac{15}{18} \end{array}$$

The fraction $\frac{15}{18}$ cannot be subtracted from $\frac{4}{18}$, since it is larger than $\frac{4}{18}$. First, borrow 1 from 36.

$$36\frac{4}{18} = 35 + 1 + \frac{4}{18}$$

$$= 35 + \frac{18}{18} + \frac{4}{18} \quad 1 = \frac{18}{18}$$

$$= 35\frac{22}{18}$$

$$35\frac{22}{18} = \left(36\frac{4}{18}\right)$$

$$-27\frac{15}{18}$$

$$8\frac{7}{18}$$

Check by adding $8\frac{7}{18}$ and $27\frac{5}{6}$. The answer is $36\frac{2}{9}$, so no mistakes were made.

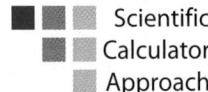

Scientific
Calculator
Approach

The calculator solution to Example 10 uses the fraction key.

$$36 \; \boxed{a^b/_c} \; 2 \; \boxed{a^b/_c} \; 9 \; \boxed{-} \; 27 \; \boxed{a^b/_c} \; 5 \; \boxed{a^b/_c} \; 6 \; \boxed{=} \; 8\frac{7}{18}$$

1.2	**Exercises**

Convert the following mixed numbers to improper fractions.

1. $1\frac{3}{8}$ $\frac{11}{8}$ **2.** $2\frac{4}{5}$ $\frac{14}{5}$ **3.** $4\frac{1}{4}$ $\frac{17}{4}$ **4.** $2\frac{8}{11}$ $\frac{30}{11}$

5. $22\frac{7}{8}$ $\frac{183}{8}$ **6.** $15\frac{2}{3}$ $\frac{47}{3}$ **7.** $12\frac{5}{8}$ $\frac{101}{8}$ **8.** $17\frac{5}{8}$ $\frac{141}{8}$

Write the following fractions in lowest terms. Use the divisibility rules as needed.

9. $\frac{8}{16}$ $\frac{1}{2}$ **10.** $\frac{15}{20}$ $\frac{3}{4}$ **11.** $\frac{40}{75}$ $\frac{8}{15}$ **12.** $\frac{36}{42}$ $\frac{6}{7}$

13. $\frac{25}{40}$ $\frac{5}{8}$ **14.** $\frac{27}{45}$ $\frac{3}{5}$ **15.** $\frac{120}{150}$ $\frac{4}{5}$ **16.** $\frac{24}{64}$ $\frac{3}{8}$

17. $\frac{132}{144}$ $\frac{11}{12}$ **18.** $\frac{40}{96}$ $\frac{5}{12}$ **19.** $\frac{96}{180}$ $\frac{8}{15}$ **20.** $\frac{32}{128}$ $\frac{1}{4}$

Convert the following improper fractions to mixed numbers and then write them in lowest terms.

21. $\frac{7}{2}$ $3\frac{1}{2}$ **22.** $\frac{9}{5}$ $1\frac{4}{5}$ **23.** $\frac{76}{20}$ $3\frac{4}{5}$ **24.** $\frac{42}{15}$ $2\frac{4}{5}$

25. $\frac{14}{11}$ $1\frac{3}{11}$ **26.** $\frac{55}{8}$ $6\frac{7}{8}$ **27.** $\frac{21}{15}$ $1\frac{2}{5}$ **28.** $\frac{85}{52}$ $1\frac{33}{52}$

29. $\frac{124}{64}$ $1\frac{15}{16}$ **30.** $\frac{190}{35}$ $5\frac{3}{7}$ **31.** $\frac{81}{32}$ $2\frac{17}{32}$ **32.** $\frac{360}{64}$ $5\frac{5}{8}$

 33. Your classmate asks you how to write a mixed number as an improper fraction. Write a couple of sentences explaining how this is done. (See Objective 2.)

34. Explain in a sentence or two how to write an improper fraction as a mixed number. (See Objective 2.)

Add each of the following and reduce to lowest terms.

35. $\dfrac{2}{5} + \dfrac{1}{5}$ $\dfrac{3}{5}$

36. $\dfrac{2}{9} + \dfrac{4}{9}$ $\dfrac{2}{3}$

37. $\dfrac{7}{10} + \dfrac{3}{20}$ $\dfrac{17}{20}$

38. $\dfrac{3}{8} + \dfrac{1}{4}$ $\dfrac{5}{8}$

39. $\dfrac{7}{12} + \dfrac{8}{15}$ $1\dfrac{7}{60}$

40. $\dfrac{5}{8} + \dfrac{7}{12}$ $1\dfrac{5}{24}$

41. $\dfrac{9}{11} + \dfrac{1}{22}$ $\dfrac{19}{22}$

42. $\dfrac{5}{6} + \dfrac{7}{9}$ $1\dfrac{11}{18}$

43. $\dfrac{3}{4} + \dfrac{5}{9} + \dfrac{1}{3}$ $1\dfrac{23}{36}$

44. $\dfrac{1}{4} + \dfrac{1}{8} + \dfrac{1}{12}$ $\dfrac{11}{24}$

45. $\dfrac{5}{6} + \dfrac{3}{4} + \dfrac{5}{8}$ $2\dfrac{5}{24}$

46. $\dfrac{7}{10} + \dfrac{8}{15} + \dfrac{5}{6}$ $2\dfrac{1}{15}$

47. $\begin{array}{r} 82\dfrac{3}{5} \\ + 15\dfrac{1}{5} \\ \hline 97\dfrac{4}{5} \end{array}$

48. $\begin{array}{r} 25\dfrac{2}{7} \\ + 14\dfrac{3}{7} \\ \hline 39\dfrac{5}{7} \end{array}$

49. $\begin{array}{r} 51\dfrac{1}{4} \\ + 29\dfrac{1}{2} \\ \hline 80\dfrac{3}{4} \end{array}$

50. $\begin{array}{r} 38\dfrac{5}{6} \\ 29\dfrac{1}{3} \\ + 47\dfrac{1}{2} \\ \hline 115\dfrac{2}{3} \end{array}$

51. $\begin{array}{r} 32\dfrac{3}{4} \\ 6\dfrac{1}{3} \\ + 14\dfrac{5}{8} \\ \hline \end{array}$ $53\dfrac{17}{24}$

52. $\begin{array}{r} 16\dfrac{7}{10} \\ 26\dfrac{1}{5} \\ + 8\dfrac{3}{8} \\ \hline \end{array}$ $51\dfrac{11}{40}$

53. $\begin{array}{r} 89\dfrac{5}{9} \\ 10\dfrac{1}{3} \\ + 87\dfrac{1}{9} \\ \hline \end{array}$ 187

54. $\begin{array}{r} 74\dfrac{1}{5} \\ 58\dfrac{3}{7} \\ + 21\dfrac{3}{10} \\ \hline \end{array}$ $153\dfrac{13}{14}$

Subtract each of the following and reduce to lowest terms.

55. $\dfrac{7}{8} - \dfrac{3}{8}$ $\dfrac{1}{2}$

56. $\dfrac{11}{12} - \dfrac{5}{12}$ $\dfrac{1}{2}$

57. $\dfrac{2}{3} - \dfrac{1}{6}$ $\dfrac{1}{2}$

58. $\dfrac{7}{8} - \dfrac{1}{2}$ $\dfrac{3}{8}$

59. $\dfrac{5}{12} - \dfrac{1}{16}$ $\dfrac{17}{48}$

60. $\dfrac{5}{6} - \dfrac{7}{9}$ $\dfrac{1}{18}$

61. $\dfrac{3}{4} - \dfrac{5}{12}$ $\dfrac{1}{3}$

62. $\dfrac{5}{7} - \dfrac{1}{3}$ $\dfrac{8}{21}$

63. $\begin{array}{r} 16\dfrac{3}{4} \\ -12\dfrac{3}{8} \\ \hline \end{array}$ $4\dfrac{3}{8}$

64. $\begin{array}{r} 25\dfrac{13}{24} \\ -18\dfrac{5}{12} \\ \hline \end{array}$ $7\dfrac{1}{8}$

65. $\begin{array}{r} 9\dfrac{7}{8} \\ -6\dfrac{5}{12} \\ \hline \end{array}$ $3\dfrac{11}{24}$

66. $\begin{array}{r} 24\dfrac{5}{6} \\ -18\dfrac{5}{9} \\ \hline \end{array}$ $6\dfrac{5}{18}$

67. $\begin{array}{r} 71\dfrac{3}{8} \\ -62\dfrac{1}{3} \\ \hline \end{array}$ $9\dfrac{1}{24}$

68. $\begin{array}{r} 19\dfrac{5}{6} \\ -12\dfrac{3}{4} \\ \hline \end{array}$ $7\dfrac{1}{12}$

69. $\begin{array}{r} 19 \\ -12\dfrac{3}{4} \\ \hline \end{array}$ $6\dfrac{1}{4}$

70. $\begin{array}{r} 374 \\ -211\dfrac{5}{6} \\ \hline \end{array}$ $162\dfrac{1}{6}$

 71. Prime numbers are used to find the least common denominator. Give the definition of a prime number in your own words. (See Objective 6.)

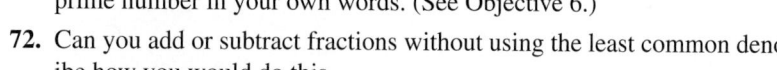 **72.** Can you add or subtract fractions without using the least common denominator? Describe how you would do this.

73. Where are fractions used in everyday life? Think in terms of business applications, hobbies, and vacations. Give three examples.

 74. When subtracting mixed numbers, explain when you need to borrow. Use an example to explain how to borrow.

Solve the following application problems.

75. CABINET INSTALLATION When installing cabinets, Kate Morgan must be certain that the proper type and size of mounting screw is used. Find the total length of the screw. $\frac{31}{40}$ inch

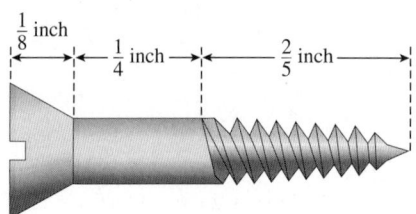

76. COMPUTER ASSEMBLY When installing a printer cable to a computer, Ann Kuick must be certain that the proper type and size of mounting hardware is used. Find the total length of the bolt shown. $\frac{47}{60}$ inch

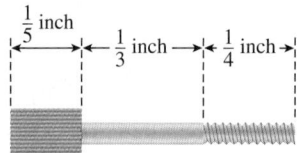

77. WETLANDS RESERVE A wetlands reserve has four sides, which measure $1\frac{7}{8}$ miles, $\frac{1}{2}$ mile, $1\frac{2}{3}$ miles, and $\frac{1}{3}$ mile. What is the total distance around the wetlands reserve? $4\frac{3}{8}$ miles

78. MEASURING BRASS TRIM To complete a custom accessory order for a customer, Ruth Berry of Home Depot must find the number of inches of brass trim needed to go around the four sides of the lamp base plate shown below. Find the length of brass trim needed. 30 inches

79. CABINET INSTALLATION Find the diameter of the hole in the mounting bracket pictured below. $\frac{3}{16}$ inch

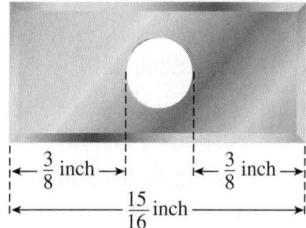

80. HYDRAULIC FLUID A hydraulic jack contains $\frac{7}{8}$ liter of hydraulic fluid. A cracked seal resulted in a loss of $\frac{1}{6}$ liter of fluid in the morning and another $\frac{1}{3}$ liter in the afternoon. Find the amount of fluid remaining. $\frac{3}{8}$ liter

81. **HIGHWAY DRIVING** On a recent vacation to Canada, Hernando Ramirez drove for $5\frac{1}{2}$ hours on the first day, $6\frac{1}{4}$ hours on the second day, $3\frac{3}{4}$ hours on the third day, and 7 hours on the fourth day. How many hours did he drive altogether? $22\frac{1}{2}$ hours

82. **WHOLESALE PRODUCE SALES** Last month, Lim's Wholesale Vegetable Market sold $3\frac{1}{4}$ tons of broccoli, $2\frac{3}{8}$ tons of spinach, $7\frac{1}{2}$ tons of corn, and $1\frac{5}{16}$ tons of turnips. Find the total number of tons of these vegetables sold by the firm last month. $14\frac{7}{16}$ tons

83. **DELIVERING CONCRETE** Chuck Stone has $8\frac{7}{8}$ cubic yards of concrete in a truck. If he unloads $2\frac{1}{2}$ cubic yards at the first stop, 3 cubic yards at the second stop, and $1\frac{3}{4}$ cubic yards at the third stop, how much concrete remains in the truck? $1\frac{5}{8}$ cubic yards

84. **TAILORED CLOTHING** Marv Levenson bought 15 yards of Italian silk fabric. He made two tops with $3\frac{3}{4}$ yards of the material, a suit for his wife with $4\frac{1}{8}$ yards, and a jacket with $3\frac{7}{8}$ yards. Find the number of yards of material remaining. $3\frac{1}{4}$ yards

85. **ORANGES** One week, sales of oranges at four different Price Chopper grocery stores were $4\frac{1}{2}$ cases, $5\frac{1}{4}$ cases, $3\frac{3}{4}$ cases, and $6\frac{1}{3}$ cases. Find the total number of cases sold. $19\frac{5}{6}$ cases

86. **PART-TIME WORK** Andrea Abriani, a college student, works part-time at Panera Bread. She worked $3\frac{3}{8}$ hours on Monday, $5\frac{1}{2}$ hours on Tuesday, $4\frac{3}{4}$ hours on Wednesday, $3\frac{1}{4}$ hours on Thursday, and 6 hours on Friday. How many hours did she work altogether? $22\frac{7}{8}$ hours

87. **WORK WEEK** Julie Davis worked 40 hours during one week. She worked $8\frac{1}{4}$ hours on Monday, $6\frac{1}{6}$ hours on Tuesday, $7\frac{2}{3}$ hours on Wednesday, and $8\frac{3}{4}$ hours on Thursday. How many hours did she work on Friday? $9\frac{1}{6}$ hours

88. **LEADED GLASS FRAMING** A craftsperson must attach a lead strip around all four sides of a leaded glass window before it is installed in a local church. The window measures $34\frac{1}{2}$ by $23\frac{3}{4}$ inches. Find the length of lead stripping needed.

$23\frac{3}{4}$ inch

$116\frac{1}{2}$ inches

$34\frac{1}{2}$ inch

89. **PARKING LOT FENCING** Three sides of a parking lot are $108\frac{1}{4}$ feet, $162\frac{3}{8}$ feet, and $143\frac{1}{2}$ feet. If the distance around the lot is $518\frac{3}{4}$ feet, find the length of the fourth side. $104\frac{5}{8}$ feet

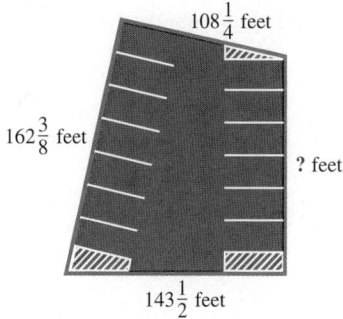

$108\frac{1}{4}$ feet

$162\frac{3}{8}$ feet

? feet

$143\frac{1}{2}$ feet

90. **SECURITY FENCING** The exercise yard at the correction center has four sides and is enclosed with $527\frac{1}{24}$ feet of security fencing around it. If three sides of the yard measure $107\frac{2}{3}$ feet, $150\frac{3}{4}$ feet, and $138\frac{5}{8}$ feet, find the length of the fourth side. 130 feet

1.3	**Multiplication and Division of Fractions**

OBJECTIVES

1 *Multiply fractions.*

2 *Divide fractions.*

3 *Convert decimals to fractions.*

4 *Round decimals.*

5 *Convert fractions to decimals.*

6 *Know common decimal equivalents.*

Objective

1 *Multiply Fractions.* Multiply two fractions by first multiplying the numerators to form a new numerator and then multiplying the denominators to form a new denominator. Write the answer in lowest terms. For example, multiply $\frac{2}{3}$ and $\frac{5}{8}$.

Multiply numerators.

$$\frac{2}{3} \times \frac{5}{8} = \frac{2 \times 5}{3 \times 8} = \frac{10}{24} = \frac{5}{12} \quad \text{(in lowest terms)}$$

Multiply denominators.

This problem can be simplified by **cancellation**, a modification of the method of writing fractions in lowest terms. If a number divides evenly into a numerator and a denominator without remainder, then divide (cancel).

$$\frac{\overset{1}{\cancel{2}}}{3} \times \frac{5}{\underset{4}{\cancel{8}}} = \frac{1 \times 5}{3 \times 4} = \frac{5}{12} \quad \text{Divide 2 into both 2 and 8.}$$

> **NOTE** It is not necessary to use a common denominator when multiplying or dividing fractions.

EXAMPLE 1   **Multiplying Common Fractions**

Multiply the following fractions.

(a) $\dfrac{6}{11} \times \dfrac{7}{8}$ (b) $\dfrac{35}{12} \times \dfrac{32}{25}$

Solution

Use cancellation in both of these problems.

(a) $\dfrac{\overset{3}{\cancel{6}}}{11} \times \dfrac{7}{\underset{4}{\cancel{8}}} = \dfrac{3 \times 7}{11 \times 4} = \dfrac{21}{44}$ 2 was divided into both 6 and 8.

(b) $\dfrac{\overset{7}{\cancel{35}}}{\underset{3}{\cancel{12}}} \times \dfrac{\overset{8}{\cancel{32}}}{\underset{5}{\cancel{25}}} = \dfrac{7 \times 8}{3 \times 5} = \dfrac{56}{15} = 3\dfrac{11}{15}$ 4 was divided into both 12 and 32 while 5 was divided into both 35 and 25.

> **NOTE** In order to cancel, the numerator and denominator must both be evenly divisible without remainder by the same number.

To multiply mixed numbers, first change the mixed numbers to improper fractions and cancel; then multiply. For example, multiply $6\frac{1}{4}$ and $2\frac{2}{3}$.

First change to improper fractions.

$$6\frac{1}{4} \times 2\frac{2}{3} = \frac{25}{4} \times \frac{8}{3} = \frac{25}{\overset{}{4}_{1}} \times \frac{\overset{2}{8}}{3} = \frac{25 \times 2}{\underbrace{1 \times 3}} = \frac{50}{3} = 16\frac{2}{3}$$

Multiply.

Cancel.

EXAMPLE 2 Multiplying Mixed Numbers

Multiply the following.

(a) $5\frac{5}{8} \times 4\frac{1}{6}$ **(b)** $1\frac{3}{5} \times 3\frac{1}{3} \times 1\frac{3}{4}$

Solution

(a) $\frac{\overset{15}{\cancel{45}}}{8} \times \frac{25}{\underset{2}{\cancel{6}}} = \frac{15 \times 25}{8 \times 2} = \frac{375}{16} = 23\frac{7}{16}$

(b) $\frac{\overset{2}{\cancel{8}}}{\underset{1}{\cancel{5}}} \times \frac{\overset{2}{\cancel{10}}}{3} \times \frac{7}{\underset{1}{\cancel{4}}} = \frac{2 \times 2 \times 7}{1 \times 3 \times 1} = \frac{28}{3} = 9\frac{1}{3}$

 Scientific Calculator Approach

The calculator solution to Example 2(b) uses the fraction key.

$1 \; \boxed{a^b/_c} \; 3 \; \boxed{a^b/_c} \; 5 \; \boxed{\times} \; 3 \; \boxed{a^b/_c} \; 1 \; \boxed{a^b/_c} \; 3 \; \boxed{\times} \; 1 \; \boxed{a^b/_c} \; 3 \; \boxed{a^b/_c} \; 4 \; \boxed{=} \quad 9\frac{1}{3}$

Multiply by a whole number by first writing the whole number as a fraction with 1 in the denominator.

$$3\frac{3}{4} \times 16 = 3\frac{3}{4} \times \frac{16}{1} \quad \text{Whole number over 1}$$

$$= \frac{15}{4} \times \frac{16}{1} \quad \text{Write } 3\frac{3}{4} \text{ as a fraction.}$$

$$= \frac{15}{\underset{1}{\cancel{4}}} \times \frac{\overset{4}{\cancel{16}}}{1} = 15 \times 4 = 60$$

NOTE Mixed numbers must always be changed to *improper fractions* before multiplying. When multiplying by mixed numbers, do not multiply whole numbers by whole numbers and fractions by fractions.

Objective

2 *Divide Fractions.* Divide two fractions by inverting the divisor and then multiplying. A fraction is inverted by exchanging the numerator and denominator.

NOTE It is not necessary to use a common denominator when dividing fractions.

EXAMPLE **3** **Dividing Common Fractions**

Divide.

(a) $\dfrac{25}{36} \div \dfrac{15}{18}$ (b) $\dfrac{21}{8} \div \dfrac{14}{16}$

Solution

Invert the second fraction and then multiply.

(a) $\dfrac{25}{36} \div \dfrac{15}{18} = \dfrac{\overset{5}{\cancel{25}}}{\underset{2}{\cancel{36}}} \times \dfrac{\overset{1}{\cancel{18}}}{\underset{3}{\cancel{15}}} = \dfrac{5 \times 1}{2 \times 3} = \dfrac{5}{6}$ (b) $\dfrac{21}{8} \div \dfrac{14}{16} = \dfrac{\overset{3}{\cancel{21}}}{\underset{1}{\cancel{8}}} \times \dfrac{\overset{\overset{1}{\cancel{2}}}{\cancel{16}}}{\underset{\underset{1}{\cancel{2}}}{\cancel{14}}} = \dfrac{3 \times 1}{1 \times 1} = 3$

Invert fraction.

> **NOTE** When dividing by a fraction, the second fraction (divisor) is inverted. Cancellation is done *only after inverting*.

Divide mixed numbers by first changing all mixed numbers to improper fractions, as follows.

$$3\dfrac{5}{9} \div 2\dfrac{2}{5} = \dfrac{32}{9} \div \dfrac{12}{5} = \dfrac{\overset{8}{\cancel{32}}}{9} \times \dfrac{5}{\underset{3}{\cancel{12}}} = \dfrac{8 \times 5}{9 \times 3} = \dfrac{40}{27} = 1\dfrac{13}{27}$$

To divide a mixed number by a whole number, first write the whole number as a fraction over a denominator of 1. Then, proceed as if dividing fractions.

$$2\dfrac{2}{5} \div 3 = \dfrac{12}{5} \div \dfrac{3}{1} = \dfrac{\overset{4}{\cancel{12}}}{5} \times \dfrac{1}{\underset{1}{\cancel{3}}} = \dfrac{4 \times 1}{5 \times 1} = \dfrac{4}{5}$$

After opening her bakery, Jacquelene Dlat taste tested various cookie recipes with her customers. The following recipe was a customer favorite and is easy to follow using the proper measuring cups and spoons. Sometimes she needs to double or triple the recipe or perhaps, baking a small order, she needs to cut the recipe in half. To double the recipe, multiply each ingredient by 2. To triple the recipe, multiply by 3. To halve the recipe, divide by 2.

Chocolate/Oat-Chip Cookies

1 cup (2 sticks) margarine or butter, softened	$1\frac{3}{4}$ cups all-purpose flour
$1\frac{1}{4}$ cups firmly packed brown sugar	1 teaspoon baking soda
$\frac{1}{2}$ cup granulated sugar	$\frac{1}{2}$ teaspoon salt (optional)
2 eggs	$2\frac{1}{2}$ cups uncooked oats
2 tablespoons milk	One 12-ounce package (2 cups) semisweet chocolate morsels
2 teaspoons vanilla	1 cup coarsely chopped nuts (optional)

Heat oven to 375°F. **Beat** margarine and sugars until creamy.
Add eggs, milk, and vanilla; beat well.
Add combined flour, baking soda, and salt, mix well. **Stir** in oats, chocolate morsels, and nuts; mix well.
Drop by rounded measuring tablespoonfuls onto ungreased cookie sheet.
Bake 9 to 10 minutes for a chewy cookie or 12 to 13 minutes for a crisp cookie.
Cool 1 minute on cookie sheet; remove to wire rack. Cool completely.
MAKES ABOUT 5 DOZEN

EXAMPLE 4 **Multiplying a Whole Number by a Mixed Number**

(a) Find the amount of uncooked oats needed if the preceding recipe for chocolate/oat-chip cookies is doubled (multiplied by 2).

(b) How many cups of all-purpose flour are needed when 12 times the recipe is needed?

Solution

Change mixed numbers to improper fractions, use cancellation, and then multiply.

(a) $2\frac{1}{2} \times 2 = \frac{5}{\overset{}{\underset{1}{2}}} \times \frac{\overset{1}{2}}{1} = \frac{5 \times 1}{1 \times 1} = \frac{5}{1} = 5$ cups

(b) $1\frac{3}{4} \times 12 = \frac{7}{\overset{}{\underset{1}{4}}} \times \frac{\overset{3}{12}}{1} = \frac{7 \times 3}{1 \times 1} = \frac{5}{1} = 21$ cups

Objective

3 *Convert Decimals to Fractions.* A **decimal number** is really a fraction with a denominator that is a power of 10, such as 10, 100, or 1000. The digits written to the right of the decimal point have place values as shown in Figure 1.3.

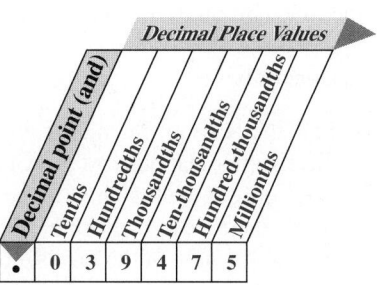

Figure 1.3

Convert a decimal to a fraction by thinking of the decimal as being written in words. For example, think of 0.47 as "forty-seven hundredths." Then write this in fraction form.

$$0.47 = \frac{47}{100}$$

In the same way, 0.3, read as "three tenths," is written in fraction form as follows:

$$0.3 = \frac{3}{10}$$

Also, 0.963, read as "nine hundred sixty-three thousandths," is written

$$\frac{963}{1000}$$

NOTE To read a number, use the word *and* for the decimal point. For example, the number 2.71 is read as "two and seventy-one hundredths." The mixed number form, $2\frac{71}{100}$ is read exactly the same.

EXAMPLE 5 **Converting Decimals to Fractions**

Convert the following decimals to fractions.

(a) 0.75 **(b)** 0.028

Solution

(a) 0.75 is read as "seventy-five hundredths."

$$0.75 = \frac{75}{100} = \frac{3}{4}$$

Here, $\frac{75}{100}$ is written in lowest terms as $\frac{3}{4}$.

(b) 0.028 is read as "twenty-eight thousandths," and the resulting fraction is written in lowest terms.

$$0.028 = \frac{28}{1000} = \frac{7}{250}$$

Objective

4 *Round Decimals.* It is important to be able to **round decimals**. For example, the 7-Eleven store sells two small candy bars for $0.79, but you want to buy only one candy bar. The price of one bar is $0.79 ÷ 2, which is $0.395. Since you cannot pay part of a cent, the store rounds the price to $0.40 for one bar.

Use the following steps for rounding decimals.

Rounding Decimals

Step 1 Find the place to which the rounding is being done. Draw a vertical line immediately after that place to show that you are deleting the digits to the right.

Step 2 Look only at the first digit to the right of your cutoff line. If the first digit is **5 or more**, increase by 1 the digit in the place to which you are rounding. If the first digit to the right of the line is **4 or less**, do not change the digit in the place to which you are rounding.

Step 3 **Drop** all digits to the right of the place to which you have rounded.

NOTE Do not move the decimal point when rounding.

EXAMPLE 6 **Rounding to the Nearest Tenth**

Round 98.5892 to the nearest tenth.

Solution

STEP 1 Locate the tenths digit and draw a line immediately to the right.

$$98.5\,|\,892$$

⎿————— Tenths digit

The tenths digit is 5.

STEP 2 Locate the digit just to the right of the line.

$$98.5\,|\,892$$

⎿——— First digit to the right of the line

The digit just to the right of the line is 8, so increase the 5 by 1, to 6.

STEP 3 Dropping all digits to the right results in 98.6.

EXAMPLE 7 **Rounding to the Nearest Thousandth**

Round 0.008572 to the nearest thousandth.

Solution   Locate the thousandths digit and draw a line.

$$0.008 \mid 572$$

Thousandths digit

Since the digit to the right of the line is 5, increase the thousandths digit by 1. Therefore, 0.008572 rounded to the nearest thousandth is 0.009.

EXAMPLE 8 **Rounding Decimals**

When doing business with a foreign country, you must convert the foreign currency using the U.S. exchange rate. Round the following currencies to the indicated place value.

(a) Euro (dollar): 0.8086 to the nearest thousandth
(b) Canada (dollar): 1.0750 to the nearest tenth
(c) Britain (pound): 0.5459 to the nearest hundredth
(d) Mexico (peso): 10.62351 to the nearest ten-thousandth

Solution   Use the method described.

(a) 0.8086 to the nearest thousandth is 0.809.
(b) 1.0750 to the nearest tenth is 1.1.
(c) 0.5459 to the nearest hundredth is 0.55.
(d) 10.62351 to the nearest ten-thousandth is 10.6235.

Objective

---

5   *Convert Fractions to Decimals.* To convert a fraction to a decimal, divide the numerator of the fraction by the denominator. Place a decimal point after the numerator and attach additional zeros, one at a time, to the right of the decimal point as the division is performed. Keep going until the division ends or until the desired degree of precision is reached. As a general rule, divide until the quotient has one more digit than the desired degree of precision and then round from the last digit. The result is the decimal equivalent of the fraction.

For example, to convert $\frac{1}{8}$ to a decimal, divide 1 by 8.

$$8\overline{)1}$$

Since 8 will not divide into 1, place a 0 to the right of the decimal point. Now 8 divides into 10 once, with a remainder of 2.

$$
\begin{array}{r}
0.1 \\
8\overline{)1.0} \\
\underline{8} \\
2
\end{array}
$$

Be sure to move the decimal point up.

Continue placing 0s to the right of the decimal point and continue dividing. The division now gives a remainder of 0.

$$
\begin{array}{r}
0.125 \\
8)\overline{1.000} \quad \text{Keep attaching zeros.} \\
\underline{8} \\
20 \\
\underline{16} \\
40 \\
\underline{40} \\
0 \quad \text{Remainder of 0.}
\end{array}
$$

Therefore, $\frac{1}{8} = 0.125$.

NOTE The decimal answer of 0.125 was not rounded. Instead, the division was continued until there was no remainder. In most problems, the answer must be rounded to the required accuracy.

EXAMPLE **9** **Rounding of a Repeating Decimal**

Convert $\frac{2}{3}$ to a decimal. Round to the nearest ten-thousandth.

Solution

Divide 2 by 3.

$$
\begin{array}{r}
0.6666 \\
3)\overline{2.0000} \quad \text{Keep attaching zeros.} \\
\underline{18} \\
20 \\
\underline{18} \\
20 \\
\underline{18} \\
20 \\
\underline{18} \\
2
\end{array}
$$

This division results in a **repeating decimal**, which is often indicated by placing a bar over the digit or digits that repeat. The answer could be written as follows.

$$0.\overline{6} \quad \text{or} \quad 0.6\overline{6} \quad \text{or} \quad 0.66\overline{66}$$

However, rounded to the nearest ten-thousandth,

$$\frac{2}{3} = 0.6667$$

■ ■ ■ Scientific
■ ■ Calculator
■ Approach

The calculator solution to Example 9 follows.

$$2 \boxed{\div} 3 \boxed{=} \quad 0.666666667$$

Objective

6 *Know Common Decimal Equivalents.* Some of the more common **decimal equivalents** of fractions are listed below. These decimals appear from least to greatest value and are rounded to the nearest ten-thousandth. Sometimes decimals must be carried out further to give greater accuracy. At other times they are not carried out as far and are rounded sooner.

Decimal Equivalents

$\frac{1}{16} = 0.0625$	$\frac{5}{16} = 0.3125$	$\frac{11}{16} = 0.6875$
$\frac{1}{10} = 0.1$	$\frac{1}{3} = 0.3333$ (rounded)	$\frac{7}{10} = 0.7$
$\frac{1}{9} = 0.1111$ (rounded)	$\frac{3}{8} = 0.375$	$\frac{3}{4} = 0.75$
$\frac{1}{8} = 0.125$	$\frac{2}{5} = 0.4$	$\frac{4}{5} = 0.8$
$\frac{1}{7} = 0.1429$ (rounded)	$\frac{7}{16} = 0.4375$	$\frac{13}{16} = 0.8125$
$\frac{1}{6} = 0.1667$ (rounded)	$\frac{1}{2} = 0.5$	$\frac{5}{6} = 0.8333$ (rounded)
$\frac{3}{16} = 0.1875$	$\frac{9}{16} = 0.5625$	$\frac{7}{8} = 0.875$
$\frac{1}{5} = 0.2$	$\frac{3}{5} = 0.6$	$\frac{9}{10} = 0.9$
$\frac{1}{4} = 0.25$	$\frac{5}{8} = 0.625$	$\frac{15}{16} = 0.9375$
$\frac{3}{10} = 0.3$	$\frac{2}{3} = 0.6667$ (rounded)	

1.3 Exercises

Multiply each of the following and write in lowest terms.

1. $\frac{5}{8} \times \frac{2}{3}$ $\frac{5}{12}$

2. $\frac{3}{8} \times \frac{1}{6}$ $\frac{1}{16}$

3. $\frac{9}{10} \times \frac{11}{16}$ $\frac{99}{160}$

4. $1\frac{1}{4} \times 3\frac{1}{2}$ $4\frac{3}{8}$

5. $1\frac{2}{3} \times 2\frac{7}{10}$ $4\frac{1}{2}$

6. $6 \times 4\frac{2}{3}$ 28

7. $4\frac{3}{5} \times 15$ 69

8. $\frac{3}{4} \times \frac{8}{9} \times 2\frac{1}{2}$ $1\frac{2}{3}$

9. $\frac{5}{9} \times 2\frac{1}{4} \times 3\frac{2}{3}$ $4\frac{7}{12}$

10. $\frac{2}{3} \times \frac{9}{8} \times 3\frac{1}{4}$ $2\frac{7}{16}$

11. $12 \times 2\frac{1}{2} \times 3$ 90

12. $18 \times 1\frac{2}{3} \times 2$ 60

Divide each of the following and write in lowest terms.

13. $\frac{1}{6} \div \frac{1}{3}$ $\frac{1}{2}$

14. $\frac{5}{8} \div \frac{3}{16}$ $3\frac{1}{3}$

15. $\frac{13}{20} \div \frac{26}{30}$ $\frac{3}{4}$

16. $\frac{7}{8} \div \frac{3}{4}$ $1\frac{1}{6}$

17. $\frac{15}{16} \div \frac{5}{8}$ $1\frac{1}{2}$

18. $\frac{12}{11} \div \frac{3}{22}$ 8

19. $2\frac{1}{2} \div 3\frac{3}{4}$ $\frac{2}{3}$

20. $6\frac{1}{2} \div \frac{1}{2}$ 13

21. $3\frac{1}{8} \div \frac{15}{16}$ $3\frac{1}{3}$

22. $5\frac{1}{2} \div 4$ $1\frac{3}{8}$

23. $6 \div 1\frac{1}{4}$ $4\frac{4}{5}$

24. $3 \div 1\frac{1}{4}$ $2\frac{2}{5}$

 25. Write in your own words the rule for multiplying fractions. Make up an example problem of your own showing how this works. (See Objective 1.)

26. Use cancellation before multiplying fractions as a useful shortcut. Describe how to do this and give an example. (See Objective 1.)

Find the time-and-a-half pay rates for the following regular hourly pay rates.

27. $8 $12

28. $14 $21

29. $17 $25.50

30. $9 $13.50

31. $10.50 $15.75

32. $18.50 $27.75

Convert the following decimals to fractions and reduce to lowest terms.

33. 0.8 $\dfrac{4}{5}$ **34.** 0.6 $\dfrac{3}{5}$ **35.** 0.24 $\dfrac{6}{25}$ **36.** 0.64 $\dfrac{16}{25}$

37. 0.73 $\dfrac{73}{100}$ **38.** 0.625 $\dfrac{5}{8}$ **39.** 0.875 $\dfrac{7}{8}$ **40.** 0.805 $\dfrac{161}{200}$

41. 0.0375 $\dfrac{3}{80}$ **42.** 0.8125 $\dfrac{13}{16}$ **43.** 0.1875 $\dfrac{3}{16}$ **44.** 0.3125 $\dfrac{5}{16}$

Round the following decimals to the nearest tenth and to the nearest hundredth.

45. 3.5218   3.5; 3.52   **46.** 4.8361   4.8; 4.84   **47.** 0.0837   0.1; 0.08

48. 2.548   2.5; 2.55   **49.** 8.643   8.6; 8.64   **50.** 86.472   86.5; 86.47

51. 58.956   59.0; 58.96   **52.** 8.065   8.1; 8.07   **53.** 23.047   23.0; 23.05

54. 65.464   65.5; 65.46   **55.** 39.496   39.5; 39.50   **56.** 92.337   92.3; 92.34

Convert the following fractions to decimals. Round the answer to the nearest thousandth if necessary.

57. $\dfrac{3}{4}$ 0.75   **58.** $\dfrac{7}{8}$ 0.875   **59.** $\dfrac{3}{8}$ 0.375   **60.** $\dfrac{5}{6}$ 0.833

61. $\dfrac{1}{6}$ 0.167   **62.** $\dfrac{2}{3}$ 0.667   **63.** $\dfrac{13}{16}$ 0.813   **64.** $\dfrac{19}{50}$ 0.38

65. $\dfrac{8}{25}$ 0.32   **66.** $\dfrac{1}{3}$ 0.333   **67.** $\dfrac{1}{99}$ 0.010   **68.** $\dfrac{73}{93}$ 0.785

69. $\dfrac{5}{8}$ 0.625   **70.** $\dfrac{5}{9}$ 0.556   **71.** $\dfrac{5}{6}$ 0.833   **72.** $\dfrac{7}{16}$ 0.438

 73. A classmate of yours is confused about how to convert a decimal to a fraction. Write an explanation of this for your classmate, including changing the fraction to lowest terms. (See Objective 3.)

 74. Explain how to convert a fraction to a decimal. Be sure to mention rounding in your explanation. (See Objective 5.)

 75. Explain in your own words the difference between hundreds and hundredths. (See Objective 3.)

 76. Write the directions for rounding an answer involving money to the nearest cent. Why must this be done? (See Objective 4.)

Solve the following application problems.

77. **PRODUCING CRAFTS** Angela Gragg wants to make 16 holiday wreaths to sell at the craft fair. Each wreath needs $2\frac{1}{4}$ yards of ribbon. How many yards does she need? 36 yards

78. **FILL DIRT** A contractor needs to add 345 cubic yards of fill dirt before compacting the soil and building a parking lot at a community college. His truck carries an average of $11\frac{1}{2}$ cubic yards of dirt each trip. Find the number of trips required by the truck. 30 trips

79. **DISPENSING EYEDROPS** How many $\frac{1}{8}$-ounce eyedrop dispensers can be filled with 11 ounces of eyedrops? 88 dispensers

80. **CONCRETE FOOTINGS** Each building footing requires $\frac{5}{16}$ cubic yard of concrete. How many building footings can be constructed from 10 cubic yards of concrete? 32 footings

81. **FINISH CARPENTRY** Each home of a certain design needs $109\frac{1}{2}$ yards of prefinished baseboard. How many homes can be fitted with baseboards if there are 1314 yards of baseboard available? 12 homes

82. **COMMERCIAL FERTILIZER** For 1 acre of crop, $7\frac{1}{2}$ gallons of fertilizer must be applied. How many acres can be fertilized with 1200 gallons of fertilizer? 160 acres

83. **INSECT CONTROL** An insect spray manufactured by Dutch Chemicals Inc. is mixed with $1\frac{3}{4}$ ounces of chemical per gallon of water. How many ounces of chemical are needed for $12\frac{1}{2}$ gallons of water? $21\frac{7}{8}$ ounces

84. **RESIDENTIAL ROOFING** Each home in a new development requires $37\frac{3}{4}$ pounds of roofing nails. How many pounds of roofing nails are needed for 36 homes? 1359 pounds

85. **FUEL CONSUMPTION** A fishing boat uses $12\frac{3}{4}$ gallons of fuel on a full-day fishing trip and $7\frac{1}{8}$ gallons of fuel on a half-day trip. Find the total number of gallons of fuel used in 28 full-day trips and 16 half-day trips. 471 gallons

86. **HANDCRAFTED JEWELRY** One necklace can be completed in $6\frac{1}{2}$ minutes, and a bracelet takes $3\frac{1}{8}$ minutes. Find the total time that it takes to complete 36 necklaces and 22 bracelets. $302\frac{3}{4}$ minutes

87. **FIREWOOD SALES** Linda Reynolds had a small pickup truck that would carry $\frac{2}{3}$ cord of firewood. Find the number of trips needed to deliver 40 cords of wood. 60 trips

88. **AUTOMOBILE DEALERSHIP** An automobile dealer has 220 cars on the lot. If $\frac{1}{5}$ of them are sold in a month, find the number of cars remaining on the lot. 176 cars

89. **MATERIALS MANAGEMENT** A manufacturer of floor jacks is ordering steel tubing to make the handles for this jack. How much steel tubing is needed to make 135 of these jacks? (The symbol for inch is ".) $2632\frac{1}{2}$ inches

2-Ton Compact Floorjack
4000 LB CAPACITY

- $19\frac{1}{2}$" handle
- Lifts 5" to $15\frac{1}{4}$"
- Fully rolled edge for added tray strength
- 21" L × $9\frac{1}{2}$" W × 6" H
- Compact & lightweight for portability—perfect for the trunk

90. **MATERIALS MANAGEMENT** A wheelbarrow manufacturer uses handles made of hardwood. Find the amount of wood that is necessary to make 182 handles. The longest dimension shown is the handle length. 11,193 inches

6.0 CUBIC FT WHEELBARROW

- Steel construction with hardwood handles
- 14" tubeless pneumatic tire
- Fully rolled edge for added tray strength
- Overall dimensions: $61\frac{1}{2}$" L × 27" W × 24.9" H

CHAPTER TERMS

Review the following terms to test your understanding of the chapter. For each term you do not know, refer to the page number found next to that term.

borrowing [p. 15]
cancellation [p. 20]
common denominator [p. 11]
decimal equivalent [p. 27]
decimal number [p. 23]
denominator [p. 8]

divisibility rules [p. 11]
fraction [p. 8]
improper fraction [p. 8]
indicators [p. 2]
inspection [p. 12]
least common denominator (LCD) [p. 12]

like fractions [p. 11]
lowest terms [p. 10]
method of prime numbers [p. 12]
mixed number [p. 9]
numerator [p. 8]
prime number [p. 12]

proper fraction [p. 8]
repeating decimal [p. 26]
rounding decimals [p. 24]
rules for divisibility [p. 10]
unlike fractions [p. 12]

CONCEPTS

EXAMPLES

1.1 Solving application problems

Step 1 Read the problem carefully and identify the unknown.

Step 2 Develop a plan to work the problem.

Step 3 Estimate a reasonable answer using rounding.

Step 4 Solve the problem.

Step 5 Check to see if the answer is reasonable.

Mr. Rice earns \$118 on Sunday, \$87 on Monday, and \$83 on Tuesday. Find his total earnings.

Using an average of \$100 in earnings per day, the total earnings are about \$300. Add to find the exact amount and check to see if the answer is reasonable.

$$
\begin{array}{ll}
\$118 & \text{Sunday's earnings} \\
87 & \text{Monday's earnings} \\
\underline{83} & \text{Tuesday's earnings} \\
\$288 & \text{Total earnings (which is close to \$300)}
\end{array}
$$

1.2 Types of fractions

Proper (common): Numerator smaller than denominator.

Improper: Numerator equal to or greater than denominator.

Mixed: Whole number and proper fraction.

Proper $\dfrac{2}{3}, \dfrac{3}{4}, \dfrac{15}{16}, \dfrac{1}{8}$

Improper $\dfrac{17}{8}, \dfrac{19}{12}, \dfrac{11}{2}, \dfrac{5}{3}, \dfrac{7}{7}$

Mixed $2\dfrac{2}{3}, 3\dfrac{5}{8}, 9\dfrac{5}{6}$

1.2 Converting fractions

Mixed to improper: Multiply whole number by denominator and add numerator. The denominator is unchanged.

Improper to mixed: Divide numerator by denominator and place remainder over denominator.

$$7\frac{2}{3} = \frac{(7 \times 3) + 2}{3} = \frac{23}{3}$$

$$\frac{17}{5} = 3\frac{2}{5} \qquad \begin{array}{r} 3 \\ 5\overline{)17} \\ \underline{15} \\ 2 \end{array}$$

1.2 Writing fractions in lowest terms

Divide the numerator and denominator by the same number.

$$\frac{30}{42} = \frac{30 \div 6}{42 \div 6} = \frac{5}{7}$$

1.2 Adding like fractions

Add numerators and reduce to lowest terms.
The denominator is unchanged.

$$\frac{3}{4} + \frac{1}{4} + \frac{5}{4} = \frac{3 + 1 + 5}{4} = \frac{9}{4} = 2\frac{1}{4}$$

1.2 Finding a least common denominator

Inspection method: Look to see if the least common denominator can be found.

Method of prime numbers: Use prime numbers to find the least common denominator.

$$\frac{1}{3} + \frac{1}{4} + \frac{1}{10}$$

$$
\begin{array}{r|ccc}
 & 1 & 1 & 1 \\
5) & 1 & 1 & 5 \\
3) & 3 & 1 & 5 \\
2) & 3 & 2 & 5 \\
2) & 3 & 4 & 10
\end{array}
$$

Multiply the prime numbers.

$$2 \times 2 \times 3 \times 5 = 60 \, \text{LCD}$$

1.2 Adding unlike fractions

1. Find the least common denominator.
2. Rewrite fractions with the least common denominator.
3. Add numerators, placing answers over LCD, and reduce to lowest terms.

$$\frac{1}{3} + \frac{1}{4} + \frac{1}{10} \quad \text{LCD} = 60$$

$$\frac{1}{3} = \frac{20}{60}, \frac{1}{4} = \frac{15}{60}, \frac{1}{10} = \frac{6}{60}$$

$$\frac{20 + 15 + 6}{60} = \frac{41}{60}$$

1.2 Adding mixed numbers

1. Add fractions.
2. Add whole numbers.
3. Combine the sums of whole numbers and fractions. Write answer in simplest terms.

$$
\begin{aligned}
9\frac{2}{3} &= 9\frac{8}{12} \\
+ 6\frac{3}{4} &= 6\frac{9}{12} \\
\hline
&\quad 15\frac{17}{12} = 16\frac{5}{12}
\end{aligned}
$$

1.2 Subtracting fractions

1. Find the least common denominator.
2. Subtract numerators, borrowing if necessary.
3. Write the difference over the LCD and reduce to lowest terms.

$$\frac{5}{8} - \frac{1}{3} = \frac{15}{24} - \frac{8}{24} = \frac{7}{24}$$

1.2 Subtracting mixed numbers

1. Subtract fractions, borrowing if necessary.
2. Subtract whole numbers.
3. Combine the differences of whole numbers and fractions.

$$
\begin{aligned}
8\frac{5}{8} &= 8\frac{15}{24} \\
- 3\frac{1}{12} &= 3\frac{2}{24} \\
\hline
&\quad 5\frac{13}{24}
\end{aligned}
$$

1.3 Multiplying proper fractions

1. Cancel if possible; then multiply numerators and denominators.
2. Reduce answer to lowest terms if canceling was not done.

$$\frac{6}{11} \times \frac{7}{8} = \frac{\overset{3}{\cancel{6}}}{11} \times \frac{7}{\underset{4}{\cancel{8}}} = \frac{21}{44}$$

1.3 Multiplying mixed numbers

1. Change mixed numbers to improper fractions.
2. Cancel if possible.
3. Multiply as with proper fractions. Always reduce to lowest terms.

$$1\frac{3}{5} \times 3\frac{1}{3} = \frac{8}{\underset{1}{\cancel{5}}} \times \frac{\overset{2}{\cancel{10}}}{3} = \frac{8}{1} \times \frac{2}{3}$$

$$= \frac{16}{3} = 5\frac{1}{3}$$

1.3 Dividing proper fractions

Invert the divisor, cancel, and then multiply as fractions.

$$\frac{25}{36} \div \frac{15}{18} = \frac{\overset{5}{\cancel{25}}}{\underset{2}{\cancel{36}}} \times \frac{\overset{1}{\cancel{18}}}{\underset{3}{\cancel{15}}} = \frac{5}{2} \times \frac{1}{3} = \frac{5}{6}$$

1.3 Dividing mixed numbers

Change mixed numbers to improper fractions. Then invert the divisor, cancel if possible, and multiply as proper fractions.

$$3\frac{5}{9} \div 2\frac{2}{5} = \frac{32}{9} \div \frac{12}{5} = \frac{\overset{8}{\cancel{32}}}{9} \times \frac{5}{\underset{3}{\cancel{12}}}$$

$$= \frac{40}{27} = 1\frac{13}{27}$$

1.3 Converting decimals to fractions

Think of the decimal as being written in words, then write in fraction form. Reduce to lowest terms.

Convert 0.47 to a fraction. Think of 0.47 as "forty-seven hundredths" and then write as $\frac{47}{100}$.

1.3 Rounding decimals

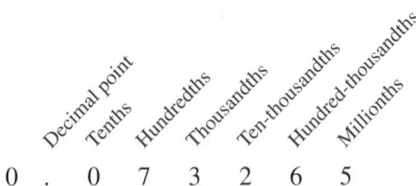

$$0 \ . \ 0 \ 7 \ 3 \ 2 \ 6 \ 5$$

Round 0.073265 to the nearest ten-thousandth.

$$0.0732\,|\,65$$
$$\uparrow$$
Ten-thousandths position

Since the digit to the right of the line is 6, increase the ten-thousandths digit by 1. Thus, 0.073265 rounds to 0.0733.

1.3 Converting fractions to decimals

Divide the numerator by the denominator. Round if necessary.

Convert $\frac{1}{8}$ to a decimal.

$$
\begin{array}{r}
0.125 \\
8\,\overline{)1.000} \\
\underline{8} \\
20 \\
\underline{16} \\
40 \\
\underline{40} \\
0
\end{array}
$$

So, $\frac{1}{8} = 0.125$

The answer section includes answers to all Review Exercises.

Write the following fractions in lowest terms. [1.2]

1. $\dfrac{24}{40}$ $\dfrac{3}{5}$
2. $\dfrac{32}{64}$ $\dfrac{1}{2}$
3. $\dfrac{27}{81}$ $\dfrac{1}{3}$
4. $\dfrac{147}{294}$ $\dfrac{1}{2}$

5. $\dfrac{63}{70}$ $\dfrac{9}{10}$
6. $\dfrac{84}{132}$ $\dfrac{7}{11}$
7. $\dfrac{24}{1200}$ $\dfrac{1}{50}$
8. $\dfrac{375}{1000}$ $\dfrac{3}{8}$

Convert the following improper fractions to mixed numbers and write in lowest terms. [1.2]

9. $\dfrac{65}{8}$ $8\dfrac{1}{8}$
10. $\dfrac{56}{12}$ $4\dfrac{2}{3}$
11. $\dfrac{38}{24}$ $1\dfrac{7}{12}$
12. $\dfrac{55}{7}$ $7\dfrac{6}{7}$

13. $\dfrac{120}{45}$ $2\dfrac{2}{3}$
14. $\dfrac{196}{24}$ $8\dfrac{1}{6}$
15. $\dfrac{258}{32}$ $8\dfrac{1}{16}$
16. $\dfrac{194}{64}$ $3\dfrac{1}{32}$

Solve the following problems and write in lowest terms. [1.2]

17. $\dfrac{5}{8} + \dfrac{7}{12}$ $1\dfrac{5}{24}$
18. $\dfrac{1}{5} + \dfrac{3}{10} + \dfrac{3}{8}$ $\dfrac{7}{8}$
19. $\dfrac{5}{7} - \dfrac{1}{3}$ $\dfrac{8}{21}$
20. $\dfrac{3}{4} - \dfrac{2}{3}$ $\dfrac{1}{12}$

21. $\begin{aligned} 25\dfrac{1}{6} \\ + 46\dfrac{2}{3} \\ \hline 71\dfrac{5}{6} \end{aligned}$

22. $\begin{aligned} 18\dfrac{3}{5} \\ 47\dfrac{7}{10} \\ + 25\dfrac{8}{15} \\ \hline \end{aligned}$ $91\dfrac{5}{6}$

23. $\begin{aligned} 6\dfrac{7}{12} \\ - 2\dfrac{1}{3} \\ \hline 4\dfrac{1}{4} \end{aligned}$

24. $\begin{aligned} 92\dfrac{5}{16} \\ - 11\dfrac{1}{4} \\ \hline 81\dfrac{1}{16} \end{aligned}$

Solve the following application problems. [1.1 and 1.2]

25. A quality oak floor costs $4.95 per square foot. Additionally, a capable installer charges $3.40 per square foot for labor. Find the total cost, not including any taxes, to lay the flooring in a 580-square-foot living room. $4843

26. A federal law requires that all residential toilets sold in the United States use no more than 1.6 gallons of water per flush. Prior to this legislation, conventional toilets used 3.4 gallons of water per flush. Find the amount of water saved in one year by a family of 6 flushing the toilet 22 times each day. 14,454 gallons saved

27. Desiree Ramirez worked $5\dfrac{1}{2}$ hours on Wednesday, $6\dfrac{1}{4}$ hours on Thursday, $3\dfrac{3}{4}$ hours on Friday, and 7 hours on Saturday. How many hours did she work altogether? $22\dfrac{1}{2}$ hours

28. A painting contractor arrived at a 60-unit apartment complex with $147\dfrac{1}{2}$ gallons of exterior paint. His crew sprayed $68\dfrac{1}{2}$ gallons on the wood siding, rolled $37\dfrac{3}{8}$ gallons on the masonry exterior, and brushed $5\dfrac{3}{4}$ gallons on the trim. Find the number of gallons of paint remaining. $35\dfrac{7}{8}$ gallons

29. Three sides of Sheri Minkner's kiwi ranch are $202\dfrac{1}{8}$ feet, $370\dfrac{3}{4}$ feet, and $274\dfrac{1}{2}$ feet. If the distance around the ranch is $1166\dfrac{7}{8}$ feet, what is the length of the fourth side? $319\dfrac{1}{2}$ feet

30. The Catering Crew served $12\dfrac{2}{3}$ pounds of American cheese, $16\dfrac{1}{8}$ pounds of jack cheese, $15\dfrac{1}{2}$ pounds of sharp cheddar cheese, and $10\dfrac{1}{6}$ pounds of muenster cheese at a catered event. Find the total weight of the cheese served. $54\dfrac{11}{24}$ pounds

Solve each problem and reduce to lowest terms. [1.2]

31. $\dfrac{5}{8} \times \dfrac{2}{3}$ $\dfrac{5}{12}$
32. $\dfrac{1}{3} \times \dfrac{7}{8} \times \dfrac{3}{5}$ $\dfrac{7}{40}$
33. $\dfrac{1}{6} \div \dfrac{1}{3}$ $\dfrac{1}{2}$
34. $10 \div \dfrac{5}{8}$ 16

35. $2\dfrac{1}{2} \div 3\dfrac{3}{4}$ $\dfrac{2}{3}$
36. $3\dfrac{3}{4} \div \dfrac{27}{16}$ $2\dfrac{2}{9}$
37. $12\dfrac{1}{2} \times 1\dfrac{2}{3}$ $20\dfrac{5}{6}$
38. $12\dfrac{1}{3} \div 2$ $6\dfrac{1}{6}$

Solve the following application problems. [1.1 and 1.3]

39. A department head has $19,200 to purchase new office furniture and equipment. She purchases 11 office suites consisting of a desk, chair, and filing cabinets, 8 laptops, and 3 notebooks. The office suites cost $985 each, the laptops cost $540 each, and the notebooks cost $349 each. Find the amount remaining after the purchases. $2998

40. The earnings of Sierra West Bancorp last year were $1.4 million, or $0.39 per share of stock. Find the number of shares of stock in the company. Round to the nearest tenth of a million.   3.6 million shares

41. The area of a piece of land is $63\frac{3}{4}$ acres. One-third of the land is sold. What is the area of the land that is left? $42\frac{1}{2}$ acres

42. A fishing boat anchor requires $10\frac{3}{8}$ pounds of steel. Find the number of anchors that can be manufactured with 25,730 pounds of steel.   2480 anchors

43. Find the number of window-blind pull cords that can be made from $157\frac{1}{2}$ yards of cord if $4\frac{3}{8}$ yards of cord are needed for each blind.   36 pull cords

44. Waterford Plumbing is a partnership formed by three people. After-tax profits one year amounted to $562,200. The partners decided to retain $\frac{1}{4}$ of the profit in the firm for remodeling costs and disburse the remaining profit equally to the partners. Find the amount going to each partner. $140,550

Convert the following decimals to a fraction and reduce to lowest terms. [1.3]

45. 0.25 $\frac{1}{4}$ **46.** 0.625 $\frac{5}{8}$ **47.** 0.93 $\frac{93}{100}$ **48.** 0.005 $\frac{1}{200}$

Round the following decimals to the nearest tenth and to the nearest hundredth. [1.3]

49. 68.433   68.4; 68.43   **50.** 975.536   975.5; 975.54

51. 0.3549   0.4; 0.35   **52.** 8.025   8.0; 8.03

53. 6.965   7.0; 6.97   **54.** 0.428   0.4; 0.43

55. 0.955   1.0; 0.96   **56.** 71.249   71.2; 71.25

Convert the following fractions to a decimal. Round to the nearest thousandth when necessary. [1.3]

57. $\frac{5}{8}$ 0.625   **58.** $\frac{3}{4}$ 0.75   **59.** $\frac{5}{6}$ 0.833   **60.** $\frac{7}{16}$ 0.438

CHAPTER 1	Business Application Case #1
	Operating Expenses

It is often said that a picture is worth a thousand words. Visual presentation of data is often used in business in the form of graphs. A commonly used graph that shows the relationships of various data is the circle graph, also called a pie chart. The circle is divided into slices or fractional parts. The size of each slice helps to show the relationship of the various slices to each other and to the whole.

The annual operating expenses for Woodline Moldings and Trim are shown below. Use this information to answer the questions that follow.

WOODLINE MOLDINGS AND TRIM		(OPERATING EXPENSES)	
Expense Item	**Monthly Amount**	**Annual Amount**	**Fraction of Total**
Salaries	$15,000	$180,000	$\frac{5}{12}$
Rent	$ 9,000	$108,000	$\frac{1}{4}$
Utilities	$ 3,000	$ 36,000	$\frac{1}{12}$
Advertising	$ 2,250	$ 27,000	$\frac{1}{16}$
Insurance	$ 2,250	$ 27,000	$\frac{1}{16}$
Miscellaneous	$ 4,500	$ 54,000	$\frac{1}{8}$
Total Expenses		$432,000	

(a) Find the total annual operating expenses for Woodline Moldings and Trim. $432,000

(b) What fraction should be used to represent each expense item as part of the total expenses? $\frac{5}{12}, \frac{1}{4}, \frac{1}{12}, \frac{1}{16}, \frac{1}{16}, \frac{1}{8}$

(c) Draw a circle (pie) graph using the fractions you found in (b) to represent each expense item. Approximate the fractional part of the circle needed for each expense item. Label each segment of the circle graph with the fraction and the expense item.

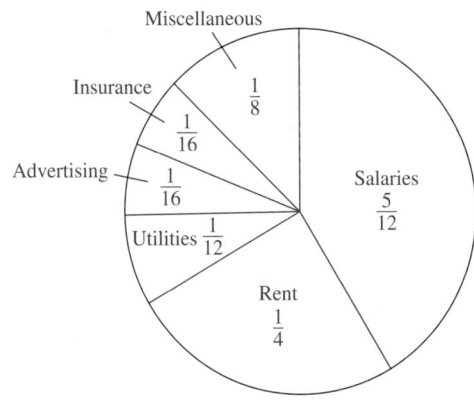

CHAPTER 1	Business Application Case #2
	Home Repair

Jonathan Ross/Cutcaster

Pete and Barbara Johnson buy an old house. They plan to make the necessary repairs before moving in with their two children, one dog, and two cats. The Johnsons buy all the needed supplies at a local Home Depot store (see www.home-depot.com) and work on the house during evenings and weekends as they have time and money. Pete believes it will take about 6 months before they can move into the house.

(a) A gutter downspout is 10 feet long. If a piece of gutter downspout 8 feet $8\frac{3}{8}$ inches is needed for a job, find the length of the remaining piece. (*Hint:* 1 foot equals 12 inches.)   1 foot $3\frac{5}{8}$ inches

(b) Home Depot stock is selling for $34.40 per share. Find the number of shares that can be purchased for $10,000. 290 shares

(c) Give three specific situations in which fractions and mixed numbers would be used in a home-improvement store. Answers will vary.

(d) From your own experiences and those of family members and classmates, list three specific activities where the ability to work with fractions would be needed.   Answers will vary.

javier brosch / Fotolia.com

CHAPTER

2

Equations and Formulas

Managers often use algebra-based equations to forecast demand for products and services. It is important to use good forecasts. A forecast that is too low means customers cannot buy what they want—lower corporate profits. A forecast that is too high means too much inventory and too many employees—and lower corporate profits. But it is often very difficult to get a good forecast.

Figure 2.1 shows annualized new vehicle sales in the United States. Sales were running at more than 16 million a year in 2007 but fell sharply throughout 2008 to fewer than 10 million a year in early 2009 in the midst of a financial crisis. Wow—a reduction of *6 million cars per year*! Forecasts had been for higher sales, and the automobile makers had far too many cars on the lots. They responded by marking the prices of the automobiles down to sell them, even as they shut down factories and laid off employees. Many families suffered when workers suddenly lost jobs and were unable to find another.

In response, the government offered an incentive to trade in that old clunker for a new car, called *cash for clunkers.* People received rebates of between $3500 and $4500 to trade in an old car for a new one that got better gas mileage. The goals were to help the automobile companies, reduce dependence on foreign oil, and try to stabilize employment along the automobile supply chains made up of thousands of companies and tens of thousands of workers. The cost of the cash for clunkers quickly swelled from the planned $1 billion to $3 billion due to very high demand. You can see the effect of the subsidy on vehicle sales in Figure 2.1 when you look at the spike in August 2009.

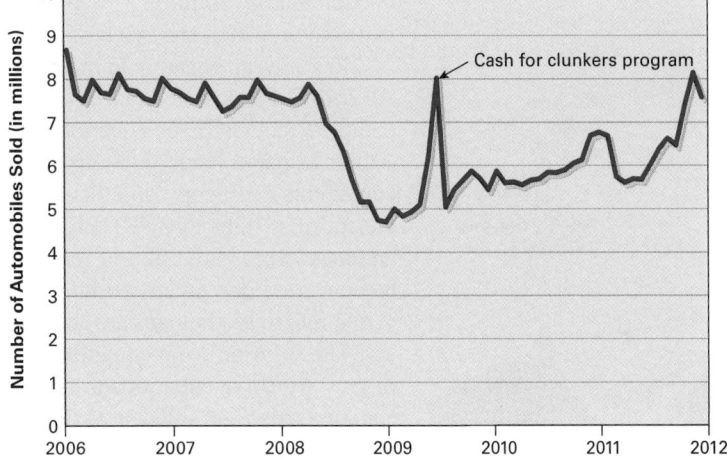

Source: U.S. Department of Commerce.

Figure 2.1 Effect of Financial Crisis on New Vehicle Sales

▶ STOP&THINK

By how much did the cash for clunkers incentive increase car sales? How long did the subsidy affect sales? What happened immediately after the subsidy ended? What effects do you think the 2008 collapse in vehicle sales had on the managers of the automakers? Is it fair for managers to fire employees at a time like this? What is (are) the alternative(s)?

| **2.1** | **Solving Equations** |

OBJECTIVES

1 *Learn the basic terminology of equations.*

2 *Use basic rules to solve equations.*

3 *Combine like terms in equations.*

4 *Use the distributive property to simplify equations.*

Equations and formulas are often used in business. For example, formulas are used to find markup, interest, depreciation, annuities, and several other values as well. In this chapter, we show how to work with and solve basic equations and formulas.

An **equation** is a statement that says two expressions are equal. For example, the equation

$$x + 5 = 9$$

says that the expression $x + 5$ and 9 are equal.

Objective

1   *Learn the Basic Terminology of Equations.* A **variable** is a letter, such as x or s, that is used to represent an unknown number. The variable x, in the equation above, as well as the numbers 5 and 9, are called terms. A **term** is a single letter, a single number, or the product (or quotient) of a number and one or more letters. Examples of terms include $80z$, $30y$, $19.5z$, and $3\frac{1}{2}t$. The number in front of the variable in a term is called the **coefficient**. So the coefficient in the term $3\frac{1}{2}t$ is $3\frac{1}{2}$ and the variable is t. Terms in expressions are separated from one another by addition $(+)$ or subtraction $(-)$ signs, as in the following **expression**, which has two terms: $75z - 15y$.

In a way, an equation in math is similar to a sentence in written language. An equation shows a complete relationship, just as each sentence must give a complete thought. Each equation has a left side and a right side. For example, Albert Einstein made the equation $E = mc^2$ famous. The **left side** of this equation is E (Energy) and the **right side** of the equation is mc^2 (mass times the speed of light squared). Einstein's theoretical work showed that energy and mass were two different forms of the same thing—essentially mass can be converted into energy (think of a nuclear bomb) and energy can be converted into mass (humans are still trying to do this).

The **solution** to an equation is the number that makes the equation true. In fact, we solve equations to find the value of the variable that makes the equation true. The solution to the equation $x + 5 = 9$ is 4, since replacing the variable x with the number 4 makes the equation true.

$E = mc^2$

Albert Einstein

$$x + 5 = 9$$
$$4 + 5 \stackrel{?}{=} 9 \quad \text{Let } x = 4.$$
$$9 = 9 \quad \text{True.}$$

The preceding check is an example of **substitution**: the variable x was replaced with 4.

Objective

2   *Use Basic Rules to Solve Equations.* We solve an equation to find the number that the variable must equal to make the equation true. The equation is true if the left side equals the right side. This is done by modifying the equation so that all terms containing a variable are on one side of the equation and all numbers are on the other side. The two sides of an equation remain equal if the same change is made to both sides.

The rules for solving equations follow.

> **Addition Rule:** The same number may be added to or subtracted from both sides of an equation.
>
> **Multiplication Rule:** Both sides of an equation may be multiplied or divided by the same nonzero number.

> **NOTE**   Remember, whatever mathematical operation is done to one side of an equation must also be done to the other side.

EXAMPLE 1   **Solving Equations Using Addition**

Solve $x - 17 = 34$.

Solution

To solve this equation, x must be alone on one side of the equal sign, and all numbers collected on the other side. To change the $x - 17$ to x, perform the opposite operation to "undo" what was done. The *opposite* of subtraction is addition, so add 17 to both sides.

$$x - 17 = 34$$
$$x - 17 + 17 = 34 + 17 \quad \text{Add 17 to both sides.}$$
$$x + 0 = 51 \quad \text{The sum of } -17 + 17 \text{ is 0.}$$
$$x = 51 \quad \text{So, } x \text{ must be 51.}$$

To check this answer, substitute 51 for x in the original equation.

$$x - 17 = 34 \quad \text{Original equation.}$$
$$51 - 17 \overset{?}{=} 34 \quad \text{Replace } x \text{ with 51.}$$
$$34 = 34 \quad \text{True.}$$

The answer checks, so $x = 51$.

EXAMPLE 2   **Solving Equations Using Subtraction**

Solve $y + 12.3 = 20.5$.

Solution

To isolate y on the left side, do the opposite of adding 12.3, which is *subtracting* 12.3 from both sides.

$$y + 12.3 = 20.5$$
$$y + 12.3 - 12.3 = 20.5 - 12.3 \quad \text{Subtract 12.3 from both sides.}$$
$$y + 0 = 8.2$$
$$y = 8.2$$

Check the answer by substituting 8.2 for y in the original equation.

$$y + 12.3 = 20.5$$
$$8.2 + 12.3 \stackrel{?}{=} 20.5$$
$$20.5 = 20.5$$

The answer checks.

EXAMPLE 3   Solving Equations Using Division

Solve $5p = 60$.

Solution

The term $5p$ indicates the product of 5 and p. Since the opposite of multiplication is division, solve the equation by *dividing* both sides by 5.

$$5p = 60$$
$$\frac{\cancel{5}p}{\cancel{5}} = \frac{60}{5} \quad \text{Divide both sides by 5.}$$
$$p = 12$$

Check by substituting 12 for p in the original equation.

EXAMPLE 4   Solving Equations Using Multiplication

Solve $\dfrac{r}{8} = 13$.

Solution

The bar in the fraction $\dfrac{r}{8}$ means to divide $(r \div 8)$. Since the opposite operation of division is multiplication, multiply both sides of the equation by 8. Note in the following that a heavy dot is used to indicate multiplication.

$$\frac{r}{8} = 13$$

$$\frac{r}{8} \cdot 8 = 13 \cdot 8 \quad \text{Multiply both sides by 8.}$$

$$\frac{r}{\cancel{8}} \cdot \cancel{8} = 104 \quad \text{Cancel } \tfrac{8}{8}, \text{ which is 1.}$$

$$r = 104$$

Example 5 shows how to solve an equation using a reciprocal. The product of a number and its **reciprocal** is 1. To get the reciprocal of a nonzero fraction, exchange the numerator and the denominator. For example, the reciprocal of $\frac{7}{9}$ is $\frac{9}{7}$.

$$\frac{\cancel{7}^{1}}{\cancel{9}_{1}} \cdot \frac{\cancel{9}^{1}}{\cancel{7}_{1}} = 1$$

EXAMPLE 5   Solving Equations Using Reciprocals

Solve $\frac{4}{5}n = 20$.

Solution

Solve this equation by multiplying both sides by $\frac{5}{4}$, which is the reciprocal of $\frac{4}{5}$. This process will give just $1n$, or n, on the left.

$$\frac{4}{5}n = 20$$

$$\overset{1}{\underset{1}{\frac{\cancel{5}}{\cancel{4}}}} \cdot \overset{1}{\underset{1}{\frac{\cancel{4}}{\cancel{5}}}}n = \frac{5}{4} \cdot 20 \quad \text{Multiply both sides by } \frac{5}{4}.$$

$$n = \frac{100}{4}$$

$$n = 25$$

The equation in Example 6 requires two steps to solve.

EXAMPLE 6   Solving Equations Involving More than One Step

Solve $2m + 5 = 17$.

Solution

To solve equations that require more than one step, first isolate the terms involving the unknown (variable) on one side of the equation and constants (numbers) on the other side by using addition and subtraction.

$$2m + 5 = 17$$

$$2m + 5 - 5 = 17 - 5 \quad \text{Subtract 5 from both sides.}$$

$$2m = 12$$

$$\frac{2m}{2} = \frac{12}{2} \quad \text{Divide both sides by 2.}$$

$$m = 6$$

Check by substituting 6 for m in the original equation.

$$2m + 5 = 17$$

$$2(6) + 5 \overset{?}{=} 17$$

$$17 = 17$$

Thus, $m = 6$ is the solution.

NOTE The unknown can be on either side of the equal sign. The equation $6 = m$ is the same as $m = 6$. The number is the solution whether the equation has the variable by itself on either the left *or* the right side.

Objective

3   *Combine Like Terms in Equations.* Some equations have more than one term with the same variable. Terms with the same variables are called **like terms**, or **similar terms**. Like terms can be *combined* by adding or subtracting the coefficients, as shown. Intuitively, you can think of $(8x + 2x)$ below as $(8 \text{ apples} + 2 \text{ apples})$. Just as 8 apples + 2 apples is 10 apples, so too is $8x + 2x$ equal to $10x$. Terms such as $3x$ and $5y$ are *not* like terms, so they cannot be combined into one term, just as 3 apples + 5 oranges cannot be combined.

Like Terms

$$8x + 2x = 10x$$
$$11y - 3y = 8y$$
$$12p - 5p + 2p = 9p$$
$$2z + z = 2z + 1z = 3z$$

Terms such as $3x$ and $2y$ are *not* like terms, so $2x + 3y$ cannot be combined into one term.

> **NOTE** Since multiplying by 1 does not change the value of a quantity, $1 \cdot z$ is the same as z.

EXAMPLE 7 Solving Equations with Like Terms

Solve the equation $9z - 3z + 2z = 50$ for the unknown.

Solution

The unknown in this equation is the variable z. The three terms on the left-hand side of the equation are like terms since they all contain the same variable z. So, the first step is to combine the three terms on the left-hand side of the equation.

$$9z - 3z + 2z = 50$$

$$8z = 50 \qquad \text{Combine the coefficients, that is, } 9 - 3 + 2 = 8.$$

$$\frac{8z}{8} = \frac{50}{8} \qquad \text{Divide both sides by 8.}$$

$$z = 6\tfrac{1}{4} \text{ or } 6.25$$

Substitute 6.25 for the variable z in the original equation to verify that it is the solution.

Objective

4   *Use the Distributive Property to Simplify Equations.* One very useful property from mathematics is called the **distributive property**. Actually, we already used the distributive property to add the coefficients of like terms in the previous example. However, this property also allows us to multiply a number on the outside of the parentheses by each term inside the parentheses, as shown here.

$$a(b + c) = ab + ac$$

The following diagram may help in remembering the distributive property.

$$a(b + c) = ab + ac$$

The term on the outside, a, is *distributed* over all terms in the parentheses.

$$2(m + 7) = 2m + 2 \cdot 7 = 2m + 14$$
$$8(k - 5) = 8k - 8 \cdot 5 = 8k - 40$$

EXAMPLE | 8 | **Solving Equations Using the Distributive Property**

Solve $6(p - 2) = 30$.

Solution

First use the distributive property on the left to remove the parentheses.

$$6(p - 2) = 30$$
$$6p - 12 = 30$$
$$6p - 12 + 12 = 30 + 12 \quad \text{Add 12 to both sides.}$$
$$6p = 42$$
$$\frac{6p}{6} = \frac{42}{6} \quad \text{Divide by 6.}$$
$$p = 7$$

NOTE Recall that the product of a positive and a negative number is negative. So, in the last example, $6(-2) = -12$, and therefore $6(p - 2) = 6p - 12$.

NOTE Also recall that a negative number times a negative number is a positive number, so $(-10)(-5) = +50$. A negative number divided by a negative number is also a positive number, so $(-10) \div (-5) = +2$.

The distributive property can be used to help understand the adding or subtracting of like terms, as follows.

$$6y + 14y = (6 + 14)y = 20y$$

$$2t + 7t - 3.5t = (2 + 7 - 3.5)t = 5.5t$$

Use the following steps to solve an equation.

Solving Linear Equations

Step 1 Remove all parentheses on both sides of the equation using the distributive property.

Step 2 Combine all similar terms on both sides of the equation.

Step 3 Add to or subtract from both sides whatever is needed to produce a term with the variable on one side and a number on the other side.

Step 4 Multiply or divide the variable term by whatever is needed to produce a term with a coefficient of 1. Multiply or divide the number term on the other side by the same quantity.

EXAMPLE | 9 | **Solving Equations Involving Several Steps**

Solve $5r - 2 = 2(r + 5)$.

Solution

$$5r - 2 = 2(r + 5)$$
$$5r - 2 = 2r + 10 \quad \text{Use distributive property on the right.}$$
$$5r - 2 + 2 = 2r + 10 + 2 \quad \text{Add 2 to both sides to get all numbers on the right-hand side.}$$

$$5r = 2r + 12$$

$$5r - 2r = 2r + 12 - 2r \quad \text{Subtract } 2r \text{ from both sides to get}$$
all variables on the left-hand side.

$$5r - 2r = 12$$

$$3r = 12 \qquad \text{Combine like terms on the right.}$$

$$\frac{3r}{3} = \frac{12}{3} \qquad \text{Divide both sides by 3 to}$$
get 1 as a coefficient.

$$r = 4$$

NOTE Be sure to check the answer in the *original* equation and not in any other step.

| **2.1** | **Exercises** |

Solve each equation. Check each answer.

1. $z + 8 = 50$ 42

2. $r + 13 = 83$ 70

3. $z + 95 = 400$ 305

4. $25 = x + 12$ 13

5. $v - 29 = 17$ 46

6. $312 = m - 40$ 352

7. $10k = 42$ 4.2

8. $7s = 84$ 12

9. $12q = 144$ 12

10. $8z = 136$ 17

11. $60 = 30m$ 2

12. $94 = 2z$ 47

13. $5.9y = 17.7$ 3

14. $16.5x = 39.6$ 2.4

15. $1.54 = 0.7y$ 2.2

16. $3.9a = 15.6$ 4

17. $3.92w = 3.136$ 0.8

18. $2.773m = 3.3276$ 1.2

19. $0.0002x = 0.08$ 400

20. $0.0324 = 0.0135y$ 2.4

21. $\dfrac{s}{7} = 42$ 294

22. $\dfrac{m}{5} = 6$ 30

23. $\dfrac{r}{7} = 1$ 7

24. $\dfrac{c}{7} = 2$ 14

25. $\dfrac{2}{3}b = 8$ 12

26. $22 = \dfrac{5}{4}s$ 17.6

27. $35 = \dfrac{7}{5}t$ 25

28. $\dfrac{7}{3}s = 21$ 9

29. $2x = \dfrac{5}{3}$ $\dfrac{5}{6}$

30. $4y = \dfrac{1}{3}$ $\dfrac{1}{12}$

31. $3p = \dfrac{5}{12}$ $\dfrac{5}{36}$

32. $\dfrac{3}{4} = 9a$ $\dfrac{1}{12}$

33. $7b + 9 = 37$ 4

34. $4x + 12 = 75$ 15.75

35. $7y - 23 = 58$ $11\dfrac{4}{7}$

36. $12r - 60 = 100$ $13\dfrac{1}{3}$

37. $6p + 41.5 = 69.4$ 4.65

38. $12.2s + 13.8 = 47.96$ 2.8

39. $6c + \dfrac{3}{4} = 8$ $1\dfrac{5}{24}$

40. $5z + \dfrac{2}{3} = 2$ $\dfrac{4}{15}$

41. $7q - \dfrac{2}{3} = 4$ $\dfrac{2}{3}$

42. $7a - \dfrac{5}{4} = \dfrac{9}{4}$ $\dfrac{1}{2}$

43. $5.2z - 4 = 1.2$ 1

44. $3.6m + 2 = 6.32$ 1.2

45. $27.85 = 3 + 7.1p$ 3.5

46. $0.9 = 4t - 3.5$ 1.1

47. $7m + 4m - 5m = 78$ 13

48. $13r - 7r + 3r = 81$ 9

49. $2s + s + 3s = 12$ 2

50. $3.5k + k + k = 11.55$ 2.1

51. $5y + 2 = 3(y + 4)$ 5

52. $4z + 2 = 2(z + 2)$ 1

53. $3(m - 4) = m + 2$ 7

54. $s + 8 = 3(s - 6)$ 13

55. $4(y + 8) = 3(y + 14)$ 10

56. $7(z - 5) = 4(z + 8)$ $22\dfrac{1}{3}$

57. $\dfrac{3}{4}s + \dfrac{1}{5}s = \dfrac{4}{5}$ $\dfrac{16}{19}$

58. $\dfrac{3}{4}q - \dfrac{1}{9} = \dfrac{1}{3} + \dfrac{1}{4}q$ $\dfrac{8}{9}$

59. $\dfrac{3}{8}y + \dfrac{1}{4} = \dfrac{9}{8}y - \dfrac{1}{4}$ $\dfrac{2}{3}$

60. $3(2p - 1) = 4(2.2 - p)$ 1.18

61. $2(y + 1) = 4(4 - 2.5y)$ $1\dfrac{1}{6}$

62. $9.1765y + 0.3284y = 6.65343$ 0.7 **63.** $0.7452(3k - 1) = 3.94956$ 2.1

64. $0.3255(1 + 7.5s) = 6.67275$ 2.6 **65.** $1.2(2 + 3r) = 0.8(2r + 5)$ 0.8

 66. Explain why all terms with a variable should be placed on one side of the equation and all terms without a variable should be placed on the opposite side when solving an equation.

 67. A student obtains the equation $6x = 5x$ after applying several steps correctly. The student then divides both sides by x and obtains the result $6 = 5$ and gives "no solution" as the answer. Is this correct? If not, state why not and give the correct solution. (See Objective 3.)

 68. Explain the distributive property and give an example. (See Objective 4.)

2.2	**Applications of Equations**

OBJECTIVES

1 *Translate phrases into mathematical expressions.*

2 *Write equations from given information.*

3 *Solve application problems.*

Most problems in business are expressed in words. Before these problems can be solved, they must be converted into mathematical language.

Objective

1 *Translate Phrases into Mathematical Expressions.* Applied problems tend to have certain phrases that occur again and again. The key to solving such problems is to correctly translate these phrases into mathematical expressions. The next few examples illustrate this process.

EXAMPLE 1 Translating Phrases Involving Addition

Write the following verbal expressions as mathematical expressions. Use p as the variable that represents the unknown number.

Verbal Expression	Mathematical Expression	Comments
(a) q plus a number	$q + p$	to q, add the unknown (p.)
(b) Add 17 to a number?	$p + 17$	p represents the number to which 17 is added
(c) The sum of a number and 12.7	$p + 12.7$	"sum" indicates addition
(d) 18 more than a number	$p + 18$	"more than" indicates addition

---

EXAMPLE 2 Translating Phrases Involving Subtraction

Write each of the following verbal expressions as a mathematical expression. Use y as a variable.

Verbal Expression	Mathematical Expression	Comments
(a) 5.5 less than a number	$y - 5.5$	"less than" indicates subtraction
(b) A number decreased by $12\frac{1}{4}$	$y - 12\frac{1}{4}$	"decreased" indicates subtraction
(c) Eight fewer than a number	$y - 8$	"fewer than" indicates subtraction
(d) Eighteen minus a number	$18 - y$	"minus" indicates subtraction

EXAMPLE **3** Translating Phrases Involving Multiplication and Division

Write the following verbal expressions as mathematical expressions. Use z as the variable.

Verbal Expression	Mathematical Expression	Comments
(a) The product of a number and 7.5	$7.5z$	"product" indicates multiplication
(b) Ten times a number	$10z$	"times" indicates multiplication
(c) One-fourth of a number	$\frac{1}{4}z$	"of" indicates multiplication
(d) The quotient of a number and 9	$\dfrac{z}{9}$	"quotient" indicates division
(e) The quotient of 8 and a number	$\dfrac{8}{z}$	"quotient" indicates division
(f) The sum of 6 and a number, multiplied by 8.3	$8.3(6 + z)$	multiplying a sum requires parentheses

■

NOTE If you are adding or multiplying, the order of the variable and the number does not matter. For example,

$$3 + x = x + 3 \quad \text{and} \quad 5 \cdot y = y \cdot 5$$

However, the order *does make a difference* in both division and subtraction, as you can see.

Is not equal to

$$8 - 3 \neq 3 - 8$$
$$12 \div 5 \neq 5 \div 12$$

Translating statements into mathematical expressions and equations helps us solve many real-world application problems. Use the following steps *every time* you solve a problem to become a better problem solver.

Solving Application Problems

Step 1 **First, read the problem very carefully**. Then reread the problem to make sure that its meaning is clear. Sometimes a sketch helps.

Step 2 **Identify the unknown** and give it a variable name such as x. If possible, write other unknowns as mathematical expressions in terms of the same variable.

Step 3 **Write an equation** describing the relationship given in the problem.

Step 4 **Solve the equation**.

Step 5 **Answer the question(s)** asked in the problem.

Step 6 **Check the solution** using the *original* words of the problem.

Step 7 **Be sure your answer is reasonable**.

NOTE The third step is often the hardest. To write an equation from the information given in the problem, convert the facts stated in words into mathematical expressions and then into equations.

Objective

2 *Write Equations from Given Information.* Any words that mean *equals* or *same* translate into an equal sign ($=$), producing an equation that can be solved for the unknown.

EXAMPLE **4** **Solving Number Problems**

Translate the following statement into an equation: The product of 5, and a number decreased by 8, is 100. Use y as the variable. Solve the equation.

Solution

The phrase "and a number decreased by 8" is set off by commas from the other parts of the sentence. So, it should have parentheses around it to keep that logic intact.

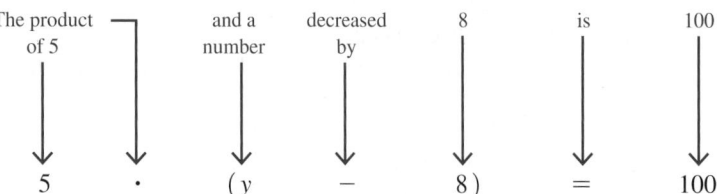

| The product of 5 | | and a number | decreased by | 8 | is | 100 |

$$5 \cdot (y - 8) = 100$$

Simplify and complete the solution of the equation.

$$5 \cdot (y - 8) = 100$$
$$5y - 40 = 100 \quad \text{Apply the distributive property.}$$
$$5y = 140 \quad \text{Add 40 to both sides.}$$
$$y = 28 \quad \text{Divide by 5.}$$

Check the answer to make sure it is correct.

∎

NOTE If Example 4 had been written as "The product of 5 and a number, decreased by 8, is 100," then the corresponding equation would be $5y - 8 = 100$ rather than $5(y - 8) = 100$.

Objective

3 *Solve Application Problems.*

EXAMPLE **5** **Solving an Application Problem**

A mattress for a single bed is on sale for $200, which is $\frac{4}{5}$ of its original price. Find the original price.

Solution

STEP 1 The mattress is on sale for $200, so it must have been priced at more than $200 originally. Let p represent the original price; $200 is the sale price, and the sale price is $\frac{4}{5}$ of the original price. Use all this information to write the equation.

STEP 2 Identify the unknown.   Sale price is $\frac{4}{5}$ of original price.

$$\downarrow \quad \downarrow \quad \downarrow \quad \downarrow$$

STEP 3 Write the equation. $\$200 = \frac{4}{5} \cdot p$

STEP 4 Solve the equation.

$$200 = \frac{4}{5} \cdot p$$

$$\frac{5}{4} \cdot 200 = \frac{5}{4} \cdot \frac{4}{5} \cdot p \quad \text{Multiply by reciprocal.}$$

$$\frac{1000}{4} = 1 \cdot p$$

$$250 = p$$

STEP 5 The original price was $250.

STEP 6 Check the solution.

$$\$200 = \frac{4}{5} \cdot p$$

$$\$200 \stackrel{?}{=} \frac{4}{5} \cdot \$250 \quad \text{Substitute \$250 for } p.$$

$$\$200 = \$200$$

The answer checks.

STEP 7 Is $250 a reasonable price for a mattress before it was on sale? Yes.

EXAMPLE **6** **Solving an Inventory Problem**

The Eastside Nursery ordered 27 saplings. Some of the saplings were elms, costing $17 each, while the rest were maples at $11 each. The total cost of the saplings was $375. Find the number of elms and the number of maples.

Solution

STEP 1 Let x represent the number of elm saplings, then $(27 - x)$ is the number of maple saplings. The total cost of the elm saplings is $17x$ and the total cost of the maple saplings is $11(27 - x)$. A table can be very helpful in identifying the knowns and unknowns.

STEP 2

	Number of Saplings	Cost per Sapling	Total Cost
Elms	x	$17	$17x$
Maples	$(27 - x)$	$11	$11(27 - x)$
Totals	**27**		**$375**

STEP 3 The information in the rightmost column of the table is used to produce the following equation.

$$\text{Cost of elms} + \text{cost of maples} = \text{total cost}$$

$$17x + 11(27 - x) = 375$$

STEP 4 Now solve this equation. First use the distributive property.

$$17x + 297 - 11x = 375$$

$$6x + 297 = 375 \quad \text{Combine terms with } x.$$

$$6x = 78 \quad \text{Subtract 297 from each side.}$$

$$x = 13 \quad \text{Divide each side by 6.}$$

STEPS 5–6 Answer the question and check the solution.

Number of elm saplings is $x = 13$

Number of maple saplings is $(27 - x) = (27 - 13) = 14$

Total number of saplings is $13 + 14 = 27$

Total cost of sapling is $(13 \times \$17) + (14 - \$11) = \$375$

STEP 7 Are the values reasonable? Yes.

EXAMPLE 7 **Solving Investment Application Problems**

After selling her small dress shop, Laurie Zimmerman has $15,000 to invest. She places a portion of the funds in a savings account and $3000 more than twice this amount in a retirement account. How much is put into the savings account? How much is placed in the retirement account?

Solution

Let z be the amount invested in the savings account. To find the amount invested in the retirement account, translate as follows.

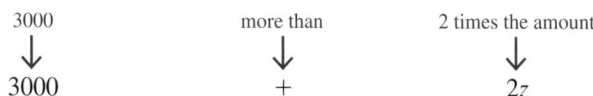

3000	more than	2 times the amount
↓	↓	↓
3000	+	$2z$

Since the sum of the two investments must be $15,000, an equation can be formed as follows.

Amount invested in savings	+	Amount invested in retirement account	=	Total amount invested
z	+	$(3000 + 2z)$	=	$15,000

Now solve the equation.

$$z + (3000 + 2z) = 15{,}000$$

$z + 3000 + 2z = 15{,}000$ Remove parentheses.

$3z + 3000 = 15{,}000$ Combine like terms.

$3z = 12{,}000$ Subtract 3000 from both sides.

$z = 4000$ Divide by 3.

The amount invested in the savings account is $4000. The amount invested in the retirement account is $3000 + 2z$, or $3000 + 2($4000) = $11,000.

Check the solution as follows:

$$\$4000 + (\$3000 + 2 \cdot \$4000) = \$15{,}000$$

The answer checks.

NOTE In the parentheses above, remember to multiply $2 \cdot \$4000$ before adding $3000.

2.2	**Exercises**

Write the following as mathematical expressions. Use x as the variable.

1. 27 plus a number $27 + x$

2. the sum of a number and $16\frac{1}{2}$ $x + 16\frac{1}{2}$

3. a number added to 22 $22 + x$

4. 6.8 added to a number $6.8 + x$

5. 4 less than a number $x - 4$

6. 12 fewer than a number $x - 12$

7. subtract $3\frac{1}{2}$ from a number $x - 3\frac{1}{2}$

8. subtract a number from 5.4 $5.4 - x$

9. triple a number $3x$

10. the product of a number and 9 $9x$

11. three-fifths of a number $\frac{3}{5}x$

12. four-thirds of a number $\frac{4}{3}x$

13. the quotient of 9 and a number $\frac{9}{x}$

14. the quotient of a number and 11 $\frac{x}{11}$

15. 16 divided by a number $\frac{16}{x}$

16. a number divided by 4 $\frac{x}{4}$

17. the product of 2.1 and the sum of 4 and a number $2.1(4 + x)$

18. the quantity of a number plus 4, divided by 9 $(x + 4) \div 9$

19. 7 times the difference of a number and 3 $7(x - 3)$

20. the difference of a number and 2, multiplied by 7 $(x - 2)7$

Write mathematical expressions for each of the following.

21. PURCHASING DVDs   Find the cost of 12 DVDs at y dollars each. $12y$

22. TUITION FEES   Find the cost of x students paying tuition of $2800 each. $2800x$

23. LIVESTOCK FEED   The demand forecast for next month is 472 tons of livestock feed. Find the amount that should be ordered if inventory is x tons. $472 - x$

24. LAPTOP USERS   Eighty-three of the x employees have laptops. How many do not have laptops? $x - 83$

25. UNION MEMBERSHIP   A company has 73 employees of whom x are members of a union. How many employees are not union members? $73 - x$

26. CARD SALES   The inventory of a small card shop is valued at $73,000. The value of the greeting cards is x. Find the value of the rest of the inventory. $73,000 - x$

27. TEXTBOOK PURCHASES   A college bookstore paid $20,210 to purchase x textbooks for a biology class. Find the cost of one textbook. $\frac{20,210}{x}$

28. SKI LODGE A group paid $1853 to a ski lodge so that its x members can ski for the day. Find the cost per person. $\frac{1853}{x}$

29. CHARITABLE DONATIONS   Robin has 21 books on computers. She donates x of them to the school library. How many does she have left? $21 - x$

30. TIRE SHOP   A tire shop is x years od. How old was it 8 years ago? $x - 8$

Solve the following application problems. Steps 1–7 are repeated here for your convenience—use them.

Solving Applied Problems

Step 1 Read the problem carefully. Sometimes a sketch helps.
Step 2 Identify the unknown and choose a variable to represent it. If possible, write any other unknowns in terms of the same variable.
Step 3 Translate the problem into an equation.
Step 4 Solve the equation.
Step 5 Answer the question(s) asked in the problem.
Step 6 Check your solution using the original words of the problem.
Step 7 Be sure your answer is reasonable.

31. Four times a number, plus 6, equals 58. Find the number.   13

32. Seventeen times a number, plus 5, equals 107. Find the number.   6

33. Six times the quantity of 4 minus a number is 15. Find the number.   1.5

34. Twelve times the quantity of a number less 1 is 72. Find the number.   7

35. When 6 is added to a number, the result is 7 times the number. Find the number.   1

36. If 6 is subtracted from three times a number, the result is 4 more than the number. Find the number.   5

37. When 5 times a number is added to twice the number, the result is 10. Find the number. $1\frac{3}{7}$

38. If 7 times a number is subtracted from 11 times the number, the result is 9. Find the number. $2\frac{1}{4}$

39. CAR STEREO   Last month, Ben Jamison sold 17 more car stereos than did the other salesperson at the store. If the two salespeople sold a total of 101 stereos, find the number sold by Jamison.   59 stereos

40. SODA SALES   A grocery store sold 19 more cases of Coke than Sprite. Given that 43 cases were sold, find the number of cases of Coke sold.   31 cases

41. PLEASURE BOATS   One hundred eighty-five more people work in building the boats than are in management, accounting, finance, and marketing. Given a total of 229 employees, find the number working in building the boats.   207

42. EXCHANGE PROGRAM TO MEXICO   Twenty-one students went on a student exchange program to Guadalajara, Mexico. There were 11 more women than men. Find the number of women.   16

43. AUTOMOBILE   A 1-year-old automobile is marked "on sale" for $18,450, which is $\frac{9}{10}$ of its original price. Find the original price. $20,500

44. INTERNATIONAL SHIPMENTS   Because of handling and freight charges, Western Oil Equipment charges $\frac{5}{4}$ of the list price for an item shipped to Indonesia. Find the list price of an item that was charged at $725. $580

45. HOME CONSTRUCTION   A contractor built 105 homes last year, some economy models and some deluxe models. The number of economy models was $\frac{3}{2}$ the number of deluxe models. Find the number of each type of home that was built.   42 deluxe; 63 economy

46. CULINARY SCHOOL   Last quarter, the Regency Culinary School spent $18,000 on advertising using radio and newspaper. The amount spent on newspaper advertising was $\frac{5}{4}$ that spent on radio advertising. Find the amount spent on each type of advertising. $8000 radio ads; $10,000 newspaper ads

47. RADIO STATION SALARIES   Radio station KLRS spent $32,490 on salaries one month. The amount spent on announcers was $\frac{4}{5}$ the amount spent on all other employees. Find the amount spent on announcers and on all other employees. $14,440 announcers; $18,050 all other employees

48. BUSY INTERSECTION   An engineer is studying a busy intersection. In 1 hour, the number of cars going north-south was $\frac{3}{4}$ of those going east-west, and the total number of cars was 1400. Find the number of cars going north-south and east-west.   east-west = 800; north-south = 600

49. COMMERCIAL BUILDING   Jane Anderson purchased a run-down, empty commercial building and plans to fix it up. The building can be used for both retail stores and office space. She thinks she can get a total annual rent of $135,000 with $3\frac{1}{2}$ times as much rent coming from retail stores as from office space. Find the rent she expects from office space and also the rent she expects from retail stores.   office space $30,000; retail stores $105,000

50. OAK FLOOR   Jimmie Gonzales is laying a wood floor. He has a piece of wood that is 106 inches long that needs to be cut so that one piece is 12 inches longer than the other. What is the length of each piece?   47 inches; 59 inches

51. HARLEY DAVIDSON   Excluding managers, there are 22 full-time employees working at a large Harley Davidson shop. New employees receive $9.50 per hour, while more experienced workers average $12.90 per hour. The company spends $273.60 per hour in wages, not counting benefits. Find the number of each type of nonmanagement worker.   3 new; 19 experienced

52. VEGETABLE SALES   Jumbo Market makes $0.10 on a head of lettuce and $0.08 on a bunch of carrots. Last week, a total of 12,900 heads of lettuce and bunches of carrots were sold, with a total profit of $1174. How many heads of lettuce and how many bunches of carrots were sold?   7100 heads of lettuce; 5800 bunches of carrots

53. NISSAN SALES   Profits on Nissan Altimas and Sentras average $1200 and $850, respectively, at one dealership. The total profit in a month in which they sold 120 of these models was $130,350. Find the number of each sold.   81 Altimas; 39 Sentras

54. AUTO REPAIR   One month, revenue from the 95 repairs at an auto repair shop totaled $20,040. The average charges for repairs on personal and commercial vehicles were $250 and $180, respectively. Find the number of each type of vehicle repaired.   42 personal; 53 commercial

55. Are the problems in this section difficult for you? Explain why or why not. Explain two things you would recommend to a classmate who is having difficulty.

56. Write out the steps necessary to solve an applied problem. (See Objective 3.)

2.3	**Formulas**

OBJECTIVES

1 *Evaluate formulas for given values of the variables.*

2 *Solve formulas for a specific variable.*

3 *Use standard business formulas to solve word problems.*

4 *Evaluate formulas containing exponents.*

In business, **formulas** are often used to show the relationships between variables. Sooner or later, almost all businesses borrow money from banks to buy inventory, make payroll, pay bills, build a new showroom, etc. The following formula is commonly used to find the interest when borrowing:

$$\text{Interest} = \text{principal} \times \text{rate} \times \text{time}$$
$$I = \quad P \quad \times R \times T$$

This equation is usually written without the multiplication signs as $I = PRT$, where

$I =$ interest in dollars

$P =$ principal, or amount borrowed, in dollars

$R =$ interest rate, *which must be written as a decimal number*

$T =$ time written as a fraction of a year

Objective

1 *Evaluate Formulas for Given Values of the Variables.* Once any three values are substituted into the formula $I = PRT$, we can then find the value of the remaining variable.

EXAMPLE 1 **Finding Interest**

Use the formula $I = PRT$ to find I if $P = \$12{,}500$, R is 8%, or 0.08, and $T = 1$ year.

Solution

Substitute \$12,500 for P, 0.08 for R, and 1 for T in the formula $I = PRT$.

$$I = PRT$$
$$I = \$12{,}500 \times 0.08 \times 1 \qquad \text{Substitute values.}$$
$$I = 1000 \qquad\qquad\qquad \text{\$1000 interest.}$$

EXAMPLE 2 **Finding Time**

Use the formula $I = PRT$ to find T if $P = \$4000$, $I = \$720$, and R is 9%, or 0.09.

Solution

Substitute the given numbers for the variables in the formula.

$$I = PRT$$
$$\$720 = \$4000(0.09)T$$
$$\$720 = 360T$$
$$\frac{\$720}{360} = \frac{360T}{360} \qquad \text{Divide by 360.}$$
$$2 = T$$

Since T is in years, the answer is 2 years. Check by substituting values for P, R, and T.

$$I = PRT$$
$$= \$4000 \cdot 0.09 \cdot 2$$
$$= \$720$$

The interest checks.

Objective

2   *Solve Formulas for a Specific Variable.* In Example 2 we found the value of T when given the values of P, I, and R. If several problems of this type must be solved, it may be better to rewrite the formula $I = PRT$ so that T is alone on one side of the equation. Do this using the rules to solve equations given earlier. Since T is multiplied by PR, get T alone by dividing both sides of the equation by PR.

$$I = PRT$$

$$\frac{I}{PR} = \frac{PRT}{PR} \qquad \text{Divide by } PR.$$

$$\frac{I}{PR} = \frac{\cancel{PR}T}{\cancel{PR}} \qquad \text{Cancel.}$$

$$\frac{I}{PR} = T \quad or \quad T = \frac{I}{PR}$$

This process of rearranging a formula is sometimes called *solving a formula for a specific variable*.

EXAMPLE 3   **Solving for a Specific Variable**

Solve for T in the formula $M = P(1 + RT)$.

Solution

This formula is explained in Chapter 11, so for now even though you may not be familiar with this formula, just work with the variables. Start by using the distributive property on the right side.

$$M = P(1 + RT)$$
$$M = P + PRT$$

Work to isolate T on the right hand side by subtracting P from both sides.

$$M - P = P + PRT - P$$
$$M - P = PRT$$

Divide each side by PR.

$$\frac{M - P}{PR} = \frac{\cancel{PR}T}{\cancel{PR}} \qquad \text{Cancel.}$$

$$\frac{M - P}{PR} = T \quad or \quad T = \frac{M - P}{PR}$$

The original formula is now solved for T.

EXAMPLE **4** **Solving for a Specific Variable**

An employee earns \$7.89 per hour plus \$0.45 for each circuit board she assembles. **(a)** Write an equation for her total income (T) in terms of hours (H) and number of circuit boards assembled (C). **(b)** Solve for the variable C. **(c)** Use this to find the number of circuit boards she must assemble in a 40-hour week in order to earn \$450.

Solution

(a) Her total earnings are the sum of her hourly wage times the number of hours plus the amount for each circuit board times the number of circuit boards assembled.

$$T = 7.89H + 0.45C$$

(b) $T - 7.89H = 7.89H + 0.45C - 7.89H$ Subtract 7.89H from both sides.

$$T - 7.89H = 0.45C$$

$$\frac{T - 7.89H}{0.45} = \frac{0.45C}{0.45}$$ Divide by 0.45.

$$C = \frac{T - 7.89H}{0.45}$$

(c) Substitute \$450 in place of T and 40 in place of H.

$$C = \frac{450 - 7.89(40)}{0.45}$$

$$C = \frac{450 - 315.6}{0.45}$$ Multiply first.

$$C = \frac{134.4}{0.45}$$

$$C = 298.666\ldots$$ Round to 299.

She must assemble 299 circuit boards.

 **Scientific Calculator Approach**

Solve this euquation using a scientific calculator as follows.

First find the numerator: 450 $\boxed{-}$ 7.89 $\boxed{\times}$ 40 $\boxed{=}$ 134.4 $\boxed{\text{STO}}$.

Divide by the denominator: $\boxed{\text{RCL}}$ $\boxed{\div}$ $.45$ $\boxed{=}$ $298.666\ldots$

Objective

3 **_Use Standard Business Formulas to Solve Word Problems._** In the following two examples, application problems that use some common business formulas are solved. These formulas are discussed in more detail later in the book.

EXAMPLE **5** **Finding Gross Sales**

Use $G = NP$ to find the gross sales from selling 339 DVDs at \$14.95 each.

Solution

In this formula, N is the number of items sold and P is the price per item.

$$G = NP$$
$$G = 339 \cdot \$14.95$$
$$G = \$5068.05$$

The gross sales are \$5068.05.

EXAMPLE 6 Finding Selling Price

Use $S = C + M$ to find the selling price of a battle-simulator computer game if the cost is $19.08 and the markup is $10.87.

Solution

The variable C is the cost of the item, and M is the markup, which is added to cover expenses and profit.

$$S = C + M$$
$$S = \$19.08 + \$10.87$$
$$= \$29.95$$

The selling price of each game is $29.95.

Objective

4 *Evaluate Formulas Containing Exponents.* Exponents are used to show repeated multiplication of some quantity. For example,

Exponent: number of times quantity is multiplied by itself

$$x \cdot x = x^2$$

Base: quantity being multiplied

Similarly, $z \cdot z \cdot z = z^3$ and $5 \cdot 5 \cdot 5 \cdot 5 = 5^4$, which is 625. Exponents are also referred to as "powers." For example, x^5 is "x to the fifth power."

EXAMPLE 7 Finding Monthly Sales

Trinity Home Furnishings has found that total monthly sales for its small chain of stores can be estimated as follows.

$$\text{Sales} = \$148{,}500 + 0.48 \cdot A^2$$

where A = amount spent on advertising. Estimate sales for a month when $500 is spent for advertising.

Solution

Substitute $500 in place of A in the equation.

$$\text{Sales} = \$148{,}500 + 0.48 \cdot A^2$$
$$= \$148{,}500 + 0.48 \cdot \$500^2 \quad \text{Substitute \$500 in place of } A.$$
$$= \$148{,}500 + 0.48 \cdot \$250{,}000 \quad \text{First evaluate the exponent.}$$
$$= \$268{,}500 \quad \text{Then multiply, and finally add.}$$

Total monthly sales are projected to be $268,500 for the month.

2.3	**Exercises**

In the following exercises a formula is given, along with the values of all but one of the variables in the formula. Find the value of the variable that is not given. Round to the nearest hundredth, if applicable.

1. $I = PRT$; $P = \$4600$, $R = 0.085$, $T = 1\frac{1}{2}$ $586.50

2. $F = ma$; $m = 820$, $a = 12$ 9840

3. $P = B \times R$; $B = \$168,000, R = 0.06$ $\$10,080$

4. $B = \dfrac{P}{R}$; $P = \$1200, R = 0.08$ $\$15,000$

5. $s = c + m$; $c = \$14, m = \$2.50$ $\$16.50$

6. $m = s - c$; $s = \$24,200, c = \$2800$ $\$21,400$

7. $P = 2L + 2W$; $P = 40, W = 6$ 14

8. $P = 2L + 2W$; $P = 340; L = 70$ 100

9. $P = \dfrac{1}{RT}$; $T = 3, I = 540, R = 0.08$ 2250

10. $M = P(1 + RT)$; $R = 0.15, T = 2, M = 481$ 370

11. $y = mx^2 + c$; $m = 3, x = 7, c = 4.2$ 151.2

12. $C = \$5 + \$0.10N$; $N = 38$ $\$8.80$

13. $M = P(1 + i)^n$; $P = \$640, i = 0.02, n = 8$ $\$749.86$

14. $M = P(1 + i)^n$; $M = \$2400, i = 0.05, n = 4$ $\$1974.49$

15. $E = mc^2$; $m = 7.5, c = 1$ 7.5

16. $x = \dfrac{1}{2}at^2$; $t = 5, x = 150$ 12

17. $A = \dfrac{1}{2}(b + B)h$; $A = 105, b = 19, B = 11$ 7

18. $A = \dfrac{1}{2}(b + B)h$; $A = 70, b = 15, B = 20$ 4

19. $P = \dfrac{S}{1 + RT}$; $S = 24,600, R = 0.06, T = \dfrac{5}{12}$ $24,000$

20. $P = \dfrac{S}{1 + RT}$; $S = 23,815, R = 0.09, T = \dfrac{11}{12}$ $22,000$

Solve each formula for the indicated variable.

21. $A = LW$; for L $\dfrac{A}{W}$

22. $d = rt$; for t $\dfrac{d}{r}$

23. $PV = nRT$; for V $\dfrac{nRT}{P}$

24. $I = PRT$; for R $\dfrac{I}{PT}$

25. $M = P(1 + i)^n$; for P $\dfrac{M}{(1 + i)^n}$

26. $R(1 - DT) = D$; for R $\dfrac{D}{1 - DT}$

27. $P = \dfrac{A}{1 + i}$; for i $\dfrac{(A - P)}{P}$

28. $M = P(1 + RT)$; for R $\dfrac{M - P}{PT}$

29. $P = M(1 - DT)$; for D $\dfrac{(M - P)}{MT}$

30. $P = \dfrac{M}{1 + RT}$; for R $\dfrac{M - P}{PT}$

31. $A = \dfrac{1}{2}(b + B)h$; for h $\dfrac{2A}{(b + B)}$

32. $P = 2L + 2W$; for L $\dfrac{P - 2W}{2}$

Solve the following application problems.

33. **CARNIVAL**   A carnival purchases 1800 stuffed animals to give to people who win at carnival games. Given a total cost of $4320, find the cost per stuffed animal. $\$2.40$

34. **WEB PAGES**   A retailer paid $1305 to a college student who designed and added 15 pages to the firm's Web site. Find the cost per Web page. $\$87$

35. **MUSICAL INSTRUMENTS**   The Guitar Shoppe bought 6 sets of bongo drums and 7 Alvarez guitars for $2445.80. The guitars cost $269 apiece. Find the cost for a set of bongo drums. $\$93.80$

36. **REFRIGERATORS**   An appliance store bought 8 high-efficiency refrigerators and 10 washer/dryer combination sets. The store's cost for a washer/dryer was $462 and the total paid for all of the appliances was $10,860. Find the cost of a refrigerator. $\$780$

37. CLOTHING STORE   The weekly salary for each salesperson at a clothing store is found using the formula $S = \$280 + 0.05x$, where $x =$ employee's total sales for the week. Find the salary of two employees with the following weekly sales: **(a)** $2940 and **(b)** $4450.   (a) $427 (b) $502.50

38. LENGTH OF AN INVESTMENT   A principal (P) of $3500 invested over an unknown amount of time (T) at 9.5% $(R = 0.095)$ yields $748.13 in interest (I). Use $I = PRT$ to find the time rounded to the nearest hundredth of a year.   2.25 years

39. COMPUTER CHIPS   A computer chip manufacturer had net sales of $230 million with returns equal to $\frac{1}{40}$ of gross sales. Find gross sales rounded to the nearest million given that net sales equals gross sales less returns. $236 million

40. BRIDAL SHOP   One month, the Bridal Shop had net sales of $33,000 and return(s) of $\frac{1}{12}$ of gross sales. If net sales equal gross sales minus returns, find gross sales. $36,000

41. MOVIES   The manager of one theatre marks up the cost of chocolate-covered raisins by $\frac{3}{4}$ of the cost of the raisins. Find the cost to the theater cent if the theatre sells the raisins for $5.95. (*Hint:* Selling price is cost plus markup.) $3.40

42. TEXTBOOK COSTS   A college bookstore marks textbooks up by $\frac{1}{4}$ the cost of the book. Find the cost to the bookstore of a book it sells for $160, where selling price is cost plus markup. $128

43. PIZZA   Last year, the expenses at Mack's Pizzeria were $\frac{5}{6}$ of the total revenue and the remainder was profit. The profit, or the total revenue less expenses, was $107,400. Find the total revenue. $644,400

44. COMPUTER SALES   Computerworld has expenses that run $\frac{15}{16}$ of revenue. One month's profit (the difference between revenue and expenses) was $18,000. Find the revenue. $288,000

In Exercises 45–49, use the formula $I = PRT$ where $I =$ *interest* in dollars, $P =$ *principal* or loan amount, $R =$ *interest rate* written as a decimal, and $T =$ *time* in years.

45. FINDING INTEREST   Find the interest if principal of $5200 is invested at $7\frac{1}{2}\%$ (or 0.075) for 1 year. $(I = PRT)$ $390

46. LOAN TO AN UNCLE   Ben Cross loaned $8000 to his uncle for 4 years and received $1920 in interest. Find the interest rate. $(I = PRT)$ 0.06, or 6%

47. AUTO PARTS STARTUP   Terry Twitty made a $22,000 loan so that Melissa Graves could start an auto parts business. The loan was for 2 years, and interest of $5720 was high since the loan was risky. Find the rate of interest. $(I = PRT)$ 0.13, or 13%

48. FINDING TIME   Fred Tausz loaned $39,000 to his sister. The loan was at 7% (or 0.07), with interest of $13,650. Find the time for the loan. $(I = PRT)$ 5 years

49. STUDENT LOAN   Joan Summers borrowed $5850 (P) from her brother to help pay for her last year in college. They agreed to an interest rate (R) of 3% and a final interest amount (I) of $702. Use $I = PRT$ to find the time of the loan.   4 years

In Exercises 50–54, $M =$ *maturity value* at the end of the loan, $P =$ *principal* or loan amount, $I =$ *interest rate* written as a decimal, $n =$ *number of years*, and $R =$ *annual interest rate* written as a decimal.

50. MATURITY VALUE   Mary Scott invests $1000 at 4% (or 0.04) for 5 years. What maturity value M did Mary have in her account at the end of 5 years? $[M = P(1 + RT)]$ $1200

51. SAVING   John Wood had $4560 in his retirement account after 2 years. If the account returned 7% (or 0.07), how much did John initially deposit in his account? $[M = P(1 + RT)]$ $4000

52. ANTIQUES   Jan Reus borrowed $12,500 from her uncle to help start an antique shop. She repaid $14,750 exactly 2 years later. Find the interest rate. $[M = P(1 + RT)]$ 9%

53. LOAN AMOUNT Bill Abel paid a maturity value of $5668.20 on a 3-year note with annual interest of 8% (or 0.08). Use $M = P(1 + i)^n$, where n is the number of years in this problem, to solve for the amount borrowed rounded to the nearest dollar. $4500

54. INHERITANCE Maybelle Jackson inherited $8500 when her grandfather died. She placed the money in a bank certificate of deposit that paid 3.5% per year and planned to leave it there for 20 years until she retires. Use $M = P(1 + i)^n$ to solve for the maturity value, assuming the interest rate stays the same. $16,913.21

 55. Write a step-by-step explanation of the procedure you would use to solve the equation $A = P + PRT$ for R. (See Objective 2.)

 56. Formulas are used in business, physics, biology, chemistry, engineering, and many other fields. Why are formulas so commonly used? (See Objective 1.)

2.4	**Ratios and Proportions**

OBJECTIVES

1 *Define a ratio.*

2 *Set up a proportion.*

3 *Solve a proportion for any unknown value.*

4 *Use proportions to solve problems.*

Objective

1 *Define a Ratio.* A **ratio** is a quotient of two quantities that is used to compare the quantities. The ratio of the number a to the number b is written in any of the following ways.

$$a \text{ to } b \quad a : b \quad \frac{a}{b}$$

This last way of writing a ratio is most common in algebra, and $a : b$ is perhaps most common in business. Read $a : b$ as "a is to b." Both quantities in a ratio should be in *the same units if possible*—that is, cents to cents or dollars to dollars, not dollars to cents. However, many ratios will not have the same units in the numerator and denominator, such as one involving a worker's pay of $9 per hour or a rate such as 45 miles per hour.

EXAMPLE **1** **Writing Ratios from Words**

Write a ratio in the form $\frac{a}{b}$ for each phrase. (Notice in each phrase that the number mentioned first always becomes the numerator.)

Solution

(a) The ratio of 3 women to 5 children is $\frac{3}{5}$.

(b) To find the ratio of $12 to 20 cents, first convert $12 to cents ($12 = 1200 cents); then write the ratio.

$$\frac{1200}{20} = \frac{60}{1} \quad or \quad 60 : 1$$

The exact same ratio results if you first convert 20 cents to $0.20 (dollars) and then work in dollars, as shown here.

$$\frac{12}{0.20} = \frac{60}{1} \quad or \quad 60 : 1$$

(c) General Motors car and truck sales fell from 1,900,000 units in 1929 to 525,000 units during 1932, the worst year of the Depression. Write unit sales as a ratio.

$$\frac{1,900,\cancel{000}}{525,\cancel{000}} = \frac{1900}{525} = \frac{76}{21}$$

↳ Cancel matching final zeros.

(d) A dairy farmer received $1000 for 5000 pounds of milk. Write this as a ratio.

$$\frac{1000}{5000} = \frac{1}{5} \quad or \quad \$1 \text{ for every 5 pounds}$$

■

NOTE   As done in Example 1(b), always change the numbers to the same units before writing as a ratio.

Objective

2   *Set Up a Proportion.* A ratio is used to compare two numbers or amounts. A **proportion** says that two ratios are equal, as in the following example.

$$\frac{3}{4} = \frac{15}{20}$$

The ratios $\frac{a}{b}$ and $\frac{c}{d}$ are said to form a proportion if $\frac{a}{b} = \frac{c}{d}$. This can be determined by multiplying both sides of the equation by the product of the two denominators.

$$\frac{a}{b} = \frac{c}{d}$$

$$\cancel{b}d \cdot \frac{a}{\cancel{b}} = b\cancel{d} \cdot \frac{c}{\cancel{d}} \quad \text{Multiply both sides by the product of the two denominators.}$$

$$ad = bc$$

Therefore, $\frac{a}{b} = \frac{c}{d}$ if, and only if, $ad = bc$. This is referred to as the **method of cross products.**

is equivalent to $ad = bc$.

NOTE   The numbers in a proportion need not be whole numbers.

EXAMPLE 2   Determining True Proportions

Decide if the following proportions are true.

(a) $\dfrac{3}{4} = \dfrac{25}{30}$ **(b)** $\dfrac{6.5}{\frac{3}{4}} = \dfrac{130}{15}$

Solution

(a) Find each cross product.

$$\frac{3}{4} \diagup\!\!\!\!\diagdown \frac{25}{30}$$

$$3 \cdot 30 = 4 \cdot 25$$

$$90 \ne 100 \quad \text{The symbol } \ne \text{ means "not equal."}$$

Since the cross products are not equal, the proportion is false.

(b) Find each cross product.

$$6.5 \cdot 15 = \frac{3}{4} \cdot 130$$

$$97.5 = 0.75 \cdot 130$$

$$97.5 = 97.5$$

The proportion is true.

Objective

3   *Solve a Proportion for Any Unknown Value.* Four numbers are used in a proportion. If *any* three of these numbers are known, *the fourth can be found.*

EXAMPLE **3**   **Finding Unknown Values in a Proportion**

Find the unknown that makes each proportion true.

(a) $\dfrac{4}{9} = \dfrac{36}{x}$ **(b)** $\dfrac{3.4}{12} = \dfrac{z}{96}$

Solution

(a) Set the cross products equal to one another and then solve the resulting equation.

$$4 \cdot x = 9 \cdot 36$$

$$4x = 324$$

$$\frac{4x}{4} = \frac{324}{4} \qquad \text{Divide by 4.}$$

$$x = 81$$

Check by confirming that $\frac{4}{9}$ does equal $\frac{36}{81}$.

(b) Set the cross products equal to one another.

$$3.4 \cdot 96 = 12 \cdot z$$

$$326.4 = 12z$$

$$\frac{326.4}{12} = \frac{12z}{12} \qquad \text{Divide by 12.}$$

$$27.2 = z$$

Objective

4   *Use Proportions to Solve Problems.* Proportions are used in many practical applications, including the following.

EXAMPLE **4**   **Foreign Currency Exchange**

While in Mexico on an exchange trip, Laura Axtell needed to exchange $75 U.S. for Mexican pesos. If $1 U.S. is equivalent to 11 Mexican pesos, how many pesos will she receive?

Solution

Set the problem up as a proportion and solve for the unknown.

$$\frac{\$1 \text{ U.S.}}{11 \text{ Mexican pesos}} = \frac{\$75 \text{ U.S.}}{x \text{ Mexican pesos}}$$

$$1 \cdot x = 11 \times 75$$

$$x = 825$$

Axtell will receive 825 Mexican pesos.

■

EXAMPLE 5   Solving Applications

A hospital charges a patient $117 for 12 capsules. How much will it charge for 18 capsules?

Solution

Let x be the cost of 18 capsules. Set up a proportion: one ratio in the proportion can involve the number of capsules, while the other ratio can use the costs. Make sure that corresponding numbers appear in the numerator and the denominator. Use this pattern.

$$\frac{\text{Capsules}}{\text{Capsules}} = \frac{\text{cost}}{\text{cost}}$$

Now substitute the given information.

$$\frac{12}{18} = \frac{\$117}{x}$$

Use cross products to solve the proportion.

$$12x = 18(\$117)$$

$$12x = \$2106$$

$$x = \$175.50$$

The 18 capsules will cost $175.50.

■

NOTE   In Example 5, you can also arrange the proportion as follows.

$$\frac{\text{cost}}{\text{capsule}} = \frac{\text{cost}}{\text{capsule}} \quad \text{or as} \quad \frac{\$117}{12 \text{ capsules}} = \frac{x}{18 \text{ capsules}}$$

EXAMPLE 6   Solving Applications

A firm in Hong Kong and one in Thailand agree to jointly develop a controller chip to be sold to North American auto manufacturers. They agree to split the development costs in a ratio of 8 : 3 (Hong Kong firm to Thailand firm), resulting in a cost of $9,400,000 to the Hong Kong firm. Find the cost to the Thailand firm.

Solution

Let x represent the cost to the Thailand firm, then

$$\frac{8}{3} = \frac{9,400,000}{x}$$

$$8x = 3 \cdot 9,400,000 \quad \text{Cross multiply.}$$

$$8x = 28,200,000$$

$$x = 3,525,000 \quad \text{Divide by 8.}$$

The Thailand firm's share of the costs is $3,525,000.

■

EXAMPLE **7** **Solving Applications**

Bill Thomas wishes to estimate the amount of timber on some forested land that he owns. One value he needs to estimate is the average height of the trees. One morning, Thomas notices that his own 6-foot body casts an 8-foot shadow at the same time that a tree casts a 34-foot shadow. Find the height of the tree.

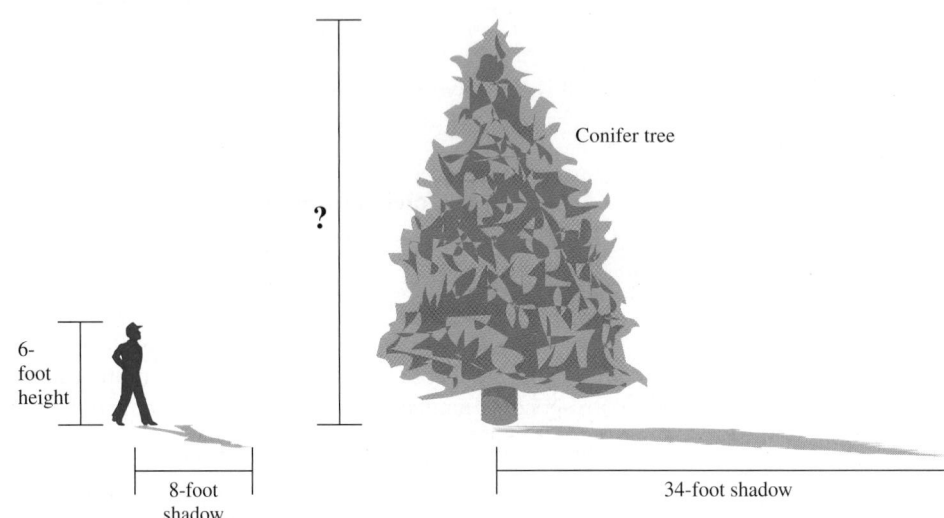

Solution

Set up a proportion in which the height of the tree is given the variable name x. Set up the ratios as height to length of shadow. All numbers are in feet.

$$\frac{6}{8} = \frac{x}{34}$$

$$6 \cdot 34 = 8 \cdot x \qquad \text{Cross multiply.}$$

$$\frac{204}{8} = \frac{8 \cdot x}{8} \qquad \text{Divide by 8.}$$

$$x = 25.5 \text{ feet}$$

Bill Thomas estimates that the tree is 25.5 feet tall.

2.4	**Exercises**

Write the following ratios. Write each ratio in lowest terms.

1. 18 kilometers to 64 kilometers $\dfrac{9}{32}$

2. 18 defects out of 580 items $\dfrac{9}{290}$

3. 216 students to 8 faculty $\dfrac{27}{1}$

4. \$80 in returns to \$8360 in sales $\dfrac{2}{209}$

5. 8 men to 6 women $\dfrac{4}{3}$

6. 12 feet to 1 inch $\dfrac{144}{1}$

7. 30 kilometers (30,000 meters) to 8 meters $\dfrac{3750}{1}$

8. 30 inches to 5 yards $\dfrac{1}{6}$

9. 90 dollars to 40 cents $\dfrac{225}{1}$

10. 148 minutes to 4 hours $\dfrac{37}{60}$

11. 4 dollars to 10 quarters $\dfrac{8}{5}$

12. 35 dimes to 6 dollars $\dfrac{7}{12}$

13. 20 hours to 5 days $\dfrac{1}{6}$

14. 6 days to 9 hours $\dfrac{16}{1}$

15. \$0.80 to \$3 $\dfrac{4}{15}$

16. \$1.20 to \$0.75 $\dfrac{8}{5}$

17. \$3.24 to \$0.72 $\dfrac{9}{2}$

18. \$3.57 to \$0.42 $\dfrac{17}{2}$

Decide whether the following proportions are true or false.

19. $\dfrac{3}{5} = \dfrac{21}{35}$ T

20. $\dfrac{6}{13} = \dfrac{30}{65}$ T

21. $\dfrac{9}{7} = \dfrac{720}{480}$ F

22. $\dfrac{54}{14} = \dfrac{270}{70}$ T

23. $\dfrac{69}{320} = \dfrac{7}{102}$ F

24. $\dfrac{17}{19} = \dfrac{72}{84}$ F

25. $\dfrac{19}{32} = \dfrac{33}{77}$ F

26. $\dfrac{19}{30} = \dfrac{57}{90}$ T

27. $\dfrac{110}{18} = \dfrac{160}{27}$ F

28. $\dfrac{46}{17} = \dfrac{212}{95}$ F

29. $\dfrac{32}{75} = \dfrac{61}{108}$ F

30. $\dfrac{28}{75} = \dfrac{224}{600}$ T

31. $\dfrac{7.6}{10} = \dfrac{76}{100}$ T

32. $\dfrac{95}{64} = \dfrac{320}{217}$ F

33. $\dfrac{2\frac{1}{4}}{5} = \dfrac{9}{20}$ T

34. $\dfrac{\frac{3}{4}}{80} = \dfrac{\frac{9}{8}}{120}$ T

35. $\dfrac{4\frac{1}{5}}{6\frac{1}{8}} = \dfrac{27}{41}$ F

36. $\dfrac{1\frac{1}{2}}{12} = \dfrac{5\frac{1}{4}}{42}$ T

37. $\dfrac{8.15}{2.03} = \dfrac{61.125}{15.225}$ T

38. $\dfrac{423.88}{17.119} = \dfrac{330.6264}{13.35282}$ T

Solve the following proportions.

39. $\dfrac{x}{15} = \dfrac{49}{105}$ 7

40. $\dfrac{y}{35} = \dfrac{27}{315}$ 3

41. $\dfrac{6}{9} = \dfrac{r}{108}$ 72

42. $\dfrac{16}{41} = \dfrac{112}{t}$ 287

43. $\dfrac{63}{s} = \dfrac{3}{5}$ 105

44. $\dfrac{260}{390} = \dfrac{x}{3}$ 2

45. $\dfrac{1}{2} = \dfrac{r}{7}$ $3\frac{1}{2}$

46. $\dfrac{2}{3} = \dfrac{5}{s}$ $7\frac{1}{2}$

47. $\dfrac{\frac{3}{4}}{6} = \dfrac{3}{x}$ 24

48. $\dfrac{3}{x} = \dfrac{11}{9}$ $2\frac{5}{11}$

49. $\dfrac{12}{p} = \dfrac{23.571}{15.714}$ 8

50. $\dfrac{86.112}{57.408} = \dfrac{k}{15}$ 22.5

 51. Explain the difference between ratio and proportion. (See Objective 2.)

 52. Explain cross products using the rules of algebra. (See Objective 2.)

Solve the following application problems.

53. **TICKET SALES** One Ticketmaster outlet sold 350 rock-concert tickets in 2 days. At that rate, find the number of tickets it can expect to sell in 9 days. 1575 tickets

54. **BLOOD CELLS** A 170-pound person has about 30 trillion blood cells. Estimate the number of blood cells in a 140-pound person to the nearest tenth of a trillion. 24.7 trillion

55. **REAL ESTATE DEVELOPMENT** Mike George paid $215,000 for a nice 5-unit apartment house. Estimate the cost for a 12-unit apartment house. $516,000

56. **TIGER FOOD** A 450-pound circus tiger eats 15 pounds of meat per day. How many pounds of meat would you expect a 360-pound tiger to eat per day? 12 pounds

57. **SEWING** If 22 children's dresses cost $660, what is the cost of 12 dresses? $360

58. **BISCUITS** A biscuit recipe that feeds 7 requires 2 cups of flour. How much flour is needed for enough biscuits to feed a church group of 125? Round to the nearest whole number. 36 cups

59. **AUTO PRODUCTION** An auto plant produces 3 red sports models for every 7 blue family models. Find the number of red sports models produced if the plant produces 868 blue family models. 372 red sports models

60. **FERTILIZER COVERAGE** Suppose that 7 sacks of fertilizer cover 3325 square feet at a rose farm. Find the number of sacks needed for 7125 square feet. 15 sacks

61. **MAP READING** The distance between two cities on a road map is 2 inches. Actually, the cities are 120 miles apart. The distance between two other cities is 17 inches. How far apart are these cities? 1020 miles

62. WOMEN'S CLOTHING SHOP   Martha Vinn opened a women's clothing shop and had sales of $3720 during the first 3 weeks. At that rate, estimate sales for the first 4 weeks. $4960

63. HEALTH FOOD SALES   Natural Harvest had sales of $274,312 for the first 20 weeks of the year. Estimate sales for the entire 52-week year. $713,211.20

64. PARTNERSHIP PROFITS   Chester and Gaines have a partnership agreement that calls for profits to be paid in the ratio of 2 : 5, respectively. Find the amount that goes to Chester if Gaines receives $45,000. $18,000

65. OIL PROFITS   The two partners in Alamo Energy agreed to split profits in a ratio of 3 : 8. If the first partner received $48,000 in profits one year, find the profit earned by the second partner. $128,000

66. PRODUCTION EMPLOYEES   The owner of a factory has always kept the ratio of salespeople to production employees at 2 : 7. If she currently has 24 salespeople, how many production employees are there?   84 employees

67. SONGBIRD MIGRATION   Small songbirds in one area migrate at about 20 miles per hour, whereas eider ducks migrate at 35 miles per hour. How far would the eider ducks migrate in the same amount of time it would take songbirds to migrate 200 miles?   350 miles

68. ISLAND AREA   Indonesia has an area of 741,101 square miles and is made up of 13,677 islands. Assume the United States, with an area of 3,618,770 square miles, were similarly broken up into islands. How many islands would there be (to the nearest whole number)?   66,784 islands

69. ICEBERG VOLUME   Seven-eighths of an iceberg is found below the water. Find the amount of an iceberg that is underwater if the amount above water has a volume of 500,000 cubic meters. (*Hint:* $1 - \frac{7}{8} = \frac{1}{8}$ above water.)   3,500,000 cubic meters

70. GLOBAL WARMING   The concentration of carbon dioxide in the atmosphere has increased from 315 parts per million to 380 parts per million in the past 48 years. During the same period of time, the global average temperature increased by 1° Fahrenheit. Estimate the amount of further increase in global average temperature to the nearest tenth of a degree if the concentration of carbon dioxide in the atmosphere increases from 380 parts per million up to 550 parts per million.   Further increase of 2.6° Fahrenheit

71. JAPANESE YEN   Benjamin Lopez was in Japan for 2 months on a business trip. Find the number of U.S. dollars he will receive for 20,355 Japanese yen if $1 U.S. can be exchanged for 80 yen. Round to the nearest cent.   U.S. $254.44

72. WORKING IN CHINA   Gina Harden was offered a job as a teacher at an elite private high school in Beijing at an annual salary of 471,200 yuan. Find the salary in U.S. dollars if 7.25 yuan can be exchanged for $1 U.S. $64,993.10 U.S.

2.5	**Exponents and the Order of Operations**

OBJECTIVES

1 *Understand the basics of exponents.*

2 *Multiply and divide using exponents.*

3 *Apply the Order of Operations.*

4 *Evaluating expressions containing exponents.*

5 *Solving application problems.*

Objective

1   *Understand the Basics of Exponents.* Exponents show repeated multiplication of a quantity by itself. The quantity being multiplied by itself is called the **base**. The number of times it is be multiplied by itself is the **exponent**. For example, $6 \cdot 6$ can be written as follows.

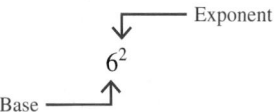

$$6^2$$

Base

Read 6^2 any of the following ways: "6 to the second power," "6 raised to the second power," or "6 squared." Note that the base is the number 6 and the exponent is the number 2, which is written in a smaller type to the upper right of the number 6. Here are several more examples.

	Read as	Base	Exponent	Equal to
5^4	"5 to the 4th power"	5	4	$5 \cdot 5 \cdot 5 \cdot 5$
x^2	"x to the 2nd power, or x squared"	x	2	$x \cdot x$
y^3	"y to the 3rd power, or y cubed"	y	3	$y \cdot y \cdot y$
e^4	"e to the 4th power"	e	4	$e \cdot e \cdot e \cdot e$

If both the base and the exponent are known, we can evaluate the term by simply multiplying.

$$6^2 = 6 \cdot 6 = 36 \quad \text{or} \quad 5^4 = 5 \cdot 5 \cdot 5 \cdot 5 = 625$$

A few important special situations involving exponents are shown in the following table.

Explanation	Examples
Any nonzero value to the power of 0 is defined to be equal to 1.	$4^0 = 1$ $x^0 = 1$ as long as x is not equal to zero
0 to the 0th power is not defined. In other words, it has no meaning and should not be used.	0^0 has no meaning y^0 is undefined when $y = 0$
Any value to the power of 1 is the value itself.	$5^1 = 5$ $z^1 = z$ $0^1 = 0$

Note that the base can be 0 as long as the exponent is not zero. For example,

$$0^3 = 0 \cdot 0 \cdot 0, \quad \text{which equals } 0$$

EXAMPLE **1** **Writing and Evaluating Exponents**

(a) Write $t \cdot t \cdot t$ and $4 \cdot 4$ using exponents.
(b) Evaluate 9^3 and $(25.1)^2$.
(c) Simplify 54^0 and x^1.

Solution

(a) $t \cdot t \cdot t = t^3$ $4 \cdot 4 = 4^2$
(b) $9^3 = 9 \cdot 9 \cdot 9 = 729$ $(25.1)^2 = 25.1 \cdot 25.1 = 630.01$
(c) $54^0 = 1$ $x^1 = x$

Objective

2   *Multiply and Divide Using Exponents.*   There are several convenient rules that make it easier to work with exponents. We will show one rule at a time, give examples for each using both integers and variables, and, finally, explain the concept behind each rule using an example.

RULE 1 $X^m \cdot X^n = X^{(m+n)}$ When multiplying with the same base, add the exponents.

Examples: $7^2 \cdot 7^3 = 7^{(2+3)} = 7^5$ Add the exponents.

$y^4 \cdot y^2 = y^{(4+2)} = y^6$ Add the exponents.

Concept: $7^2 \cdot 7^3 = (7 \cdot 7) \cdot (7 \cdot 7 \cdot 7) = 7^5$ The number of 7s being multiplied is found by adding the two exponents.

RULE 2 $\dfrac{X^m}{X_n} = X^{(m-n)}$ When dividing with the same base, subtract the exponents.

Examples: $\dfrac{9^5}{9^2} = 9^{(5-2)} = 9^3$ Subtract the exponents

$\dfrac{Z^4}{Z^2} = Z^{(4-2)} = Z^2$ Subtract the exponents

Concept: $\dfrac{9^5}{9^2} = \dfrac{9 \cdot 9 \cdot 9 \cdot 9 \cdot 9}{9 \cdot 9} = 9^3$ The number of 9s remaining after canceling is found by subtracting the exponents.

RULE 3 $(X \cdot Y)^n = X^n \cdot Y^n$ Apply the exponent to both values in the parentheses.

Examples: $(8 \cdot 9)^2 = 8^2 \cdot 9^2$ Apply the exponent to both numbers.

$(S \cdot Z)^n = S^n \cdot Z^n$ Apply the exponent to both variables.

Concept: $(8 \cdot 9)^2 = (8 \cdot 9) \cdot (8 \cdot 9)$ Two 8s and two 9s are being multiplied.

$= (8 \cdot 8) \cdot (9 \cdot 9) = 8^2 \cdot 9^2$ The exponent applies to both numbers.

RULE 4 $\left(\dfrac{X}{Y}\right)^n = \dfrac{X^n}{Y^n}$ Apply the exponent to both the numerator and denominator.

Examples: $\left(\dfrac{7}{9}\right)^2 = \dfrac{7^2}{9^2}$ Apply the exponent to both numbers.

$\left(\dfrac{Z}{T}\right)^3 = \dfrac{Z^3}{T^3}$ Apply the exponent to both variables.

Concept: $\left(\dfrac{7}{9}\right)^2 = \dfrac{7}{9} \cdot \dfrac{7}{9} = \dfrac{7 \cdot 7}{9 \cdot 9} = \dfrac{7^2}{9^2}$ Apply the exponent to the numerator and denominator.

RULE 5 $(X^m)^n = X^{m \times n}$ Multiply the two exponents.

Examples: $(5^2)^3 = 5^{2 \cdot 3} = 5^6$ Multiply the two exponents.

$(R^4)^2 = R^{4 \cdot 2} = R^8$ Multiply the two exponents.

Concept: $(5^2)^3 = (5^2) \cdot (5^2) \cdot (5^2)$

$= 5^{(2+2+2)} = 5^{3 \cdot 2} = 5^6$

Here are all the rules for working with exponents in one place.

Rules for Exponents Quick Directions

1. $X^m \cdot X^n = X^{(m+n)}$ Add the exponents.

2. $\dfrac{X^m}{X^n} = X^{(m-n)}$ Subtract the exponents.

3. $(X \cdot Y)^n = X^n \cdot Y^n$ Apply the exponent n to both variables in the parentheses.

4. $\left(\dfrac{X}{Y}\right)^n = \dfrac{X^n}{Y^n}$ Apply the exponent to both the numerator and denominator of the fraction.

5. $(X^m)^n = X^{m \times n}$ Multiply the two exponents.

NOTE In Rule 3, notice that $(X \cdot Y)^n$ and $X^n \cdot Y^n$ can be written without the multiplication dot ($\cdot$) as $(XY)^n$ and $X^n Y^n$, respectively.

In Rule 1, it is important to realize that you cannot combine two values with different bases. For example, you cannot combine the following into one variable raised to a power because the bases are not the same.

$$X^2 \cdot Y^3$$

It has already been written as simply as possible unless the values for X and Y are known. Nor can you simplify $\dfrac{y^3}{t^2}$ because these bases also differ.

EXAMPLE 2 **Working With Exponents**

Simplify each of these using the preceding rules.

(a) $\dfrac{y^4}{y^2}$

(b) $(9^2)^3$

(c) $z^2 \cdot z^3$

(d) $(5 \cdot 6)^2$

(e) $\left(\dfrac{r}{S}\right)^3$

(f) T^1

(g) $x^3 + x^3$

(h) 0^0

Solution

(a) $\dfrac{y^4}{y^2} = y^{(4-2)} = y^2$

(b) $(9^2)^3 = 9^{2 \cdot 3} = 9^6$

(c) $z^2 \cdot z^3 = z^{(2+3)} = z^5$

(d) $(5 \cdot 6)^2 = 5^2 \cdot 6^2$

(e) $\left(\dfrac{r}{S}\right)^3 = \dfrac{r^3}{S^3}$

(f) $T^1 = T$

(g) $x^3 \div x^3 = x^{(3-3)} = x^0 = 1$

(h) 0^0 has no meaning; it is undefined.

Objective

3 *Apply the Order of Operations.* Every expression must be evaluated in the sequence given by the **order of operations** shown in the following table. Be careful to always do the operations in an expression in the order listed in the table.[1]

Order of Operations — Calculate from the Top Down

1. Do all operations inside parentheses.
2. Evaluate square roots and exponents.
3. Multiply and divide from left to right.
4. Add and subtract from left to right.

To see why it is important to agree on the order of operations, look at the following. How should we evaluate it?

$$7 \cdot 8 - 3$$

Should we subtract first, or should we multiply first? A different answer is found depending on which mathematical operation is done first. There are only two math operations in the expression, namely, multiplication and subtraction. Since multiplication (3 in preceding table) is listed above subtraction (4 in the table), multiply first. Then subtract.

$$7 \cdot 8 - 3$$

$56 - 3$ First multiply 7 by 8.

53 Then subtract.

It is very important that you always use the order of operations when evaluating expressions. In complicated expressions, it is best to *do only one mathematical operation at a time* to prevent mistakes. The solution in the next example does that—only one operation is done at a time.

[1]More practice is given using the order of operations in the appendix on basic calculators.

EXAMPLE **3** **Evaluating Arithmetic Expressions**

Use the order of operations to evaluate each.

(a) $7^2 - (5 \times 2)$
(b) $6 \cdot 5^3 + 3$

Solution

Notice that operations are done in the sequence listed in the order of operations.

(a) $7^2 - (5 \times 2)$

$\quad 7^2 - 10$ First, evaluate the contents in the parentheses.

$\quad 49 - 10$ Next, evaluate the term with the exponent.

$\quad 39$ Finally, subtract.

(b) $6 \cdot 5^3 + 3$

$\quad 6 \cdot 125 + 3$ First, evaluate 5^3, which is $5 \cdot 5 \cdot 5 = 125$.

$\quad 750 + 3$ Next, multiply.

$\quad 753$ Finally, add.

Objective

4   *Evaluating expressions containing exponents.* To evaluate an expression with a variable, first substitute the value of the variable into the equation. Then do the operations in the sequence listed in the order of operations to evaluate.

EXAMPLE **4** **Evaluating an Expression with an Exponent**

Evaluate each of the following.

(a) $X^3 - 7.8 \cdot 3$ when $X = 8$
(b) $(R - 0.7)^2 \cdot (9.2 - 1)$ when $R = 19$

Solution

(a) $X^3 - 7.8 \cdot 3$

$\quad 8^3 - 7.8 \cdot 3$ Substitute 8 for the variable X.

$\quad 512 - 7.8 \cdot 3$ First evaluate 8^3, which is $8 \cdot 8 \cdot 8 = 512$.

$\quad 512 - 23.4$ Next, multiply.

$\quad 488.6$ Finally, subtract.

(b) $(R - 0.7)^2 \cdot (9.2 - 1)$

$\quad (19 - 0.7)^2 \cdot (9.2 - 1)$ Substitute 19 for the variable R.

$\quad (18.3)^2 \cdot (8.2)$ Do the operations inside both parentheses.

$\quad 18.3^2 \cdot 8.2$ Remove parentheses since only one number is inside each.

$\quad 334.89 \cdot 8.2$ Evaluate the exponent.

$\quad 2746.098$ Finally, multiply.

Objective

5   *Solving Application Problems.* The following example shows an application that uses exponents.

EXAMPLE 5 **Solving an Application Problem**

The manager of Benthos Diving has perfected and patented a new valve for deep-sea scuba diving. An economist friend tells him his profit can be approximated as follows.

$$P = 0.15N^2 + \$168N - \$300,000$$

where P = annual profit and N = number of valves sold in a year. Find the expected profit if 1100 valves are sold in the first year.

Solution

$$P = 0.15N^2 + \$168N - \$300,000$$
$$= 0.15 \cdot 1100^2 + 168 \cdot 1100 - 300,000 \qquad \text{Substitute 1100 for } N$$
$$= 0.15 \cdot 1,210,000 + 168 \cdot 1100 - 300,000 \qquad \text{Evaluate the exponent.}$$
$$= 181,500 + 184,800 - 300,000 \qquad \text{Multiply before adding.}$$
$$= 366,300 - 300,000 \qquad \text{Add.}$$
$$P = \$66,300$$

The expected profit is only \$66,300. The balance of the revenue is "eaten up" by cost, which include labor, materials, rent, interest on bank loans, etc.

2.5	**Exercises**

Write each using exponents.

1. $p \cdot p$ p^2
2. $3 \cdot 3$ 3^2
3. $r \cdot r \cdot r$ r^3
4. $7 \cdot 7 \cdot 7$ 7^3
5. $x \cdot x \cdot x \cdot x$ x^4
6. $5 \times 5 \times 5$ 5^3

Evaluate each of the following.

7. 7^2 49
8. $(0.75)^2$ 0.5625
9. X^0 when $X = 7$ 1
10. 5^1 5
11. 19^0 1
12. 12^3 1728

Simplify each of the following, leaving exponents in each answer.

13. $(t \cdot g)^4$ $t^4 g^4$
14. $(S^3)^2$ S^6
15. $9^2 \cdot 9^2$ 9^4
16. $\dfrac{6^5}{6^3}$ 6^2
17. $\left(\dfrac{3}{4}\right)^2$ $\dfrac{3^2}{4^2}$
18. $\dfrac{7^m}{7^n}$ $7^{(m-n)}$
19. $(x \cdot y)^2$ $x^2 y^2$
20. $\left(\dfrac{Y}{R}\right)^3$ $\dfrac{y^3}{R^3}$

Evaluate the following expressions.

21. $17 - 3 \cdot 4$ 5
22. $9 \cdot 8 - 7$ 65
23. $5 \cdot 4^2 + 3$ 83
24. $(9.1 - 1) \cdot 13$ 105.3
25. $191 - 5^3$ 66
26. $(14 - 7)^2 - 3 \cdot 8$ 25
27. $\dfrac{2^5}{2^3} \cdot 5$ 20
28. $1 - \left(\dfrac{3}{4}\right)^2$ 0.4375
29. $\dfrac{12^3}{12^3} \cdot 75^2$ 5625
30. $17.2^3 + (5 - 2^2)$ 5089.448
31. $(16 - 2 \cdot 7)^0$ 1
32. $(4^1 + 2^3 \div 2)^1$ 8

Substitute the value(s) for the variable(s) and then evaluate.

33. $x^2 - 4 \cdot 2; x = 13$ 161

34. $(9 - y)^2 + 5y; y = 3$ 51

35. $7r \div 3^2; r = 27$ 21

36. $\left(\dfrac{s}{x}\right) - 4; s = 42, x = 6$ 3

37. $(y^2 - 7.8) \cdot 3t; y = 10, t = 2$ 553.2

38. $\left(\dfrac{12}{x}\right)^2 \cdot r^2; x = 3, r = 9$ 1296

39. $(S - 7)^n \cdot 9.2 - 1; S = 13, n = 1$ 54.2

40. $\dfrac{Gr^2}{2} \cdot 7 - 2^2; G = 21, r = 6$ 2642

Solve the following application exercises.

41. The daily cost to produce a new memory chip for a smartphone is given by $C = 0.17N^2 + 12N + \$18,900$, where $C =$ daily cost and $N =$ average number produced in a day. Find the daily cost if $N = 420$.   \$53,928

42. The daily profit from selling a new Barbie doll is given by $P = 0.027N^2 + \$4.50N - \$62,700$, where $P =$ daily profit and $N =$ average number sold per day. Find the daily profit if $N = 1860$.   \$39,079.20

43. The future value of an investment is given by $M = P(1 + i)^t$, where $M =$ maturity value, $P =$ amount initially invested, $i =$ interest rate written as a decimal, and $t =$ number of time periods. Find the future value of a \$4800 investment expected to earn 5% per year for 4 years.   \$5834.43

44. The future value of an investment is given by $M = P(1 + i)^t$, where $M =$ maturity value, $P =$ amount initially invested $i =$ interest rate written as a decimal, and $t =$ number of time periods. Find the future value of a \$15,000 investment expected to earn 7% per year in a mutual fund for 40 years.   \$224,616.87 (rounded)

CHAPTER TERMS

Review the following terms to test your understanding of the chapter. For each term you do not know, refer to the page number found next to that term.

addition rule [p. 39]
base [p. 64]
coefficient [p. 38]
distributive property [p. 42]
equation [p. 38]
exponent [p. 65]

expression [p. 38]
formulas [p. 52]
left side [p. 38]
like terms [p. 41]
method of cross
　products [p. 58]

multiplication
　rule [p. 39]
order of operations [p. 67]
proportion [p. 58]
ratio [p. 58]
reciprocal [p. 40]

right side [p. 38]
similar terms [p. 41]
solution [p. 38]
substitution [p. 38]
term [p. 38]
variable [p. 38]

CONCEPTS

EXAMPLES

2.1 Solving equations

1. Remove all parentheses on each side of the equation using the distributive property.
2. Combine all like terms on each side of the equation.
3. **Addition Rule** Add to or subtract from both sides whatever is needed to produce a term with the variable on one side and a number on the other side.
4. **Multiplication Rule** Multiply or divide the variable term by whatever is needed to produce a term with a coefficient of 1. Multiply or divide the number term on the other side by the same quantity.

$$12(y + 2) = 84$$
$$12y + 24 = 84 \quad \text{Use distributive rule.}$$
$$12y + 24 - 24 = 84 - 24 \quad \text{Subtract 24 from both sides.}$$
$$12y = 60 \quad \text{Simplify.}$$
$$y = 5 \quad \text{Divide both sides by 12.}$$

2.2 Translating phrases

Use mathematical symbols to represent verbal expressions.

6 times a number plus 3: $6x + 3$

14 minus $2\frac{1}{2}$ times a number: $14 - 2\frac{1}{2}y$

2.2 Solving applied problems

1. **First, read the problem very carefully.** Reread the problem to make sure that its meaning is clear. Sometimes a sketch helps.
2. **Identify the unknown** and give it a variable name such as x. If possible, write other unknowns as mathematical expressions in terms of the same variable.
3. **Write an equation** describing the relationship given in the problem.
4. **Solve the equation.**
5. **Answer the question(s)** asked in the problem.
6. **Check the solution** using the *original* words of the problem.
7. **Be sure your answer is reasonable.**

A committee had 7 fewer men than women. The total number of people on the committee was 19. Find the number of women.

Let x represent the number of women.

$$x + (x - 7) = 19$$
$$2x - 7 = 19$$
$$2x = 26$$
$$x = 13 \text{ women}$$
$$x - 7 = 13 - 7 = 6 \text{ men}$$

Check the answer.

$$13 + (13 - 7) \stackrel{?}{=} 19$$
$$19 = 19$$

The answer checks.

2.3 Evaluating formulas for given values of the variable Substitute numerical values for variables and evaluate.	Use $I = PRT$ with $P = \$10{,}500$, $R = 0.09$, and $T = \frac{3}{4}$ year to find interest (I). $$I = PRT$$ $$I = 10{,}500 \cdot 0.09 \cdot \frac{3}{4}$$ $$= \$708.75$$
2.3 Solving formulas for a specific variable Use the rules for solving equations.	Solve $M = P + PRT$ for T. $$M = P + PRT$$ $$M - P = PRT \qquad \text{Subtract } P \text{ from both sides.}$$ $$\frac{M - P}{PR} = T \qquad \text{Divide both sides by } PR.$$
2.4 Solving a proportion for a missing part Use the principle of cross products and solve the resulting equation. $$\frac{a}{b} = \frac{c}{d} \text{ if } a \cdot d = b \cdot c$$	Find x in the proportion. $$\frac{5}{x} \diagup\!\!\!\!\diagdown \frac{35}{63}$$ $$5 \cdot 63 = 35x \quad \text{Cross products.}$$ $$315 = 35x$$ $$9 = x$$
2.4 Using proportions to solve problems Set up the proportion, use the principle of cross products, and solve the resulting equation.	A retail store charges \$20 to rent 5 movies on DVDs. How much does it charge for 8 movies? $$\frac{20}{5} = \frac{x}{8}$$ $$20 \cdot 8 = 5 \cdot x$$ $$160 = 5x$$ $$32 = x$$ It charges \$32 for 8 movies.
2.5 Understanding exponents The exponent is the number of times a number is to be multiplied by itself.	Find 6^4. $\qquad$ Exponent $$6^4 = 6 \cdot 6 \cdot 6 \cdot 6$$ $$= 1296$$
2.5 Some basics of exponents A number greater than 0 to the 0th power is 1. 0 to the 1st or greater power equals 0. 0 to the 0th power is undefined (has no meaning).	$7^0 = 1$ $0^5 = 0$ 0^0 is undefined

2.5 Multiply and divide exponents using the rules.

1. $X^m \cdot X^n = X^{(m+n)}$ Add the exponents. $9^2 \cdot 9^3 = 9^{(2+3)} = 9^5$

2. $\dfrac{X^m}{X^n} = X^{(m-n)}$ Subtract the exponents. $\dfrac{8^5}{8^2} = 8^{(5-2)} = 8^3$

3. $(X \cdot Y)^n = X^n \cdot Y^n$ Apply the exponent n to both $(5 \cdot 7)^2 = 5^2 \cdot 7^2$
   values in the parentheses.

4. $\left(\dfrac{X}{Y}\right)^n = \dfrac{X^n}{Y^n}$ Apply the exponent to $\left(\dfrac{3}{7}\right)^2 = \dfrac{3^2}{7^2}$
   both the numerator and
   denominator of the fraction.

5. $(X^m)^n = X^{m \times n}$ Multiply the two exponents. $(8^2)^3 = 8^{2 \cdot 3} = 8^6$

2.5 Evaluate expressions using the order of operations

Evaluate in the order listed.

1. Do all operations inside parentheses.
2. Evaluate square roots and exponents.
3. Multiply and divide from left to right.
4. Add and subtract from left to right.

Evaluate $(7 - 5)^3 \div (1 + 1) \cdot 2^0$.

$(7 - 5)^3 \div (1 + 1) \cdot 2^0$

$(2)^3 \div (2) \cdot 2^0$ Contents of parentheses.

$8 \div 2 \cdot 1$ Evaluate exponents.

$4 \cdot 1$ Division/multiplication from left to right.

4

2.5 Evaluating algebraic expressions with exponents

Substitute values for variables and then solve using the order of operations.

Evaluate $x^2 + 7(x - 4)$ when $x = 5$.

$x^2 + 7(x - 4)$

$5^2 + 7(5 - 4)$ Substitute 5 for x.

$5^2 + 7 \cdot (1)$ Evaluate contents of parentheses.

$25 + 7$ Evaluate exponents.

32 Add.

CHAPTER 2	Review Exercises

The answer section includes answers to all Review Exercises.

Solve each equation. [2.1]

1. $x + 45 = 96$ 51

2. $r - 36 = 14.7$ 50.7

3. $8t + 45 = 175.4$ 16.3

4. $4t - 6 = 15$ $5\frac{1}{4}$

5. $\dfrac{s}{6} = 42$ 252

6. $\dfrac{5z}{8} = 85$ 136

7. $\dfrac{m}{4} - 5 = 9$ 56

8. $5(x - 3) = 3(x + 4)$ $13\frac{1}{2}$

9. $6y = 2y + 28$ 7

10. $3r - 7 = 2(4 - 3r)$ $1\frac{2}{3}$

11. $0.15(2x - 3) = 5.85$ 21

12. $0.6(y - 3) = 0.1y$ 3.6

Write a mathematical expression. Use x as the variable. [2.2]

13. Ninety-four times a number $94x$

14. One half times a number $\frac{1}{2}x$

15. Six times a number is added to the number $6x + x$

16. Five times a number is decreased by 11 $5x - 11$

17. The sum of 3 times a number and 7 $3x + 7$

Solve the following application problems. [2.2]

18. Molly Videtto wishes to purchase three DVDs at $14.95 each and a Liz Claiborne sweater for $95. Given that she has $47.50, find the additional amount she needs. (Ignore taxes.) $92.35

19. The owner of three bicycle stores has found that profits *(P)* are related to advertising *(A)* according to $P = 18.5A + 4.5$, where all figures are in thousands of dollars. How much must she spend on advertising in order to obtain a quarterly profit of \$60,000?   \$3000

20. Phone and water bills together cost a company \$540 for March. If the phone bill costs 4 times as much as the water bill, find each.   \$108 water; \$432 phone

21. Five more than $\frac{1}{4}$ of the employees of a company have 25 years or more of service. If 24 employees have 25 or more years of service, how many employees does the company have?   76

22. The local movie theater sold 100 tickets for \$780. If children's tickets cost \$6 and adult tickets \$12, how many of each were sold?   70 child; 30 adult

Use the formula to find the value of the variable that is not given. [2.3]

23. $I = PRT$; $I = \$960, R = 0.12, T = 2$ $P = \$4000$

24. $M = P(1 + RT)$; $M = \$3770, R = 0.04, T = 4$ $P = \$3250$

25. $M = P(1 + i)^n$; $M = \$14{,}526.80, i = 0.1, n = 6$ $P = \$8200$ (rounded)

Solve the equation for the variable indicated. [2.3]

26. $I = PRT$; for R $\dfrac{I}{PT}$

27. $M = P(1 + RT)$; for T $\dfrac{M - P}{PR}$

28. $B = PR$; for P $\dfrac{B}{R}$

Write the following ratios and simplify. [2.4]

29. \$17 to 50 cents $\dfrac{34}{1}$

30. 9 days to 12 hours $\dfrac{18}{1}$

31. \$5000 to \$250 $\dfrac{20}{1}$

32. 3 years to 15 months $\dfrac{12}{5}$

33. \$2 to 75 cents $\dfrac{8}{3}$

Solve the following proportions. [2.4]

34. $\dfrac{v}{14} = \dfrac{27}{126}$ 3

35. $\dfrac{5}{y} = \dfrac{20}{27}$ $6\dfrac{3}{4}$

36. $\dfrac{3}{8} = \dfrac{z}{12}$ $4\dfrac{1}{2}$

37. $\dfrac{6}{11} = \dfrac{90}{t}$ 165

38. $\dfrac{20}{r} = \dfrac{60}{72}$ 24

Solve the following application problems. [2.4]

39. Bass in a lake are sampled for a particular parasite, and 14 of 60 bass have the parasite. Given that there are an estimated 18,400 bass in the lake, find the number with parasites. Round to the nearest whole number.   4293 bass

40. A college student majoring in petroleum engineering worked on an oil-drilling site. She noticed a down-hole pressure of 3220 pounds per square inch at 6700 feet below the surface. Estimate the pressure at the 9850-foot total depth of the well to the nearest pound per square inch. Assume that the ratio of pressure to depth does not change with different depths.   4734 pounds per square inch (rounded)

41. Last year, a shelter purchased 5760 pounds of beef to feed its 120 inhabitants. Find the total amount of beef needed next year if the manager anticipates 138 inhabitants.   6624 pounds

42. John proofreads 7 pages in 12 minutes. How many pages does he proofread in 3 hours?   105

43. A company makes pension contributions of \$89,391 per quarter for its 83 employees. It anticipates a merger that will bring in another 21 employees, and managers plan to give them the same average pension. Find the new quarterly pension contribution required.   \$112,008

44. If 8 shirts cost \$223.20, how much would 5 shirts cost?   \$139.50

Write each using exponents. [2.5]

45. $y \cdot y \cdot y$ y^3

46. $5 \cdot 5$ 5^2

47. $9 \times 9 \times 9 \times 9$ 9^4

48. $3.1 \cdot 3.1$ 3.1^2

Evaluate each of the following. **[2.5]**

49. $(1/2)^3$ $\dfrac{1}{8}$

50. s^0 for $s = 4$ 1

51. 102^1 102

52. 0^0 undefined

Simplify the following leaving exponents in the answer. **[2.5]**

53. $7^2 \cdot 7^3$ 7^5

54. $(r^3)^2$ r^6

55. $(s \cdot t)^4$ $s^4 t^4$

56. $\left(\dfrac{z}{y}\right)^2$ $\dfrac{z^2}{y^2}$

Evaluate the following expressions.

57. $75 - 4^2 \cdot 2$ 43

58. $(1 + 2^3)^2 \div 3$ 27

59. $(16 - 8 \cdot 2)^0$ undefined

60. $(5^1 + 2^3 - 2)^1$ 11

61. $(y - 9)^2 + 5y$ for $y = 50$ 1931

62. $4x^2 \div 3^2$ for $x = 27$ 324

Solve the following application problems. **[2.5]**

63. The weekly profit from selling a brand new smart chip used in military aircraft is given by $P = 1.85N^2 + \$535.2N - \$862,700$, where P = weekly profit and N = number sold per week. Find the total weekly profit if $N = 780$.
$680,296

64. The future value of an investment is given by $M = P(1 + i)^t$, where M = maturity value, P = amount initially invested, i = interest rate written as a decimal, and t = number of time periods. Find the future value of a \$93,200 retirement account balance expected to earn 6.5% per year for 25 years.   \$449,941.56

CHAPTER 2	**Business Application Case #1** ***Breakeven in Retail***

The average selling price of a book at Discount Books is $24.80. Typically, just $\frac{7}{10}$ of this amount goes to pay for the cost of the book, including shipping and handling. Monthly expenses at Discount Books are:

Salaries with benefits	$8500 includes owner's salary
Rent and utilities	$2100
Janitorial	$350
Other	$1620

These definitions may help you:

> *Gross revenue* is the total of all revenue from all sales.
> *Breakeven* is the point at which total revenues equals cost of goods sold plus total expenses.
> *Profit, or net profit,* is the amount left over after all expenses have been paid.
> *Percents* are parts out of 100, so $\frac{7}{10}$ is 70 parts out of 100 equal parts, or 70%.

(a) Find the total monthly expenses. $12,570

(b) If $\frac{7}{10}$ of the revenues is used to pay for books, what fraction of the revenue remains? $\frac{3}{10}$

(c) Write an equation for monthly net profit. Net profit is gross revenue from the sale of books less monthly expenses. Use N for the number of books sold in a month. $\left(\frac{3}{10} \cdot \$24.80 \cdot N\right) - \$12,570$ or $7.44N - \$12,570$

(d) How many books must the store sell to break even? Round to the nearest whole number.   1690 books

(e) What happens if the store does not sell enough books to break even one month?   The owner would probably receive a lower salary.

(f) How many books must the store sell to reach a profit of $6000 over and above all expenses in a month? Round to the nearest whole number.   2496 books

CHAPTER 2	**Business Application Case #2**
	Expanding the Number of Stores

McDonald's (see www.mcdonalds.com) is a successful company that has stores (restaurants) in more than 115 countries. In fact, managers predict that at some point in the future as much as 80% of company profits will be from countries other than the United States. In 2012, the chain had about 31,000 stores, and managers expect total revenue of over $25 billion. Now that is a lot of hamburgers, or actually veggie burgers in India! Most people in India are vegetarians, so when McDonald's goes to India the menus are radically changed.

(a) Estimate the average sales per store to the nearest dollar. $806,452

(b) Use the average sales per store found in part (a) and write an algebraic expression for total revenue if managers add N stores next year. Assume that average sales for all of the stores remain the same and that none of the stores are closed. $806,452 \cdot (31,000 + N)$

(c) Estimate revenue for McDonald's if the revenue is increased by $\frac{1}{5}$ in 2 years. $30 billion

(d) List the pros and cons of working at a fast-food restaurant such as McDonald's. Why might upper management not want to hire someone to manage a store unless he or she has worked in one?   Answers will vary.

javier brosch / Fotolia.com

Percent

It is important to understand percents, since they are used daily in newspapers, magazines, government, and certainly in business. The word **percent** means "parts out of one hundred," and percents are often used to compare data. For example, monthly data can have a lot of **variability**. So, managers often look at quarterly data and then look at percent gains or losses to better understand the trend.

For example, managers at Abercrombie & Fitch are trying to understand how well the company is doing. A newly hired college graduate looks at quarterly total revenue, shown in Figure 3.1. At first, he is alarmed by what appears to be a sharp falloff in sales from the fourth quarter of 2010 ($1,150,000,000) to the first quarter of 2011 ($840,000,000). However, the same thing happened at the end of 2009, and he realizes that sales are very high in the months leading up to Christmas in the fourth quarter. So, he instead needs to compare sales for the same quarter in successive years. He compares sales in the first quarter of 2010 ($600,000,000) to those in the first quarter of 2011 ($690,000,000). The sales increased 15%. If sales increase that same amount each quarter compared to the same quarter of the previous year, then corporate sales will be up 15% for the year—not a bad yearly growth rate.

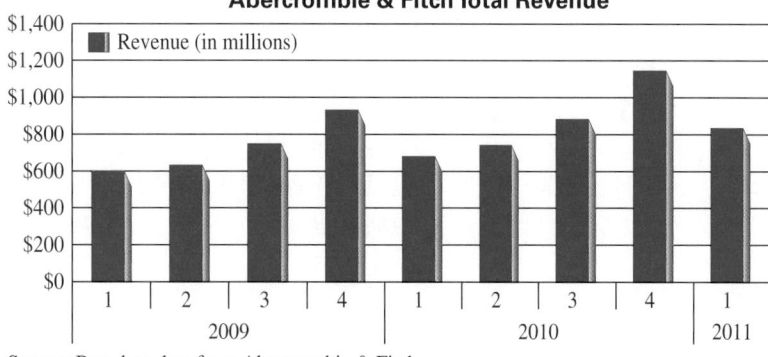

Source: Based on data from Abercrombie & Fitch.

Figure 3.1

▶ STOP&THINK

Sales at Abercrombie & Fitch increase throughout each year and peak in the fourth quarter before falling sharply in the first quarter of the next year. Estimate the difference in revenue between quarters 1 and 4 of 2010. How can managers cope with such a sharp seasonality? Think in terms of inventory and number of employees (or hours of work scheduled for existing employees). Do the sales of all businesses differ by season of the year? Name some that do not.

3.1	**Writing Decimals and Fractions as Percents**

OBJECTIVES

1 *Write a decimal as a percent.*

2 *Write a fraction or mixed number as a percent.*

3 *Write a percent as a decimal.*

4 *Write a percent as a fraction.*

5 *Write a fractional percent as a decimal.*

Percents represent parts of a whole, just as fractions or decimals do. **Percents** are **hundredths**, or parts of a hundred. "One percent" means 1 of 100 parts. Percents are written with a percent sign, %. For example:

Decimal Equivalent

$$25\% = 25 \text{ parts out of } 100 = \frac{25}{100} \qquad\qquad 0.25$$

$$50\% = 50 \text{ parts out of } 100 = \frac{50}{100} \qquad\qquad 0.50$$

$$100\% = 100 \text{ parts out of } 100 = \frac{100}{100} \qquad\qquad 1.00$$

So, 100% is 100 parts out of 100 parts, or the entire (or whole) amount. Any percent greater than 100% is more than the whole. For example, 250% is 250 parts out of 100, or 2.5 times the whole.

> **NOTE** It is important to realize that the % sign is *not* a variable.

Objective

1 *Write a Decimal as a Percent.* Write a decimal as a percent by moving the decimal point two places to the right and attaching a % sign. For example, write 0.75 as a percent by moving the decimal point two places to the right and attaching a % sign, giving 75% as the result.

Decimal   *Percent*

0.75 (0.75.)   75% ←— Attach a percent sign.

         ↑— 2 places to the right

EXAMPLE **1**   **Changing Decimals To Percents**

When completing some market research you must express your findings using percents. Write the following decimals as percents.

(a) 0.25   **(b)** 0.38   **(c)** 0.65

Solution

Move the decimal point two places to the right and attach a percent sign.

(a) 25%   **(b)** 38%   **(c)** 65%

If there is nothing in the hundredths position, place zeros to the right of the number to hold the hundredths position. For example, the decimal 0.5 is expressed as 50%, and the number 1.2 is 120%.

$$0.5 = 0.50. = 50\% \qquad\qquad 1.2 = 1.20. = 120\%$$

$$\text{Attach a zero.} \qquad\qquad \text{Attach a zero.}$$

NOTE Another method of changing a decimal to a percent is to multiply the decimal by 100%. For example,

$$0.25 \times 100\% = 25\% \qquad 0.5 \times 100\% = 50\% \qquad 1.2 \times 100\% = 120\%$$

EXAMPLE 2 Writing Decimals as Percents

Write the following decimals as percents.

(a) 0.7   **(b)** 1.3   **(c)** 0.1   **(d)** 3

Solution

Attach zeros to the right side of each number before moving the decimal point two places to the right and adding a % sign.

(a) 70%   **(b)** 130%   **(c)** 10%   **(d)** 300%

If the decimal extends farther than the hundredths position, the resulting percent includes decimal parts of whole percents.

EXAMPLE 3 Writing Decimals as Percents

When reading a newsletter, an auto parts manager sees the following decimals. Write these decimals as percents.

(a) 0.857   **(b)** 0.0057   **(c)** 0.0025

Solution

(a) 85.7%   **(b)** 0.57%   **(c)** 0.25%

NOTE In Example 3 both (b) and (c) are less than 1%; they are decimal parts of 1%.

Objective

2 *Write a Fraction or Mixed Number as a Percent.* There are two ways to write a fraction as a percent. One way is to first convert the fraction to a decimal, as explained in **Section 1.3**. For example, to express the fraction $\frac{2}{5}$ as a percent, write $\frac{2}{5}$ as a decimal by dividing 2 by 5. Then write the decimal as a percent.

Fraction		*Decimal*		*Percent*
$\dfrac{2}{5}$	$=$	0.4	$=$	40%

EXAMPLE 4   Writing Fractions and Mixed Numbers as Percents

An advertising account representative is given the following data in fraction form and must change the data to percents.

(a) $\frac{1}{4}$ **(b)** $\frac{3}{5}$ **(c)** $\frac{7}{8}$ **(d)** $1\frac{3}{4}$ **(e)** $1\frac{2}{3}$

Solution

First write each as a decimal. Then write the decimal as a percent.

(a) $\frac{1}{4} = 0.25 = 25\%$ **(b)** $\frac{3}{5} = 0.6 = 60\%$ **(c)** $\frac{7}{8} = 0.875 = 87.5\%$

(d) $1\frac{3}{4} = 1.75 = 175\%$ **(e)** $1\frac{2}{3} = 1.667$ (rounded) $= 166.7\%$

A second way to write a fraction as a percent is to multiply the fraction by 100%. For example, write the fraction $\frac{2}{5}$ as a percent by multiplying $\frac{2}{5}$ by 100%.

$$\frac{2}{5} = \frac{2}{5} \times 100\% = \frac{200\%}{5} = 40\%$$

EXAMPLE 5   Writing Fractions and Mixed Numbers as Percents

Write the following fractions as percents.

(a) $\frac{3}{4}$ **(b)** $\frac{1}{3}$ **(c)** $\frac{5}{8}$ **(d)** $1\frac{1}{2}$ **(e)** $2\frac{1}{3}$

Solution

Write as percents by multiplying each by 100%.

(a) $\frac{3}{4} \times 100\% = 75\%$ **(b)** $\frac{1}{3} \times 100\% = 33.3\%$ (rounded)   **(c)** $\frac{5}{8} \times 100\% = 62.5\%$

(d) $1\frac{1}{2} \times 100\% = 150\%$ **(e)** $2\frac{1}{3} \times 100\% = 233.3\%$ (rounded)

Objective

3   *Write a Percent as a Decimal.* Write a percent as a decimal by moving the decimal point two places to the left and dropping the percent sign. For example, 50% becomes 0.50 or 0.5, 100% becomes 1, and 352% becomes 3.52.

EXAMPLE 6   Writing Percents as Decimals

To calculate some insurance claims an insurance agent must change the following percents to decimals.

(a) 25%   **(b)** 142%   **(c)** $37\frac{1}{2}\%$ (*Hint:* $37\frac{1}{2}\% = 37.5\%$)

Solution

Move the decimal point two places to the left and drop the percent sign.

(a) 0.25   **(b)** 1.42   **(c)** 0.375

NOTE Another method of changing a percent to a decimal number is to divide by 100%. For example,

$25\% \div 100\% = 0.25$ $142\% \div 100\% = 1.42$ $37.5\% \div 100\% = 0.375.$

Objective

4   *Write a Percent as a Fraction.* Write a percent as a fraction by first changing the percent to a decimal. Then write the decimal as a fraction in lowest terms.

> **EXAMPLE 7   Writing Percents as Fractions**
>
> The following table has data from the American Red Cross, an organization that helps people in times of need, such as after hurricanes, floods, and tornadoes. Convert each percent to a fraction and reduce the fraction to its lowest term.
>
> **Are People Ready for Disasters?**
>
> People along the Gulf Coast who have:
>
> | (a) Disaster supply kits | 28% |
> | (b) Evacuation plans | 36% |
> | (c) First aid or CPR training | 40% |
>
> *Source:* Data from American Red Cross.
>
> **Solution**
>
> First write each as a decimal. Then convert to a fraction and reduce if possible.
>
> **(a)** $28\% = 0.28 = \dfrac{28}{100} = \dfrac{7}{25}$ **(b)** $36\% = 0.36 = \dfrac{36}{100} = \dfrac{9}{25}$
>
> **(c)** $40\% = 0.40 = \dfrac{40}{100} = \dfrac{2}{5}$

Objective

5   *Write a Fractional Percent as a Decimal.* A fractional percent such as $\frac{1}{2}\%$ has a value less than 1%. In fact, $\frac{1}{2}\%$ is equal to $\frac{1}{2}$ of 1%. Write a fractional percent as a decimal by first changing the fraction to a decimal, leaving the percent sign. For example, first write $\frac{1}{2}\%$ as 0.5%. Then write 0.5% as a decimal by moving the decimal point two places to the left and dropping the percent sign.

$$\frac{1}{2}\% = 0.5\% = 0.005$$

↑— Written as decimal

> **EXAMPLE 8   Writing Fractional Percents as Decimals**
>
> Write each fractional percent as a decimal.
>
> **(a)** $\frac{1}{5}\%$ **(b)** $\frac{3}{4}\%$ **(c)** $1\frac{1}{8}\%$
>
> **Solution**
>
> Begin by writing the fraction as a decimal.
>
> **(a)** $\frac{1}{5}\% = 0.2\% = 0.002$
>
> **(b)** $\frac{3}{4}\% = 0.75\% = 0.0075$
>
> **(c)** $1\frac{1}{8}\% = 1.125\% = 0.01125$

> **NOTE**   When writing a fractional percent as a decimal, first, change the fraction to a decimal, leaving the percent sign. Then move the decimal point two places to the left and drop the percent sign.

The following chart shows many fractions, as well as their decimal and percent equivalents. **It is helpful to memorize the more commonly used ones.**

FRACTION, DECIMAL, AND PERCENT EQUIVALENTS

$\frac{1}{100} = 0.01 = 1\%$	$\frac{9}{16} = 0.5625 = 56.25\%$ or $56\frac{1}{4}\%$
$\frac{1}{50} = 0.02 = 2\%$	$\frac{3}{5} = 0.6 = 60\%$
$\frac{1}{25} = 0.04 = 4\%$	$\frac{5}{8} = 0.625 = 62.5\%$ or $62\frac{1}{2}\%$
$\frac{1}{20} = 0.05 = 5\%$	$\frac{2}{3} = 0.66\overline{6} = 66\frac{2}{3}\%$
$\frac{1}{16} = 0.0625 = 6.25\%$ or $6\frac{1}{4}\%$	$\frac{11}{16} = 0.6875 = 68.75\%$ or $68\frac{3}{4}\%$
$\frac{1}{12} = 0.083\overline{3} = 8\frac{1}{3}\%$	$\frac{7}{10} = 0.7 = 70\%$
$\frac{1}{10} = 0.1 = 10\%$	$\frac{3}{4} = 0.75 = 75\%$
$\frac{1}{9} = 0.111\overline{1} = 11\frac{1}{9}\%$	$\frac{4}{5} = 0.8 = 80\%$
$\frac{1}{8} = 0.125 = 12.5\%$ or $12\frac{1}{2}\%$	$\frac{13}{16} = 0.8125 = 81.25\%$ or $81\frac{1}{4}\%$
$\frac{1}{7} = 0.1428 = 14\frac{2}{7}\%$	$\frac{5}{6} = 0.833\overline{3} = 83\frac{1}{3}\%$
$\frac{1}{6} = 0.166\overline{6} = 16\frac{2}{3}\%$	$\frac{7}{8} = 0.875 = 87\frac{1}{2}\%$
$\frac{3}{16} = 0.1875 = 18.75\%$ or $18\frac{3}{4}\%$	$\frac{9}{10} = 0.9 = 90\%$
$\frac{1}{5} = 0.2 = 20\%$	$\frac{15}{16} = 0.9375 = 93.75\%$ or $93\frac{3}{4}\%$
$\frac{1}{4} = 0.25 = 25\%$	$1 = 1.00 = 100\%$
$\frac{3}{10} = 0.3 = 30\%$	$1\frac{1}{10} = 1.1 = 110\%$
$\frac{5}{16} = 0.3125 = 31.25\%$ or $31\frac{1}{4}\%$	$1\frac{1}{4} = 1.25 = 125\%$
$\frac{1}{3} = 0.333\overline{3} = 33\frac{1}{3}\%$	$1\frac{1}{3} = 1.333\overline{3} = 133\frac{1}{3}\%$
$\frac{3}{8} = 0.375 = 37.5\%$ or $37\frac{1}{2}\%$	$1\frac{1}{2} = 1.5 = 150\%$
$\frac{2}{5} = 0.4 = 40\%$	$1\frac{2}{3} = 1.66\overline{6} = 166\frac{2}{3}\%$
$\frac{7}{16} = 0.4375 = 43.75\%$ or $43\frac{3}{4}\%$	$1\frac{3}{4} = 1.75 = 175\%$
$\frac{1}{2} = 0.5 = 50\%$	$2 = 2.00 = 200\%$

3.1   Exercises

Write the following decimals as percents.

1. 0.2   20%   **2.** 0.5   50%   **3.** 0.72   72%   **4.** 0.86   86%

5. 1.4   140%   **6.** 3.017   301.7%   **7.** 0.375   37.5%   **8.** 0.875   87.5%

9. 4.625   462.5%   **10.** 7.8   780%   **11.** 0.0025   0.25%   **12.** 0.0008   0.08%

13. 0.0015   0.15%   **14.** 0.221   22.1%   **15.** 3.45   345%   **16.** 5.5   550%

Write the following fractions as percents.

17. $\frac{1}{4}$ 25%   **18.** $\frac{5}{8}$ 62.5%   **19.** $\frac{1}{10}$ 10%   **20.** $\frac{1}{20}$ 5%

21. $\frac{1}{50}$ 2%   **22.** $\frac{1}{125}$ 0.8%   **23.** $\frac{3}{8}$ 37.5%   **24.** $\frac{4}{5}$ 80%

25. $\frac{1}{8}$ 12.5%   **26.** $\frac{13}{20}$ 65%   **27.** $\frac{1}{200}$ 0.5%   **28.** $\frac{1}{400}$ 0.25%

29. $\frac{7}{8}$ 87.5%   **30.** $\frac{1}{100}$ 1%   **31.** $\frac{3}{50}$ 6%   **32.** $\frac{4}{25}$ 16%

Write the following percents as decimals.

33. 65% 0.65   **34.** 32% 0.32   **35.** 75% 0.75   **36.** 58% 0.58

37. 0.6% 0.006   **38.** 0.5% 0.005   **39.** 0.25% 0.0025   **40.** 0.125% 0.00125

41. 315% 3.15   **42.** 150% 1.5   **43.** 200.6% 2.006   **44.** 475.6% 4.756

45. 540.6% 5.406   **46.** 135.6% 1.356   **47.** 0.07% 0.0007   **48.** 0.05% 0.0005

 49. Fractions, decimals, and percents are all used to describe a part of something. The use of percent is much more common than fractions and decimals. Why do you suppose this is true?

 50. List five uses of percent that are or will be part of your life. Consider the activities of working, shopping, saving, borrowing, and planning for the future.

 51. To change a fraction to a percent you must first change the fraction to a decimal. Why is this? (See Objective 2.)

 52. The fractional percent $\frac{1}{2}$% is equal to 0.005. Explain each step as you change $\frac{1}{2}$% to its decimal equivalent (See Objective 5.)

Determine the fraction, decimal, or percent equivalents for each of the following, as necessary. Write fractions in lowest terms.

	Fraction	Decimal	Percent
53.	$\frac{1}{2}$	0.5	50%
54.	$\frac{3}{25}$	0.12	12%
55.	$\frac{3}{20}$	0.15	15%
56.	$\frac{7}{8}$	0.875	87.5%
57.	$\frac{1}{4}$	0.25	25%
58.	$\frac{7}{20}$	0.35	35%
59.	$6\frac{1}{8}$	6.125	612.5%
60.	$3\frac{1}{2}$	3.5	350%
61.	$7\frac{1}{4}$	7.25	725%
62.	$1\frac{3}{4}$	1.75	175%
63.	$\frac{1}{400}$	0.0025	0.25%
64.	$\frac{1}{800}$	0.00125	0.125%

	Fraction	Decimal	Percent
65.	$\frac{1}{3}$	0.33$\overline{3}$	33$\frac{1}{3}$%
66.	$\frac{17}{400}$	0.0425	4$\frac{1}{4}$%
67.	$\frac{3}{400}$	0.0075	$\frac{3}{4}$%
68.	$\frac{9}{200}$	0.045	4.5%
69.	$\frac{1}{8}$	0.125	12.5%
70.	$\frac{1}{40}$	0.025	2.5%
71.	$2\frac{1}{2}$	2.5	250%
72.	$3\frac{3}{4}$	3.75	375%
73.	$10\frac{767}{2000}$	10.3835	1038.35%
74.	$23\frac{41}{50}$	23.82	2382%
75.	$4\frac{3}{8}$	4.375	437.5%
76.	$\frac{3}{8}$	0.375	37$\frac{1}{2}$%
77.	$\frac{27}{400}$	0.0675	6$\frac{3}{4}$%
78.	$\frac{35}{200}$	0.175	17.5%
79.	$8\frac{4}{5}$	8.8	880%
80.	$6\frac{3}{8}$	6.375	637.5%
81.	$\frac{1}{400}$	0.0025	$\frac{1}{4}$%
82.	$\frac{1}{125}$	0.008	$\frac{4}{5}$%

3.2   Applications: Finding the Part

OBJECTIVES

1 *Identify the three elements of a percent problem.*

2 *Use the percent formula.*

3 *Apply the percent formula to a business problem.*

4 *Recognize the terms associated with base, rate, and part.*

5 *Use the basic percent equation.*

Objective

1   *Identify the Three Elements of a Percent Problem.* Problems involving percent have three main quantities. Usually two of these quantities are given and the third must be found. The three key quantities in a percent problem are as follows.

Base. The whole or total, the starting point, or that to which something is being compared.
Rate. A number followed by "%" or "percent."
Part. The result of multiplying the base and the rate. It is a part of the base.

Rate (percent) acts on some value, the base. It may help to ask yourself this question: percent of what? The answer to the question will help you identify the base. Here are some examples.

Part (*P*)	= Rate (*R*)	×	Base (*B*)
Sales tax	= Sales tax rate	×	Total cost
Commission	= Commission rate	×	Sale price of home
Markdown	= Discount rate	×	Original price
Increase	= Percent of increase	×	Original amount
Interest	= Interest rate	×	Investment

Objective

2 *Use the Percent Formula.* The above three quantities are related by the basic **percent formula**.

$$\text{Part} = \text{Rate} \times \text{Base} \quad or \quad P = R \times B \quad or \quad P = RB$$

A couple selling their home for \$220,000 discovered that they must pay a 6% real estate commission on the sales price, which is the base. Use the **basic percent equation** to find the commission.

$$\text{Part } (P) = \text{Rate } (R) \times \text{Base } (B)$$
$$\text{Commission} = 0.06 \times \$220,000 \quad \text{Write 6\% as 0.06.}$$
$$\text{Commission} = \$13,200$$

The couple must pay \$13,200 in commission. The commission is often split among four parties: the real estate broker of the agent that listed the house, the listing agent at that brokerage, the real estate broker of the selling agent, and the agent that actually sold the house. The commission is not necessarily split evenly among the four parties and varies from one location to another.

EXAMPLE 1 Solving for Part

Solve for part (*P*) using $P = R \times B$.

(a) 4% of 50   (b) 1.2% of 180
(c) 140% of 225   (d) $\frac{1}{4}$% of 560 (*Hint:* $\frac{1}{4}$% = 0.25%)

Solution

(a) $R \times B = P$ (b) $R \times B = P$
     $0.04 \times 50 = 2$ $0.012 \times 180 = 2.16$

(c) $R \times B = P$ (d) $R \times B = P$
     $1.4 \times 225 = 315$ $0.0025 \times 560 = 1.4$

Objective

3   *Apply the Percent Formula to a Business Problem.* Calculating **sales tax** is an excellent example of finding part. States, counties, and cities often collect taxes on sales to the consumer. The sales tax is a percent or portion of the sale. This percent varies from as low as 3% in some states to 8% or more in other states. The percent formula is used for finding sales tax.

$$P \quad = \quad R \quad \times \quad B$$

$$\text{Sales tax} = \text{sales tax rate} \times \text{sales}$$

·EXAMPLE   2   Calculating Sales Tax

Racy Feed and Pet Supply sold $284.50 worth of merchandise. If the sales tax rate was 5%, what was the sales tax and the total sale, including the tax?

Solution

The amount of sales, $284.50, is the starting point or base, and 5% is the rate. Since the tax is a *part* of total sales, use the formula $P = RB$ to find the part.

$$P = 5\% \times \$284.50$$
$$P = 0.05 \times \$284.50$$
$$P = 14.225 = \$14.23 \quad \text{Rounded}$$

The tax, or part, was $14.23.

$$\text{Total} = \text{amount of sale} + \text{tax}$$
$$= \$284.50 \qquad + \$14.23$$
$$= \$298.73$$

NOTE An alternative approach to finding the combined sales and tax is to multiply $284.50 by 105% (100% sales + 5% sales tax).

$$\$284.50 \times 105\% = 284.5 \times 1.05 = \$298.73$$

EXAMPLE   3   Finding Part

Jerome and Patsy Whitney live in Texas and have a combined income of $72,850. They are debating moving to New York but have heard that the taxes are very high there. Use information from the figure to estimate the increase in state and local tax should they move and have the same combined income in New York.

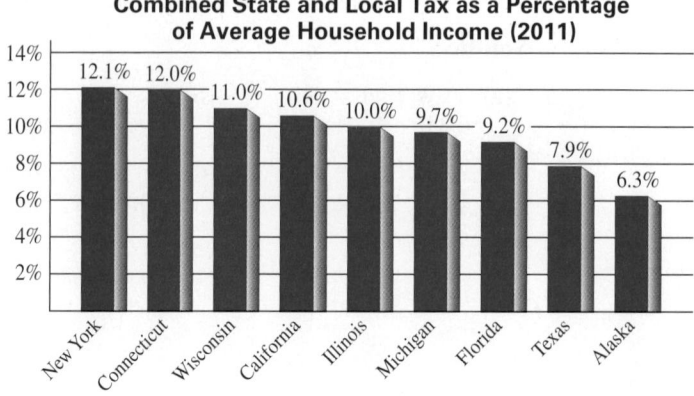

Combined State and Local Tax as a Percentage of Average Household Income (2011)

Source: © Tax Foundation 2011. All rights reserved.

Solution

The tax rate in the figure is a percent of income. So, income is the base and the amount of tax is the part. Estimate the state and local tax on the combined income of $72,850 for each state as shown.

$$P \quad = \quad R \quad \times \quad B$$

Tax in Texas $\quad = 0.079 \times \$72,850 = \$5755.15$

Tax in New York $= 0.121 \times \$72,850 = \$8814.85$

Next, subtract the two taxes to find the increase in taxes that must be paid on moving to New York.

Difference $= \$8814.85 - \$5755.15 = \$3059.70$, or about $3060 a year

Each year, the couple would pay an extra $3060 in state and local taxes if they moved. Housing costs may also be more expensive for the family in New York compared to Texas.

 Scientific
Calculator
Approach

The calculator solution to Example 3 follows.

$72850 \boxed{\times} 7.9 \boxed{\%} \boxed{=} 5755.15$

$72850 \boxed{\times} 12.1 \boxed{\%} \boxed{=} 8814.85 \boxed{STO}$

$\boxed{RCL} \boxed{-} 5755.15 \boxed{=} 3059.70$

Objective

4 *Recognize the Terms Associated with Base, Rate, and Part.* Percent problems have certain similarities. For example, some phrases are associated with the base in the problem. Other phrases lead to the part, while "%" or "percent" following a number identifies the rate. Table 3.1 helps distinguish between the base and the part.

Table 3.1 WORDS AND PHRASES ASSOCIATED WITH BASE AND PART

Usually Indicates the Base (*B*)	Usually Indicates the Part (*P*)
Sales $\longrightarrow$	Sales tax
Investment $\longrightarrow$	Return
Savings $\longrightarrow$	Interest
Value of bonds $\longrightarrow$	Interest
Retail price $\longrightarrow$	Discount
Last year's anything $\longrightarrow$	Increase or decrease
Value of real estate $\longrightarrow$	Rents
Old salary $\longrightarrow$	Raise
Total sales $\longrightarrow$	Commission
Value of stocks $\longrightarrow$	Dividends
Revenue $\longrightarrow$	Expenditures
Original $\longrightarrow$	Change

Objective

5   *Use the Basic Percent Equation.* Most percent problems can be written in the form of the basic percent equation.

$$
\begin{array}{ccccc}
\boldsymbol{R} & \times & \boldsymbol{B} & = & \boldsymbol{P} \\
\text{Rate} & \times & \text{Base} & = & \text{Part} \\
\downarrow & \downarrow & \downarrow & \downarrow & \downarrow \\
\underline{\quad}\% & \text{of} & \underline{\quad} & \text{is} & \underline{\quad}
\end{array}
$$

Examples: 5% of the automobiles are red.
4.2% of the workers are unemployed.
28% of the income is income tax.
75% of the students are full-time.

> **NOTE** Rate is identified by "%" (the percent sign); the word "of" means "×" (multiplication); the *multiplicand,* or number being multiplied, is the base; the word "is" means " = " (equals); and the product, or answer, is a part of the base.

EXAMPLE 4   **Identifying the Elements in Percent Problems**

Identify the values given in the following percent problems and determine which value must be found.

(a) During a recent sale, Stockdale Marine offered a 15% discount on all new recreational equipment. Find the discount on a jet ski originally priced at $9800.

Solution

Identify the values in the percent equation: Rate = 15%; Base = Price = $9800; and Part = discount, which is the unknown.

$$
\begin{array}{ccccc}
\boldsymbol{R} & \times & \boldsymbol{B} & = & \boldsymbol{P} \\
\underline{\quad}\% & \text{of} & \underline{\quad} & \text{is} & \text{discount.} \\
15\% & \text{of} & \$9800 & = & \text{discount} \\
0.15 & \times & \$9800 & = & P
\end{array}
$$

$$P = \$1470 \text{ discount}$$

(b) Round Table Pizza spends an amount equal to 5.8% of its sales on advertising. If sales for the month were $28,500, find the amount spent on advertising.

Solution

Identify the values in the percent equation: Rate = 5.8%; Base = Sales = $28,500; and Part = amount spent on advertising, which is the unknown.

$$
\begin{array}{ccccc}
\boldsymbol{R} & \times & \boldsymbol{B} & = & \boldsymbol{P} \\
\underline{\quad}\% & \text{of} & \underline{\quad} & \text{is} & \text{amount spent on advertising.} \\
5.8\% & \text{of} & \$28,500 & = & \text{amount spent on advertising} \\
0.058 & \times & \$28,500 & = & P
\end{array}
$$

$$P = \$1653 \text{ spent on advertising}$$

3.2	Exercises

Solve for part in each of the following.

1. 20% of 80 bicycles   16 bicycles

2. 25% of 3500 Web sites   875 Web sites

3. 22.5% of $1086 $244.35

4. 20.5% of $1500 $307.50

5. 4% of 120 feet   4.8 feet

6. 125% of 2000 products   2500 products

7. 175% of 5820 miles   10,185 miles

8. 15% of 75 cases   11.25 cases

9. 17.5% of 1040 homes   182 homes

10. 52.5% of 1560 trucks   819 trucks

11. 118% of 125.8 yards   148.444 yds

12. 500% of 142 units   710 units

13. $90\frac{1}{2}$% of $5930 $5366.65

14. $7\frac{1}{2}$% of $150 $11.25

15. 0.5% of $1300 $6.50

16. 0.75% of 180,000 calls   1350 calls

 17. Name the three components in a percent problem and tell how you can identify each of these components. (See Objective 1.)

18. There are words and phrases that are usually associated with base and part. Give three examples of words that usually identify base and the accompanying word for the part. (See Objective 4.)

Solve for part in the following application problems. Round to the nearest cent unless otherwise indicated.

19. WEDDING PREFERENCES   In a recent survey of 480 adults, 55% said that they would prefer to have their wedding at a religious site. How many said they would prefer the religious site?   264 adults

20. NEWS ON INTERNET   One poll of 822 people showed that 47.2% get their news from the Internet. Find the number of people who said they get their news from the Internet. Round to the nearest whole number.   388 people

21. SALES TAX   A real estate broker wants to purchase a laptop priced at $599. If the sales tax rate is 7.75%, find the total price including the sales tax. $645.42

22. MORTGAGE BROKER   Thomas Dugally of Century 21 Realty works with a mortgage company that charges borrowers a fee of $350 plus 2% of the loan amount. What is the total charge for a home loan of $128,000? $2910

23. SUPERMARKET SHOPPING   The Point of Purchase Advertising Institute says that 55% of all supermarket shoppers have a written list of their needs. If there are 3680 shoppers per day entering the supermarket that you manage, what number of shoppers would you expect to have a written shopping list?   2024 shoppers

24. BAR SOAP   A bar of Ivory Soap is $99\frac{44}{100}$% pure. If the bar of soap weighs 9 ounces, how many ounces are pure? Round to the nearest hundredth.   8.95 ounces

25. GLOBAL WARMING   Of 240 climate scientists polled, 85.8% strongly believe that humans contribute significantly to global warming. Find the number of scientists that strongly believe. Round to the nearest whole number.   206 scientists

26. DRIVING DISTRACTIONS   It is estimated that 29.5% of automobile crashes are caused by driver distractions, such as texting or talking on a cell phone. If there are 16,450 automobile crashes in a study, what number would be caused by driver distractions? Round to the nearest whole number.   4853 accidents

27. GERMAN LABOR FORCE   The size of the workforce in Germany is 44 million. If 62.5% of the labor force is male, find (a) the percent of the labor force that is female and (b) the number of workers who are female.   (a) 37.5% (b) 16.5 million female workers

28. U.S. LABOR FORCE   In the United States, there are 158 million people in the labor force. If 68% of the labor force is male, find (a) the percent of the workforce that is female and (b) the number of workers who are female to the nearest tenth of a million.   (a) 32% (b) 50.6 million female workers

29. **WORKPLACE REQUIREMENTS** A study of office workers found that 27% would like more storage space. If there are 14 million office workers, how many would want more storage space? 3.78 million office workers

30. **FEMALE LAWYERS** There are 1,143,050 active lawyers living in the United States. If 53.1% of these lawyers are male, find (a) the percent of the lawyers who are female and (b) the number of lawyers who are female. Round to the nearest whole number. (a) 46.9% female (b) 536,090 female

31. **NEW PRODUCT FAILURE** Marketing Intelligence Service says that there were 15,401 new products introduced last year. If 86% of the products introduced last year failed to reach their business objectives, find the number of products that did reach their objectives. Round to the nearest whole number. 2156 products

32. **FAMILY BUDGET** A family of four with an after-tax monthly income of $4400 spends 90% and saves the balance. Find (a) the monthly savings and (b) the annual savings. (a) $440 per month (b) $5280 annual savings

33. **ORANGE JUICE IN CHINA** This year the sales of Tropicana orange juice in China are $100 million. Seagram's Tropicana Beverage Group estimates that sales will increase by 35% next year. Find the amount of orange juice sales estimated for next year. $135 million

34. **SUPER BOWL ADVERTISING** The average cost of a 30-second ad during the Super Bowl 4 years ago was $2.6 million. If the increase in cost is 3.64% per year, find the average cost this year. Round to the nearest tenth of a million. $3.0 million

35. **SALES TAX COMPUTATION** As the owner of a copy and print shop, you must collect $6\frac{1}{2}$% of the amount of each sale for sales tax. If sales for the month are $48,680, what is the combined amount of sales and tax? $51,844.20

36. **HDTV** A high-definition TV is priced at $1149. If sales tax of $7\frac{3}{4}$% is charged, find the total cost paid by the customer. $1238.05

37. **REAL ESTATE COMMISSIONS** Thomas Dugally of Century 21 Realty sold a home for $174,900. The commission was 6% of the sale price. However, Dugally receives only 20% of the total commission. Find the amount of commission received by Dugally. $2098.80

38. **BUSINESS OWNERSHIP** Rick Wilson has an 82% ownership in a company called Puppets and Clowns. The company has a value of $49,200 and Wilson receives an income of 30% of the value of his ownership. Find the amount of his income. $12,103.20

INTERNET SALES Country Store has a unique selection of merchandise that it sells by mail and over the Internet. Use the shipping and insurance delivery chart below and a sales tax rate of 8% to solve Exercises 39–42. There is no sales tax on shipping and insurance.

Shipping and Insurance Delivery Chart

Up to $25.00	add $3.95
$25.01 to $50.00	add $6.95
$50.01 to $99.99	add $8.95
$100.00 or more	add $10.95

39. Find the total cost of 6 electric skillets at a price of $29.99 each. $205.29

40. A customer ordered 5 sets of flour-sack towels at a price of $12.99 each. What is the total cost? $79.10

41. Find the total cost of 3 pop-up hampers at a price of $18.99 each and 4 nonstick mini-donut pans at $10.99 each. $119.93

42. Find the total cost of a small night lamp at a price of $49.99 and 2 sweaters at a price of $38.50 each. $148.10

3.3	**Applications: Finding the Base**

OBJECTIVES

1 *Use the basic percent equation to solve for base.*

2 *Find the amount of sales when taxes and rate of tax are known.*

3 *Find the amount of investment when expense and rate of expense are known.*

4 *Find the base when rate and part are for different quantities.*

Objective

1

Use the Basic Percent Equation to Solve for Base. In some problems, the rate and part are given and the base must be found. For example, suppose that a couple, interested in purchasing a home, can make a monthly payment of $1155, which is 28% of their monthly income. To find their monthly income, use the rate (28%) and part ($1155) to find the base by using the basic percent equation, rate × base = part. The word "of" in "28% of their monthly income" is the key word that indicates monthly income is the base.

$$R \times B = P$$
$$28\% \text{ of } \underline{\qquad} = \$1155$$
$$0.28 \times B = \$1155 \qquad \text{Base } (B) \text{ is unknown.}$$
$$\frac{0.28B}{0.28} = \frac{\$1155}{0.28} \qquad \text{Divide both sides by 0.28.}$$
$$B = \frac{\$1155}{0.28}$$
$$B = \$4125 \qquad \text{Monthly income.}$$

EXAMPLE 1 Solving for Base

Solve for base using the basic percent equation.

(a) 8 is 4% of _____   **(b)** 135 is 15% of _____   **(c)** 1.25 is 25% of _____

Solution

(a)
$$P = R \times B$$
$$8 = 4\% \text{ of } \underline{\qquad}$$
$$8 = 4\% \times B$$
$$8 = 0.04B$$
$$\frac{8}{0.04} = \frac{0.04B}{0.04}$$
$$B = \frac{8}{0.04} = 200$$

(b)
$$P = R \times B$$
$$135 = 15\% \text{ of } \underline{\qquad}$$
$$135 = 15\% \times B$$
$$135 = 0.15B$$
$$\frac{135}{0.15} = \frac{0.15B}{0.15}$$
$$B = \frac{135}{0.15} = 900$$

(c)
$$P = R \times B$$
$$1.25 = 25\% \text{ of } \underline{\qquad}$$
$$1.25 = 25\% \times B$$
$$1.25 = 0.25B$$
$$\frac{1.25}{0.25} = \frac{0.25B}{0.25}$$
$$B = \frac{1.25}{0.25} = 5$$

Objective

2 *Find the Amount of Sales When Taxes and Rate of Tax Are Known.* A common business application of percent involves sales tax and the sales tax rate.

> **EXAMPLE** **2** **Finding Sales When Sales Tax Is Given**
>
> The 7.75% sales tax collected one week by Famous Footwear was $980. What was the amount of total sales?
>
> **Solution**
>
> Here the rate of tax collection is 7.75% and taxes collected are a part of total sales. The rate is 7.75% and the part is $980. Use the percent equation.
>
> $$R \times B = P$$
>
> $$7.75\% \text{ of } \underline{\hspace{1cm}} = \$980$$
>
> $$0.0775B = \$980$$
>
> $$\frac{0.0775B}{0.0775} = \frac{\$980}{0.0775}$$
>
> $$B = \frac{\$980}{0.0775} = \$12{,}645.16$$
>
> The total sales of the company were $12,645.16.

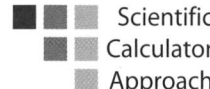

Scientific	In the calculator solution to Example 2, the percent key may be used when dividing.
Calculator	
Approach	$980 \boxed{\div} 7.75 \boxed{\%} \boxed{=} 12645.16$ (rounded)

> **NOTE** It is important to consider whether an answer is reasonable. A common error in a base problem is to confuse the base and part. In Example 2, if the taxes, $980, had been mistakenly used as the base, the resulting answer would have been $75.95 ($980 × 7.75%). Obviously, $75.95 is not a reasonable amount for total sales, given $980 as sales tax.

Objective

3 *Find the Amount of Investment When Expense and Rate of Expense Are Known.* The amount of an investment is the base. When the amount of expenses and the rate of expenses are known, the percent equation may be used to find the amount of the investment.

> **EXAMPLE** **3** **Finding the Amount of an Investment**
>
> The yearly lawn and pool maintenance cost of an apartment complex is $3\frac{1}{2}\%$ of its value. If the maintenance cost amounts to $73,500 per year, find the value of the complex.
>
> **Solution**
>
> To find the total value of the complex, which is the base, use the percent equation.
>
> $$R \times B = P$$
>
> $$3\frac{1}{2}\% \text{ of } \underline{\hspace{1cm}} = \$73{,}500$$
>
> $$0.035B = \$73{,}500$$
>
> $$\frac{0.035B}{0.035} = \frac{\$73{,}500}{0.035}$$

$$B = \frac{\$73,500}{0.035} = \$2,100,000$$

The total value of the complex is $2,100,000.

NOTE   When working with a fraction of a percent, it is best to change the fraction to a decimal. In Example 3, $3\frac{1}{2}\%$ was changed to 3.5%, which equals 0.035.

Objective

4   *Find the Base When Rate and Part Are for Different Quantities.*   The rate used and the part given in a problem do not always refer to the same quantity. *Always pay careful attention when reading to understand a problem.*

Sometimes you need to subtract a percent from 100% to solve a problem. For example, assume 8% of the bananas in a shipment have been damaged. The percent of the bananas with good quality is found as follows.

$$\begin{array}{ll} 100\% & \text{All bananas in the shipment} \\ \underline{-8\%} & \text{Damaged bananas} \\ 92\% & \text{Good quality bananas} \end{array}$$

The value 92% is said to be the **complement** with respect to 100% of 8%, or it is simply called the complement of 8%.

EXAMPLE **4**   **Finding Base When Rate and Part Are for Different Quantities**

United Hospital finds that 25% of its employees are men and 720 are women. Find the total number of employees.

Solution

First find the percent of women employees.

$$\begin{array}{ll} 100\% & \text{All employees} \\ \underline{-25\%} & \text{Men} \\ 75\% & \text{Women} \end{array}$$

Then use the percent equation knowing that the 720 women employees (part) correspond to 75% of the total number of employees.

$$R \times B = P$$

$$75\% \text{ of } \underline{\hspace{2cm}} = 720$$

$$0.75B = 720$$

$$\frac{0.75B}{0.75} = \frac{720}{0.75}$$

$$B = \frac{720}{0.75} = 960$$

The total number of employees is 960.

| **3.3** | **Exercises** |

Solve for base in each of the following. Round to the nearest hundredth.

1. 265 bowlers is 25% of _____1060_____ bowlers.

2. 240 letters is 80% of _____300_____ letters.

3. 75 miles is 40% of _____187.5_____ miles

4. 32 shipments is 8% of _____400_____ shipments.

5. 55 packages is 5.5% of _____1000_____ packages.

6. $850 is $4\frac{1}{4}$% of _____$20,000_____.

7. 36 employees is 0.75% of _____4800_____ employees.

8. 23 workers is 0.5% of _____4600_____ workers.

9. 33 rolls is 0.15% of _____22,000_____ rolls.

10. 54,600 boxes is 60% of _____91,000_____ boxes.

11. 50 doors is 0.25% of _____20,000_____ doors.

12. 39 bottles is 0.78% of _____5000_____ bottles.

13. $33,870 is $37\frac{1}{2}$% of _____$90,320_____.

14. $8,500 is $27\frac{1}{2}$% of _____$30,909.09_____.

15. 20% of _____1750_____ sacks is 350 sacks.

16. 16% of _____$281.25_____ is $45.

17. 375 crates is 0.12% of _____312,500_____ crates.

18. 3.5 quarts is 0.07% of _____5000_____ quarts.

19. 0.5% of _____65,400_____ homes is 327 homes.

20. 6.5 barrels is 0.05% of _____13,000_____ barrels.

21. 12 audits is 0.03% of _____40,000_____ audits.

22. 8 banks is 0.04% of _____20,000_____ banks.

 23. The basic percent formula is $P = B \times R$. Show how to find the formula to solve for B (base). (See Objective 1.)

 24. A problem includes amount of sales, sales tax, and a sales tax rate. Explain how you could identify the base, rate, and part in this problem. (See Objective 2.)

Solve for base in the following application problems. Round to the nearest whole number as needed.

25. **STUDENT DEBT**   A survey at one large university showed that 1843 juniors and seniors had more than $10,000 in student loans. This amounted to 36.7% of the entire group of juniors and seniors. Find the number of juniors and seniors at the college.   5022 juniors and seniors

26. **EMPLOYEE POPULATION BASE**   In a large metropolitan area, 81% of the employed population is enrolled in a health maintenance organization (HMO). If 700,650 employees are enrolled, find the total number of people in the employed population.   865,000 people

27. **COLLEGE ENROLLMENT**   This semester there are 1785 married students on campus. If this figure represents 23% of the total enrollment, what is the total enrollment?   7761 students

28. **WOMEN MOTORCYCLISTS**   The Motorcycle Industry Council estimated that there were 635,000 women motorcycle riders in the United States. Since this is 9.6% of all motorcycle riders in the United States, what is the total number of motorcycle riders? Round to the nearest thousand.   6,615,000 motorcycle riders

29. **LOAN QUALIFICATION**   Lauren Morse found a home for Sharon and Howard Martin that will require a monthly loan payment of $1140. If the lender insists that the buyer's monthly payment not exceed 30% of the buyer's monthly income, find the minimum monthly income required by the lender. $3800

30. **PERSONAL BUDGETING** Byron Hopkins spends 30% of his income on rent, 24% on food, 8% on clothing, 15% on transportation, 11% on education, and 7% on recreation and saves the balance. If his savings amount to $150 per month, what are his monthly earnings? $3000 monthly earnings

31. **DIABETES SURVEY** In a telephone survey, 749 people said that diabetes is a serious problem in the United States. If this was 71% of the survey group, find the total number of people in the telephone survey. 1055 people

32. **DRIVING TESTS** In analyzing the success of driver's license applicants, the state finds that 58.3% of those examined received a passing mark. If the records show that 8370 new driver's licenses were issued, what was the number of applicants? 14,357 applicants

33. **APPLE INC.** After paying income taxes of $4.5 billion last year, Apple Inc. earned $14 billion in profit. Estimate total revenue to the nearest tenth of a billion if profit was 21.5% of total revenue. $65.1 billion

34. **COMMUNICATIONS INDUSTRY LAYOFFS** Telecommunications equipment maker Nortel Networks says it will lay off 4000 workers globally. If this amounts to 4% of its total workforce, how many workers will remain after the layoffs? 96,000 workers after layoffs

35. **GAMBLING PAYBACK** An Atlantic City casino advertises that it gives a 97.4% payback on slot machines, and the balance is retained by the casino. If the amount retained by the casino is $4823, find the total amount played on the slot machines. $185,500

36. **SMOKERS AND CANCER** The National Cancer Institute estimates that 87% of all deaths due to lung cancers are caused by smoking. Assume that 1.1 million people who developed lung cancer from smoking died from the cancer. Find the number who died of lung cancer from all causes. Round to the nearest tenth of a million. 1.3 million

Supplementary Exercises: Base and Part

Solve for base or part as indicated in the following application problems.

1. **SHAMPOO INGREDIENTS** Most shampoos contain 75% to 90% water. If there are 12.5 ounces of water in a bottle of shampoo that contains 78% water, what is the size of the bottle of shampoo? Round to the nearest whole number. 16 ounces

2. **HOUSEHOLD LUBRICANT** The lubricant WD-40 is used in 82.3 million U.S. homes, which is 79% of all homes. Find the total number of homes in the United States. Round to the nearest tenth of a million. 104.2 million homes

3. **PROPERTY INSURANCE** A dental office is valued at $423,750 and is insured for 68% of its value. Find the amount of insurance coverage. $288,150

4. **FLU SHOTS** In a survey of 3860 people who were 18–49 years of age, 16.3% had received an influenza vaccination (flu shot). How many of those surveyed received the vaccination? Round to the nearest whole number. 629 people

5. **CAMAROS AND MUSTANGS** The Chevy Camaro was introduced in 1967. Sales that year were 220,917, which was 46.2% of the number of Ford Mustangs sold in the same year. Find the number of Mustangs sold in 1967. Round to the nearest whole number. 478,175 Mustangs

6. **AUTO-LOAN INDUSTRY** The Money Store Inc. announced that it held auto loans valued at $776 million. If this is 5.1% of the company's total loan portfolio, what is the total amount of loans? Round to the nearest tenth of a million. $15,215.7 million or $15,215,700,000

7. **FROZEN YOGURT SALES** The total sales of frozen yogurt were $594 million in the past 12 months. If 15.8% of the sales were private-label brands, what is the amount of sales that were private-label brands? Round to the nearest tenth of a million. $93.9 million

8. **CALORIES FROM FAT**   Häagen-Dazs vanilla ice cream has 270 calories per serving. If 60% of these calories come from fat, find the number of calories coming from fat.   162 calories

9. **RETIREMENT ACCOUNTS**   Jo O'Neill has 9.5% of her earnings deposited into a retirement account. This amounts to $308.75 per month. Find her annual earnings. $39,000

10. **SOCIAL SECURITY**   After graduating from college, James O'Neill was surprised that $52.08 was taken out of his first weekly paycheck for something he had never heard of called FICA. He learned that FICA is also called Social Security tax, and that the tax rate was 6.2%. Find his income for the week. $840

11. **DRIVER SAFETY SURVEY**   A survey at an intersection in Spain found that of 2200 drivers, 38% were wearing seat belts. How many drivers in the survey were wearing seat belts?   836 drivers

12. **BLOOD CHOLESTEROL LEVELS**   At a recent health fair 32% of the people tested were found to have high blood cholesterol levels. If 350 people were tested, find the number having high blood cholesterol.   112 people

13. **CAT FOOD SALES**   Sales of Whiskas canned cat food dropped 3%, or $1.9 million, in the past year. Find the sales of Whiskas cat food after the decrease. Round to the nearest tenth of a million. $61.4 million

14. **CANNED CAT FOOD**   In the past year there has been a 14% increase in the sales of Tender Morsels canned cat food. If this increase amounts to $1.41 million, find the sales of Tender Morsels canned cat food after the increase. Round to the nearest tenth of a million. $11.48 million

3.4   Applications: Finding the Rate

OBJECTIVES

1 *Use the percent equation to solve for rate.*

2 *Find the rate of return when the amount of the return and the investment are known.*

3 *Solve for the percent remaining when the total amount and amount used are given.*

4 *Find the percent of change.*

In the third type of percent problem, the part and base are given and the rate must be found. The rate is identified by the "%" sign, or "percent." For example, what percent of 32 is 8? Use the percent equation as shown next.

Objective

1   *Use the Percent Equation to Solve for Rate.*

$$R \times B = P$$

$$\underline{}\% \text{ of } 32 = 8$$

$$R \times 32 = 8$$

$$32R = 8$$

Now divide both sides by 32.

$$\frac{\cancel{32}R}{\cancel{32}} = \frac{8}{32}$$

$$R = \frac{8}{32} = 0.25 = 25\%$$

Finally, 8 is 25% of 32, or 25% of 32 is 8.

NOTE When solving for rate, you *must* change the resulting decimal answer to a percent.

EXAMPLE **1** **Solving for Rate**

Solve for rate.

(a) 63 is what percent of 180?
(b) What percent of 500 is 100?
(c) 54 is what percent of 12?

Solution

(a) 63 is _____ % of 180

$$R \times B = P$$

$$\text{_____} \% \text{ of } 180 = 63$$

$$180R = 63$$

$$\frac{180R}{180} = \frac{63}{180} \qquad \text{Divide both sides by 180.}$$

$$R = \frac{63}{180} = 0.35 = 35\%$$

(b) 100 is _____ % of 500

$$R \times B = P$$

$$\text{_____} \% \text{ of } 500 = 100$$

$$500R = 100$$

$$\frac{500R}{500} = \frac{100}{500} \qquad \text{Divide both sides by 500.}$$

$$R = \frac{100}{500} = 0.2 = 20\%$$

(c) 54 is _____ % of 12

$$R \times B = P$$

$$\text{_____} \% \text{ of } 12 = 54$$

$$12R = 54$$

$$\frac{12R}{12} = \frac{54}{12} \qquad \text{Divide both sides by 12.}$$

$$R = \frac{54}{12} = 4.5 = 450\%$$

Objective

2 *Find the Rate of Return When the Amount of the Return and the Investment Are Known.* It is often necessary to find the rate of return when the amount of the return and investment are known.

EXAMPLE **2**   **Finding the Rate of Return**

Joan Baker invested $8000 in a certificate of deposit (CD) at a bank and received interest of $123.60 one year later. Find the rate of return (the interest rate) to the nearest tenth of a percent.

Solution

The original investment of $8000 is the base and the interest of $123.60 is the part.

$$R \times B = P$$

$$\underline{\qquad}\% \times \$8000 = \$123.60$$

$$R \times \$8000 = \$123.60$$

$$\$8000R = \$123.60$$

$$\frac{\cancel{\$8000}R}{\cancel{\$8000}} = \frac{\$123.60}{\$8000} \qquad \text{Divide both sides by \$3000.}$$

$$R = 1.545\%$$

The annual interest rate was 1.545%, which rounds to 1.5%.

Objective

3   *Solve for the Percent Remaining When the Total Amount and Amount Used Are Given.* When the total amount of something and the amount used are known, it is common to solve for the percent remaining.

EXAMPLE **3**   **Solving for the Percent Remaining**

A roof is expected to last 12 years before it needs replacement. If the roof is 10 years old, what percent of the roof's life remains? Round to the nearest tenth of a percent.

Solution

The total life of the roof is 12 years, which is the whole or base. The number of years of life remaining is $12 - 10 = 2$ years, which is the part.

$$R \times B = P$$

$$\underline{\qquad}\% \text{ of } 12 \text{ is } 2$$

$$R \times 12 = 2$$

$$12R = 2$$

$$\frac{\cancel{12}R}{\cancel{12}} = \frac{2}{12} \qquad\qquad \text{Divide both sides by 12.}$$

$$R = \frac{2}{12} = \frac{1}{6} = 0.166\ldots = 16.7\% \quad \text{Rounded}$$

This problem can also be solved by first finding the percent of the life that has been used (10 years/12 years), which is 83.3% rounded to the nearest tenth of a percent. The percent of total life remaining is found as follows.

$$\begin{array}{ll} 100.0\% & \text{Total life of the roof} \\ \underline{-83.3\%} & \text{Amount of life that has been used} \\ 16.7\% & \text{Remaining life} \end{array}$$

This results in the same answer found above.

NOTE Remember that the base is always 100%.

Objective

4 *Find the Percent of Change.* A common business problem is to find the percent of change in amounts involved in operating a business, such as sales and returns, and to determine the percent of gain or loss of an investment.

> **EXAMPLE** **4** **Finding the Percent of Increase**
>
> Slow sales at Consumer Electronics Inc. early in the fall prompted the managers to mark down prices by 15% and to advertise the sale widely on radio and in the newspaper. Sales climbed from $36,600 in the month before the advertising campaign to $113,460 the next month. Find the percent increase.

Solution

The base is the sales last month, or $36,600. Find the part, the increase in sales, as follows.

$$\text{Increase in sales} = \$113,460 - \$36,600 = \$76,860$$

Use the basic percent equation as follows.

$$R \times B = P$$
$$\underline{}\% \text{ of } \$36,600 = \$76,860$$
$$R \times \$36,600 = \$76,860$$
$$\$36,600R = \$76,860$$
$$\frac{\$36,600R}{\$36,600} = \frac{\$76,860}{\$36,600} \qquad \text{Divide both sides by } \$36,600.$$
$$R = \frac{76,860}{36,600} = 2.1 = 210\%$$

Sales increased by 210%. Since this percent is over 200%, the *increase in sales* was more than twice the original sales amount of $36,600. Clearly, customers responded strongly to the advertising campaign. This is a *huge increase* for one month!

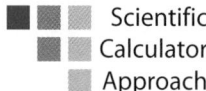 Scientific Calculator Approach

The calculator solution to this example is to subtract to find the difference and then divide.

NOTE Remember, to find the **percent of increase**, the first step is to determine the amount of increase. The base is *always* the original amount, such as last year's or last month's amount, and the amount of increase is the part.

Percents are commonly used to show the amount of change, for example, from one year to another. Figure 3.2 shows the increase in the cost of several foods from 2010 to 2011. Several prices increased significantly, but the 13.4% increase in the price of eggs was very high. Price increases of this magnitude may cause some lower-income families to buy fewer eggs and turn to other foods.

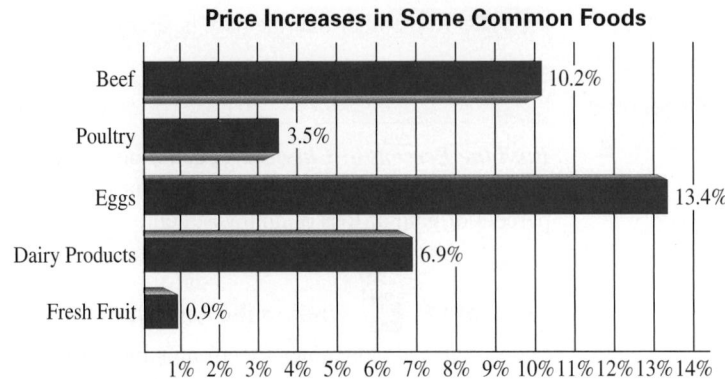

Price Increases in Some Common Foods

Source: United States Department of Agriculture.

Figure 3.2

EXAMPLE 5 **Finding the Percent of Decrease**

As a result of lower mortgage interest rates, Scott and Andrea Abriani will be able to decrease their monthly mortgage payment from $1155 to $1050. Find the **percent of decrease**.

Solution

The base is the old monthly payment of $1155. First find the part, which is the decrease in the payment.

$$\text{Decrease in payment} = \text{old payment} - \text{new payment}$$
$$= \$1155 - \$1050 = \$105$$

Use the basic percent equation.

$$R \times B = P$$
$$\underline{\hspace{2cm}}\% \text{ of } \$1155 = \$105$$
$$R \times \$1155 = \$105$$
$$\$1155R = \$105$$
$$\frac{\$1155R}{\$1155} = \frac{\$105}{\$1155} \qquad \text{Divide both sides by \$1155.}$$
$$R = \frac{105}{1155} = 0.0909 = 9.1\% \qquad \text{Rounded to the nearest tenth of a percent}$$

The monthly mortgage payment went down by 9.1%.

■■■ Scientific
■■ Calculator
■ Approach

The calculator solution to this example is to subtract to find the difference and then divide.

$$1155 \boxed{-} 1050 \boxed{=} 105 \boxed{\div} 1155 \boxed{=} 0.0909 = .091 \text{ (rounded)}$$

NOTE To find the percent of decrease, the first step is to determine the *amount of decrease*. The amount of decrease is the part in the problem and the base is the original amount or last year's, last month's, or last week's amount.

3.4	**Exercises**

Solve for rate in each of the following. Round to the nearest tenth of a percent.

1. _____10_____% of 2760 listings is 276 listings.

2. _____40_____% of 850 showings is 340 showings.

3. 310 phones is _____125_____% of 248 phones.

4. 144 desks is _____48_____% of 300 desks.

5. _____28.3_____% of 78.57 ounces is 22.2 ounces.

6. _____70_____% of 728 miles is 509.6 miles.

7. 73.1 quarts is _____9.3_____% of 786.8 quarts.

8. $310.75 is _____250_____% of $124.30.

9. _____4.1_____% of $53.75 is $2.20.

10. _____0.4_____% of 850 liters is 3.4 liters.

11. 46 shirts is _____5.9_____% of 780 shirts.

12. 5.2 vats is _____18.3_____% of 28.4 vats.

13. _____102.5_____% of 2 acres is 2.05 acres.

14. _____0.75_____% of $8 is $0.06.

15. 13,830 books is _____17.6_____% of 78,400 books.

16. _____480_____% of 73 cases is 350.4 cases.

17. _____27.8_____% of $330 is $91.74.

18. _____62.5_____% of 752 employees is 470 employees.

 19. The basic percent formula is $P = B \times R$. Show how to use the formula to solve for R (rate). (See Objective 1.)

 20. A problem includes last year's sales and this year's sales and asks for the percent of increase. Explain how you would identify the base, rate, and part in this problem. (See Objective 4.)

Solve for rate in the following application problems. Round to the nearest tenth of a percent.

21. **ADVERTISING EXPENSES** Fernanda Lai of Wired Education Systems reports that sales were $132,900 while advertising expenses were $7442.40. What percent of last month's sales was spent on advertising? 5.6%

22. **MUSIC STORES** Music Land Group Inc. will close 150 of its 1119 Sam Goody and Suncoast Motion Picture Company Stores. What percent of the stores will close? 13.4%

23. **WOMEN IN THE MILITARY** A recent study by Rand's National Defense Research Institute examined 48,000 military jobs, such as Army attack-helicopter pilot or Navy gunner's mate. It was found that only 960 of these jobs were filled by women. What percent of these jobs were filled by women? 2.0%

24. **VOCABULARY KNOWLEDGE** There are 55,000 words in Webster's Dictionary, but most educated people can identify only 20,000 of these words. What percent of the words in the dictionary can these people identify? 36.4%

25. **ADVERTISING MEDIA** Advertising expenditures for Bailey's Roofers are as follows.

Newspaper	$2250	Television	$1425
Radio	$954	Yellow Pages	$1605
Outdoor	$1950	Miscellaneous	$2775

What percent of the total advertising expenditures is spent on radio advertising? 8.7%

26. **MAIL DELIVERY** The manager of a small country post office estimates that of the roughly 3850 mailings handled each day, about 2400 fall in the category that some homeowners called junk mail advertising. Find the percent of the mailings that are advertising. 62.3%

27. **HARLEY-DAVIDSON MOTORCYCLES** Harley-Davidson, the only major U.S.-based motorcycle maker, says that it expects to build 317,000 motorcycles this year, up from 290,600 last year. Find the percent of increase in production. 9.1%

28. **AVERAGE HOME PRICE** The average selling price of a home in the United States last year was $202,250 while the average selling price this year was $207,300. What is the percent of increase? 2.5%

29. **FALLING PHONE BILLS** Sarah Walker's long-distance phone bills plummeted to an average of $24.40 a month from last year's monthly average of $30.50. What was the percent of decrease? 20%

30. **SOLAR POWER** In the past 5 years, the cost of generating electricity from the sun has been brought down from 24 cents per kilowatt hour to 7 cents per kilowatt hour. Find the percent of decrease. 70.8%

Supplementary Exercises: Rate, Base, and Part

Solve for rate, base, or part as indicated in the following. Round rates to the nearest tenth of a percent or whole number, as needed.

1. **OVERWEIGHT PATIENTS** A telephone survey of doctors found that 63% of the doctors reported an increase in the number of patients who are overweight. If the number of doctors reporting this was 189, find the number of doctors in the survey. 300 doctors

2. **EMPLOYEE HEALTH PLANS** When larger firms (over 1000 employees) were surveyed, it was found that 27% of the firms offered only one health plan to employees. If 1800 firms were surveyed, find the number offering only one health plan. 486 firms

3. **MOTORCYCLE SAFETY** Only 20 of the 50 states require motorcycle riders to wear helmets. What percent of the states require motorcycle riders to wear helmets? 40%

4. **DANGER OF EXTINCTION** Scientists tell us that there are 9688 species of birds and that 1211 of these species are in danger of extinction. What percent of the bird species are in danger of extinction? 12.5%

5. **ECONOMY LODGING** According to industry figures, there are 44,500 hotels and motels in America. Economy hotels and motels account for 38% of this total. Find the number of economy hotels and motels. 16,910 hotels

6. **AMERICAN CHIROPRACTIC ASSOCIATION** There are 60,000 licensed chiropractors in the nation. If 25% of these chiropractors belong to the American Chiropractic Association (ACA), find the number of chiropractors in the ACA. 15,000 chiropractors

7. **DRUNK-DRIVING ACCIDENTS** In the United States, 275,000 people were injured in alcohol-related driving accidents last year. This was 9.48% of all traffic injuries. Find the number of traffic injuries last year. 2,900,844 injuries

8. **LAPTOP COMPUTER SALES** Last year, Get Wired Company sold 7038 laptop computers. If this was 56% of its total computer sales, find the total number of computers sold. 12,568 computers sold

9. **COST AFTER MARKDOWN** A fax machine priced at $398 is marked down 7% to promote the new model. If the sales tax is also 7%, what is the cost of the fax machine including sales tax? $396.05

10. **TEAM SWEATERS** After a losing basketball season, a college bookstore offers sweaters emblazoned with a large, colorful team mascot at a 10% discount. If the original price was $58 and sales tax is 7.5%, find the total cost with sales tax. (*Hint:* First find the discount and then add the tax.) $56.12

11. BLOOD-ALCOHOL LEVELS In the United States, 15 of the 50 states limit blood-alcohol levels for drivers to 0.08%. The remaining states limit these levels to 0.10%.

(a) What percent of the states have a blood-alcohol limit of 0.08%? (a) 30%

(b) What percent have a limit of 0.10%? (b) 70%

12. ENDANGERED FROGS About 2700 of the 6000 known species of frogs are threatened with extinction. Find the percent threatened with extinction. 45%

13. WOMEN'S COATS A "60%-off sale" begins today. What is the sale price of women's wool coats normally priced at $335? $134 sale price

14. APPLIANCES What is the sale price of a $769 Sears Kenmore washer/dryer set with a discount of 25%? $576.75 sale price

15. SOCIAL SECURITY BENEFITS The Social Security Administration announced that the average monthly benefit to single retirees will be increased from $1108 to $1141. Find the percent of increase. Round to the nearest hundredth of a percent. 2.98%

16. BENEFIT INCREASE The average monthly Social Security benefit to couples will be increased to $1523. If the current monthly benefit is $1492, what is the percent of increase? 2.1%

CELL PHONE SALES The cell phone sales by one company in four regions of the country are shown in the table. Use the data to answer Exercises 17–20.

CELL PHONE SALES		
Region	**Last Year**	**This Year**
Northeast	32,000	36,000
Midwest	65,000	66,300
South	82,000	77,500
West	54,000	49,600

17. Find the percent of increase in sales in the northeastern region. 12.5%

18. Find the percent of increase in sales in the midwestern region. 2%

19. What is the percent of decrease in sales in the southern region? 5.5%

20. What is the percent of decrease in sales in the western region? 8.1%

21. VENDING MACHINE SALES Of the total candy bars contained in a vending machine, 240 bars have been sold. If 25% of the bars have been sold, find the total number of candy bars that were in the machine. 960 candy bars

22. TOTAL SALES If the sales tax rate is 6% and the sales tax collected is $478.20, what are the sales? $7970

23. FAMILY BUDGETING Toni and Jay Shellan set up a budget allowing 30% for rent and household expenses, 25% for food, 8% for clothing, 10% for car payments and insurance, and 20% for medical and recreation. The balance is put into savings. Jay takes home $2950 per month after taxes and Toni brings home $28,500 per year after taxes. Assuming no emergencies that use up funds, find the amount the couple will save in a year. $4473

24. CHICKEN NOODLE SOUP In one year there were 350 million cans of chicken noodle soup sold (all brands). If 60% of this soup is sold in the cold-and-flu season (October through March), how many cans were sold in the cold-and-flu season? 210 million cans

25. FLOOD INSURANCE According to the Federal Emergency Management Agency (FEMA), there are 11 million buildings at risk of flooding. The agency finds that only 2.6 million of these are currently insured for flooding. Find the percent that are insured. 23.6%

26. REFRIGERATION CAPACITY A Hotpoint refrigerator has a capacity of 11.5 cubic feet in the refrigerator and 5.5 cubic feet in the freezer. What percent of the total capacity is the capacity of the freezer? 32.4%

27. **GLOBAL INTERNET USE**   The World Wide Web first became available in 1993, but it has grown rapidly and there are 2.5 billion users today. At 44% of the total number of users, Asia has far more users than any other continent. Estimate the number of Asian users to the nearest tenth of a billion.   1.1 billion

28. **INTERNET USE**   Approximately 78.3% of the 362 million people living in North America use the Internet. Estimate the number of users to the nearest million   283 million

29. **U.S. PATENT RECIPIENTS**   Among the 50 companies receiving the greatest number of U.S. patents last year, 18 were Japanese companies. What percent of the top 50 companies were Japanese companies?   36%

30. **LAYOFF ALTERNATIVE**   Instead of laying off workers, a company cut all employee hours from 40 hours a week to 30 hours a week. What was the percent cut in employee hours?   25%

3.5	**Increase and Decrease Problems**

OBJECTIVES

1 *Learn to identify an increase or a decrease problem.*

2 *Apply the basic diagram for increase problems.*

3 *Use an equation to solve for base in increase problems.*

4 *Apply the basic diagram for decrease problems.*

5 *Use an equation to solve for base in decrease problems.*

Businesses commonly look at how amounts change, either up or down. For example, a manager might need to know the percent by which sales have increased, or the percent by which costs have decreased, while a consumer might need to know the percent by which the price of an item has changed. Identify these **increase and decrease problems** as follows.

Objective

1 *Learn to Identify an Increase or a Decrease Problem.*

Increase Problem

The base (100%) plus some portion of the base, gives a new value, which is part. Phrases such as *after an increase of, more than,* or *greater than* often indicate an increase problem. The basic formula for an increase problem is

$$\underset{\uparrow}{\text{Original}} + \text{increase} = \underset{\uparrow}{\text{new value}}$$
$$\text{Base} \qquad\qquad\qquad \text{Part}$$

Decrease Problem

The part equals the base (100%) minus some portion of the base, resulting in a new value. Phrases such as *after a decrease of, less than,* or *after a reduction of* often indicate a decrease problem. The basic formula for a decrease problem is

$$\underset{\uparrow}{\text{Original}} - \text{decrease} = \underset{\uparrow}{\text{new value}}$$
$$\text{Base} \qquad\qquad\qquad \text{Part}$$

> **NOTE** Base is always the original amount and we can solve for base in both increase and decrease problems. Base is always 100%.

EXAMPLE 1 Using a Diagram to Understand an Increase Problem

The price of a home sold by real estate agent Tricia Marinaro this year is $187,000, which is 10% more than last year's value. Find the value of the home last year.

Solution

The phrase "10% more than last year's value" tells us that last year's value is the base, and it is also the unknown. Figure 3.3 shows last year's value, which is 100%, and this year's value, which is

$$(\text{The base} + 10\% \text{ more than last year's value}) = 110\% \text{ of the base}$$

Objective

2 *Apply the Basic Diagram for Increase Problems.*

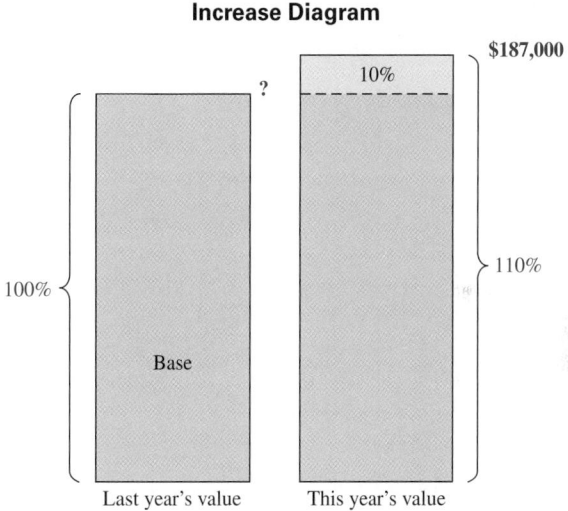

Increase Diagram

Figure 3.3

Objective

3 *Use an Equation to Solve for Base in Increase Problems.* So, 110% of the base equals this year's value of $187,000. Use the increase formula from the previous page to find the base (*B*), which is last year's value.

$$\text{Original} + \quad\quad\quad \text{increase} = \text{new value}$$

$$\text{Last year's value} + 10\% \text{ of last year's value} = \text{this year's value}$$

$$100\% \times B + 10\% \times B = \$187{,}000$$

$$110\% \times B = \$187{,}000$$

$$1.1B = \$187{,}000$$

$$\frac{\cancel{1.1}B}{\cancel{1.1}} = \frac{\$187{,}000}{1.1} \quad \text{Divide both sides by 1.1.}$$

$$B = \frac{\$187{,}000}{1.1}$$

$$B = \$170{,}000 \quad \text{Last year's value}$$

Check the answer by finding 10% of last year's value and adding it to last year's value.

$170,000   Last year's value
+   17,000   (10% of $170,000)
$187,000   This year's value

NOTE The common error in solving for the base in an increase problem is thinking that the base is given and that the solution can be found by solving for part. However, the number given in Example 1, ($187,000) is the result of having added 10% of the base, to the base. In fact, $187,000 is the part, and base must be found.

Figure 3.4 shows world population with forecasts to 2050. Although world population growth has slowed since early in the last century, experts predict that it will still grow rapidly for decades since there are so many young people of childbearing age in the world. To capture some of the uncertainty in the rate of population growth, three different forecasts are shown.

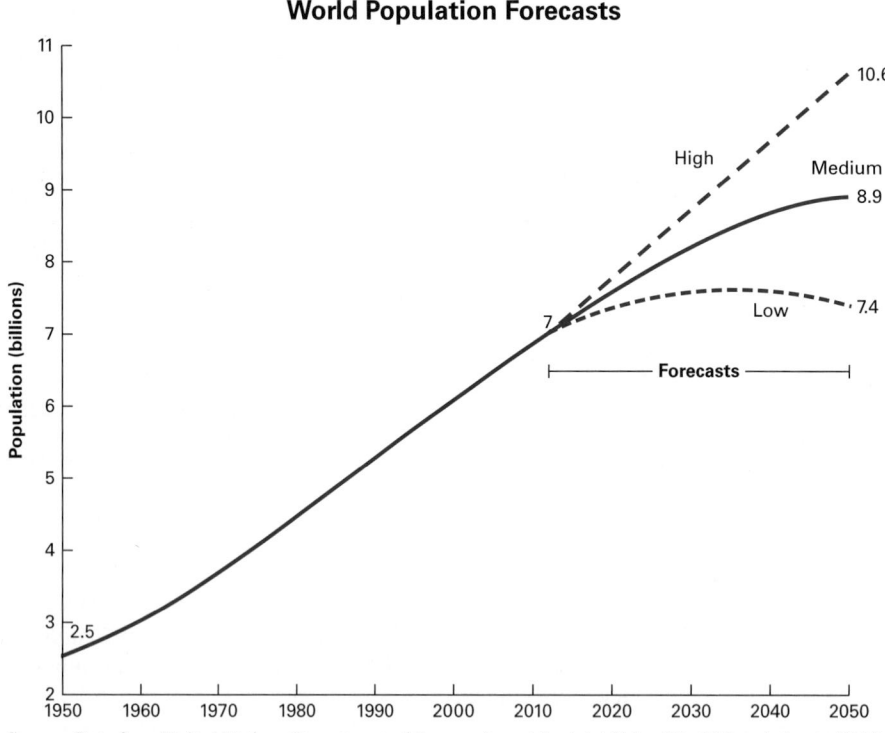

World Population Forecasts

Source: Data from United Nations Department of Economic and Social Affairs–World Population to 2300.

Figure 3.4

The low rate of population growth results in a peak in population of about 7.5 billion in 2038. World population in 2050 will be 8.9 billion under the medium growth rate and 10.6 billion under the high growth rate. Clearly, this information is very relevant to industry and world leaders trying to make plans to ensure sufficient food, water, energy, etc. for the growing population on planet Earth.

Example 2 shows how to solve a problem with two increases.

EXAMPLE 2 Finding Base after Two Increases

Sales of Icon's newest Web-enabling device have grown by 20% per year for each of the past 2 years. If 93,600 are sold this year, find sales 2 years ago.

Solution

The two 20% increases cannot be added together. Rather, two steps are needed to solve this problem, one for each of the two 20% increases. First, use the diagram in Figure 3.5 to help find last year's production.

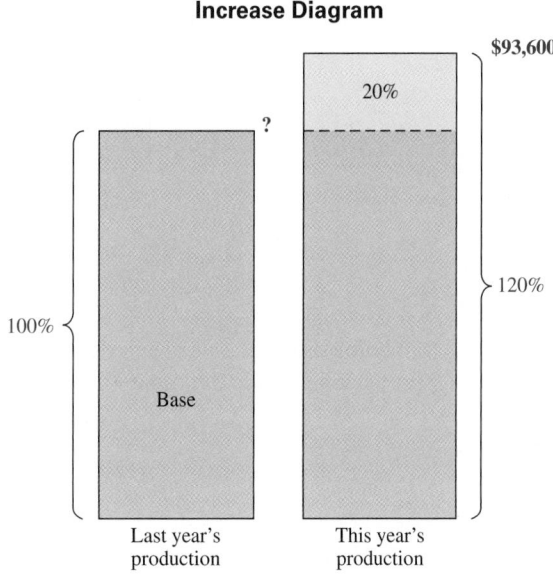

Increase Diagram

Figure 3.5

Last year's production plus 20% of last year's production equals this year's production. Use the following formula:

$$100\% \times B + 20\% \times B = 93{,}600$$

$$120\% \times B = 93{,}600$$

$$1.2B = 93{,}600$$

$$\frac{1.2B}{1.2} = \frac{93{,}600}{1.2}$$

$$B = \frac{93{,}600}{1.2}$$

$$B = 78{,}000 \quad \text{Last year's production}$$

Production last year was 78,000 units. Use this number and the knowledge that production also increased by 20% from 2 years ago to last year to find production 2 years ago. Figure 3.6 may help.

Increase Diagram

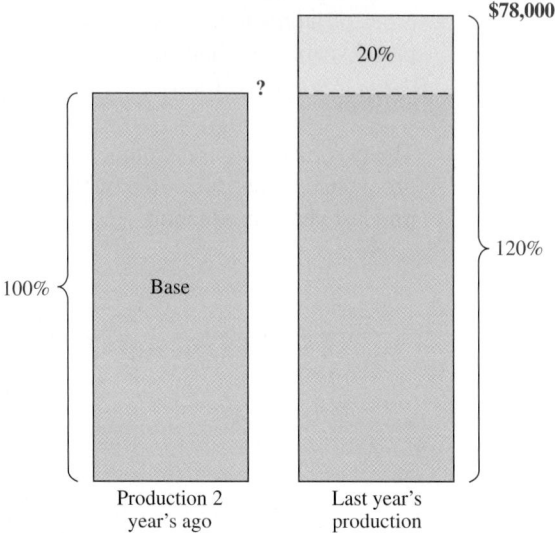

Figure 3.6

To minimize confusion and since the letter *B* was used in the earlier equations, we will use *b* for the unknown in the equations that follow.

$$100\% \times b + 20\% \times b = 78{,}000$$

$$120\% \times b = 78{,}000$$

$$1.2b = 78{,}000$$

$$\frac{\cancel{1.2}b}{\cancel{1.2}} = \frac{78{,}000}{1.2}$$

$$b = \frac{78{,}000}{1.2}$$

$$b = 65{,}000 \quad \text{Production 2 years ago}$$

So, the production two years ago, after two consecutive years of 20% growth, was 65,000 units. Check the answer as follows.

$$
\begin{array}{ll}
65{,}000 & \text{Production 2 years ago} \\
+\ 13{,}000 & \text{20\% increase} \\
\hline
78{,}000 & \text{Production last year} \\
+\ 15{,}600 & \text{20\% increase} \\
\hline
93{,}600 & \text{Production this year}
\end{array}
$$

Scientific
Calculator
Approach

The calculator solution to this example divides in a series.

$$93{,}600 \;\boxed{\div}\; 1.2 \;\boxed{\div}\; 1.2 \;\boxed{=}\; 65{,}000$$

NOTE It is important to realize that the two 20% increases cannot be added together to equal one increase of 40%. Each 20% increase is calculated on a *different base*.

Objective

4 *Apply the Basic Diagram for Decrease Problems.*

> **EXAMPLE** **3** **Using a Diagram to Understand a Decrease Problem**
>
> After Fleetfeet deducted 10% from the price of a pair of running shoes, Craig Bleyer paid $135. What was the original price of the shoes?
>
> **Solution**
>
> We know this is a decrease problem based on the phrase "deducted 10% from the price." Figure 3.7 is a decrease diagram that shows the decrease from the original price. The original price is the unknown.

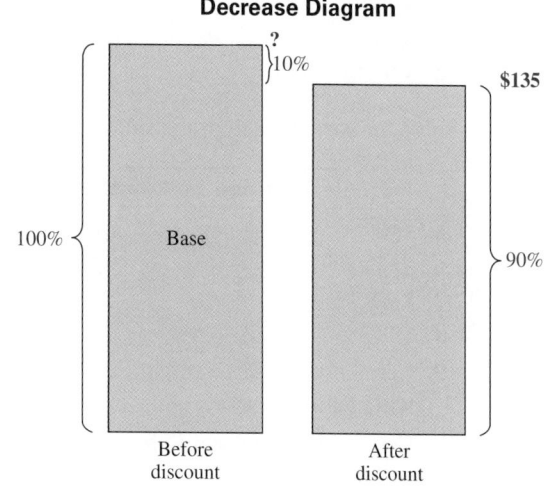

Decrease Diagram

?
10%
$135
100%
Base
90%
Before discount
After discount

Figure 3.7

Objective

5 *Use an Equation to Solve for Base in Decrease Problems.* The original price is decreased by 10% of the original price. In other words, subtract 10% of the original price from the original price to find the sale price.

$$\text{Original} - \text{decrease} = \text{sale price}$$
$$\text{Original price} - 10\% \text{ of the original price} = \text{price paid}$$
$$100\% \times B - 10\% \times B = \$135$$
$$90\% \times B = \$135$$
$$0.9B = \$135$$
$$\frac{0.9B}{0.9} = \frac{\$135}{0.9}$$
$$B = \frac{\$135}{0.9}$$
$$B = \$150 \quad \text{Original price}$$

Check the answer.

$$\begin{array}{r r l} & \$150 & \text{Original price} \\ - & 15 & \text{10\% discount} \\ \hline & \$135 & \text{Price paid} \end{array}$$

> **NOTE** The common mistake made in Example 3 is thinking that the reduced price, $135, is the base. The original price is the base, while the reduced price, $135, is a *result* of subtracting 10% of the base from the base. The reduced price is the part or 90% *of the base* (100% − 10% = 90%).

3.5	**Exercises**

Solve for base in each of the following. Round to the nearest cent.

	Part (After Increase)	**Rate of Increase**	
1.	$450	20%	$375
2.	$800	25%	$640
3.	$30.70	10%	$27.91
4.	$10.09	5%	$9.61

Solve for base in each of the following. Round to the nearest cent.

	Part (After Decrease)	**Rate of Decrease**	
5.	$20	20%	$25
6.	$1530	15%	$1800
7.	$598.15	30%	$854.50
8.	$98.38	15%	$115.74

9. Certain words or word phrases help to identify an increase problem. Discuss how you will identify an increase problem. (See Objective 1.)

10. Certain words or word phrases help to identify a decrease problem. Discuss how you will identify a decrease problem. (See Objective 1.)

Solve the following application problems. Read each carefully to determine which are increase or decrease problems and work accordingly. Round to the nearest cent when necessary.

11. **HOME VALUE APPRECIATION** Zoe Werner of Century 21 Realty just listed a home for $178,740. If this is 3% more than what the home sold for last year, what was last year's selling price to the nearest dollar? $173,534

12. **DEALER'S COST** John Chavez Auto Stereos sold a high-quality auto stereo for $337.92, a loss of 12% of the dealer's original cost. Find the original cost. $384

13. **FAMILY RESTAURANT** Santiago Rowland owns a small restaurant and charges 8% sales tax on all orders. At the end of the day, he has a total of $2052, including the sales and sales tax in his cash register. (a) What were his sales not including sales tax? (b) Find the amount that is sales tax. (a) $1900 (b) $152

14. **SALES TAX** A hotel manager purchased a notebook computer for $958.50, including $6\frac{1}{2}$% sales tax. Find (a) the price of the personal computer, and (b) the amount of sales tax. (a) $900 (b) $58.50

15. **STARBUCKS** Revenue at Starbucks increased to $2.5 billion this quarter, or 8.7% higher than the same quarter last year. Find the total revenue for the same quarter last year to the nearest tenth of a billion. $2.3 billion

16. **ANTILOCK BRAKES** In a recent test of an automobile antilock braking system (ABS) on wet pavement, the stopping distance was 114 feet. If this was 28.75% less than the distance needed to stop the same automobile without the ABS, find the distance needed to stop without the antilock braking system. 160 feet

17. **WEDDING COSTS** The average cost of a wedding today is $24,066, which is 26% more than the average cost 5 years ago. Find the average cost of a wedding 5 years ago. Round to the nearest cent. $19,100

18. **POPULATION OF CHINA** The population of China is about 1.35 billion. It has grown at a rate of 1.1% per year for each of the past 2 years. Find the population 2 years ago and round to the nearest hundredth of a billion. 1.32 billion

19. **WALLPAPER SALES** Erika Guitierrez, owner of Wallpaper Plus, says that her sales have increased exactly 20% per year for the last 2 years. Her sales this year are $340,070.40. Find her sales 2 years ago. $236,160

20. **VOLVO SALES** In 5 years, Volvo plans to boost worldwide sales 25%, to 500,000 units a year. Find the Volvo sales this year. 400,000 units

21. **NURSING HOME COSTS** Next year, the average annual cost of nursing home care is expected to increase to $83,585. Find the cost this year to the nearest dollar if costs increase by 6%. $78,854

22. **NETFLIX** Netflix rents movies on the Internet. The firm recently announced that it has 28.2 million subscribers, or 25% more than last year. Find the number of subscribers last year rounded to the nearest tenth of a million. 22.6 million

23. **SURPLUS-EQUIPMENT SALES** In a 3-day public sale of Jackson County surplus equipment, the first day brought $5750 in sales and the second day brought $4186 in sales, with 28% of the original equipment left to be sold on the third day. Find the value of equipment left to sell. $3864

24. **COLLEGE EXPENSES** After spending $4800 for tuition and $4350 for dormitory fees, Donald Cole finds that 15% of his original savings remains. Find the amount of his savings that remains. $1614.71

25. **TIRE MANUFACTURING** International Tires reported a 16% drop in third quarter earnings. If earnings dropped to $122 million, find the earnings before the drop. Round to the nearest hundredth of a million. 145.24 million

26. **NATIONAL HOME SALES** Sales of existing homes decreased 7.4% to an annual number of 6.2 million units. Find the annual number of homes sold before the decrease. Round to the nearest hundredth of a million. 6.70 million homes

27. **WINTER-WHEAT PLANTING** Even though wheat prices are rising during the planting season, farmers have planted only 50.2 million acres of winter-wheat varieties. If this is 2% fewer acres than last year, find the number of acres planted last year. Round to the nearest tenth of a million. 51.2 million

28. **LEATHER-CLOTHING SALES** Department stores and specialty chains sold 4.1 million leather jackets and coats this year. If this is a 38% drop in sales from last year, find last year's sales. Round to the nearest tenth of a million. 6.6 million

29. **COMMUNITY COLLEGE** For the past 2 years, the enrollment at American River College has grown by 3.2% per year. If there are currently 37,000 students enrolled, estimate the number of students enrolled 2 years ago. 34,741 students

30. **TUITION** The tuition and fees at one public university have increased by an average of 8.2% for each of the past 2 years. If tuition and fees are currently $4600 per semester, find the cost 2 years ago. $3929.20

31. **CONE ZONE DEATHS** This year there were 1181 deaths related to road construction zones in the United States. If this is an increase of 70% in the last 5 years, what was the number of deaths 5 years ago? Round to the nearest whole number. 695 deaths

32. **MINORITY LOANS** A mortgage lender made 8% more loans to minorities this year than last year. If the number of loans to minorities this year is 2660, find the number of loans made to minorities last year. 2463 loans

33. **SMART PHONE SALES** Sales of one model of smart phone fell 18% in one year, to 296,398 units. Find the number of these phones sold last year rounded to the nearest whole number. 361,461 phones

34. **JOB LOSSES** Jameson Foundry announced that it expects to reduce its union workforce to 59,000 workers, a decrease of 20%. Find the size of the workforce before the decrease. 73,750

CHAPTER TERMS

Review the following terms to test your understanding of the chapter. For each term you do not know, refer to the page number found next to that term.

base [p. 85]
basic percent equation [p. 85]
complement [p. 93]

decrease problem [p. 104]
hundredths [p. 78]
increase problem [p. 104]
part [p. 85]

percent [p. 77]
percent formula [p. 85]
percent of decrease [p. 100]
percent of increase [p. 99]

percents [p. 78]
rate [p. 85]
sales tax [p. 86]
variability [p. 77]

CONCEPTS	EXAMPLES
3.1 Writing a decimal as a percent Move the decimal point two places to the right and attach a % sign.	$0.75\ (0.75.) = 75\%$
3.1 Writing a fraction as a percent First change the fraction to a decimal and then write the decimal as a percent.	$\dfrac{2}{5} = 0.4$ $0.4\ (0.40.) = 40\%$
3.1 Writing a percent as a decimal Move the decimal point two places to the left and drop the % sign.	$50\%\ (0.50.\%) = 0.5$
3.1 Writing a percent as a fraction First change the percent to a decimal. Then write the decimal as a fraction in lowest terms.	$15\%\ (0.15.\%) = 0.15 = \dfrac{15}{100} = \dfrac{3}{20}$
3.1 Writing a fractional percent as a decimal First change the fraction to a decimal leaving the % sign; then move the decimal point two places to the left and drop the % sign.	$\dfrac{1}{2}\% = 0.5\%$ $0.5\% = 0.00.5$ $\dfrac{1}{2}\% = 0.005$
3.2 Solving for part using the percent formula $\text{Part} = \text{Base} \times \text{Rate}$ $P = B \times R$ $P = BR$ ____% of ____ is ____	A company offered a 15% discount on all sales. Find the discount on sales of $1850. _____% of *sales* is discount 15% of $1850 = discount $R \times B = P$ $0.15 \times \$1850 = P$ $0.15 \times \$1850 = \$277.50$ discount

3.3 Using the basic percent equation to solve for base

Remember that base is the starting point, reference point, all of something, or 100%.

Rate × Base = Part

_____% × _____ is _____

If the sales tax rate is 8%, find the sales if the sales tax is $18.

$$R \times B = P$$
$$8\% \times \underline{} = \$18$$
$$0.08B = \$18$$
$$\frac{0.08B}{0.08} = \frac{\$18}{0.08}$$
$$B = \frac{\$18}{0.08}$$
$$B = \$225 \text{ sales}$$

3.4 Using the basic percent equation to solve for rate

Remember that rate is a percent and is followed by a % sign.

Rate × Base = Part

_____% × _____ is _____

The return is $307.80 on an investment of $6840. Find the rate of return.

$$R \times B = P$$
$$\underline{}\% \text{ of } \$6840 \text{ is } \$307.80$$
$$R \times \$6840 = \$307.80$$
$$\$6840R = \$307.80$$
$$R = \$307.80$$
$$\frac{\$6840R}{\$6840} = \frac{\$307.80}{\$6840}$$
$$R = 0.045$$
$$R = 4.5\%$$

3.4 Finding the percent of change

Calculate the change (increase or decrease), which is the part. Base is the amount before the change.

$$\text{Use } R = \frac{P}{B}$$

Weekly air conditioner production rose from 3820 units to 5157 units. Find the percent of increase.

$$5157 - 3820 = 1337 \text{ increase}$$
$$R = \frac{1337}{3820} = 0.35 = 35\%$$

3.5 Drawing a diagram and using an equation to solve an increase problem

Increase Diagram

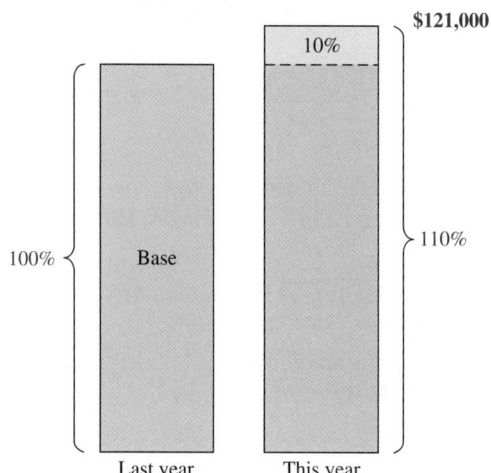

Solve for base given rate (110%) and part (after increase).

This year sales of $121,000 are 10% more than last year's sales. Find last year's sales.

Original + increase = new value
$$100\% \times B + 10\% \times B = \$121,000$$
$$1B + 0.1B = \$121,000$$
$$1.1B = \$121,000$$
$$B = \frac{\$121,000}{1.1}$$
$$B = \$110,000 \text{ last year's sales}$$

3.5 Drawing a diagram and using an equation to solve a decrease problem

Decrease Diagram

100% $\left\{$ Base

Original price

Discounted price

10%

$135

90%

Solve for base given rate (90%) and part (after decrease).

After a deduction of 10% from the price, a customer paid $135. Find the original price.

$$\text{Original} - \text{decrease} = \text{new value}$$
$$100\% \times B - 10\% \times B = \$135$$
$$1B - 0.1B = \$135$$
$$0.9B = \$135$$
$$B = \frac{\$135}{0.9}$$
$$B = \$150 \text{ original price}$$

CHAPTER 3 | Review Exercises

The answer section includes answers to all Review Exercises.

Solve each of the following. [3.1–3.4]

1. 18 members is 12% of what number of members? 150 members

2. What is 5% of 480 vans? 24 vans

3. 33 shippers is 3% of what number of shippers? 1100 shippers

4. 36 accounts is what percent of 1440 accounts? 2.5%

5. What is $\frac{1}{4}$% of $1500? $3.75

6. Find the fractional equivalent of 24%. $\frac{6}{25}$

7. 24 loads is $2\frac{1}{2}$% of how many loads? 960 loads

8. Change 87.5% to its fractional equivalent. $\frac{7}{8}$

9. $70.55 is what percent of $830? 8.5%

10. What is the fractional equivalent of $\frac{1}{2}$%? $\frac{1}{200}$

Solve the following application problems, reading each carefully to determine whether base, part, or rate is being asked for. Also, check to see which are increase or decrease problems, and work accordingly. Round to the nearest cent or tenth of a percent, as necessary.

11. Due to low demand related to high gas prices, a Ford Explorer is offered at 17% off the manufacturer's suggested retail price. Find the discount and the sale price of this Explorer, originally priced at $30,500. **[3.2]** $5185; $25,315

12. A supervisor at Barrett Manufacturing finds that rejects (poor quality) amount to 1120 units per month. If this is 0.5% of total monthly production, find the total monthly production. **[3.3]** 224,000 units

13. During a recent economic downturn in the United States, automobile sales were expected to fall 1.2% from the previous year's sales of 6.30 million. Find the expected sales for this year, rounded to the nearest hundredth of a million. **[3.2]** 6.22 million

14. It is estimated that 3 million people in the United States who are between the ages 55 and 64 have no health insurance. If this is 14% of the people in this age bracket, find the number of Americans in this age bracket. Round to the nearest hundredth of a million. **[3.3]**   21.43 million people

15. A district manager for Olive Garden has a monthly advertising budget of $6800. She budgets 25% for television, 40% for radio, and the remainder for newspapers. (a) Find the percent of the total budget to be spent on newspapers. (b) Find the total amount to be spent on newspaper advertising for an entire year. **[3.2]**   (a) 35% (b) $28,560

16. James River Corporation has had a tough couple of years and offers a $25,000 bonus to any employee wishing to retire early. An account estimates that the average employee would only be able to keep $17,800 of the $25,000 due to taxes and other deductions. What percent of the bonus will a retiring employee be able to keep?   71.2%

17. A Sony digital camera is marked "reduced 25%, now only $262.50." Find the original price of the digital camera. **[3.5]** $350

18. Last year's backpack sales were 10% more than they were the year before. This year's sales are 1452 units, which is 10% more than last year. Find the number of backpacks sold 2 years ago. **[3.5]**   1200 backpacks

19. One day on the London Stock Exchange, Unilever's stock shares increased 12.3 pence to 449.5 pence. Find the percent of increase. **[3.4]**   2.8%

20. Automobile sales in Asia were 23.4 million this year, a 9.4% increase over last year. Find the number of auto sales in Asia last year, rounded to the nearest tenth of a million. **[3.5]**   21.4 million

21. Americans lose about 300 million golf balls each year, and about 225 million of these are recovered and resold in what has become a $200 million annual business. What percent of the lost golf balls are recovered and resold? **[3.4]**   75%

22. Most window cleaners contain 75% to 90% water. If a 16-ounce bottle of window cleaner contains 78% water, find the number of ounces of water in the 16-ounce bottle. Round to the nearest tenth of an ounce. **[3.2]**   12.5 ounces

23. Bookstore sales of the *Physicians Desk Reference,* which contains prescription drug information, rose 13.7% this year. If sales this year were 111,150 copies, find last year's sales. Round to the nearest whole number. **[3.5]**   97,757 copies

24. After deducting 11.8% of total sales as her commission, George-Ann Hornor, a salesperson for Marx Toy Company, deposited $35,138.88 to the company account. Find the total amount of her sales. **[3.5]** $39,840

25. The U.S. Patent Office received 230,000 patent applications last year and issued 112,091 patents. What percent of the patent applications resulted in patents? Round to the nearest tenth of a percent. **[3.4]**   48.7%

26. Doctors in Argentina reported that 480,000 Argentines will have plastic surgery this year. If the population of the entire country is 41 million, what percent of the Argentines will have plastic surgery this year? **[3.4]**   1.2%

27. World population is about 6,925,000,000. If 4.54% of the world's population lives in the United States, estimate the number of people living in the United States. **[3.2]**   314,395,000 people

28. Tupperware, which was built on parties in people's homes where sellers demonstrated the use of plastic containers, is part of Premark International, Incorporated. Last year, Tupperware products accounted for 39% of Premark's $3.5 billion in sales. Find the amount of the Tupperware sales. **[3.2]** $1.365 billion

29. The whooping crane, which is the tallest bird (5 feet) in North America, now has a population of 300 after dropping to near extinction in 1941, when there were only 15 birds. Find the percent of increase, to the nearest percent, in the number of whooping cranes since 1941. **[3.4]**   1900%

30. The Small Business Administration (SBA) guaranteed 42,500 loans this year, compared with 40,100 loans last year. Find the percent of increase in the number of loans guaranteed. **[3.4]**   6.0%

31. The number of business failures this year was 64,031, compared with 64,743 business failures last year. Find the percent of decrease. **[3.4]**   1.1%

32. The number of Canadian tourists traveling to Florida this year has decreased 25% since 1990, when a record 2.4 million visited the "Sunshine State." Find the number of Canadian tourists visiting Florida this year. **[3.2]**   1,800,000 tourists

33. Sales at Baker Electronics increased 1.7% this quarter to $143.2 million. Find sales last quarter to the nearest tenth of a million. **[3.4]** $140.8 million

34. Online sales of an item were up 2% from last year. If sales this year were 151,477 units, find the number of units sold last year. Round to the nearest whole number. **[3.5]** 148,507 units

35. Average hourly wages at a distribution center have risen 4.2% to $12.40 over the last year. Find the average hourly wages last year. **[3.5]** $11.90 per hour

36. Navistar International Corporation will cut daily production of class 8 trucks—those that can haul more than 33,000 pounds—by 26%, reducing daily production to 72 units. Find the daily production before the cutback. Round to the nearest whole number. **[3.5]** 97 units

CHAPTER 3	Business Application Case #1
	Stocks

Understanding the stock market can be an important part of financial planning. Looking toward retirement, you may invest a portion of your savings by buying stock in various companies. Every day the changes in stock prices are shown in some major newspapers and on the Internet. Listed below are some well-known companies along with stock price information for this year and last year. Find the stock price last year, the percent of change from last year, or the stock price this year, as necessary. Round dollar amounts to the nearest cent and percents to the nearest tenth.

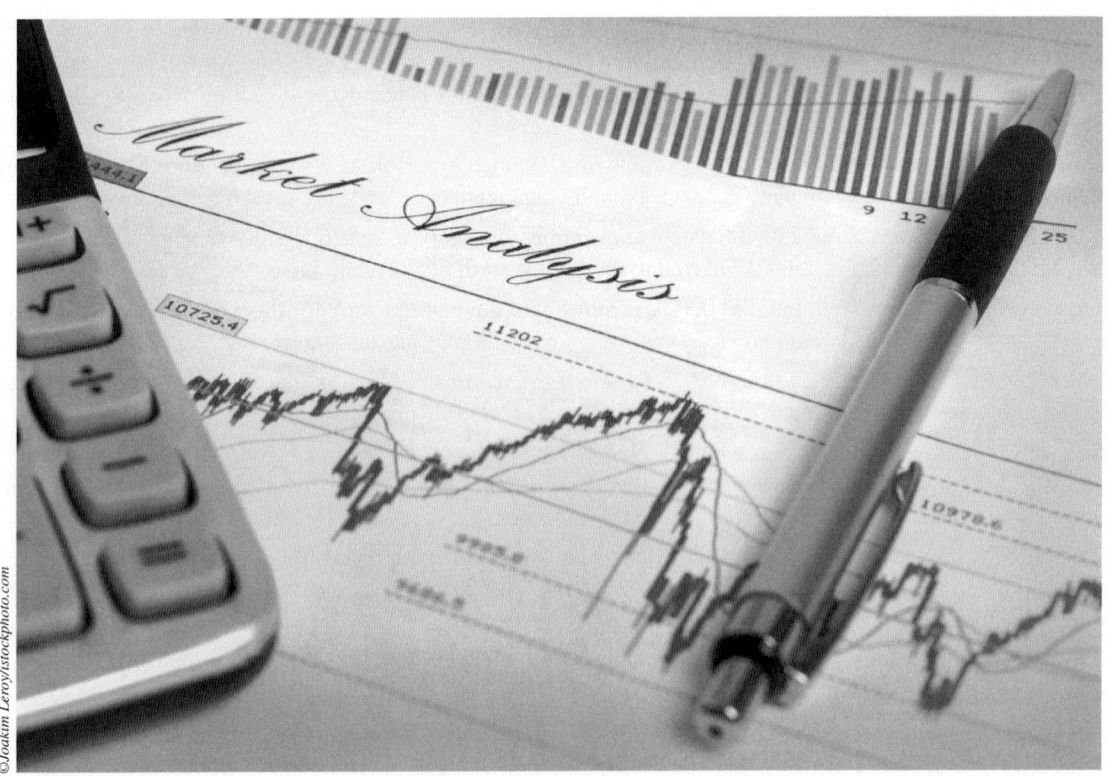

©Joakim Leroy/istockphoto.com

THE UPS AND DOWNS OF LAST YEAR

Company Name	Stock Symbol	Stock Price Last Year	Stock Price This Year	% Change from Last Year
Amazon.com	AMZN	$120.03	$212.87	77.3%
Apple, Inc.	AAPL	$248.08	$364.92	47.1%
Coca-Cola, Inc.	KO	$54.60	$67.54	23.7%
Google	GOOG	$492.68	$597.62	21.3%
Krispy Kreme	KKD	$4.25	$9.30	118.8%
McDonald's	MCD	$70.80	$85.50	20.8%
Merck	MRK	$55.30	$43.63	−21.1%
Pepsi Bottling	PBG	$25.71	$23.27	−9.5%
Starbucks	SBUX	$26.75	$39.80	48.8%
Wal-Mart	WMT	$50.51	$52.68	4.3%

CHAPTER 3	**Business Application Case #2** *Real Estate Sales*

Century 21 Real Estate Corporation (www.century21.com) is the world's largest franchiser of real estate offices and operates in more than 60 countries. The firm provides comprehensive training, management, administrative, and market support for more than 6000 independently owned and operated offices. It is considered the number-one consumer brand in the real estate industry.

Sometimes homeowners complain when they see the 6% sales commission that they must pay when listing their homes for sale with Century 21. However, they may not realize that the commission is usually split among the following four parties: listing agent, selling agent, and the two offices for which each of these real estate agents work.

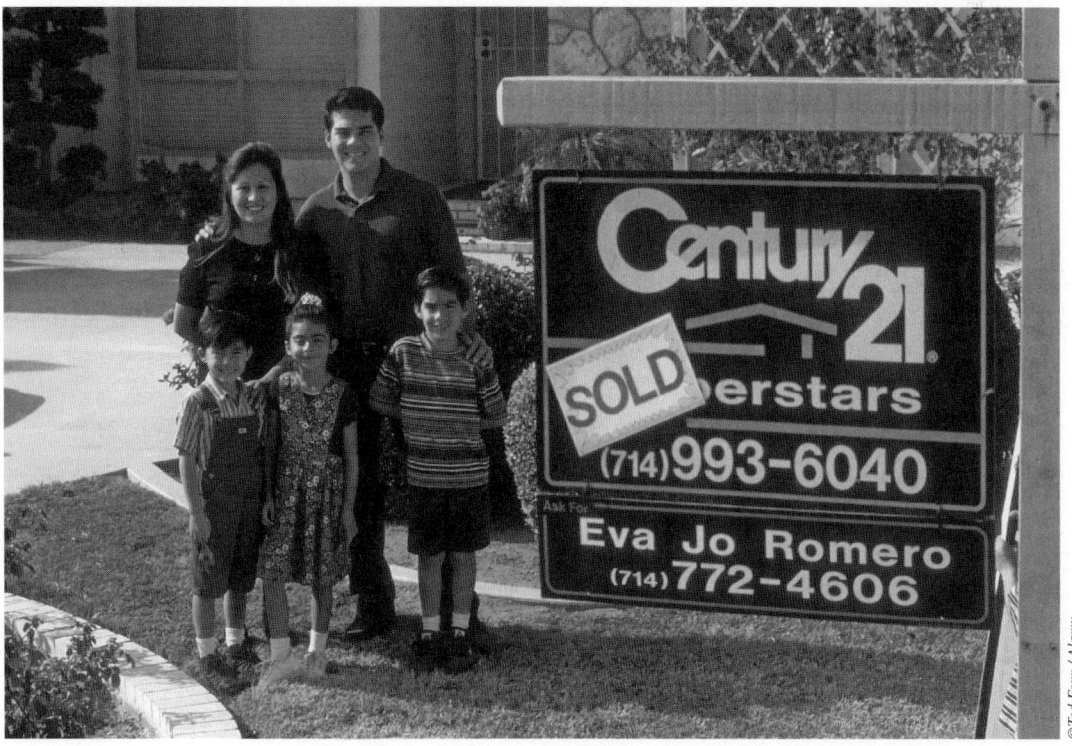

©Ted Foxx / Alamy

(a) The value of homes in one area went up by an average of 2.3% in the past year. Estimate the value today of a home that was valued at $265,000 last year. $271,095

(b) This year, the annual sales through one Century 21 office with 12 sales agents were $42 million. Estimate the revenue for the office if it received an average of 20% of the 6% commission on sales. $504,000

(c) From the revenue in part (b) above, the office manager must pay all costs of operating the sales office, including advertising, utilities, phones, insurance, and salaries for all noncommission employees. For the current year, these costs amount to $468,000. Find the profit as a percent of total revenue to the real estate office and round to the nearest tenth of a percent.   7.1%

(d) Describe at least four examples in which percent is used in the real estate industry.   Answers will vary.

(e) Visit any local real estate office. Ask the manager and/or agents about advantages and disadvantages of a career as a real estate agent. Would a career as a real estate agent interest you? Why or why not?   Answers will vary.

javier brosch / Fotolia.com

CHAPTER 4

Business Statistics

Sometimes the word **statistics** refers to data from business, economics, or other areas. At other times, *statistics* refers to techniques used to study data, such as looking for trends or making forecasts. For example, Figure 4.1 shows two different sets of data on the same line graph. One set is world population with a forecast to 2100 made by the United Nations. World population is read in billions of people using the scale on the left side of the graph. Notice that world population is predicted to peak at about 2080, followed by a slow decline.

The other set of data in the figure is total world oil production based on a projection made by Cambridge Energy Research Associates (CERA), a well-respected group of experts on oil. Actually, CERA assumes higher levels of oil production for a longer period of time than many other groups of scientists studying the same issue. So, some suggest the world oil production line in Figure 4.1 is optimistic. The idea that there will be a peak in world oil production followed by a decline is known as **peak oil**. World oil production in millions of barrels per day is read using the scale on the right-hand side of the graph.

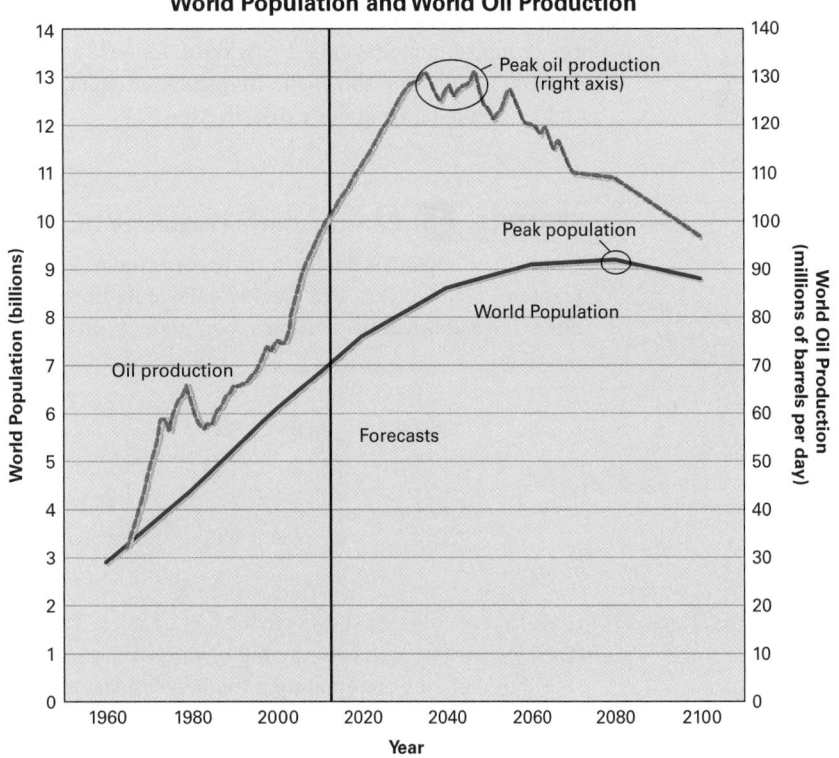

World Population and World Oil Production

Figure 4.1

Notice that world oil production is predicted to peak about 2040, or about 40 years before world population peaks in 2080. It is important to remember that everything beyond 2013 in the graph is a forecast and therefore subject to significant error.

▶STOP&THINK

The forecasts in Figure 4.1 predict that world crude oil production will peak about 40 years before the peak in world population. First, list as many things as you can think of for which we humans use oil—it may help to use the Internet. Then, describe possible major issues if oil production peaks and falls off as population continues to grow. Finally, describe how business and government may be affected.

Managers use statistics daily. Sometimes the data are given in tables, but frequency distributions and graphs are often used as well. This chapter introduces basic concepts in statistics. To learn more on this important subject, we encourage you to take a class in statistics at your college.

| 4.1 | **Frequency Distributions and Basic Graphs** |

OBJECTIVES

1 *Construct a frequency distribution.*

2 *Make a bar graph.*

3 *Make a line graph.*

4 *Make a circle graph.*

Objective

1 *Construct a Frequency Distribution.* It can be difficult to interpret or find patterns in a large group of numbers called **raw data**. One way of analyzing the numbers is to organize them into a table that shows the frequency of occurrence of the various numbers. This type of table is called a **frequency distribution**.

EXAMPLE **1** **Constructing a Frequency Distribution**

Stephanie Simpson is analyzing sales over the past 24 weeks at her new outdoor restaurant, Garden Plaza Coffee. The weekly sales data have been rounded to the nearest thousand dollars. Read down the columns, beginning with the left column, for successive weeks of the year.

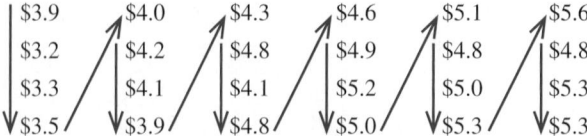

Construct a table that shows each value of sales. Then go through the data and place a tally mark $\left(|\right)$ next to each corresponding value. By counting the number of occurrences of each sales number, you are creating a frequency distribution table.

Solution

Table 4.1 shows that the most common weekly sales amount was $4800, although there were 3 weeks with sales of $5300.

Table 4.1 FREQUENCY DISTRIBUTION TABLE

Sales (thousands)	Tally	Frequency	Sales (thousands)	Tally	Frequency	Sales (thousands)	Tally	Frequency
$3.2	|	1	$4.2	|	1	$5.1	|	1
$3.3	|	1	$4.3	|	1	$5.2	|	1
$3.5	|	1	$4.6	|	1	$5.3	|||	3
$3.9	||	2	$4.8	||||	4	$5.6	|	1
$4.0	|	1	$4.9	|	1			
$4.1	||	2	$5.0	||	2			

The frequency distribution given in the previous example contains a great deal of information, perhaps more than is needed. It can be simplified by combining weekly sales into groups, forming the grouped data shown in Table 4.2.

NOTE   The number of groups in the left column of Table 4.2 is arbitrary and usually varies between 5 and 15.

Table 4.2 GROUPED DATA

Sales (thousands)	Frequency (number of weeks)
$3.1–$3.5	3
$3.6–$4.0	3
$4.1–$4.5	4
$4.6–$5.0	8
$5.1–$5.5	5
$5.6–$6.0	1

Simpson must pay all expenses, including cost of foods and beverages, equipment repairs, employee salaries, rent, taxes, utilities, and insurance before anything is left for her to take out of the company as profit.

EXAMPLE 2   Analyzing Data

Based on the grouped data in Table 4.2, answer the following questions.

a. If sales are $4000 or less per week, Simpson can take no salary and she must actually put money into the company to pay the bills. Find the number of weeks during which this occurred. Show this as a percent of the total number of weeks.

b. If weekly sales are greater than $4000 but not more than $5000, Simpson does not have to put money into the company, but she still cannot take anything out of the company for herself in profit. Find the number of weeks during which this occurred. Show this as a percent of the total number of weeks.

c. Simpson can take out at least a small profit for herself if sales exceed $5000 per week. Find the number of weeks during which this occurred and show this as a percent of the total number of weeks.

Solution

First, add the numbers in the right column in Table 4.2 to find that there are 24 weeks of data. Then answer the questions.

Sales	Number of Occurrences	Percent
(a) Less than or equal to $4000 per week	6 weeks	25%
(b) More than $4000 but less than or equal to $5000 per week	12 weeks	50%
(c) More than $5000 per week	6 weeks	25%

Simpson had to put money into her business during 25% of the weeks. She was able to take a salary out of the company during only 25% of the weeks—the weeks with the highest sales. Example 3 gives a better sense of which weeks she was able to take a salary.

Objective

2 *Make a Bar Graph.* The next step in analyzing this information is to use it to make a graph. A **graph** is a visual presentation of numerical data. One of the most common graphs is a **bar graph**, where the height of a bar represents the frequency of a particular value. A bar graph for the sales data is shown in Figure 4.2.

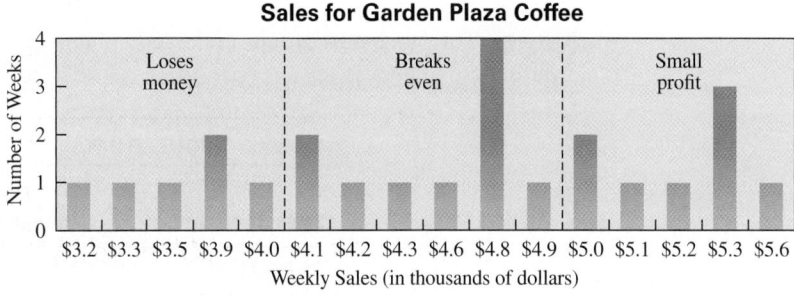

Figure 4.2

The information from the grouped data is shown in Figure 4.3. This graph shows that weekly sales of between $4600 and $5000 were the most common. Notice that this graph *does not* show any trend that may be occurring over time.

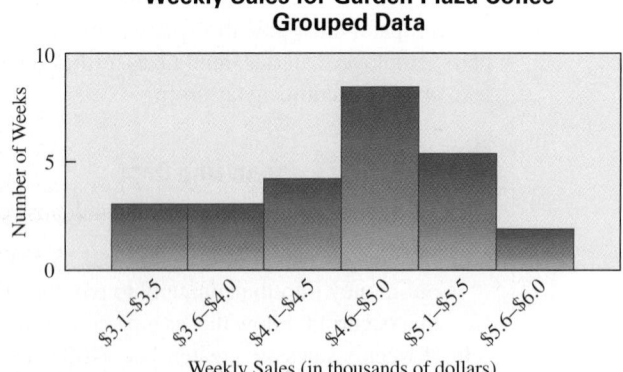

Figure 4.3

Objective

3 *Make a Line Graph.* Bar graphs show which numbers occurred and how many times but do not necessarily show the order in which the numbers occurred. To discover any trends that may have developed, draw a **line graph** of the data over time.

EXAMPLE 3 Draw a Line Graph

Show the progression of weekly sales at Garden Plaza Coffee through the year using a line graph. Do this by totaling the first 4 weeks (the first column) of data in Example 1 for the first data point. Similarly, total the second 4 weeks (second column) of data for the next data point, and so on.

Solution First find total sales for each 4-week period of time. We will just show the calculations for the first two 4-week time periods to show how it is done.

$$\text{First 4 weeks' sales} = \$3.9 + \$3.2 + \$3.3 + \$3.5 = \$13.9 \text{ or } \$13,900$$
$$\text{Next 4 weeks' sales} = \$4.0 + \$4.2 + \$4.1 + \$3.9 = \$16.2 \text{ or } \$16,200$$

Continuing in this manner, the six data points for the graph are $13.9, $16.2, $18, $19.7, $20.2, and $21 in thousands of dollars.

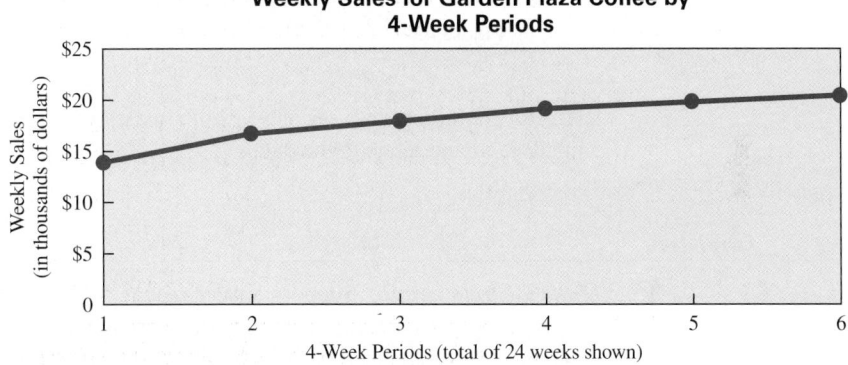

Weekly Sales for Garden Plaza Coffee by 4-Week Periods

Figure 4.4

It is apparent from Figure 4.4 that weekly sales are increasing. Stephanie Simpson is excited about this trend and she is determined to continue the trend since her livelihood depends on the restaurant. She plans to work very hard in the restaurant over the next few months.

One advantage of line graphs is that two or more sets of data can be shown on the same graph. For example, suppose the managers of a company called River City Auto Parts want to compare total sales, profits, and overhead. Assume that they have extracted the data in Table 4.3 from their records.

Table 4.3 RIVER CITY AUTO PARTS

Year	Total Sales	Overhead	Profit
2010	$740,000	$205,000	$83,000
2011	$860,000	$251,000	$102,000
2012	$810,000	$247,000	$21,000
2013	$1,040,000	$302,000	$146,000

Separate lines can be made on a line graph for each category so that necessary comparisons can be made. A graph such as this is called a **comparative line graph** (see Figure 4.5).

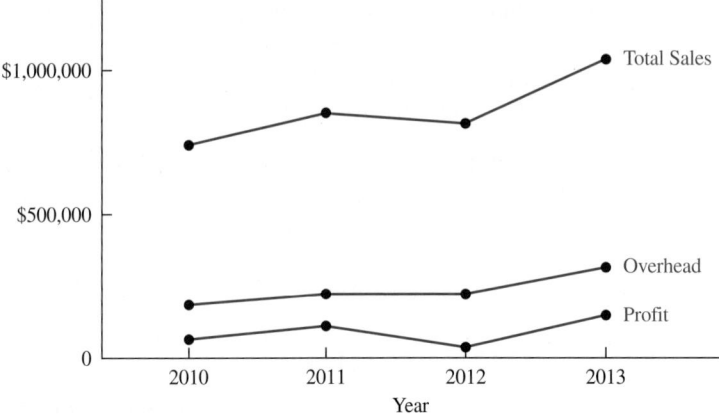

Figure 4.5

NOTE Including zero on one or both scales of a line graph *often helps* the viewer understand and relate to the data.

Objective

4 *Make a Circle Graph.* Suppose a sales manager for Blues Recording makes a record of the expenses involved in keeping a sales force on the road. After finding the total expenses, she converts each expense into a percent of the total, as shown in Table 4.4.

Table 4.4 BLUES RECORDING EXPENSES

Item	Percent of Total
Car and plane	30%
Lodging	25%
Food	15%
Entertainment	10%
Sales meetings	10%
Other	10%
Total:	100%

NOTE The percents should total 100%, although the total sometimes differs slightly due to rounding.

The sales manager can show these percents using a **circle graph**, which is sometimes called a **pie chart**. Every circle has 360 degrees, which is written as 360°. The degrees used here have nothing to do with temperature degrees such as 75° Fahrenheit or 15° Celsius. A degree as used in a circle graph simply represents $\frac{1}{360}$ of the circle in the shape of a piece of pie. To find the portion of the circle graph for each expense, multiply the percents in Table 4.4 by 360°.

Item	Percent × 360°	Fraction of Circle
Car and plane	30% × 360° = 108°	$\frac{108°}{360°} = \frac{3}{10}$
Lodging	25% × 360° = 90°	$\frac{90°}{360°} = \frac{1}{4}$
Food	15% × 360° = 54°	$\frac{54°}{360°} = \frac{3}{20}$
Entertainment	10% × 360° = 36°	$\frac{36°}{360°} = \frac{1}{10}$
Sales meetings	10% × 360° = 36°	$\frac{36°}{360°} = \frac{1}{10}$
Other	10% × 360° = 36°	$\frac{36°}{360°} = \frac{1}{10}$

These figures are used to build the pie chart in Figure 4.6.

**Blues Recording
Breakdown of Expenses**

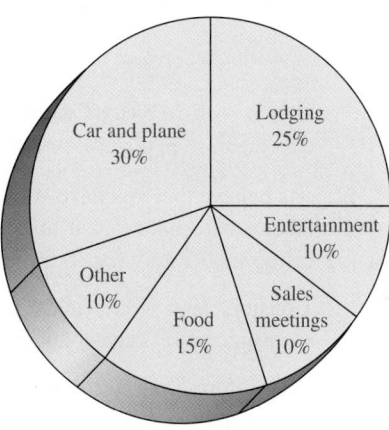

Figure 4.6

Circle graphs are used to show comparisons when one item represents a small portion compared to another. In the circle graph shown here, an item representing 1% of the total could be drawn as a small but noticeable slice; such a small item would hardly show up in a line graph.

EXAMPLE **4** **Interpreting a Circle Graph**

Based on the circle graph of expenses, answer the following questions.

a. What percent of expenses was spent on travel and entertainment?
b. What percent of expenses was spent on food and lodging?

Solution

a.

Travel	30%	Car and plane
Entertainment	+10%	
Total spent	40%	

b.

Food	15%
Lodging	+25%
Total spent	40%

Health Alert—The Diabetes Crisis

Diabetes is the most rapidly growing disease in the United States. The Centers for Disease Control estimates that 105 million Americans now have either diabetes or prediabetes. That is about one out of every three Americans! The bar chart in Figure 4.7 shows the percentage of Americans over 20, by race, who now have full-blown diabetes.

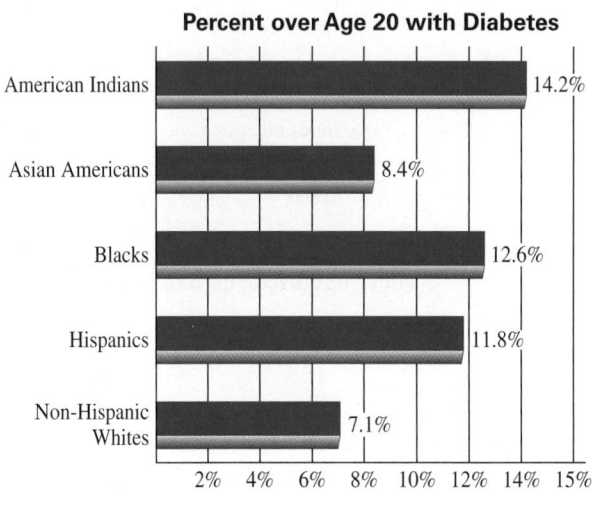

Source: Centers for Disease Control

Figure 4.7

Experts believe that you have some control over your chance of getting diabetes. The risk of diabetes decreases if you lose weight, exercise, and improve your diet. In addition to exercising moderately for 30 minutes on most days, experts recommend that you.

Consume less: sodas, candy, fatty meat, chips, sugar, rich desserts, fried foods, calories
Consume more: vegetables, fish, baked foods, whole grain foods, soy protein, tofu, fruit

For more information, see www.diabetes.org and www.cdc.gov.

| 4.1 | **Exercises** |

Solve the following application problems using the information provided.

Answer Exercises 1–3 using the bar chart on the left and answer Exercises 4–6 using the line graph on the right.

Source: Federal Board Survey of Consumer Finances.

Source: U.S. Bureau of the Census.

1. **BANK DEPOSITS**   Find the total percent on deposit at banks, including checking accounts and savings deposits.   17.7%

2. **INVESTMENT DEPOSITS**   Find the total percent in investments, including stocks and bonds, mutual funds, and retirement accounts.   69.2%

3. **RATIO COMPARISON**   Compare the percent in investment deposits to the percent in bank deposits using the answers in Exercises 1 and 2 above.   3.91 times as much in investments as in banks

4. **MARRIED**   Approximately what percent of the U.S. population was married in 1950 and in 2010?   67%; 50%

5. **DIVORCED**   What has happened to the percent of people divorced during the past 50+ years?   It has increased.

6. **WIDOWED**   Estimate the percent of widowed people in 2010.   4.8%

COLLEGE CREDITS   The following list shows the number of college credits completed by 30 employees of Franklin Bank.

74	133	4	127	20	30
103	27	139	118	138	121
149	132	64	141	130	76
42	50	95	56	65	104
4	140	12	88	119	64

Use these numbers to complete the following table.

Number of Credits Completed	Frequency
7. 0–24	4
8. 25–49	3
9. 50–74	6
10. 75–99	3
11. 100–124	5
12. 125–149	9

13. Make a line graph using the frequencies that you found.

14. How many employees completed fewer than 25 credits?   4

15. How many employees completed 50 or more credits?   23

16. How many employees completed from 50 to 124 credits?   14

17. How many employees completed from 0 to 49 credits?   7

18. What percent of the employees have completed at least 100 credits? Round to the nearest tenth of a percent.   46.7%

College Credits Completed By Franklin Bank Employees

19. Compare bar graphs, line graphs, and circle graphs. (See Objectives 2–4.)

20. Explain the purpose of a comparative line graph. (See Objective 3.)

21. **FARM TRACTOR** The following graph is used to estimate the acreage covered by a farm implement per hour, when its width and speed of travel are known. For example, a $7\frac{1}{2}$-foot (90-inch) mower blade moving 4 miles per hour would cover about $3\frac{5}{8}$ acres per hour. This is found by going across the graph from the working width (90 inches) to the diagonal line for speed (4 mph), then down to the bottom to find acreage per hour.

  a. What is the acreage per hour for a 36-inch implement moving $2\frac{1}{2}$ miles per hour?   almost 1 acre

  b. What is the acreage per hour for an 8-foot-wide combine moving 4 miles per hour?   almost $3\frac{7}{8}$ acres

  c. How fast must a tractor pull a 48-inch plow in order to plow 1 acre per hour?   2 mph

  d. How wide a spray pattern is needed in order to spray $4\frac{1}{2}$ acres per hour at a speed of $4\frac{1}{2}$ miles per hour?   99 inches

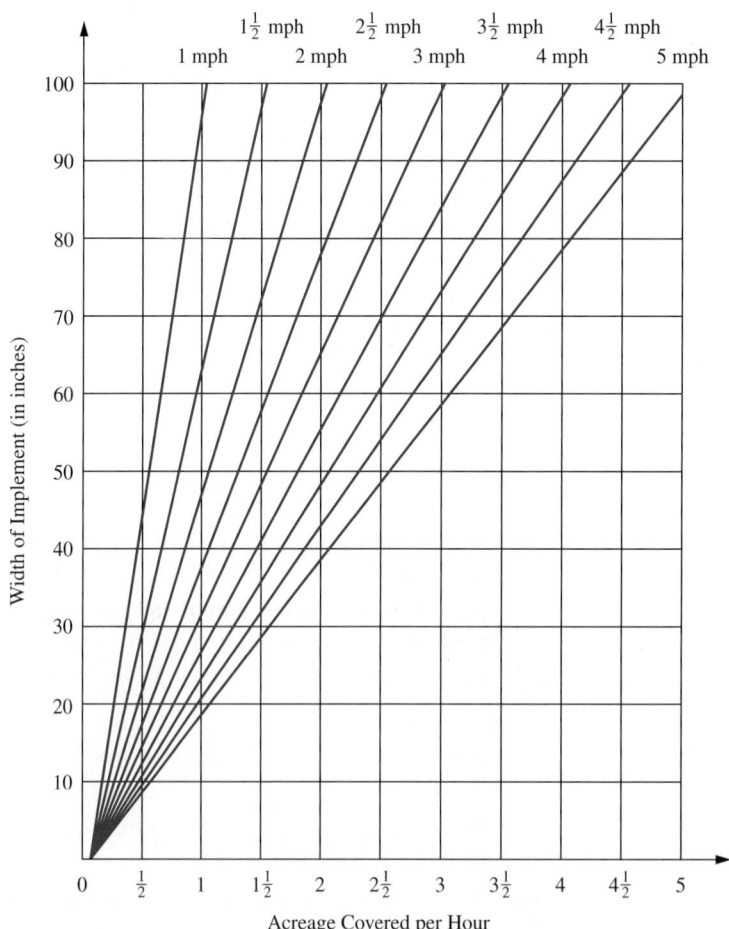

Acreage Covered by Farm Tractor

22. **AVERAGE WEIGHT AND HEIGHT**   The comparative line graph shows the change in average weight (in pounds) for a recent 20-year period for various categories of American adults. Find the change in weight for each of the following groups of people.

    a. Men aged 20–24 who are 5 feet 10 inches tall (*Hint:* First find 5′ 10″ on the horizontal line in the center of the graph.)   +10 pounds
    b. Women aged 40–49 whose height is 5 feet 8 inches   −5 pounds
    c. 5-foot-tall women aged 20–24   +4 pounds

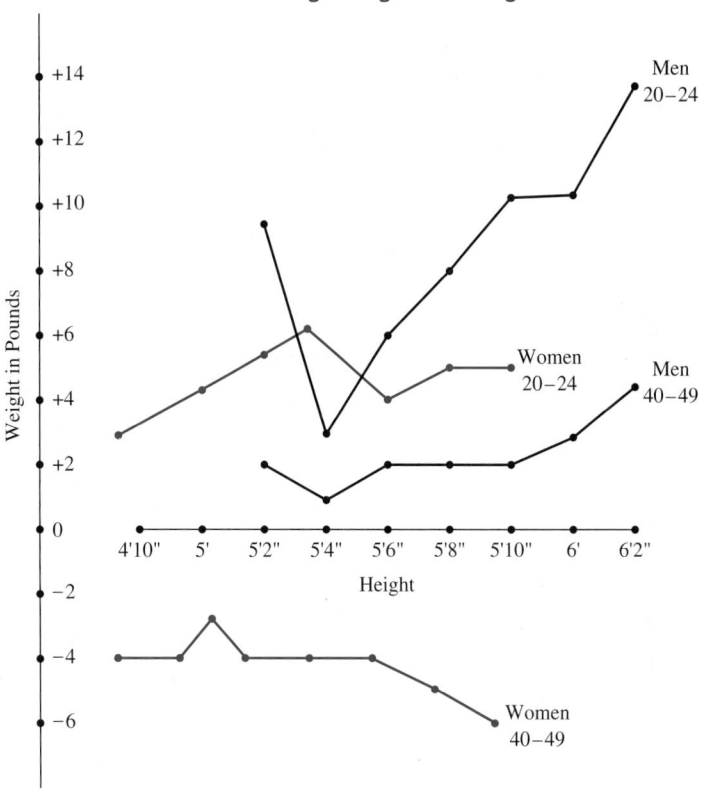

Average Weight and Height

20-Year Change in Average Weight of Americans

23. **COMPUTER SKILLS**   In today's business environment it is important for administrative and office-support professionals to possess computer skills. A recent survey asked this question of employers: "What does your company use as the primary method for evaluating a job candidate's software proficiency?" Draw a circle graph using the data.

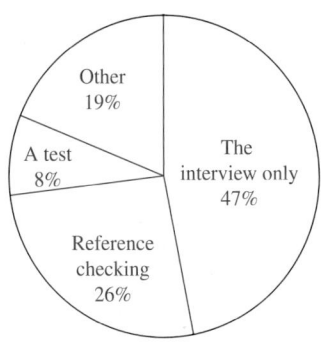

Computer Skills Evaluation

The interview only	47%
Reference checking	26%
A test on a computer	8%
Other	19%
	100%

24. **SOURCES OF RETIREMENT INCOME**   The Social Security Administration recently found that the average retired couple has the following sources of retirement income. Show the data in a circle graph.

Social Security	40%
Personal assets	21%
Earnings	17%
Pensions	19%
Other	3%
	100%

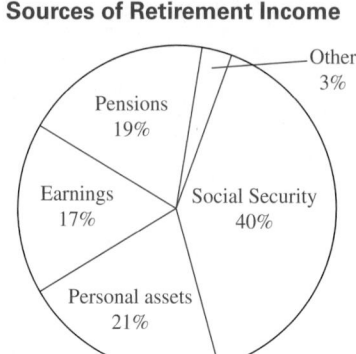

Sources of Retirement Income

25. **INTEREST RATES**   Interest rates in the United States have changed considerably during the past 100 years, creating an environment that either nourishes business growth and associated stock market rallies or stunts their growth. Use the data in the line chart to answer the questions that follow.

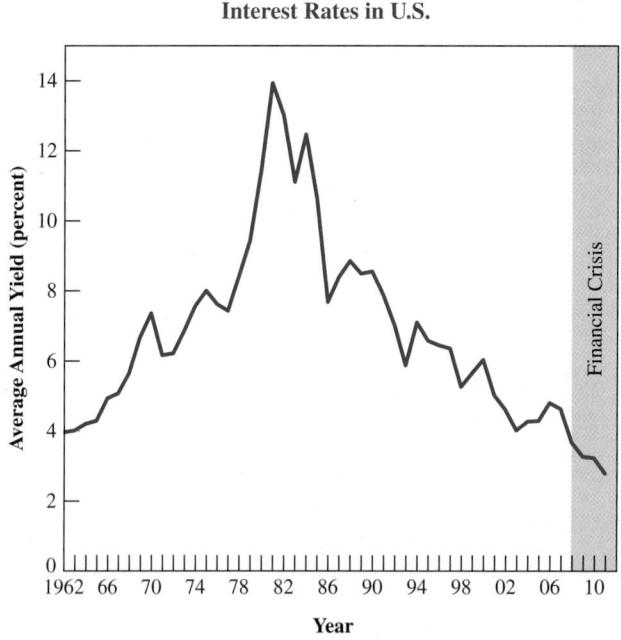

Interest Rates in U.S.

a. Estimate the peak annual yield in 1982.   14%
b. Over what range did yields fluctuate between 1980 and 1990?   8% to 13%
c. Over what range did yields fluctuate between 2000 and 2010?   2% to $6\frac{1}{2}$%
d. Identify the long-term trend of rates during 1940–1982 and during 1982–2010. up; down

26. FAST FOOD   Sales data for several companies in the fast-food business are shown. Show the data in a pie chart.

Market Share of Several Fast-Food Restaurants

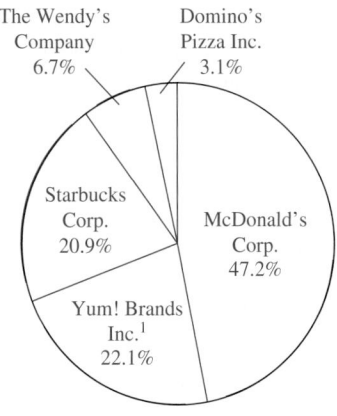

[1]Yum! Brands, Inc. owns Pizza Hut, Kentucky Fried Chicken, Taco Bell, and Long John Silvers.

Global Fast-Food Sales

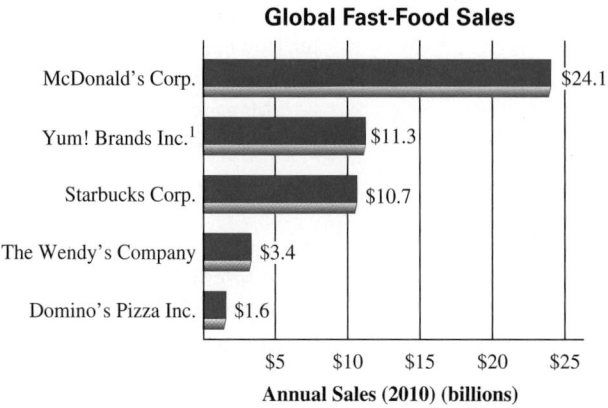

[1]Yum! Brands, Inc. owns Pizza Hut, Kentucky Fried Chicken, Taco Bell, and Long John Silver's.

27. COST OF COLLEGE   The table shows that tuition and fees at colleges have continued to increase during the recession. Find the percent increase for each and plot the data using a bar chart.

Percent Increase in Average College Tuition and Fees from 2010–11 to 2011–12

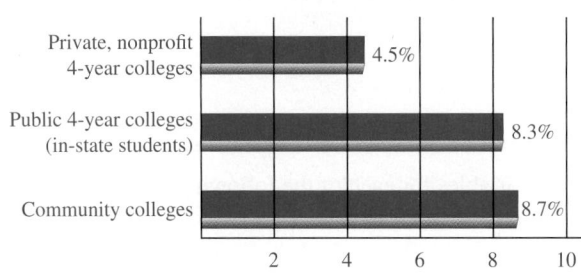

AVERAGE COLLEGE TUITION AND FEES		
	2010–2011	2011–2012
Private, nonprofit four-year colleges	$27,265	$28,500
Public four-year colleges (in-state students)	$7,613	$8,244
Community colleges	$2,727	$2,963

Source: Trends in college Pricing. © 2011 The College Board. www.collegeboard.org. Reproduced with permisson.

4.2	**Graphing Equations Using Line Graphs**

OBJECTIVES

1 *Understand dependent and independent variables.*

2 *Choose the axes and labels carefully.*

3 *Graph linear equations.*

4 *Graph nonlinear equations.*

Objective

1   *Understand Dependent and Independent Variables.* A **dependent variable** is one whose value *depends on* the value of a different variable. On the other hand, an **independent variable** is one whose value *does not depend on* the value of another variable. Think about the amount of rain in the past 24 hours and amount of water flowing down a local creek. Does the amount of rain in the past 24 hours depend on the amount of water flowing down the creek? No! However, the amount of water flowing down the creek probably does depend on the amount of rain in the past 24 hours. So, the dependent variable is the amount of water flowing down the creek and the independent variable is the amount of rain in the past 24 hours. Here is an example from business.

Managers at Andiamo's Pizza have studied monthly sales and advertising data and have found that the relationship can be estimated as follows:

$$\text{Sales} = 37.5 \cdot \text{advertising} + \$12{,}200$$
$$S = 37.5A + 12{,}200$$

Since *sales* (S) depend on the amount of *advertising* (A), *sales* (S) is the dependent variable and *advertising* (A) is the independent variable. Another way to think about it is to realize that the amount of advertising does not depend on sales. Rather, the amount of advertising is chosen by management. More advertising should call more attention to the restaurant and result in higher sales.

Every equation has one dependent variable and at least one independent variable. Here are some common examples—the key is to decide which variable depends on the other.

Dependent Variable		Independent Variable
Real estate commission	depends on	sale price of house
Sales tax	depends on	amount of purchase
Interest earned	depends on	amount invested

Actually, there can be more than one independent variable in an equation. For example, the amount of *interest earned* in an account at a bank depends on *amount invested, interest rate,* and *length of time* funds are on deposit. In this *case, interest earned* is the dependent variable and the other three variables (*amount invested, interest rate,* and *length of time* funds are on deposit) are all independent variables.

EXAMPLE 1 **Identifying Independent and Dependent Variables**

Identify the independent and dependent variables for each of the following by asking yourself which variable depends on another variable or variables.

a. Income, income tax to be paid
b. Amount of debt on VISA card, monthly interest charge
c. Property tax, assessed value of a house
d. Interest rate earned, years to retirement, amount at retirement, annual investment

Solution

	Dependent Variable		Independent Variable(s)
(a)	Income tax to be paid	depends on	income
(b)	Monthly interest charge	depends on	amount of debt on VISA card
(c)	Property tax	depends on	assessed value of a house
(d)	Amount at retirement	depends on	annual investment, years to retirement, and interest rate earned

2 *Choose the Axes and Labels Carefully.* Data is often shown using a **line graph**, which is a graph with a line or curve drawn on it. A graph does not have the precision of an algebraic equation in that you cannot use it to find an exact number. However, line graphs are very commonly used since they help convey ideas and trends so well.

Before constructing a graph, think about each axis. An **axis** is a horizontal or vertical line along the edge of a graph that usually has a **scale** with units of measurement. An axis is required in order to construct the graph, and it is an important aide to help understand the information and data in the graph. The horizontal axis is used for the *independent variable,* and it is often called the ***x*-axis.** It should have a label below it unless the value on the axis is obvious to anyone reading the graph. Here is one choice for the *x*-axis for the equation introduced above: $S = 37.5A + 12,200$.

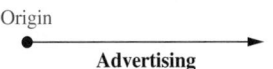

Advertising

Independent variable

The purpose of a graph is to *clearly communicate* data and ideas. The *x*-axis above can be improved by adding a scale showing different amounts of advertising. Commonly, the amount of Advertising at the leftmost point, which is called the **origin**, is $0. However, the **origin** can be a number other than 0. Here we have added the origin at the left.

Origin

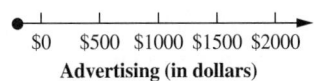

Advertising

The next questions to ask are: What scale should be used for the *x*-axis, and how should it be labeled? A scale divides the length of the axis into sections that show amounts for the independent variable. In our example, it should be based on the amounts of advertising that managers would consider. If they would consider up to $2000 per month in advertising, then the scale should divide $2000 into 4 to 8 intervals. A reasonable label is "Advertising (in dollars)."

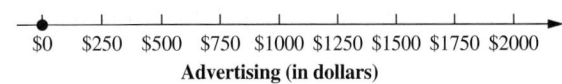

$0 $500 $1000 $1500 $2000
Advertising (in dollars)

However, the following choice of a scale may also be appropriate.

$0 $250 $500 $750 $1000 $1250 $1500 $1750 $2000
Advertising (in dollars)

However, this last axis seems a little "too busy" with too many numbers on it, so we will use the axis just above the last one.

In a similar fashion, the **y-axis** chosen to represent the reasonable values for the outcome of *Sales* based on the values of *Advertising* shown on the *x*-axis. The *y*-axis is commonly vertical. To determine the scale on the *y*-axis, first find the minimum and maximum amount of sales that are possible using the equation from above: $S = 37.5A + 12,200$.

Minimum sales occur if Advertising (*A*) is $0:	$S = 37.5 \cdot \$0 + \$12,200 = \$12,200$
Maximum sales occur at the maximum advertising of $2000:	$S = 37.5 \cdot \$2000 + \$12,200 = \$87,200$

Therefore, the scale on the *y*-axis should go from below $12,200 to a little over $87,200. A reasonable scale is shown here.

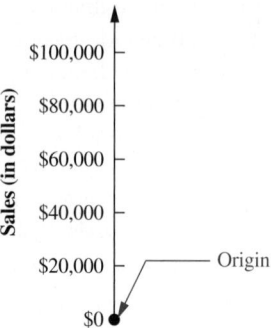

Combining the *x*- and *y*-axes at the origin results in the following.

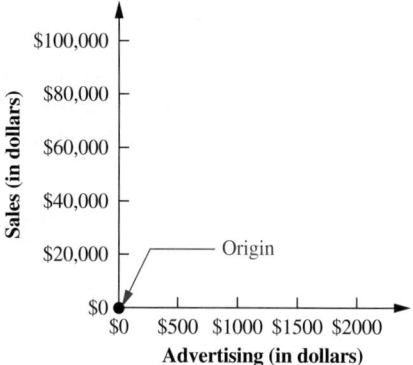

Remember, the purpose of a graph is to communicate CLEARLY. We have not yet graphed the equation, but is there something we can do to improve the quality of the communication in the basic graph itself? Yes, we can add a title to it. The title is very important, and it should clearly indicate the main theme of the information or data in the graph. In our example, the title should include some or all of the following words: Andiamo's Pizza, sales, advertising, and monthly data. The graph should be labeled so well that you can put it aside and still understand the graph a month or two later when you look at it again.

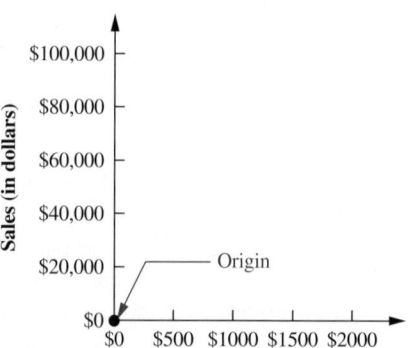

NOTE Always try to use a title, label for your axes and a scale that will be clearly understood.

EXAMPLE **2** **Setting Up a Reasonable Graph**

At the request of a financial planner, the Hernandez family of three is setting up a personal budget and they want to graph the amount spent each week on groceries. Help them set up an appropriate graph.

NOTE The first step in building a graph is to identify the independent and dependent variables.

Solution

First identify the dependent and independent variables. Since the amount of food purchased depends on the week, the dependent variable *amount of food purchased* and the independent variable is *week*. Thus, the *y*-axis label should be *Amount of Food Purchased (in dollars)* or simply *Amount Purchased (in dollars)*. The *x*-axis label should be *Week* (either week number 1, 2, 3, etc., or a date associated with the first day of successive weeks such as Jan. 9, Jan. 16, Jan. 23, etc.).

To determine the scale on the *y*-axis, decide what the maximum amount of food purchased in a week might be. Assuming a maximum purchase of $300, a scale of $0, $100, $200, and $300 is reasonable. To determine the scale on the *x*-axis, decide on the number of weeks for which you wish to track the data. Assuming you want to track the data for 8 weeks, the scale would be 1, 2, 3, 4, 5, 6, 7, and 8.

Here is a reasonable graph.

Objective

3

Graph Linear Equations. A **linear equation** is an equation that does not have any variables raised to a power (such as x^2) or multiplied by another variable (such $x \cdot y$). Here are some examples of linear equations:

$$S = 37.5A + 12,200$$

$$y = 35x + 94$$

$$P = 1700 - 47.3s$$

These equations are called linear equations, since the graph of each is a straight line.

Now let's put several of these ideas together and graph the equation of sales at Andiamo's Pizza that we worked with above: $S = 37.5A + \$12,200$. First, note that it is a linear equation because no variable is raised to a power, nor are any variables multiplied by one another. So, the graph of the equation will be a straight line. For a straight line, we need to plot only two data points on the line graph before connecting them with a ruler. The exact same straight line results no matter which two points we use, and the same straight line would occur if we used three or more points.

Graphing a Straight Line

Step 1 Pick two different values of the independent variable.
Step 2 Calculate the corresponding value of the dependent variable.
Step 3 Draw a straight line through the two points.

It is better to chose values of the independent variable that are not too close to one another. Choosing points that are too close to one another may result in data points that are too close together to use in drawing the straight line. Reasonable *Advertising* expenses range from $0 to $2000, so we arbitrarily choose advertising values of $500 and $2000. Next, substitute these two values for A on the right side of the equation to find the predicted sales.

NOTE A 3rd point can be used to check. It should be on the straight line.

Amount of *Advertising* (A)	Corresponding *Sales* (S) amount
$500	$S = 37.5 \cdot \$500 + \$12{,}200 = \$30{,}950$
$2000	$S = 37.5 \cdot \$2000 + \$12{,}200 = \$87{,}200$

The next step is to graph the following data points on the graph developed above. Often the points are written in this format: (value of independent variable, value of dependent variable), or as shown in the right column below. We sometimes refer to this notation as (x, y) where x is the value for the independent variable and y is the value for the dependent variable.

Advertising	Sales	Data Point
$500	$30,950	($500, $30,950)
$2000	$87,200	($2000, $87,200)

y-variable (dependent)
x-variable (independent)

To plot the data point ($500, $30,950), place a point directly above $500 on the x-axis and aligned horizontally to $30,950 on the y-axis. You cannot see the difference between $30,950 versus, say, $31,200 on the graph, so do the best you can. As stated earlier, graphs do not have the precision of an algebraic equation, but they often show the overall relationship more clearly than an algebraic equation. Next, plot ($2000, $87,200) by placing a dot aligned with $2000 on the x-axis and with $87,200 on the y-axis.

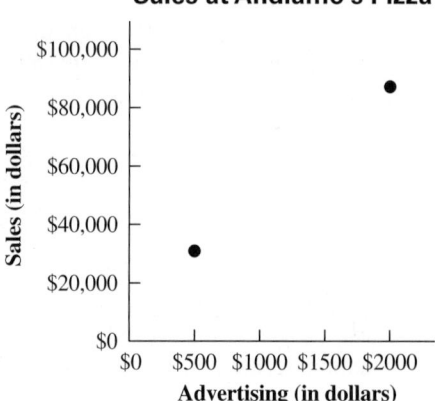

Sales at Andiamo's Pizza

Finally, connect the lines with a ruler.

Sales at Andiamo's Pizza

The formula $S = 37.5A + \$12,200$ is the algebraic form of the relationship. However, the graph is a visual representation of the same relationship. In a very real way, these are two very different ways of showing the *same information*. Graphs are extremely common in business, since they allow us to use our visual ability to quickly understand a relationship or pattern. Is it easier for you to work with a graph or an equation?

The **y-intercept** is the point at which the line intersects the y-axis. The y-axis for this graph corresponds to $0 in advertising. You can either substitute $0 into the equation in place of A and solve to find that the y-intercept is $12,200 or estimate the y-intercept by looking at the graph. Monthly sales would be $12,200 even with no advertising.

EXAMPLE **3** **Constructing a Graph**

The real estate commission in Albuquerque, New Mexico, is 6% of the sales price of the home. The average price of homes sold in one part of Albuquerque last month was $223,000, but prices of homes sold ranged from $100,000 to $480,000 during the month. Write an equation for commission versus sales price and graph it in a well-labeled graph.

Solution

The algebraic relationship is based on the fact that *Real Estate Commission* equals 6% of *Sales Price,* so commission depends on price as follows.

$$C = 0.06 \times P$$

where $C =$ Real Estate Commission
$P =$ Selling Price of Home

Since the independent variable *Selling Price of Home* (P) ranged between $100,000 to $480,000, a reasonable scale for the x-axis would be $0, $100,000, $200,000, $300,000, $400,000, and $500,000. Using thousands, the scale would be $0, $100, $200, $300, $400, and $500. Although we can start the x-axis at $100 (in thousands) on the left since that is the lowest value of the independent variable, we choose to use $0 for the origin.

The dependent variable is *Real Estate Commission*, which can be as high as 6% of $480,000, or $28,800. So, a reasonable scale for the y-axis would be $0, $10,000, $20,000, and $30,000. If the label on the y-axis indicates that the commissions are in thousands of dollars, then the numbers shown along the axis would be $0, $10, $20, and $30.

Again, the equation is linear, so we need to plot only two data points. Remember to choose values for the independent variables that are spread out a little—we choose $100,000 and $300,000.

Independent Variable	Value of Dependent Variable	Data Point (in thousands of dollars)
$100,000	$C = 0.06 \times \$100{,}000 = \$6000$	($100, $6)
$300,000	$C = 0.06 \times \$300{,}000 = \$18{,}000$	($300, $18)

Now construct the chart with a good title, appropriate axes, and a reasonable scale.

Real Estate Commission versus Selling Price of Home Albuquerque, New Mexico

NOTE Software such as Microsoft Excel can be used to create professional-looking graphs.

Objective

4 *Graph Nonlinear Equations.* Up to this point, we have worked only with linear equations, which graph as straight lines. However, many situations in business require **nonlinear equations**, which have graphs that are not straight lines. Compound interest calculations used daily by banks and others require the use of the following nonlinear equation. It shows how to find the maturity value of an investment of P dollars at an interest rate of i for n time periods.

$$M = P(1 + i)^n$$

where M = total amount accumulated at the end of the investment period

P = principal amount invested

i = interest rate per year written as a decimal number (e.g., write 6% as 0.06)

n = number of years the investment is held[3]

The dependent variable M (maturity value) depends on the three independent variables: P (original investment), i (interest rate), and n (number of years). The equation is nonlinear since it includes an exponent and also since the variable P is being multiplied by $(1 + i)$, which has a variable itself. Thus, it will not graph as a straight line. As a result, it is *necessary to plot several data points* before connecting them with a smooth line—two data points are not enough for a nonlinear graph.

EXAMPLE 4 Graphing an Equation that Involves Exponents

Trisha Patterson inherits $8000 from her grandmother and decides to put the money into a mutual fund that she hopes will earn 5% per year. She hopes the accumulated funds will help her 2-year-old pay for college. Graph the equation $M = P(1 + i)^n$ using the data given.

---

[3]Here we will work only with annual interest rate and number of years. Chapter 14 discusses several other options.

> **NOTE** Before graphing an equation with exponents or variables multiplied together, plot several points.

Solution

The original investment is $P = \$8000$ and the interest rate per year is $i = 5\%$, or 0.05. Putting the values for P and i into the equation simplifies it.

$$M = \$8000 \cdot (1 + 0.05)^n$$

Or, simpler still, as

$$M = \$8000 \cdot (1.05)^n$$

A reasonable scale for the x-axis is 0, 5, 10, 15, and 20 years. Next, find the value of M that corresponds to each of these values of the independent variable. Notice below that the largest value on the y-axis is $\$21,226$, so label the y-axes as Maturity Value (in thousands), and use this scale: $\$0, \$5, \$10, \$15, \$20, \$25$.

Dependent Variable	Maturity Value (*M*), Rounded to the Nearest Dollar
0 years	$M = \$8000 \cdot (1.05)^n = \$8000 \cdot 1.05^0 = \$8000 \cdot 1 = \$8000$
5 years	$M = \$8000 \cdot (1.05)^n = \$8000 \cdot 1.05^5 = \$8000 \cdot 1.27628 = \$10,210$
10 years	$M = \$8000 \cdot (1.05)^n = \$8000 \cdot 1.05^{10} = \$8000 \cdot 1.62889 = \$13,031$
15 years	$M = \$8000 \cdot (1.05)^n = \$8000 \cdot 1.05^{15} = \$8000 \cdot 2.07893 = \$16,631$
20 years	$M = \$8000 \cdot (1.05)^n = \$8000 \cdot 1.05^{20} = \$8000 \cdot 2.65330 = \$21,226$

Finally, plot the points (0, \$8), (5, \$10), (10, \$13), (15, \$17) and (20, \$21) and connect the points with a smooth line.

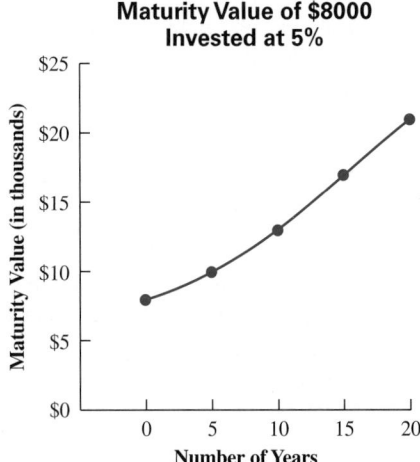

Maturity Value of $8000 Invested at 5%

Notice that the line is not a straight line. Rather, it curves upward slightly, showing that the maturity value grows more rapidly with time. In actuality, in the later years the investment is earning interest on larger and larger amounts since interest is being paid on interest already paid to the account. Nonlinear relationships such as these are both very common and very important in business. As we will see in the chapter on annuities, the increasing amounts of interest earned over time is a key to building up investments.

A common application of exponents uses a number represented by the symbol e, which is approximately equal to 2.7182818. This number is so commonly used in business, engineering, and scientific calculations that it can be found on most calculators. Is it on yours? Maturity value M depends on the following three things:

- The original investment of P dollars
- Invested for t years
- At an interest rate of r per year.

The formula for the maturity value is given here.[4]

$$M = Pe^{rt}$$

The value for e is a constant that is found on your calculator, so you will not have to key it in each time. Since e is raised to the power of r (interest rate) multiplied by t (time), the equation is nonlinear. The next example shows the huge difference both time and interest rate make in accumulating money for a future event, such as saving for an automobile or a down payment on a home.

EXAMPLE 5 **Graphing an Equation that Uses the Number e**

Sara Walker won a scratch-off lottery. After buying a Toyota Camry, she has $7000 to invest. A financial advisor shows her the difference that interest rate and length of investment can make using the following two investment options.

a. A conservative investment expected to earn 4% per year for 10 years, or
b. A mutual fund expected to earn 7% for 40 years.

Graph maturity value against year for both of these investment options on the same graph.

Solution

It is necessary to make a separate calculation for option (a) and (b) at each of the years to be used on the x-axis. Option (a) is only for 10 years, so we choose to calculate the maturity values for this option for years 0, 5, and 10. However, option (b) is for 40 years, so we will calculate the maturity values for it for 0, 5,10, 20, 30, and 40 years. Here are the calculations for maturity value for both options for 5 years, with maturity value rounded to the nearest dollar.

a. $M = Pe^{rt} = \$7000 \cdot e^{0.04 \times 5} = \$7000 \cdot e^{0.2} = \$7000 \cdot 1.22140 = \$8550$
b. $M = Pe^{rt} = \$7000 \cdot e^{0.07 \times 5} = \$7000 \cdot e^{0.35} = \$7000 \cdot 1.41907 = \$9933$

The remaining maturity values are calculated in the same way using the appropriate interest rate and number of years in place of the variables r and t, respectively.

The initial investment is $7000 under both option (a) and (b) above, so $7000 is the amount at time 0 for both options. Check the maturity values in the table that follows to make sure they are correct. Notice that no calculation is needed under option (a) beyond 10 years.

	Maturity Values		
Year	Option (a)	Option (b)	
0	$7,000	$7,000	Initial investment.
5	$8,550	$9,933	
10	$10,443	$14,096	
20	*	$28,386	
30	*	$57,163	
40	*	$115,113	

[4]This formula applies in the situation of continuous compounding. See Chapter 14 for more details.

Sara is amazed that a $7000 investment can grow to about $115,000 in 40 years. The amount of interest that the investment will earn in 40 years is found by subtracting the original investment from the maturity value as follows.

$$\$115,113 - \$7,000 = \$108,103$$

She likes the thought of her money working for her over the years. Option (b) clearly results in far more money than option (a), but of course it takes much longer to accumulate.

The left column of the table on page 140, labeled *Year*, shows the values for the *x*-axis. The *y*-axis of the graph should go higher than $115,113, so we choose to label it as *Maturity Value* (in thousands) with a scale of $0, $25, $50, $75, $100, $125.

Maturity Value of a $7000 Investment at 4% and 7%

The difference in the effects of the two different interest rates of 4% and 7% are shown by the difference in the two curves up to year 10. Option (b) has the higher interest rate and results in larger maturity values. So, both interest rate and time are very important to building investments. The chapter on annuities and sinking funds (Chapter 15) will show you practical ways to accumulate a large sum of money over time.

4.2	**Exercises**

Identify the dependent and independent variable(s) based on your internal sense of which variable depends on the other(s).

	Dependent	**Independent**
1. Interest earned, total investment	Interest earned	Total Investment
2. Calories eaten, weight gain	Weight gain	Calories eaten
3. Profit, sales	Profit	Sales
4. Number of employees, payroll	Payroll	Number of Employees
5. Weight of calf, age of calf	Weight of Calf	Age of Calf
6. Total sales, number of smart phones sold	Total sales	Number of smart phones sold
7. Sales, profit, total expenses	Profit	Sales. Total Expenses
8. Size of roof, material used, cost of new roof	Cost of new roof	Size of roof, Materials used

Construct a reasonable graph for each of the following.

9. **FLOODING** Due to severe flooding in the past, administrators in Pakistan carefully watch the flow of water in the Indus River which flows out of China and India and into Pakistan. Water flows are estimated each day based on the height of the river in meters taken at the upstream monitoring station. One of the worst floods on record occurred when the height of the water at the monitoring station peaked at 32.1 meters. It resulted in 1600 deaths and affected 14 million people.

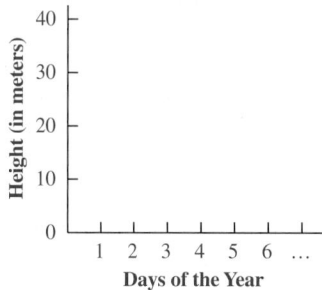

10. **MCDONALDS** An entrepreneur sets up a new McDonald's franchise and plans to carefully watch weekly sales for the first 10 weeks of operation. He hopes weekly sales will approach $16,000.

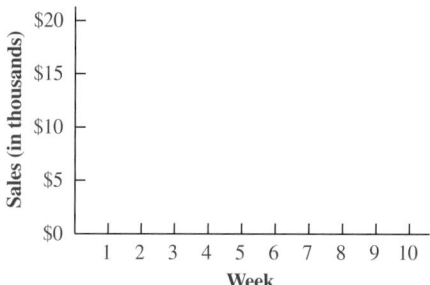

11. **APPLE, INC.** An investor loves her iPad and iPhone and is debating whether to buy stock in the company that makes them, Apple Inc. She wants to look at a graph of the firm's after-tax quarterly profit for each quarter of the past year. Quarterly profit ranges up to nearly $8 billion.

12. **QUALITY** A quality-control inspector is concerned with the number of bottles of beer that are not being capped appropriately at a bottling machine on a production line. Although the production line runs very rapidly, he has a machine that scans every bottle

for quality problems. He doesn't expect more than 30 defective bottles in an hour, and he wants a graph that will show results for a 24-hour day.

**Number of Defects at
Bottling Machine**

Construct the graphs indicated.

13. **MONTHLY SALES** Monthly sales for one product line are based on advertising and can be approximated by $S = 40.2A + \$17{,}500$. Graph this relationship if advertising does not exceed \$2000 per month.

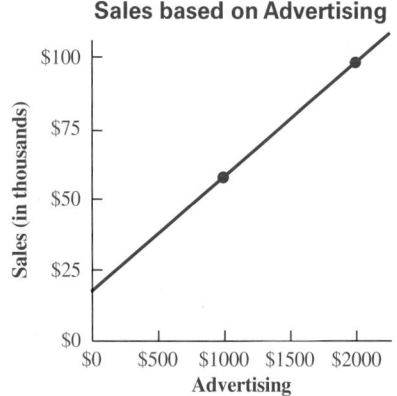

Sales based on Advertising

14. **STOCK PRICE** Recently, the share price of LemonKing Inc. has increased with the firm's earnings per share of stock according to $S = 24.1E + \$12.3$, where $S =$ share price and $E =$ quarterly earnings per share of stock. Graph this relationship, assuming that earnings per share do not exceed \$0.90.

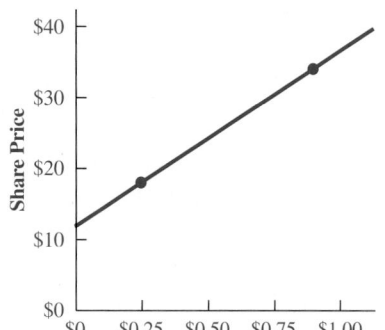

**Lemon King Inc. Share Price versus
Recent Quarterly Earnings per Share**

15. **ENTREPRENEUR** Bill Thomas is thinking about working part-time tutoring gifted children. He will charge $25 per hour and will rent a small office with a total cost of $275 a month. First, write an equation for his monthly profit based on the number of students he tutors in a month. (*Hint:* monthly profit = monthly revenue − monthly expense.) Then, graph the equation assuming that he will tutor between 15 and 80 students in any given month.

$P = \$25N - \$275$, where P = profit and N = number tutored in a month

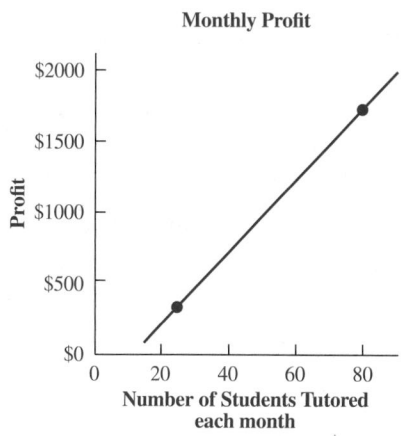

16. **CELL PHONE** Verizon advertises a low-cost beginner special on cell phone use to attract new users. The monthly cost is $14.95 a month plus $0.07 per minute for each minute of time (excluding taxes) used for calls made in the United States. Write an equation for monthly cost versus cell phone use and graph it, assuming users do not use over 400 minutes per month.

$C = \$0.07M + \$14.95$, where C = monthly cost and M = minutes used per month

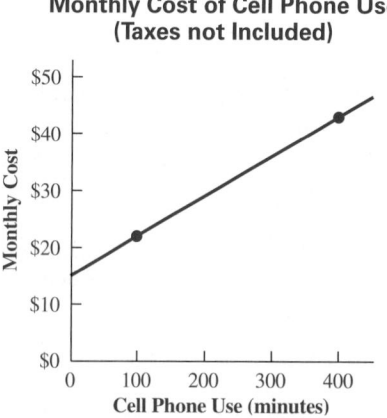

17. **LAWN MOWING** Calvin Tigard is only 15, but he has decided to start a lawn-mowing business. He plans to charge an average of $40 to mow and trim each yard. He thinks that the cost of buying and maintaining the equipment needed plus operational expenses such as gasoline will be about $7 per yard mowed. Write an equation for weekly profit and graph it, assuming he does not mow more than 8 yards per week.

Tigard's profit per yard is $40 − $7 = $33 per yard. He has no other costs.

$P = \$33N$ where P = profit per week and N = number of yards mowed per week

Weekly Profit Based on Number of Yards Mowed

18. VACATION After college, Tina Duncan and her husband decide to drive the 3000 miles across the United States to visit her grandparents. They can average 60 miles per hour on the highways, but Tina is not sure how many hours per day they will drive. Write an equation to show miles driven per day based on the number of hours driven and graph it, assuming they are not willing to drive more than 10 hours in any one day.

$M = 60H$, where M = miles driven per day and H = number of hours driven in a day

Miles Driven Per Day Versus Number of Hours Driven Per Day

19. COMPUTER SALES Computer Shoppe is a high-volume seller of computers on the Intenet. The total cost of selling computers can be approximated by TC = $95,000 + 680N + $0.21N^2$, where TC = total annual cost and N = number of computers sold in a month. Graph this nonlinear equation, assuming fewer than 1000 computers are sold. (*Hint:* Since it is a nonlinear equation, you must plot several different values of the independent variable before connecting points with a smooth line.)

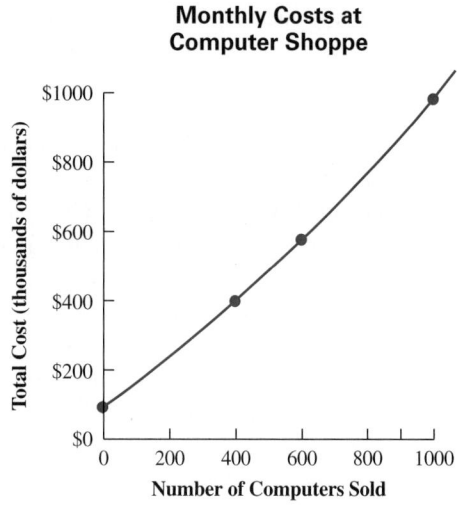

Monthly Costs at Computer Shoppe

20. **SMARTPHONES** Discount*Smartphones.com sells smartphones cheaply, both through their store location and on the Internet. The total weekly profit is approximated by $P = -\$85{,}000 + 645N - 0.3N^2$, where P = total weekly profit and N = number of smartphones sold during the week. Use the equation to create a graph, assuming that smartphone sales range between 200 and 800 per week. (*Hint:* Since it is a nonlinear equation, you must plot several different values of the independent variable before connecting points with a smooth line.)

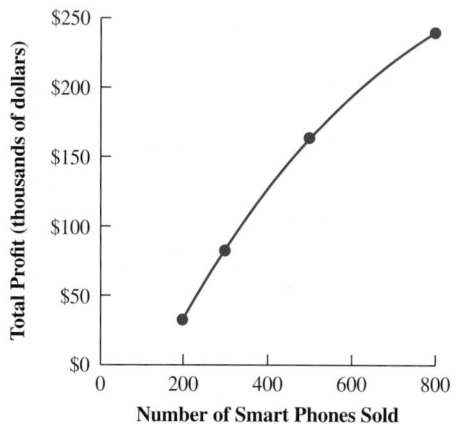

**Weekly Profit at
Discount* Smartphones.com**

4.3   The Mean

OBJECTIVES

1 *Understand the difference between population and sample.*

2 *Find the mean of a set of data.*

3 *Find a weighted mean.*

4 *Find the mean for grouped data.*

Objective

1 *Understand the Difference between Population and Sample.*   In statistics, it is important to distinguish between the concepts of population and sample. **Population** is the entire group being studied, whereas **sample** is a portion of the entire group. Samples should be chosen randomly, meaning that no one individual in the population is more likely to be chosen than is another. The idea is for the sample to represent the population.

An administrator might be interested in the grade point average (GPA) of all freshmen at a community college. The GPA of the *entire population* of freshmen can be obtained, but this might be time-consuming to compile. Or, if an estimate of the GPA is adequate, the administrator can randomly choose a sample of perhaps 50 freshmen and find their grade point averages. The administrator might then *assume* that the grade point average of *this sample of students* is close to that of the entire population of all freshmen.

Objective

2 *Find the Mean of a Set of Data.*   Businesses are often faced with the problem of analyzing a mass of raw data. Reports come in from many different branches of a company. For example, salespeople may send in a large number of expense claims. In analyzing all the data, one of the first things to look for is a **measure of central tendency**—a single number that is designed to represent the middle of the entire list of numbers. One such measure of central tendency is the **mean**, which is just the common **average** used in everyday life.

For example, suppose the sales of carnations at Tom's Flower Shop for each of the days last week were $86, $103, $118, $117, $126, $158, and $149. To find a single number that is representative of this list, use the following formula.

$$\text{Mean} = \frac{\text{sum of all values}}{\text{number of values}}$$

For Tom's Flower Shop, the mean is

$$\text{Mean} = \frac{\$86 + \$103 + \$118 + \$117 + \$126 + \$158 + \$149}{7}$$

$$= \frac{\$857}{7}$$

$$= \$122.43 \quad \text{Rounded to the nearest cent}$$

NOTE   The symbol $\overline{X}$ is often used for the mean.

EXAMPLE **1**   **Finding the Mean**

Stephanie Simpson has promised 7 of her employees at Garden Plaza Coffee that they will all work about the same number of hours. One employee complained that she worked considerably more hours than the other employees last month. The number of hours worked by each of the 7 employees during the past month are given. Find the mean to the nearest hour.

Hours worked: 75, 63, 76, 82, 70, 81, 149

Solution

The mean can be *estimated* by first rounding each number to the tens position. Therefore, 75 rounds to 80, 63 to 60, and so on, providing the following.

80, 60, 80, 80, 70, 80, 150

Add these numbers and divide by 7 to find an estimate of the mean.

$$600 \div 7 = 86 \quad \text{Rounded to the nearest whole number}$$

Now find the exact value by adding the original numbers and dividing by 7. Check that the sum of numbers is 596.

$$\text{Mean} = \frac{596}{7} = 85 \quad \text{Rounded}$$

Notice that our estimate of 86 is close to the exact mean of 85. Estimating an answer before calculating the exact value helps minimize errors. However, the mean of 85 seems a bit large since 1 employee did work a lot more than the other 6 employees. The mean without this value of 149 is the sum of the remaining hours worked divided by 6.

$$\text{Mean} = \frac{447}{6} = 75 \quad \text{Rounded}$$

This value seems more in line with the average number of hours worked. Perhaps there was an unusual reason why the one employee worked 149 hours (someone else was sick, etc.).

Student Credit-Card Debt at One College

Figure 4.8

Averages are commonly used. Figure 4.8 shows the average credit-card debt owed by students at one private college. To find the averages shown in Figure 4.8, someone went through the following steps for just the freshman class:

1. Identify all freshmen students at the college (the population);
2. Take a random sample from the population of all freshmen; and
3. Estimate the average credit-card debt of freshmen in the random sample.

If the sample was taken randomly, then results from the sample can be used as an estimate of the average credit-card debt for the population of all freshman students at the college. All three steps must be done separately for sophomores, again for juniors, and again for seniors to get the data in the table. As you can see, a lot of work was needed to get the data, including taking four different samples from four different populations of students at the one college.

Objective

3   *Find a Weighted Mean.*   Table 4.5 shows a frequency distribution of annual salaries received by employees of a corporation. The table shows that 27 employees were paid $32,000 each, 16 were paid $40,000 each, and so on. The average salary paid to these employees cannot be found by just adding the salaries, since different salaries are earned by different numbers of employees.

To find the mean of the salaries, it is necessary to first multiply each annual salary by the number of employees receiving that salary. This process produces a **weighted mean**, where each number (a salary here) is "weighted" by multiplying it by the number of times it occurs.

Table 4.5 EMPLOYEE SALARIES

Salary	Number of Employees	Salary × Number of Employees
$32,000	27	$864,000
40,000	16	640,000
50,000	11	550,000
72,000	6	432,000
90,000	4	360,000
96,000	4	384,000
110,000	3	330,000
160,000	2	320,000
$296,000	1	296,000
	Total: 74	**Total:** $4,176,000

Use the totals of both columns of data in the table to find the mean by dividing total salaries by total number of employees.

$$\text{Mean salary} = \frac{\$4,176,000}{74} = \$56,432 \quad \text{Rounded}$$

Importantly, look at the large size of the total payroll: $4,176,000. The company must pay this amount in salaries *each year* for the 74 employees. This may not be a problem for a company making money, but imagine the difficulty paying this amount in salaries if the company is facing a severe financial problem. In fact, managers at companies in financial trouble often lay off employees to save funds. One long-standing debate in society relates to the fairness of laying workers off even as top managers continue to earn high salaries and bonuses.

As you can see in the next example, weighted means are also used to find grade point averages.

EXAMPLE 2　Finding Grade Point Average

Find the grade point average for the following student. Assume $A = 4$, $B = 3$, $C = 2$, and $D = 1$, and $F = 0$.

Solution

Course	Units	Grade	Grade × Units
Business mathematics	3	$A\,(=4)$	$4 \times 3 = 12$
Retailing	4	$C\,(=2)$	$2 \times 4 = 8$
English	3	$B\,(=3)$	$3 \times 3 = 9$
Computer science	2	$A\,(=4)$	$4 \times 2 = 8$
Lab for computer science	2	$D\,(=1)$	$1 \times 2 = 2$
	Total: 14		**Total:** 39

The grade point average for this student is

$$\frac{39}{14} = 2.79, \textit{ or } \text{a B}-$$

NOTE　Grade point averages are frequently rounded to the nearest hundredth.

Objective

4　*Find the Mean for Grouped Data.*　The mean can also be found for data that have been grouped into a frequency distribution. To do so, find the midpoint of each interval or class. This midpoint is found by averaging the highest and lowest numbers that can go into a class. For example, the midpoint, or **class mark**, of the interval 100–109 in the next example is the mean of 100 and 109.

$$\text{Class midpoint} = \frac{100 + 109}{2} = \frac{209}{2} = 104.5$$

EXAMPLE **3** **Finding the Mean for Grouped Data**

A researcher surveyed a number of farmers on their use of a particular brand of fertilizer. Although the recommended usage is 135 pounds per acre, she found that the usage varied from that. Find the mean for the frequency distribution shown.

	Intervals	Frequency	
	100–109	9	
	110–119	12	
	120–129	17	
Pounds per acre	130–139	28	Number of farmers
	140–149	21	
	150–159	16	
	160–169	4	

Solution

Begin by finding the class mark for each class of fertilizer use. As explained, the class mark or midpoint of the first class is 104.5, and the midpoint of the second class is

$$\frac{110 + 119}{2} = \frac{229}{9} = 114.5$$

Find the other midpoints in a similar way. Then multiply the frequencies by the class marks, completing the column at the right labeled Frequency × Class Mark. Next, find the totals in the Frequency column and the Frequency × Class Mark column.

Intervals	Frequency	Class Mark	Frequency × Class Mark
100–109	9	104.5	9 × 104.5 = 940.5
110–119	12	114.5	12 × 114.5 = 1,374.0
120–129	17	124.5	17 × 124.5 = 2,116.5
130–139	28	134.5	28 × 134.5 = 3,766.0
140–149	21	144.5	21 × 144.5 = 3,034.5
150–159	16	154.5	16 × 154.5 = 2,472.0
160–169	4	164.5	4 × 164.5 = 658.0
	Total: 107		**Total: 14,361.5**

NOTE The intervals in a frequency table should not overlap with one another.

Finally, the mean is the quotient of these totals, or

$$\text{Mean} = \frac{14,361.5}{107} = 134.2 \quad \text{To the nearest tenth}$$

The mean usage rate of 134.2 pounds per acre is close to the recommended usage rate of 135 pounds per acre. The researcher was concerned with fertilizer use. Farmers using too much fertilizer could damage their crops, and those using too little fertilizer could have reduced yields. Either way, farmers would produce less and make less profit.

NOTE When a set of data is divided into classes, it is no longer possible to tell where a particular item falls in a class. For this reason, *a mean found from grouped data is only approximate.*

| **4.3** | **Exercises** |

Find the mean for the following sets of data. Round to the nearest tenth.

1. 128, 240, 164, 380   228
2. 60, 65, 67, 62, 59, 58, 70   63
3. 3800, 3625, 3904, 3296, 3400, 3650, 3822, 4020   3689.6
4. 10.3, 11.7, 12.4, 8.6, 9.9, 12.1, 13.2, 10.8, 9.6, 8.8   10.7

Round to the nearest whole number or as indicated.

5. **DOG WEIGHTS**   A kennel owner likes Labs and owns four registered Labs with the following weights: 65 pounds, 58 pounds, 90 pounds, and 79 pounds. Find the mean weight.   73 pounds

6. **AUTO PRODUCTS**   Weekly sales of products from the automotive department at a large discount store rounded to the nearest dollar were: $7327, $6849, $8104, and $6598. Find the mean. $7220

7. **COST OF DINING ROOM SET**   A young couple is shopping for a formal dining room set. The prices of the ones they have looked at so far are $1280, $2650, $870, $940, and $760. Find the mean. $1300

8. **LIFE INSURANCE SALES**   The amount of life insurance sold last month by the 6 new agents of National Insurance Agency totaled $294,000, $580,000, $722,000, $463,000, $814,000, and $1,785,000. Find the mean total of life insurance sold. $776,333

9. **RAINFALL**   Annual rainfall in a small city in the desert of southern Arizona is given for the past few years: 12 inches, 9.8 inches, 12.2 inches, 9.3 inches, 10.2 inches, and 8 inches. Find the mean amount of rainfall to the nearest tenth.   10.3 inches

10. **TELEPHONE SALES**   AgriFarm employs 9 people to make telephone calls to sell irrigation pumps. Last year, these people produced total sales of $492,811, $763,455, $901,852, $179,806, $244,193, $382,574, $591,873, $1,003,058, and $473,902. Find the mean sales per employee. $559,280

Find the weighted mean for the following. Round to the nearest tenth.

11.

Value	Frequency	
30	5	
40	3	39.4
45	2	
48	4	

12.

Value	Frequency	
10	8	
12	5	11.5
15	1	
18	1	

13.

Value	Frequency	
125	6	
130	4	
150	5	167.2
190	3	
220	2	
230	5	

14.

Value	Frequency	
25	1	
26	2	
29	5	30.2
30	4	
32	3	
33	5	

 15. Explain the difference between population and sample. (See Objective 1.)

16. Think of an example in which the mean really does not give a good understanding of the situation involving the data. (See Objective 2.)

In the following problems, find the weighted mean salary for the employees. Round to the nearest thousand dollars.

17. Salary	Number of Employees		18. Salary	Number of Employees
$18,000	8		$15,000	8
$21,000	10		$20,000	15
$28,000	8		$22,000	13
$29,000	6	$31,000	$25,000	9	$28,200
$38,000	4		$30,000	4
$41,000	3		$42,000	3
$53,000	2		$57,000	2
$162,000	1		$260,000	1

Find the grade point average for the following students. Assume A = 4, B = 3, C = 2, D = 1, and F = 0. Round to the nearest hundredth.

19. Credits	Grade		20. Credits	Grade
4	D		4	B
2	A		3	B
3	C	1.62	3	C	2.25
1	F		3	C
3	D		3	D

Find the mean for the following grouped data. Rounded to the nearest tenth.

21. Interval	Frequency		22. Interval	Frequency	
50–59	15		320–339	7	
60–69	20		340–359	9	
70–79	21	76.3	360–379	12	375.5
80–89	27		380–399	11	
90–99	18		400–419	6	
100–109	2		420–439	5	

23. Interval	Frequency		24. Interval	Frequency	
25–49	18		150–154	4	
50–74	15		155–159	7	
75–99	30	105.8	160–164	9	167.5
100–124	18		165–169	12	
125–149	32		170–174	16	
150–174	14		175–179	8	
175–199	7		180–184	3	

Solve the following application problems.

25. **MINIMUM GRADE TO PASS**   The final grade in a history class is the average of three tests taken during the semester. Wanda Kroll made 74% and 68% on the first two tests. Find the minimum score she can make on the third test and still have a 70% average.   68%

26. CATTLE TRAILER   A trailer can hold 4200 pounds. The front of the trailer is loaded with scrap steel weighing 1300 pounds and an engine block weighing 840 pounds. Find the number of cows with a mean weight of 660 pounds that can be safely added to the trailer.   3 cows

27. STUDENT HEIGHT   A teacher wanted to demonstrate the mean of the grouped data to her class and asked everyone to write down his or her height to the nearest inch. Find the mean to the nearest inch.

Interval	Frequency
46–50 inches	4
51–55 inches	12
56–60 inches	9
61–65 inches	3

55 inches

28. WEIGHT LIFTING   At the end of a one-semester class in weight lifting, a high school football coach tabulated data showing the amount of weight each student could dead lift. Find the mean to the nearest pound.

Interval	Frequency
101–150 pounds	1
151–200 pounds	9
201–250 pounds	16
251–300 pounds	5

216 pounds

4.4   The Median and the Mode

OBJECTIVES

1 *Find the median of a set of data.*

2 *Find the mode of a set of data.*

3 *Find the median and the mode of data in a frequency table.*

In everyday life, the word "average" usually refers to the mean. However, there are two other "averages" in common use, the **median** and the **mode**. Median and mode are discussed in this section.

Suppose the owner of a small company pays 5 employees annual salaries of $17,500, $18,000, $18,200, $19,000, and $20,000. The average, or mean, salary paid to the employees is

$$\text{Mean} = \frac{\$17,500 + \$18,000 + \$18,200 + \$19,000 + \$20,000}{5}$$

$$= \frac{\$92,700}{5} = \$18,540$$

Now suppose that the employees go on strike and demand a raise. To get public support, they appear on television to talk about their low salaries, which average only $18,540 per year.

The television station sends a reporter to interview the owner of the company. Before the interviewer arrives, the owner decides to find the average salary of *all employees*, including the 5 on strike, plus his own. To do this, he adds the 5 salaries given to the employees, plus his salary of $127,000. This gives an average of

$$\text{Mean} = \frac{\$17,500 + \$18,000 + \$18,200 + \$19,000 + \$20,000 + \$127,000}{6}$$

$$= \frac{\$219,700}{6} = \$36,617 \quad \text{Rounded}$$

When the television reporter arrives, the owner says that there is no reason for the employees to be on strike, since "the average salary of all company employees is $36,617."

There are two points to this story. First, both averages are correct, depending on what is being measured. *This shows how easily statistics can be manipulated.* Second, *the mean is often a poor indicator of the "middle"* of a list of numbers. In fact, when the mean was computed by the owner, it was greater than 5 of the 6 employees' salaries. The mean may be greatly affected by extreme values, such as the owner's salary of $127,000.

Objective

1   *Find the Median of a Set of Data.* To avoid such a misleading result, use a different measure of the "middle" of a list of numbers, the **median**. The median divides a list of numbers in half: one-half of the numbers lie at or above the median and one-half lie at or below the median.

Since the median divides an ordered list of numbers in half, the first step in finding a median is to rewrite the list of numbers as an **ordered array**, or list, with the numbers going from *smallest to largest.* For example, the list of numbers 9, 6, 11, 17, 14, 12, 8 would be written in order as the following ordered array.

$$6, 8, 9, 11, 12, 14, 17$$

The median is found from the ordered array as explained in the following box. Notice that the procedure for finding the median depends on whether the number of numbers in the list is even or odd.

Finding the Median

1. If the ordered array has an *odd* number of values, divide the number of values by 2. The next higher whole number gives the *location* of the median.

2. If the ordered array has an *even* number of values, there is no single middle number. Find the median by first dividing the number of values by 2. The median is the average (mean) of the number in this position and the number in the next higher position.

Example 1 shows a list of numbers having an *odd* number of values. Example 2 shows an *even* number of values.

| **EXAMPLE** **1**   Finding the Median (Odd Number of Numbers) |

Find the median for the annual salaries of the 5 employees introduced earlier in this section ($18,000, $20,000, $17,500, $19,000, and $18,200).

Solution

First, list the numbers from smallest to largest.

$$\$17,500, \$18,000, \$18,200, \$19,000, \$20,000$$

There are 5 numbers in the list. Divide 5 by 2 to get $\frac{5}{2} = 2.5$. The *next higher number* is 3 so that the median is the third number, or $18,200. Two numbers are larger than $18,200 and two are smaller.

EXAMPLE **2** **Finding the Median (Even Number of Numbers)**

Find the median of the salaries of the employer and the 5 employees introduced earlier in this section ($127,000, $17,500, $18,000, $18,200, $19,000, and $20,000).

Solution

First arrange the numbers from smallest to largest.

$17,500, $18,000, $18,200, $19,000, $20,000, $127,000

There are 6 numbers (an even number of numbers) in the list. Divide 6 by 2 to get 3. The median is the *mean of the numbers in the third and fourth positions.*

$$\text{Median} = \frac{\$18,200 + \$19,000}{2} = \$18,600$$

The median of this set of numbers is $18,600 and the mean is $36,617. The median is probably a better measure of central tendency for this set of numbers than is the mean, which is distorted by one large number, i.e., $127,000.

Objective

2 *Find the Mode of a Set of Data.* The last important statistical measure of central tendency is called the **mode**. The mode is the number that occurs *most often.* For example, 10 students earned the following scores on a business law examination.

74, 81, 39, 74, 82, 80, 100, 92, 74, 85

The mode is 74, since more students obtained this score than any other.

NOTE A bar graph can be used to find the mode.

EXAMPLE **3** **Finding the Mode**

Professor Miller gave the same test to both his day and evening sections of business math at American College. Find the mode of the tests given in each class. Which class had the lower mode?

a. Day class: 85, 92, 81, 73, 78, 80, 83, 80, 74, 69, 80, 65, 71, 65, 80, 93, 54, 78, 80, 45, 70, 76, 73, 80, 71, 68
b. Evening class: 68, 73, 59, 76, 79, 73, 85, 90, 73, 69, 73, 75, 93, 73, 76, 70, 73, 68, 82, 84, 77

Solution

a. The number 80 is the mode for the day class because it occurs more often than any other number.
b. The number 73 is the mode for the evening class because it occurs more often than any other number.

The evening class has the lower mode.

NOTE It is not necessary to place the numbers in numerical order when looking for the mode, but it helps with a large array of numbers.

A set of data is called **bimodal** if it has two different modes, i.e., two numbers that occur the same number of times with each occurring more than any other number in the data set. A data set in which every number occurs the same number of times is said to have *no mode.*

NOTE The mean, median, and mode are different ways of estimating the middle or center of a list of numbers. Each of these three ways is a measure of central tendency.

Objective

3 *Find the Median and the Mode of Data in a Frequency Table.* The same basic ideas of median and mode are applied to data in a frequency table, as shown in the next example.

EXAMPLE **4** **Finding the Mean, Median, and Mode**

The diameter of a part coming out of a machining process is measured regularly. The diameters vary some, as shown in the frequency table. Find (a) the mean, (b) the median, and (c) the mode.

Diameter (inches)	Frequency
0.720–0.729	3
0.730–0.739	12
0.740–0.749	8
0.750–0.759	9
0.760–0.769	2

Solution

a. The mean of the grouped data is found using the technique shown in the previous section. The class mark for the first class is

$$\frac{0.720 + 0.729}{2} = 0.7245$$

and so on for the other classes.

Class Mark	Frequency × Class Mark	
0.7245	3 × 0.7245 =	2.1735
0.7345	12 × 0.7345 =	8.814
0.7445	8 × 0.7445 =	5.956
0.7545	9 × 0.7545 =	6.7905
0.7645	2 × 0.7645 =	1.529
Total: 34		= 25.263

The group average is

$$\frac{25.263}{34} = 0.743 \quad \text{Rounded}$$

b. There are 34, or an even number, of values. Divide 34 by 2 to get 17. Thus, the 17th and 18th numbers from the smallest are averaged to find the median. The numbers have already been arranged from smallest to largest in the table. Three numbers fall in the first class (0.720–0.729) and 15 numbers fall in the first and second classes combined (0.720–0.729 and 0.730–0.739). The 17th and 18th numbers fall in the third class (0.740–0.749). The median is the class mark of the class containing the 17th and 18th values, or 0.7445.

c. The mode is the class mark of the class with the highest frequency of occurrences, or 0.7345.

Thus, we have the following.

Mean = 0.743   Median = 0.7445   Mode = 0.7345

4.4	**Exercises**

Find the median for the following sets of data.

1. 37, 14, 65, 12, 32   32
2. 46, 27, 91, 34, 68, 53, 39   46
3. 95, 98, 75, 81   88
4. 6.8, 9.7, 5.2, 6.0, 6.8, 6.3   6.55
5. 0.81, 0.82, 0.86, 0.84   0.83
6. 900, 860, 840, 880, 920, 940   890

Find the mode or modes for the following sets of data.

7. 60, 50, 60, 40, 70, 60, 40   60
8. 12, 13, 10, 13, 14, 13   13
9. 65, 60, 68, 72, 56, 70, 85   none
10. 180, 195, 162, 173, 184, 195, 186, 170   195
11. 6, 4, 8, 4, 6, 9, 3, 2   4 and 6
12. 5.8, 5.6, 5.8, 5.5, 5.3, 5.4, 5.6, 5.2   5.8 and 5.6

 13. Compare mean, median, and mode. (See Objectives 1–3.)

 14. Give an example in which values for the mean, median, and mode of a set of data still do not provide a good understanding of the situation involving the data. (See Objectives 1–3.)

Solve the following application problems.

15. SCUBA DIVING   A scuba diver used his log book to review the depths of his last 5 dives in the waters of the Caribbean.

    68 feet, 90 feet, 56 feet, 82 feet, 110 feet

    Find the mean and median.   81.2 feet; 82 feet

16. SKYDIVING   The altitudes of a skydiver's recent jumps are given in feet.

    4300, 5000, 3800, 4800, 3400, 3600

    Find the mean and median.   4150 feet; 4050 feet

17. If you want to avoid a single extreme value having a large effect on the average, would you use the mean or the median? Explain.

18. SHOE INVENTORY   A manager trainee at a shoe store is trying to figure out how many pairs of each size shoe of a particular style to order. Should she use the mean, median, or mode of the number of each size sold? Or, are none of these values adequate? Explain. (See Sections 4.2 and 4.3.)

Find the mean, median, and mode for the following grouped data sets. Round to the nearest tenth.

19.

Interval	Frequency
100–109	10
110–119	12
120–129	8
130–139	2

115.1; 114.5; 114.5

20.

Interval	Frequency
10–14	2
15–19	1
20–24	5
25–29	7

22.7; 22; 27

Solve the following application problems.

21. HEATING OIL A manufacturing company made 4 purchases of 3000 gallons each of heating oil to heat its facility during the winter. The prices it paid for the heating oil follow: $3.78 per gallon, $3.59 per gallon, $3.81 per gallon, and $3.45 per gallon. Find the mean and median. Mean $3.66; Median $3.69

22. WHALE WATCH Blue Ray Tours takes people off the coast of Newfoundland twice daily and records the number of whales spotted. The number of whales varies by season of the year. Late one spring, the following weekly counts were observed during four successive weeks: 14, 21, 48, and 37. Find the mean, median, and mode. Mean 30; Median 29; No mode

23. CHEMICAL PRODUCTION A biochemical company tries to place exactly 3 pounds of a particular enzyme in each bag that it produces. However, a tolerance of ± 0.1 pound is considered acceptable. A recent sample of 56 bags of enzyme showed the following.

Pounds of Enzyme	Frequency
2.76–2.85	0
2.86–2.95	3
2.96–3.05	48
3.06–3.15	5
3.16–3.25	0

Find the mean of the grouped data. Based on the data available, does the company appear to have a successful bagging operation rounded to the nearest one-hundredth of a pound? 3.01 pounds; probably so

24. ROBOT-DRILLED HOLES A robot designed to drill a hole to a depth of 1.5 centimeters in a block of steel is being tested, with the following results.

Depth of Hole (centimeters)	Frequency
1.16–1.25	0
1.26–1.35	1
1.36–1.45	18
1.46–1.55	20
1.56–1.65	0

Find the mean of the grouped data. Does the robot appear to be working as desired? 1.45; The robot is not working as desired.

4.5 Range and Standard Deviation

OBJECTIVES

1 *Find the range for a set of data.*

2 *Find the standard deviation.*

3 *Use the normal curve to estimate data.*

The mean and median can be used to indicate the middle, or central tendency, of a set of data, but *more is needed* to gain a good understanding of the data. It is also very important to get some sense about how widely the data are scattered.

To see why, look at the data in Table 4.6. Both sets of numbers have the same mean and median. The number of admittances in emergency room A go from a low of 5 to a high of 9 and the number of admittances in data set B go from a low of 1 to a high of 13. Even though the means and medians are the same, the manager of emergency room B needs to plan for a higher number of people since that emergency room sometimes has significantly more admittances per hour. A term used to describe the scatter of the data is **dispersion**.

Table 4.6	HOURLY ADMITTANCES TO EMERGENCY ROOMS	
	A	**B**
	5	1
	6	2
	7	7
	8	12
	9	13
Mean	7	7
Median	7	7

Objective

1   *Find the Range for a Set of Data.* Two of the most common measures of dispersion, the range and the standard deviation, are discussed here.

The **range** for a set of data is defined as the *difference between the largest value and the smallest value in the set*. The range is *never* a negative number. In column A in Table 4.6, the largest value is 9 and the smallest is 5. The range is

$$\text{Highest} - \text{lowest} = \text{range}$$
$$9 - 5 = 4$$

In column B, the range is $13 - 1 = 12$, or much higher than the range in column A.

The range can be misleading if it is interpreted unwisely. For example, suppose three executives rate two employees, Mark and Myrna, on five different jobs, as shown in the following table.

Job	Mark	Myrna
1	28	27
2	22	27
3	21	28
4	26	6
5	18	27
Mean	23	23
Median	22	27
Range	10	22

By looking at the range for each person, we might be tempted to conclude that Mark is a more consistent worker than Myrna. However, by checking more closely, we might decide that Myrna is actually more consistent with the exception of one very poor score, which may be due to some special circumstance. Myrna's median score is not affected much by the single low score and is more typical of her performance as a whole than is her mean score.

One of the most useful measures of dispersion, the standard deviation, is based on the *deviation (or spread) from the mean* of the data. To find how much each value deviates from the mean, first find the mean, and then subtract it from each data value.

EXAMPLE **1**   **Finding Deviations from the Mean**

Find the deviations from the mean for the data values 32, 41, 47, 53, 57.

Solution

Divide the sum of the numbers by 5 to find the mean of 46. Then find the deviations from the mean by subtracting the mean of 46 from each number. The subtraction can result in a negative number.

Date Value	−	Mean	=	Deviation from the Mean
32	−	46	=	−14
41	−	46	=	−5
47	−	46	=	1
53	−	46	=	7
57	−	46	=	11

NOTE   To check the work in Example 1, add the deviations. The sum of the deviations for a set of data is always 0, as long as the mean was not rounded.

NOTE   The deviation between a number and the mean is 0 if the two numbers are identical.

Objective

2   *Find the Standard Deviation.* To find the measure of dispersion or scatter in the data, it might be tempting to find the mean of the deviations. However, this number always turns out to be 0 no matter how much the dispersion in the data is, because the positive deviations simply cancel out the negative ones.

Get around this problem of adding positive and negative numbers by first squaring each deviation. Note that the square of a negative number is a positive number. Looking at the first row in the following table we have:

$$(-14)^2 = (-14) \cdot (-14) = +196$$

The square of the deviations from the mean are shown in the rightmost column.

Data Value	Deviation from the Mean	Square of Deviation
32	−14	196
41	−5	25
47	1	1
53	7	49
57	11	121

Before defining standard deviation, we need to define square root. The **square root** of a number n is written $\sqrt{n}$. It is the number that when multiplied by itself equals n. Thus, $\sqrt{144} = 12$ since $12 \times 12 = 144$, $\sqrt{1} = 1$ since $1 \times 1 = 1$, and so on.

Here is the formula to find the **standard deviation**.

$$\text{Standard deviation} = \sqrt{\frac{\Sigma \, (\text{deviation}^2)}{\text{number of observations}}}$$

where (deviation^2) is the deviation from the mean for each value squared and $\Sigma \, (\text{deviation}^2)$ is the sum of the squared deviations.

Finding the Standard Deviation

1. For each number, find the deviation from the mean.
2. Square each deviation.
3. Add the squared deviations together.
4. Divide the sum of the squared deviations by the number of observations.
5. Find the square root of the result found in Step 4.

Find the standard deviation using the data in the previous table, which is based on the same raw data found in Example 1.

$$s = \sqrt{\frac{196 + 25 + 1 + 49 + 121}{5}}$$

$$= \sqrt{\frac{392}{5}}$$

$$= \sqrt{78.4}$$

$$= 8.9 \qquad \text{Rounded to the nearest tenth}$$

 Scientific
Calculator
Approach

The calculator solution to this problem is as follows.

(196 + 25 + 1 + 49 + 121) ÷ 5 = 78.4 STO

RCL √X 8.854377448

The algebraic expression for the standard deviation is

$$s = \sqrt{\frac{\Sigma d^2}{n}}$$

where d = a deviation from the mean, n is the *number of data points in the group of numbers*, and the Greek letter Σ (sigma) represents a "sum of."

NOTE Some calculators have statistical function keys that can be used to calculate means and standard deviations. Check your calculator manual to see if your calculator has these keys.

EXAMPLE 2 Finding Standard Deviation

The number of attendees at recent children's soccer games is 7, 9, 18, 22, 27, 29, 32, 40. Find the standard deviation.

Solution

STEP 1 Find the mean of the values.

$$\frac{7 + 9 + 18 + 22 + 27 + 29 + 32 + 40}{8} = 23$$

STEP 2 Find the deviations from the mean by subtracting the mean from each value.

Data values	7	9	18	22	27	29	32	40
Deviations	−16	−14	−5	−1	4	6	9	17

STEP 3 Square each deviation.

Squares of deviations: 256 196 25 1 16 36 81 289

These numbers are the d^2 values in the formula.

STEP 4 Find the sum of the d^2 values.

$$\Sigma d^2 = 256 + 196 + 25 + 1 + 16 + 36 + 81 + 289 = 900$$

Now divide Σd^2 by n, which is 8 since there are 8 soccer game scores.

$$\frac{\Sigma d^2}{n} = \frac{900}{8} = 112.5$$

STEP 5 Take the square root of the answer in Step 4. The standard deviation of the given list of numbers is

$$s = \sqrt{112.5} = 10.6$$

The standard deviation is an important measure of the scatter in data. For example, suppose two different soccer teams score the following number of goals in subsequent games.

Team	Number of Goals Scored
Rockets	2, 1, 2, 2, 1
Bulls	0, 4, 5, 1, 9

The data for the Bulls is more widely scattered and will have a larger standard deviation than that for the Rockets. It is important to know both measures of central tendency, such as the mean, median, or mode, and measures of dispersion (or scatter), such as range and standard deviation. Information on both is needed to better understand the data.

> **NOTE** The **variance**, which is used in some textbooks, is the square of the standard deviation.
>
> $$\text{Variance} = (\text{standard deviation})^2$$
>
> Similarly, the standard deviation is the square root of the variance.
>
> $$\text{Standard deviation} = \sqrt{\text{variance}}$$

Objective

3 *Use the Normal Curve to Estimate Data.* Soft-drink bottlers such as the Coca-Cola Company wish to deliver a quality product to their customers. Of course, a primary measure of quality is taste. The level of liquid placed in each container during the bottling process affects the level of carbonation, which, in turn, influences taste. Thus, these bottlers try to put a very specific amount of the liquid drink into each container. Some even X-ray each bottle as it rapidly moves down the production line in order to make sure that the amount of liquid is "close enough" to the desired level.

If the bottling process is working well, the amount of liquid in successive containers will be centered around the desired amount. However, there will always be **variation** since not every bottle will be filled with exactly the same amount of fluid. Even though the difference in the amount of fluid in each bottle may be small, it is an important measure of quality that producers are very concerned about. The differences in the fluid levels between bottles can usually be described by the **normal curve**. The normal curve is also called the **normal probability distribution** or the **bell-shaped curve**. The normal curve is shown in Figure 4.9.

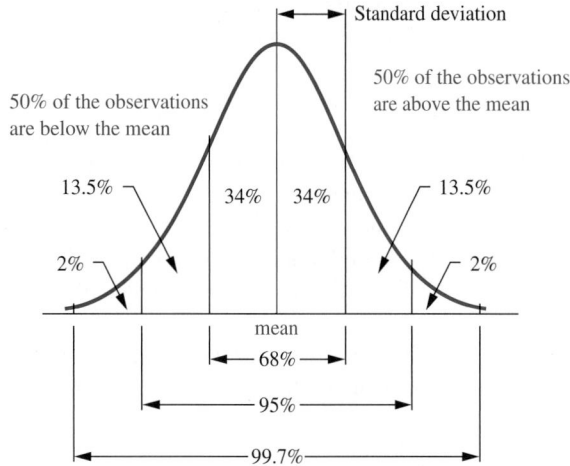

Figure 4.9 Normal Distribution

To illustrate how the normal curve shown in Figure 4.9 is used, assume that the amount of fluid in bottles being produced at a bottling company is normally distributed with a mean of 16 ounces and a standard deviation of 0.1 ounce. Then the following are true.

50% of the bottles contain 16 ounces or less.

50% of the bottles contain 16 ounces or more.

The following are also true.

68% of the bottles are filled to within 1 standard deviation of the mean of 16 ounces.

95% of the bottles are filled to within 2 standard deviations of the mean of 16 ounces.

99.7% of the bottles are filled to within 3 standard deviations of the mean of 16 ounces.

Although the amount of fluid in the next bottle to be produced is never known exactly ahead of time, the output of the process can be approximated by the normal curve.

In this example, the amount of fluid is measured in ounces. However, the next example discusses fluid levels in bottles using the height of fluid in a bottle. The same percentages that are shown above apply to this example as well. In fact, the same percentages *apply to every application* of the normal probability distribution!

EXAMPLE **3**   **Using the Normal Distribution**

Measurements are used by a worker to determine the fluid-level fill of bottles. The worker has found that the fluid-level fill can be described by the normal curve with a mean of 6 inches and a standard deviation of 0.04 inch.

a. Find the mean minus 3 standard deviations and the mean plus 3 standard deviations.
b. Use Figure 4.9 to find the number of bottles out of 1000 that should fall between the two limits found in part (a). This represents the number of appropriately filled bottles.
c. Find the number of bottles out of 1000 expected to have a fluid-level fill of less than or equal to a number defined as the mean minus 1 standard deviation.

Solution

a. Mean − 3 standard deviations = 6 − (3 · 0.04) = 5.88 inches
   Mean + 3 standard deviations = 6 + (3 · 0.04) = 6.12 inches
b. Looking along the bottom of Figure 4.9, notice that 99.7% of the observations fall within 3 standard deviations of the mean, or between the following:

(Mean − 3 standard deviations)   and   (Mean + 3 standard deviations)

Thus, the number of bottles that should fall within the 3 standard deviation limits of 5.88 inches and 6.12 inches is found by multiplying 99.7% by 1000 bottles.

$$0.996 \times 1000 = 997 \text{ bottles}$$

So, 997 out of every 1000 bottles should fall within the 3 standard deviation limits as long as the bottling process is operating correctly. If a random sample of 1000 results in more than 3 bottles with fluid-level fills that fall outside the acceptable range, then the production line is stopped and everything is checked for quality problems. This is done to prevent over- or under-filled bottles from leaving the bottling facility and being sold to customers.

c. The question asks us to find the number of bottles out of 1000 expected to have a fill rate of less than or equal to the mean minus 1 standard deviation.

Mean − 1 standard deviation = 6 − 0.04 = 5.96 inches

We need to find the area under the normal curve that is to the left of 5.96 inches, as shown in Figure 4.9. The entire area to the left of the mean is 0.50. From the area of 0.50, subtract the area in the first standard deviation to the left of the mean, which is 0.34.

Area to the left of mean   0.50
−Area in first standard deviation −0.34
                                    0.16 Area to left of the mean − 1 standard deviation

The area of interest is 0.16, or 16%. So, 16% of the 1000 bottles should have a fill level that is less than or equal to 5.96 inches. This amounts to 160 bottles out of the 1000.

$$0.16 \times 1000 = 160 \text{ bottles}$$

NOTE Workers from all over the world have been trained in statistics so that they can monitor the quality of their own work using the technique shown in the previous example.

| **4.5** | **Exercises** |

Find the mean and standard deviation for each set of data. Round answers to the nearest tenth.

1. 15, 18, 20, 19   18; 1.9
2. 6.8, 5.4, 3.7, 7.2, 6.4   5.9; 1.3
3. 20, 22, 23, 18, 21, 22   21; 1.6
4. 120, 118, 109, 115, 112, 110   114; 4.0
5. 55, 58, 54, 52, 51, 59, 58, 60   55.9; 3.1
6. 7.5, 7.3, 7.2, 7.5, 7.8, 7.1, 7.4, 8.0, 7.2, 7.6   7.5; 0.3

Find the range for each set of data.

7. 18, 24, 60, 42, 51, 61   43
8. 10, 15, 12, 17, 21, 13   11
9. 500, 274, 361, 295, 112   388
10. 10.3, 7.4, 8.1, 6.5, 9.7   3.8

11. When can the range of a set of numbers be misleading? (See Objective 1.)

12. Explain the meaning of range and standard deviation. (See Objectives 1 and 2.)

STUDENT WEIGHT The weights of two hundred 11-year-old students were measured. The results can be approximated by a normal curve with a mean weight of 80 pounds and a standard deviation of 0.5 pound. Use the following graph to find the number of students weighing as indicated in Exercises 13–20.

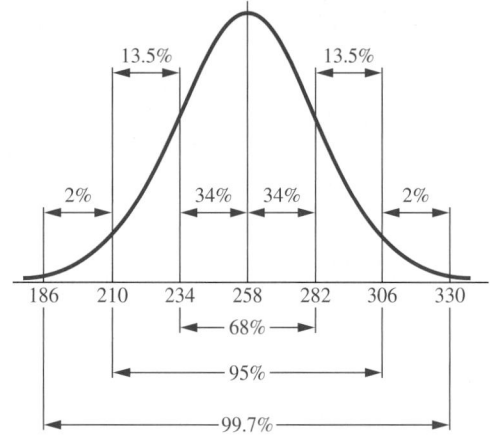

13. More than 80 pounds   100

14. More than 79.5 pounds   168

15. Between 79.5 and 80.5 pounds   136

16. Between 79 and 81 pounds   190

17. Between 80.5 and 81 pounds   27

18. Between 79.5 and 81 pounds   163

19. Within 1 pound of the mean   190

20. More than $1\frac{1}{2}$ pounds away from the mean   2

JOCKEY WEIGHT The weight of each jockey who rides horses at the race track is carefully measured before any race. The jockeys at one race had a mean weight of 107.8 pounds with a standard deviation of 2.6 pounds. Use the concepts of the normal curve to estimate the likelihood that one jockey chosen at random falls in the following weight classes.

21. Less than 107.8 pounds   50%

22. More than 110.4 pounds   16%

23. Between 102.6 and 113 pounds   95%

24. Between 100 and 115.6 pounds   99%

IQ = TEST RESULTS On standard IQ tests, the mean is 100 and the standard deviation is 15. The results are very close to fitting a normal curve. Suppose an IQ test is given to a very large group of people. Find the percent of people whose IQ score is the following.

25. More than 100   50%

26. Less than 100   50%

27. Greater than 115   16%

28. Between 85 and 115   68%

29. Between 70 and 130   95%

30. Between 55 and 145   99%

31. Less than 55 $\frac{1}{2}$%

32. More than 145 $\frac{1}{2}$%

TIRE WEAR After a 30,000-mile road test, the average wear on a particular brand of tire averaged 0.2 inch, with a standard deviation of 0.015 inch. The tire wear fits a normal curve closely. What percent of the tire wear would be the following?

33. 0.185 inch or more?   84%

34. Less than 0.185 inch?   16%

35. 0.23 inch or less?   97.5%

36. More than 0.23 inch?   2.5%

RACE TIMES The average amount of time taken by runners to complete a 10-kilometer race was 47.6 minutes, with a standard deviation of 2.7 minutes. Given that the times are approximately normally distributed, what percent of the runners required the following?

37. At least 44.9 minutes?   84%

38. No more than 44.9 minutes?   16%

39. No more than 53 minutes?   97.5%

40. At least 53 minutes?   2.5%

41. Between 44.9 minutes and 50.3 minutes?   68%

42. Between 42.2 minutes and 53 minutes?   95%

43. SWIMMING   A graduate student is doing research using students on a high school swim team. She found that the average time to swim the 100-yard freestyle was 54.6 seconds, with a standard deviation of 1.2 seconds. Out of 20 swimmers, use the normal distribution to estimate the number that would be expected to swim 100 yards freestyle in less than 53.4 seconds.   3 swimmers

44. TEST GRADES   The exact same final exam in world history was given to 263 students. The results can be approximated by the normal probability distribution, with a mean of 72% and a standard deviation of 9%. Find the number of students scoring less than 63% on the test.   42 students

---

4.6   Index Numbers

OBJECTIVES

1 *Find the price relative.*

2 *Use the Consumer Price Index to compare costs.*

Objective

1   *Find the Price Relative.* A house that cost $85,000 ten years ago now sells for $182,500. Tuition at one community college has increased from $380 per semester 15 years ago to $2600 per semester today. The price of both the house and college tuition increased over time. In fact, the cost of most items, including houses, cars, food, and beverages, tends to go up from year to year. Salaries also often increase from year to year.

Rather than thinking that prices continually increase, you can also think of it as the value of each dollar continuing to fall as time passes. Over the years, each dollar buys less and less, so the value of the dollar goes down. This is true for most currencies in the world, most of the time.

Price relatives are used to study the increase in prices over time. They can be used to compare two different items to see which price has increased more during a certain period of time. The **price relative** is the current price divided by the price in a specific past year, which is called the **base year**. The formula for price relative follows.

$$\text{Price relative} = \frac{\text{price this year}}{\text{price in base year}} \times 100$$

EXAMPLE 1 **Finding the Price Relative**

Using the prices just given, find the price relative for the house.

$$\text{Price relative} = \frac{\$182,500}{\$85,000} \times 100 = 214.7 \qquad \text{Rounded}$$

Today, the house sells for 214.7% of the price it did 10 years ago. Notice that a price relative is really just a percent. It gives the percent that this year's price is compared to the base year.

Find the price relative for the community college tuition as follows.

$$\text{Price relative} = \frac{\$2600}{\$380} \times 100 = 684.2 \quad \text{Rounded}$$

Since the price relative of 684.2 for the increase in college tuition is much larger than the price relative of 214.7 for the house, it is clear that the price of the college tuition has increased far more rapidly than the price of the house.

EXAMPLE 2 Finding the Price Relative

The price of a particular Intel computer chip dropped from $500 two years ago to $200 today. The price relative is found as follows.

$$\frac{\$200}{\$500} \times 100 = 40$$

The computer chip sells for 40% of its original price. This example shows that a price relative is below 100 when the price of the item falls. Although the price of most items increases with time, the price of a few items goes down with time. Most price relatives are over 100 during periods of high inflation when prices are generally increasing.

NOTE The price relative gives a way of comparing the two prices and showing a percent increase.

Objective

2 *Use the Consumer Price Index to Compare Costs.* The **Consumer Price Index (CPI)**, published by the Bureau of Labor Statistics, can be given in terms of price relatives. The bureau keeps track of the costs of a great many items in different cities throughout the country and publishes its findings monthly. A recent portion of the report for one month is included in Table 4.7.

Table 4.7 URBAN PRICES INDEX*

Item	Chicago	Houston	Los Angeles	New York
All items	220.1	201.6	233.4	248.1
Food and beverages	222.9	210.3	232.3	235.3
Transportation	210.1	196.6	215.5	230.0
Medical	417.4	382.0	386.9	391.1
Recreation	113.2	109.1	104.8	115.8

*Each figure is given as a percent of the 1982–1984 base of 100.
Source: U.S. Bureau of Labor Statistics

The numbers in Table 4.7 show the price relatives using a base year of 1982–1984. For example, medical costs in New York are now 391.1% of those in 1982–1984. The price relatives in Table 4.7 can be used to compare price increases for the different cities shown. For example, since 1982–1984 the cost of recreation has gone up by 109.1% in Houston versus 104.8% in Los Angeles. The data in the table cannot be used to estimate the actual cost of recreation in, say, Houston without first knowing what recreation costs were in the base year.

NOTE It is easy to see that the largest price relatives in Table 4.7 are those for medical costs. Thus, medical costs have increased far more rapidly than any of the other costs shown in the table.

Medical Costs Increase

The results of a recent survey of area firms indicate that increasing medical costs have become a big concern for managers. The survey showed an average annual increase in the cost of medical insurance of 9.8%. Managers are debating how to keep medical costs under control and wondering how they can pass part of the costs along to consumers and to employees. . . .

EXAMPLE 3 **Using the CPI**

One kidney transplant in Chicago cost $11,050 in 1984. Use the price relative to estimate the cost of the same surgery today.

Solution

The price relative for medical costs in Chicago is 417.4, or 417.4%.

$$\text{Today's cost} = \$11,050 \times 417.4\% = \$46,122.70$$

This high cost shows why people need help with the expenses from any catastrophic illness.

4.6	Exercises

Find the price relatives for the following items. Round to the nearest tenth.

Item	Price Then	Price Now	
1. Rent	$225 per month	$680 per month	302.2
2. Ski boat	$2600	$8700	334.6
3. Laptop	$2000	$840	42
4. Jeans	$25 per pair	$40 per pair	160
5. Natural gas	$1.25 per thousand cubic feet	$4.25 per thousand cubic feet	340
6. House	$122,100	$198,200	162.3

Use the Urban Prices Index in Table 4.7 to complete the following chart.

Urban Area	Item	$100 Worth in 1982 Will Cost Today
7. Chicago	All items	$220.10
8. New York	Food and beverage	$235.30
9. Houston	Transportation	$196.60
10. Los Angeles	Food and beverage	$232.30
11. Chicago	Medical	$417.40
12. Los Angeles	Recreation	$104.80

Solve the following application problem using Table 4.7.

13. HEART BYPASS Assume the total cost of a heart bypass in New York in 1982 was $34,500. Estimate the cost today to the nearest $1000. $135,000

14. FAMILY BUDGET Find today's equivalent of $22,000 family budget in 1982 in Houston to the nearest $1000. This would include all items. $44,000

15. FOOD AND BEVERAGE Assume a 1983 food and beverage budget for a family of 4 in Chicago of $285 per week. Find today's equivalent amount. $635.27

16. RECREATION Assume a 1982 family budget of $3000 for recreation in Los Angeles and find today's equivalent amount. $3144

17. INCREASING PRICES Of the items listed in Table 4.7, which has increased the most?   Medical costs

18. INCREASING PRICES Use Table 4.7 to find the city in which all item costs increased the least.   Houston

 19. Explain price relative and inflation. Are they identical to one another? Explain. (See Objectives 1 and 2.)

 20. Go to the library or use the Internet and find the government's estimate of the CPI for the past 3 years. Compare the average inflation of these 3 years to inflation during the early 1930s, when inflation was actually negative. Also compare to inflation in the late 1970s, when inflation was very high. (See Objective 2.)

CHAPTER TERMS

Review the following terms to test your understanding of the chapter. For any terms you do not know, refer to the page number found next to that term.

average [p. 147]
axis [p. 133]
bar graph [p. 122]
base year [p. 166]
bell-shaped curve
  [p. 162]
bimodal [p. 156]
circle graph [p. 124]
class mark [p. 149]
comparative line graph
  [p. 123]
Consumer Price Index
  (CPI) [p. 167]

dependent variable [p. 131]
dispersion [p. 159]
frequency distribution
  [p. 120]
graph [p. 122]
independent variable
  [p. 131]
linear equation [p. 135]
line graph [p. 133]
mean [p. 147]
measure of central
  tendency [p. 146]
median [p. 153]

mode [p. 153]
nonlinear equation [p. 138]
normal curve [p. 162]
normal probability
  distribution [p. 162]
ordered array [p. 154]
origin [p. 133]
peak oil [p. 119]
pie chart [p. 124]
population [p. 146]
price relative [p. 166]
range [p. 159]
raw data [p. 120]

sample [p. 146]
scale [p. 133]
square root [p. 160]
standard deviation
  [p. 160]
statistics [p. 119]
variance [p. 162]
variation [p. 162]
weighted mean [p. 148]
x-axis [p. 133]
y-axis [p. 133]
y-intercept [p. 137]

CONCEPTS

4.1 Constructing a frequency distribution from raw data

1. Construct a table listing each value and the number of times this value occurs.
2. For a distribution with grouped data, combine the data into classes.

EXAMPLES

For the following data, construct a frequency distribution.
12, 15, 15, 14, 13, 20, 10,
12, 11, 9, 10, 12, 17, 20, 16,
17, 14, 18, 19, 13

Data	Tally	Frequency
9	|	1
10	||	2
11	|	1
12	|||	3
13	||	2
14	||	2
15	||	2
16	|	1
17	||	2
18	|	1
19	|	1
20	||	2

Classes	Frequency
9–11	4
12–14	7
15–17	5
18–20	4

4.1 Constructing a bar graph from a frequency distribution

Draw a bar for each class using the frequency of the class as the height of the bar.

Construct a bar graph from the frequency distribution of the previous example.

4.1 Constructing a line graph

1. Plot each year on the horizontal axis.
2. For each year, find the value for that year and plot a point for each value.
3. Connect all points with straight lines.

Construct a line graph for the following data.

Year	Value
2010	$850,000
2011	920,000
2012	875,000
2013	975,000

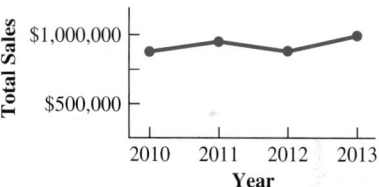

4.1 Constructing a circle graph

1. Determine the percent of the total for each item.
2. Find the number of degrees represented by each percent.
3. Draw the circle.

Construct a circle graph for the following weekly expenses.

Item	Amount	Percent
Car	$200	20%
Lodging	300	30%
Food	250	25%
Entertainment	150	15%
Other	100	10%

Multiply each percent by 360° to find the angle for each sector.

Car: $360° \times 0.2 = 72°$
Lodging: $360° \times 0.3 = 108°$
Food: $360° \times 0.25 = 90°$
Entertainment: $360° \times 0.15 = 54°$
Other: $360° \times 0.1 = 36°$

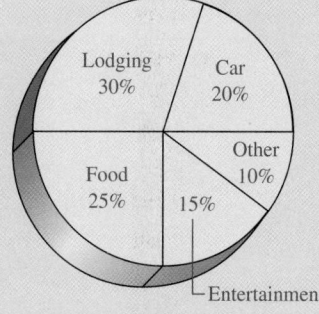

4.2 Identifying independent and dependent variables

Decide which variable depends on the other variable(s).

Runners sometimes develop shin splints that cause pain in the lower leg. Further stress on the leg can lead to even more pain. Think of "amount of pain" and "stress from running" as variables and decide which is the independent variable and which is the dependent variable.

Since "amount of pain" depends on "stress from running": Independent variable: stress from running, Dependent variable: amount of pain

4.2 Setting up an appropriate graph

Decide on the variables for the *x*- and *y*-axes. Decide on scales and give an appropriate title and axes labels.

A professor wants to construct a graph comparing legal and illegal music downloads on the Internet by year. No one knows for sure, but estimates are that there are more than a billion illegal downloads each year. Legal downloads are a fraction of the illegal downloads. Set up a graph from 2000 to the present.

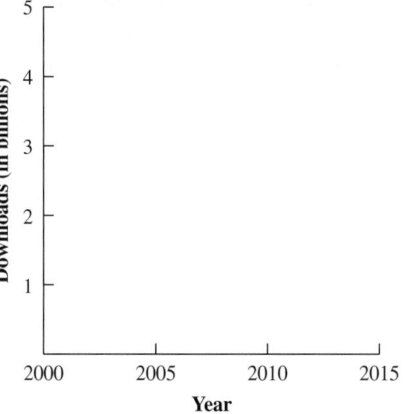

4.2 Graphing a straight line

Substitute two values for the independent variable and find corresponding values of the dependent variable. Set up the graph, plot the two points, and connect them with a ruler.

A running coach wants to know how many calories are burned by mile run for various athletes he coaches. The athletes weight between 125 and 190 pounds. Construct a graph given the following.

Calories burned per mile = $0.75 \cdot$ body weight

4.2 Graphing a nonlinear line

Evaluate the equation for several different values of the independent variable. Plot the points and connect them with a smooth line.

The maturity value for an $8500 investment at 3.5% is given by $M = \$8500(1.035)^n$, where n is the number of years. Graph this relationship for 20 years.

The equation is nonlinear since it includes an exponent.

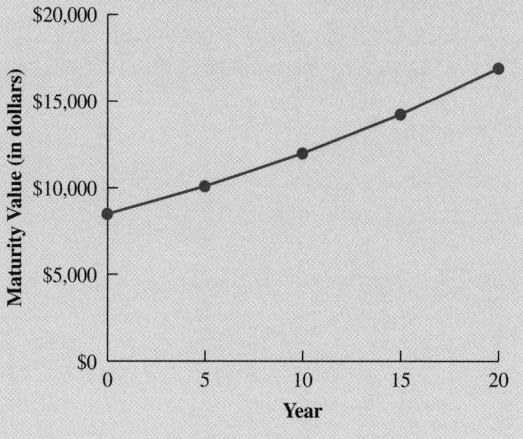

Maturity Value of an $8500 Investment

4.3 Finding the mean of a set of data

Divide the sum of the data by the number of data points.

The test scores for Pat Phelan in her business math course were 85, 76, 93, 91, 78, 82, 87, and 85. Find Phelan's test average.

$$\text{Mean} = \frac{85 + 76 + 93 + 91 + 78 + 82 + 87 + 85}{8}$$

$$= \frac{677}{8} = 84.63$$

4.3 Finding the weighted mean

1. Multiply frequency by value.
2. Add all products obtained in Step 1.
3. Divide the sum in Step 2 by the total number of data points.

No. of School-Age Children	Frequency
0	12
1	6
2	7
3	3
4	2
Total families:	30

Find the mean number of school-age children per family.

No.	Frequency	No. × Frequency
0	12	0
1	6	6
2	7	14
3	3	9
4	2	8
		37

$$\text{Mean} = \frac{37}{30} = 1.23$$

4.3 Finding the mean of a grouped frequency distribution

1. Determine the class mark (the midpoint) for each class.
2. Multiply the class mark by the frequency of each class.
3. Add all the products obtained in Step 2.
4. Divide by the number of observations.

Find the mean.

Intervals	Frequency
3–5	2
6–8	10
9–11	12
12–14	9
15–17	7

Intervals	Freq.	Class Mark	Frequency × Class Mark
3–5	2	4	8
6–8	10	7	70
9–11	12	10	120
12–14	9	13	117
15–17	7	16	112
	Total: 40		Total: 427

$$\text{Mean} = \frac{427}{40} = 10.68$$

4.4 Finding the median of a set of data

1. Arrange the data from lowest to highest.
2. If there is an *odd* number of numbers, the median is the number in the middle.
3. If there is an *even* number of numbers, the median is the average of the two in the middle.

Find the median for Pat Phelan's grades from an earlier example. The data arranged from lowest to highest are 76, 78, 82, 85, 85, 87, 91, and 93.

The average of the middle two values is $\frac{85 + 85}{2} = 85$.

4.4 Determining the mode of a set of data

The mode is the most frequently occurring value.

Find the mode for Phelan's grades in the previous example.
The mode is 85, which occurs most frequently (twice).

4.4 Finding the median of a grouped frequency distribution

The median is the class mark associated with the middle number or with the average of the middle numbers.

Intervals	Frequency
10–19	5
20–29	8
30–39	2

There are 15 observations. Divide 15 by 2 to find 7.5. Thus, the class mark associated with the eighth value from the smallest, or 24.5, is the median.

4.4 Finding the mode of a grouped frequency distribution

The mode is the class mark of the class with the highest frequency.

Intervals	Frequency
10–19	5
20–29	8
30–39	2

The second class has the highest frequency. The mode is the associated class mark of 24.5.

4.5 Finding the range of a set of data

$$\text{Range} = \text{largest} - \text{smallest}$$

Find the range of the values 7, 6, 10, 7, 9, 5, 2, 8, and 9.

$$\text{Range} = \text{highest} - \text{lowest}$$
$$= 10 - 2 = 8$$

4.5 Finding the standard deviation

1. Determine the mean of the data.
2. Subtract the mean from each value to obtain individual deviations, d.
3. Square each deviation.
4. Sum all the squared deviations.
5. Divide the sum by the number of observations.
6. Take the square root of the number obtained in Step 5.

$$s = \sqrt{\frac{\sum d^2}{n}}$$

Find the standard deviation of the values, 7, 6, 10, 7, 9, 5, 2, 8, and 9.

Data Value	Deviation d	Deviation Squared, d^2
7	0	0
6	−1	1
10	3	9
7	0	0
9	2	4
5	−2	4
2	−5	25
8	1	1
9	2	4
Total: 63		**Total: 48**

$$\text{Mean} = 63 \div 9 = 7$$
$$\text{Variance} = \frac{\sum d^2}{n} = \frac{48}{9} = 5.33$$
$$\text{Std. deviation} = \sqrt{5.33} = 2.31$$

4.6 Finding the price relative

Divide the price this year by the price in a base year and multiply by 100.

A car cost $16,000 10 years ago. It now costs $22,500. Find the price relative for the car.

$$\text{Price relative} = \frac{\text{price this year}}{\text{price in base year}} \times 100$$
$$= \frac{\$22,500}{\$16,000} \times 100 = 140.6$$

4.6 Finding cost today using the Consumer Price Index (CPI)

Multiply CPI by cost in the base year to estimate current cost.

A family budget in Los Angeles in 1982 was $23,500. Estimate the same budget today using Table 4.7.

$$\text{Cost today} = \$23,500 \times 233.4\%$$
$$= \$23,500 \times 2.334$$
$$= \$54,849$$

CHAPTER 4 | Review Exercises

The answer section includes answers to all Review Exercises.

Work the following application problems. The following numbers are the number of gallons of gasoline sold at a convenience store by week for the past 20 weeks. [4.1]

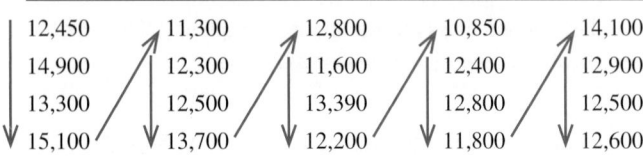

12,450	11,300	12,800	10,850	14,100
14,900	12,300	11,600	12,400	12,900
13,300	12,500	13,390	12,800	12,500
15,100	13,700	12,200	11,800	12,600

1. Use these numbers to complete the following table.

Gallons of Gasoline	Number of Weeks
10,000–10,999	1
11,000–11,999	3
12,000–12,999	10
13,000–13,999	3
14,000–14,999	2
15,000–15,999	1

2. How many weeks had sales of 13,000 gallons or more?   6

3. Use the numbers in Exercise 1 to draw a bar graph. Be sure to put a heading and labels on the graph.

4. During a 1-year period, the student newspaper at Comfort Community College had the following expenses. Find all numbers missing from the table.

Item	Dollar Amount	Percent of Total	Degrees of a Circle
Newsprint	$12,000	20%	72°
Printing costs	$6,000	10%	36°
Wire service	$18,000	30%	108°
Salaries	$18,000	30%	108°
Other	$6,000	10%	36°

5. Draw a circle graph using the information in Exercise 4.

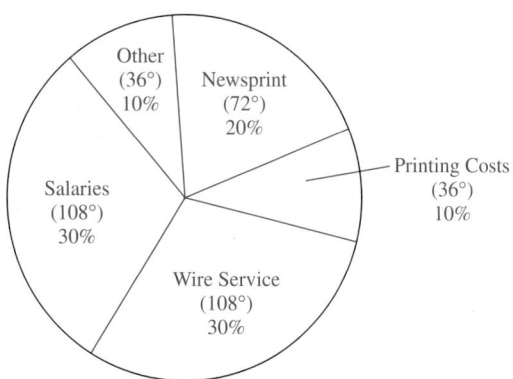

6. What percent of the expenses were for newsprint, printing costs, and wire service?   60%

Graph as indicated. [4.2]

7. There are two common systems used to measure temperatures: Celsius and Fahrenheit. Use the following equation to convert from Celsius to Fahrenheit: $F = \frac{9}{5} C + 32$. Show this relationship from the freezing point of water at 0° Celsius to the boiling point of water at 100° Celsius.

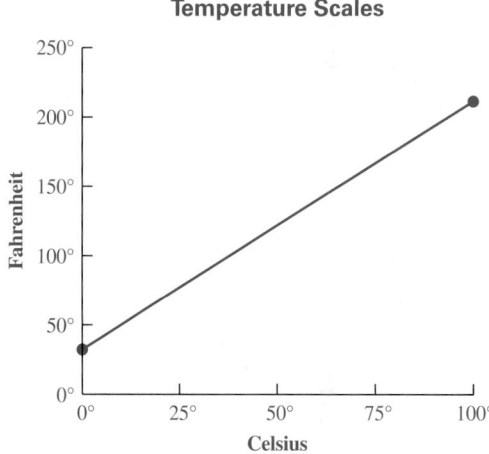

8. Bob and Linda Jolicka are medical doctors with their own medical practice. They share income equally and pay taxes jointly as a married couple. Bob estimates that the total tax due on combined income of between $100,000 and $200,000 can be estimated using $T = 0.28I + 0.153I + 0.06I + \$36{,}700$. Note that I is taxable income in excess of $100,000, $0.28I$ is federal income tax, $0.153I$ is Social Security and Medicare tax, $0.06I$ is state income tax, and $36,700 is the total tax on the first $100,000 in income. Show this relationship in a graph for incomes between $100,000 and $200,000.

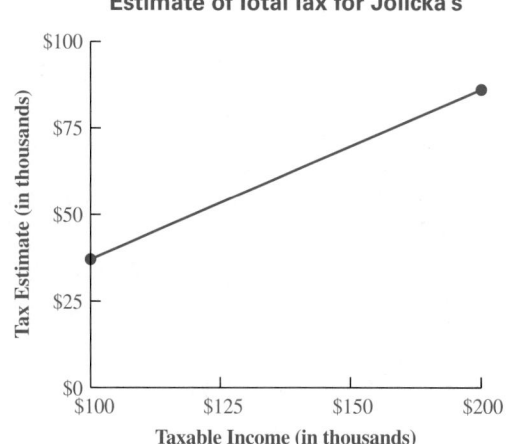

9. Profit in thousands is given by $P = -\$80,300 + 512N - 0.26N^2$, where N is the number of items sold in a week. Sales are expected to range between 400 and 800 per week. Graph this equation. (*Hint:* Since the equation is nonlinear, you need to plot more than two points.)

10. The eventual maturity value of an investment of $85,000 that earns 6% in a retirement plan is found using $M = \$85,000 \cdot 1.06^n$, where n is the number of years the investment is held. Graph this equation, given that the owner of the retirement plan is interested in the maturity when he retires in 20 to 35 years. (*Hint:* Since the equation is nonlinear, you need to plot more than two points.)

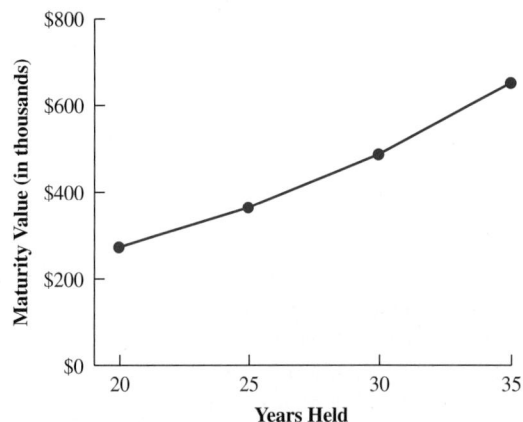

Calculate the mean, median, and mode for the following sets of data. Round answers to the nearest tenth. [4.3–4.4]

11. 25, 20, 18, 35, 19   23.4; 20; no mode

12. 85, 80, 82, 82, 88, 90, 92   85.6; 85; 82

13. 21, 20, 20, 18, 21, 19, 21, 22   20.3; 20.5; 21

14. 42, 44, 41, 44, 45, 44   43.3; 44; 44

15. 8, 7, 6, 6, 7, 7, 5, 9   6.9; 7; 7

16. 2.5, 2.4, 2.4, 2.3, 2.4, 2.6, 2.0, 2.2   2.4; 2.4; 2.4

Calculate the mean for the frequency distribution given in Exercises 13 and 14. Round answers to the nearest tenth. [4.3]

17.	Intervals	Frequency	
	10–14	6	
	15–19	3	
	20–24	5	26.1
	25–29	7	
	30–34	5	
	35–39	9	

18.	Intervals	Frequency	
	10–19	6	
	20–29	5	
	30–39	9	34.8
	40–49	4	
	50–59	7	

Calculate the median and the mode for the frequency distributions given in Exercises 15 and 16. [4.4]

19.	Intervals	Frequency	
	1–5	20	
	6–10	12	
	11–15	14	8; 3
	16–20	10	
	21–25	5	

20.	Intervals	Frequency	
	50–59	3	
	60–69	5	
	70–79	18	74.5; 74.5
	80–89	12	
	90–99	4	

Find the range and standard deviation for Exercises 17–20. Round answers to the nearest hundredth. [4.5]

21. 62, 24, 38, 91, 56   67; 22.77

22. 5, 7, 12, 10, 7, 12, 18   13; 4.05

23. 82, 86, 78, 74, 65   21; 7.21

24. 150, 145, 130, 120, 162, 158   42; 14.88

Find the price relative for Exercises 25–28. Round to the nearest tenth. [4.6]

Item		Price in Base Year	Price in Current Year	
25.	Automobile	$22,500	$32,300	143.6
26.	Television	$250	$410	164.0
27.	Personal computer	$1800	$950	52.8
28.	Lawn mower	$185	$300	162.2

Solve the following application problems.

29. A Brazilian brought his critically ill 18-year-old daughter to Houston, Texas, to receive the same medical procedure he had received there in 1984 as a young man. The cost of the procedure in 1984 was $12,170. Use the price relatives in Table 4.7 to estimate the cost of the medical procedure to the nearest dollar. [4.6] $46,489

30. The thickness of an alloy coating on a military weapon can be approximated by a normal curve with mean 7.2 millimeters and standard deviation 0.08 millimeter. Find the percent of items expected to have a coating thicker than 7.12 millimeters. [4.5]   84%

31. Jawya Rhomber needs to buy a used automobile. He uses the Internet to find the prices of several similar, acceptable automobiles and finds that the mean price is $9412, with a standard deviation of $760. Sketch the normal curve and then find the price range that corresponds to a 95% chance of finding an acceptable automobile.

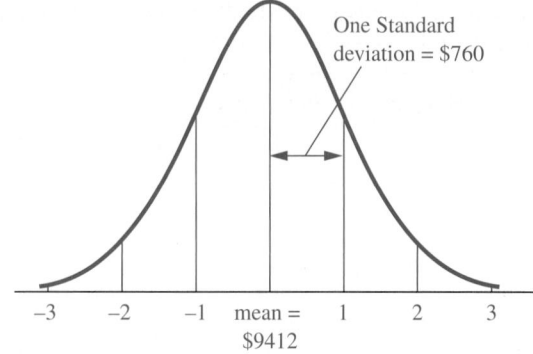

Since the mean ± 2 standard deviations includes 95% of the area, the price range that corresponds to a 95% chance of finding an acceptable automobile is $9412 ± $1520, or between $7892 and $10,932.

32. Okba Asad, the owner of Current's Restaurant, has monitored weekly sales for the past 6 weeks. Plot these data in a line graph. Do sales appear to be increasing or can you tell from the data given? [4.2]   Sales are relatively flat.

Week	Sales	Week	Sales
1	$4227	4	$5009
2	$4806	5	$4198
3	$4559	6	$5126

33. Ted Smith sells stocks and bonds at Merrill Lynch. His wife developed a serious illness at the beginning of 2011 and her condition slowly improved through the balance of the year. Do you think his personal problems may have influenced his work performance? [4.1]

Year	Quarterly Commissions			
2011	$14,250	$12,375	$15,750	$13,682
2012	$13,435	$14,230	$11,540	$15,782
2013	$8,207	$7,350	$10,366	$11,470

Support your view by drawing a line graph. Be sure to label the quarter in which Mrs. Smith became ill.

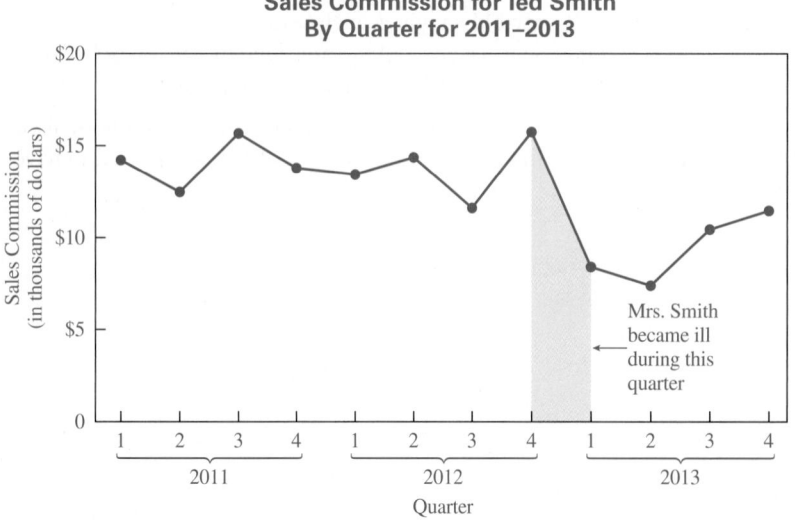

Mrs. Smith's illness affected Mr. Smith's work

34. Marie Dee wishes to calculate her grade point average for the semester. Round your answers to the nearest hundredth. (A = 4.0, B = 3.0, C = 2.0, D = 1.0, F = 0.0)

Also, find her grade point average if she had been unable to pull her Spanish grade up from the F she had in the course prior to the final exam. [4.3]   2.54; 2.31

Course	Semester Hours	Grade
Business Math	3	A
English	3	C
Biology	4	B
Spanish	3	D

35. The average price of a nursing home in Philadelphia went from $1950 per month in 1990 to $5340 per month today. Find the price relative. [4.6]   273.8

36. In the past month, a landscaper completed jobs for which he was paid these amounts: $3280, $4650, $8116, $5000, $2400, and $5000. (**a**) Find the mean, median, and mode, (**b**) Find the standard deviation.

a. Mean = $4741; median = $4825; mode = $5000

b. Standard deviation = 1786.4 (rounded)

CHAPTER 4	Business Application Case #1
	Growth of a New Business

For years, Pat Farmer managed an oil and gas services company in Midland, Texas, that provided well services for oil and gas operators. Finally, she decided to start her own company in Midland, where she knew a lot of people. Six months later, she opened a second office in Lockhart, Texas, to service oil and gas operators in that area even though she did not know nearly as many people in that area. Here are the sales in thousands of dollars for the two shops.

	Mar.	Apr.	May	June	July	Aug.	Sep.	Oct.	Nov.	Dec.
Midland	8.9	12.2	15.4	18.4	18.9	16.1	18.5	20.2	28.3	31.4
Lockhart							4.8	8.6	10.2	10.2

a. Find the mean, median, and mode for both stores to the nearest tenth of a thousand.

Midland:	18.8, 18.5, no mode
Lockhart:	8.5, 9.4, 10.2

b. Plot sales for both stores on the same line graph. Put month on the horizontal axis and sales on the vertical axis.

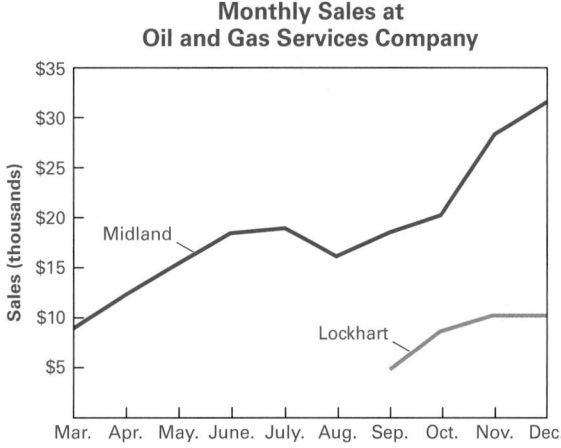

c. Identify any trends in the line graph.   Sales grew rapidly in Midland and are also growing in Lockhart.

d. In which city have sales grown more rapidly? Explain why this may be the case.   Sales have grown more rapidly in Midland. Pat Farmer has worked in Midland for several years and knows a lot of people. She does not know as many people in Lockhart.

CHAPTER 4	Business Application Case #2
	Sales at the Retailing Giant: Wal-Mart Stores Inc.

Sam Walton opened the first Wal-Mart store in Arkansas in 1962. The first giant supercenters were built 26 years later in 1988. Wal-Mart now serves more than 49 million customers each week, employs more than 620,000 people, and has over 3100 international stores in 13 different countries, including Mexico, Canada, China, the United Kingdom, and Japan. Amazingly, more than 1,000,000 different products are for sale on the Wal-Mart Web site, www.walmart.com. The following financial data were taken from Wal-Mart's financial statements, which are public.

Wal-Mart Stores, Inc. (all numbers in billions)			
Year	Net Sales	Income Taxes Paid	After-Tax Profit
2007	$345.0	$6.7	$11.3
2008	$374.5	$6.3	$12.7
2009	$404.2	$7.1	$13.4
2010	$408.1	$7.2	$14.4
2011	$421.8	$7.6	$16.4

a. First, find the mean and median income taxes paid. Then find the mean and median after-tax profit.
Income taxes paid: mean = $6.98 billion, median = $7.1 billion
Profit: mean = $13.64 billion, median = $13.4 billion

b. Find the sum of the Income Taxes Paid and After-Tax Profit columns. Next, add those two sums together to find the total before-tax income for Wal-Mart for the 5 years shown. Find the effective income tax rate for Wal-Mart by dividing the sum of 5 years of income taxes paid by the sum of the 5-year total before-tax income. Round to the nearest tenth of a percent.   Sum of columns: $34.9, 68.2; total before-tax income: $103.1; 33.9% tax rate

c. Graph net sales versus year using a line graph. Identify any particular trend.   Sales have a clear upward trend, indicating that Wal-Mart Stores continues to grow even though the company is the largest retailer in the world.

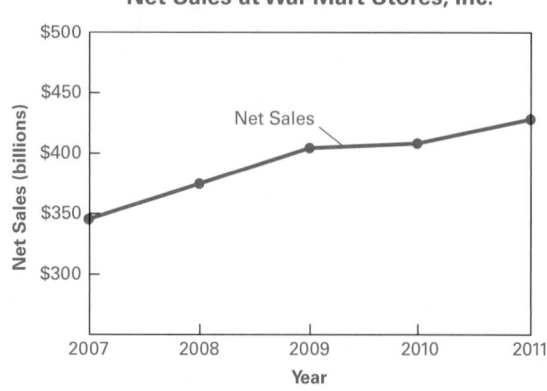

Net Sales at Wal-Mart Stores, Inc.

| **PART 1** | Cumulative Review: Chapters 1–4 |

To help you review, the numbers in brackets show the section in which the topic was introduced.

Solve the following application problem. [1.1]

1. One of the first things Alyssa Datoli did after getting a divorce was to set up a budget for herself and her young son. She spends $875 for rent and utilities, $400 for food, $320 for child care, and $182 for transportation and plans to limit herself to $600 for all other expenses. She puts any remaining money in a saving account at a local bank. Find the amount going into savings each month if her take-home pay is $2437 per month including child-care payments. $60 per month

2. The Enabling Supply House purchases 6 motorized wheelchairs at $1256 each and 15 speech-compression recorder-players at $895 each. Find the total cost. $20,961

3. Software Supply had a bank balance of $29,742.18 at the beginning of April. During the month, the firm made deposits of $14,096.18 and $6529.42. A total of $18,709.51 in checks was paid by the bank during the month. Find the firm's checking account balance at the end of April. $31,658.27

4. Jessica Waters purchases a hot tub on contract and must pay $185 per month until she has paid a total of $4440. Find the number of payments she must make.   24 payments

Solve the following problems. [1.2–1.3]

5. Write $\frac{48}{54}$ in lowest terms. $\frac{8}{9}$

6. Write $8\frac{1}{8}$ as an improper fraction. $\frac{65}{8}$

7. Write $\frac{107}{15}$ as a mixed number. $7\frac{2}{15}$

8. $1\frac{2}{3} + 2\frac{3}{4} =$ $4\frac{5}{12}$

9. $5\frac{7}{8} + 7\frac{2}{3} =$ $13\frac{13}{24}$

10. $6\frac{1}{3} - 4\frac{7}{12} =$ $1\frac{3}{4}$

11. $8\frac{1}{2} \times \frac{9}{17} \times \frac{2}{3} =$ 3

12. $3\frac{3}{4} \div \frac{27}{16} =$ $2\frac{2}{9}$

Solve the following application problems. [1.2–1.3]

13. The area of a piece of land is $63\frac{3}{4}$ acres. One-third of the land is sold. What is the area of the land that is left? $42\frac{1}{2}$ acres

14. To prepare for the state real estate exam, Pam Prentiss studied $5\frac{1}{2}$ hours on the first day, $6\frac{1}{4}$ hours on the second day, $3\frac{3}{4}$ hours on the third day, and 7 hours on the fourth day. How many hours did she study altogether? $22\frac{1}{2}$ hours

15. The storage yard at American River Raft Rental has four sides and is enclosed with $527\frac{1}{24}$ feet of security fencing around it. If three sides of the yard measure $107\frac{2}{3}$ feet, $150\frac{3}{4}$ feet, and $138\frac{5}{8}$ feet, what is the length of the fourth side?   130 feet

16. Play-It-Now Sports Center has decided to divide $\frac{2}{3}$ of the company's profit-sharing funds evenly among the 8 store managers. What fraction of the total amount will each receive? $\frac{1}{12}$ of the total

Solve the following problems. [1.3]

17. Change 0.35 to a fraction. $\frac{7}{20}$

18. Change $\frac{2}{3}$ to a decimal. Round to the nearest thousandth.   0.667

Round each of the following numbers as indicated. [1.3]

19. 78.572 to the nearest hundredth   78.57

20. 4732.489 to the nearest hundredth   4732.49

21. 62.65 to the nearest tenth   62.7

22. 215.6749 to the nearest thousandth   215.675

Solve each equation. [2.1]

23. $x + 17 = 43$ 26

24. $y - 33 = 52.4$ 85.4

25. $\frac{z}{4} - 10 = 18$ 112

26. $4(r - 2) = 2(r + 8)$ 12

Write a mathematical expression. Use x as the variable. [2.2]

27. $\frac{3}{4}$ times a number $\quad \frac{3}{4}x$

28. 5 times a number is added to the number $\quad 5x + x$

29. 8 times a number is decreased by 8 $\quad 8x - 8$

30. The sum of 6 times a number and 5 $\quad 6x + 5$

For each problem, use the formula to find the value of the variable that is not given. [2.3]

31. $I = PRT; I = \$2880, R = 0.08, P = \$12,000 \quad T = 3$

32. $M = P(1 + RT); M = \$2035, R = 0.05, T = 2 \quad P = \$1850$

Write the following ratios. [2.4]

33. \$2000 to \$400 $\quad \frac{5}{1}$

34. 21 feet to 5 yards $\quad \frac{7}{5}$

Solve the following proportions. [2.4]

35. $\frac{3}{x} = \frac{14}{42} \quad 9$

36. $\frac{5}{8} = \frac{22}{y} \quad 35\frac{1}{5}$

Solve the following application problems. [2.4]

37. Thirty-five out of a random sample of 200 students at a 4-year liberal arts college play some type of sport. Based on results of this sample, estimate the number playing sports out of a student body of 3000 students. $\quad$ 525 students

38. A company spends 4 times as much on product development as it does on advertising. If \$38,500 is spent on advertising, how much is spent on product development? $\quad$ \$154,000

Write each using exponents. [2.5]

39. $t \cdot t \cdot t \quad t^3$

40. $17 \cdot 17 \quad 17^2$

Evaluate each of the following. [2.5]

41. $20^2 \quad 400$

42. $(7.2)^0 \quad 1$

Simplify each of the following leaving exponents in each answer. [2.5]

43. $\left(\frac{r}{t}\right)^2 \quad \frac{r^2}{t^2}$

44. $(s \cdot t)^3 \quad s^3 t^3$

45. $\frac{9^5}{9^3} \quad 9^2$

46. $(T^2)^4 \quad T^8$

Evaluate the following expressions. [2.5]

47. $8 \cdot 9 - (14 - 7)^2 \quad 23$

48. $9^2 \cdot 72 - (6^2 \div 2)^3 \quad 0$

49. $75 - \frac{x^3}{4}; x = 6 \quad 21$

50. $(r - 1)^2 + 2^3 - r, r = 12 \quad 117$

Solve the following problems. [3.1–3.4]

51. Change $\frac{5}{8}$ to a percent. $\quad$ 62.5%

52. Change 0.25% to a decimal. $\quad$ 0.0025

53. Find 18% of 2500 prospects. $\quad$ 450 prospects

54. Find 134% of \$80. $\quad$ \$107.20

55. 275 sales is what percent of 1100 sales? $\quad$ 25%

56. 375 patients is what percent of 250 patients? $\quad$ 150%

Solve the application problems.

57. During the real estate crisis of 2008–2012, a mayor in California estimated that 18,300 of the 140,000 homes in his community went through foreclosure. Foreclosure occurs when the homeowner cannot make the payments and the mortgage company takes over ownership of the home. Find the percent of foreclosures to the nearest tenth of a percent. [3.4]   13.1%

58. The population of Elk Grove is 76,800 people. If 28.5% of the population is under the age of 18, find the number of people under the age of 18. [3.2]   21,888 people

59. The number of students enrolled in the Los Rios Community College District rose 9.5% this year. If the number of students enrolled this year is 64,040, find last year's enrollment. Round to the nearest whole number. [3.5]   58,484 students

60. As an antique dealer, Clarence Hanks charges a 25% selling fee. After deducting this fee, Hanks recently paid out $12,570 to his sellers. Find the total amount of his sales. [3.5] $16,760

61. Early investors in Dell Computer stock saw the value of the stock go up 900 times their original cost. What percent increase did they experience? Show your work explaining how you arrived at your answer. [3.1]   90,000%

62. The value of a stock used to be 6 times what it is worth today. The value today is what percent of the past value? Round to the nearest tenth of a percent. Show your work explaining how you arrived at your answer. [3.1]   16.7% (rounded)

63. The graph shows both actual minimum wage and the minimum wage in constant 2009 dollars which makes adjustment for the effects of inflation. Use the graph to estimate each of the following.

    a. The actual minimum wage for 1990 and 2010 and the percent increase from 1990 to 2010.   1990 — $3.25; 2010 — $7.25; 123.1%

    b. The minimum wage in constant 2009 dollars for 1990 and 2010 and the percent increase.   1990 — $5.75; 2010 — $7.00; 21.7%

    c. The year at which the minimum wage in constant 2009 dollars peaked, the amount in constant 2009 dollars at which it peaked, and the percent decline from that year to 2010.   Peaked in 1968; peaked at $10 per hour; 30% decline

    d. What has happened to the purchasing power of the minimum wage over the years?   The purchasing power of the minimun-wage worker has continued to fall since 1968. In other words, those working for minimum wage are worse off today than in 1968.

U.S. Federal Minimum Wage

Source: U.S. Bureau of Labor Statistics

64. Use the data in the table to construct a bar chart. [4.1]

PRICE OF A GALLON OF REGULAR GASOLINE			
Year	Price	Year	Price
1995	$1.14	2005	$2.28
2000	$1.50	2010	$2.91

Price of a Gallon of Regular Gasoline

65. Benson's Medical Supplies had quarterly sales of $85.2, $102, $92, and $124, in millions, last year. Show this data using both a bar chart and a pie chart. [4.1]

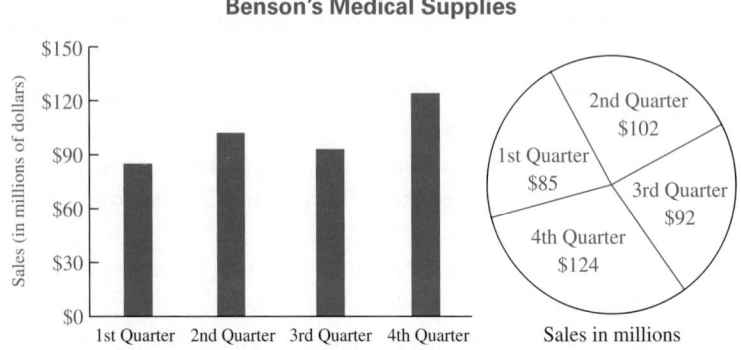

66. A farmer wants to install an irrigated field in the shape of a circle. He has yet to decide on the size of the field, but he is thinking in terms of a circle with a radius of between 200 and 800 meters. The larger the area, the deeper the irrigation well needed and the more expensive the pumping equipment, so he is worried about the cost. Construct a graph using the equation for the area of a circle: $A = \pi \cdot r^2$, where r is the radius of the circle and $\pi = 3.14159$. (*Hint:* Since the equation is nonlinear, you need to plot more than two points.) [4.2]

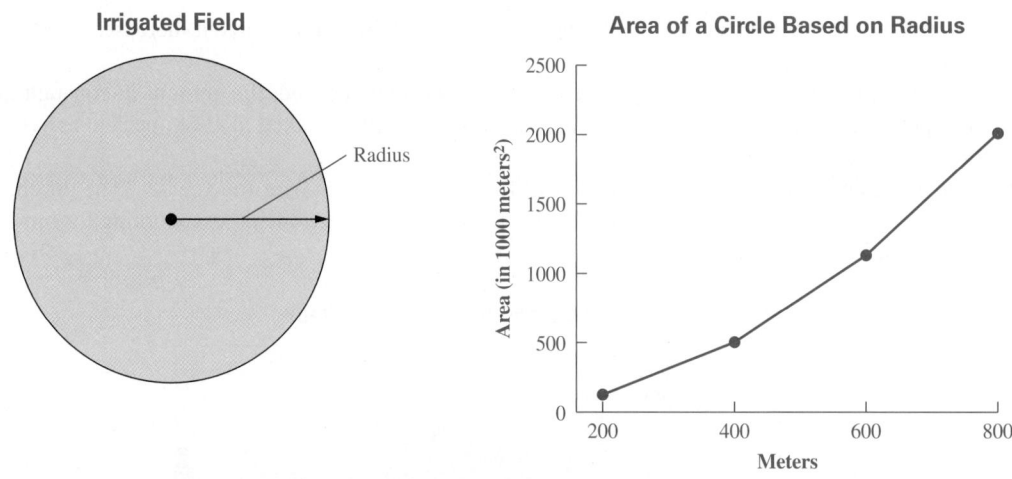

67. Glenda Hickey made the grades shown below. Find her grade point average to the nearest hundredth. (Note: A = 4, B = 3, C = 2, D = 1, and F = 0.) [4.3]

Course	Credits	Grade	
Math	3	B (=3)	
English	4	C (=2)	
Sociology	3	C (=2)	2.69
Music	3	A (=4)	
	Total: 13		

68. Find the mean, range, and standard deviation for the following data: 78, 82, 71, 69. Round to the nearest tenth where applicable. [4.3 and 4.4]   75; 13; 5.2

69. The diameter of a metal transmission shaft fits a normal curve, with a mean of 0.625 inch and a standard deviation of 0.045 inch. Find the percent of the shafts with a diameter of between 0.625 inch and 0.715 inch, assuming a normal curve. [4.5]   47.5%

70. The mean weight of a random sample of 80 professional football players is 258 pounds, and the standard deviation is 24 pounds. Assume the data are normally distributed and sketch the probability distribution showing the mean. Mark 3 standard deviations on each side of the mean. Find the percent of players with a weight of more than 1 standard deviation to the right of the mean ($258 + 24 = 282$). How many of the sample of 80 are expected to weigh more than 282 pounds? [4.5]

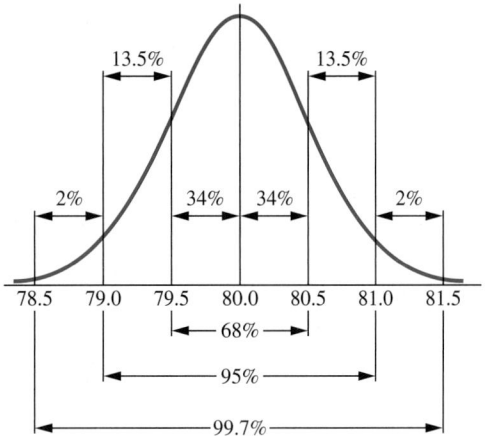

Area to the right of the mean: 0.50

Area in first standard deviation to the right of the mean: $\underline{-0.34}$

Area of interest   0.16

So, 16% of the players have a weight of more than 282 pounds. About 13 of the players should weigh more than 282 pounds.

71. The price of a network card for a computer network dropped from $1200 one year ago to $680 today. Find the price relative, rounded to the nearest whole number. [4.6]   57

72. A family of 4 in Chicago averaged $270 per month for food and beverages in 1984. Use Table 4.7 to estimate the monthly cost of food and beverages for a family of 4 in Chicago today. Round to the nearest dollar. [4.6] $602

javier brosch / Fotolia.com

Banking Services

Banks and savings institutions are far more than simply places to deposit funds and take out loans. They also offer many services, including automated teller machines (ATMs), credit cards, debit cards, safe deposit boxes, online banking, investment services, automatic withdrawals and payments, and even payroll services for businesses. This chapter explores electronic banking, checking accounts and registers, business checking account services, credit-card transactions, and bank reconciliation, which is also referred to as balancing a checking account.

The use of **electronic banking** and **electronic commerce (e-commerce)** on the Internet does not come without risk. For example, Figure 5.1 shows the number of complaints related to various Internet crimes on the government's Internet crime Web site, called IC3. Note that the number of complaints has increased dramatically since 2000. Internet theft now exceeds $500,000,000 per year, and identity theft is on the rise. You need to be careful!

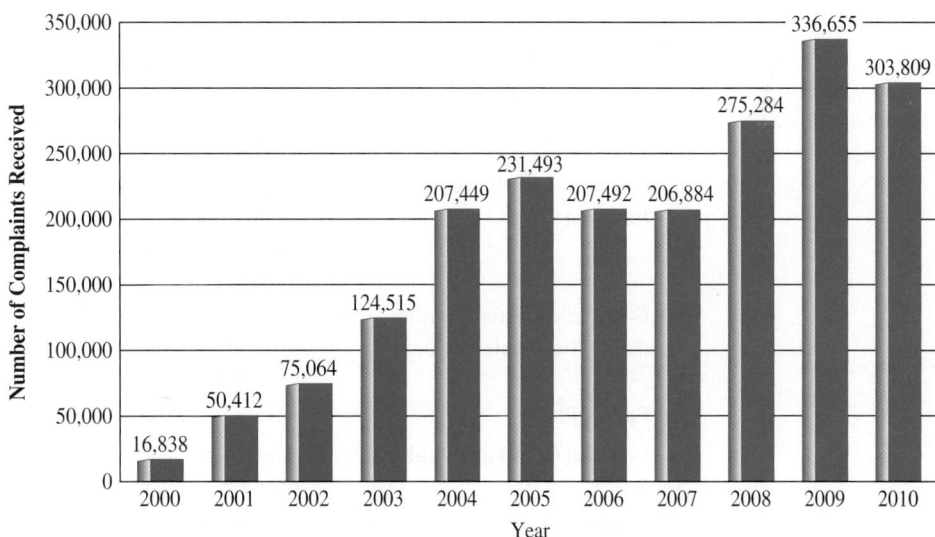

Number of Complaints Related to Online Internet Crime

Source: Internet Crime Complaint Center, U.S. Government.

Figure 5.1

▶ STOP&THINK

> Do you think that Internet crime will continue to be a problem in the future? List several ways in which people may be able to steal from you, or access your personal records, using the Internet. How can law enforcement control this growing threat? Can you think of job opportunities related to this growing threat? What training would be needed?

| 5.1 | **Checking Accounts and Check Registers** |

OBJECTIVES

1 *Compare traditional and electronic banking.*

2 *Know the types of checking accounts.*

3 *Identify the parts of a check.*

4 *Find the monthly service charges.*

5 *Identify the parts of a deposit slip.*

6 *Identify the parts of a check stub.*

7 *Complete the parts of a check register (transaction register).*

Objective

1 *Compare Traditional and Electronic Banking.* **Traditional banking** involves the use of paper checks and check registers to record deposits and checks. Many people still use the traditional system, as do some small businesses. Quite a few people use both traditional banking and electronic banking. However, increasing numbers of people are moving toward electronic banking.

Electronic banking allows customers to make financial transactions on secure Web sites through computer networks such as the Internet. Electronic banking is also referred to as **home banking, online banking**, or **Internet banking**. The table that follows shows some of the many features of electronic banking. Electronic commerce (EC) refers to the buying or selling of products or services over the Internet or other computer networks.

Feature	Description
Automated Teller Machine (ATM)	Worldwide network of electronic machines with 24-hour-a-day access. Used to make deposits, transfer money, or get cash. Use of the ATM machine at a bank at which you are not an account holder often results in a charge.
Direct Deposit/Direct Payment	Allows you to authorize regularly occurring deposits (e.g., payroll checks) directly into your checking account. It also allows you to authorize direct payments from your accounts (e.g., house payment or utility bills).
Electronic Funds Transfer (EFT)/Electronic Payment	Allows you to electronically make transfers of funds and pay bills. Many small and most large businesses use this feature extensively.
Pay by Phone	Allows you to use the phone to transfer money.
Personal Computer Banking	Allows you to use a computer hooked up to the Internet to remotely check balances, pay bills, and transfer funds.
Debit Card	A card that looks very similiar to a credit card. When used, the payment amount is immediately subtracted from the account, even if late at night. It requires a **personal identification number (PIN)**.
Prepaid Card	A card on which a user has stored monetary value before making any purchases.
Smart Card	A card with a microchip that receives electronic signals, makes calculations, and sends signals. Some can be used for identification.
Point-of-Sale (POS)	Refers to the checkout register where a transaction occurs in a business.

Source: Clendenen, Gary; Salzman, Stanley; Miller, Charles D., BUSINESS MATHEMATICS, 12th Ed., © 2012. Reprinted and Electronically reproduced by permission of Pearson Education, Inc., Upper Saddle River, New Jersey.

Let's compare the three common payment systems for a customer making a purchase at a merchant such as a Wal-Mart store.

Payment Method	
Check	Depending on the amount of the check, the teller may ask for identification and write on the back of the check. The check is soon deposited in Wal-Mart's local bank, which electronically requests payment from the customer's bank through a clearing house.
Credit Card	The customer swipes the card through the card reader. Depending on factors such as the amount of the charge and whether the customer has purchased there before, he or she may be asked to sign the credit slip. Often, the merchant's system will electronically check to make sure the credit card is valid.
Debit Card	The customer swipes the card through the reader and enters his or her personal identification number (PIN) when requested. Wal-Mart immediately routes the charge to a bank, which authorizes payment and debits the account balance, all within seconds or perhaps minutes.

In the past, it took a week to process a check. But now, checks are often processed in just a few days. However, the percent of all consumer payments made by check has fallen from 50% in 2000 to about 16% in 2012. So, the era of the check is slowly but surely coming to an end as checks are replaced by credit cards, debit cards, and **electronic payments**.

A credit-card transaction is not completely settled until the end of the customer's billing cycle. A debit-card transaction is completed in a few seconds or a few minutes at most. The cheapest and fastest of the three is the debit card, which is often processed over a network such as the Internet. According to msnmoney.com <http://msnmoney.com/>, Internet transaction costs average only $0.01. That compares to average costs for telephone transactions of $0.27, by mail at $0.73, and by a teller at $1.07.

However, electronic banking is not without problems. For example, it is relatively easy to authorize one or more payments for which you do not have available funds. This may occur when a payroll check is for less than expected, yet the date for a scheduled payment arrives. This has resulted in up to 10 charges for insufficient funds in one day for some individuals. Clearly, you need to monitor your account balances carefully and continuously.

Another problem is unauthorized use of your account, or even identity theft. **Identity theft** occurs when someone gathers enough information about you to fraudulently establish credit cards or borrow money using your name and personal information. It can be very difficult to stop the thief since it is difficult to find him or her. It is extremely important to protect your financial information as well as your log-on ID and password to all financial accounts. Experts recommend using complex passwords that cannot easily be discovered by criminals. They also recommend destroying documents that include credit-card numbers, account numbers, Social Security numbers, and all bank records.

Thief from the Past

Thief of Today

A trend called **mobile payments** uses specially equipped mobile phones instead of cash, checks, credit cards, or debit cards to make payments. For example, in some places you can pay charges for a commuter train simply by holding your phone as you walk through the turnstile. Some banks allow customers to use cell phones to check account balances on credit cards, pay bills, transfer money, and view transactions. Some banks even communicate balances using **texting**. Expect more applications in the future as banks look to both satisfy customers and cut costs.

Objective

2 *Know the Types of Checking Accounts.* Two main types of checking accounts are available.

Personal checking accounts are used by individuals. The bank supplies printed checks (normally charging a check-printing fee) for the customer to use. Some banks offer the checking account at no charge to the customer, but most require that a minimum monthly balance remain in the checking account. If the minimum balance is not maintained during any month, a service charge is applied to the account. Today, the **flat-fee checking account** is common. For a fixed charge per month, the bank supplies the checking account, check printing, a bank credit card, an ATM card, a debit card, and a host of other services. **Interest paid on checking account balances** is common with personal checking accounts. **Money market** accounts are offered by savings and loan associations, credit unions, and banks and are available to individuals as well as business customers. These accounts often require much higher minimum balances than regular accounts, but pay higher interest.

Business checking accounts often receive more services than do personal accounts. For example, banks often arrange to receive payments on debts payable to business firms. The bank automatically credits the amount to the business account.

> **NOTE** Those on vacation in Europe, Canada, Mexico, and many other countries can often obtain cash in the local currency using ATM machines.

Objective

3 *Identify the Parts of a Check.* Although the majority of transactions are done electronically today, there are still billions of checks written every year. So, it is important to understand checks. Figure 5.2 shows a diagram of one.

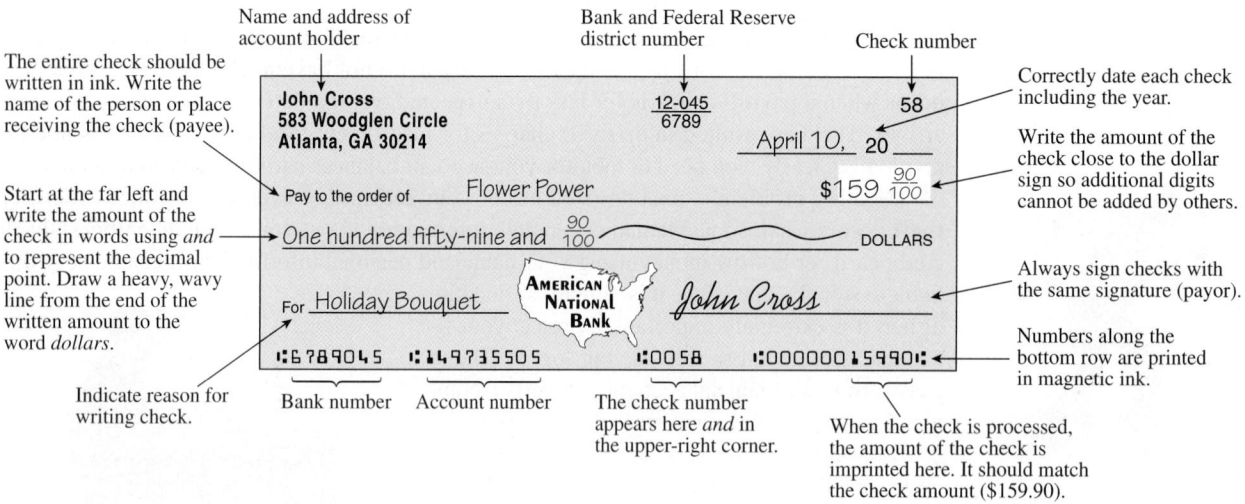

Figure 5.2

Objective

4 *Find the Monthly Service Charges.* Service charges for business checking accounts are based on the average balance for the period covered by the statement. This average balance determines the **maintenance charge per month**, to which a **per debit charge** (per check charge) is added. The charges generally apply regardless of the amount of account activity. Some typical bank charges for a business checking account appear in Table 5.1.

Table 5.1 TYPICAL BANK CHARGES FOR A BUSINESS CHECKING ACCOUNT

Average Balance	Maintenance Charge per Month	Per Check Charge
Less than $500	$12.00	$0.20
$500–$1999	$ 7.50	$0.20
$2000–$4999	$ 5.00	$0.10
$5000 or more	$ 0	$0

EXAMPLE 1   Finding the Checking Account Service Charge

Find the monthly service charge for the following business accounts using Table 5.1.

a. Pittsburgh Glass, 38 checks written, average balance $833

Solution

a. An account with an average balance between $500 and $1999 has a maintenance charge of $7.50 per month plus a debit (check) charge of $0.20 each.

Monthly charge = maintenance charge + number of checks × per check charge

= $7.50   +   38   × $0.20

= $15.10

b. Fargo Western Auto, 87 checks written, average balance $2367

Solution

a. An account with an average balance between $2000 and $4999 has a maintenance charge of $5.00 and a per check charge of $0.10.

Monthly charge = maintenance charge + number of checks × per check charge

= $5.00   +   87   × $0.10

= $13.70

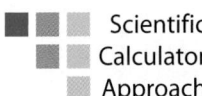 Scientific Calculator Approach

The calculator solutions to Example 1 use chain calculations, with the calculator observing the order of operations.

(a) 7.5 $\boxed{+}$ 38 $\boxed{\times}$ .2 $\boxed{=}$ 15.1

(b) 5 $\boxed{+}$ 87 $\boxed{\times}$ .1 $\boxed{=}$ 13.7

Objective

5 *Identify the Parts of a Deposit Slip.* Money, either cash or checks, is placed into a checking account with a **deposit slip** or **deposit ticket**, such as the one in Figure 5.3. The account number is written at the bottom of the slip in magnetic ink. The slip contains blanks on which are entered any cash (either currency or coins), as well as checks that are to be deposited.

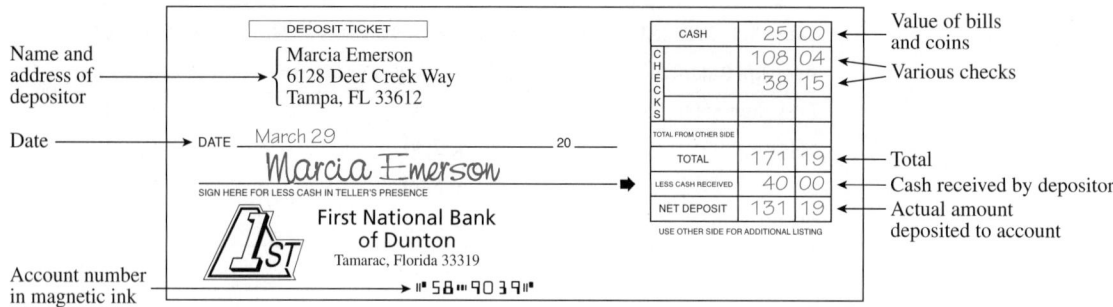

Name and address of depositor

Date

Account number in magnetic ink

Value of bills and coins

Various checks

Total

Cash received by depositor

Actual amount deposited to account

Figure 5.3

When a check is deposited, it should have "for deposit only" and either the depositor's signature or the company stamp placed on the back within 1.5 inches of the vertical top edge. In this way, if a check is lost or stolen on the way to the bank, it will be worthless to anyone finding it. Such an endorsement, which limits the ability to cash a check, is called a **restricted endorsement**. An example of a restricted endorsement is shown in Figure 5.4, along with two other types of endorsements. The most common endorsement by individuals is the **blank endorsement**, where only the name of the person being paid is signed. This endorsement should be used only at the moment of cashing a check. The **special endorsement**, used to pass on the check to someone else, might be used to pay a bill on another account.

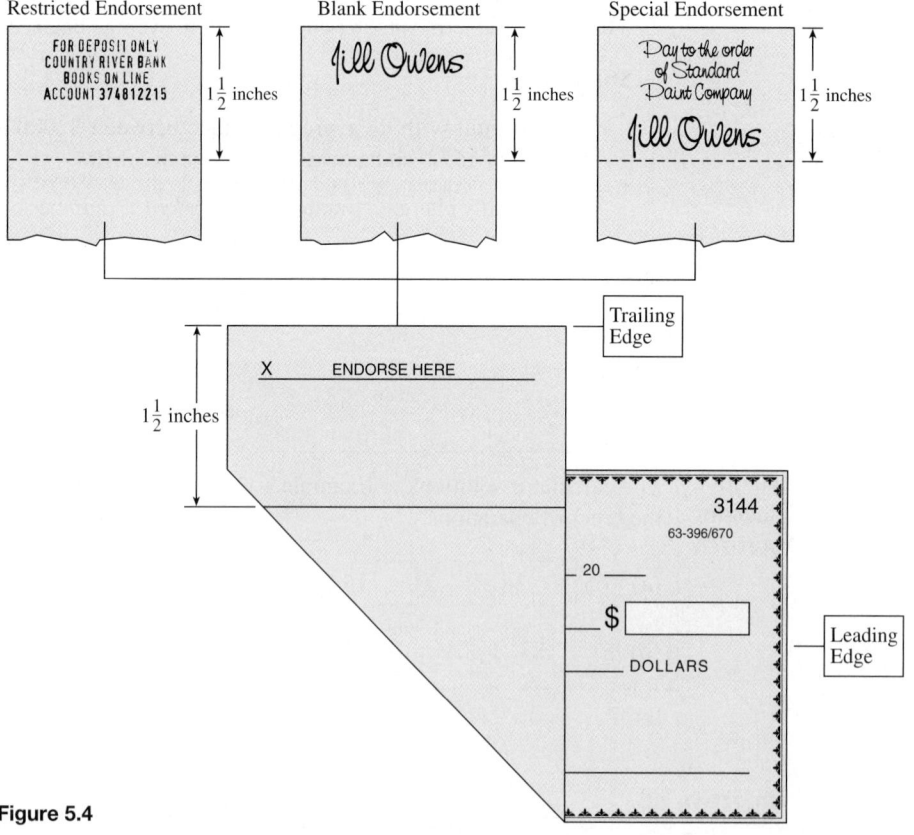

Figure 5.4

After the check is endorsed, it is normally cashed or deposited at a bank. The payee either is given cash or receives a credit in the account for the amount of the check. The check is then routed to a Federal Reserve bank, which forwards the check to the payer's bank. After going through this procedure, known as **processing**, the check is then **canceled** and returned to the payer. The check will now have additional processing information on its back, as shown in Figure 5.5.

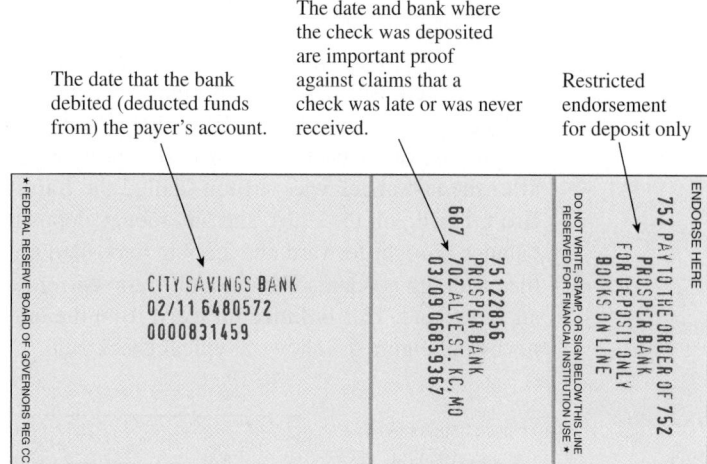

The date that the bank debited (deducted funds from) the payer's account.

The date and bank where the check was deposited are important proof against claims that a check was late or was never received.

Restricted endorsement for deposit only

Figure 5.5

A federal law known as **Check 21** took effect in October of 2004. Check 21, short for the 21st Century Act, resulted in several changes to the handling of checking account transactions. These changes in the federal banking laws allow banks to take electronic photos of all canceled checks and to exchange checks electronically. The bank retains the photos and the canceled checks are destroyed instead of being returned to the payer. The 1- to 5-day window between the time you write a check and the time your money is withdrawn from your account (known as "**float**") has been reduced greatly.

A two-sided commercial deposit slip is shown in Figure 5.6. Notice that more space is given for an itemized list of customers' checks that are being deposited to the business account. Some financial institutions require that the bank and Federal Reserve district numbers be shown in the description column of the deposit slip. These numbers appear in the upper center portion of the check and are identified in the sample check on page 192.

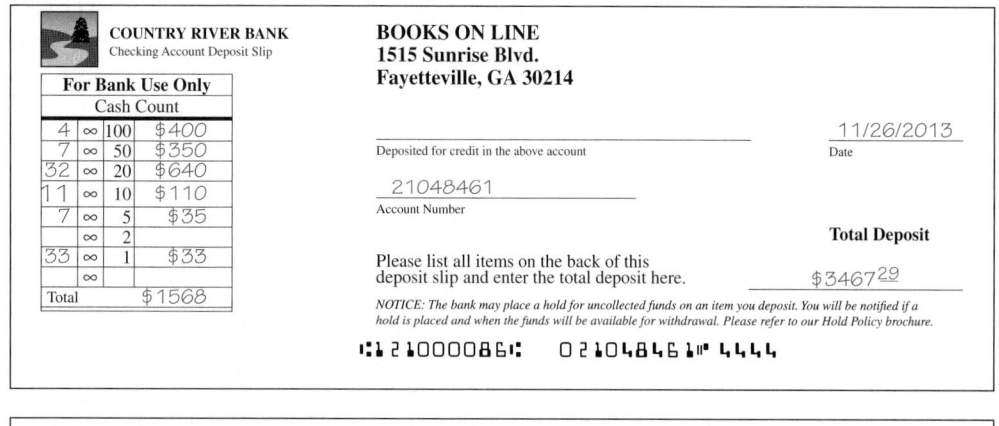

Please list each check separately Specify by number the bank on which each check is drawn	Description	Dollars	Cents
	Currency	$1568	00
	Coin	$135	00
	Checks - List Below		
1	90-7030/1	$38	18
2	11-8	$462	53
3	119	$79	24
4	2208	$57	14
5	514	$118	32
6	111	$68	76
7	35/8	$25	14
8	721	$99	05
9	76-218	$188	29
10	4421	$8	56
11	119	$220	15
12	218	$79	86
13	90-725	$26	19
14	90-725	$18	74
15	71-668	$134	55
16	119	$156	24
17	721	$73	35
18			
19			
20			
21			
22			
23			
24			
25			
26			
27			
28			
29			
30			
31			
32			
33			
34			
35			
36			
	TOTAL	$3467	29
	Please enter total on front of this slip		

Figure 5.6

Objective

6 *Identify the Parts of a Check Stub.* A record must be kept of every deposit made and every check written. Business firms normally do this with one **check stub** for each check. These stubs provide room to list the date, the person or firm to whom the check will be paid, and the purpose of the check. Also, the stub provides space to record the balance in the account after the last check was written (called the **balance brought forward**, abbreviated Bal. Bro't. For'd., on the stub), and any money deposited since the last check was written. The balance brought forward and amount deposited are added to provide the current balance in the checking account. The amount of the current check is then subtracted, and a new balance is found. This **balance forward** from the bottom of the stub should be written on the next stub. Figure 5.7 shows a typical check stub.

Figure 5.7

EXAMPLE **2** **Completing a Check Stub**

Check number 2724 is made out on June 8 to Lillburn Utilities as payment for water and power. Assume that the check is for $182.15, that the balance brought forward is $4245.36, and that deposits of $337.71 and $193.17 have been made since the last check was written. Complete the check stub as shown in Figure 5.8.

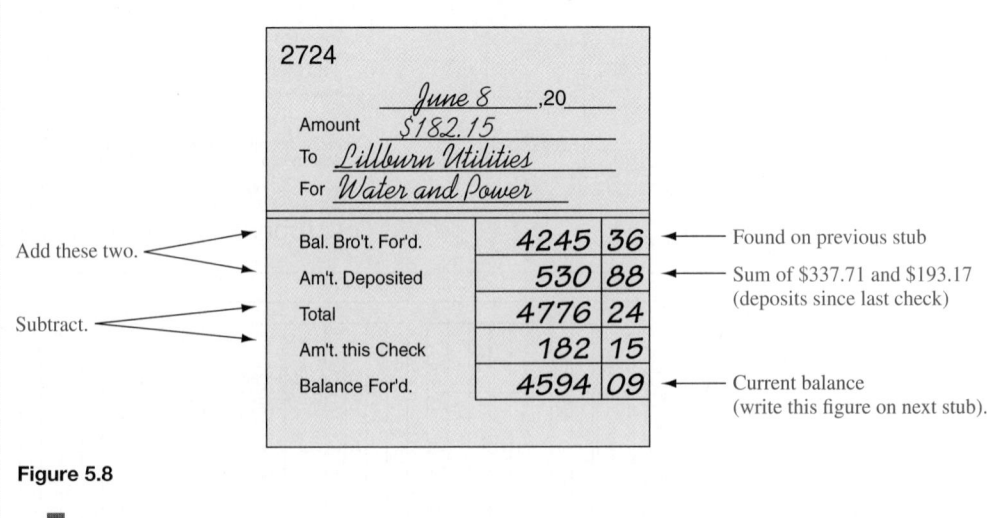

Figure 5.8

Banks offer many styles of checkbooks. Notice that the two styles shown in Figure 5.9 offer two stubs and may be used for payrolls. The stub next to the check can be used as the employee's record of earnings and deductions. The second style provides space on the check itself for listing a group of invoices or bills that are being paid with that same check.

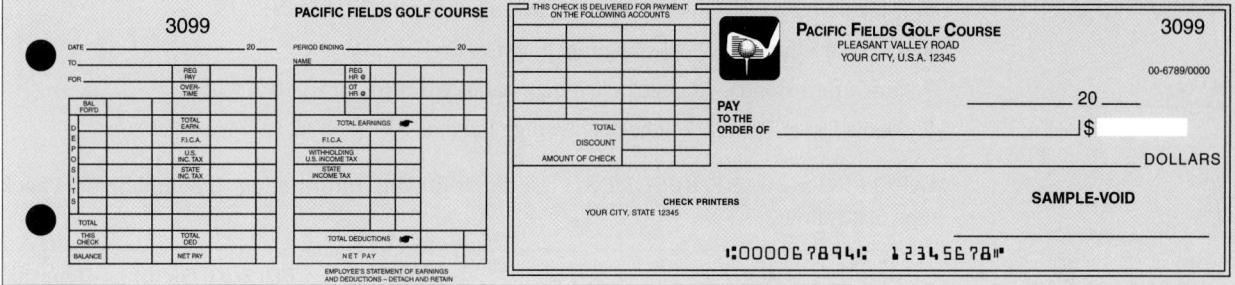

Figure 5.9

Objective

7

Complete the Parts of a Check Register (Transaction Register). Some depositors prefer a check register to the check stubs, while others use both. The **check register**, also called a **transaction register**, shows at a glance the checks written and deposits made, as seen in Figure 5.10. The column headed ✓ is used to check off each check or check image after it is received back from the bank.

CHECK NO.	DATE	CHECK ISSUED TO	AMOUNT OF CHECK		✓	DATE OF DEP.	AMOUNT OF DEPOSIT		BALANCE	
			BALANCE BROUGHT FORWARD →						3518	72
e*	5/8	Swan Brothers	378	93					3139	79
1436	5/8	Class Acts	25	14					3114	65
1437	5/9	Mirror Lighting	519	65					2595	00
		Deposit				5/10	3821	17	6416	17
e	5/10	Woodlake Auditorium	750	00					5666	17
		Deposit				5/12	500	00	6166	17
1438	5/12	Rick's Clowns	170	80					5995	37
1439	5/14	Y.M.C.A.	219	17					5776	20
	5/14	ATM	120	00					5656	20
		Deposit				5/15	326	15	5982	35
e	5/16	Stage Door Playhouse	825	00					5157	35
e	5/17	Gilbert Eckern	1785	00					3372	35
		Deposit				5/19	1580	25	4952	60

e = refers to an electronic payment or debit.

Figure 5.10

NOTE ATM transactions for cash withdrawals and purchases must be entered on check stubs or in the check register. The transaction amount and the charge for each transaction must then be subtracted to maintain an accurate balance.

5.1	**Exercises**

Use Table 5.1 to find the monthly checking account service charge for the following business accounts.

1. Maxine Vitamins, 92 checks, average balance $4618 $14.20
2. Mandarin Restaurant, 76 checks, average balance $3318 $12.60
3. Auto Parts, 112 checks, average balance $7832 $0
4. Quality Gifts, 64 checks, average balance $3490 $11.40
5. Mak's Smog and Tune, 48 checks, average balance $1763 $17.10
6. Cellular One, 315 checks, average balance $6424 $0
7. Jim's Bail Bonds, 28 checks, average balance $1965 $13.10
8. Ben's Lawn Repair, 74 checks, average balance $875 $22.30

MAINTAINING BANK RECORDS   Use the following information to complete the check stubs that follow.

	Date	To	For	Amount	Bal. Bro't. For'd.	Deposits
9.	Mar. 8	Patty Demko	Tutoring	$380.71	$3971.28	$79.26
10.	Oct. 15	Elizabeth Linton	Rent	$850.00	$2973.09	$1853.24
11.	Dec. 4	Paul's Pools	Chemicals	$37.52	$1126.73	—

9.

857		
Mar. 8 _____ 20 ____		
Amount $380.71		
To Patty Demko		
For Tutoring		
Bal. Bro't. For'd.	3971	28
Am't. Deposited	79	26
Total	4050	54
Am't. this Check	380	71
Balance For'd.	3669	83

10.

1248		
Oct. 15 _____ 20 ____		
Amount $850.00		
To Elizabeth Linton		
For Rent		
Bal. Bro't. For'd.	2973	09
Am't. Deposited	1853	24
Total	4826	33
Am't. this Check	850	00
Balance For'd.	3976	33

11.

735		
Dec. 4 _____ 20 ____		
Amount $37.52		
To Paul's Pools		
For Chemicals		
Bal. Bro't. For'd.	1126	73
Am't. Deposited		
Total	1126	73
Am't. this Check	37	52
Balance For'd.	1089	21

12. List and explain at least six parts of a check. Draw a sketch showing where these parts appear on a check. (See Objective 1.)

 13. Explain to a friend at least two advantages and two possible disadvantages of using an ATM card. Do this in writing. (See Objective 2.)

 14. Write an explanation for a friend of two types of check endorsements. Describe where these endorsements must be placed. (See Objective 4.)

 15. Explain in your own words the factors that determine the service charges on a business checking account. (See Objective 3.)

COMPLETING CHECK STUBS   Using the information below, complete the following check stubs for Books On Line. The balance brought forward for check stub 5311 is $7223.69.

CHECKS WRITTEN						DEPOSITS MADE	
Number	Date	To	For	Amount		Date	Amount
5311	Oct. 7	Anessa Davis	Books	$1250.80		Oct. 8	$752.18
5312	Oct. 10	County Clerk	License	$39.12		Oct. 9	$23.32
5313	Oct. 15	United Parcel	Shipping	$356.28		Oct. 13	$1025.45

16.

```
5311

              Oct. 7          20 ____
Amount    $ 1250.80
To   Anessa Davis
For  Books

  Bal. Bro't. For'd.        7223 | 69
  Am't. Deposited
  Total                     7223 | 69
  Am't. this Check          1250 | 80
  Balance For'd.            5972 | 89
```

17.

```
5312

              Oct. 10         20 ____
Amount    $39.12
To   County Clerk
For  License

  Bal. Bro't. For'd.        5972 | 89
  Am't. Deposited            752 | 18
                             23 | 32
  Total                     6748 | 39
  Am't. this Check            39 | 12
  Balance For'd.            6709 | 27
```

18.

```
5313

              Oct. 15         20 ____
Amount    $356.28
To   United Parcel
For  Shipping

  Bal. Bro't. For'd.        6709 | 27
  Am't. Deposited           1025 | 45
  Total                     7734 | 72
  Am't. this Check           356 | 28
  Balance For'd.            7378 | 44
```

BANK BALANCES For Exercises 19–22, complete the balance column in the following check registers after each check or deposit transaction. Electronic payments and debits are indicated using *e*.

19.

CHECK NO.	DATE	CHECK ISSUED TO	AMOUNT OF CHECK		✓	DATE OF DEP.	AMOUNT OF DEPOSIT		BALANCE	
						BALANCE BROUGHT FORWARD →			1629	86
e	7/3	Ahwahnee Hotel	250	45					1379	41
862	7/5	Willow Creek	149	00					1230	41
863	7/5	Void								
		Deposit				7/7	117	73	1348	14
864	7/9	Del Campo High School	69	80					1278	34
		Deposit				7/10	329	86	1608	20
		Deposit				7/12	418	30	2026	50
e	7/14	Big 5 Sporting Goods	109	76					1916	74
e	7/14	Dr. Yates	614	12					1302	62
865	7/16	Greyhound	32	18					1270	44
		Deposit				7/16	520	95	1791	39

20.

CHECK NO.	DATE	CHECK ISSUED TO	AMOUNT OF CHECK		✓	DATE OF DEP.	AMOUNT OF DEPOSIT		BALANCE	
						BALANCE BROUGHT FORWARD →			832	15
e	3/17	AirTouch Cellular	257	29					574	86
1122	3/18	Curry Village	190	50					384	36
		Deposit				3/19	78	29	462	65
		Deposit				3/21	157	42	620	07
e	3/22	San Juan District	38	76					581	31
1123	3/23	Macy's Gourmet	175	88					405	43
		Deposit				3/23	379	28	784	71
1124	3/24	Class Video	197	20					587	51
e	3/24	Water World	25	10					562	41
e	3/25	Bel Air Market	75	00					487	41
		Deposit				3/28	722	35	1209	76

21.

CHECK NO.	DATE	CHECK ISSUED TO	AMOUNT OF CHECK		✓	DATE OF DEP.	AMOUNT OF DEPOSIT		BALANCE	
						BALANCE BROUGHT FORWARD →			3852	48
e	12/6	Web Masters	143	16					3709	32
e	12/7	Water and Power	118	40					3590	92
		Deposit				12/8	286	32	3877	24
	12/10	ATM (cash)	80	00					3797	24
2310	12/11	Ann Kuick	986	22					2811	02
e	12/11	Account Temps	375	50					2435	52
		Deposit				12/14	1201	82	3637	34
e	12/14	Central Chevrolet	735	68					2901	66
2311	12/15	Miller Mining	223	94					2677	72
		Deposit				12/17	498	01	3175	73
2312	12/18	Federal Parcel	78	24					3097	49

22.

CHECK NO.	DATE	CHECK ISSUED TO	AMOUNT OF CHECK	✓	DATE OF DEP	AMOUNT OF DEPOSIT	BALANCE
		BALANCE BROUGHT FORWARD →					8284 18
e	6/4	Valley Electric	188 18				8096 00
e	6/5	Harrold Ford	433 56				7662 44
1919	6/5	Paul Altier (photography)	138 17				7524 27
		Deposit			6/6	453 28	7977 55
		Deposit			6/8	1475 69	9453 24
e	6/9	U.S. Rentals	335 82				9117 42
1920	6/11	Quick Turn Merchandise	573 27				8544 15
	6/11	ATM (wine)	16 35				8527 80
1921	6/14	Broadly Plumbing	195 15				8332 65
		Deposit			6/16	635 85	8968 50
e	6/16	National Dues F.F.A.	317 20				8651 30

5.2	**Checking Services and Credit-Card Transactions**

OBJECTIVES

1 *Identify bank services available to customers.*

2 *Deposit credit-card transactions.*

3 *Calculate the discount fee on credit-card deposits.*

Objective

1

Identify Bank Services Available to Customers. Banks must make a profit in order to survive and prosper. Furthermore, banking has become so fiercely competitive that bank managers must continually look for ways to increase revenue and cut costs. They have cut costs by moving to online banking and increased revenue by charging for many services. Listed below are some of the services that banks offer along with possible associated charges. Of course, charges vary greatly and also depend on the amount the customer has on deposit at the bank. Fees are usually waived for individuals with a lot of money on deposit. Still, U.S. banks pull in over $50 billion a year in charges!

ATM services—Banks often let their own customers use the bank's ATM machine for free but charge $1.00 or more to a noncustomer. The ATM charges can be even higher for any out-of-country users.

Bank teller—Some banks now charge if you talk to a teller.

Cashier's check (bank check)—This is a check guaranteed by the bank. The charge for a cashier's check depends on the amount of the check, but it is commonly $5 or more.

Money order—A money order is proof that funds have been prepaid in cash. In addition to banks, retail stores such as Wal-Mart and even U.S. post offices sell money orders. Depending on the amount of money involved, money orders can cost up to $4.

Notary—Some documents require a signature by a person called a notary. Once this service was free, but bank customers now often have to pay for it.

Online banking—Online banking allows individuals to check account balances, make payments, and transfer funds between accounts from any personal computer anywhere in the world. This service is often free but some banks charge a small fee.

Overdraft or insufficient funds (NSF)—You will get an insufficient funds charge of $20 to $45 if you write a check for more than you have on deposit in your account. The same charge may be applied if a check is returned because it was not completed correctly.

Overdraft protection—The bank will honor the check even though there are currently insufficient funds in the account to cover it. Charges for overdraft protection vary, but some banks give overdraft protection to those with sufficient funds on deposit, for example, in a certificate of deposit.

Returned deposit—A fee of $10 to $40 is charged on any item deposited that is then returned to the bank due to insufficient funds.

Stop payment—Banks charge as much as $35 to stop payment on a check you have written.

The following table shows that students rely widely on credit cards.

Students and Credit Cards

75% have credit cards.

25% have paid a late fee.

Average balance is $2200 for undergraduates, $5800 for graduates.

Devote 22% of their income to servicing debt.

Some students see a penalty of 30% after one late payment.

Source: Based on data from Nellie Mae.

Objective

2 *Deposit Credit-Card Transactions.* Most retailers and chain stores complete credit-card transactions electronically. After your credit card is swiped, the system either authorizes or does not authorize the purchase, depending on your credit. The verification of your ability to buy and the actual purchase both happen at the same time. To be effective, this process requires a high-speed network link to the merchant's bank. The magnetic "strip" on the back of the credit card contains information that uniquely identifies you, the number of the credit card, and the bank that issued the card. The use of electronic verification systems allows merchants to eliminate paper transactions and reduce costs.

Objective

3 *Calculate the Discount Fee on Credit-Card Deposits.* **Credit-card sales** are very common in business. Even customers that are not comfortable using the Web for purchases often use credit cards without hesitation. The customer swipes his or her credit card at the point-of-sale terminal, which scans information from the card. The system seeks authorization for the charge, which is quickly given or denied. Credit charges are accumulated by the financial institution in batches and then submitted for funding, which takes a few days. The customer receives a bill at the end of the month and has the option to pay all or part of the balance due (See Figure 5.12).

"How It Works"

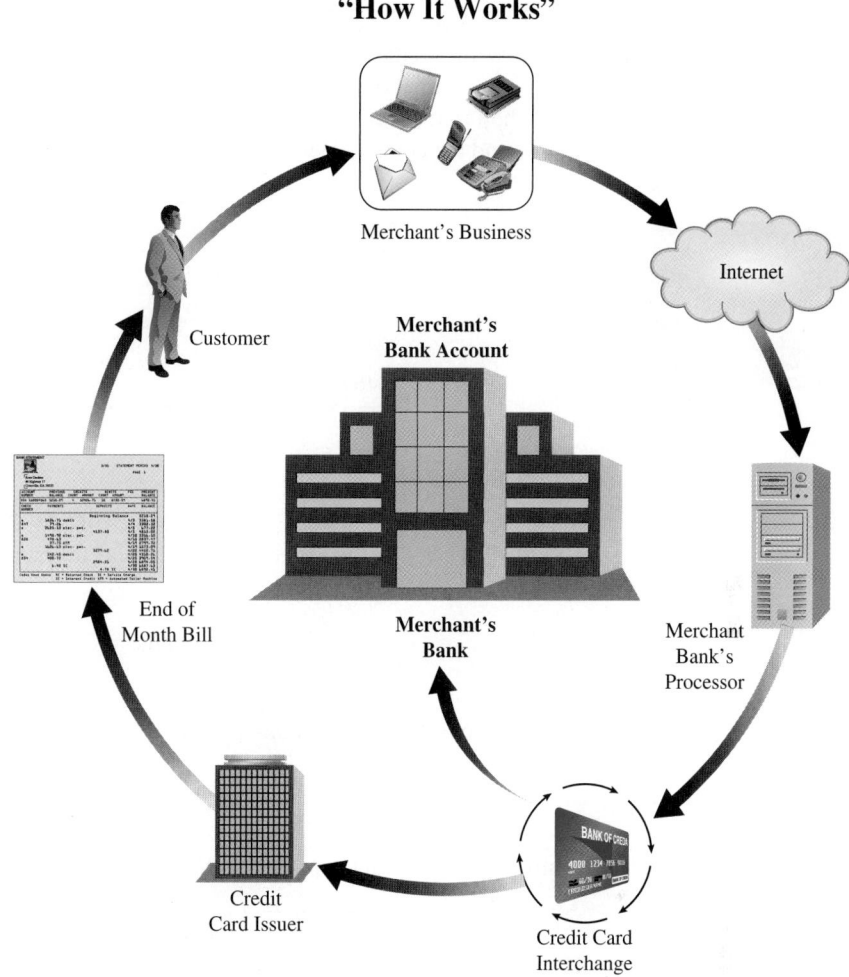

Source: Clendenen, Gary; Salzman, Stanley; Miller, Charles D., BUSINESS MATHEMATICS, 12th Ed., c 2012. Reprinted and Electronically reproduced by permission of Pearson Education, Inc., Upper Saddle River, New Jersey.

Figure 5.12

The cost to the merchant of processing credit-card transactions is often higher than processing debit-card transactions. In fact, merchants must pay a fee averaging about 2% on credit-card sales made on VISA® and MasterCard®. The merchant is willing to pay the fee since it increases sales. The banks that offer the credit cards like this business because it generates a lot of income. Many consumers like to use credit cards since it allows them to either delay the payment until the end of the billing cycle or spread the cost out over several months. To avoid the fee charged by the issuer of the credit card, some merchants offer discounts to customers who pay using cash, debit, or check. Still, most merchants take payments in any form to maximize sales.

Finding Net Deposit for Credit-Card Sales

1. Net credit card sales = total credit card sales − total credit card refunds
2. Total fee = appropriate percent × net credit card sales
3. Net deposit = total credit card sales − total fee

EXAMPLE **1** **Find the Fees and Net Deposit on Credit-Card Sales**

Here are some credit-card sales and credit-card refunds made one afternoon at Rose Gardens. Find the total credit card sales, the total credit card refunds, and the net credit card sales. Then find the bank fee charged, assuming a fee of 2% of the net credit card sales. Finally, find the amount deposited to Rose Garden's checking account.

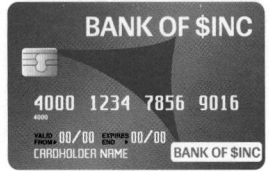

CREDIT-CARD SALES		CREDIT-CARD REFUNDS
$82.31	$146.50	$43.83
$38.18	$78.80	$85.95
$249.33	$470.15	
$46.80	$320.90	

Solution

Add the preceding to find total credit-card sales of $1432.97 and total credit-card refunds of $129.78. Then find the net credit-card sales as follows.

$$\begin{aligned} \text{Total sales} &= \$1432.97 \\ \text{Total refunds} &= \underline{-129.78} \\ \text{Net sales} &\quad \mathbf{\$1303.19} \end{aligned}$$

The bank fee is 2% of net credit-card sales.

$$\begin{aligned} \textbf{Bank fee} &= \textbf{2\% of \$1303.19} \\ &= \textbf{\$26.06} \quad \textbf{(rounded)} \end{aligned}$$

Finally, find the amount deposited to Rose Garden's checking account.

$$\text{Amount} = \$1303.19 - \mathbf{\$26.06} = \$1277.13$$

Interestingly, some banks that issue MasterCard® and Visa® give rewards to credit-card users. When you receive cash back or some other reward based on your credit-card use, you are really getting a small rebate based on your previous credit-card use.

In 2009, a credit-card reform bill was signed into law. It resulted in the following changes, which were designed to help people better understand and, therefore, manage their credit-card debt.

1. Limits when credit-card interest rates can be increased on existing balances

2. Prohibits over-limit fees unless consumers allow transactions exceeding their credit limit to go through rather than be denied.

3. Requires fees for late payments and other penalty fees to be reasonable.

4. Bans credit cards for people under 21 unless they have adult cosigners or show proof that they have the means to repay the debts.

5. Requires card issuers to disclose how long it will take to pay off a credit-card balance if the cardholder pays the minimum payment each month.

| **5.2** | **Exercises** |

For each of the following businesses, find (a) the total charges, (b) the total credits, (c) the amount of the gross deposit, (d) the amount of the discount charged at the statement date, and (e) the amount of credit given after the fee is subtracted.

1. **CREDIT-CARD DEPOSITS** Fry's Electronics does most of its business on a cash basis or through its own credit department, although it does honor major bank charge cards. In a recent period, the business had the following credit-card charges and credits. The bank charges a 3% discount.

Sales		Credits	
$78.56	$38.15	$29.76	(a) $2419.76
$875.29	$18.46	$102.15	(b) $203.86
$330.82	$22.13	$71.95	(c) $2215.90
$55.24	$707.37		(d) $66.48
$47.83	$245.91		(e) $2149.42

2. **CREDIT-CARD DEPOSITS** Baker Auto accepts credit cards from customers for work ranging from oil changes to small repairs on automobiles. The following credit-card transactions occurred during a recent period. The bank charges a 2% discount.

Sales		Credits	
$66.68	$18.95	$62.16	(a) $1595.36
$119.63	$496.28	$106.62	(b) $207.69
$53.86	$21.85	$38.91	(c) $1387.67
$178.62	$242.78		(d) $27.75
$219.78	$176.93		(e) $1359.92

3. **CREDIT-CARD DEPOSITS** Bayside Jeepers does most of its business on a cash basis or through its own credit department, although it does honor major bank charge cards. In a recent period, the business had the following credit-card charges and credits. The bank charges a 4% discount.

Sales			Credits	
$25.18	$77.51	$14.73	$38.15	(a) $1591.44
$15.73	$357.18	$106.78	$106.86	(b) $189.39
$138.97	$72.73	$88.34	$44.38	(c) $1402.05
$58.73	$29.68	$72.21		(d) $56.08
$255.18	$15.76	$262.73		(e) $1345.97

4. **CREDIT-CARD DEPOSITS** Jamison Hardware had the following credit-card transactions during a recent period. The bank charges a 2% discount.

Sales		Credits	
$42.60	$29.50	$22.10	(a) $381.61
$38.25	$72.85	$14.67	(b) $67.07
$16.60	$19.30	$30.30	(c) $314.54
$52.40	$6.75		(d) $6.29
$14.38	$88.98		(e) $308.25

5. **CREDIT-CARD DEPOSITS**   Maureen Tomlin Studios had the following credit-card transactions during a recent period. The bank charges a 3% discount.

Sales		Credits	
$7.84	$98.56	$13.86	(a) $1064.72
$33.18	$318.72	$58.97	(b) $72.83
$50.76	$116.35		(c) $991.89
$12.72	$23.78		(d) $29.76
$9.36	$38.95		(e) $962.13
$118.68	$235.82		

6. **CREDIT-CARD DEPOSITS**   Jena's Small Gifts is located near a college campus. The following credit-card charges and credits took place during a recent period. The bank charges a 2% discount.

Sales		Credits	
$16.40	$184.16	$23.17	(a) $516.15
$18.98	$137.61	$7.26	(b) $44.96
$6.76	$24.69	$14.53	(c) $471.19
$11.75	$86.17		(d) $9.42
$29.63			(e) $461.77

 7. List and describe in your own words four services offered to business checking account customers. (See Objective 1.)

 8. The merchant accepting a credit card from a customer must pay a fee of 2% to 5% of the transaction amount. Why is the merchant willing to do this? Who really pays this fee?

5.3 Reconciliation

OBJECTIVES

1 *Know the importance of reconciling a checking account.*

2 *Reconcile a bank statement with a checkbook.*

3 *List the outstanding checks.*

4 *Find the adjusted bank balance or current balance.*

5 *Use the T-account form of reconciliation.*

Objective

1 *Know the Importance of Reconciling a Checking Account.* Once a month, a bank creates a bank statement that shows all activity for each account. Some customers want the bank to mail them a copy. Others prefer to look at the **bank statement** on the bank's Web site, where it can also be printed out if desired. The bank statement shows all deposits and credits as well as disbursements, such as checks, debits, electronic payments, ATM cash withdrawals, and any fees. Here is a list of a few reasons for an account owner to look at the bank statement every month.

1. The fee charged by the bank often varies from month to month.

2. A deposited check may be returned due to **insufficient funds**, also called **nonsufficient funds**. The amount of the check and any fees must be deducted. **Returned checks** are also called **bounced checks**.

3. A scheduled deposit may or may not have been made.

4. The account holder may have made an error in the check register.

If someone owed you money and was supposed to make an automatic payment into your checking account but did not do so one month, would you be concerned? Of course; funds in a bank account are an asset that individuals and business managers should manage carefully.

Objective

2 *Reconcile a Bank Statement with a Checkbook.* The process of checking the bank statement against the check register is called **reconciliation**. Figure 5.13 shows a bank statement for Rose Gardens. Two columns of information on the bank statement are further explained below.

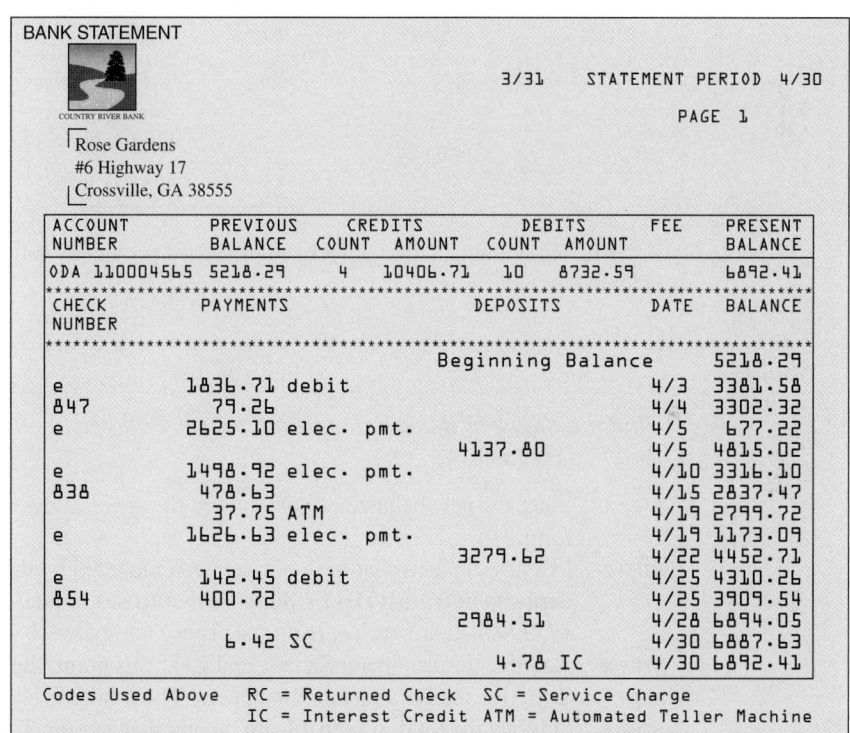

BANK STATEMENT

COUNTRY RIVER BANK

3/31   STATEMENT PERIOD 4/30
PAGE 1

Rose Gardens
#6 Highway 17
Crossville, GA 38555

ACCOUNT NUMBER	PREVIOUS BALANCE	CREDITS COUNT	AMOUNT	DEBITS COUNT	AMOUNT	FEE	PRESENT BALANCE
ODA 110004565	5218.29	4	10406.71	10	8732.59		6892.41

CHECK NUMBER	PAYMENTS	DEPOSITS	DATE	BALANCE
		Beginning Balance		5218.29
e	1836.71 debit		4/3	3381.58
847	79.26		4/4	3302.32
e	2625.10 elec. pmt.		4/5	677.22
		4137.80	4/5	4815.02
e	1498.92 elec. pmt.		4/10	3316.10
838	478.63		4/15	2837.47
	37.75 ATM		4/19	2799.72
e	1626.63 elec. pmt.		4/19	1173.09
		3279.62	4/22	4452.71
e	142.45 debit		4/25	4310.26
854	400.72		4/25	3909.54
		2984.51	4/28	6894.05
	6.42 SC		4/30	6887.63
		4.78 IC	4/30	6892.41

Codes Used Above   RC = Returned Check   SC = Service Charge
IC = Interest Credit   ATM = Automated Teller Machine

Source: Clendenen, Gary; Salzman, Stanley; Miller, Charles D., BUSINESS MATHEMATICS, 12th Ed., c 2012. Reprinted and Electronically reproduced by permission of Pearson Education, Inc., Upper Saddle River, New Jersey.

Figure 5.13

PAYMENTS—include checks, electronic payments, debits, electronic transfers of funds to other accounts, ATM withdrawals, returned checks, and fees.
DEPOSITS—include regular deposits, electronic deposits, transfers of money into the account, and interest credited during the month.

Electronic transfers are easy to track since they show up very quickly on the bank's computer system. Checks are different. For example, you may send your aunt a check for her birthday that she does not deposit for 5 weeks. A firm often has written checks that do not yet show up on the bank statement. These unpaid checks are called **checks outstanding**. The next example shows how to identify checks outstanding and reconcile an account.

> **EXAMPLE** | **1** | **Reconciling a Checking Account**
>
> The most recent bank statement for Rose Gardens shows a balance of $6892.41 after a bank service charge of $6.42 and an interest credit of $4.78. The check register for Rose Gardens shows a current balance of $7576.38. Reconcile the account as follows.

Objective

3

List the Outstanding Checks. Find the checks outstanding by comparing the list of checks on the bank statement against the list of checks written by the firm. You may wish to put a check mark on the bank statement and/or check register as you compare them. In particular, note any differences in the amounts for any check. Here are the outstanding checks.

NUMBER	AMOUNT
846	$42.73
852	$598.71
853	$68.12
857	$79.80
858	$160.30

After listing the outstanding checks in the space provided on the form, total them. The total is $949.66.

Objective

4

Find the Adjusted Bank Balance or Current Balance. Follow the steps listed here and shown in Figure 5.14.

STEP 1 Enter the new balance of $6892.41 in the space at the top of the reconciliation form.

STEP 2 List any deposits that have not yet been recorded by the bank. These are called **deposits in transit (DIT)**. Suppose that Rose Gardens has deposits of $892.41 and $739.58 that are not yet recorded. These numbers are written at Step 2 on the form.

STEP 3 Add the numbers from Steps 1 and 2. At this point, the total is $8524.40.

STEP 4 Write the total of outstanding checks. The total is $949.66.

STEP 5 Subtract the total in Step 4 from the number in Step 3. The result here is $7574.74, which is the **adjusted bank balance**, or the current balance. This number should represent the current checking-account balance.

Now look at the firm's own records.

STEP 6 List the firm's check register balance of $7576.38 on line 6 on the form.

STEP 7 Enter total service charges of $6.42 on line 7.

STEP 8 Subtract the charges on line 7 from the checkbook balance on line 6 to get $7569.96.

STEP 9 Enter the interest credit of $4.78 on line 9. This is interest paid on money in the account.

STEP 10 Add the interest on line 9 to line 8 to get $7574.74, the same result as in step 5.

Since the result from step 10 is the same as the result from step 5, the account is **balanced** (reconciled). The correct current balance in the account is $7574.74.

Reconciliation		
Checks Outstanding		
Number	Amount	
846	$	42 | 73
852	598 | 71	
853	68 | 12	
857	79 | 80	
858	160 | 30	
Total	$	949 | 66

Compare the list of checks paid by the bank with your records. List and total the checks not yet paid.

(1) Enter new balance from bank statement: $ 6892.41

(2) List any deposits made by you and not   + 892.41
      yet recorded by the bank: + 739.58
                                              +
                                              +

(3) Add all numbers from lines above.
      Total: 8524.40
(4) Write total of checks outstanding: − 949.66

(5) Subtract (4) from (3).
      This is adjusted bank balance: $ 7574.74

To reconcile your records:

(6)   List your checkbook balance: $ 7576.38

(7)   Write the total of any fees or charges deducted
       by the bank and not yet subtracted by you from
       your checkbook: − 6.42

(8)   Subtract line (7) from line (6).   7569.96

(9)   Enter interest credit: (Add to your checkbook)   + 4.78

(10) Add line (9) to line (8).
       Adjusted checkbook balance. $ 7574.74

New balance of your account; this number should be same as (5).

Source: Clendenen, Gary; Salzman, Stanley; Miller, Charles D., BUSINESS MATHEMATICS, 12th Ed., c 2012. Reprinted and Electronically reproduced by permission of Pearson Education, Inc., Upper Saddle River, New Jersey.

Figure 5.14

There are several typical reasons checking accounts do not balance.

Why Checking Accounts Do Not Balance

- Forgetting to enter a check in the check register.
- Forgetting to enter a deposit in the check register.
- Transposing numbers (writing $961.20 as $916.20, for example).
- Making addition or subtraction errors.
- Forgetting to subtract one of the bank service fees, such as those charged for using your debit card or for ATM use.
- Charging the customer an amount different from the check amount.
- Having checks that are altered or forged.

If an account does not reconcile, employees must slowly work through the transactions, comparing the company's check register to the bank statement, until the error is found. It can be a pain to find the error, and often there will be more than one error or discrepancy in a very active business account. Usually, the errors are made by the account owner rather than the bank, but banks sometimes make mistakes too.

The following graph shows how much consumers pay for monthly banking fees. The business person, as well as the consumer, must look for the best value and convenience when selecting a banking-services provider.

Numbers in the News

How Much does your bank charge you?
Of 1000 customers surveyed, 57% stated their bank charged them a monthly fee.

- Less than $3 — 17%
- $3 to $6 — 20%
- $6 to $8 — 7%
- $8 to $10 — 6%
- $10 or more — 14%
- Don't know/not sure — 2%
- Nothing — 41%

DATA: Ipsos Reid poll of 1000 consumers for the American Bankers Association

---

EXAMPLE **2** **Reconciling a Checking Account**

Using the information on the check register and the bank statement in Figure 5.15, reconcile the checking account. Compare the items appearing on the check register to the bank statement a check √ indicates that the transaction was on the prior months bank statement,

CHECK NO.	DATE	TRANSACTION DESCRIPTION	AMOUNT OF WITHDRAWAL	✓	DATE OF DEP.	AMOUNT OF DEPOSIT/CREDIT	BALANCE	
		BALANCE BROUGHT FORWARD →					2782	95
e	7/11	Miller's Outpost	138 50	✓			2644	45
e	7/12	Barber Advertising	73 08				2571	37
723	7/18	Wayside Lumber	318 62	✓			2252	75
		Deposit			7/20	980 37	3233	12
724	7/25	I.R.S.	836 15				2396	97
e	7/26	John Lessor	450 00				1946	97
e	7/28	Sacramento Bee	67 80				1879	17
726	8/2	T.V.A.	59 25				1819	92
727	8/3	Carmichael Office	97 37				1722	55
		Deposit			8/6	875 45	2598	00
ATM	8/5	ATM Cash	80 00				2518	00

Bank Statement

```
*************************************************************
CHECK   WITHDRAWALS              DEPOSITS      DATE    BALANCE
NUMBER
*************************************************************
                                              7/20    2325.83
        73.08 elec. pmt.                      7/22    2252.75
                              980.37          7/24    3233.12
724     836.15                                7/28    2396.97
725     450.00 debit 49.07 RC                 7/30    1897.90
726      59.25         80.00 ATM   3.22 IC    8/4     1761.87
                        7.60 SC               8/5     1754.27
```

Reconciliation

Checks Outstanding		
Number	Amount	
725	$ 67	80
727	97	37
Total	$ 165	17

Compare the list of checks paid by the bank with your records. **List and total the checks not yet paid.**

(1) Enter new balance from bank statement: $ 1754.27

(2) List any deposits made by you and not yet recorded by the bank:
+ 875.45
+
+
+

(3) Add all numbers from lines above.
Total: 2629.72

(4) Write total of checks outstanding: − 165.17

(5) Subtract (4) from (3).
This is adjusted bank balance: $ 2464.55

To reconcile your records:

(6) List your checkbook balance: $ 2518.00

(7) Write the total of any fees or charges deducted by the bank and not yet subtracted by you from your checkbook: − 56.67 (Returned check and service charge)

(8) Subtract line (7) from line (6). 2461.33

(9) Enter interest credit: (Add to your checkbook) + 3.22

(10) Add line (9) to line (8).
Adjusted checkbook balance: $ 2464.55

New balance of your account; this number should be same as (5).

Source: Clendenen, Gary; Salzman, Stanley; Miller, Charles D., BUSINESS MATHEMATICS, 12th Ed., c 2012. Reprinted and Electronically reproduced by permission of Pearson Education, Inc., Upper Saddle River, New Jersey.

Figure 5.15

so does not need to be added or subtracted again. (Codes indicate the following: RC means returned check; SC means service charge; IC means interest credit; ATM means automated teller machine.)

Since the adjusted bank balance from Step 5 is the same as the new balance from Step 10, the account is reconciled (balanced). The correct current balance in the account is $2464.55.

Objective

5 *Use the T-Account Form of Reconciliation.* Many businesspeople and accountants prefer a **T-account form** for bank reconciliation. With this method, the bank statement balance is written on the left and the checkbook balance is written on the right. Adjustments are made to either the bank balance or the checkbook balance, depending on which side was unaware of the transaction or charge. T-account reconciliation uses the format in Figure 5.16. The adjusted balances must agree, with the result showing the actual amount remaining in the account.

Bank Reconciliation

Bank statement balance	$ _____	Checkbook balance	$ _____
Add:		**Add:**	
1. Add all deposits not yet recorded.	$ _____	1. Add all miscellaneous credits, collections, and interest.	$ _____
Less:		**Less:**	
2. Subtract all outstanding checks.	$ _____	2. Subtract previously deposited overdrafts and bank charges.	$ _____
Adjusted balance	$ ═══════	**Adjusted balance**	$ ═══════

Figure 5.16

EXAMPLE 2   Using the T-Account Form

The bank statement of Hazel Nut Gifts shows a balance of $4385.88. Checks outstanding are $292.70, $75.16, and $636.55. Deposits not yet recorded are $483.11 and $89.95. Also appearing are a service charge of $7.90, a check-printing charge of $9.20, a returned check (NSF) for $94.25, and an interest credit of $10.06. The checkbook now shows a balance of $4055.82. Use the T-method to reconcile the checking account.

Solution

The reconciliation is shown using a T-account in Figure 5.17.

Bank Reconciliation

Bank statement balance	$4385.88	Checkbook balance	$4055.82

Add:

Deposits not recorded   add these to get
$483.11
+ 89.95   + 573.06

4958.94

Less:

Outstanding checks

$292.70   add these to get
75.16
+636.55   −1004.41

Adjusted balance $3954.53

Add:

Interest credit   + 10.06

4065.88

Less:

Service charge $7.90
Check printing charge   9.20   add these to get
Returned check   +94.25   − 111.35

Adjusted balance $3954.53

found by adding $4385.88 and $573.06, and subtracting $1004.41

found by adding $4055.82 and $10.06, and subtracting $111.35

Figure 5.17

EXAMPLE 2 Reconciling a Checking Account

A checking account register is shown in Figure 5.18. A $\sqrt{}$ on the register indicates that the check appeared on the previous month's bank statement. Reconcile the account with a bank statement shown in Figure 5.19. (Codes on the statement have the following meaning: RC, Returned Check; SC, Service Charge; IC, Interest Credit; ATM, Automated Teller Machine.)

CHECK NO.	DATE	CHECK ISSUED TO	AMOUNT OF CHECK		✓	DATE OF DEP.	AMOUNT OF DEPOSIT		BALANCE	
		BALANCE BROUGHT FORWARD →							2782	95
*e**	7/11	Miller's Outpost	138	50	✓				2644	45
722	7/12	Barber Advertising	73	08					2571	37
723	7/18	Wayside Lumber	318	62	✓				2252	75
		Deposit				7/20	1060	37	3313	12
e	7/25	I.R.S.	836	15					2476	97
e	7/26	John Lessor	450	00					2026	97
724	7/28	Sacramento Bee	67	80					1959	17
e	8/2	T.V.A.	59	25					1899	92
725	8/3	Carmichael Office	97	37					1802	55
		Deposit				8/6	795	45	2598	00
ATM	8/5	ATM Cash	80	00					2518	00

e=refers to electronic payment or debit.

Figure 5.18 *e refers to and electronic payment or debit.

```
Bank Statement
*****************************************************************
CHECK      CHECKS                    DEPOSITS    DATE    BALANCE
NUMBER     AND DEBITS
*****************************************************************
                                                 7/20   2325.83
722        73.08                                 7/22   2252.75
                                     1060.37      7/24   3313.12
           836.15  elec. pmt.                    7/28   2476.97
            45.00  elec. pmt.    49.07 RC  7/30   1977.90
            59.25  elec. pmt.     3.22 IC   8/4    1921.87
                   80.00 ATM                      8/5    1841.87
                    7.60 SC                       8/5    1834.27
```

Figure 5.19

Bank Reconciliation

Bank statement balance	$1834.27		Checkbook balance	$2518.00
Add:			**Add:**	
Deposits not recorded	+ 795.45		Interest credit (IC)	+3.22
	2629.72			2521.22
Less:			**Less:**	
Outstanding checks			*Bank charges* Returned check (RC) $49.07	
$67.80 +97.37	−165.17		Service charge (SC) +7.60	−56.67
Adjusted balance	$2464.55		**Adjusted balance**	$2464.55

Figure 5.20

Solution

Follow the instructions on the form in Figure 5.16. The completed reconciliation is shown in T-form in Figure 5.20.

■

NOTE It is important to guard against identity theft and other criminal activities. Destroy all documents that include savings, checking, and credit-card account numbers, Social Security numbers, and all bank records. Check washing is a crime in which the thief removes the amount written on the check and changes it to a higher amount.

5.3	Exercises

Find the current balance for each of the following accounts.

	Balance from Bank Statement	Checks Outstanding		Deposits Not Yet Recorded	
1.	$4572.15	$97.68 $418.25	$348.17	$816.14 $571.28	$5095.47
2.	$6274.76	$381.40 $875.14	$681.10 $83.15	$346.65 $198.96	$4799.58
3.	$7911.42	$52.38 $95.42	$528.02 $76.50	$492.80 $38.72	$7690.62
4.	$9343.65	$840.71 $78.68	$665.73 $87.00	$971.64 $3382.71	$12,025.88
5.	$19,523.20	$6853.60 $795.77	$340.00 $22.85	$6724.93 $78.81	$18,314.72
6.	$32,489.50	$3589.70 $263.15	$18,702.15 $7269.78	$7110.65 $2218.63	$11,994.00

RECONCILING CHECKING ACCOUNTS Use the steps given in Example 1 and Figure 5.14 to reconcile the following accounts.

		7.		8.		
Balance from bank statement			$6875.09		$14,928.42	7. $6967.88
Checks outstanding (check number is given first)	421		$371.52	112	$84.76	8. $14,714.14
	424		$429.07	115	$109.38	
	427		$883.69	117	$42.03	
	429		$35.62	119	$1429.12	
Deposits not yet recorded			$701.56		$54.21	
			$421.78		$394.76	
			$689.35		$1002.04	
Bank charge			$8.75		$7.00	
Interest credit			$10.71		$22.86	
Checkbook balance			$6965.92		$14,698.28	

RECONCILING CHECKING ACCOUNTS   Use the T-account form, Figure 5.16, to reconcile the following accounts.

9. The checkbook of Toys for Tots Inc. shows a balance of $7779. When the bank statement was received, it showed a balance of $6237.44, a returned check amounting to $246.70, a service charge of $15.60, and a check-printing charge of $18.50. There were unrecorded deposits of $1442.44 and $479.50 and checks outstanding of $146.36, $91.52, $43.78, and $379.52. $7498.20

10. Carole Venezio received a bank statement showing a balance of $1248.63, a returned check amounting to $35.17, a service charge of $7.70, and an interest credit of $2.51. Checks outstanding were $380, $36.66, $15.29, and $143.18; deposits not yet recorded were $478.18 and $359.12. The checkbook showed a balance of $1551.16. $1510.80

11. The bank statement of William Poole Enterprises showed a bank balance of $4074.65, a returned check amounting to $168.40, a service charge of $7.08, and an interest credit of $10.18. There were unrecorded deposits of $907.82 and $1784.15 and checks outstanding of $642.55, $1082.98, $73.25, and $471.83. The checkbook showed a balance of $4661.31. $4496.01

12. The bank statement of Allysa Paige Decorating showed a balance of $1270.08. The checkbook balance showed $1626.63. There were unrecorded deposits of $370.64 and $219.38 and outstanding checks of $38.18, $185.10, $14.75, and $90.14. Check-printing charges were $8.50; the service charge was $3.80; there was a returned check of $83.85 and an interest credit of $1.45. $1531.93

 13. Explain in your own words the significance of writing a bad check. What might the cost be in dollars? What are the other consequences? (See Objective 1.)

 14. What happens when you as a businessperson receive a bad check? What are the financial costs to the business? What are you likely to do regarding this customer? (See Objective 1.)

 15. Briefly describe the importance of reconciling a checking account. What are the benefits derived from keeping good checking records? (See Objective 1.)

 16. Suppose your checking account will not balance. Name four types of errors that you will look for in trying to correct this problem.

Reconcile the following checking accounts. Compare the items appearing on the bank statement to the check register. A ✓ indicates that the check appeared on the previous month's statement. (Codes indicate the following: RC means Returned Check, SC means Service Charge, CP means Check-Printing Charge, IC means Interest Credit, ATM means Automated Teller Machine.) Electronic payments are indicated by *e*.

17. Rose Gardens

CHECK NO.	DATE	TRANSACTION DESCRIPTION	AMOUNT OF WITHDRAWAL		✓	DATE OF DEP.	AMOUNT OF DEPOSIT/CREDIT		BALANCE	
		BALANCE BROUGHT FORWARD →							6669	34
e	2/8	Floors to Go	248	96					6420	38
762	2/9	Healthways Dist.	125	63					6294	75
		Deposit				2/11	618	34	6913	09
763	2/12	Franchise Tax	770	41	✓				6142	68
764	2/14	Foothill Repair	22	86	✓				6119	82
e	2/15	Yellow Pages	91	24					6028	58
		Deposit				2/17	826	03	6854	61
e	2/17	Morning Herald	71	59					6783	02
765	2/18	San Juan Electric	63	24					6719	78
ATM	2/22	ATM Gas	15	26					6704	52
766	2/23	West Construction	405	07					6299	45
767	2/24	Heater Repairs	525	00					5774	45
		Deposit				2/26	220	16	5994	61
768	2/28	Capital Alarm	135	76					5858	85

Bank Statement

```
************************************************************
CHECK           WITHDRAWALS              DEPOSITS       DATE      BALANCE
NUMBER
************************************************************
                                                        2/14      5876.07
                 91.24  elec. pmt.        618.34        2/16      6403.17
                248.96  debit             826.03        2/17      6980.24
                 71.59  elec. pmt.                       2/19      6908.65
  762           125.63                                   2/21      6783.02
                        198.17  RC                       2/22      6584.85
                         15.26  ATM          8.12  IC    2/24      6577.71
  766           405.07    4.85  CP                        2/26      6167.79
                          6.28  SC                        2/27      6161.51
  767           525.00                                    2/28      5636.51
```

Reconciliation

Checks Outstanding		
Number	Amount	
765	$ 63	24
768	135	76
Total	$ 199	00

Compare the list of checks paid by the bank with your records. List and total the checks not yet paid.

(1) Enter new balance from bank statement: $ 5636.51

(2) List any deposits made by you and not yet recorded by the bank:
+ 220.16
+
+
+

(3) Add all numbers from lines above.
Total: 5856.67

(4) Write total of checks outstanding: − 199.00

(5) Subtract (4) from (3).
This is adjusted bank balance: $ 5657.67

To reconcile your records:

(6) List your checkbook balance: $ 5858.85

(7) Write the total of any fees or charges deducted by the bank and not yet subtracted by you from your checkbook: − 209.30

(8) Subtract line (7) from line (6). 5649.55

(9) Enter interest credit: (Add to your checkbook) + 8.12

(10) Add line (9) to line (8).
Adjusted checkbook balance: $ 5657.67

New balance of your account; this number should be same as (5).

18. Play It Again Sports

CHECK NO.	DATE	CHECK ISSUED TO	AMOUNT OF WITHDRAWAL		✓	DATE OF DEP.	AMOUNT OF DEPOSIT/CREDIT		BALANCE	
		BALANCE BROUGHT FORWARD →							7682	07
e	3/3	Action Packing Supplies	451	16					7230	91
663	3/3	Crown Paper	954	29	✓				6276	62
664	3/5	ATM Cash	80	00	✓				6196	62
		Deposit				3/7	913	28	7109	90
e	3/10	Fairless Water District	72	37					7037	53
665	3/12	Audia Temporary	340	88					6696	65
e	3/13	Lionel Toys	618	65					6078	00
666	3/14	Fairless Hills Power	100	50					5977	50
		Deposit				3/16	450	18	6427	68
		Deposit				3/18	163	55	6591	23
667	3/20	Hunt Roofing	238	50					6352	73
668	3/22	Standard Brands	315	62					6037	11
669	3/23	Penny-Saver Products	67	29					5969	82
		Deposit				3/24	830	75	6800	57

Bank Statement

CHECK NUMBER	WITHDRAWALS		DEPOSITS		DATE	BALANCE
					3/5	6647.78
			913.28		3/7	7561.06
	451.16	elec. pmt.			3/11	7109.90
665	340.88	82.15 RC	450.18		3/16	7137.05
	72.37	debit	22.48 IC		3/20	7087.16
	618.65	elec. pmt.	163.55		3/22	6632.06
667	238.50	12.70 SC			3/26	6380.86

Reconciliation

Checks Outstanding		
Number	Amount	
666	$ 100	50
668	315	62
669	67	29
Total	$ 483	41

Compare the list of checks paid by the bank with your records. List and total the checks not yet paid.

(1) Enter new balance from bank statement: $ 6380.86

(2) List any deposits made by you and not yet recorded by the bank: { + 830.75 / + / + / + }

(3) Add all numbers from lines above. Total: 7211.61

(4) Write total of checks outstanding: − 483.41

(5) Subtract (4) from (3). This is adjusted bank balance: $ 6728.20

To reconcile your records:

(6) List your checkbook balance: $ 6800.57

(7) Write the total of any fees or charges deducted by the bank and not yet subtracted by you from your checkbook: − 94.85

(8) Subtract line (7) from line (6).   6705.72

(9) Enter interest credit: (Add to your checkbook)   + 22.48

(10) Add line (9) to line (8). Adjusted checkbook balance: $ 6728.20 ←

New balance of your account; this number should be same as (5).

Source: Clendenen, Gary; Salzman, Stanley; Miller, Charles D., BUSINESS MATHEMATICS, 12th Ed., c 2012. Reprinted and Electronically reproduced by permission of Pearson Education, Inc., Upper Saddle River, New Jersey.

CHAPTER TERMS

Review the following terms to test your understanding of the chapter. For each term you do not know, refer to the page number found next to that term.

adjusted bank balance [p. 208]
ATM services [p. 201]
automated teller machine (ATM) [p. 190]
balance brought forward [p. 196]
balanced [p. 208]
balance forward [p. 196]
bank check [p. 201]
bank statement [p. 206]
bank teller [p. 201]
blank endorsement [p. 194]
bounced check [p. 206]
business checking account [p. 192]
canceled (check) [p. 194]
cashier's check [p. 201]
check [p. 191]
Check 21 [p. 195]

check register [p.197]
checks outstanding [p. 207]
check stub [p. 196]
credit card [p. 191]
credit card sales [p. 202]
debit card [p. 191]
deposit slip [p. 193]
deposit ticket [p. 193]
deposits in transit [p. 208]
direct deposit [p. 190]
direct payment [p. 190]
e-commerce [p. 189]
electronic banking [p. 189]
electronic commerce [p. 189]
electronic payment [p. 191]
flat-fee checking account [p. 192]
float [p. 195]
home banking [p. 190]

identity theft [p. 191]
insufficient funds [NSF] [p. 206]
interest-paying checking accounts [p. 192]
Internet banking [p. 190]
maintenance charge per month [p. 192]
mobile payments [p. 191]
money market [p. 192]
money order [p. 201]
notary [p. 201]
online banking [p. 201]
overdraft [p. 202]
overdraft protection [p. 202]
pay by phone [p. 190]
per debit charge [p. 192]
personal checking account [p. 192]

personal identification number (PIN) [p. 190]
point of sale (POS) [p. 190]
prepaid card [p. 190]
processing (check) [p. 194]
reconciliation [p. 207]
restricted endorsement [p. 194]
returned check [p. 206]
returned-deposit [p. 202]
smart card [p. 190]
special endorsement [p. 194]
stop payment [p. 202]
T-account form [p. 211]
texting [p. 191]
traditional banking [p. 190]
transaction register [p. 197]

CONCEPTS

EXAMPLES

5.1 Checking account service charges

There is usually a checking account maintenance charge and often a per check charge.

Find the monthly checking account service charge for a business with 36 checks and transactions, given a monthly maintenance charge of $7.50 and a $0.20 per check charge.

$$\$7.50 + 36(\$0.20) = \$7.50 + \$7.20$$
$$= \$14.70 \text{ monthly service charge}$$

5.2 Banking services offered

The checking account customer must be aware of various banking services that are offered.

Overdraft protection: offered to protect the customer from bouncing a check (NSF)

Stop-payment order: stops payment on a check written in error or a lost check

Cashier's check: a check written by the financial institution itself

Money order: an instrument used in place of cash

Notary service: an official certification of a signature or document

Online banking: allows the customer to perform banking functions using the Internet

Safe deposit box: box in a bank vault in which important and valuable items can be stored

5.2 Depositing credit-card transactions

Subtract credit-card refunds from total credit-card sales to find the gross deposit. Then subtract the discount charge from this total.

The following are credit-card charges and credits.

Sales		Credits
$28.15	$78.59	$21.86
$36.92	$63.82	$19.62

a. Find total sales.

$$\$28.15 + \$36.92 + \$78.59 + \$63.82 = \$207.48$$

b. Find total credits.

$$\$21.86 + \$19.62 = \$41.48$$

c. Find gross amount.

$$\$207.48 - \$41.48 = \$166$$

d. Given a 2% fee, find the amount of the charge.

$$\$166 \times 0.02 = \$3.32$$

e. Find the amount of credit given to the business.

$$\$166 - \$3.32 = \$162.68$$

5.3 Reconciliation of a checking account

A checking account customer must periodically verify checking account records with those of the bank or financial institution. The bank statement is used for this.

The accuracy of all checks written, deposits made, service charges incurred, and interest paid is checked and verified. The customer's checkbook balance and bank balance must be the same for the account to reconcile, or balance.

CHAPTER 5 | Review Exercises

The answer section includes answers to all Review Exercises.

Use Table 5.1 on page 191 to find the monthly checking account service charge for the following accounts. [5.1]

1. The Sub Shop, 42 checks, average balance $1478 $15.90

2. Sangi Market, 35 checks, average balance $485 $19

3. Old English Chimney Sweep, 52 checks, average balance $3017 $10.20

Complete the following three check stubs for Cypert Propane. The balance brought forward for stub 1561 is $16,409.82. Find the balance forward at the bottom of each stub. [5.1]

CHECKS WRITTEN

Number	Date	To	For	Amount
1561	Aug. 6	Fuel Depot	Fuel	$6892.12
1562	Aug. 8	First Bank	Payment	$1258.36
1563	Aug. 14	Security Service	Guard dogs	$416.14

Deposits made: $1572 on Aug. 7, $10,000 on Aug. 10.

4.

1561		
Aug. 6, 20____		
Amount $6892.12		
To Fuel Depot		
For Fuel		
Bal. Bro't. For'd.	$16,409	82
Am't. Deposited		
Total	16,409	82
Am't. this Check	6,892	12
Balance For'd.	9,517	70

5.

1562		
Aug. 8, 20____		
Amount $1258.36		
To First Bank		
For Payment		
Bal. Bro't. For'd.	$9,517	70
Am't. Deposited	1,572	00
Total	11,089	70
Am't. this Check	1,258	36
Balance For'd.	9,831	34

6.

1563		
Aug. 14, 20____		
Amount $416.14		
To Security Service		
For Guard dogs		
Bal. Bro't. For'd.	$9,831	34
Am't. Deposited	10,000	00
Total	19,831	34
Am't. this Check	416	14
Balance For'd.	19,415	20

Jim Havey owns The Toy Train Shop. The shop sells new and collectible toy trains and does repairs as well. The following credit-card transactions occurred during a recent period. [5.2]

	Sales	Credits
$118.68	$235.82	$15.36
$7.84	$98.56	$57.47
$33.18	$318.72	
$50.76	$116.35	
$12.72	$23.78	
$9.36	$38.95	

7. Find the total charges for the store. $1064.72

8. What is the total amount of the credits? $72.83

9. Find the amount of the gross deposit when these credit-card transactions are deposited. $991.89

10. If the bank charges the retailer a 2% discount charge, what is the amount of the discount charge at the statement date? $19.84

11. Find the amount of credit given to The Toy Train Shop after the fee is subtracted. $972.05

Solve the following application problems.

12. Clancy Strock Collectibles received a bank statement showing a balance of $4964.52, a returned check amounting to $140.68, a service charge of $30.84, and an interest credit of $10.04. Checks outstanding are $1520, $146.64, $31.16, and $572.76; deposits not yet recorded are $1912.72 and $1436.48. The checkbook shows a balance of $6204.64. Use Figure 5.15 to reconcile the checking account. [5.3] $6043.16

13. The bank statement of Jerry's Pizza showed a bank balance of $8149.30, a returned check amounting to $336.80, a service charge of $14.16, and an interest credit of $20.36. There were unrecorded deposits of $1815.64 and $3568.30, and checks outstanding of $1285.10, $2165.96, $146.50, and $943.66. The checkbook shows a balance of $9322.62. Use Figure 5.16 to reconcile the checking account. [5.3] $8992.02

14. Use Figure 5.16 and the following check register and bank statement to reconcile the checking account. Compare the items appearing on the bank statement to the check register. A ✓ indicates that the check appeared on the previous month's statement and *e* refers to an electronic payment. (Codes indicate the following: RC means Returned Check, SC means Service Charge, CP means Check-Printing Charge, IC means Interest Credit, ATM means Automated Teller Machine.) [5.3] $1267.21

CHECK NO.	DATE	CHECK ISSUED TO	AMOUNT OF CHECK	✓	DATE OF DEP.	AMOUNT OF DEPOSIT	BALANCE
					BALANCE BROUGHT FORWARD →		1876 93
e	9/6	MUIR TRAVEL	76 18	✓			1800 75
e	9/6	NORTH COAST TOURS	322 40				1478 35
320	9/8	AMES PHOTO	41 12	✓			1437 23
		DEPOSIT			9/10	851 62	2288 85
e	9/14	AMERICAN FLYERS	970 40				1318 45
e	9/15	REVERE INTER.	386 92				931 53
		DEPOSIT			9/18	995 20	1926 73
321	9/20	IDAHO EDISON	68 17				1858 56
e	9/20	WESSON SUPPLY	195 76				1662 80
e	9/22	PARKER PACKERS	348 33				1314 47
322	9/23	FREEZE DRY SUPPLY	215 84				1098 63
323	9/24	COUNTY WATER	169 56				929 07
		DEPOSIT			9/28	418 35	1347 42

BANK STATEMENT

Check Number (or electronic transaction)	Checks and Debits		Deposits	Date	Balance
				9/9	1759.63
			851.62	9/10	2611.25
e	970.40			9/15	1640.85
e	322.40			9/18	1318.45
e	386.92	78.93 RC	995.20	9/20	1847.80
e	195.76		6.52 IC	9/23	1658.56
e	348.33	7.80 SC		9/25	1302.43

CHAPTER 5	# Business Application Case #1
	Retailer Banking

Keiah Fulgham owns a retail store specializing in track-and-field equipment and accessories. She sells athletic shoes, clothing, and equipment to individuals, athletic clubs, and schools. Many of her customers use credit cards for their purchases and her credit-card sales in a recent week amounted to $8752.40. During the same period she had $573.94 in credit slips; Ms. Fulgham pays a credit-card fee of $2\frac{1}{2}\%$.

When she received her bank statement, the balance was $4228.34. The checks outstanding were $758.14, $38.37, $1671.88, $120.13, $2264.75, $78.11, $3662.73, $816.25, and $400. Both her credit-card deposit and bank deposits of $458.23, $771.18, $235.71, $1278.55, $663.52, and $1475.39 were not recorded.

a. Find the gross deposit when the credit-card sales and credits are deposited. $8178.46 gross profit

b. Find the amount of the credit given to Ms. Fulgham after the fee is subtracted. $7974 credit

c. What is the total of the checks outstanding? $9810.36 total of checks outstanding

d. Find the total of the deposits that were not recorded. $4882.58 deposits not recorded

e. Find the current balance in Ms. Fulgham's checking account. $7274.56 balance

CHAPTER 5	Business Application Case #2
	Internet Startup

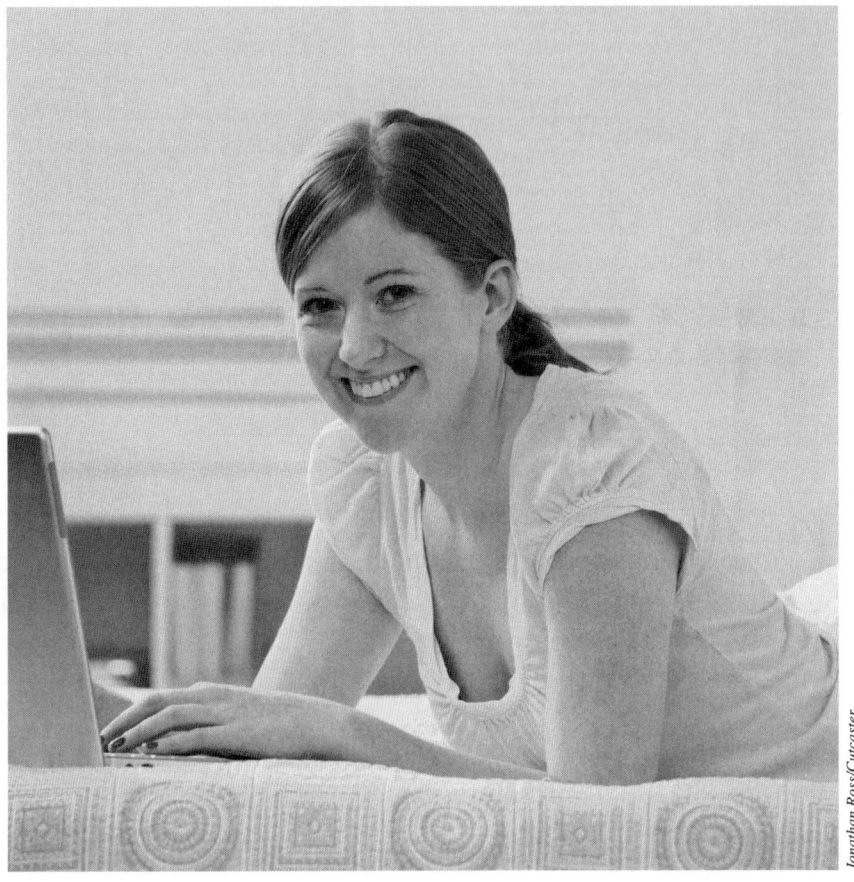

Jonathan Ross/Cutcaster

After having a baby, Melissa Hilton started her own business on Ebay (www.ebay.com). She buys items on sale at various stores in the mall or at garage sales. She then sells them to the highest bidder on Ebay and also on a Web site she has created where people can make purchases using a credit card.

Melissa likes working at home since it allows her to take care of her new baby and supplement the family income at the same time. She also likes the fact that being active with a new business keeps her mentally stimulated. At the recommendation of an accountant, she uses a separate checking account for all of her business transactions. Although many of her payments are made online, she still writes checks to some individuals.

a. If Hilton pays a monthly checking account fee of $5 plus $0.05 per check, find the total charge for a month in which 48 checks were written. $7.40

b. The total credit-card sales during one month were $2682 with only a single credit-card return of $112. Find (i) the gross amount of the credit-card deposit and (ii) the amount of credit after a fee of $1\frac{1}{2}\%$ is subtracted.   (a) $2570 (b) $2531.45

c. List items you or your friends have purchased on the Internet. Would you buy again on the Internet? What was the service like? Did you have any problems or issues? Do you trust the Internet as a place to shop and buy?   Answers will vary.

d. List pros and cons from your perspective of having a home-based business on the Internet. Have you ever tried to sell something on Ebay? If not, we suggest you try it. It is easier than you may think.   Answers will vary.

javier brosch / Fotolia.com

CHAPTER 6

Payroll

Business owners, managers, and employees alike take a strong interest in payroll. The amount of pay earned by an employee is most often determined by the number of hours worked or by specific tasks accomplished. Workers' pay varies around the world. Figure 6.1 shows average hourly manufacturing wages in different countries. Clearly the highest wages are paid in Norway, Germany, France, the United States, the United Kingdom, and Japan. Wages are far lower in Brazil, Mexico, India, and China.

The primary reason companies **offshore**, or move jobs abroad, is to take advantage of the lower wage rates. Factory workers in China may not speak English and may not have the training and skills of U.S. or German workers, but they will work for much less, as shown in Figure 6.1. Other problems that arise when firms offshore jobs include differences in time zones, high shipping costs, language problems, quality problems, unreliable electricity and water, and cultural differences.

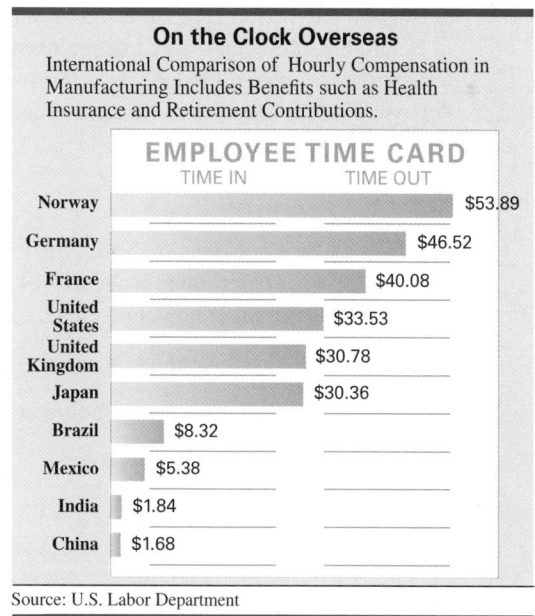

On the Clock Overseas

International Comparison of Hourly Compensation in Manufacturing Includes Benefits such as Health Insurance and Retirement Contributions.

EMPLOYEE TIME CARD		
TIME IN	TIME OUT	
Norway		$53.89
Germany		$46.52
France		$40.08
United States		$33.53
United Kingdom		$30.78
Japan		$30.36
Brazil	$8.32	
Mexico	$5.38	
India	$1.84	
China	$1.68	

Source: U.S. Labor Department

Figure 6.1

▶ STOP&THINK

Use Figure 6.1 to compare the average hourly compensation in the United States, Mexico, India, and China. Estimate the annual savings in compensation for a company with 100 manufacturing jobs if managers move the jobs from the United States to China. Now, list several reasons why it might be disadvantageous to offshore.

Preparing the payroll is one of the most important jobs in any office. Payroll records must be accurate, and the payroll must be prepared on time so that the necessary checks can be written. The first step in preparing the payroll is to determine the **gross earnings**, or the total amount earned for each employee. Many methods are used to find gross earnings and several of these are discussed in this chapter. A number of **deductions** may be subtracted from gross earnings to find **net pay**, the amount actually received by the employee. These deductions and employer payroll records will also be discussed in this chapter.

6.1	Gross Earnings (Wages and Salaries)

OBJECTIVES

1 *Use hourly rate to calculate gross earnings.*

2 *Find overtime earnings for over 40 hours of work per week.*

3 *Use overtime premium method of calculating gross earnings.*

4 *Find overtime earnings for over 8 hours of work per day.*

5 *Understand double time, shift differential, and split-shift premiums.*

6 *Find equivalent earnings for different pay periods.*

7 *Find gross earnings when overtime is paid to salaried employees.*

Several methods are used to determine an employee's pay. Two of these methods, salaries and wages, are discussed in this section. Commissions and piecework are discussed in the next two sections.

The first step in calculating pay is to determine how many hours each employee worked during the pay period. The times are often stamped on a **time card**, such as the one shown in Figure 6.2, although time cards are usually stored electronically. This information is then transferred to a **payroll ledger**, which is used to help calculate gross pay for each employee. A payroll ledger is shown in the next example.

Objective

1 *Use Hourly Rate to Calculate Gross Earnings.* Eboni Perkins, whose time card is shown in Figure 6.2, is paid an **hourly wage** of $14.80 (see the time card). Her gross earnings would be calculated with the following formula.

$$\text{Gross earnings} = \text{number of hours worked} \times \text{rate per hour}$$

For example, if Perkins works 8 hours at $14.80 per hour, her gross earnings would be

$$\text{Gross earnings} = 8 \times \$14.80 = \$118.40$$

> **EXAMPLE 1　Completing a Payroll Ledger**
>
> Meg Holden is doing the payroll for two employees, S. Abruzzo and N. Williams. The first thing she must do is complete a payroll ledger.

Employee	Hours Worked							Total Hours	Rate	Gross Earnings
	S	M	T	W	Th	F	S			
Abruzzo, S.	—	2	4	8	6	3	—		$8.40	
Williams, N.	—	3.5	3	7	6.75	7	—		$10.40	

Solution

The first step is to find the total number of hours worked by each person.

$$\text{Abruzzo:}\quad 2 + 4 + 8 + 6 + 3 = 23 \text{ hours}$$
$$\text{Williams: } 3.5 + 3 + 7 + 6.75 + 7 = 27.25 \text{ hours}$$

To find the gross earnings, multiply the number of hours worked and the rate per hour.

$$\text{Abruzzo:}\quad 23 \times \$8.40 = \$193.20$$
$$\text{Williams: } 27.25 \times \$10.40 = \$283.40$$

The payroll ledger can now be completed.

| Employee | Hours Worked | | | | | | | Total Hours | Rate | Gross Earnings |
	S	M	T	W	Th	F	S			
Abruzzo, S.	—	2	4	8	6	3	—	23	$8.40	$193.20
Williams, N.	—	3.5	3	7	6.75	7	—	27.25	$10.40	$283.40

PAYROLL CARD
NO TIME CLOCK REQUIRED

EMPL. NO. 1375   CARD NO. _____

FULL NAME Eboni Perkins   AGE (IF UNDER 18)

ADDRESS 412 Fawndale Drive   SOCIAL SECURITY NO. 123-45-6789

DATE EMPLOYED   POSITION Shift MGR   RATE $14.80

PAY PERIOD STARTING 7/23   ENDING 7/27

| DATE | REGULAR TIME | | | | | OVER TIME | | |
	IN	OUT	IN	OUT	DAILY TOTALS	IN	OUT	DAILY TOTALS
7/23	8:00	11:50	12:20	4:30	8	4:30	6:30	2
7/24	7:58	12:00	12:30	4:30	8	5:00	7:30	2.5
7/25	8:00	12:00	12:30	4:32	8			
7/26	7:58	12:05	12:35	4:30	8	4:30	5:00	0.5
7/27	8:01	12:00	1:00	5:00	8			

APPROVED BY   MJH

TOTAL REGULAR TIME 40   5

REGULAR DAYS WORKED 5 @ 8 HRS. @ EARNINGS 14.80 $ 592.00

ADDITIONAL COMPENSATION: VALUE OF MEALS, LODGING, GIFTS, ETC.   AMOUNT $ _____

COMMISSIONS, FEES, BONUSES, GOODS, ETC. OT 5 @ 22.20   AMOUNT $ 111.00

OTHER REMUNERATIONS (KIND) $ _____

DEDUCTIONS: TOTAL EARNINGS $ 703.00

I CERTIFY THE FOREGOING TO BE A CORRECT ACCOUNT OF THE TIME WORKED AND WAGES RECEIVED:

SIGNATURE   DATE PAID

Figure 6.2

Objective

2   *Find Overtime Earnings for Over 40 Hours of Work Per Week.* The **Fair Labor Standards Act (FLSA)** is a federal law that establishes a workweek of 40 hours per week and requires **overtime** pay for hours worked beyond 40 per week. It also sets the federal **minimum wage**, which was $7.25 per hour in 2013. Some states, such as California, set their minimum wage at levels higher than the federal minimum wage. FLSA does not control vacation or sick pay, holidays off, vacations, or fringe benefits such as medical insurance. Many employees are not covered by FLSA, including executives, professionals, managers, administrative workers, teachers, outside sales employees, waiters and waitresses, salespeople, farm workers, and casual babysitters. So, for example, FLSA does not require that mangers or teachers who work more than 40 hours per week be paid overtime.

Many companies not covered by the FLSA follow the practice of paying **time-and-a-half**, or 1.5 times the normal wage rate, for any work over 40 hours per week. Calculate overtime earnings as follows. Add regular earnings to overtime earnings to find gross earnings.

$$\text{Gross earnings} = \text{earnings at regular rate} + \textbf{overtime earnings}$$
$$\text{where } \textbf{overtime earnings} = \text{hourly wage} \times 1.5$$

EXAMPLE 2   **Completing a Payroll Ledger with Overtime**

Complete the following payroll ledger.

Employee	Hours Worked S	M	T	W	Th	F	S	Total Hours Reg.	O.T.	Gross Earnings Reg. Rate	Reg.	O.T.	Total
Chung, E.	6	9	8.25	8	9	4.5	—			$8.30			
Jenders, P.	—	10	6.75	9	6.25	10	4.25			$9.48			

Solution

First find the total number of hours worked.

$$\text{Chung:} \qquad 6 + 9 + 8.25 + 8 + 9 + 4.5 = 44.75 \text{ hours}$$
$$\text{Jenders:} \quad 10 + 6.75 + 9 + 6.25 + 10 + 4.25 = 46.25 \text{ hours}$$

Both employees worked more than 40 hours. Chung earned $40 \times \$8.30 = \$332$ at the regular rate, and Jenders earned $40 \times \$9.48 = \$379.20$ at the regular rate. To find overtime earnings, first find the number of overtime hours worked by each employee.

Regular hours

$$\text{Chung:} \quad 44.75 - 40 = 4.75 \text{ overtime hours}$$
$$\text{Jenders:} \quad 46.25 - 40 = 6.25 \text{ overtime hours}$$

The regular rate given for each employee can be used to find the time-and-a-half rate.

$$\text{Chung:} = 1\frac{1}{2} \times \$8.30 = \$12.45 \quad \text{Per hour of overtime}$$

$$\text{Jenders:} = 1\frac{1}{2} \times \$9.48 = \$14.22 \quad \text{Per hour of overtime}$$

Now find the overtime earnings.

$$\text{Chung: 4.75 hours} \times \$12.45 \text{ per hour} = \$59.14 \quad \text{Rounded to the nearest cent}$$
$$\text{Jenders: 6.25 hours} \times \$14.22 \text{ per hour} = \$88.88 \quad \text{Rounded}$$

The ledger can now be completed.

Employee	Hours Worked							Total Hours		Gross Earnings			
	S	M	T	W	Th	F	S	Reg.	O.T.	Reg. Rate	Reg.	O.T.	Total
Chung, E.	6	9	8.25	8	9	4.5	—	40	4.75	$8.30	$332	$59.14	$391.14
Jenders, P.	—	10	6.75	9	6.25	10	4.25	40	6.25	$9.48	$379.20	$88.88	$468.08

Objective

3   *Use Overtime Premium Method of Calculating Gross Earnings.* Gross earnings with overtime is sometimes calculated with the **overtime premium method** (sometimes called the **overtime excess method**). This method produces the same result as the method just described. The total hours at the regular rate are added to the overtime hours at one-half of the regular rate to arrive at gross earnings.

The formula for the overtime premium method is

$$
\begin{array}{ll}
\text{Total hours} \times \text{ regular rate} & = \text{straight-time earnings} \\
+ \text{ Overtime hours} \times \dfrac{1}{2} \text{regular rate} & = \text{overtime premium} \\
\hline
& = \text{gross earnings}
\end{array}
$$

EXAMPLE 3   **Using the Overtime Premium Method**

This week, Marcy Pleu worked 40 regular hours and 12 overtime hours. Her regular rate of pay is $17.40 per hour. Find her total gross pay using the overtime premium method.

Solution

The total number of hours worked by Pleu is 52 ($40 + 12$) and her overtime premium rate is $8.70 ($\frac{1}{2} \times \$17.40$).

$$
\begin{array}{rll}
52 \text{ hours} \times \$17.40 = & \$904.80 & \text{Regular-rate earnings} \\
12 \text{ overtime hours} \times \ \ \$8.70 = & \underline{\$104.40} & \text{Overtime} \\
& \$1009.20 & \text{Gross earnings}
\end{array}
$$

 Scientific Calculator Approach

Using chain calculations and the order of operations to solve Example 3, the regular earnings are calculated. Next the overtime earnings are calculated. Finally, they are added together.

52 $\boxed{\times}$ 17.4 $\boxed{+}$ 12 $\boxed{\times}$ 17.4 $\boxed{\times}$ .5 $\boxed{=}$ 1009.2

NOTE Some companies prefer the overtime premium method since it readily identifies the extra cost of overtime labor and can be seen easily. Quite often, excessive use of overtime indicates inefficiencies in management.

Objective

4   *Find Overtime Earnings for Over 8 Hours of Work Per Day.* Some companies pay the time-and-a-half rate for all time worked over 8 hours in any one day, no matter how many hours are worked in a week. An example of **daily overtime** is shown in the next example.

EXAMPLE 4 **Finding Overtime Each Day**

Peter Harris worked 10 hours on Monday, 5 on Tuesday, 7 on Wednesday, and 12 on Thursday. His regular rate of pay is $10.10. Find his gross earnings for the week if everything over 8 hours in one day is overtime.

	S	M	T	W	Th	F	S	Total Hours
Reg.	—	8	5	7	8	—	—	28
O.T.	—	2	—	—	4	—	—	6

Solution

Harris worked more than 8 hours on both Monday and Thursday. On Monday, he had $10 - 8 = 2$ hours of overtime, with $12 - 8 = 4$ hours of overtime on Thursday. For the week, he earned $2 + 4 = 6$ hours of overtime. His regular hours are 8 on Monday, 5 on Tuesday, 7 on Wednesday, and 8 on Thursday, or

$$8 + 5 + 7 + 8 = 28 \text{ hours at the regular rate}$$

His hourly earnings are $10.10, giving

$$28 \times \$10.10 = \$282.80 \text{ at the regular rate}$$

If the regular rate is $10.10, the time-and-a-half rate is

$$\$10.10 \times 1\frac{1}{2} = \$15.15$$

He earned time-and-a-half for 6 hours.

$$6 \times \$15.15 = \$90.90$$

His gross earnings are found by adding regular earnings and overtime earnings.

$$\underbrace{\$282.80}_{\substack{\text{Total} \\ \text{regular pay}}} + \underbrace{\$90.90}_{\substack{\text{Total} \\ \text{overtime}}} = \underbrace{\$373.70}_{\substack{\text{Gross} \\ \text{earnings}}}$$

NOTE There are many careers that require unusual schedules and do not pay overtime for over 40 hours worked in one week or over 8 hours worked in one day. One example is a firefighter, who may work 24 hours and then get 48 hours off. In this case the firefighter is working an average of 8 hours per day.

Objective

5 *Understand Double Time, Shift Differential, and Split-Shift Premiums.* In addition to premiums paid for overtime, other **premium payment plans** include **double time** for holidays and, in some industries, Saturdays and Sundays. A **shift differential** is often given to compensate employees for working less desirable hours. For example, an additional amount per hour or per shift might be paid to swing shift (4:00 P.M. to midnight) and graveyard shift (midnight to 8:00 A.M.) employees. These shifts are worked by nurses, emergency personnel, telephone operators, and workers at power plants.

Restaurant employees and telephone operators often receive a **split-shift premium**. The employees' hours are staggered so that the employees are on the job only during the busiest times. For example, an employee may work 4 hours, be off 4 hours, then work 4 hours. The employee is paid a premium because of this less desirable schedule.

Some employers offer **compensatory time**, or **comp time**, for overtime hours worked. Instead of receiving additional money, an employee is given time off from the regular work schedule as compensation for overtime hours already worked. Quite often, the compensatory time is given at $1\frac{1}{2}$ times the overtime hours worked. For example, 12 hours might be given as compensation for 8 hours of previously worked overtime. Occasionally an employee is given a choice of overtime pay or comp time. Many companies reserve the use of compensatory time for their supervisors or managerial employees. Also, compensatory time is very common in government agencies.

Objective

6 *Find Equivalent Earnings for Different Pay Periods.* The second common method of finding gross earnings uses a **salary**, a fixed amount given as so much per **pay period** (time between paychecks). Common pay periods are weekly, biweekly, semimonthly, and monthly (Table 6.1).

Table 6.1 COMMON PAY PERIODS

Monthly	12 paychecks each year
Semimonthly	Twice each month or 24 paychecks each year
Biweekly	Every two weeks or 26 paychecks each year
Weekly	52 paychecks each year

In Chapter 1, Figure 1.1 shows the average earnings for workers, depending on the level of education that they have achieved. Figure 6.3 shows that there are good careers that do not require a 4-year college degree. Notice, however, that many of these careers do require special training or an associate's degree.

Jobs That Do Not Require an Undergraduate Degree

Profession	Median Annual Earnings	Profession	Median Annual Earnings
Air traffic controller	$107,780	Funeral director	$57,660
Commercial pilot	$71,270	Police officer	$50,670
Nuclear power		Aircraft mechanic	$49,670
reactor operator	$71,220	Court reporter	$48,330
Elevator installer/		Electrician	$48,100
repairer	$66,330	Flight attendant	$33,470
Dental hygienist	$64,910	Pest control worker	$30,280
Locomotive		Restaurant cook	$21,960
engineer	$63,180	Bartender	$19,740
Registered nurse	$62,480		

Source: U.S. Department of Labor.
Figure 6.3

EXAMPLE 5 Determining Equivalent Salaries

You are a career counselor and want to compare the earnings of four clients for whom you have helped find jobs. John Cross receives a weekly salary of $546, Melanie Goulet, a biweekly salary of $1686, Carla Lampsa, a semimonthly salary of $736, and Tom Shaffer, a monthly salary of $1818. For each worker, find the following: (a) earnings per year, (b) earnings per month, and (c) earnings per week.

Solution

John Cross
(a) $546 × 52 = $28,392 per year
(b) $28,392 ÷ 12 = $2366 per month
(c) $546 per week

Melanie Goulet
(a) $1686 × 26 = $43,836 per year (biweekly = 26 per year)
(b) $43,836 ÷ 12 = $3653 per month
(c) $1686 ÷ 2 = $843 per week

Carla Lampsa
(a) $736 × 24 = $17,664 per year
(b) $736 × 2 = $1472 per month
(c) $17,664 ÷ 52 = $339.69 per week

Tom Shaffer
(a) $1818 × 12 = $21,816 per year
(b) $1818 per month
(c) $21,816 ÷ 52 = $419.54 per week

OBJECTIVE

7 *Find Gross Earnings When Overtime Is Paid to Salaried Employees.* A salary is paid for the performance of a certain job, without keeping track of the number of hours worked. However, the Fair Labor Standards Act requires that certain salaried positions receive additional compensation for overtime. Just as with wage earners, the salaried employee is often paid time-and-a-half for all hours worked over the normal number of hours per week.

EXAMPLE 6 Finding Overtime for Salaried Employees

Caralee Woods is paid $872 a week as an executive assistant. If her normal workweek is 40 hours, and she is paid time-and-a-half for all overtime, find her gross earnings for a week in which she works 45 hours.

Solution

The executive assistant's salary has an hourly equivalent of

$$\frac{\$872}{40 \text{ hours}} = \$21.80 \text{ per hour}$$

Since she must be paid overtime at the rate of $1\frac{1}{2}$ times her regular pay, she will get $32.70 per hour $\left(1\frac{1}{2} × \$21.80\right)$ for overtime. Her gross earnings for the week are calculated as follows:

Salary for 40 hours =	$ 872.00	Regular-rate earnings
Overtime for 5 hours (5 × $32.70) =	163.50	Overtime
	$1035.50	Gross earnings

■ ■ ■ Scientific
■ ■ Calculator
■ Approach

The calculator solution to Example 6 is as follows:

$$872 \boxed{\div} 40 \boxed{\times} 1.5 \boxed{\times} 5 \boxed{=} 163.5 \boxed{STO}$$

$$872 \boxed{+} \boxed{RCL} \boxed{=} 1035.5$$

EXAMPLE 7 **Finding Gross Earnings with Overtime**

A technician working in a crime lab is paid a salary of $648 per week. If his regular work-week is 36 hours, find his gross earnings for a week in which he works 46 hours. All over-time hours are paid at time-and-a-half.

Solution

The technician's salary has an hourly equivalent of

$$\frac{\$648}{36 \text{ hours}} = \$18 \text{ per hour}$$

Amount of overtime: $46 - 36 = 10$ hours

Since he is paid $1\frac{1}{2}$ times the regular rate per hour, he will receive $27 per hour $\left(1\frac{1}{2} \times \$18\right)$ for overtime. His gross earnings for the week are as follows.

Salary for 36 hours $=$	$648	Regular-rate earnings
Overtime for 10 hours $(10 \times \$27) =$	270	Overtime
	$918	Gross earnings

Figure 6.4 lists the 10 best firms to work for as rated by *Fortune* magazine. Besides salaries, the editors also look at factors such as benefits and working environment when trying to identify the best companies.

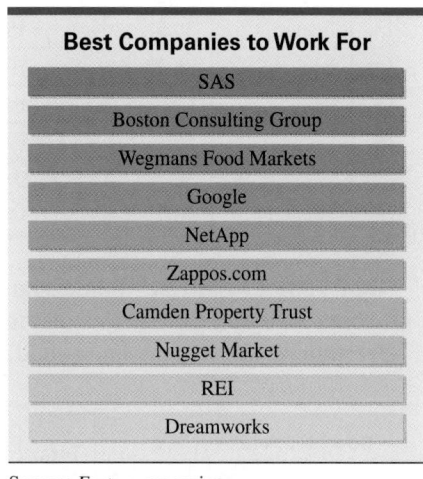

Best Companies to Work For

SAS
Boston Consulting Group
Wegmans Food Markets
Google
NetApp
Zappos.com
Camden Property Trust
Nugget Market
REI
Dreamworks

Source: *Fortune* magazine.

Figure 6.4

6.1 | **Exercises**

THE PAYROLL LEDGER Find the number of regular hours and overtime hours (any hours over 40) for each of the following employees. Then calculate the overtime rate (time-and-a-half) for each employee.

	Employee	S	M	T	W	Th	F	S	Reg. Hrs.	O.T. Hrs.	Reg. Rate	O.T. Rate
1.	Allen, K.	—	7	4	7	10	8	4	40	0	$8.10	$12.15
2.	Doran, C.	—	6.5	9	7.5	8	9.5	7	40	7.5	$8.24	$12.36
3.	Jaworski, B.	3	6	8.25	8	8.5	5	—	38.75	0	$7.80	$11.70
4.	Sheehan, A.	8.5	9	7.5	8	10	8.25	—	40	11.25	$9.50	$14.25
5.	Ulman, L.	—	9.5	7	9	9.25	10.5	—	40	5.25	$11.48	$17.22
6.	Fuqua, B.	—	8	8	9	7.25	6	7	40	5.25	$9.80	$14.70

GROSS EARNINGS Find the earnings at the regular rate, the earnings at the overtime rate, and the gross earnings for each of the employees in Exercises 1–6.

7. Allen, K. $324; $0; $324

8. Doran, C. $329.60; $92.70; $422.30

9. Jaworski, B. $302.25; $0; $302.25

10. Sheehan, A. $380; $160.31; $540.31

11. Ulman, L. $459.20; $90.41; $549.61

12. Fuqua, B. $392; $77.18; $469.18

Find the overtime rate at time-and-a-half, the amount of earnings at regular pay, the amount at overtime pay, and the total gross wages for each employee.

		Total Hours		Reg.	O.T.	Gross Earnings		
	Employee	Reg.	O.T.	Rate	Rate	Reg.	O.T.	Total
13.	Fenton, C.	39.5	—	$8.80	$13.20	$347.60	$0	$347.60
14.	Klein, A.	36.25	—	$10.20	$15.30	$369.75	$0	$369.75
15.	Schultz, J.	40	4.5	$14.40	$21.60	$576	$97.20	$673.20
16.	Light, P.	40	6.75	$9.80	$14.70	$392.00	$99.23	$491.23
17.	Weisher, W.	40	4.25	$9.18	$13.77	$367.20	$58.52	$425.72
18.	Dong, L.	40	5	$8.25	$12.38	$330.00	$61.90	$391.90

OVERTIME PREMIUM Some companies use the overtime premium method to determine gross earnings. Use this method to complete the following partial payroll register. Overtime is paid at time-and-a-half rate for all hours over 40.

		Hours Worked							Total Hours	Reg. Rate	O.T. Hours	O.T. Premium Rate	Gross Earnings		
	Employee	S	M	T	W	Th	F	S					Reg.	O.T.	Total
19.	Aragona, B.	10	9	8	5	12	7	—	51	$7.40	11	$3.70	$377.40	$40.70	$418.10
20.	Biron, C.	7.75	10	5	9.75	8	10	—	50.5	$9.50	10.5	$4.75	$479.75	$49.88	$529.63
21.	Cheever, P.	—	12	11	8	8.25	11	—	50.25	$8.60	10.25	$4.30	$432.15	$44.08	$476.23
22.	Abeya, C.	—	8.5	5.5	10	12	10.5	7	53.5	$13.50	13.5	$6.75	$540	$273.38	$813.38
23.	Sherlock, F.	—	10	9.25	9.5	11.5	10	—	50.25	$10.20	10.25	$5.10	$512.55	$52.28	$564.83
24.	Firavich, S.	8.5	7	9.75	—	10.5	12	—	47.75	$12.50	7.75	$6.25	$596.88	$48.44	$645.32

DAILY OVERTIME PAYMENT   Some companies pay overtime for all time worked over 8 hours in a given day. Use this method to complete the following payroll register. Overtime is paid at time-and-a-half rate.

	Employee	\multicolumn{7}{c}{Hours Worked}			Total Hours		Reg. Rate	O.T. Rate	\multicolumn{3}{c}{Gross Earnings}		
		S	M	T	W	Th	F	S	Reg.	O.T.	Reg. Rate	O.T. Rate	Reg.	O.T.	Total
25.	Belinder, M.	—	10	9	11	6	5	—	35	6	$9.50	$14.25	$332.50	$85.50	$418.00
26.	Cechvala, C.	—	9	8.75	7	8.5	10	—	39	4.25	$7.60	$11.40	$296.40	$48.45	$344.85
27.	Deininger, M.	—	7.5	8	9	10.75	8	—	39.5	3.75	$11.40	$17.10	$450.30	$64.13	$514.43
28.	Gingrich, D.	—	9	10	8	6	9.75	—	38	4.75	$8.60	$12.90	$326.80	$61.28	$388.08
29.	Kaplan, L.	—	9.5	8.5	7.75	8	9.5	—	39.75	3.5	$10.20	$15.30	$405.45	$53.55	$459.00
30.	Lerner, M.	6	8	6.5	8.75	—	10.25	—	36.5	3	$14.40	$21.60	$525.60	$64.80	$590.40

31. Explain in your own words what premium payment plans are. Select a premium payment plan and describe it. (See Objective 5.)

32. If you were given a choice of overtime pay or compensatory time, which would you choose? Why? (See Objective 5.)

EQUIVALENT EARNINGS   Find the equivalent earnings for each of the following salaries as indicated.

	Weekly Earnings	Biweekly Earnings	Semimonthly Earnings	Monthly Earnings	Annual Earnings
33.	$248	$496	$537.33	$1074.67	$12,896
34.	$323.08	$646.15	$700	$1400	$16,800
35.	$426	$852	$923	$1846	$22,152
36.	$530.77	$1061.54	$1150	$2300	$27,600
37.	$501.92	$1003.85	$1087.50	$2175	$26,100
38.	$436	$872	$944.67	$1889.33	$22,672
39.	$618.46	$1236.92	$1340	$2680	$32,160
40.	$384	$768	$832	$1664	$19,968
41.	$830	$1660	$1798.33	$3596.67	$43,160
42.	$1003.85	$2007.69	$2175	$4350	$52,200

SALARY WITH OVERTIME   Find the weekly gross earnings for the following people who are on salary and are paid time-and-a-half for overtime. (*Hint:* Round hourly equivalents and overtime amounts to the nearest cent.)

	Employee	Regular Hours per Week	Weekly Salary	Hours Worked	Weekly Gross Earnings
43.	Atkins, G.	40	$520	56	$832
44.	Berry, M.	40	$360	42	$387
45.	Bridges, C.	45	$418	50	$487.70
46.	Kelley, R.	38	$340	40	$366.86
47.	Magot, D.	32	$450	44	$703.08
48.	Sypniewski, D.	30	$484	45	$847

Solve the following application problems. Round hourly equivalents, regular rates, and overtime rates to the nearest cent.

49. STARBUCKS   Last week, Lori Merrill worked 48 hours at Starbucks. Find her gross earnings for the week if she is paid $8.40 per hour and earns time-and-a-half for all hours over 40. $436.80

50. EMERGENCY ROOM　Angela Gragg works as a nurse's aide in an emergency room. She is paid $13.60 per hour for straight time and time-and-a-half for all hours over 40 worked in a week. Find her gross earnings for a week in which she worked 52 hours.　$788.80

51. CHEF　James Simpson is paid $14.60 per hour to work as a chef. He is paid time-and-a-half for all hours over 8 hours worked on a given day. Find his gross earnings for a week during which he worked the following hours: Monday, 9.5 hours; Tuesday, 7 hours; Wednesday, 8 hours; Thursday, 10 hours; and Friday, 9.5 hours.　$678.90

52. DENTAL ASSISTANT　Jenny Fang is a dental assistant and worked 10 hours on Monday, 9.75 hours on Tuesday, 5.5 hours on Wednesday, 12 hours on Thursday, and 7.25 hours on Friday. Her regular rate of pay is $11.50 an hour, with time-and-a-half paid for all hours over 8 worked in a given day. Find her gross earnings for the week.　$556.32

53. ESCROW OFFICER　Anne Felsted is paid $920 a week as an escrow officer at a bank. Her normal workweek is 40 hours. She is paid time-and-a-half for overtime. Find her gross earnings for a week in which she worked 46 hours.　$1127

54. FEEDSTORE SALES　An employee at Valley Feed Stores is paid $298 for a normal workweek of 35 hours. If she is paid time-and-a-half for overtime, find her gross earnings for a week in which she worked 48 hours.　$464.01

55. SALARY WITH OVERTIME　Charles Dawkins, manager of the Cellular Phone Center, is paid a salary of $638 per week, has a normal workweek of 40 hours, and is paid time-and-a-half for overtime. Find his gross earnings in a week in which he worked 52 hours.　$925.16

56. HOME MORTGAGE BUSINESS　Lesly Jaramillo, an assistant manager at Bank of America, worked 54 hours this week. If she is paid a weekly salary of $800 and has a normal workweek of 45 hours, find her gross earnings for the week. She is paid time-and-a-half for all overtime.　$1040.03

57. EQUIVALENT EARNINGS　An employee earns $630 weekly. Find the equivalent earnings if paid (a) biweekly, (b) semimonthly, (c) monthly, and (d) annually. (a) $1260 biweekly (b) $1365 semimonthly (c) $2730 monthly (d) $32,760 annually

58. FIREMAN　Tom Canales is a fireman and is paid $42,900 annually. Find the equivalent earnings if this amount is paid (a) weekly, (b) biweekly, (c) semimonthly, and (d) monthly.　(a) $825 weekly (b) $1650 biweekly (c) $1787.50 semimonthly (d) $3575 monthly

 59. Semimonthly pay periods result in 24 paychecks per year. Biweekly pay periods result in 26 paychecks per year. Which of these pay periods gives three checks in two months of the year? Will it always be the same two months? Explain.

 60. Which would you prefer: a monthly pay period or a weekly pay period? What special budgetary considerations might you consider regarding the pay period that you choose?

6.2 Gross Earnings (Commission)

OBJECTIVES

1 *Find gross earnings using commission rate × sales (P = R × B).*
2 *Determine commission using a variable commission rate.*
3 *Use salary and commission rate to find gross earnings.*
4 *Use a drawing account and quota to find gross earnings.*
5 *Determine override as part of gross earnings.*

Many people in sales and marketing are paid on **commission**, usually a fixed percent of sales. This is an incentive system of compensation and the commissions are designed to produce maximum employee output, since pay is directly dependent on sales. This section discusses several common types of sales commissions.

Objective

1   *Find Gross Earnings Using Commission Rate × Sales (P = R × B).* With a **straight commission**, the salesperson is paid a fixed percent of sales. Gross earnings are found by the following formula.

$$P \quad = \quad R \quad \times \quad B$$
Gross earnings = commission rate × amount of sales

EXAMPLE 1   **Determining Earnings Using Commission**

The real estate commission to sell a house is 6% of the sale price. Find the commission on a small three-bedroom, two-bath home that sold for $188,500.

Solution

$$\text{Commission} = 6\% \text{ of } \$188,500$$
$$= 0.06 \times \$188,500 = \$11,310$$

Any returned items must be subtracted from gross sales before calculating a commission. Gross sales less **returns** is called **net sales**.

EXAMPLE 2   **Subtracting Returns When Using Commissions**

Jessie Winkler sells food supplements and vitamins and is paid commission of 4.5% of net sales. His territory includes several states in the northeastern part of the United States and also Quebec, Canada. Find his commission for a month with $98,450 in sales and $2650 in returns.

Solution

Find net sales before finding the commission.

$$\text{Net sales} = \$98,450 - \$2650 = \$95,800$$
$$\text{Commission} = 4.5\% \text{ of } \$95,800$$
$$= 0.045 \times \$95,800 = \$4311$$

Objective

2   *Determine Commission Using a Variable Commission Rate.* The **sliding-scale**, or **variable**, **commission** plan is a method of pay designed to retain top-producing salespeople. With these plans, a higher rate of commission is paid as sales get larger and larger.

EXAMPLE 3   **Finding Earnings Using Variable Commission**

Roberto Virez sells smart phones to retail chains in the Dallas–Ft. Worth area. His commission is based on the monthly sales that he generates, as follows.

Sales Generated	Rate
First $10,000 in sales	7.5%
Sales between $10,001 and $20,000	9%
All sales above $20,000	10%

Find Virez's gross earnings if he generates $42,003 in sales in June.

Solution

It may help to think of Virez's earnings as shown.

$$\underset{\$10,000 \text{ in sales}}{7.5\% \text{ of the first}} + \underset{\$10,000 \text{ in sales}}{9\% \text{ on the next}} + \underset{\text{above } \$20,000}{10\% \text{ on any sales}}$$

Amount of sales above \$20,000 = \$42,003 − \$20,000 = \$22,003

	Calculation	Commission
On first \$10,000 in sales =	\$10,000 × 0.075 =	\$750.00
On next \$10,000 in sales =	\$10,000 × 0.09 =	\$900.00
On last \$22,003	= \$ 22,003 × 0.10 =	\$2200.30
	Total	\$3850.30

Virez's gross earnings are \$3850.30.

It may be easier to first find the commission earned at the highest rate and *place* it in memory.

(42003 − 20000) × 10 % = 2200.3 STO

Next, find the commission at the second-highest rate and *add* this to memory.

(20000 − 10000) × 9 % = + RCL = 3100.3 STO

Finally, find the commission at the lowest rate and *add* it to memory. The result is the total commission.

10000 × 7.5 % = + RCL = 3850.3

Objective

3 *Use Salary and Commission Rate to Find Gross Earnings.* With a **salary plus commission**, the salesperson is paid a fixed sum per pay period, plus a commission on all sales. This method of payment is commonly used by large retail stores. Gross earnings with salary plus commission are found by the following formula.

Gross earnings = fixed amount per pay period + amount earned on commission

Many salespeople favor this method of determining gross earnings. It is especially attractive to the beginning salesperson who lacks selling experience and personal self-confidence. While providing an incentive, it offers the security of a guaranteed income to cover basic living costs.

EXAMPLE 4 **Adding Commission to a Salary**

Pat Quinlin is paid \$225 per week by the Potters Exchange, plus 3% on all sales. Find her gross earnings for a week in which her sales were \$7250.

Solution

$$
\begin{aligned}
\text{Gross earnings} &= \text{fixed earnings} + \text{commission} \\
&= \$225 \quad\quad + (0.03 \times \$7250) \\
&= \$225 \quad\quad + \$217.50 \\
&= \$442.50
\end{aligned}
$$

NOTE Workers paid by commission may include salespeople in clothing stores and even waiters and waitresses in high-end restaurants who are paid a commission on sales of wine or other items.

Objective

4 *Use a Drawing Account and Quota to Find Gross Earnings.* The fixed amount of earnings is often a **draw**, or loan, against future commissions. A **drawing account** is set up with the amounts drawn repaid with future commissions. This is a loan against future commissions but offers the salesperson the assurance of a fixed sum per pay period. The salesperson must repay the drawing account as commissions are earned.

EXAMPLE 5 **Subtracting a Draw from Commission**

Elizabeth Owens, a computer sales representative, has sales of $77,120 for the month and is paid a 7% commission rate. Find her gross earnings at the end of the month given that she took a $750 draw mid-month.

Solution

$$\text{Gross earnings (end of month)} = \text{commissions} - \text{draw}$$
$$= (0.07 \times \$77,120) - \$750$$
$$= \$5398.40 - \$750$$
$$= \$4648.40$$

However, Owens' total income for the month is $5398.40, since she also keeps the draw of $750.

NOTE It can be risky to work only for commissions since sales can be low some months, resulting in low earnings for the month. As a result, many companies offer a plan that includes a low base salary plus a commission used to motivate people to greater achievements.

Figure 6.5 shows the occupations with the highest number of projected jobs.

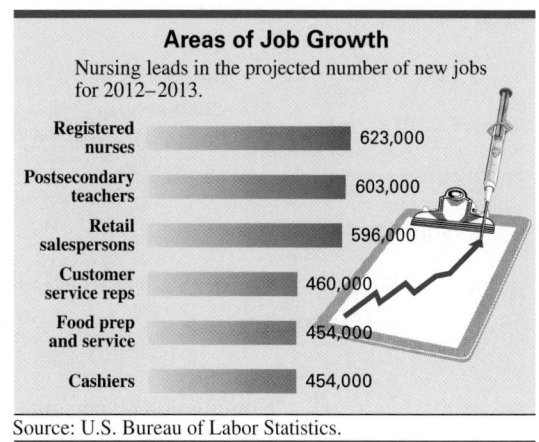

Source: U.S. Bureau of Labor Statistics.

Figure 6.5

A sales quota is often established for salespeople. The **quota** is the minimum amount of sales expected from the employee. If the salesperson continually falls short of the sales quota, the person may be terminated. Normally, however, the salesperson is rewarded with a bonus or commission for passing the sales quota. This plan is called a **quota bonus system**.

EXAMPLE 6　**Using the Quota Bonus System**

David Shea is a sales representative for a mountain bike manufacturer. During a recent week, he had sales of $18,780 and was paid a commission of 8% after meeting the sales quota of $5000. Find his gross earnings.

Solution

The commission is paid only on sales above the quota.

$$
\begin{aligned}
\text{Gross earnings} &= \text{commission rate} \times (\text{sales} - \text{quota}) \\
&= 0.08 \times (\$18{,}780 - \$5000) \qquad \text{No commission on} \\
&= 0.08 \times \$13{,}780 \qquad\qquad\qquad \text{the first \$5000} \\
&= \$1102.40
\end{aligned}
$$

Objective

5　*Determine Override as Part of Gross Earnings.* Sales supervisors and department heads are often paid from two sources. First, they receive a commission on their own personal sales. Second, they also receive a commission called an **override** on the total sales of their department. The override is used to reward the manager for training and motivating sales staff. It is difficult to do a great job managing people, and managers are usually rewarded by making more than nonmanagers, although some salespeople earn high incomes.

EXAMPLE 7　**Finding Gross Earnings with Commission and Override**

Taylor's Men's Shoppe pays the manager of one department a salary plus commission and override on department sales. Find the earnings for a manager given the following information for one week.

	Manager	Department
Sales	$5850	$23,650
Returns	$187	$768
Base Salary	$400	—
Quota	$2000	—
Commission Rate	5%	
Override Rate	1%	

Solution

First, find the commission on personal sales.

$$
\begin{aligned}
\text{Personal sales} - \text{returns} - \text{quota} &= \$5850 - \$187 - \$2000 \\
&= \$3663
\end{aligned}
$$

$$
\text{Commission on personal sales} = 5\% \times \$3663 = \$183.15
$$

Then, find the override commission on department sales.

$$
\text{Department sales} - \text{returns} = \$23{,}650 - \$768 = \$22{,}882
$$

$$
\text{Override on department sales} = \$22{,}882 \times 0.01 = \$228.82
$$

Finally, find the manager's gross earnings.

$$\text{Gross earnings} = \text{salary} + \text{commission} + \text{override}$$
$$= \$400 + \$183.15 + \$228.82$$
$$= \$811.97$$

 Scientific Calculator Approach

In solving Example 7, the approach here is to first find the manager's commission on personal sales and *place* it in memory.

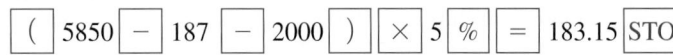

(5850 − 187 − 2000) × 5 % = 183.15 STO

Next, find the override on department sales and *add* it to memory.

(23650 − 768) × 1 % = + RCL = 411.97 STO

Finally, *add* the salary to the commission and override in memory. The result is the gross earnings.

400 + RCL = 811.97

6.2 Exercises

COMMISSION WITH RETURNS Find the gross earnings for each of the following salespeople.

	Employee	Total Sales	Returns and Allowances	Rate of Commission	
1.	McKee, J.	$2810	$208	8%	$208.16
2.	Brown, D.	$5734	$415	5%	$265.95
3.	Pasnick, J.	$2875	$64	15%	$421.65
4.	Beckenstein, J.	$2603	$76	18%	$454.86
5.	Brown, K.	$25,658	$4083	9%	$1941.75
6.	Dramatinos, M.	$18,765	$386	8%	$1470.32
7.	Dobbins, G.	$45,618	$2281	1%	$433.37
8.	Phares, H.	$34,183	$1169	2%	$660.28

VARIABLE COMMISSION In addition to a small monthly base salary, Jetta Pools and Spas pays its salespeople a monthly commission, determined as follows:

6% on first $7500 in sales

8% on next $7500 in sales

10% on any sales over $15,000

Find the commission for each of the following employees.

	Employee	Total Sales			Employee	Total Sales	
9.	Dean, D.	$18,550	$1405	10.	Davis, C.	$17,640	$1314
11.	Brueck, G.	$10,480	$688.40	12.	Koch, R.	$16,250	$1175
13.	Sanchez, J.	$11,225	$748	14.	Fisher, L.	$22,650	$1815
15.	Butter, M.	$25,860	$2136	16.	Manly, C.	$23,340	$1884

17. When you are paid a commission, there is always the possibility of higher earnings and also the uncertainty about a paycheck. Explain in your own words the special budgetary planning you would have to do if you were paid on commission.

 18. A variable commission plan is often referred to as an incentive within an incentive. Explain why this might be an accurate description of a variable commission plan. (See Objective 2.)

COMMISSION PAYROLL LEDGER Complete the following commission payroll to find gross earnings.

	Employee	Gross Sales	Sales Returns	Net Quota	Commission Sales	Commission Rate	Gross Commission	Salary	Gross Earnings
19.	Potter, D.	$5250	$220	—	$5030	4%	$201.20	$290	$491.20
20.	Schwartz, A.	$9370	$840	$3000	$5530	10%	$553	—	$553
21.	Reska, L.	$6380	$295	$2000	$4085	6%	$245.10	$500	$745.10
22.	Wetherbee, S.	$3270	$420	—	$2850	7%	$199.50	$280	$479.50
23.	Chen, C.	$22,420	$390	$2500	$19,530	3%	$585.90	—	$585.90
24.	Ng, B.	$10,680	$490	$1500	$8690	6%	$521.40	—	$521.40
25.	Jidobu, B.	$4215	$318	$1000	$2897	5%	$144.85	$310	$454.85
26.	Kroeger, T.	$3850	$310	$1400	$2140	6%	$128.40	$350	$478.40

Solve the following application problems.

27. **ART SUPPLIES** Laura Akahori is a sales representative for Wholesale Art. She is paid an 11% commission rate and has had a draw of $450 this week. If her sales are $12,420 this week, find her gross earnings after repaying the drawing account. $916.20

28. **COMMISSION DRAW** Kim Craft has sales of $78,560 for the month and is paid a 6% commission rate. She has had draws totaling $1500 for the month. Find her gross earnings after repaying the drawing account. $3213.60

29. **SALARY PLUS COMMISSION** Stacy Dwyer, a salesperson for Zapp Music, has sales of $194,800 this month and is paid a 2% commission by her company. She also receives a salary of $1750 each month. Find her gross earnings for the month. $5646

30. **EDUCATIONAL SALES** Nancy White, an account representative for Kreative Kids, is paid a 4% commission rate and a salary of $200 each week. If her sales are $25,510 this week, find her gross earnings for the week. $1220.40

31. **OFFICE SYSTEMS** Arthur Zinshyang is a commissioned salesperson for Office Systems, Inc., which allows him to draw $800 per month. His commission is 6% of the first $6000 in sales, 8% of the next $16,000, and 15% of all sales over $22,000. If his sales for the month were $27,700, find (a) his total commission and (b) the earnings due at the end of the month after repaying the drawing account balance of $800. (a) $2495 (b) $1695

32. **SALES** Emma Clarke is a sales representative for Hi Side Greeting Card Company. She is paid a monthly draw of $650. Her commission is 10% of the first $2000 in sales, 12% of the next $4000, and 20% of all sales over $6000. If her sales for the month were $13,750, find (a) her total commission and (b) the gross earnings due at the end of the month after repaying the drawing account. (a) $2230 (b) $1580

33. **COMMISSION PLUS OVERRIDE** A manager at Medco Health is paid a weekly salary plus commission and an override. Find his gross earnings given the following.

Personal sales	$5650	Personal returns	$168
Department sales	$17,312	Department returns	$634
Salary	$400	Personal quota	$1000
Commission rate	5%	Override	$1\frac{1}{2}\%$

$874.27

34. APPLIANCE SALES MANAGER   The sales manager for A&A Appliance is paid a salary plus commission and an override. Find her gross earnings given the following.

Personal sales	$5856	Personal returns	$185	
Store sales	$19,622	Store returns	$358	$715.41
Salary	$250	Personal quota	$3000	
Commission rate	3%	Override	2%	

6.3	**Gross Earnings (Piecework)**

OBJECTIVES

1 *Find the gross earnings for piecework.*

2 *Find the gross earnings for differential piecework.*

3 *Determine chargebacks or dockings.*

4 *Find overtime earnings for piecework.*

The salaries and wages discussed in **Section 6.1** are called **time rates**, since they depend only on the amount of time an employee was actually on the job. Commission earnings in **Section 6.2** and the piecework methods discussed in this section are called **incentive rates**. These gross earnings are based on production and pay an employee for actual performance on the job. The 10 help-wanted ads from the classified section of the newspaper are for jobs offering incentive rates of pay. The ad for lathers and stucco construction workers offers piecework and hourly compensation; the ad for truck drivers lists piece rates of $0.45 per mile (cpm). The ads for bill collectors and commercial roofing, health insurance, Better Business Bureau membership, automobile, swimming pool, and home security system sales positions pay on a commission plan.

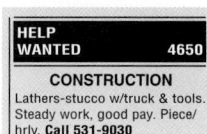

Objective

1   *Find the Gross Earnings for Piecework.*   A **piecework rate** pays an employee so much per item produced. Gross earnings are found using the following formula.

$$\text{Gross earnings} = \text{pay per item} \times \text{number of items}$$

For example, a truck driver who drives 2000 miles in a week and is paid a piecework rate of $0.45 per mile earns

$$\text{Gross earnings} = 2000 \times \$0.45 = \$900$$

for the week.

EXAMPLE 1   Finding Gross Earnings for Piecework

Dona Kenly was paid $0.85 for sewing a jacket collar, $0.98 for a sleeve with a cuff, and $1.10 for a lapel. One week she sewed 318 jacket collars, 112 sleeves with cuffs, and 37 lapels. Find her gross earnings.

Solution

Multiply the rate per item by the number of that type of item.

Item	Rate × Number = Total
Jacket collars	$0.85 × 318 = $270.30
Sleeves with cuffs	$0.98 × 112 = $109.76
Lapels	$1.10 × 37 = $40.70
	Gross earnings = $420.76

Objective

2   *Find the Gross Earnings for Differential Piecework.*   A **straight-piecework plan**, such as in Example 1, is perhaps the oldest of all incentive payment plans. It is used in many manufacturing and production jobs such as fine jewelry finishing, agricultural and farm work, garment manufacturing, as well as in the building trades for structural framing, roofing, and floor laying. While many workers prefer working under a piecework plan, there are just as many who dislike it. Labor unions and other employee organizations, senior employees, and others claim that piecework plans result in unsafe work habits and poor workmanship.

Companies still using piecework have often made various modifications and changes to the straight-piecework plan. Many of these modified plans incorporate initial quotas and then offer an additional **premium rate** for each item produced beyond the quota. These plans offer an added incentive within an incentive. For example, in the **differential-piecework plan** the rate paid per item depends on the number of items produced.

EXAMPLE 2   Using Differential Piecework

Jabil Circuits pays assemblers as follows.

1–100 units	$2.10 each
101–150 units	$2.25 each
151 or more units	$2.40 each

Find the gross earnings of an employee producing 214 items.

Solution

Be sure you understand how the employee is paid. It may help to rewrite as follows.

$$\frac{\$2.10 \text{ on the}}{\text{first 100 units}} + \frac{\$2.25 \text{ on the}}{\text{next 50 units}} + \frac{\$2.40 \text{ on all units}}{\text{beyond 150}}$$

The number of units produced beyond above 150 is $214 - 150 = 64$.

	Calculation	Commission
On first 100 units	$= 100 \times \$2.10 =$	\$210.00
On next 50 units	$= 50 \times \$2.25 =$	\$112.50
On last 64 units	$= 64 \times \$2.40 =$	\$153.60
	Total	\$476.10

The gross earnings are \$476.10.

Objective

3 *Determine Chargebacks or Dockings.* While companies are often pleased to reward employees with premium rates for surpassing quotas, management is very concerned with unacceptable quality and unusable production. Ruined items may produce a total loss of material and labor or correctable flaws that require additional handling, resulting in added costs and decreased profits. To discourage carelessness and mistakes, many companies require the employee to share in the cost of the spoiled item. These penalties, called **chargebacks** or **dockings**, are normally at a lower rate than the employee receives for producing that piece. This lower rate is used because a small amount of production error is expected.

EXAMPLE **3** **Understanding and Using Chargebacks**

In Example 2, suppose the company had a chargeback of \$2.50 per spoiled item and the employee had spoiled 14 items. Find the gross earnings after the chargeback.

Solution

Gross earnings are found by subtracting the chargeback from piece rate earnings.

$$\begin{aligned}
\text{Gross earnings} &= \text{piecework earnings} - (\text{spoiled items} \times \text{chargeback rate}) \\
&= \$476.10 - (14 \text{ items} \times \$2.50) \\
&= \$476.10 - \$35 \\
&= \$441.10
\end{aligned}$$

Piecework and differential-piecework rates are frequently modified to include some guaranteed hourly rate of pay. Often this is necessary to meet minimum wage laws. To satisfy the law, the employer may either pay minimum wage or piecework earnings, *whichever is higher.*

EXAMPLE 4   **Finding Earnings with a Guaranteed Hourly Wage**

A tire installer at the Tire Center is paid $8.40 per hour for an 8-hour day, or $0.95 per tire installed—whichever is higher. Find the weekly earnings for an employee having the following rate of production.

Monday	86 installations
Tuesday	70 installations
Wednesday	88 installations
Thursday	68 installations
Friday	82 installations

Solution

The hourly earnings for an 8-hour day are $67.20 (8 × $8.40). If the piecework earnings for the day are less than this amount, the hourly earnings will be paid.

Monday	86 × $0.95 =	$81.70	Piece rate
Tuesday	~~70 × $0.95~~ =	$67.20	Hourly (piece rate is $66.50)
Wednesday	88 × $0.95 =	$83.60	Piece rate
Thursday	~~68 × $0.95~~ =	$67.20	Hourly (piece rate is $64.60)
Friday	82 × $0.95 =	$77.90	Piece rate
		$377.60	Weekly earnings

The worker *cannot* earn less than $8.40 per hour, or $67.20 ($8.40 × 8) for the day. Since the piecework earnings on Tuesday and Thursday in this example fall below the hourly minimum, the hourly rate, or $67.20 for the day, is paid on those days.

Objective

4   *Find Overtime Earnings for Piecework.* Piecework employees, just as other workers, are paid time-and-a-half for overtime. The overtime rate may be computed as $1\frac{1}{2}$ times the hourly rate, but most often the overtime rate is $1\frac{1}{2}$ times the regular rate per piece.

EXAMPLE 5   **Determining Earnings with Overtime Piecework**

Ryan Andrews is paid $0.98 per child's bicycle assembled. During one week, he assembles 480 bicycles on regular time and 104 bicycles during overtime hours. Find his gross earnings for the week if time-and-a-half per assembly is paid for overtime.

Solution

$$\text{Gross earnings} = \text{earnings at regular piece rate} + \text{earnings at overtime piece rate}$$
$$= 480 \times \$0.98 + (104 \times 1\frac{1}{2} \times \$0.98)$$
$$= \$470.40 + \$152.88$$
$$= \$623.28$$

Scientific
Calculator
Approach

The calculator solution to Example 5 uses parentheses to first calculate the overtime piece rate.

480 ⨉ .98 + (104 ⨉ 1.5 ⨉ .98) = 623.28

| 6.3 | Exercises |

PETCO Complete the following payroll ledger given that employees are paid a straight piece rate. Rates per unit vary depending on worker skills involved.

	Employee	\multicolumn{5}{c}{Units Produced}	Total Pieces	Rate per Unit	Gross Earnings
		M	T	W	Th	F			
1.	Mora, E.	150	124	172	110	96	652	$0.58	$378.16
2.	Motton, T.	120	108	89	130	95	542	$0.87	$471.54
3.	Young, C.	98	86	79	108	80	451	$0.75	$338.25
4.	McIntosh, R.	67	54	72	83	59	335	$0.93	$311.55
5.	Todd, R.	118	124	143	132	148	665	$0.68	$452.20
6.	Eckern, G.	157	148	169	145	178	797	$0.59	$470.23
7.	King, M.	125	118	115	132	98	588	$0.46	$270.48
8.	Demaree, D.	152	136	170	144	192	794	$0.43	$341.42
9.	Parker, R.	149	135	118	125	143	670	$0.78	$522.60
10.	Pearson, D.	96	84	115	102	96	493	$0.72	$354.96

FRUIT INSPECTION Production workers at Classic Fruit Distributors are paid as follows to inspect and package crates of fruit.

1–200 crates	$1.00 each
201–400 crates	$1.08 each
Over 400 crates	$1.15 each

Find the weekly gross earnings for each of the full- and part-time workers.

	Employee	Number of Crates				Employee	Number of Crates	
11.	Dalton, S.	190	$190.00		**12.**	Peterson, K.	180	$180.00
13.	Zhao, F.	228	$230.24		**14.**	Nguyen, A.	310	$318.80
15.	Simms, B.	405	$421.75		**16.**	Getz, J.	420	$439.00

HOURLY/PIECEWORK RATES Find the gross earnings for each of the following agricultural employees. Each has an 8-hour workday and is paid $0.75 for each unit of production or the hourly rate, whichever is greater. Note that agricultural workers are not covered by the Fair Labor Standards Act, so they are often paid less than the minimum wage.

	Employee	\multicolumn{5}{c}{Units Produced}	Hourly Rate	Gross Earnings
		M	T	W	Th	F		
17.	Knab, C.	66	75	58	72	68	$6.18	$260.19
18.	DeCicco, A.	62	78	79	80	81	$7.20	$296.10
19.	Wilson, M.	80	60	75	78	74	$6.80	$284.65
20.	Viale, D.	72	70	62	88	82	$6.50	$286
21.	Zurcher, S.	75	84	72	93	67	$6.75	$297
22.	Frase, E.	63	57	67	75	70	$5.70	$251.85
23.	Pantera, A.	73	62	78	64	81	$6.30	$274.80
24.	Enos, C.	90	77	89	102	99	$8.10	$349.80

PIECEWORK WITH OVERTIME   Find the gross earnings for each of the following employees. Overtime is $1\frac{1}{2}$ times the normal per piece rate. Rejected units are charged at the chargeback rate.

	Employee	Units Produced Reg.	Units Produced O.T.	Rejected Units	Rate per Unit	Chargeback per Unit	Gross Earnings
25.	Miller, J.	510	74	20	$0.72	$0.38	$439.52
26.	Kavanagh, M.	380	26	6	$0.69	$0.56	$285.75
27.	Boghoussian, A.	493	74	34	$0.86	$0.46	$503.80
28.	Carlson, K.	508	38	16	$0.59	$0.42	$326.63
29.	Balbi, G.	286	38	4	$0.95	$0.82	$322.57
30.	Fukano, H.	315	64	35	$0.74	$0.65	$281.39
31.	Hughes, G.	403	72	15	$0.68	$0.45	$340.73
32.	Dos Reis, A.	452	12	6	$0.59	$0.50	$274.30

33. Wages and salaries are known as time rates, while commissions are called incentive rates of pay. Explain in your own words the difference between these payment methods.

34. Describe what a chargeback or docking is for rejected units. Why do you think that the chargeback per unit is usually less than the rate paid per unit? (See Objective 3.)

Solve the following application problems.

35. MINIATURE TRAIN   Greg Jackson is paid $4.75 for each train assembled, charged $2.25 for each rejection, and paid time-and-a-half for overtime production. Find his gross earnings for the 2-week period when he assembles 142 trains at the regular rate and 26 at the overtime rate and has 7 chargebacks. $844

36. CAKE DECORATING   John Davis decorates cakes at the French Meadow Bakery, for which he is paid $2.42 each. He is charged $1.40 per rejection and paid time-and-a-half for all overtime production. Find his gross earnings when production for the week is 128 cakes at the regular rate and 19 cakes at the overtime rate. He has a total of 5 chargebacks. $371.73

37. FAUCET ASSEMBLY   Mike Kinney is paid $2.35 per faucet assembled, charged $1.05 for each rejection, and paid time-and-a-half for overtime production. Find his gross earnings for the week when he assembles 228 faucets at the regular rate, 74 faucets at the overtime rate, and has 18 chargebacks. $777.75

38. COSTUME PRODUCTION   Kristen Clement sews lace on dance costumes, for which she is paid $1.18 each. She is charged $0.90 per rejection and is paid time-and-a-half for all overtime production. Find her gross earnings when production during a 3-day workweek is 138 costumes at the regular rate and 28 costumes at the overtime rate. She has a total of 9 chargebacks. $204.30

39. TOY TRAIN PACKAGING   Anna Kauffman packages toy train sets. She is paid $1.15 per unit and is charged $0.45 for each rejection. Find her gross earnings for the week given the following production.

	M	T	W	Th	F	Totals	
Production	142	106	118	98	110	574	$648.40
Chargebacks	6	3	5	8	4	26	

40. PACKING AND SHIPPING   Steve Zagorin checks and ships customer orders for Feathers and Stream Fishing Lures. He receives $0.48 per package and is charged $0.40 for each rejection. Find his gross earnings for the week given the following production.

	M	T	W	Th	F	Totals	
Production	178	165	186	171	174	874	$411.12
Chargebacks	5	3	2	7	4	21	

| 6.4 | **Social Security, Medicare, and Other Taxes** |

OBJECTIVES

1 *Understand FICA.*

2 *Find the maximum FICA tax paid by an employee in one year.*

3 *Understand Medicare tax.*

4 *Find FICA tax and Medicare tax.*

5 *Determine the FICA tax and the Medicare tax paid by a self-employed person.*

6 *Find state disability insurance deductions.*

Finding the gross earnings is simply the first step for an employer. The amount actually paid to an employee is called the **net pay**. Look at the long list of required and potential deductions from gross pay. Imagine having to calculate payroll on dozens or hundreds of employees, each with some or most of these deductions.

Gross pay

- Social Security tax (FICA)
- Medicare tax
- Federal income taxes
- State income taxes
- Group health, life, and/or dental insurance (if any)
- Retirement contributions by individual (if any)
- State disability insurance (if any)
- Savings, bonds, loan payments (if any)
- Union dues (if any)
- Payments to charities (if any)

Net pay

Objective

1 *Understand FICA.* The **Federal Insurance Contributions Act (FICA)** was passed into law in the 1930s during the middle of the Great Depression. This plan, now called **Social Security,** was originally designed to give monthly benefits to retired workers and their survivors. Also included today are death benefits and **Medicare** payments. As the number of people receiving benefits has increased along with the individual benefit amounts, people paying into Social Security have had to pay a larger amount of earnings into this fund each year. From 1937 through 1950 an employee paid 1% of income into Social Security, up to a maximum of $30 per year. This amount has increased over the years until an employee in 2009 paid 6.2% of income to FICA and 1.45% to Medicare, which together can total $8170 or more per year.

For many years, both the Social Security tax rate and the Medicare tax rate were combined. However, since 1991 these tax rates have been expressed individually. Table 6.2 shows the tax rates and the maximum earnings on which Social Security and Medicare taxes are paid by the employee. The employer pays the same rate as the employee, matching all employee contributions dollar for dollar. Self-employed people pay double the rate paid by those who are employees, since they are effectively both the employee and the employer.

Notice in Table 6.2 that the Social Security and Medicare tax rates have remained constant since 2000. However, the maximum amount of earnings subject to the FICA and Medicare taxes often increased. At first glance, one might think that these data suggest that more of the cost of these programs is being shifted to people with higher earnings. But, the increase in maximum earnings subject to tax is really just an adjustment for inflation. In other words, earnings of $76,200 in 2000 provided about the same purchasing power as earnings of $110,100 in 2012. Inflation is a very important topic and we cover it in more detail in Chapter 12.

Table 6.2 MAXIMUM EARNINGS ON WHICH SOCIAL SECURITY AND MEDICARE TAXES ARE PAID

	Social Security Tax		Medicare Tax	
Year	Social Security Tax Rate	Employee Earnings Subject to the Tax	Medicare Tax Rate	Employee Earnings Subject to the Tax
2000	6.2%	$76,200	1.45%	all
2005	6.2%	$90,000	1.45%	all
2010	6.2%	$106,800	1.45%	all
2012	6.2%[1]	$110,100	1.45%	all

[1] The social security tax rate was temporarily reduced in 2012 due to the financial crisis.

NOTE Since both the maximum amount of earnings subject to tax and the tax rates change annually, we will use 6.2% of the first $110,000 for Social Security taxes and 1.45% of all earnings for Medicare taxes. Use the Social Security Administration's Web page at www.ssa.gov to find the current rates and maximum earnings subject to taxes.

Each employee in the United States must have a Social Security number. You can apply for one at a local post office. Future benefits depend on the amount of money contributed to the fund during an individual's working years. Each year, the Social Security Administration sends out a statement to workers 25 and older showing how much they will be paid in the event of retirement, disability, or death. You can submit a **Request for Earnings and Benefit Estimate Statement**, as shown in Figure 6.6, to get an estimate of your future benefits. Check it carefully for errors! Errors can only be corrected within the first three years. Not catching an error may be like throwing money into the trash!

Request for *Social Security Statement*

☐ Please check this box if you want to get your *Statement* in Spanish instead of English.

Please print or type your answers. When you have completed the form, fold it and mail it to us. If you prefer to send your request using the Internet, go to *www.socialsecurity.gov.*

1. Name shown on your Social Security card:

First Name _____ Middle Initial ____

Last Name Only _____

2. Your Social Security number as shown on your card:

☐☐☐-☐☐-☐☐☐☐

3. Your date of birth (Mo.-Day-Yr.)

☐☐-☐☐-☐☐☐☐

4. Other Social Security numbers you have used:

☐☐☐-☐☐-☐☐☐☐
☐☐☐-☐☐-☐☐☐☐

5. Your Sex: ☐ Male ☐ Female

For items 6 and 8, show only earnings covered by Social Security. Do NOT include wages from state, local or federal government employment that are NOT covered by Social Security or that are covered ONLY by Medicare.

6. Show your actual earnings (wages and/or net self-employment income) for last year and your estimated earnings for this year.

A. Last year's actual earnings: *(Dollars Only)*

$☐☐☐,☐☐☐.☐0☐0

B. This year's estimated earnings: *(Dollars Only)*

$☐☐☐,☐☐☐.☐0☐0

7. Show the age at which you plan to stop working:

☐☐ *(Show only one age)*

8. Below, show the average yearly amount (not your total future lifetime earnings) that you think you will earn between now and when you plan to stop working. Include performance and/or scheduled pay increases or bonuses, but not cost-of-living increases.

If you expect to earn significantly more or less in the future due to promotions, job changes, part-time work or an absence from the work force, enter the amount that most closely reflects your future average yearly earnings.

If you don't expect any significant changes, show the same amount you are earning now (the amount in 6B).

Future average yearly earnings: *(Dollars Only)*

$☐☐☐,☐☐☐.☐0☐0

9. Do you want us to send the *Statement:*
   • To you? Enter your name and mailing address.
   • To someone else (your accountant, pension plan, etc.)? Enter your name with "c/o" and the name and address of that person or organization.

"C/O" or Street Address (Include Apt. No., P.O. Box, Rural Route)

_____
Street Address

_____
Street Address (If Foreign Address, enter City, Province, Postal Code)

_____
U.S. City, State, ZIP code (If Foreign Address, enter Name of Country only)

NOTICE:
I am asking for information about my own Social Security record or the record of a person I am authorized to represent. I declare under penalty of perjury that I have examined all the information on this form, and on any accompanying statements or forms, and it is true and correct to the best of my knowledge. I authorize you to use a contractor to send the *Social Security Statement* to the person and address in item 9.

►

Please sign your name (Do Not Print)

_____
Date   (Area Code) Daytime Telephone No.

Form **SSA-7004-SM** (06-2008) EF (06-2008)
10-2006 edition may be used

Printed on recycled paper

Figure 6.6

Objective

2 *Find the Maximum FICA Tax Paid by an Employee in One Year.* Since Social Security rates and maximum earnings change annually, we assume throughout the book that the taxes are paid only on gross earnings up to $110,000 per year.

Social Security tax = 6.2% of gross earnings up to $110,000 per year

No Social Security taxes are paid on any gross earnings above $110,000 in one year.

> **NOTE** Only about 7% of all income earners reach the cutoff point of $110,000 for Social Security taxes.

Objective

3 *Understand Medicare Tax.* Medicare tax is paid on *all* earnings. Multiply the earnings by 1.45% to find the tax.

Objective

4 *Find FICA Tax and Medicare Tax.* When finding the amounts to be withheld for Social Security tax and Medicare tax, the employer must use the current rates and the maximum earnings amount.

EXAMPLE **1** **Finding FICA Tax and Medicare Tax**

Find the Social Security tax and the Medicare tax for the following gross earnings.

(a) D. Horwitz; $478.15   **(b)** C. Christensen; $522.83

Solution

(a) Social Security tax = 6.2% × $478.15

$\qquad\qquad\qquad$ = 0.062 × $478.15 = $29.65   Rounded

$\quad$ Medicare tax = 1.45% × $478.15

$\qquad\qquad\qquad$ = 0.0145 × $478.15 = $6.93   Rounded

(b) Social Security tax = 6.2% × $522.83

$\qquad\qquad\qquad$ = 0.062 × $522.83 = $32.42   Rounded

$\quad$ Medicare tax = 1.45% × $522.83

$\qquad\qquad\qquad$ = 0.0145 × $522.83 = $7.58   Rounded

EXAMPLE **2** **Finding FICA Tax**

Shannon Woolums has earned $107,634.05 so far this year. Her gross earnings for the current pay period are $5224.03. Find her Social Security tax.

Solution

Social Security tax is paid on only the first $110,000 earned in a year. Woolums has already earned $107,634.05. Subtract $107,634.05 from $110,000, to find the amount subject to Social Security tax.

$\qquad$ $110,000.00   Maximum earning subject to Social Security tax

$\qquad$ − $107,634.05   Earnings to date

$\qquad$ $2,365.95   Earnings on which tax is due

The Social Security tax on $2365.95 is $146.69 ($2365.95 × 6.2%) (rounded). Therefore, Woolums pays $146.69 for the current pay period and no additional Social Security tax for the rest of the year.

Table 6.3 compares the contributions to social programs (Social Security and Medicare) in selected countries around the world. How do U.S. workers' (employee) contributions compare to those in other countries?

Table 6.3 SOCIAL INSURANCE CONTRIBUTIONS AS A PERCENT OF TOTAL GROSS EARNINGS

Country	Employee	Employer
Italy	10.26	48.00
France	20.66	42.57
Sweden	33.00	7.00
Belgium	14.24	32.73
Mexico	22.00	3.00
Germany	21.12	21.12
Netherlands	7.04	13.05
Japan	11.00	12.00
Ireland	5.52	10.54
U.K.	7.08	10.00
Switzerland	6.55	8.37
Canada	5.00	8.00
U.S.A.	7.65	7.65

Sources: Benefits Report Europe, USA, and Canada; Watson Wyatt Worldwide, and Knight Ridder Tribune.

Objective

5 *Determine the FICA Tax and the Medicare Tax Paid by a Self-Employed Person.* People who are self-employed pay higher Social Security tax and higher Medicare tax than people who work for others. There is no employer to match the employee contribution so the self-employed person pays a rate that is double that of the employee. The gross earnings of the self-employed person are first multiplied by 92.35% (0.9235) to find the adjusted earnings. These adjusted earnings are then multiplied by the current rates. In our examples the self-employed person pays 12.4% (6.2% × 2) of adjusted earnings for Social Security tax and 2.9% (1.455% × 2) of adjusted earnings for Medicare tax.

EXAMPLE 3 Finding FICA and Medicare Tax for the Self-Employed

Find the Social Security tax and the Medicare tax paid by Sashaya Davis, a self-employed Web-page designer who had adjusted earnings of $53,820 this year.

Solution

$$\text{Social Security tax} = \$53,820 \times 12.4\% = \$53,820 \times 0.124 = \$6673.68$$
$$\text{Medicare tax} = \$53,820 \times 2.9\% = \$53,820 \times 0.029 = \$1560.78$$

NOTE Social Security taxes apply only to the first $110,000 in self-employment income, whereas Medicare taxes apply to total gross earnings with no upper limit.

NOTE Always use the current tax rates for both Social Security and Medicare. These can always be found in Circular E, *Employer's Tax Guide*, which is available from the Internal Revenue Service.

Objective

6 *Find State Disability Insurance Deductions.* Many states have a state disability insurance program that is paid for by employees. If disabled, the employee would receive weekly benefits. A typical state program defines "disability" as "any illness or injury incurred on or off the job, either physical or mental, including pregnancy, childbirth, or related condition, that prevents you from doing your regular work." The employee processes the claim after obtaining certification from a doctor or other qualified examiner.

A typical state program also requires the qualifying employee to pay a **state disability insurance (SDI)** deduction of 1% of the first $31,800 earned each year. There are no payments on earnings above this amount. Some states have similar programs, but their insurance is placed with private insurance companies rather than with the state.

EXAMPLE **4** **Finding State Disability Insurance Deductions**

Find the state disability deduction for an employee at Comet Auto Parts with gross earnings of $418 this pay period. The SDI rate is 1%, and the employee has not earned $31,800 this year.

Solution

$$\text{State disability deduction} = 1\% \text{ of } \$418$$
$$= 0.01 \times \$418 = \$4.18$$

EXAMPLE **5** **Finding State Disability Insurance Deductions**

Milo Lacy has earned $30,620 so far this year. Find the SDI deduction if gross earnings this pay period are $3096. Use an SDI rate of 1% on the first $31,800.

Solution

The SDI deduction will be taken on $1180 of the current gross earnings.

$$
\begin{array}{ll}
\$31,800 & \text{Maximum earning subject to SDI} \\
- \$30,620 & \text{Earnings this year} \\
\hline
\$1,180 & \text{Earnings this year subject to SDI}
\end{array}
$$

The SDI deduction is $11.80 ($1180 × 1%).

NOTE Those involved in payroll work must always be up-to-date on the current rates and the maximum annual earning amounts against which FICA, Medicare, and SDI payroll deductions may be taken.

| **6.4** | **Exercises** |

SOCIAL SECURITY AND MEDICARE TAX Find the Social Security tax and the Medicare tax for each of the following amounts of gross earnings. Assume a 6.2% FICA rate and a 1.45% Medicare tax rate.

1. $324.72 $20.13; $4.71   **2.** $207.25 $12.85; $3.01

3. $463.24 $28.72; $6.72   **4.** $606.35 $37.59; $8.79

5. $854.71 $52.99; $12.39   **6.** $683.65 $42.39; $9.91

7. $1086.25 $67.35; $15.75   **8.** $1243.18 $77.08; $18.03

MAXIMUM SOCIAL SECURITY TAX   Find the Social Security tax for each of the following managers for the current pay period. Assume a 6.2% FICA rate up to a maximum of $110,000.

Manager	Gross Earnings This Year (So Far)	Earnings Current Pay Period	
9. Dandridge, T.	$98,460.10	$4218.48	$261.55
10. Hale, R.	$107,950.10	$3200	$127.09
11. Hall, T.	$109,360.40	$5260	$39.66
12. Maurin, J.	$112,040.18	$2487.52	$0
13. Saraniti, S.	$109,540.96	$1053.73	$28.46
14. De Bouchel, V.	$108,820.12	$4160.86	$73.15

PAYROLL DEDUCTIONS   Find the regular earnings, overtime earnings, gross earnings, Social Security tax (6.2%), Medicare tax (1.45%), and state disability insurance deduction (1%) for each of the following employees. Assume that no employee will have earned more than the FICA or SDI maximum at the end of the current pay period. Assume time-and-a-half is paid for any overtime in a 40-hour week.

Employee	Hours Worked	Regular Rate	
15. Thunstrom, P.	45.5	$9.22	$368.80; $76.07; $444.87; $27.58; $6.45; $4.45
16. Fernandez, P.	47.75	$7.52	$300.80; $87.42; $388.22; $24.07; $5.63; $3.88
17. Odom, R.	44	$10.30	$412; $61.80; $473.80; $29.38; $6.87; $4.74
18. Ruppart, A.	45	$12.40	$496; $93; $589; $36.52; $8.54; $5.89
19. Leonard, B.	45	$8.18	$327.20; $61.35; $388.55; $24.09; $5.63; $3.89
20. Taggart, G.	47	$11.68	$467.20; $122.64; $589.84; $36.57; $8.55; $5.90
21. Zhao, T.	46.75	$17.50	$700; $177.19; $877.19; $54.39; $12.72; $8.77
22. Shotwell, E.	48.25	$7.40	$296; $91.58; $387.58; $24.03; $5.62; $3.88

Solve the following application problems. Assume that the FICA rate is 6.2%, the Medicare rate is 1.45%, the SDI rate is 1%, and that earnings will not exceed $31,800.

23. SOCIAL SECURITY AND MEDICARE   Kwei Riang worked 43.5 hours last week at McDonald's. He is paid $8.58 per hour, plus time-and-a-half for overtime (over 40 hours per week). Find his (a) Social Security tax and (b) Medicare tax for the week.   (a) $24.07 (b) $5.63

24. SOCIAL SECURITY AND MEDICARE   Beth Kaufman receives 7% commission on all sales. Her sales on Monday of last week were $1412.20, with $1928.42 on Tuesday, $598.14 on Wednesday, $1051.12 on Thursday, and $958.72 on Friday. Find her (a) Social Security tax and (b) Medicare tax for the week.   (a) $25.82 (b) $6.04

25. STATE DISABILITY DEDUCTION   Lynn Peterson is paid an 8% commission on sales. During a recent pay period, she had sales of $19,482 and returns and allowances of $193. Find the amount of (a) her Social Security tax, (b) her Medicare tax, and (c) her state disability for this pay period.   (a) $95.67 (b) $22.38 (c) $15.43

26. STATE DISABILITY DEDUCTIONS   Peter Phelps is a representative for Delta International Machinery and is paid $675 per week plus a commission of 2% on sales. His sales last week were $17,240. Find the amount of (a) his Social Security tax, (b) his Medicare tax, and (c) his state disability for the pay period.   (a) $63.23 (b) $14.79 (c) $10.20

SELF-EMPLOYMENT DEDUCTIONS   The following problems refer to self-employed individuals. These people pay Social Security tax of 12.4% and Medicare tax of 2.9%. Find the taxes on each of the following annual adjusted earnings. (See Example 3.)

27. Tony Romano, owner of The Cutlery, earned $58,238.74. $7221.60; $1688.92

28. Rachel Leach, an interior decorator, earned $28,286.20. $3507.49; $820.30

29. Krystal McClellan, retail sales, earned $34,817.16. $4317.33; $1009.70

30. Ron Morris, a Chick-fil-A franchise owner, earned $48,007.14. $5952.89; $1392.21

31. Lauren Midgley, teaching assistant, earned $26,843.60. $3328.61; $778.46

32. Eric Lemmon, commission salesperson, earned $52,748.32. $6540.79; $1529.70

 33. A young person who has just received her first paycheck is puzzled by the amounts that have been deducted from gross earnings. Briefly explain both the FICA and Medicare deductions to this person. (See Objectives 1–4.)

 34. Describe the difference between the FICA paid by an employee and that paid by a self-employed person. (See Objective 5.)

6.5	**Income Tax Withholding**

OBJECTIVES

1 *Understand the Employee's Withholding Allowance Certificate (Form W-4).*

2 *Find the federal withholding tax using the wage bracket method.*

3 *Find the federal tax using the percentage method.*

4 *Find the state withholding tax using the state income tax rate.*

5 *Find net pay when given gross wages, taxes, and other deductions.*

Figure 6.7 shows the sources of income for the U.S. federal government. Note that the **personal income taxes** that are paid by many people in the country account for 26% of the government's income. The law requires that these taxes be paid as individuals earn income throughout the year. So, employers withhold money from the gross earnings of their employees (**income tax withholding**) and send the funds to the **Internal Revenue Service (IRS)**. The IRS is the branch of the government that collects taxes and works to find individuals and corporations that cheat on their income taxes. Most people file electronically, which is sometimes referred to as **e-file**. The amount withheld for income taxes depends on an employee's earnings—high earners pay higher income taxes and many lower-income individuals and families pay no income taxes.

Currently, there is a lot of discussion about changing the tax code in the United States. Further, the so-called Bush tax cuts are set to expire at the end of 2012. However, that may or

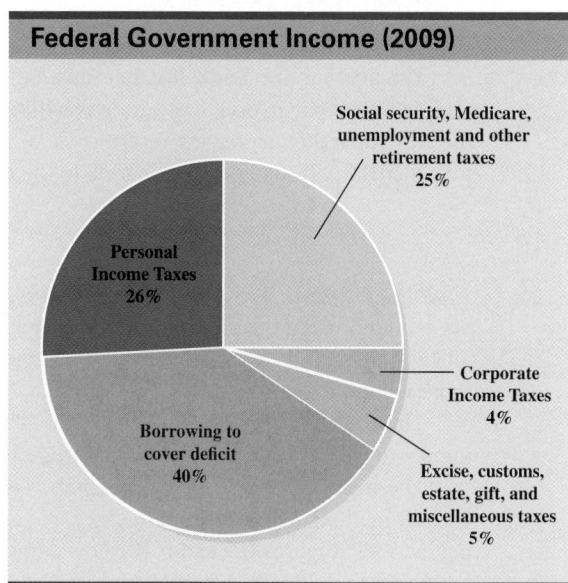

Figure 6.7

may not happen given the differences in the views among politicians today. So, the laws are always changing. It is very important to use the most recent laws and forms when working on income tax returns.

Objective

1 *Understand the Employee's Withholding Allowance Certificate (Form W-4).* Each employee must file a W-4 form (Figure 6.8) that shows whether the individual is married or single and how many **withholding allowances** are claimed. This information is used when calculating the amount of money withheld for income taxes. The number of withholding allowances is often the number of individuals in the household. For example, a married person with 1 child will normally claim 3 allowances, one for each spouse and one for the child. But an employee can choose to have extra income tax withheld by claiming fewer exemptions, or vice versa. One reason for overpaying income taxes through the year is to get cash back from the IRS at the end of the year.

- Cut here and give Form W-4 to your employer. Keep the top part for your records. -

Form **W-4** Department of the Treasury Internal Revenue Service	**Employee's Withholding Allowance Certificate** ► Whether you are entitled to claim a certain number of allowances or exemption from withholding is subject to review by the IRS. Your employer may be required to send a copy of this form to the IRS.	OMB No. 1545-0074 2011

1 Type or print your first name and middle initial.	Last name	**2 Your social security number**

Home address (number and street or rural route)	**3** ☐ Single ☐ Married ☐ Married, but withhold at higher Single rate. **Note.** If married, but legally separated, or spouse is a nonresident alien, check the "Single" box.
City or town, state, and ZIP code	**4 If your last name differs from that shown on your social security card, check here. You must call 1-800-772-1213 for a replacement card.** ► ☐

5 Total number of allowances you are claiming (from line **H** above **or** from the applicable worksheet on page 2) **5** ____

6 Additional amount, if any, you want withheld from each paycheck . . . . **6** $ ____

7 I claim exemption from withholding for 2011, and I certify that I meet **both** of the following conditions for exemption.
- Last year I had a right to a refund of **all** federal income tax withheld because I had **no** tax liability **and**
- This year I expect a refund of **all** federal income tax withheld because I expect to have **no** tax liability.

If you meet both conditions, write "Exempt" here . . . . ► **7** ____

Under penalties of perjury, I declare that I have examined this certificate and to the best of my knowledge and belief, it is true, correct, and complete.

Employee's signature
(This form is not valid unless you sign it.) ► _____ Date ► _____

8 Employer's name and address (Employer: Complete lines 8 and 10 only if sending to the IRS.)	**9** Office code (optional)	**10** Employer identification number (EIN)

For Privacy Act and Paperwork Reduction Act Notice, see page 2. Cat. No. 10220Q Form **W-4** (2011)

Figure 6.8

The amount of income tax that must be paid for the year is not affected by the amount withheld each pay period. If too little is withheld during the year, extra money must be sent to the IRS when the income tax return is filed. If too much money is withheld during the year, then the IRS will send the excess back to the taxpayer when the income tax return is filed.

Objective

2 *Find the Federal Withholding Tax Using the Wage Bracket Method.* The withholding tax is found using the gross earnings per pay period. Income tax withholding is applied to all earnings, unlike Social Security tax. Generally, the higher a person's gross earnings, the more withholding tax is paid.

There are two methods that employers use to determine the amount of federal withholding tax to deduct from paychecks: the **wage bracket method** and the **percentage method**.

The Internal Revenue Service supplies withholding tax tables to be used with the wage bracket method. These tables are extensive and cover weekly, biweekly, monthly, and daily pay periods. Figures 6.9 and 6.10 show samples of the withholding tables. Figure 6.9 is for both single and married people who are paid weekly and Figure 6.10 is for both single and married people who are paid monthly.

SINGLE Persons—WEEKLY Payroll Period

(For Wages Paid through December 2011)

And the wages are—		And the number of withholding allowances claimed is—										
At least	But less than	0	1	2	3	4	5	6	7	8	9	10
		The amount of income tax to be withheld is—										
350	360	39	28	18	10	3	0	0	0	0	0	0
360	370	41	30	19	11	4	0	0	0	0	0	0
370	380	42	31	21	12	5	0	0	0	0	0	0
380	390	44	33	22	13	6	0	0	0	0	0	0
390	400	45	34	24	14	7	0	0	0	0	0	0
400	410	47	36	25	15	8	1	0	0	0	0	0
410	420	48	37	27	16	9	2	0	0	0	0	0
420	430	50	39	28	18	10	3	0	0	0	0	0
430	440	51	40	30	19	11	4	0	0	0	0	0
440	450	53	42	31	21	12	5	0	0	0	0	0
450	460	54	43	33	22	13	6	0	0	0	0	0
460	470	56	45	34	24	14	7	0	0	0	0	0
470	480	57	46	36	25	15	8	1	0	0	0	0
480	490	59	48	37	27	16	9	2	0	0	0	0
490	500	60	49	39	28	17	10	3	0	0	0	0
500	510	62	51	40	30	19	11	4	0	0	0	0
510	520	63	52	42	31	20	12	5	0	0	0	0
520	530	65	54	43	33	22	13	6	0	0	0	0
530	540	66	55	45	34	23	14	7	0	0	0	0
540	550	68	57	46	36	25	15	8	1	0	0	0
550	560	69	58	48	37	26	16	9	2	0	0	0
560	570	71	60	49	39	28	17	10	3	0	0	0
570	580	72	61	51	40	29	19	11	4	0	0	0
580	590	74	63	52	42	31	20	12	5	0	0	0
590	600	75	64	54	43	32	22	13	6	0	0	0

MARRIED Persons—WEEKLY Payroll Period

(For Wages Paid through December 2011)

And the wages are—		And the number of withholding allowances claimed is—										
At least	But less than	0	1	2	3	4	5	6	7	8	9	10
		The amount of income tax to be withheld is—										
550	560	44	33	26	19	12	5	0	0	0	0	0
560	570	46	35	27	20	13	6	0	0	0	0	0
570	580	47	36	28	21	14	7	0	0	0	0	0
580	590	49	38	29	22	15	8	1	0	0	0	0
590	600	50	39	30	23	16	9	2	0	0	0	0
600	610	52	41	31	24	17	10	3	0	0	0	0
610	620	53	42	32	25	18	11	4	0	0	0	0
620	630	55	44	33	26	19	12	5	0	0	0	0
630	640	56	45	35	27	20	13	6	0	0	0	0
640	650	58	47	36	28	21	14	7	0	0	0	0
650	660	59	48	38	29	22	15	8	1	0	0	0
660	670	61	50	39	30	23	16	9	2	0	0	0
670	680	62	51	41	31	24	17	10	3	0	0	0
680	690	64	53	42	32	25	18	11	4	0	0	0
690	700	65	54	44	33	26	19	12	5	0	0	0
700	710	67	56	45	35	27	20	13	6	0	0	0
710	720	68	57	47	36	28	21	14	7	0	0	0
720	730	70	59	48	38	29	22	15	8	0	0	0
730	740	71	60	50	39	30	23	16	9	1	0	0
740	750	73	62	51	41	31	24	17	10	2	0	0
750	760	74	63	53	42	32	25	18	11	3	0	0
760	770	76	65	54	44	33	26	19	12	4	0	0
770	780	77	66	56	45	34	27	20	13	5	0	0
780	790	79	68	57	47	36	28	21	14	6	0	0
790	800	80	69	59	48	37	29	22	15	7	0	0

Figure 6.9

SINGLE Persons—MONTHLY Payroll Period
(For Wages Paid through December 2011)

And the wages are—		And the number of withholding allowances claimed is—										
At least	But less than	0	1	2	3	4	5	6	7	8	9	10
		The amount of income tax to be withheld is—										
1,400	1,440	151	105	63	32	1	0	0	0	0	0	0
1,440	1,480	157	111	67	36	5	0	0	0	0	0	0
1,480	1,520	163	117	71	40	9	0	0	0	0	0	0
1,520	1,560	169	123	77	44	13	0	0	0	0	0	0
1,560	1,600	175	129	83	48	17	0	0	0	0	0	0
1,600	1,640	181	135	89	52	21	0	0	0	0	0	0
1,640	1,680	187	141	95	56	25	0	0	0	0	0	0
1,680	1,720	193	147	101	60	29	0	0	0	0	0	0
1,720	1,760	199	153	107	64	33	2	0	0	0	0	0
1,760	1,800	205	159	113	68	37	6	0	0	0	0	0
1,800	1,840	211	165	119	73	41	10	0	0	0	0	0
1,840	1,880	217	171	125	79	45	14	0	0	0	0	0
1,880	1,920	223	177	131	85	49	18	0	0	0	0	0
1,920	1,960	229	183	137	91	53	22	0	0	0	0	0
1,960	2,000	235	189	143	97	57	26	0	0	0	0	0
2,000	2,040	241	195	149	103	61	30	0	0	0	0	0
2,040	2,080	247	201	155	109	65	34	4	0	0	0	0
2,080	2,120	253	207	161	115	69	38	8	0	0	0	0
2,120	2,160	259	213	167	121	74	42	12	0	0	0	0
2,160	2,200	265	219	173	127	80	46	16	0	0	0	0
2,200	2,240	271	225	179	133	86	50	20	0	0	0	0
2,240	2,280	277	231	185	139	92	54	24	0	0	0	0
2,280	2,320	283	237	191	145	98	58	28	0	0	0	0
2,320	2,360	289	243	197	151	104	62	32	1	0	0	0
2,360	2,400	295	249	203	157	110	66	36	5	0	0	0

MARRIED Persons—MONTHLY Payroll Period
(For Wages Paid through December 2011)

And the wages are—		And the number of withholding allowances claimed is—										
At least	But less than	0	1	2	3	4	5	6	7	8	9	10
		The amount of income tax to be withheld is—										
2,400	2,440	193	147	115	84	53	22	0	0	0	0	0
2,440	2,480	199	153	119	88	57	26	0	0	0	0	0
2,480	2,520	205	159	123	92	61	30	0	0	0	0	0
2,520	2,560	211	165	127	96	65	34	3	0	0	0	0
2,560	2,600	217	171	131	100	69	38	7	0	0	0	0
2,600	2,640	223	177	135	104	73	42	11	0	0	0	0
2,640	2,680	229	183	139	108	77	46	15	0	0	0	0
2,680	2,720	235	189	143	112	81	50	19	0	0	0	0
2,720	2,760	241	195	149	116	85	54	23	0	0	0	0
2,760	2,800	247	201	155	120	89	58	27	0	0	0	0
2,800	2,840	253	207	161	124	93	62	31	0	0	0	0
2,840	2,880	259	213	167	128	97	66	35	4	0	0	0
2,880	2,920	265	219	173	132	101	70	39	8	0	0	0
2,920	2,960	271	225	179	136	105	74	43	12	0	0	0
2,960	3,000	277	231	185	140	109	78	47	16	0	0	0
3,000	3,040	283	237	191	145	113	82	51	20	0	0	0
3,040	3,080	289	243	197	151	117	86	55	24	0	0	0
3,080	3,120	295	249	203	157	121	90	59	28	0	0	0
3,120	3,160	301	255	209	163	125	94	63	32	2	0	0
3,160	3,200	307	261	215	169	129	98	67	36	6	0	0
3,200	3,240	313	267	221	175	133	102	71	40	10	0	0
3,240	3,280	319	273	227	181	137	106	75	44	14	0	0
3,280	3,320	325	279	233	187	141	110	79	48	18	0	0
3,320	3,360	331	285	239	193	146	114	83	52	22	0	0
3,360	3,400	337	291	245	199	152	118	87	56	26	0	0

Figure 6.10

EXAMPLE 1 Finding Federal Withholding Using the Wage Bracket Method

Lisa Revies is single and claims no withholding allowances so that she will receive a refund from the government or avoid owing taxes at the end of the year. The proper number will be used when filing her income tax return. Use the wage bracket method to find her withholding tax if her weekly gross earnings are $395.27.

Solution

Use the table in Figure 6.9 for Single Persons—Weekly Payroll Period. The given earnings are found in the row "at least $390 but less than $400." Go across this row to the column headed "0" (for no withholding allowances). From the table, the withholding is $45 per week.

EXAMPLE 2 Using the Wage Bracket Method for Federal Withholding

Larry Sifford is married, claims three withholding allowances, and has monthly gross earnings of $3016.47. Find his withholding tax using the wage bracket method.

Solution

Use the table in Figure 6.10 for Married Persons—Monthly Payroll Period. Look down the two left columns and find the range that includes Sifford's gross earnings: "at least $3000 but less than $3040." Read across the table to the column headed "3" for the three withholding allowances. The withholding tax is $145 per month.

Objective

3 *Find the Federal Tax Using the Percentage Method.* Many companies today prefer to use the **percentage method** to determine federal withholding tax. The percentage method does not require the many pages of tables needed with the wage bracket method and is more easily adapted to computer applications in the processing of payrolls. Instead, the table shown in Figure 6.11 is used.

EXAMPLE 3 Finding Federal Withholding Using the Percentage Method

Joseph Fillipi is married, claims four withholding allowances, and has weekly gross earnings of $1575. Use the percentage method to find his withholding tax.

Solution

STEP 1 Find the withholding allowance for *one* on the weekly payroll period in Figure 6.11. The amount is $71.15. Since Fillipi claims four allowances, multiply the one withholding allowance ($71.15) by the number of withholding allowances (4).

$$\$71.15 \times 4 = \$284.60$$

Amount for one withholding allowance ⎯⎯⎯⎯⎯⎯⎯⎯ Amount for four withholding allowances

STEP 2 Subtract the amount in Step 1 from gross earnings.

$$\$1575 - \$284.60 = \$1290.40$$

Gross earnings ⎯⎯⎯⎯⎯⎯ Amount used in Table 1(b)

STEP 3 Find the "married person weekly" section of the percentage method withholding in Figure 6.11. Since $1290.40 is over $479 but not over $1479, the amount to be withheld is $32.70 plus 15% of the excess over $479.

$$\text{Amount to withhold} = \$32.70 + 15\% \text{ of excess over } \$479$$
$$= \$32.70 + 0.15 \times (\$1290.40 - \$479)$$
$$= \$32.70 + \$121.71 = \$154.41$$

Therefore, the amount to be withheld each week for income taxes is $154.41.

Percentage Method Tables for Income Tax Withholding
(For Wages Paid in 2011)

TABLE 1—WEEKLY Payroll Period

(a) SINGLE person (including head of household)—

If the amount of wages (after subtracting withholding allowances) is: The amount of income tax to withhold is:

Not over $40 . . . . $0

Over—	But not over—		of excess over—
$40	—$204	. . . $0.00 plus 10%	—$40
$204	—$704	. . . $16.40 plus 15%	—$204
$704	—$1,648	. . . $91.40 plus 25%	—$704
$1,648	—$3,394	. . . $327.40 plus 28%	—$1,648
$3,394	—$7,332	. . . $816.28 plus 33%	—$3,394
$7,332	. . . .	. . . $2,115.82 plus 35%	—$7,332

(b) MARRIED person—

If the amount of wages (after subtracting withholding allowances) is: The amount of income tax to withhold is:

Not over $152 . . . . $0

Over—	But not over—		of excess over—
$152	—$479	. . . $0.00 plus 10%	—$152
$479	—$1,479	. . . $32.70 plus 15%	—$479
$1,479	—$2,832	. . . $182.70 plus 25%	—$1,479
$2,832	—$4,235	. . . $520.95 plus 28%	—$2,832
$4,235	—$7,443	. . . $913.79 plus 33%	—$4,235
$7,443	. . . .	. . . $1,972,43 plus 35%	—$7,443

TABLE 2—BIWEEKLY Payroll Period

(a) SINGLE person (including head of household)—

If the amount of wages (after subtracting withholding allowances) is: The amount of income tax to withhold is:

Not over $81 . . . . $0

Over—	But not over—		of excess over—
$81	—$408	. . . $0.00 plus 10%	—$81
$408	—$1,408	. . . $32.70 plus 15%	—$408
$1,408	—$3,296	. . . $182.70 plus 25%	—$1,408
$3,296	—$6,788	. . . $654.70 plus 28%	—$3,296
$6,788	—$14,663	. . . $1,632.46 plus 33%	—$6,788
$14,663	. . . .	. . . $4,231.21 plus 35%	—$14,663

(b) MARRIED person—

If the amount of wages (after subtracting withholding allowances) is: The amount of income tax to withhold is:

Not over $304 . . . . $0

Over—	But not over—		of excess over—
$304	—$958	. . . $0.00 plus 10%	—$304
$958	—$2,958	. . . $65.40 plus 15%	—$958
$2,958	—$5,663	. . . $365.40 plus 25%	—$2,958
$5,663	—$8,469	. . . $1,041.65 plus 28%	—$5,663
$8,469	—$14,887	. . . $1,827.33 plus 33%	—$8,469
$14,887	. . . .	. . . $3,945.27 plus 35%	—$14,887

TABLE 3—SEMIMONTHLY Payroll Period

(a) SINGLE person (including head of household)—

If the amount of wages (after subtracting withholding allowances) is: The amount of income tax to withhold is:

Not over $88 . . . . $0

Over—	But not over—		of excess over—
$88	—$442	. . . $0.00 plus 10%	—$88
$442	—$1,525	. . . $35.40 plus 15%	—$442
$1,525	—$3,571	. . . $197.85 plus 25%	—$1,525
$3,571	—$7,354	. . . $709.35 plus 28%	—$3,571
$7,354	—$15,885	. . . $1,768.59 plus 33%	—$7,354
$15,885	. . . .	. . . $4,583.82 plus 35%	—$15,885

(b) MARRIED person—

If the amount of wages (after subtracting withholding allowances) is: The amount of income tax to withhold is:

Not over $329 . . . . $0

Over—	But not over—		of excess over—
$329	—$1,038	. . . $0.00 plus 10%	—$329
$1,038	—$3,204	. . . $70.90 plus 15%	—$1,038
$3,024	—$6,135	. . . $395.80 plus 25%	—$3,204
$6,135	—$9,175	. . . $1,128.55 plus 28%	—$6,135
$9,175	—$16,127	. . . $1,979.75 plus 33%	—$9,175
$16,127	. . . .	. . . $4,273.91 plus 35%	—$16,127

TABLE 4—MONTHLY Payroll Period

(a) SINGLE person (including head of household)—

If the amount of wages (after subtracting withholding allowances) is: The amount of income tax to withhold is:

Not over $175 . . . . $0

Over—	But not over—		of excess over—
$175	—$883	. . . $0.00 plus 10%	—$175
$883	—$3,050	. . . $70.80 plus 15%	—$883
$3,050	—$7,142	. . . $395.85 plus 25%	—$3,050
$7,142	—$14,708	. . . $1,418.85 plus 28%	—$7,142
$14,708	—$31,771	. . . $3,537.33 plus 33%	—$14,708
$31,771	. . . .	. . . $9,168.12 plus 35%	—$31,771

(b) MARRIED person—

If the amount of wages (after subtracting withholding allowances) is: The amount of income tax to withhold is:

Not over $658 . . . . $0

Over—	But not over—		of excess over—
$658	—$2,075	. . . $0.00 plus 10%	—$658
$2,075	—$6,408	. . . $141.70 plus 15%	—$2,075
$6,408	—$12,271	. . . $791.65 plus 25%	—$6,408
$12,271	—$18,350	. . . $2,257.40 plus 28%	—$12,271
$18,350	—$32,254	. . . $3,959.52 plus 33%	—$18,350
$32,254	. . . .	. . . $8,547.84 plus 35%	—$32,254

TABLE 5. Percentage Method—2011
Amount for One Withholding Allowance

Payroll Period	One With holding Allowance
Weekly.	$ 71.15
Biweekly.	142.31
Semimonthly.	154.17
Monthly.	308.33
Quarterly.	925.00
Semiannually.	1,850.00
Annually.	3,700.00
Daily or miscellaneous (each day of the payroll period).	14.23

Figure 6.11

> **NOTE** In Step 1, for an employee who is paid monthly, the number of withholding allowances would be multiplied by $308.33, the amount from the table for one monthly withholding allowance.

Scientific
Calculator
Approach

The calculator solution to Example 3 follows.

$$1575 \boxed{-} \$71.15 \boxed{\times} 4 \boxed{-} 479 \boxed{=} 811.40 \boxed{\text{STO}}$$

$$\boxed{\text{RCL}} \boxed{\times} .15 \boxed{+} 32.70 = 154.41 \text{ (rounded)}$$

EXAMPLE **4** **Finding Federal Withholding Using the Percentage Method**

Sharon MacDonald is married, claims 3 withholding allowances, and has monthly gross earnings of $6820. Use the percentage method to find her withholding tax.

Solution

STEP 1 Find the withholding allowance for *one* on the monthly payroll period in the percentage method income tax withholding table. The amount is $308.33. Since MacDonald claims 3 withholding allowances, multiply the withholding allowance for one by her number of withholding allowances (3).

$$\$308.33 \times 3 = \$924.99$$

Amount for 1 withholding allowance ⟍ ⟋ Amount for 3 withholding allowances

STEP 2 Subtract the amount in Step 1 from gross earnings.

$$\$6820 - \$924.99 = \$5895.01$$

Gross earnings ⟍ ⟋ Amount used in Table 4(b), Figure 6.11

STEP 3 Find the married person monthly section of the percentage method withholding table. Since $5895.01 is over $2075 but not over $6408, the monthly withholding is found by adding $141.70 to 15% of the excess over $2075.

$$\text{Amount to withhold} = \$141.70 + 0.15 \times (\$5895.01 - \$2075)$$

$$= \$141.70 + \$573.00 = \$714.70$$

EXAMPLE **5** **Finding Federal Withholding Using the Percentage Method**

Yadi Isleta is divorced, so she files as a single person. Use the percentage method to find her withholding tax for a 2-week pay period (biweekly) with gross earnings of $3850.

Solution

Yadi Isleta claims one withholding allowance.

$$\text{Biweekly withholding allowance} = \$142.31 \times 1 = \$142.31$$

$$\text{Gross earnings} - \text{withholding allowances} = \$3850 - \$142.31$$

$$= \$3707.69$$

Since $3707.69 falls between $3296 and $6788 in the single-biweekly table, the amount to be withheld is $654.70 + 28% of the excess over $3296.

$$\text{Withholding} = \$654.70 + 0.28 \times (\$3707.69 - \$3296)$$
$$= \$769.97$$

The amount that will be withheld is $769.97.

NOTE The amount of withholding tax found using the wage bracket method can vary slightly from the amount of withholding tax found using the percentage method. Any differences would be eliminated when the income tax return is filed.

Objective

4 *Find the State Withholding Tax Using the State Income Tax Rate.* Many states and cities have a **state income tax** that is collected by withholding. Notice in Figure 6.12 the big differences in state tax rates. States with no state income tax often have high property taxes, and vice versa. However, state income tax rates are particularly high in California, New York, and Oregon.

Some believe that high earners do not pay much in taxes—but this is not always true. For example, look at the taxes on a married couple, each of whom work for an organization and who make about the same incomes as one another, live in Oregon, and have a combined taxable income of $400,000. One example of a couple that would have this kind of income is a medical doctor and an attorney. They would pay the following taxes, which add up to about $164,740, or to about 41.2% of their taxable income.

FICA taxes:	6.2% of the first $220,000, since there are 2 wage earners
Medicare taxes:	1.45% of $400,000
Federal income taxes:	Roughly $107,000 in federal income taxes
Oregon income taxes:	Roughly $38,300 in state income taxes

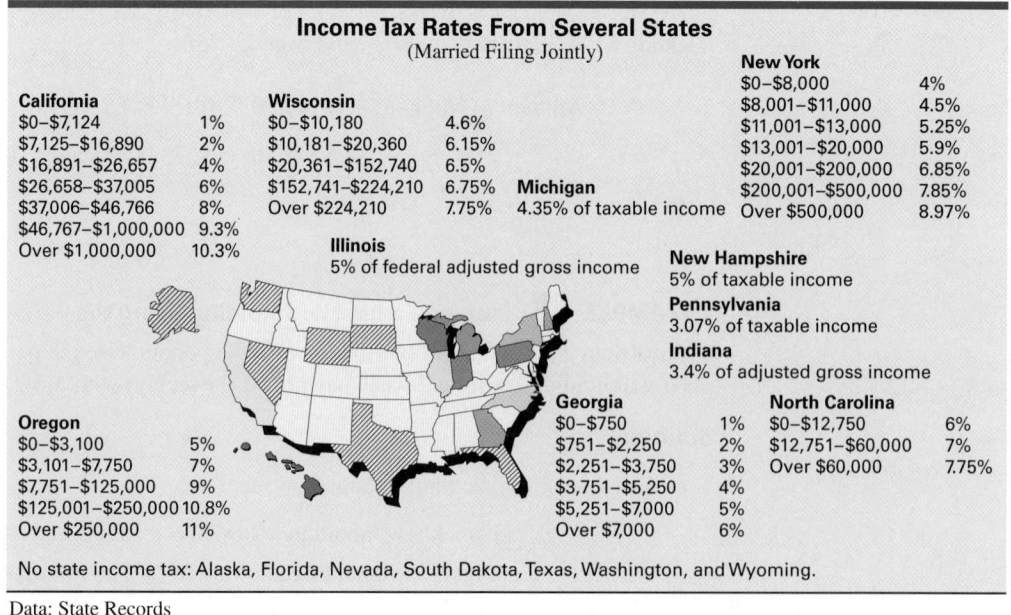

Figure 6.12

Note that income taxes in Oregon are higher than in most other states. The taxes listed above do not include the other taxes that the couple must also pay, which include property taxes, sales taxes on purchases, and taxes on gasoline. Although the taxes may seem high to this couple, it is important to remember the following two points.

1. Benefits such as a good transportation system, police and fire protection, retirement payments and heath care in the later years of life, national defense, etc., must be paid for somehow. No taxes, no benefits! So, people receive benefits from the taxes that they pay, and many benefits occur daily.
2. There are several countries in Europe where taxes are significantly higher, as are benefits.

▶ **STOP&THINK**

> Do you think the couple listed above pays enough in taxes, or should they pay more? This is a common debate in Congress and the press today as the United States struggles with many serious financial issues and seeks additional income.

EXAMPLE 6 **Finding State Withholding Tax**

After receiving his Bachelor's degree in computer science, Imtiaz Ahmed moved to Michigan and began a new job. The gross amount of his first paycheck is $4240. Use Figure 6.12 to (**a**) find the applicable state tax rate and then (**b**) estimate the state tax.

Solution

(**a**) The tax rate for Michigan is 4.35% of taxable income.
(**b**) State tax = gross earnings × tax rate

$$= \$4240 \times 0.0435$$
$$= \$184.44$$

NOTE Several software programs are available to find state income tax. For example, Quickbooks, Turbo Tax, and Peachtree Accounting are often used.

Objective

5 *Find Net Pay When Given Gross Wages, Taxes, and Other Deductions.* It is common for employees to request additional deductions, such as union dues and credit union payments. The final amount of pay received by the employee, called the net pay, is given by the following formula.

Gross earnings
− FICA tax (Social Security)
− Medicare tax
− Federal withholding tax
− State withholding tax
− Other deductions
──────────────
Net pay

Wow, that is a lot of deductions! But remember, later in life you will probably benefit greatly from both Social Security and Medicare. Federal and state taxes pay for things we all benefit from, including roads, police, military defense, and so on.

EXAMPLE 7 **Determining Net Pay after Deductions**

Bernice L. White is married and claims three withholding allowances. Her weekly gross earnings are $643.35. Her state withholding is 2.5% and her union dues are $25. Find her net pay using the percentage method of withholding.

Solution

First, we will find the federal withholding tax since it requires several steps.

From Figure 6.11, one withholding allowance is $71.15.

Total withholding allowance = $71.15 × 3 allowances = $213.45

Gross earnings − Total withholding allowance = $643.35 − $213.45 = $429.90

From Figure 6.11, married, weekly, the federal tax is 10% of ($429.90 − $152) = $27.79

Next, find the other deductions and add them to find the total of weekly deductions.

FICA: $643.35 × 0.062	= $ 39.89
Medicare: $643.35 × 0.0145	= $ 9.33
Federal: (from above)	= $ 27.79
State: $643.35 × 0.025	= $ 16.08
Union dues:	= $ 25.00
Total deductions	$118.09

Finally, find the net pay by subtracting total deductions from gross earnings.

$643.35   Gross earnings
−118.09   Total deductions
$525.26   Net pay

White will receive a paycheck for $525.26, about 81.6% of her gross income. The other 18.4% of her income goes to pay various taxes and union dues.

6.5	**Exercises**

FEDERAL WITHHOLDING TAX Find the federal withholding tax for each of the following employees. Use the wage bracket method.

	Employee	Gross Earnings	Married?	Withholding Allowances	
1.	Stanegna, J.	$3128.51 monthly	yes	3	$163
2.	De Simone, D.	$395.76 weekly	no	2	$24
3.	Koehler, J.	$587.20 weekly	yes	0	$49
4.	Jones, C.	$2416.88 monthly	yes	1	$147
5.	Jenders, P.	$1568.12 monthly	no	2	$83
6.	Hollabaugh, A.	$1953.35 monthly	no	1	$183
7.	Esposito, C.	$2817.32 monthly	yes	6	$31
8.	Miller, M.	$541.32 weekly	no	1	$57
9.	Mehta, S.	$1622.41 monthly	no	4	$21
10.	Sommerfield, K.	$785.49 weekly	yes	0	$79
11.	Weisner, W.	$1834.57 monthly	no	3	$73
12.	NgauTibbits, C.	$618.43 weekly	yes	2	$32

STATE WITHHOLDING TAX Use the state income tax rate given to find the state withholding tax for each of the following employees. Round to the nearest cent.

	Employee	Gross Weekly Earnings	State Income Tax Rate	
13.	Owens, E.	$480.60	4.4%	$21.15
14.	Childs, M.	$520.10	5.0%	$26.01
15.	Christensen, C.	$392.12	1.4%	$5.49
16.	deJamaer, K.	$547.54	3.4%	$18.62
17.	Galvin, M.	$1476.32	6.0%	$88.58
18.	Hampson, N.	$2720.85	5.95%	$161.89

EMPLOYEE NET PAY Use the percentage method of withholding to find federal withholding tax, a 6.2% FICA rate to find FICA tax, and 1.45% to find Medicare tax for each of the following employees. Then find the net pay for each employee. The number of withholding allowances and the marital status are listed after each employee's name. Assume that no employee has earned over $110,000 so far this year. (See Examples 3 and 5.)

	Employee	Gross Earnings	FICA	Medicare Tax	Federal Withholding Tax	Net Pay
19.	Hamel; 4, M	$576.28 weekly	$35.73	$8.36	$13.97	$518.22
20.	Guardino; 3, S	$2878.12 monthly	$178.44	$41.73	$231.32	$2426.63
21.	Foster; 1, S	$2512.53 monthly	$155.78	$36.43	$268.98	$2051.34
22.	Erb; 2, M	$625 weekly	$38.75	$9.06	$33.26	$543.93
23.	Terry; 3, M	$2276.83 semimonthly	$141.16	$33.01	$187.35	$1915.31
24.	Galluccio; 1, S	$420.17 weekly	$26.05	$6.09	$38.15	$349.88
25.	Derma; 6, M	$1971.06 semimonthly	$122.21	$28.58	$72.11	$1748.16
26.	Eddy; 2, M	$1020 weekly	$63.24	$14.79	$92.51	$849.46
27.	Tang; 3, S	$2710 biweekly	$168.02	$39.30	$401.47	$2101.21
28.	Zamost; 2, S	$6625.24 monthly	$410.76	$96.07	$1135.50	$4982.91
29.	Reilly; 1, S	$1786.44 weekly	$110.76	$25.90	$346.24	$1303.54
30.	Gertz; 4, M	$2618.50 biweekly	$162.35	$37.97	$229.09	$2189.09
31.	Bryn; 3, M	$1852.20 semimonthly	$114.84	$26.86	$123.65	$1586.85
32.	Hahn; 2, S	$1240 weekly	$76.88	$17.98	$189.83	$955.31

 33. Write an explanation of how to determine the federal withholding tax using the wage bracket (tax tables) method. (See Objective 2.)

 34. Write an explanation of how to find the federal withholding tax using the percentage method. (See Objective 3.)

Use the percentage method of withholding, a FICA rate of 6.2%, a Medicare rate of 1.45%, an SDI rate of 1%, and a state withholding tax of 3.4% in the following problems.

35. MARKETING REPRESENTATIVE Doug Gilbert, marketing representative, has weekly earnings of $975. He is married and claims four withholding allowances. His deductions include FICA, Medicare, federal withholding, state disability insurance, state withholding, union dues of $15.50, and credit union savings of $25. Find his net pay for a week in February. $752.60

36. TEACHER PAY Sheila Jones received her 4-year degree and is in her first year of teaching mathematics at a high school in the Midwest. Her semimonthly income is $1835 before deductions for FICA, Medicare, federal withholding, state disability insurance, state withholding, a United Way contribution of $20, and a savings deduction of $30. If she is single and claims four withholding allowances, find her net pay. $1412.03

37. EDUCATIONAL SALES A new salesperson for Pearson Education is paid a salary of $410 per week plus 7% of all sales over $5000. She is single and claims two withholding allowances. Her deductions include FICA, Medicare, federal withholding, state disability insurance, state withholding, credit union savings of $50, and a Salvation Army contribution of $10. Find her net pay for a week in April during which she has sales of $11,284 with returns and allowances of $425. $573.84

38. TRAVEL AGENCY SALES Mindy Carter, an account executive for a travel agency specializing in executive travel to Asia, is paid on a variable commission, is married, and claims four withholding allowances. She receives 3% of the first $20,000 in sales, 4% of the next $10,000 in sales, and 6% of all sales over $30,000. This week she has sales of $45,550 and the following deductions: FICA, Medicare, federal withholding, state disability insurance, state withholding, a retirement contribution of $45, a savings bond of $50, and charitable contributions of $20. Find her net pay after subtracting all of her deductions. $1360.02

39. HEATING COMPANY REPRESENTATIVE Sheri Minkner, a commission sales representative for Alternative Heating Company, is paid a monthly salary of $4200 plus a bonus of 1.5% on monthly sales. She is married and claims three withholding allowances. Her deductions include FICA, Medicare, federal withholding, state disability insurance, credit union savings of $150, charitable contributions of $25, and a savings bond of $50. Find her net pay for a month in which her sales were $42,618. The state in which Minkner works has no state income tax. $3778.09

40. RIVER RAFTING MANAGER River Raft Adventures pays its manager Susan Estey a monthly salary of $2880 plus a commission of 0.8% based on total monthly sales volume. In the month of May, River Raft Adventures has total sales of $86,280. Estey is married and claims five withholding allowances. Her deductions include FICA, Medicare, federal withholding, state disability insurance, state withholding of $159.30, credit union payment of $300, March of Dimes contributions of $20, and savings bonds of $250. Find her net pay for May. $2395.06

6.6 Payroll Records and Quarterly Returns

OBJECTIVES

1 *Understand payroll records kept by employers.*

2 *Calculate employer's matching Social Security and Medicare contributions.*

3 *Find the quarterly amount due the Internal Revenue Service.*

4 *Find the amount of federal unemployment tax due.*

Employers keep payroll records for many reasons. Individual payroll records for each employee are used to keep track of Social Security tax, Medicare tax, federal and state withholding, and many other items. The amounts withheld from employee earnings are sent periodically to the proper agency. Most are paid entirely by the employee and others are matched by the employer. Usually these records are filed quarterly. These quarters and the filing dates are shown in Table 6.4.

Table 6.4 COMPANY FILING SCHEDULES FOR EMPLOYEE WITHHOLDING

Quarter	Ending	Due Date
January, February, March	March 31	April 30
April, May, June	June 30	July 31
July, August, September	September 30	October 31
October, November, December	December 31	January 31

Objective

1 *Understand Payroll Records Kept by Employers.* The payroll ledger, discussed in **Section 6.1**, was a record of the number of hours worked by all of the employees during a certain time period. The Employee's Earnings Record shown in Figure 6.13 details quarterly totals for an individual employee. This record shows the gross earnings, deduction amounts, and net pay for each pay period during the quarter.

NAME Lisa Kamins						CLOCK NUMBER 114		DEPT Production		M	3	RECORD OF PAY CHANGES 1/1/20—	7.20	
STREET 407 Glen Oak Dr.						SOC.SEC. NUMBER 123-45-6789				MARITAL STATUS ☐ M. ☒ F.	NO. OF EXEMPT			
CITY Fort Worth, Texas						PHONE NO. 482-6319		DATE STARTED DATE LEFT						

TIME WORKED	DATE PAY PERIOD ENDING	YEAR 200___				ENCIRCLE QUARTERS ① 2 3 4		GROSS PAYROLL	F.W.T.	SOC. SEC.	MEDI	S.W.T.	U.D.	D. INS.	CHECK NO.	DEDUCTION AMOUNTS	
		TIME WORKED													NET PAY	
		SUN	M	TU	W	TH	F	SAT				DEDUCTIONS					
	BROUGHT FORWARD ➡																
	1/7		8	8	7	8	10		298^{80}	18^{00}	19^{42}	4^{48}	13^{80}	5^{00}	18^{00}	1186	220^{10}	1
	1/14		8	8	8	8	8		288^{00}	16^{00}	18^{72}	4^{32}	13^{40}	5^{00}	18^{00}	1295	212^{56}	2
	1/21		8	10	8	9	8	4	363^{60}	28^{00}	23^{63}	5^{45}	15^{06}	5^{00}	18^{00}	1378	268^{46}	3
	1/28		8	8	8	8	8		288^{00}	16^{00}	18^{72}	4^{32}	13^{40}	5^{00}	18^{00}	1498	212^{56}	4
	2/4		8	8	6	8	8	2	288^{00}	16^{00}	18^{72}	4^{32}	13^{40}	5^{00}	18^{00}	1601	212^{56}	5
	2/11		8	8	8	8	8		288^{00}	16^{00}	18^{72}	4^{32}	13^{40}	5^{00}	18^{00}	1738	212^{56}	6
	2/18		8	8	8	8	8		288^{00}	16^{00}	18^{72}	4^{32}	13^{40}	5^{00}	18^{00}	1856	212^{56}	7
	2/25		10	8	10	6	6	5	342^{00}	25^{00}	22^{23}	5^{13}	14^{70}	5^{00}	18^{00}	2023	251^{94}	8
	3/3		8	8	8	8	8		288^{00}	16^{00}	18^{72}	4^{32}	13^{40}	5^{00}	18^{00}	2186	212^{56}	9
	3/10		8	7	8	9	10		309^{60}	19^{00}	20^{12}	4^{64}	13^{90}	5^{00}	18^{00}	2316	228^{94}	10
	3/17		8	8	8	8	8		288^{00}	16^{00}	18^{72}	4^{32}	13^{40}	5^{00}	18^{00}	2479	212^{56}	11
	3/24		10	8	10	8	8		391^{00}	33^{00}	25^{42}	5^{87}	16^{60}	5^{00}	18^{00}	2632	287^{11}	12
	3/31		8	8	8	9	8	4	403^{75}	34^{00}	26^{24}	6^{06}	17^{06}	5^{00}	18^{00}	2801	297^{39}	13
																		14
																		15
																		16
	QTR.								4124^{75}	269^{00}	268^{10}	61^{87}	184^{92}	65^{00}	234^{80}		3041^{86}	
	TO DATE																	

Figure 6.13

Objective

2 *Calculate Employer's Matching Social Security and Medicare Contributions.* The employer must check the earnings of each employee to make sure that the FICA and the federal unemployment tax cutoff points are not passed. Since the employer must also give an end-of-year wage and tax statement (Form W-2) to each employee, the records are also used as the source of this information. In addition, accurate payroll records are important because the employer is required by law to match the employee's Social Security and Medicare contributions.

Objective

3 *Find the Quarterly Amount Due the Internal Revenue Service.* An employee's contribution to Social Security and Medicare must be matched by the employer.

EXAMPLE 1   **Finding the Amount of FICA and Medicare Tax Due**

If the employees at Fair Oaks Auto pay a total of $10,258.30 in Social Security tax and $2399.12 in Medicare tax, how much must the employer send to the Internal Revenue Service?

Solution

The employer must match the contributions listed above and send the entire amount to the Internal Revenue Service.

Social Security: $10,258.30 × 2 = $20,516.60
Medicare: $2,399.12 × 2 = $4,798.24
Total to be sent to IRS $25,314.84

Note that employers must pay the matching contribution out of their own funds. The matching contributions do not come from the employee.

NOTE   In addition to sending Social Security and Medicare taxes, a company must also send in the following to the Internal Revenue Service.
1. Federal income taxes withheld from employees
2. Any corporate income taxes that are due

EXAMPLE 2   **Finding the Employer's Amount Due the IRS**

Suppose that during a certain quarter Leslie's Pool Supplies has collected $2765.42 from its employees for FICA tax, $638.17 for Medicare tax, and $3572.86 in federal withholding tax. Compute the total amount due to the Internal Revenue Service from Leslie's Pool Supplies.

Solution

$2,765.42	Collected from employees for FICA tax
$2,765.42	Equal amount paid by employer
$638.17	Collected from employees for Medicare tax
$638.17	Equal amount paid by employer
$3,572.86	Federal withholding tax
$10,380.04	Total due to Internal Revenue Service

The firm must send $10,380.04 to the Internal Revenue Service, not including any corporate income taxes due.

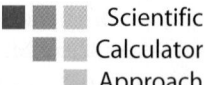 Scientific Calculator Approach

The calculator solution for Example 2 is as follows:

2765.42 ☒ 2 ⊞ 638.17 ☒ 2 ⊞ 3572.86 ☐ 10380.04

Objective

4   *Find the Amount of Federal Unemployment Tax Due.*   The **Federal Unemployment Tax Act (FUTA)** requires employers to pay yet another tax. This **unemployment insurance tax** is paid entirely by employers. These funds are used to pay unemployment benefits to individuals who have lost their jobs and cannot find work. Unemployment benefits are often very benefical to families in times of economic recession when many people are unemployed. One difference between the **developed world** and poorer **third-world countries** is that most countries in the developed world offer benefits to help people when they are sick, lose their jobs, or retire. The poorest countries in the world usually have no benefits to pay to individuals who are ill, elderly, or without sufficient food.

In general, all employers who paid wages of $1500 or more in a calendar quarter or had one or more employees for some part of a day in any 20 different weeks in a calendar year must file an employer's annual *Federal Unemployment Tax Return*. This federal return must be filed each January for the preceding year. The FUTA tax that must be paid by the employer is 6.0% of the first $7000 in earnings for that year for each employee.

States also require employers to pay unemployment taxes. Any **state unemployment tax (SUTA)** paid by an employer becomes a credit on the federal unemployment tax return. Many states decrease the unemployment tax rate for any company with low labor turnover. Since the tax rates and maximum amount subject to tax vary widely by state, we will not include them in our calculations here. However, you can be sure that your employer is paying both SUTA and FUTA taxes on your behalf.

EXAMPLE 3   **Finding the Amount of Unemployment Tax Due**

Betty Clifton earns $4800 each quarter. Find **(a)** the amount of her earnings subject to the FUTA tax in the second quarter and **(b)** the amount of the tax in that quarter.

Solution

(a) The FUTA tax applies only to the first $7000 in earnings each year. So the earnings in the second quarter subject to the FUTA tax are: $7000 − $4800 = $2200.

(b) FUTA tax = $2200 × 0.06 = $132.00

NOTE Employers pay several expenses on behalf of each employee that the employee does not see. These include the employer's one-half of FICA and Medicare taxes, unemployment taxes, and usually worker's compensation insurance which insures employees in the event they are injured on the job. Many employers also pay portions of the employee's health insurance and make contributions to a retirement plan for the employee. So the salary is only part of an employer's cost to hire someone.

6.6 | Exercises

EMPLOYER PAYROLL RECORDS   Find the total combined amount of Social Security and Medicare tax (employee's contribution plus employer's contribution) for each of the following firms. Use a FICA rate of 6.2% and a Medicare tax rate of 1.45%, and assume no employee has earned over $110,000 so far this year.

	Firm	Total Employee Earnings	
1.	Atlasta Ranch	$15,634.18	$2392.04
2.	Norm's Cell Phones	$10,046.53	$1537.12
3.	Adin Feed and Fuel	$17,462.10	$2671.70
4.	Leisure Outdoor Furniture	$15,324.15	$2344.60
5.	Computers Plus	$14,131.59	$2162.14
6.	Owl Drugstore	$21,281.60	$3256.08
7.	Plescia Produce	$62,475.80	$9558.80
8.	Brownstone Music	$122,819.50	$18,791.38

TOTAL EMPLOYER PAYMENT Calculate the total amount due from each of the following firms. Use a FICA rate of 6.2% and a Medicare tax rate of 1.45%.

Firm	Total Employee Earnings	Total Withholding for Income Tax	
9. Web Design	$6150.82	$629.18	$1570.26
10. McIntosh Meats	$8714.55	$2008.76	$3342.08
11. Childlike Publishers	$32,121.85	$8215.08	$13,129.72
12. Mart & Bottle	$20,255.60	$4436.80	$7535.92
13. Todd Consultants	$37,271.39	$7128.64	$12,831.18
14. UPS Store	$10,158.24	$2768.62	$4322.82
15. Tony Balony's	$34,547.86	$12,628.19	$17,914.01
16. Oaks Hardware	$21,394.77	$5671.30	$8944.70

17. Without changes, Social Security is projected to be bankrupt by 2038. What changes do you think should be made to the system to keep it solvent?

18. Describe in your own words four differences between Social Security and FUTA. Consider the purpose, amount paid, and who pays.

Solve the following application problems. Assume no employee has earned over $110,000 so far this year. Use a FICA rate of 6.2% and a Medicare tax rate of 1.45%.

19. HAIR SALON Total employee earnings at City Hair Care are $21,928.10. Find the combined total amount of FICA and Medicare taxes sent to the IRS by the employer. $3355

20. PAVING CONTRACTOR Biondi Paving has a weekly payroll of $13,650.30. How much FICA and Medicare taxes should be sent to the IRS? $2088.50

21. RADIO STATION KOMA has an employee payroll of $7622.84. During the same time period, $1625.68 was withheld as income tax. Find the total amount due to the IRS. $2791.98

22. FLORIST The payroll at the Oak Mill Florist is $22,607.72. During the same pay period, $3898.14 was withheld as income tax. Find the total amount that must be sent to the IRS. $7357.12

FEDERAL UNEMPLOYMENT TAX Assume a FUTA rate of 6.0% of the first $7000 in earnings in each of the following.

23. An employee earns $3280 in the first quarter of the year, $2600 in the second quarter, and $3156 in the third quarter. Find (a) the amount of earnings subject to unemployment tax in the third quarter and (b) the amount of unemployment tax due on third-quarter earnings. (a) $1120 (b) $67.20

24. As a part-time employee at an apartment complex, James Berry earns an average of $850 per month. Find (a) the amount of income subject to unemployment tax in the third quarter and (b) the amount of tax due on third-quarter earnings. (a) $1900 (b) $114

25. Emma Price is paid $1800 per month. Find (a) the amount of earnings subject to unemployment tax in the second quarter and (b) the amount of unemployment tax due on second-quarter earnings. (a) $1600 (b) $96

26. Michael Booth received $4820 in earnings in the first quarter of the year. His earnings in the second quarter are $3815. Find (a) the amount of his earnings subject to FUTA in the second quarter and (b) the amount of tax due in the second quarter. (a) $2180 (b) $130.80

CHAPTER TERMS

Review the following terms to test your understanding of the chapter. For each term you do not know, refer to the page number found next to that term.

chargebacks [p. 243]
commission [p. 234]
compensatory (comp) time [p. 229]
daily overtime [p. 227]
deductions [p. 224]
developed world [p. 267]
differential-piecework plan [p. 242]
dockings [p. 243]
double time [p. 228]
drawing account [p. 237]
Fair Labor Standards Act (FLSA) [p. 226]
Federal Insurance Contributions Act (FICA) [p. 247]
Federal Unemployment Tax Act (FUTA) [p. 266]
gross earnings [p. 224]

hourly wage [p. 224]
incentive rates [p. 241]
income tax withholding [p. 253]
Internal Revenue Service (IRS) [p. 253]
Medicare [p. 247]
minimum wage [p. 226]
net pay [p. 224]
net sales [p. 235]
offshore [p. 223]
override [p. 238]
overtime [p. 226]
overtime premium (excess) method [p. 227]
pay period [p. 229]
payroll ledger [p. 224]
percentage method [p. 254]
personal income tax [p. 253]

piecework rate [p. 242]
premium payment plan [p. 228]
premium rate [p. 242]
quota bonus system [p. 238]
quotas [p. 238]
Request for Earnings and Benefit Estimate Statement [p. 248]
returns [p. 235]
salary [p. 229]
salary plus commission [p. 236]
shift differential [p. 228]
sliding-scale commission [p. 235]
Social Security [p. 247]
split-shift premium [p. 228]
state disability insurance (SDI) [p. 251]

state income tax [p. 260]
state unemployment insurance tax (SUTA) [p. 267]
straight commission [p. 235]
straight-piecework plan [p. 242]
third-world country [p. 267]
time card [p. 224]
time rates [p. 241]
time-and-a-half rate [p. 226]
unemployment insurance tax [p. 266]
variable commission [p. 235]
wage bracket method [p. 254]
withholding allowances [p. 254]

CONCEPTS

EXAMPLES

6.1 Gross earnings

Gross earnings = hours worked × rate per hour

40 hours at $8.40 per hour

Gross earnings = 40 × $8.40 = $336

6.1 Gross earnings with overtime

First, find regular earnings. Then, determine overtime pay at overtime rate. Finally, add regular and overtime earnings.

40 hours at $8.40 per hour; 10 hours at time-and-a-half.

$$\text{Gross earnings} = (40 \times \$8.40) + (10 \times \$8.40 \times 1\tfrac{1}{2})$$
$$= \$336 + \$126$$
$$= \$462$$

6.1 Common pay periods

Pay Period	Paychecks per Year
Monthly	12
Semimonthly	24
Biweekly	26
Weekly	52

Find the earnings equivalent to $2000 per month for other pay periods.

$$\text{Semimonthly} = \frac{\$2000}{2} = \$1000$$

$$\text{Biweekly} = \frac{\$2000 \times 12}{26} = \$923.08$$

$$\text{Weekly} = \frac{\$2000 \times 12}{52} = \$461.54$$

6.1 Overtime for salaried employees

First, find the equivalent hourly rate. Next, multiply the rate by the overtime hours by $1\frac{1}{2}$. Finally, add overtime earnings to salary.

Salary is $648 per week for 36 hours. Find earnings for 46 hours.

$$\$648 \div 36 = \$18.00 \text{ per hour}$$
$$\$18.00 \times 10 \times 1\tfrac{1}{2} = \$270 \text{ overtime}$$
$$\$648 + \$270 = \$918$$

6.2 Straight commission

Gross earnings = commission rate $\times$ amount of sales

Sales of $25,800; commission rate is 5%.

$$0.05 \times \$25,800 = \$1290$$

6.2 Variable commission

Commission rate varies at different sales levels.

Up to $10,000, 6%; $10,001–$20,000, 8%; $20,001 and up, 9%. Find the commission on sales of $32,768.

$$0.06 \times \$10,000 = \$600.00 \quad \text{(First \$10,000)}$$
$$0.08 \times \$10,000 = \$800.00 \quad \text{(Next \$10,000)}$$
$$0.09 \times \underline{\$12,768} = \underline{\$1149.12} \quad \text{(Over \$20,000)}$$
$$\text{Totals } \$32,768 \quad \$2549.12$$

6.2 Salary and commission

Gross earnings = fixed earnings + commission

Salary, $250 per week; commission rate, 3%. Find gross earnings on sales of $6848.

$$\begin{aligned} \text{Gross earnings} &= \$250 + (0.03 \times \$6848) \\ &= \$250 + \$205.44 \\ &= \$455.44 \end{aligned}$$

6.2 Commissions with a drawing account

Gross earnings = commission − draw

Sales for month, $54,640; commission rate, 7%; draw, $750 for month. Find the gross earnings.

$$\begin{aligned} \text{Gross earnings} &= (0.07 \times \$54,640) - \$750 \\ &= \$3824.80 - \$750 \\ &= \$3074.80 \end{aligned}$$

6.2 Commissions with a quota bonus

Gross earnings = commission rate $\times$ (sales − quota)

Sales for week, $14,370; commission rate, 10% after meeting the sales quota of $4000. Find gross earnings.

$$\begin{aligned} \text{Gross earnings} &= 0.1 \times (\$14,370 - \$4000) \\ &= 0.1 \times \$10,370 \\ &= \$1037 \end{aligned}$$

6.3 Gross earnings for piecework

Gross earnings = payment per item $\times$ number of items

Items produced, 275; payment per item, $1.28. Find the gross earnings.

$$\$1.28 \times 275 = \$352$$

6.3 Gross earnings for differential piecework

The rate paid per item produced varies with level of production.

1–100 items, $1.20 each; 101–200 items, $1.30 each; over 200 items, $1.45 each. Find the gross earnings if 292 items are produced.

$$100 \times \$1.20 = \$120.00 \text{ First 100 items}$$
$$100 \times \$1.30 = \$130.00 \text{ Second 100 items}$$
$$\underline{92 \times \$1.45 = \$133.40} \text{ Above 200 items}$$
$$292 \qquad\qquad 383.40$$

6.3 Gross earnings with piece rate and chargebacks

Find piece rate earnings; then calculate chargebacks and subtract them from piece rate earnings to find gross earnings.

Items produced, 318; piece rate, $1.35; spoiled items, 26; chargeback, $1.60. Find the gross earnings.

$$\text{Total: } 318 \times \$1.35 = \$429.30$$
$$\text{Chargeback: } 26 \times \$1.60 = \$41.60$$
$$\text{Gross earnings: } \$429.30 - \$41.60 = \$387.70$$

6.3 Overtime earnings on piecework

Gross earnings = earnings at regular rate + earnings at overtime rate

Items produced on regular time, 530; items produced on overtime, 110; piece rate, $0.60. Find the gross earnings.

$$\text{Gross earnings} = 530 \times \$0.60 + 110\left(1\frac{1}{2} \times \$0.60\right)$$
$$= \$318 + \$99$$
$$= \$417$$

6.4 FICA; Social Security tax

The gross earnings are multiplied by the rate. When the maximum earnings are reached, no additional FICA is withheld that year.

Gross earnings, $458; Social Security tax rate, 6.2%. Find Social Security tax.

$$\$458 \times 0.062 = \$28.40$$

6.4 Medicare tax

The gross earnings are multiplied by the tax rate. There is no maximum earnings limit on Medicare.

Gross earnings, $458; Medicare tax rate, 1.45%. Find Medicare tax.

$$\$458 \times 0.0145 = \$6.64$$

6.4 State disability insurance deductions

Multiply the gross earnings by the SDI tax rate. When maximum earnings are reached, no additional taxes are paid in that year.

Gross earnings, $3210; SDI tax rate 1%. Find SDI tax.

$$\$3210 \times 0.01 = \$32.10$$

6.5 Withholding Federal Tax—Wage Bracket

Find the amount to be withheld using the tables for Wage Bracket Method of Withholding.

Single, 3 withholding allowances, weekly wage of $535.

Go to the table for single and weekly. Look at the row "at least $530 but less than $540" and column with 3 allowances.

$$\text{Withholding amount} = \$34$$

6.5 Withholding Federal Tax—Percentage Method	Married, 4 withholding allowances, monthly wage of $3400.

Find

1. Amount for one withholding allowance
2. Multiply amount times number of allowances
3. Wages – amount found in Step 2 above
4. Appropriate table for Percentage Method Withholding Allowance
5. Appropriate row in table
6. Amount to withhold by following directions

1. One monthly withholding allowance = $308.33
2. $308.33 × 4 = $1233.32
3. $3400 − $1233.32 = $2166.68
4. Table for married, monthly
5. "over $2075 but not over $6408" row
6. $141.70 + 0.15 × ($2166.68 − $2075)
   = $141.70 + $13.75
   = $155.45

6.5 State withholding tax

Tax is paid on total earnings. No maximum as with FICA.

Married employee with weekly earnings of $392. Find the state withholding tax given a state withholding tax rate of 4.5%.

$$4.5\% \times \$392 = 0.045 \times \$392 = \$17.64$$

6.6 Quarterly report

Filed each quarter; FICA and federal withholding are sent to the IRS.

(FICA + Medicare) × 2 (employer) + Federal withholding tax

Quarterly FICA withheld from employees is $5269, Medicare tax is $1581, and federal withholding tax is $14,780. Find the total due the IRS.

$$(\$5269 + \$1581) \times 2 + \$14,780 = \$28,480$$

6.6 Federal Unemployment Tax (FUTA)

FUTA is paid by the employer on the first $7000 of earnings each year for each employee.

An employee earned $3850 in the first quarter of a year. Find the amount of unemployment tax using a 6.0% tax rate.

$$\$3850 \times 6.0\% = \$231$$

CHAPTER 6	Review Exercises

The answer section includes answers to all Review Exercises.

Complete the following partial payroll ledger. Find the total gross earnings for each employee. Time-and-a-half is paid on all hours over 40 in one week. **[6.1]**

Employee	Hours Worked	Reg. Hours	O.T. Hours	Reg. Rate	Gross Earnings
1. Darasz, B.	48.5	40	8.5	$9.14	$482.14
2. Davidson, D.	48	40	8	$8.50	$442
3. Mandler, S.	38.25	38.25	0	$10.85	$415.01
4. Rosenthal, L.	57.25	40	17.25	$12.20	$803.68

Find the equivalent earnings for each of the following salaries as indicated. **[6.1]**

	Weekly	Biweekly	Semimonthly	Monthly	Annually
5.	$410.80	$821.60	$890.07	$1780.13	$21,361.60
6.	$530	$1060	$1148.33	$2296.67	$27,560
7.	$346.15	$692.31	$750	$1500	$18,000
8.	$403.85	$807.69	$875	$1750	$21,000

Find the weekly gross earnings for the following people who are on salary and are paid time-and-a-half for overtime. **[6.1]**

	Employee	Regular Hours per Week	Weekly Salary	Hours Worked	Weekly Gross Earnings
9.	Uldall, E.	40	$640	45	$760
10.	Donovan-Dickerson, K.	36	$342	42	$427.50

Find the gross earnings for each of the following salespeople. **[6.2]**

	Employee	Total Sales	Returns	Rate of Commission	
11.	Gonsalves, R.	$48,620	$3106	8%	$3641.12
12.	Kaufman, B.	$38,740	$1245	9%	$3374.55

Solve the following application problems. **[6.3]**

13. Twenty Minute Lube and Oil pays its employees $2.50 for an oil change, $2.60 for each car lubed, and $3.75 if a car gets both an oil change and a lube. This week, Andre Herrebout changed the oil in 63 cars, lubed 46 cars, and gave an oil change and lube to 68 cars. Find his gross pay for the week. $532.10

14. At Jalisco Electronics in Mexicali, Mexico, assemblers are paid as follows: 1–20 units in a week, $4.50 each; 21–30 units, $5.50 each; and more than 30 units, $7 each. Adrian Ortega assembled 28 units in one week. Find his gross pay. $134

15. Samantha Walker receives a commission of 6% for selling a $235,000 house. Half the commission goes to the broker and half of the remainder to another salesperson. Walker gets the rest. Find the amount she receives. $3525

Employees at Appliance Giant are paid a commission on the following schedule: first $2000 in sales, 6%; next $2000 in sales, 8%; sales over $4000, 10%. Use this information for Exercises 16 and 17. **[6.2]**

16. Find the gross earnings for an employee with total sales of $5850. $465

17. Find the gross earnings for an employee with total sales of $7200. $600

18. Pat Rowell ties bows on Christmas wreaths and is paid $0.12 for each bow tied. She is charged $0.09 for each rejection and is paid time-and-a-half for overtime production. Find her gross earnings for a week when she produces 1850 at the regular rate, 285 at the overtime rate, and has 92 rejections. $265.02

An employee is paid a salary of $9300 per month. If the FICA rate is 6.2% on the first $110,000 of earnings and the Medicare tax rate is 1.45% on all earnings, how much will the employee pay in (a) FICA tax and (b) Medicare tax during the following month? **[6.4]**

19. March   (a) $576.60 (b) $134.85

20. November   (a) $477.40 (b) $134.85

Find the federal withholding tax using the wage bracket method for each of the following employees. **[6.5]**

21. Flahive: 2 withholding allowances, single, $515 weekly earnings $42

22. Hoffa: 2 withholding allowances, married, $705.91 weekly earnings $45

23. Howard: 3 withholding allowances, married, $3210.55 monthly earnings $175

24. Kluesner: 4 withholding allowances, single, $1859.62 monthly earnings $45

25. Lawrence: 6 withholding allowances, married, $2864.57 monthly earnings $35

26. Tewell: 2 withholding allowances, single, $378.36 weekly earnings $21

Find the net pay for each of the following employees after FICA, Medicare, federal withholding tax, state disability, and other deductions have been made. Assume that no one has earned over $110,000 so far this year. Assume a FICA rate of 6.2%, Medicare rate of 1.45%, and a state disability rate of 1%. Use the percentage method of withholding. **[6.5]**

27. Precilo: $1852.75 monthly earnings, 1 withholding allowance, single, $37.80 in other deductions $1484.69

28. Martinez: $684.20 weekly earnings, 4 withholding allowances, married, state withholding of $15.34, credit union savings of $20 $564.92

29. Watson: $1040 weekly earnings, 6 withholding allowances, married, state withholding of $34.80, union dues of $38, charitable contribution of $15 $809.42

Solve the following application problems. Assume no employee has earned over $110,000 so far this year. Use a FICA rate of 6.2% and a rate of 1.45% for Medicare. **[6.6]**

30. Total employee earnings for Round Table Pizza are $12,720.15. Find the combined total of FICA and Medicare taxes sent to the IRS by the employer. $1946.18

31. San Juan Electric has an employee payroll of $29,185.17. During the same period $4921 was withheld as income tax. Find the total amount due the IRS. $9386.32

Solve the following application problems.

32. A salesperson is paid $452 per week plus a commission of 2% on all sales. The salesperson sold $712 worth of goods on Monday, $523 on Tuesday, $1002 on Wednesday, $391 on Thursday, and $609 on Friday. Returns and allowances for the week were $114. Find the employee's (a) Social Security tax (6.2%), (b) Medicare tax (1.45%), and (c) state disability insurance (1%) for the week. (a) $31.90 (b) $7.46 (c) $5.14

33. Kerry Conley has earned $108,210 this year and his income for the current week is $2650. Find his (a) FICA tax and (b) Medicare tax for the current week. (a) $110.98 (b) $38.43

34. The employees of Miracle Floor Covering paid a total of $1496.11 in Social Security tax last month, $345.30 in Medicare tax, and $1768.43 in federal withholding tax. Find the total amount that the employer must send to the Internal Revenue Service. $5451.25

For Exercises 35 and 36, find (a) the Social Security tax and (b) the Medicare tax for each of the following self-employed people. Use a FICA tax rate of 12.4% and a Medicare tax rate of 2.9%. **[6.4]**

35. Kula, S.: $38,795.22 (a) $4810.61 (b) $1125.06

36. Biondi, E.: $27,618.53 (a) $3424.70 (b) $800.94

Assume a FUTA rate of 6.0% on the first $7000 in earnings in each of the following. **[6.6]**

37. An employee earns $2875 in the first quarter of the year, $3212 in the second quarter, and $2942 in the third quarter. Find (a) the amount of earnings subject to unemployment tax in the third quarter and (b) the amount of unemployment tax due on third quarter earnings. (a) $913 (b) $54.78

38. Amy Berk earns $810 per month. Find (a) the amount of earnings subject to unemployment tax in the third quarter and (b) the amount of unemployment tax due on third-quarter earnings. (a) $2140 (b) $128.40

CHAPTER 6	Business Application Case #1 *Diesel Mechanic*

Jim Waters is a diesel mechanic working on truck engines for Hunter Trucking. His annual salary based on a 40-hour workweek is $38,480, but he is paid time-and-a-half for all overtime. He is single and claims two withholding allowances. Deductions include FICA, federal withholding using the percentage method, state disability insurance at 1%, state withholding at 3.5%, credit union payments of $125, retirement deductions of $55, association dues of $15, and a contribution to the Diabetes Association of $25. Find each of the following for a 52-hour workweek.

  (a) Regular wages $740

  (b) Overtime wages $333

  (c) Total gross earnings $1073

  (d) FICA $66.53

  (e) Medicare $15.56

  (f) Federal withholding $148.08

  (g) State disability insurance $10.73

  (h) State withholding $37.56

  (i) Other deductions $220.00

  (j) Net pay $574.54

CHAPTER 6	Business Application Case #2
	Social Security (www.ssa.gov)

The Great Depression of the 1930s was a very difficult time across much of the world. In the United States, unemployment rose to 25% and widespread bank failures wiped out the savings of many families. Poverty among the elderly and disabled grew dramatically, and by 1934 more than 50% of the elderly did not have enough income to support themselves.

Due to the great problems of that era, Congress and the president acted and passed the Social Security Act of 1935. It required employees and employers to contribute to a fund that would then be used to make monthly payments to retired workers. Social Security includes benefits to retired workers and dependents, child survivors of a deceased worker, and disabled workers and dependents. The graph shows the number receiving benefits over time. It is important to note that Social Security payments amount to more than one-half of the income of many retired people in the United States.

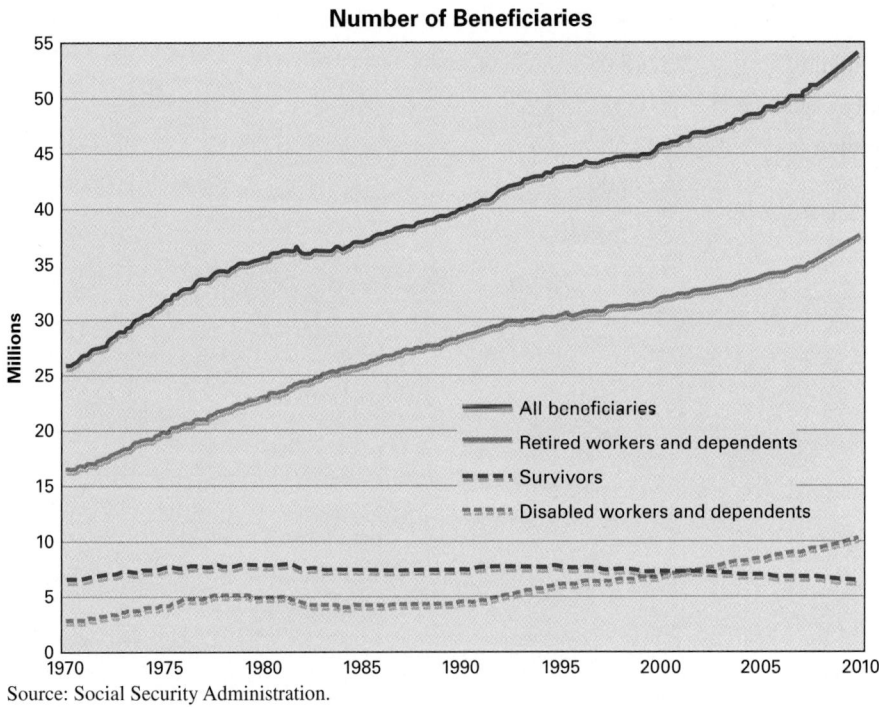

Number of Beneficiaries

Source: Social Security Administration.

(a) Estimate the total number of beneficiaries of Social Security payments in 1970 and also in 2010. Then find the percent increase from 1970 to 2010.   25.5 million; 54 million; 111.8% increase

(b) A high school senior by the name of Dong Yi has started up her own business that designs and builds Web pages for area businesses. Yi hires another high school student to assist her. Find the total FICA taxes and Medicare taxes that must be sent to the government for a quarter in which Dong made $5700 and the assistant was paid $2600.   FICA, $1029.20; Medicare, $240.70

javier brosch / Fotolia.com

Taxes

> Taxes are the price
> we pay to live in
> a civilized society.
>
> —Oliver Wendell
> Holmes, Jr.

Taxes are paid by individuals and businesses to various governments including school districts, cities, counties, states, and the federal government. Tax dollars pay for public education, national defense, streets and highways, parks and recreation facilities, police and fire protection, public assistance for the poor, libraries, street lights, and benefits to people 62 and older.

Figure 7.1 shows where the federal government spends money. The largest category of expense is Social Security, Medicare, and other retirement, which are payments to, or on behalf of, people 62 years old or older. Many of these people have worked and paid taxes for many decades. The next two largest categories of expenses are national defense and social programs.

Expenditures of the Federal Government

National defense, veterans, and foreign affairs
22%

Social Security, Medicare, and other retirement
34%

Net interest on the debt
5%

Law enforcement and general government
2%

Physical, human, and community development
15%

Social programs
21%

Source: Internal Revenue Service.

Figure 7.1

▶ STOP & THINK

> List every government expense that you can identify (local, state, and federal). Should the various governments be doing more to help people than they are currently doing? Are some of the expenditures unnecessary and a waste? Is government too big? What are your opinions on these issues that are commonly being discussed throughout the country?

Most taxes are levied on sales, property, and income. This chapter examines the basics of taxation and discusses the calculations necessary to work with each type of tax.

7.1	**Sales Tax**

OBJECTIVES

1 *Understand how sales tax is determined.*

2 *Find the amount of sales tax and the total sale.*

3 *Find the selling price when the sales tax is known.*

4 *Find the amount of the sale when the total price including tax is known.*

5 *Define excise tax.*

6 *Find the total cost including sales tax and excise tax.*

Most states and many cities and counties levy a **sales tax** on sales at retail stores. The tax rate varies from one location to another, but it is always given as a percent of the retail price. Although most states tax restaurant sales, many do not tax food items purchased in grocery stores.

Objective

1 *Understand How Sales Tax Is Determined.* Most stores have cash registers that automatically calculate the sales tax. Table 7.1 shows 2011 sales tax rates for all 50 states and also for the District of Columbia. The tax rates in the table do not include any sales taxes levied by cities and counties, so the rate you pay in your state is probably higher than the one shown in the table.

The basic percent equation is used to solve sales tax problems. The amount of *sales tax* is the part, the *amount of the sale* is the base, and the *sales tax rate* is the rate.

$$\text{Sales tax} = \text{amount of sale} \times \text{sales tax rate}$$
$$P = B \times R$$
$$\text{Part} = \text{base} \times \text{rate}$$

Objective

2 *Find the Amount of Sales Tax and the Total Sale.* A common calculation in business is to find the amount of sales tax and the total amount of the sale, including tax.

> **EXAMPLE 1** **Finding Sales Tax and the Total Sale**
>
> A customer at Round Table Pizza purchases several large pizzas for $49.95. Sales tax in the area is 6.5%. Find (a) the amount of sales tax and (b) the total amount collected from the customer.
>
> **Solution**
>
> **(a)** The amount of sales tax (part) is found by multiplying the sales tax rate (rate) by the amount of the sale (base). Use the percent equation to find the sales tax.
>
> $$P = BR$$
> $$= \$49.95 \times 6.5\%$$
> $$= \$49.95 \times 0.065 = \mathbf{\$3.25} \quad \text{Rounded}$$
>
> The sales tax is $3.25.
>
> **(b)** Add to find the total amount collected from the customer.
>
> | | |
> |---:|:---|
> | $49.95 | Amount of sale |
> | + 3.25 | Sales tax |
> | $53.20 | Total sale including tax |

Table 7.1 SALES TAX RATES (EXCLUDES CITY, COUNTY, AND OTHER LOCAL SALES TAXES)

Alabama	4%	Montana	0%
Alaska	0%	Nebraska	5.5%
Arizona	6.6%	Nevada	6.85%
Arkansas	6%	New Hampshire	0%
California	6.25%	New Jersey	7%
Colorado	2.9%	New Mexico	5.125%
Connecticut	6.35%	New York	4%
Delaware	0%	North Carolina	4.75%
District of Columbia	6%	North Dakota	5%
Florida	6%	Ohio	5.5%
Georgia	4%	Oklahoma	4.5%
Hawaii	4%	Oregon	0%
Idaho	6%	Pennsylvania	6%
Illinois	6.25%	Rhode Island	7%
Indiana	7%	South Carolina	6%
Iowa	6%	South Dakota	4%
Kansas	5.3%	Tennessee	7%
Kentucky	6%	Texas	6.25%
Louisiana	4%	Utah	4.7%
Maine	5%	Vermont	6%
Maryland	6%	Virginia	4%
Massachusetts	6.25%	Washington	6.5%
Michigan	6%	West Virginia	6%
Minnesota	6.875%	Wisconsin	5%
Mississippi	7%	Wyoming	4%
Missouri	4.225%		

Note: Alaska, Delaware, Montana, New Hampshire, and Oregon do not have a state sales tax.

NOTE The sales tax on any one sale may be small, but the sales taxes on all transactions in a state add up to a *lot of money*. States depend on revenue from sales taxes to pay expenses such as the salaries of state employees, to maintain and improve roads, to operate museums, to staff police departments, etc.

Objective

3 *Find the Selling Price When the Sales Tax Is Known.* If the amount of sales tax and the sales tax rate are known, it is possible to determine the selling price.

EXAMPLE **2** **Finding Price When Sales Tax Is Known**

The sales tax on a new sound system is $16.14. Find the price of the sound system if the sales tax rate is 6%.

Solution

Since sales tax (part) is found by multiplying the sales tax rate (rate) by the amount of the sale (base) the amount of sale is found using the percent equation and solving for base.

$$P = B \times R$$
$$\$16.14 = B \times 6\% \quad \text{Write 6\% as 0.06.}$$
$$\$16.14 = 0.06B$$
$$\frac{\$16.14}{0.06} = \frac{0.06B}{0.06}$$
$$\$269 = B$$

The sound system sells for $269.

Objective

4 *Find the Amount of the Sale When the Total Price Including Tax Is Known.* When the total price, including sales tax and the **sales tax rate** are known, the sale amount can be found, as shown in the next example.

EXAMPLE 3 Determining the Sale Price When the Total Cost Is Known

Coleman Headstart Preschool purchased some playground equipment at a total cost of $3663.36, including sales tax of 6%. Find the price of the equipment before the sales tax.

Solution

The sales tax rate of 6% applies to the cost of the equipment (base) and not to the total of $3663.36, which includes the sales tax. Let B be the cost of the equipment. Then the cost of the equipment plus the sales tax equals $3663.36.

$$\text{Cost of equipment} + \text{sales tax} = \text{total price}$$
$$B + (6\%)B = \$3663.36$$
$$1B + 0.06B = \$3663.36$$
$$1.06B = \$3663.36$$
$$B = \frac{\$3663.36}{1.06} \quad \text{Divide by 1.06.}$$
$$B = \$3456$$

The cost of the equipment is $3456.
Check the answer by finding the sales tax (part) and adding it to the original price.

$$\text{Sales tax} = \$3456 \times 0.06 = \$207.36$$
$$\text{Total cost} = \$3456 + \$207.36 = \$3663.36$$

The answer checks, so the cost before sales tax is $3456.

Objective

5 *Define Excise Tax.* Besides state sales taxes, an **excise tax**, sometimes called a **luxury tax**, is charged on certain items by the federal, state, and local governments. Similar to sales taxes, excise taxes are paid by, or passed on to, the consumer of goods and services. Excise taxes are charged on gasoline, tires, luxury cars, and services such as telephone, entertainment, air transportation, and business licenses.

Excise taxes may be either a percent of the sale price of an item, a fixed amount for each unit sold, or a combination of the two. Table 7.2 shows the current federal excise taxes charged on several items.

Table 7.2 FEDERAL EXCISE TAXES*

Product or Service	Rate	Product or Service	Rate
Local telephone service	3%	Bows	11%
Cigarettes	$1.01 per pack	Gasoline	18.3¢/gal.
Tires	$0.0945 for each 10 pounds of the maximum rated load capacity over 3500 pounds	Diesel fuel	24.3¢/gal.
		Aviation fuel	19.4¢/gal.
Air transportation	7.5%	Truck and trailer, chassis and bodies	12%
International air travel	$16.30 per person	Inland waterways fuel	20¢/gal.
Air freight	6.25%	Ship passenger tax	$3/passenger
Fishing rods	10%	Vaccines	$0.75 per dose

Source: Publication 510, I.R.S., Excise Taxes for 2010.

*In addition to the federal excise taxes shown here, there are a number of additional excise taxes that apply to alcoholic beverages, tobacco products, and firearms. Special ATF forms are used by businesses when selling these products.

Objective

6 *Find the Total Cost Including Sales Tax and Excise Tax.* Excise taxes are added to the price of an item in addition to sales tax. The excise tax is calculated on the base price of the item before sales tax is added. The amount of the excise tax is not subject to sales tax.

EXAMPLE 4 Finding the Total Cost with Sales and Excise Taxes

The purchasing manager of a large sporting goods chain orders 1230 fishing rods. The marketing manager expects to sell the fishing rods at an average price of $26.40, not including excise or sales taxes. The excise tax is 10% of the average price and sales taxes average 7.75% in that part of the country. Find the total revenue expected from the sale of all of the fishing rods, including all taxes.

Solution

First, find the total revenue per fishing rod.

$$\text{Excise tax per rod} = \$26.40 \times 10\% = \$2.64$$
$$\text{Sales tax per rod} = \$26.40 \times 7.75\% = \$2.05$$
$$\text{Total revenue per rod} = \$26.40 + \$2.64 + \$2.05 = \$31.09$$

Then, find the total revenue expected from the sale of all 1230 fishing rods.

$$\text{Total revenue} = 1230 \times \$31.09 = \$38,240.70$$

Excise and sales taxes are applied separately to the price of the item. So, another way to work this problem is to first add the two tax rates together ($10\% + 7.75\% = 17.75\%$) and then apply this rate to the price of the item.

$$\text{Excise tax} + \text{Sales tax} = 17.75\% \text{ of } \$26.40$$
$$= \$4.69$$

This method results in the exact total revenue.

| 7.1 | **Exercises** |

SALES AND EXCISE TAX   Find (a) the amount of sales tax, (b) the amount of excise tax, and (c) the total sale price including taxes in each of the following problems.

	Sale Price	Sales Tax Rate	Excise Tax Rate	
1.	$76.20	3%	11%	$2.29; $8.38; $86.87
2.	$59.80	6%	10%	$3.59; $5.98; $69.37
3.	$47.70	4.5%	3%	$2.15; $1.43; $51.28
4.	$21.15	8.25%	12%	$1.74; $2.54; $25.43
5.	$148.50	5%	18.4¢/gal.; 165 gal.	$7.43; $30.36; $186.29

	Sale Price	Sales Tax Rate	Excise Tax Rate	
6.	$216.75	3%	14¢ gal.; 190 gal.	$6.50; $26.60; $249.85
7.	$822.18	7%	12%	$57.55; $98.66; $978.39
8.	$648.52	4%	10%	$25.94; $64.85; $739.31
9.	$29,400	6.25%	$3/person; 168 people	$1837.50; $504; $31,741.50
10.	$57,552	4.5%	$3/person; 218 people	$2589.84; $654; $60,795.84

SALES TAX COMPUTATIONS   Find the sale price and total cost when given the amount of sales tax and the sales tax rate. Round to the nearest cent.

	Amount of Sales Tax	Sales Tax Rate	
11.	$9.60	6%	$160; $169.60
12.	$4.58	5%	$91.60; $96.18
13.	$6.30	4%	$157.50; $163.80
14.	$21.84	8%	$273; $294.84
15.	$21.45	6.5%	$330; $351.45
16.	$58.00	7.25%	$800; $858
17.	$63.84	5%	$1276.80; $1340.64
18.	$22.32	4%	$558; $580.32

SALES TAX APPLICATIONS   Find the amount of the sale before sales tax was added and the amount of sales tax in each of the following. Round to the nearest cent.

	Total Sale (including sales tax)	Sales Tax Rate	
19.	$107.31	5%	$102.20; $5.11
20.	$273.92	7%	$256; $17.92
21.	$551.52	6%	$520.30; $31.22
22.	$312.66	5.5%	$296.36; $16.30
23.	$20.60	4.25%	$19.76; $0.84
24.	$85.28	4%	$82; $3.28
25.	$333.90	6%	$315; $18.90
26.	$1352.01	3%	$1312.63; $39.38
27.	$2945.76	7%	$2753.05; $192.71
28.	$4469.64	5%	$4256.80; $212.84

29. What is the sales tax where you live? Is there a different tax rate in a county or city near you? Explain why this difference exists.

30. List three items that you, your family, or your employer purchased within the last year on which an excise tax was paid. (See Objective 5.)

Solve the following application problems.

31. ARCHERY EQUIPMENT   Open Range Archery sells an archery set for $119.80. If sales tax is 6% and the excise tax is 11%, find (a) the amount of the sales tax, (b) the amount of the excise tax, and (c) the total sale including sales tax and excise tax. (a) $7.19 (b) $13.18 (c) $140.17

32. TRUCK PURCHASE   Cross Town Trucking pays $43,135.20 for a truck. If sales tax is 7% and excise tax is 12%, find (a) the amount of the sales tax, (b) the amount of the excise tax, and (c) the total price including sales tax and excise tax.   (a) $3019.46 (b) $5176.22 (c) $51,330.88

33. MOUNTAIN BICYCLE PURCHASE   The sales tax on a mountain bike is $19.39. If the sales tax rate is $7\frac{1}{2}\%$, find the sales price of the mountain bike. $258.53

34. HARLEY-DAVIDSON   Sales tax on a motorcycle was $1584. If the tax rate was 8.25%, find the sales price of the motorcycle. $19,200

35. NOTEBOOK COMPUTER   The price of an HP notebook is $754.92, including an 8% sales tax. Find the sales price before tax. $699

36. FLIGHT TO AFRICA   Jeb Britney visits his son in the Peace Corps in Cameroon, Africa. The cost of the flight is $1645 before taxes. Sales taxes are 8% and the excise tax rate is given in Table 7.2 for air transportation. Find the total cost including the international air travel fee also in Table 7.2. $1792.90

37. CHARTER PLANE   A group of retired people charter an airplane for a round-trip from Houston, Texas, to Paris, France. The cost of each ticket is $462 not including a 6.5% sales tax and an excise tax as given in Table 7.2 for air transportation. Find the total cost for everyone given that 108 people sign up for the trip. (*Hint:* Don't forget the international air travel fee also in Table 7.2.) $54,899.64

38. TROPICAL FISH SALES   The Tropical Fish Place has total receipts for the day of $875.43. This includes 6.5% sales tax on all sales. Find the amount that is sales tax. $53.43

39. EMPLOYEE MATH ERROR   At the close of business one day, Mike Roche, a new employee, totaled the sales in the cash register and found $1908.01. He multiplied this sum by the sales tax rate of $8\frac{1}{2}\%$ to find the amount of sales tax. This procedure is incorrect. Find (a) the correct amount of sales tax and (b) the amount of error made by Roche.   (a) $149.48 (b) $12.70 too high

40. TAX OVERPAYMENT   Santiago Rowland has total daily receipts of $1856. His lounge manager multiplies this total by 5.5%, the tax rate in the area. This procedure is incorrect. Find (a) the correct amount of sales tax and (b) the amount of error made by the manager.   (a) $96.76 (b) $5.32

41. CIGARETTE SALES   Ryman Market purchased 800 packs of cigarettes last week for $2.35 per pack. Note that the store does not have to pay sales taxes when purchasing the cigarettes since sales taxes are paid by the final buyer. Find the total cost of buying the 800 packs including excise tax. $2688

42. JET FUEL   Bombay Aviation purchased 850,000 gallons of aviation fuel at a cost of $3.48 per gallon. Find the total cost including excise tax assuming no sales tax is paid. $3,122,900

43. VACCINES   The manager of a very active free clinic in Los Angeles anticipates giving 22,000 vaccines in the coming year. Find the total excise tax. $16,500

44. GASOLINE TAX   An accountant at a corporation wants to know the amount of excise taxes the firm pays on behalf of their outside salespeople. The accountant estimates the firm purchased 4909 gallons of gasoline last year. Find the excise tax. $898.35

7.2   Property Tax

OBJECTIVES

1 *Understand fair market value and find assessed valuation.*

2 *Use the tax rate formula.*

3 *Use the formula for property tax.*

4 *Express tax rates in percent, dollars per $100, dollars per $1000, and mills.*

5 *Find taxes given the assessed valuation and the tax rate.*

6 *Find the assessed valuation given the tax rate and the tax.*

7 *Find the tax rate given the assessed valuation and the tax.*

Virtually everywhere in the nation, the owners of **real property** such as homes or land pay a property tax *every year* based on the value of their property. In many areas **personal property** (such as mobile homes, furnishings, appliances, motor homes, trailers, boats, and other non–real estate items) is also taxed. Some areas handle these two taxes separately, while others combine them. The money raised by this property tax is used to provide services in the local community, such as police and fire protection, roads, schools, and parks.

Table 7.3 shows property tax rates on homes as a percent of the value of the home for a few states. Note that states often choose to get their funding from different sources. For example, California has low property taxes but high state income tax rates. On the other hand, Texas has high property taxes but no state income tax. Due to revenues from abundant oil and gas production, Alaska has no state income tax, low property taxes, and no sales taxes. Alaska even gives rebates to its citizens. However, some cities in Alaska levy and collect sales taxes on sales within the city.

Table 7.3 PROPERTY TAX RATES ON HOMES (2011)

State	Annual Tax as a Percent of Home Value
Arizona	0.72%
California	0.74%
Florida	0.97%
Georgia	0.83%
Illinois	1.73%
Michigan	1.62%
Minnesota	1.05%
Nebraska	1.76%
Pennsylvania	1.35%
Texas	1.81%
Wisconsin	1.76%

Source: Data from tax-rates.org

NOTE Although churches and nonprofit charitable organizations are exempt from both property taxes and income taxes, the individuals who work for these organizations are required to pay these taxes.

Objective

1 *Understand Fair Market Value and Find Assessed Valuation.* The first step in calculating the property tax on real estate is to get the property assessed. In this process, a local official, called the assessor, makes an estimate of the **fair market value** of the property, the price for which the property could reasonably be expected to be sold. The **assessed valuation** of the property is then found by multiplying the fair market value by a certain percent called the **assessment rate**. The percent that is used varies from location to location.

In some areas assessed valuation is 25% of fair market value, while in other areas, the assessed valuation is 40% to 60% or even 100% of fair market value. Occasionally, different rates will be used for homes and for businesses. In theory, this step is unnecessary in calculating property tax. However, using an assessed valuation that is a percent of fair market value has become an accepted practice over the years.

NOTE The assessed value of a property is often far below the fair market value. Assessed value has meaning only when calculating the property taxes. It is not used for any other purpose.

EXAMPLE 1 Finding the Assessed Value of Property

Find the assessed valuation for the following pieces of property owned by Lynn Colgin.

(a) Fair market value, $112,000; assessment rate (percent), 25%
(b) Fair market value, $1,382,500; assessment rate (percent), 60%

Solution

Multiply the fair market value by the assessment rate.

(a) $112,000 \times 0.25 = $28,000 assessed valuation
(b) $1,382,500 \times 0.60 = $829,500 assessed valuation

NOTE Property is often reassessed every few years, especially in areas with rapidly increasing or decreasing property values.

Objective

2 *Use the Tax Rate Formula.* After calculating the assessed valuation of all the taxable property in an area and determining the amount of money needed to provide the necessary services (the budget), the agency responsible for levying the tax announces the annual **property tax rate**. This tax rate is determined by the following formula.

$$R = \frac{P}{B}$$

$$\text{Tax rate} = \frac{\text{total tax amount needed}}{\text{total assessed value}}$$

EXAMPLE 2 Finding the Tax Rate on Property

Find the tax rate on property that is needed to generate the total tax amounts shown.

	Total Tax Amount Needed	Total Assessed Value
(a)	$1,105,200	$36,840,000
(b)	$1,900,800	$86,400,000

Solution

In each situation, divide the total tax amount needed by the total assessed value.

(a) $1,105,200 ÷ $36,840,000 = 3.0%   **(b)** $1,900,800 ÷ $86,400,000 = 2.2%

NOTE Some states reduce property taxes on homes to make home ownership more affordable. Some further reduce property taxes on homes owned by individuals who are elderly or disabled.

Senior Fights High Property Taxes

Tom and Becky Smith purchased their home in 1989. Tom retired from his engineering job in 2012 after being diagnosed with lung cancer. He died this year. His 72-year-old widow Becky is trying to figure out how to pay the bills, including the medical bills and the property taxes. The property taxes on their home have increased from $407 per year to $8640 per year in the 20+ years they have owned the home. So, Becky has decided to protest . . .

Objective

3 *Use the Formula for Property Tax.* Property tax rates are expressed in different ways in different parts of the country. However, property tax is always found with the formula

$$P = R \times B$$

$$\text{Tax} = \text{tax rate} \times \text{assessed valuation}$$

Objective

4   *Express Tax Rates in Percent, Dollars per $100, Dollars per $1000, and Mills.*
Percent. Some areas express tax rates as a percent of assessed valuation. The tax on some acreage with an assessed valuation of $86,500 at a tax rate of 4.87% is found as follows.

$$\text{Tax} = 0.0487 \times \$86,500 = \$4212.55$$

Dollars per $100. In other areas, the rate is expressed as a number of dollars per $100 of assessed valuation. For example, the rate might be expressed as $11.42 per $100 of assessed valuation. Assuming a tax rate of $11.42 per $100, find the tax on a piece of land having an assessed valuation of $42,000 as follows. First divide the assessed valuation by 100 by moving the decimal point two places to the left to find the number of hundreds in $42,000.

$$\$42,000 = 420 \text{ hundreds.} \quad \text{Move the decimal two places to the left}$$

Then, find the tax.

$$\text{Tax} = \text{tax rate} \times \text{number of hundreds of valuation}$$
$$= \$11.42 \times 420 = \$4796.40$$

Dollars per $1000. In other areas, the tax rate is expressed as a number of dollars per $1000 of assessed valuation. If the tax rate is $98.12 per $1000, a piece of property having an assessed valuation of $197,000 would be taxed as follows.

$$\$197,000 = 197 \text{ thousands} \qquad \text{Move the decimal three places to the left.}$$
$$\text{Tax} = \$98.12 \times 197 = \$19,329.64$$

Mills. Finally, some areas express tax rates in mills, where a **mill** is one-tenth of a cent, or one-thousandth of a dollar. For example, a tax rate might be expressed as 46 mills per dollar, or $0.046 per dollar of assessed evaluation. The tax on a property having an assessed valuation of $81,000, at a tax rate of 46 mills follows.

$$\text{Tax} = 0.046 \times \$81,000 \quad 46 \text{ mills} = \$0.046$$
$$= \$3726$$

Table 7.4 shows the same tax rates written in the four different systems. Although expressed differently, they are equivalent tax rates.

Table 7.4 WRITING TAX RATES IN FOUR SYSTEMS

Percent	Per $100	Per $1000	In Mills
2.25%	$2.25	$22.50	22.5
3.2%	$3.20	$32.00	32
9.87%	$9.87	$98.70	98.7

Objective

5   *Find Taxes Given the Assessed Valuation and the Tax Rate.* Property taxes are found by multiplying the tax rate by the assessed valuation, as shown in the following example. Regardless of assessment rate or tax rate, property owners are concerned with the actual tax.

EXAMPLE 3 Finding the Property Tax

Find the annual taxes on each of the following pieces of property. Assessed valuations and tax rates are given.

(a) $58,975; 8.4%   **(b)** $875,400; $7.82 per $100
(c) $129,600; $64.21 per $1000   **(d)** $221,750; 94 mills

Solution

Multiply tax rate by the assessed valuation.

(a) 8.4% = 0.084

$$\text{Tax} = \text{tax rate} \times \text{assessed valuation}$$
$$\text{Tax} = 0.084 \times \$58,975 = \$4953.90$$

(b) $875,400 = 8754 hundreds

$$\text{Tax} = \$7.82 \times 8754 = \$68,456.28$$

(c) $129,600 = 129.6 thousands

$$\text{Tax} = \$64.21 \times 129.6 = \$8321.62$$

(d) 94 mills = 0.094

$$\text{Tax} = 0.094 \times \$221,750 = \$20,844.50$$

Objective

6 *Find the Assessed Valuation Given the Tax Rate and the Tax.* The tax formula can also be used to find the assessed valuation when given the amount of tax and the tax rate.

EXAMPLE 4 Finding the Assessed Valuation

The county property tax on a car wash in Boden County is $1024. If the tax rate is $1.65 per $100, find the assessed valuation.

Solution

Use the formula for finding tax.

$$\text{Tax} = \text{tax rate} \times \text{assessed valuation}$$
$$\$1024 = \$1.65 \times \text{assessed valuation}$$
$$\frac{\$1024}{\$1.65} = \text{assessed valuation} \qquad \text{Divide by \$1.65.}$$
$$620.61 \text{ hundreds} = \text{assessed valuation}$$

The assessed valuation is $62,061 ($620.61 × 100).

 Scientific Calculator Approach

The calculator solution to Example 4 is as follows.

1024 ÷ 1.65 × 100 = 62061   Rounded to the nearest dollar.

NOTE The total property tax is usually the sum of taxes from several different taxing entities, including state, school district, county, city, and, perhaps, even local community college districts.

Objective

7 *Find the Tax Rate Given the Assessed Valuation and the Tax.* The tax rate may be found by using the tax formula when the assessed valuation and the amount of tax are given.

> **EXAMPLE 5** **Finding the Tax Rate Given Assessed Valuation and Tax**
>
> A commercial property in Hampton County has an assessed valuation of $480,000 and an annual property tax of $14,500. Find the tax rate per $1000.
>
> **Solution**
>
> Use the formula for finding tax.
>
> $$\text{Tax} = \text{tax rate} \times \text{assessed valuation}$$
>
> The assessed valuation is 480 thousands ($480,000 \div 1000$).
>
> $$\$14,500 = \text{tax rate} \times 480$$
>
> $$\frac{\$14,500}{480} = \text{tax rate} \qquad \text{Divide by 480.}$$
>
> $$\$30.21 = \text{tax rate per } \$1000$$
>
> The tax rate per $1000 is $30.21.

7.2	**Exercises**

ASSESSED VALUATION Find the assessed valuation for each of the following pieces of property.

	Fair Market Value	Rate of Assessment	
1.	$341,200	40%	$136,480
2.	$136,500	50%	$68,250
3.	$173,800	35%	$60,830
4.	$587,300	42%	$246,666
5.	$1,300,500	25%	$325,125
6.	$2,450,000	80%	$1,960,000

PROPERTY TAX RATES Find the tax rate for the following. Write the tax rate as a percent rounded to the nearest tenth.

	Total Tax Amount Needed	Total Assessed Value	
7.	$12,342,000	$220,440,000	5.6%
8.	$8,650,000	$346,000,000	2.5%
9.	$12,480,000	$337,297,297	3.7%
10.	$2,751,375	$108,750,000	2.5%
11.	$1,224,000	$40,800,000	3%
12.	$2,941,500	$81,700,000	3.6%

TAX RATE COMPARISON Complete the following list comparing tax rates.

	Percent		Per $100		Per $1000		In Mills
13.	(a) 2.8 %	(b)	$2.80	(c)	$28		28
14.	(a) 6.75 %		$6.75	(b)	$67.50	(c)	67.5
15.	2.41%	(a)	$2.41	(b)	$24.10	(c)	24.1
16.	7.42%	(a)	$7.42	(b)	$74.20	(c)	74.2
17.	(a) 7.08 %		$7.08	(b)	$70.80	(c)	70.8
18.	(a) 3.5 %	(b)	$3.50		$35	(c)	35

19. What is the difference between fair market value and assessed value? How is the assessment rate used when finding the assessed value? (See Objective 1.)

20. Select any tax rate and express it as a percent. Write this tax rate in three additional equivalent forms and explain what each form means. (See Objective 4.)

FINDING PROPERTY TAX Find the tax for each of the following.

	Assessed Valuation	Tax Rate	
21.	$86,200	$6.80 per $100	$5861.60
22.	$41,300	$46.40 per $1000	$1916.32
23.	$685,400	6.93%	$47,498.22
24.	$128,200	42 mills	$5384.40
25.	$248,000	$1.80 per $100	$4464
26.	$38,250	$89.70 per $1000	$3431.03

ASSESSED VALUE, TAX RATE, AND TAX Find the missing quantity.

	Assessed Valuation	Tax Rate	Tax
27.	$49,250	5.8 %	$2856.50
28.	$218,000	$7.18 per $100	$15,652.40
29.	$73,800	85 mills	$6273
30.	$39,500	$48.18 per $1000	$1903.11
31.	$152,680	$5.25 per $100	$8015.70
32.	$435,500	37.6 mills	$16,374.80
33.	$236,800	4.3%	$10,182.40
34.	$96,200	$35 per $1000	$3367

Solve the following application problems. Round percents to the nearest tenth of a percent.

35. RETAIL CENTER Wilma James owns a retail center with many different shops that has a fair market value of $2,870,000. Property in the area is assessed at 60% of market value and the property tax is $58,400. Find the tax rate as a percent of assessed value. 3.4%

36. MEDICAL CLINIC Dr. Robertson owns a clinic that is occupied by physicians and their medical equipment. The building has a fair market value of $1,880,000 and property is assessed at 50% of market value. Given a property tax of $52,400, find the tax rate as a percent of assessed value. 5.6%

37. FM RADIO BROADCASTING   A new FM radio station broadcasts from a building having a fair market value of $734,000. The building is in an area where property is assessed at 25% of market value and the tax rate is $75.30 per $1000 of assessed value. Find the property tax. $13,817.55

38. ICE SKATING RINK   The building containing a small ice skating rink has a fair market value of $628,000, not including the value of the equipment inside the building. Property is assessed at 35% and the tax rate is $42 per $1000 of assessed value. Find the property tax. $9231.60

39. COMMERCIAL PROPERTY   Plaza Office Park has a fair market value of $5,700,000. Property is assessed in the area at 25% of market value. The tax rate is $14.10 per $100 of assessed valuation. Find the property tax. $200,925

40. HARLEY-DAVIDSON SHOP   Harley-Davidson of Lincoln has property with a fair market value of $1,037,200. The property is located in an area that is assessed at 15% of market value. The tax rate for the local school district is $7.35 per $100. Find the school district property tax. $11,435.13

41. COUNTY PROPERTY TAX   In one county, property is assessed at 40% of market value, with a tax rate of 32.1 mills. In a second county, property is assessed at 24% of market value with a tax rate of 50.2 mills. Custom Cabinets is trying to decide where to place a building with a fair market value of $380,000. (a) Which county would charge the lower property tax? (b) Find the amount saved each year.   (a) The second county (b) $300.96

42. PROPERTY TAX COMPARISON   Property taxes vary from one county to the next. In one county, property is assessed at 30% of market value, with a tax rate of 45.6 mills. In a second county, property is assessed at 48% of market value, with a tax rate of 29.3 mills. Misty Arce is trying to decide where to build a home that she expects to have a market value of $210,000. (a) Which county would charge the lower property tax? (b) Find the annual amount saved.   (a) The first county (b) $80.64

43. MANSION   Last year the property tax on a mansion was $28,600 at a tax rate of $12.50 per $1000. After a reassessment this year, the assessed value was increased by $140,000 and the property tax due is $31,100. Find the percent increase in the tax rate.   2.5%

44. INDUSTRIAL PROPERTY TAX   Last year the property tax on a small warehouse was $3042, and the tax rate was $3.60 per $100. After a reassessment this year, the assessed value was increased by $10,500 and the property tax due is $3705. Find the percent of increase in the tax rate. Round to the nearest tenth of a percent.   8.3%

45. TAX ON A LOT   A commercial corner lot was assessed at $45,000, and the tax was $1327.50. The following year the property tax increased to $1353.75 while the tax rate decreased by $0.10 per $100. Find the amount of increase in the assessed value of the commercial lot. $2500

46. TAX ON INVESTMENT PROPERTY   An investment property was assessed at $240,000, and the tax was $5400. The following year the property tax increased to $5805, while the tax rate decreased by $1.00 per $1000. Find the amount of increase in the assessed value of the property. $30,000

7.3	**Personal Income Tax**

OBJECTIVES

1 *Know the four steps that determine tax liability.*

2 *Identify information needed to find adjusted gross income.*

3 *Calculate adjusted gross income.*

4 *Know the standard deduction amounts.*

5 *Know the tax rates.*

6 *List possible itemized deductions to find taxable income.*

7 *Calculate income tax.*

8 *Determine a balance due or a refund from the Internal Revenue Service.*

9 *Prepare a 1040A and a Schedule B federal tax form.*

Income taxes are taxes paid by individuals and businesses. They are a primary source of income for the federal government, most states, and some local governments. Figure 7.2 shows the 2009 income for the federal government. Notice that personal income taxes made up 26% of the government's income, whereas corporate income taxes made up only 4% of the government's income. Individuals paid more taxes than corporations. Also notice that 40% of the income came from borrowing. Many believe that this level of borrowing is unsustainable, but 2009 was unusual in that the government spent money to combat the effects of the financial crisis.

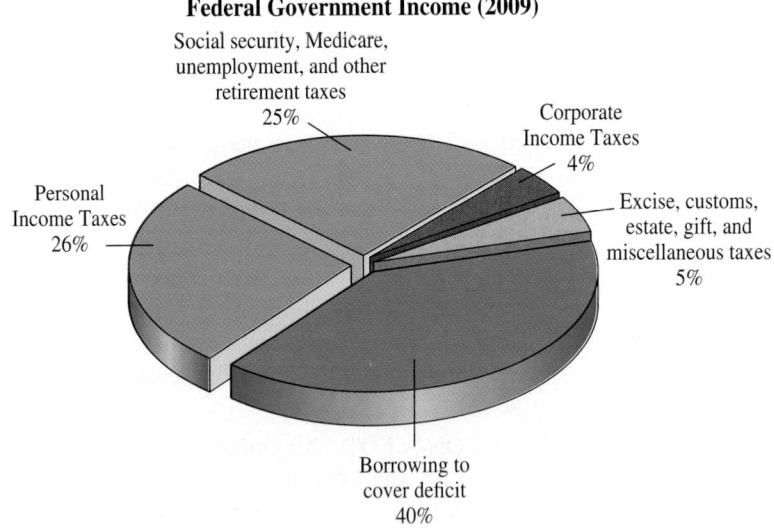

Federal Government Income (2009)

Source: Internal Revenue Service.

Figure 7.2

Some people believe that individuals with high incomes pay little or no income taxes. Figure 7.3 shows that the top 1% of all earners pay an average of 31.2% of their income in federal taxes, or about $1 out of every $3 earned. In fact, the top 1% of all earners pay more in federal income tax than the lowest 90% of all earners combined.

The **Internal Revenue Service (IRS)** is the organization in the U.S. government that is responsible for collecting income taxes from individuals and businesses. Most working adults are required to file income tax returns with the IRS each year. Married couples usually submit one joint tax return showing income and deductions for both spouses, but spouses can file separately. The most recent forms and tax rates can be found on the IRS Web site at www.irs.gov. Last year, more than 80 million families, or about 80% of the number filing in the United States,

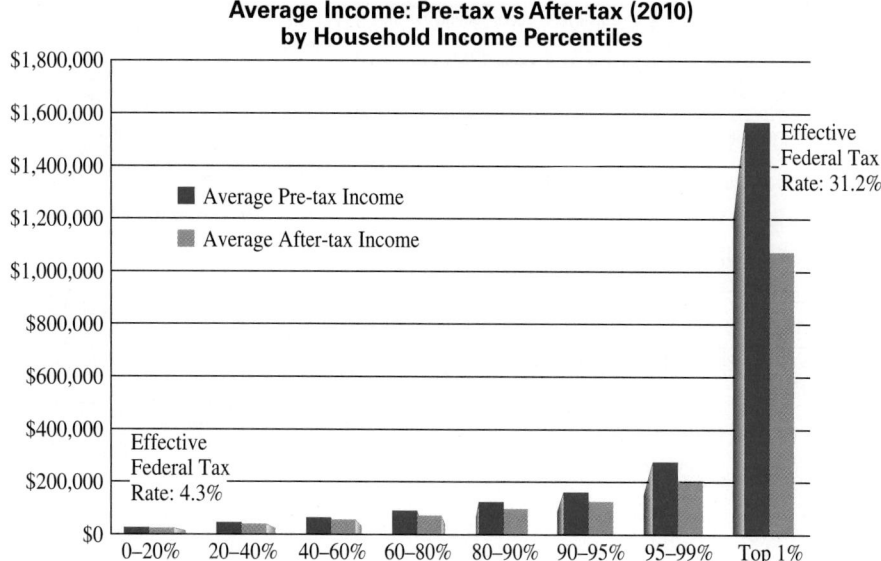

Average Income: Pre-tax vs After-tax (2010) by Household Income Percentiles

Source: Congressional Budget Office.

Figure 7.3

filed electronically. Filing electronically allows most filers access to free, commercial, online tax preparation software and can result in receiving refunds in as few as 10 days.

There are thousands of rules relating to income tax preparation and many different forms, each with its own instructions. However, many people have relatively simple income tax returns that do not require professionals to complete. Regardless of whether you use a professional to file your income tax return or if you do it yourself, you should carefully save all records related to income and expenses. These records should be kept until the statute of limitations runs out, which is 3 years from the date the tax return was filed or 2 years from the date the tax was paid, whichever is later. The IRS can audit you during this period and they require proof of income and deductions. Many accountants recommend you keep records for 7 years, but you should keep records on real estate as long as they are needed.

Objective

1 *Know the Four Steps That Determine Tax Liability.* There are four basic steps in finding a person's total tax liability.

Preparing Your Income Tax Return

Step 1 Find the adjusted gross income (AGI) for the year.
Step 2 Find the taxable income.
Step 3 Find the tax.
Step 4 Check to see if a refund is due or if more money is owed to the government.

Objective

2 *Identify Information Needed to Find Adjusted Gross Income.* The first step in finding personal income tax is to find **adjusted gross income**. Adjusted gross income is the total of all income, less certain adjustments. Employers are required to send employees **W-2 forms** showing wages paid, federal income taxes withheld, Social Security tax withheld, and Medicare tax withheld. Other types of income such as interest, dividends, and self-employment income are shown on **1099 forms**, which are also mailed to each individual. Sample W-2 and 1099-INT forms are shown.

22222	Void ☐	**a** Employee's social security number	For Official Use Only ▶ OMB No. 1545-0008		

b Employer identification number (EIN) 94-1287319		**1** Wages, tips, other compensation $24,738.41	**2** Federal income tax withheld $3275.60
c Employer's name, address, and ZIP code		**3** Social security wages $24,738.41	**4** Social security tax withheld $1533.78
The Doll House 1568 Liberty Heights Ave. Baltimore, MD 21230		**5** Medicare wages and tips $24,738.41	**6** Medicare tax withheld $358.71
		7 Social security tips	**8** Allocated tips
d Control number 123-45-6789		**9**	**10** Dependent care benefits
e Employee's first name and initial Jennifer	Last name Crum Suff.	**11** Nonqualified plans	**12a** See instructions for box 12
2136 Old Road Towson, MD 21285		**13** Statutory employee ☐ Retirement plan ☐ Third-party sick pay ☐	**12b**
		14 Other	**12c**
			12d
f Employee's address and ZIP code			

15 State Employer's state ID number MD	600-5076	**16** State wages, tips, etc.	**17** State income tax	**18** Local wages, tips, etc.	**19** Local income tax	**20** Locality name

Form **W-2** **Wage and Tax Statement**   **2012**

Department of the Treasury—Internal Revenue Service

Copy A For Social Security Administration — Send this entire page with Form W-3 to the Social Security Administration; photocopies are **not** acceptable.

For Privacy Act and Paperwork Reduction Act Notice, see the separate instructions.

Cat. No. 10134D

Do Not Cut, Fold, or Staple Forms on This Page

9292   ☐ VOID   ☐ CORRECTED

PAYER'S name, street address, city, state, ZIP code, and telephone no. Employees Credit Union 2572 Brookhaven Drive Dundalk, MD 21222 301-125-3661	Payer's RTN (optional)	OMB No. 1545-0112 **20**12 Form **1099-INT**	**Interest Income**
	1 Interest income $ 1624.01		
	2 Early withdrawal penalty $		
PAYER'S federal identification number 94-1287319	RECIPIENT'S identification number 123-45-6789	**3** Interest on U.S. Savings Bonds and Treas. obligations $	**Copy A** For Internal Revenue Service Center File with Form 1096.
RECIPIENT'S name Jennifer Crum		**4** Federal income tax withheld $	**5** Investment expenses $
Street address (including apt. no.) 2136 Old Road		**6** Foreign tax paid $	**7** Foreign country or U.S. possession
City, state, and ZIP code Towson, MD 21285		**8** Tax-exempt interest $	**9** Specified private activity bond interest $
Account number (see instructions)	2nd TIN not. ☐	**10** Tax-exempt bond CUSIP no.	**11** State	**12** State identification no.	**13** State tax withheld $

For Privacy Act and Paperwork Reduction Act Notice, see the **2012 General Instructions for Certain Information Returns.**

Form **1099-INT**   Cat. No. 14410K   Department of the Treasury - Internal Revenue Service

Do Not Cut or Separate Forms on This Page — Do Not Cut or Separate Forms on This Page

Objective

3 *Calculate Adjusted Gross Income.*

Finding Adjusted Gross Income

1. **Add** amounts from all W-2 and 1099 forms along with dividends, capital gains, unemployment compensation, and tips or other employee compensation.
2. From this sum, subtract adjustments such as contributions to a *regular* **individual retirement account (IRA)** or alimony payments.

EXAMPLE 1 **Finding Adjusted Gross Income (AGI)**

As an assistant manager at The Doll House, Jennifer Crum earned $24,738.41 last year and $1624.01 in interest from her credit union (see her W-2 and 1099 forms). She had $1500 in IRA contributions. Find her adjusted gross income.

Solution

$$\text{Adjusted gross income} = \text{wages} + \text{interest} - \text{IRA contribution}$$
$$= \$24{,}738.41 + \$1624.01 - \$1500$$
$$= \$24{,}862.42$$

NOTE A copy of all W-2 forms must be sent to the Internal Revenue Service, along with the completed tax forms. However, the IRS does not require the taxpayer to send in copies of 1099 forms.

Objective

4 *Know the Standard Deduction Amounts.* Most people are almost finished at this point. A taxpayer next subtracts *the larger of* either the itemized deductions or the standard deduction from adjusted gross income. Itemized deductions are described in Objective 5 in this section and are associated with several limitations based on adjusted gross income. The **standard deduction** amounts change each year, so be sure to use the most recent numbers when preparing your income taxes. Here are the most recent standard deductions.

$5,800—Single taxpayers
$11,600—Married couples filing jointly or qualifying widower
$5,800—Married taxpayers filing separately
$8,500—Head of household

NOTE Additional standard deductions are given for taxpayers and dependents who are blind or 65 years of age or older.

Head of household refers to an unmarried person who provides a home for other people such as a dependent child or a dependent parent of the taxpayer.

The next step is to find the number of **personal exemptions**. One exemption is allowed for yourself, another for your spouse if filing a joint return, and yet another exemption for each child or other dependent. The number of exemptions does not depend on whether the filing status is single or married. The deduction for personal exemptions is $3700 times the number of exemptions. Here are some examples.

	Number of Exemptions	Personal Exemption(s)
Single individual	1	1 × $3700 = $3,700
Married couple filing jointly, with 3 children	5	5 × $3700 = $18,500
Single woman, head of household with 2 dependent children	3	3 × $3700 = $11,100

Taxable income is found as follows.

Adjusted gross income

− Larger of itemized deductions or the standard deduction

− Personal exemptions ($3700 for each dependent)

Taxable income

NOTE Both the standard deduction amounts and the personal exemption amounts change each year. It is always important to use current information.

Objective

5 *Know the Tax Rates.* As shown in Table 7.5, income tax rates for individuals range from 10% to 35%, depending on taxable income and filing status. Assume a single filer has a taxable income of $37,300. According to the tax rate schedule for a single filer, $37,300 falls in the row Over $34,500, but not over $83,600. Use the information to the right in that row to find the tax.

$$\text{Federal income tax} = \$4750 + 25\% \text{ of the amount over } \$34,500$$
$$= \$4750 + 0.25 \times (\$37,300 - \$34,500)$$
$$= \$5450$$

Note that the 25% tax rate applies only to the amount above $34,500 and not to the full amount of taxable income.

EXAMPLE 2 Finding Taxable Income and the Income Tax Amount

Find the taxable income and tax for each.

(a) Peter Chin, single, 1 exemption; adjusted gross income $32,480
(b) The Richfields, married, filing jointly, 4 exemptions; adjusted gross income $68,250

Solution

(a)
$$\text{Taxable income} = \text{Adjusted Gross Income} - \text{Standard Deduction} - \text{Personal Exemption(s)}$$
$$\text{Taxable income} = \$32,480 - \$5800 - 1 \times \$3700$$
$$= \$22,980$$
$$\text{Tax} = \$850 + 0.15 \times (\$22,980 - \$8500)$$
$$= \$3022$$

(b)
$$\text{Taxable income} = \text{Adjusted Gross Income} - \text{Standard Deduction} - \text{Personal Exemption(s)}$$
$$\text{Taxable income} = \$68,250 - \$11,600 - 4 \times \$3700$$
$$= \$41,850$$
$$\text{Tax} = \$1700 + 0.15 \times (\$41,850 - \$17,000)$$
$$= \$5427.50$$

Table 7.5   2011 TAX RATE SCHEDULES

Schedule X—Use if your 2011 filing status is Single				Schedule Z—Use if your 2011 filing status is Head of household			
If line 5 is:		The tax is:		If line 5 is:		The tax is:	
Over—	But not over—		of the amount over—	Over—	But not over—		of the amount over—
$0	$8,500	——— 10%	$0	$0	$12,150	——— 10%	$0
8,500	34,500	$850.00 + 15%	8,500	12,150	46,250	$1,215.00 + 15%	12,150
34,500	83,600	4,750.00 + 25%	34,500	46,250	119,400	6,330.00 + 25%	46,250
83,600	174,400	17,025.00 + 28%	83,600	119,400	193,350	24,617.50 + 28%	119,400
174,400	379,150	42,449.00 + 33%	174,400	193,350	379,150	45,323.50 + 33%	193,350
379,150	———	110,016.50 + 35%	379,150	379,150	———	106,637.50 + 35%	379,150

Schedule Y-1—Use if your 2011 filing status is Married filing Jointly or Qualifying widow(er)				Schedule Y-2—Use if your 2011 filing status is Married filing separately			
If line 5 is:		The tax is:		If line 5 is:		The tax Is:	
Over—	But not over—		of the amount over—	Over—	But not over—		of the amount over—
$0	$17,000	——— 10%	$0	$0	$8,500	——— 10%	$0
17,000	69,000	$1,700.00 + 15%	17,000	8,500	34,500	$850.00 + 15%	8,500
69,000	139,350	9,500.00 + 25%	69,000	34,500	69,675	4,750.00 + 25%	34,500
139,350	212,300	27,087.50 + 28%	139,350	69,675	106,150	13,543.75 + 28%	69,675
212,300	379,150	47,513.50 + 33%	212,300	106,150	189,575	23,756.75 + 33%	106,150
379,150	———	102,574.00 + 35%	379,150	189,575	———	51,287.00 + 35%	189,575

NOTE When taxable income goes beyond the 15% tax rate amount, do not make the mistake of using the 25% tax rate on the entire amount of taxable income. Just apply the 25% rate to the amount over and above the amount listed in the table.

Objective

6 *List Possible Itemized Deductions to Find Taxable Income.* Taxpayers can deduct the larger of **itemized deductions** or the standard deduction from their adjusted gross income. The use of itemized deductions is most likely to be applicable to individuals who own their own homes. The most common **tax deductions** for individuals are listed here. Business deductions differ from those for individuals.

NOTE At the time this edition was written, Congress was talking seriously about changing the tax code. So, some of these rules introduced in this section may change in the near future.

Medical and dental expenses. Only medical and dental expenses exceeding 7.5% of adjusted gross income may be deducted. This deduction is effectively limited to catastrophic illnesses for most taxpayers. Expenses reimbursed by an insurance company are not deductible.

Taxes. Taxes that can be deducted include state and local income taxes, real estate taxes, and personal property taxes. Taxes that individuals cannot deduct include federal income taxes, excise taxes, and taxes on gasoline.

Interest. Home mortgage interest on the taxpayer's principal residence and a qualified second home is deductible. Other interest charges (such as credit-card interest) may *not* be deducted.

Contributions. Contributions to qualifying charities may be deducted.

Miscellaneous deductions. These expenses are deductible only to the extent that the total exceeds 2% of the taxpayer's adjusted gross income. They include the following: unreimbursed employee expenses, tax preparation fees, appraisal fees for tax purposes, and legal fees for tax planning or tax litigation.

> **NOTE** The taxpayer may take the larger of the standard deduction or the itemized deductions. You must have documentation that shows the itemized expenses if you itemize.

Objective

7 *Calculate Income Tax.* After the taxable income is determined, the amount of income tax must be found (see Objective 5).

EXAMPLE 3 **Using Itemized Deductions to Find Taxable Income and Income Tax**

Chris Kelly is single and has no dependents. He had an adjusted gross income of $26,735 last year. He had deductions of $1352 for other taxes, $5270 for mortgage interest, and $317 for charity. Find his taxable income and his income tax.

Solution

$$\text{Itemized deductions} = \$1352 + \$5270 + \$317 = \$6939$$

Kelly's itemized deductions of $6939 are larger than the $5800 standard deduction for a single person. Therefore, taxable income is adjusted gross income minus the itemized deductions minus the one personal exemption for being single with no dependents.

$$
\begin{aligned}
& \qquad\qquad\qquad \overset{\text{Itemized}}{\underset{\text{deductions}}{}} \quad \overset{\text{Personal}}{\underset{\text{exemption}}{}} \\
\text{Taxable income} &= \$26{,}735 - \$6935 - 1 \times \$3700 = \$16{,}096 \\
\text{Income tax} &= \$850 + 15\% \text{ of the excess over } \$8500 \\
&= \$850 + 0.15 \times (\$16{,}096 - \$8500) \\
&= \$1989.40
\end{aligned}
$$

Chris Kelly must pay $1989.40 in income taxes for the year.

■

> **NOTE** The federal government requires that individuals pay taxes. Not paying a tax can result in legal troubles, fines, and potentially the loss of an asset such as your home. Lying on a tax return is a criminal issue and may result in a prison sentence.

Objective

8 *Determine a Balance Due or a Refund from the Internal Revenue Service.* A taxpayer may have paid either too much or too little in to the IRS during the year. To check, first add up the total income of income tax paid using W-2 forms. If more was withheld than due to the IRS, a refund will be paid to the taxpayer. If not enough was withheld, the taxpayer must pay the difference along with the tax return.

EXAMPLE | **4** | **Determining Tax Due or Refund**

Tim Owen works as an attorney and his wife stays at home with their young daughter. Last year Tim had an adjusted gross income of $94,800 and $820 was withheld from his paycheck each month for federal income taxes. The Owens file a joint return and use the standard deduction and 3 exemptions. Find either the amount of income taxes they must pay or the amount they overpaid.

Solution

Adjusted gross income	$94,800	
Standard deduction	−$11,600	Married filing jointly
Personal exemptions	−$11,100	3 exemptions × $3700
Taxable income	$72,100	

$$\begin{aligned} \text{Income tax} &= \$9500 + 25\% \text{ of the amount over } \$69,000 \\ &= \$9500 + 0.25 \times (\$72,100 - \$69,000) \\ &= \$10,275 \end{aligned}$$

Total amount withheld last year $= \$820 \times 12 = \$9840$

Amount owed to IRS $= \$10,275 - \$9840 = \$435$

The Owens must send a payment of $435 to the IRS along with their income tax return.

It is best to use the simplest form needed when filing with the IRS. The **1040EZ** is the simplest form and is used by many students, but many people are not allowed to use it. Here are the IRS guidelines to help you determine the appropriate form.

Form 1040EZ—You must

1. file single or married filing jointly;
2. claim no dependents;
3. be under 65 and not blind at the end of the tax year;
4. have only wages, salaries, tips, taxable scholarship and fellowship grants, and certain other income;
5. have taxable income of less than $100,000;
6. not receive any advance earned income credit payments;
7. not owe any household employment taxes on wages you paid to a household employee;
8. not claim the additional standard deduction for real estate taxes, net disaster losses, or qualified motor vehicle taxes;
9. not claim a student loan interest deduction, an educator expense deduction, or a tuition and fees deduction; and
10. not claim an education credit, retirement savings contributions credit, or a health coverage tax credit.

Form 1040A—You must

1. have income only from wages, salaries, tips, taxable scholarships and fellowship grants, interest, or ordinary dividends, capital gain distributions, pensions, annuities, IRAs, or certain other income;
2. have taxable income of less than $100,000;
3. not itemize deductions;
4. not have an alternative minimum tax adjustment on stock you acquired from the exercise of an incentive stock option; and
5. only have the following adjustments to income: the IRA deduction, the student loan interest deduction, the educator expenses deduction, and the tuition and fees deduction.

Form 1040—Use this form if

1. your taxable income is $100,000 or more;
2. you have certain types of income such as unreported tips, certain nontaxable distributions, self-employment earnings, or income received as a partner, a shareholder in an "S" Corporation, or a beneficiary of an estate or trust;
3. you itemize deductions or claim certain tax credits or adjustments to income; or
4. you owe household employment taxes.

Objective

9 *Prepare a 1040A and a Schedule B Federal Tax Form.* Table 7.6 shows that taxes vary considerably by country and that married couples in many countries pay a far higher percent of their income in taxes than they do in the United States. Actually, income taxes in the United States are relatively low compared to many countries in the figure. However, many of the countries with higher taxes have more safety nets for employees, including higher unemployment benefits and coverage of medical expenses compared to the United States. So, generally countries with higher income tax rates offer more benefits and countries with lower levels of income taxes have fewer benefits.

Table 7.6 **PERCENTAGE OF GROSS EARNINGS PAID IN INCOME TAX AND SOCIAL SECURITY CONTRIBUTIONS (SELECTED COUNTRIES, 2010)**

Country	Income Tax (%)	Social Security Contributions (%)	Total (%)
Germany	15.7	17.2	32.9
United Kingdom	14.7	8.3	23.0
Italy	15.4	7.2	22.6
Australia	20.4	0	20.4
United States	13.9	7.0	20.0
Canada	13.3	6.5	19.8
France	9.9	9.6	19.5
Japan	6.8	11.5	18.3
Spain	11.4	4.9	16.3
Mexico	3.8	1.2	5.0

Source: Data from the Organization for Economic Cooperation and Development.

The next example shows how to complete an income tax return using **Form 1040A** and a **Schedule B (Form 1040A)**. When completing income tax forms and calculations, notice that all amounts may be rounded to the nearest dollar.

EXAMPLE 5 **Preparing a 1040A and a Schedule B**

Jennifer Crum is single and claims one exemption. Her income appears on the W-2 and 1099 forms on page 294. Crum contributes $1500 to an IRA. Crum satisfies the requirements to use Form 1040A but must also fill out Schedule B (Form 1040A) since she has more than $1500 in interest.

Form
1040A

Department of the Treasury—Internal Revenue Service

U.S. Individual Income Tax Return (99)   **2011**   IRS Use Only—Do not write or staple in this space.

Name, Address, and SSN

See separate instructions.

PRINT CLEARLY	Your first name and initial	Last name	OMB No. 1545-0074
	Jennifer	Crum	**Your social security number** 123 45 6789
	If a joint return, spouse's first name and initial	Last name	**Spouse's social security number**
	Home address (number and street). If you have a P.O. box, see instructions. Apt. no.		▲ Make sure the SSN(s) above and on line 6c are correct.
	2136 Old Road		
	City, town or post office, state, and ZIP code. If you have a foreign address, see instructions.		Checking a box below will not change your tax or refund.
	Towson, MD 21285		

Presidential Election Campaign ► Check here if you, or your spouse if filing jointly, want $3 to go to this fund ---------- ► ☑ **You** ☐ **Spouse**

Filing status

Check only one box.

1 ☑ Single
2 ☐ Married filing jointly (even if only one had income)
3 ☐ Married filing separately. Enter spouse's SSN above and full name here. ►

4 ☐ Head of household (with qualifying person). (See instructions.) If the qualifying person is a child but not your dependent, enter this child's name here. ► _____
5 ☐ Qualifying widow(er) with dependent child (See instructions.)

Exemptions

If more than six dependents, see instructions.

6a ☑ **Yourself.** If someone can claim you as a dependent, **do not** check box 6a.

b ☐ **Spouse**

c Dependents:

(1) First name Last name	(2) Dependent's social security number	(3) Dependent's relationship to you	(4) ✔ if child under age 17 qualifying for child tax credit (see page 16)
_____	¦		☐
_____	¦		☐
_____	¦		☐
_____	¦		☐
_____	¦		☐
_____	¦		☐

Boxes checked on 6a and 6b   1
No. of children on 6c who:
● lived with you   ____
● did not live with you due to divorce or separation (see instructions)   ____
Dependents on 6c not entered above   ____

d Total number of exemptions claimed.

Add numbers on lines above ►   1

Income

Attach Form(s) W-2 here. Also attach Form(s) 1099-R if tax was withheld.

If you did not get a W-2, see page 20.

Enclose, but do not attach, any payment. Also, please use Form 1040-V.

7	Wages, salaries, tips, etc. Attach Form(s) W-2.	7	$24,738
8a	**Taxable** interest. Attach Schedule B if required.	8a	$1,624
b	**Tax-exempt** interest. **Do not** include on line 8a. 8b		
9a	Ordinary dividends. Attach Schedule B if required.	9a	
b	Qualified dividends (see instructions). 9b		
10	Capital gain distributions (see instructions).	10	
11a IRA distributions. 11a	**11b** Taxable amount (see instructions).	11b	
12a Pensions and annuities. 12a	**12b** Taxable amount (see instructions).	12b	
13	Unemployment compensation and Alaska Permanent Fund dividends.	13	
14a Social security benefits. 14a	**14b** Taxable amount (see instructions).	14b	
15	Add lines 7 through 14b (far right column). This is your **total income.** ►	15	$26,362

Adjusted gross income

16	Educator expenses (see instructions). 16		
17	IRA deduction (see instructions). 17	$1,500	
18	Student loan interest deduction (see instructions). 18		
19	Tuition and fees. Attach Form 8917. 19		
20	Add lines 16 through 19. These are your **total adjustments.**	20	$1,500
21	Subtract line 20 from line 15. This is your **adjusted gross income.** ►	21	$24,862

For Disclosure, Privacy Act, and Paperwork Reduction Act Notice, see separate instructions.   Cat. No. 11327A   Form **1040A** (2010)

Form 1040A (2010)   Page **2**

Tax, credits, and payments	**22**	Enter the amount from line 21 (adjusted gross income).	**22**	$24,862

23a Check if: ☐ **You** were born before January 2, 1946, ☐ Blind } **Total boxes**
☐ **Spouse** was born before January 2, 1946, ☐ Blind } checked ► **23a** [ ]

b If you are married filing separately and your spouse itemizes deductions, see page 30 and check here ► **23b** ☐

24	Enter your **standard deduction** (see instructions).	**24**	$5,800
25	Subtract line 24 from line 22. If line 24 is more than line 22, enter -0-.	**25**	$19,062
26	**Exemptions.** Multiply $3,650 by the number on line 6d.	**26**	$3,700
27	Subtract line 26 from line 25. If line 26 is more than line 25, enter -0-. This is your **taxable income.** ►	**27**	$15,362
28	**Tax,** including any alternative minimum tax (see Instructions).	**28**	$1,879
29	Credit for child and dependent care expenses. Attach Form 2441.	**29**	
30	Credit for the elderly or the disabled. Attach Schedule R.	**30**	
31	Education credits from Form 8863, line 23.	**31**	
32	Retirement savings contributions credit. Attach Form 8880.	**32**	
33	Child tax credit (see instructions).	**33**	
34	Add lines 29 through 33. These are your **total credits.**	**34**	$0
35	Subtract line 34 from line 28. If line 34 is more than line 28, enter -0-.	**35**	$1,879
36	Advance earned income credit payments from Form(s) W-2, box 9.	**36**	
37	Add lines 35 and 36. This is your **total tax.** ►	**37**	$1,879
38	Federal income tax withheld from Forms W-2 and 1099. **38** $3,276		
39	2010 estimated tax payments and amount applied from 2009 return. **39** $0		

If you have a qualifying child, attach Schedule EIC.

40	Making work pay credit. Attach Schedule M. **40**		
41a	**Earned income credit (EIC).** **41a** $0		
b	Nontaxable combat pay election. **41b**		
42	Additional child tax credit. Attach Form 8812. **42**		
43	American opportunity credit from Form 8863, line 14. **43**		
44	Add lines 38, 39, 40, 41a, 42 and 43. These are your **total payments.** ►	**44**	$3,276

Refund	**45**	If line 44 is more than line 37, subtract line 37 from line 44. This is the amount you **overpaid.**	**45**	$1,397

Direct deposit? See instructions and fill in 46b, 46c, and 46d or Form 8888.

46a Amount of line 45 you want **refunded to you.** If Form 8888 is attached, check here ► ☐ **46a** $1,397

► **b** Routing number [1 2 3 4 5 6 7 8 9] ► **c** Type: ☐ Checking ☐ Savings

► **d** Account number [5 5 4 1 1 0 0 0 1 1 0 0 5 9 0 0 1]

47 Amount of line 45 you want **applied to your 2011 estimated tax.** **47** $0

Amount you owe	**48**	**Amount you owe.** Subtract line 44 from line 37. For details on how to pay, see instructions. ► **48**	$0
	49	Estimated tax penalty (see instructions). **49** $0	

Third party designee

Do you want to allow another person to discuss this return with the IRS (see instructions)? ☐ **Yes.** Complete the following. ☑ **No**

Designee's name ►   Phone no. ►   Personal identification number (PIN) ► [ ][ ][ ][ ][ ][ ]

Sign here

Under penalties of perjury, I declare that I have examined this return and accompanying schedules and statements, and to the best of my knowledge and belief, they are true, correct, and accurately list all amounts and sources of income I received during the tax year. Declaration of preparer (other than the taxpayer) is based on all information of which the preparer has any knowledge.

Joint return? See page 13.

Keep a copy for your records.

Your signature	Date	Your occupation	Daytime phone number
Jennifer Crum	4/15/--	Assistant Manager	(410) 286-2594
Spouse's signature. If a joint return, **both** must sign.	Date	Spouse's occupation	

Paid preparer use only

Print/type preparer's name	Preparer's signature	Date	Check ► ☐ if self-employed	PTIN
Firm's name ►			Firm's EIN ►	
Firm's address ►			Phone no.	

Form **1040A** (2010)

SCHEDULE B
(Form 1040A or 1040)

Department of the Treasury
Internal Revenue Service (99)

Interest and Ordinary Dividends

► **Attach to Form 1040A or 1040.**   ► **See instructions on back.**

OMB No.1545-0074

20**11**

Attachment
Sequence No. **08**

Name(s) shown on return
Jennifer Crum

Your social security number
123 45 6789

Part I **Interest** (See instructions on back and the instructions for Form 1040A, or Form 1040, line 8a.) **Note.** If you received a Form 1099-INT, Form 1099-OID, or substitute statement from a brokerage firm, list the firm's name as the payer and enter the total interest shown on that form.	**1**	List name of payer. If any interest is from a seller-financed mortgage and the buyer used the property as a personal residence, see instructions on back and list this interest first. Also, show that buyer's social security number and address ► *Employees Credit Union*		**Amount**
			1	$1,624
	2	Add the amounts on line 1	**2**	$1,624
	3	Excludable interest on series EE and I U.S. savings bonds issued after 1989. Attach Form 8815	**3**	
	4	Subtract line 3 from line 2. Enter the result here and on Form 1040A, or Form 1040, line 8a . . . . ►	**4**	$1,624

Note. If line 4 is over $1,500, you must complete Part III.

Part II **Ordinary Dividends** (See instructions on back and the instructions for Form 1040A, or Form 1040, line 9a.) **Note.** If you received a Form 1099-DIV or substitute statement from a brokerage firm, list the firm's name as the payer and enter the ordinary dividends shown on that form.	**5**	List name of payer ►		**Amount**
			5	
	6	Add the amounts on line 5. Enter the total here and on Form 1040A, or Form 1040, line 9a . . . . ►	**6**	

Note. If line 6 is over $1,500, you must complete Part III.

Part III **Foreign Accounts and Trusts** (See instructions on back.)	You must complete this part if you **(a)** had over $1,500 of taxable interest or ordinary dividends; **(b)** had a foreign account; or **(c)** received a distribution from, or were a grantor of, or a transferor to, a foreign trust.		**Yes**	**No**
	7a	At any time during 2010, did you have an interest in or a signature or other authority over a financial account in a foreign country, such as a bank account, securities account, or other financial account? See instructions on back for exceptions and filling requirements for Form TD F 90-22.1		✓
	b	If "Yes," enter the name of the foreign country ►		
	8	During 2010, did you receive a distribution from, or were you the grantor of, or transferor to, a foreign trust? If "Yes," you may have to file Form 3520. See instructions on back		✓

For Paperwork Reduction Act Notice, see your tax return instructions.   Cat. No. 17146N   **Schedule B (Form 1040A or 1040) 2010**

7.3   Exercises

ADJUSTED GROSS INCOME   Find the adjusted gross income for each of the following.

Name	Income from Jobs	Interest	Misc. Income	Dividend Income	Adjustments to Income	Adjusted Gross Income
1. R. Jacob	$22,840	$234	$1209	$48	$1200	$23,131
2. K. Chandler	$38,156	$285	$73	$542	$317	$38,739
3. The Hanks	$21,380	$625	$139	$184	$618	$21,710
4. The Jazwinskis	$33,650	$722	$375	$218	$473	$34,492
5. The Brashers	$38,643	$95	$188	$105	$0	$39,031
6. The Ameens	$41,379	$1174	$536	$186	$2258	$41,017

TAXABLE INCOME AND TAX   Find the amount of taxable income and the tax for each of the following. Use the tax rate schedule (Table 7.5). The letter following the name indicates marital status. Assume that all married people are filing jointly. Round figures to nearest dollar.

Name	Number of Exemptions	Adjusted Gross Income	Total Itemized Deductions	Taxable Income	Tax Owed
7. R. Rodriguez, S	1	$32,400	$2398	$22,900	$3010
8. Lesly Pacas, S	1	$22,770	$898	$13,270	$1565.50
9. The Cooks, M	3	$38,751	$5968	$16,051	$1605.10
10. The Loveridges, M	7	$52,532	$6972	$15,032	$1503.20
11. The Jordans, M	5	$71,800	$12,200	$41,100	$5315
12. G. Clarke, Married Filing Separately	2	$48,600	$6820	$32,700	$4480
13. D. Collins, Married Filing Separately	3	$35,350	$6240	$15,750	$1937.50
14. K. Tang, Head of Household	2	$93,240	$14,012	$71,828	$12,724.50
15. B. Kammerer, S	1	$58,720	$5107	$49,220	$8430
16. G. Nation, M	3	$193,440	$18,070	$164,270	$34,065.10
17. B. Albert, Head of Household	2	$62,613	$8490	$46,713	$6445.75
18. B. Nelson, Head of Household	4	$94,810	$9912	$70,098	$12,292

TAX REFUND OR TAX DUE   Find the amount of any refund or tax due for the following people. The letter following the name indicates marital status. Assume a 52-week year and that married people are filing jointly.

Name	Taxable Income	Federal Income Tax Withheld from Checks	Tax Refund or Tax Due
19. Karecki, S	$16,890	$243.10 monthly	$808.70 tax refund
20. Turner, K., S	$32,060	$347.80 monthly	$210.40 tax due
21. Hunziker, S	$23,552	$72.18 weekly	$645.56 tax refund
22. The Fungs, M	$54,180	$119.27 weekly	$1074.96 tax due
23. The Todds, M	$68,420	$510 monthly	$3293 tax due
24. The Bensons, M	$46,850	$165.30 weekly	$2418.10 tax refund

25. List four sources of income for which an individual might receive W-2 and 1099 forms. Which form would commonly be received for each? (See Objective 3.)

26. List four possible tax deductions, and explain the effect that a tax deduction will have on taxable income and on income tax due. (See Objective 6.) Round to the nearest dollar.

Find the taxable income and income tax in the following application problems.

27. MARRIED—INCOME TAX   Paul and Joanna Kidman had an adjusted gross income of $121,420 last year. Deductions included $3184 for state income tax, $1208 for city income tax, $8145 for property tax on their home, $13,512 for mortgage interest, and $1425 in charitable contributions. They file a joint return and claim 4 exemptions. $79,146; $12,036.50

28. SINGLE—INCOME TAX   Ronda Biondi works at Fashion Shoppe and had an adjusted gross income of $34,975 last year. She had deductions of $971 for state income tax, $2564 for property tax, $3820 in mortgage interest, and $235 in contributions. Biondi claims 1 exemption and files as a single person. $23,685; $3127.75

29. SINGLE—INCOME TAX   Martha Crutchfield has an adjusted gross income of $79,300 and files as a single person with only 1 exemption. Her itemized deductions amounted to $4630. $69,800; $13,575

30. MARRIED—INCOME TAX   The Simpsons had an adjusted gross income of $48,260 last year. They had deductions of $1078 for state income tax, $253 for city income tax, $4850 for property tax, $6318 in mortgage interest, and $920 in contributions. They claim 3 exemptions and file a joint return. $23,741; $2711.15

31. HEAD OF HOUSEHOLD   Martha Spencer, owner of The Doll House, had wages of $98,645, dividends of $385, interest of $672, and adjustments to income of $1058 last year. She had deductions of $2877 for state income tax, $342 for city income tax, $3840 for property tax, $8250 in mortgage interest, and $855 in contributions. She claims 4 exemptions and files as head of household. $67,680; $11,687.50

32. HEAD OF HOUSEHOLD   John Walker had wages of $30,364, other income of $2892, dividends of $240, interest of $315, and a regular IRA contribution of $750 last year. He had deductions of $1163 for state income tax, $3220 for property tax, $3680 in mortgage interest, and $540 in contributions. Walker claims 2 exemptions and files as head of household. $17,161; $1966.65

33. MARRIED TAXPAYER   Bruce and Sally Feldstein work full-time as registered nurses and had combined wages of $128,450, other income of $3200, dividend income of $530, and interest income of $1848. They do not own a home but are thinking of buying one. They contributed $10,300 to a tax-deductible retirement plan at work. Deductions include $6400 in state income tax and $1230 in charitable donations. They file a joint return and claim 3 exemptions. $101,028; $17,507

34. SINGLE TAXPAYER   Sheila Spinney works as a freelance editor and earned $78,450 last year along with interest of $2450 and dividends of $432. She contributed $1500 to an IRA and donated $3600 to her church and an additional $200 for hurricane relief. She does not own a home and lives in a state that has no state income tax. She files as a head of household with 3 exemptions. $60,232; $9825.50

CHAPTER TERMS

Review the following terms to test your understanding of the chapter. For each term you do not know, refer to the page number found next to that term.

1099 forms [p. 293]
adjusted gross income
    [p. 293]
assessed valuation [p. 285]
assessment rate [p. 285]
contributions [p. 298]
dollars per $100 [p. 287]
dollars per $1000 [p. 287]
excise (luxury) tax [p. 281]
fair market value [p. 285]
Form 1040A [p. 300]

Form 1040EZ [p. 299]
head of household [p. 295]
income taxes [p. 292]
individual retirement
    account (IRA) [p. 295]
interest [p. 298]
Internal Revenue Service
    (IRS) [p. 292]
itemized tax deduction
    [p. 297]
luxury tax [p. 281]

medical and dental
    expenses [p. 297]
mills [p. 287]
miscellaneous deductions
    [p. 298]
percent [p. 287]
personal exemptions
    [p. 295]
personal property [p. 284]
property tax rate [p. 286]
real property [p. 284]

sales tax [p. 278]
sales tax rate [p. 280]
Schedule B (Form 1040A)
    [p. 300]
standard deduction
    [p. 295]
tax deduction [p. 297]
taxable income [p. 296]
W-2 forms [p. 293]

CONCEPTS

EXAMPLES

7.1 Finding sales tax

Collected by most states, and some counties and cities. Use $P = BR$, where P is the sales tax, B is the amount of the sale, and R is the sales tax rate.

Sales tax of $7\frac{1}{2}\%$ is charged on a sale of $45.75. Find the amount of sales tax and the total including tax.

$$P = 0.075 \times \$45.75 = \$3.43 \quad \text{Rounded}$$

$$\$45.75 \text{ sale} + \$3.43 \text{ tax} = \$49.18 \quad \text{Total}$$

7.1 Finding selling price when the sales tax is known

Use the basic percent equation.

$$P = B \times R$$

Sales tax = selling price × tax rate

Sales tax is $4.59 and the sales tax rate is 6%. Find the amount of the sale.

$$\$4.59 = B \times 0.06$$

$$\frac{\$4.59}{0.06} = B$$

$$\$76.50 = B \qquad \text{Selling price}$$

7.1 Finding the amount of the sale when the total price is known

Use the percent equation and remember

Amount of sale + sales tax = total

Total price including tax, $128.96; sales tax, 7%. Find the amount of the sale.

$$B + (0.07)B = \$128.96$$

$$1.07B = \$128.96$$

$$B = \frac{\$128.96}{1.07} = \$120.52$$

7.1 Excise tax (luxury tax)

A tax charged on certain items by the federal, state, or local government. It may be either a percent of the sale price or a certain amount per item.

A firm buys a truck costing $48,700. Sales taxes are 8% and excise taxes are as shown in Table 7.2. Find the total cost.

$48,700	Truck
$3,896	Sales tax: 0.08 × $48,700
$5,844	Excise tax: 0.12 × $48,700
$58,440	Total cost

7.2 Fair market value and assessed valuation

Multiply the market value of the property by the assessment rate (a local assessed percent) to arrive at the assessed valuation.

The assessment rate is 30%; fair market value is $115,000. Find the assessed valuation.

$$0.3 \times \$115{,}000 = \$34{,}500$$

7.2 Tax rate

The tax rate formula follows.

$$\text{Tax rate} = \frac{\text{total tax amount needed}}{\text{total assessed value}}$$

Tax amount needed, $2,456,000; total assessed value, $144,470,000. Find the tax rate to nearest tenth of a percent.

$$\frac{\$2{,}456{,}000}{\$144{,}470{,}000} = 1.7\% \quad \text{Rounded}$$

7.2 Expressing tax rates in different forms and finding tax

1. Percent: multiply assessed valuation by rate.

Assessed value, $90,000; tax rate, 2.5%.

$$\$90{,}000 \times 0.025 = \$2250$$

2. Dollars per $100: move decimal 2 places to left in assessed valuation and multiply.

Tax rate, $2.50 per $100

$$900 \times \$2.50 = \$2250$$

3. Dollars per $1000: move decimal 3 places to left in assessed valuation and multiply.

Tax rate, $25 per $1000

$$90 \times \$25 = \$2250$$

4. Mills: move decimal 3 places to the left in rate and multiply by assessed valuation.

Tax rate, 25 mills

$$\$90{,}000 \times 0.025 = \$2250$$

7.3 Adjusted gross income

Adjusted gross income includes wages, salaries, tips, dividends, and interest. Regular IRA contributions or alimony payments are subtracted.

Salary, $32,540; interest income, $875; dividends, $315; IRA contribution $500. Find adjusted gross income.

$$\$32{,}540 + \$875 + \$315 - \$500 = \$33{,}230$$

7.3 Standard deduction amounts

The majority of taxpayers use the standard deduction allowed by the IRS.

$5800 for single people; $11,600 for married couples filing jointly; $5800 for married taxpayers filing separately; $8500 for head of household

7.3 Taxable income

The larger of either the total of itemized deductions or the standard deduction is subtracted from adjusted gross income along with $3700 for each personal exemption.

Adjusted gross income, $18,200; single taxpayer; 1 exemption; itemized deductions total $2850; find taxable income. Standard deduction is $5800; larger than $2850 itemized deduction.

$$\text{Taxable income} = \$18{,}200 - \$5800 - \$3700$$
$$= \$8700$$

7.3 Tax Rates

The tax rate shown applies to earnings over the amount shown in the appropriate column.

Tax Rates	Single Amount over	Married Filing Jointly Amount over	Married Filing Separately Amount over	Head of Household Amount over
10%	$0	$0	$0	$0
15%	$8,500	$17,000	$8,500	$12,150
25%	$34,500	$69,000	$34,500	$46,250
28%	$83,600	$139,350	$69,675	$119,400
33%	$174,400	$212,300	$106,150	$193,350
35%	$379,150	$379,150	$189,575	$379,150

7.3 Income tax

The amount of income tax is found by using the correct tax table and the proper tax rates.

Taxable income, $72,508; married filing jointly; find income tax.

$$\$9,500 + 0.25 \times (\$72,508 - \$69,000) = \$10,377$$

7.3 Tax due or refund

If the total amount withheld by employers is greater than the tax owed, a refund results. If the tax owed is the greater amount, a balance is due.

Tax owed, $2506; tax withheld, $226 per month for 12 months. Find balance due or refund.

$$\$226 \times 12 = \$2712 \text{ withheld}$$
$$\$2712 \text{ withheld} - \$2506 \text{ owed} = \$206 \text{ refund}$$

CHAPTER 7 | Review Exercises

The answer section includes answers to all Review Exercises.

Find the amount of the sales tax, the excise tax, and the total cost including taxes in each of the following problems. **[7.1]**

	Sale Price	Sales Tax Rate	Excise Tax Rate	
1.	$852.15	6%	10%	$51.13; $85.22; $988.50
2.	$86.15	8%	11%	$6.89; $9.48; $102.52
3.	$16,500	5%	$12.20/person; 110 people	$825; $1342; $18,667
4.	$345.96	7%	18.3¢/gal.; 285 gal.	$24.22; $52.16; $422.34

Find the item cost when given the amount of tax and the sales tax rate. **[7.1]**

	Amount of Sales Tax	Sales Tax Rate	
5.	$68.04	6%	$1134
6.	$14.20	5%	$284
7.	$19.60	$7\frac{1}{2}\%$	$261.33
8.	$26.99	$8\frac{1}{4}\%$	$327.15

Find the amount of the sale before sales tax was added in each of the following. **[7.1]**

Total Sale	Sales Tax Rate	
9. $447.32	6%	$422
10. $133.75	7%	$125
11. $292.95	$5\frac{1}{2}\%$	$277.68
12. $172.06	$7\frac{3}{4}\%$	$159.68

Complete the following list comparing tax rates. Do not round. **[7.2]**

Percent	Per $100	Per $1000	In Mills
13. 4.06 %	$4.06	$40.60	40.6
14. 2.7 %	$2.70	$27	27
15. 1.27%	$1.27	$12.70	12.7
16. 1.95 %	$1.95	$19.50	19.5

Find the missing quantity. **[7.2]**

Assessed Valuation	Tax Rate	Tax
17. $426,000	32 mills	$13,632
18. $98,200	$18.50 per $1000	$1816.70
19. $46,500	3.5%	$1627.50
20. $140,500	2.8 %	$3934
21. $96,200	$3.80 per $100	$3655.60
22. $103,600	27 mills	$2797.20

Find the taxable income and the tax rounded to the nearest dollar for the following. The letter following the name indicates the marital status. All married people are filing jointly. **[7.3]**

Name	Number of Exemptions	Adjusted Gross Income	Total Itemized Deductions	
23. G. Eckern, S	1	$38,415	$4516	$28,915; $3912.25
24. The Bridges, M	5	$88,628	$9834	$58,528; $7929.20
25. R. McIntosh, M	3	$68,490	$11,920	$45,470; $5970.50
26. B. Thomas, S, Head of Household	2	$122,380	$14,320	$100,660; $19,932.50

Solve the following application problems. **[7.1–7.2]**

27. The Oak Glen Park District budgets on the basis that it will collect $1,978,000. If the total assessed value of the property in the district is $90,550,000, find the tax rate as a percent rounded to the nearest tenth.   2.2%

28. Total receipts for the day at the Toy Circus are $3442.88. If this includes 6% sales tax, find the amount of the sales tax. $194.88

29. A shopping center has a fair market value of $2,608,300. Property in the area is assessed at 40% of fair market value, with a tax rate of $37.50 per $1000. Find the annual property tax. $39,124.50

Find the taxable income and income tax owed in each of the following application problems. **[7.3]**

30. The Bakers, married and filing a joint return, have a combined adjusted gross income of $94,320, 3 exemptions, and itemized deductions of $9450. $71,620; $10,155

31. Permelia Pervine had an adjusted gross income of $37,450 last year. She had deductions of $960 for state income tax, $3840 for property tax, $5280 in mortgage interest, and $830 to her church. She claims 2 exemptions and files as head of household. $19,140; $2263.50

32. Jennifer and Tony Romano had total wages and salaries of $69,750, other income of $852, and interest income of $2880. They are allowed an adjustment to income of $2450. Their itemized deductions are $7218 in mortgage interest, $3450 in property tax, $1680 in state income taxes, and $1040 in charitable contributions. The Romanos are filing a joint return and claim 4 exemptions. $42,844; $5576.60

Find the amount of any refund or tax due for the following people. The letter following the name indicates marital status. Assume a 52-week year and that married people are filing jointly. [7.3]

Name	Taxable Income	Federal Income Tax Withheld from Checks	
33. The Smiths, M	$60,850	$188.40 weekly	$1519.30 tax refund
34. Maria Jales, S	$32,507	$387.30 monthly	$196.55 tax refund
35. The Flores, M	$52,970	$105.07 weekly	$1631.86 tax due
36. Jake Kraft, HH	$48,300	$685.20 monthly	$1379.90 tax refund

CHAPTER 7	Business Application Case #1
	Locating a Truck Stop

Jack Armstrong, owner of All American Truck Stop, is considering two separate locations along the interstate, Anderson and Bentonville. The two locations are about 200 miles apart, and while the sites offer similar business potential, there are differences in land acquisition costs, building costs, and, importantly, property taxes. Armstrong feels that he needs 5.5 acres of land and buildings and improvements that will total 90,000 square feet. The land and building costs and property tax information are as follows.

	Anderson	Bentonville
Land cost (per square foot)	$0.80	$0.70
Building and improvement cost (per square foot)	$32.80	$36.90
Assessment rate	25%	20%
Tax rate	32 mills	$7.50 per $100

Knowing that there are 43,560 square feet in an acre and that the total cost of land improvements will be used as fair market value in both locations, Armstrong needs to answer the following questions to help him in his decision.

(a) What is the cost of the land and improvements in each location? Anderson: $3,143,664; Bentonville: $3,488,706

(b) Find the assessed valuation of the land and improvements in each location.
Anderson: $785,916; Bentonville: $697,741.20

(c) Find the annual property tax in each location. Anderson: $25,149.31; Bentonville: $52,330.59

(d) What is the total cost including land, building, and property taxes over a 10-year period in each location? Assume taxes remain constant. Anderson: $3,395,157.10; Bentonville: $4,012,011.90

(e) On the basis of cost over a 10-year period, which location should Armstrong select? Anderson

CHAPTER 7	Business Application Case #2
	Taxes Paid by a Family

To help understand why it is so difficult to pay the bills every month, Todd and Samantha Baker decided to estimate the various annual taxes they pay. Since they inherited their home from Samantha's mother, the interest on the monthly payments is too small to be a deduction on their income tax return. As a result, they plan to file using form 1040A. They also bought an inexpensive, used car this year for their 17-year-old daughter, which increased the amount spent subject to sales tax. Use the following information to answer the questions.

Estimated amount spent subject to sales tax: $23,700; sales tax rate: 7.25%

Market value of home: $173,000; assessment rate: 40%; property tax rate: $54.30 per $1000

Combined wages: $52,500; taxable interest: $3840; IRA contribution: $2000; married filing jointly with 3 deductions

Miles driven by family in year: 32,890; average miles per gallon of gasoline: 18.5; average state and federal tax on a gallon of gasoline: $0.45

(a) Sales tax = $1718.25

(b) Property tax = $3757.56

(c) FICA and Medicare tax = $4016.25

(d) Taxable income = $31,640

(e) Income tax (use Table 7.4) = $3896

(f) Tax on gasoline = $800.03

(g) Total of taxes = $14,188.09

(h) Taxes as a percent of combined wages and interest = 25.2% rounded

At first, the Bakers were surprised that their total taxes amount to over $14,000, or more than 25% of their combined wages and interest income. But after talking it over, they recognized that there was no charge for the high school education for their daughter, the roads in their neighborhoods were nicely paved, the area they lived in was relatively free of crime, and they knew that the police would come quickly when called. They also knew that Social Security would pay them an income for many years after they retire and that Medicare would pay most of their medical expenses then, too. All in all, the Bakers felt they were getting a lot out of the taxes they were paying each year. javier brosch / Fotolia.com

javier brosch / Fotolia.com

Risk Management

We buy insurance to protect us against catastrophic loss such as damage to our home by a fire or the theft of our automobile. Without insurance, one large, catastrophic loss could financially destroy a family or business. **Insurance** protects against risk. **Peril insurance** provides protection against financial loss, whereas life insurance provides protection against a death, and medical insurance provides protection against illness.

An **insured policyholder** such as a person, family, or business pays a small **premium** to the insurance company, called the **insurer or carrier**. The insurance company pools the many small payments together into large sums of money. The insurance company must pay its expenses, including commissions to insurance agents, employee salaries, mortgage payments on real estate, property taxes, and utilities. The company then uses its financial resources to pay claims made by any insured that has an accident or suffers damages for which it is insured. For example, insurance companies collect premiums for wind and flood damages from many different property owners in hurricane-prone areas along the Gulf of Mexico. However, Figure 8.1 shows that insurance companies have paid out *billions of dollars* in damages from huge hurricanes.

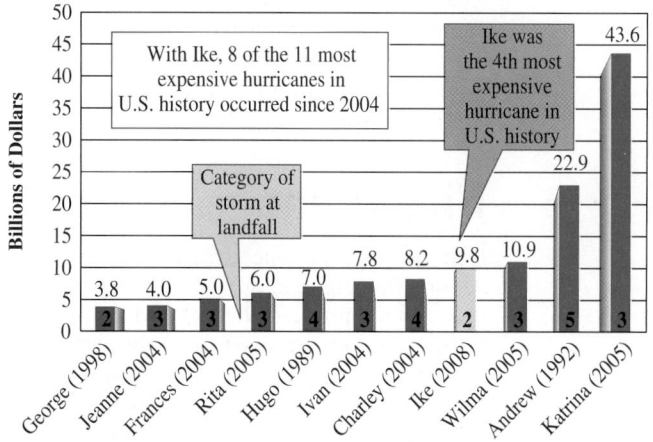

Top 11 Most Costly Hurricanes in U.S. History
(Insured Losses in 2007 dollars)

With Ike, 8 of the 11 most expensive hurricanes in U.S. history occurred since 2004

Ike was the 4th most expensive hurricane in U.S. history

Category of storm at landfall

Sources: ISO/PCS; AIR Worldwide, RMS, Eqecat; Insurance Information Institute inflation adjustments.

Figure 8.1

▶ STOP&THINK

List all insurance premiums that you (or your parents) pay and add up the combined annual cost. Why buy insurance? How do you choose the policy limits? Why do businesses buy insurance? Why do states require automobile owners to carry insurance?

Individuals buy insurance to protect against losses due to fire, theft, illness or health problems, disability, car wrecks, lawsuits, and even death. Companies buy insurance to protect against losses due to fire, automobile accidents, employee illnesses, lawsuits, and worker accidents on the job. This chapter looks first at business insurance, including fire and liability coverage. Next, motor vehicle insurance is discussed. Then, several types of life insurance policies are examined.

8.1 Business Insurance

OBJECTIVES

1 *Define the terms: policy, face value, and premium.*

2 *Identify the factors that determine the premium.*

3 *Find the annual premium for fire insurance given rating and property values.*

4 *Calculate short-term rates and cancellations.*

5 *Calculate prorated insurance premium cancellations.*

6 *Use the coinsurance formula to solve problems.*

7 *Find the insurance liability when there are multiple carriers.*

8 *Find liability of multiple carriers when coinsurance requirement is not met.*

9 *List additional risks against which a business may be insured.*

There is only a slight chance that any particular building will suffer fire damage during a given year. However, if such fire damage were to occur, the financial loss to the owner could be very large. To protect against this small chance of a large loss, people pay an amount equal to a small percent of the value of their property to a fire insurance company. Each year the company collects money from a large number of property owners, then pays for expenses due to fire damage for those few buildings that are damaged that year.

Insurance company earnings can be volatile, changing rapidly from year to year. For example, a large earthquake in the San Francisco area could result in major losses for that year for a company with many policies in force in the area. Yet, the same company might have had a good profit the year before.

Fire Damage, Water Damage

Betty Davis experienced a fire in an apartment house she owned. Thanks to the quick action of a neighbor, a fire truck was there in minutes and the firemen quickly went to work. In the process, they kicked in the doors to two apartments that backed up to the utility room and sprayed foam throughout both apartments. They did this to keep the fire from coming into the apartments and spreading, but it made a mess. As a result, repairs had to be made to the two apartments in addition to the laundry room, and someone had to pay for the clothes that tenants lost in the washers and dryers. Betty was thankful that she had insurance.

Objective

1 *Define the Terms: Policy, Face Value, and Premium.* The contract between the owner of a building and a fire insurance company is called a **policy**. The amount of insurance provided by the company is called the **face value** of the policy. The charge for the policy is called the **premium**.

Objective

2 *Identify the Factors That Determine the Premium.* The amount of premium charged by the insurance company depends on several factors, such as the type of construction of the building, the contents and use of the building, the location of the building, and the type of fire protection that is available. Wood-frame buildings are generally more likely to be damaged by fire and thus require a larger premium than masonry buildings. Building types are assigned to categories by insurance company employees called **underwriters**. These categories are usually named by letters, such as A, B, C, and so on. Underwriters also assign ratings, called **territorial ratings**, to each area served, which describe the quality of fire protection in the area. Although fire insurance rates vary from state to state, the rates in Table 8.1 are typical.

Table 8.1 ANNUAL RATES FOR EACH $100 OF FIRE INSURANCE

Territorial Rating	Building Rating: A		Building Rating: B		Building Rating: C	
	Building	Contents	Building	Contents	Building	Contents
1	$0.28	$0.40	$0.36	$0.49	$0.45	$0.60
2	$0.30	$0.44	$0.45	$0.55	$0.54	$0.75
3	$0.37	$0.46	$0.54	$0.60	$0.63	$0.80
4	$0.50	$0.52	$0.75	$0.77	$0.84	$0.90
5	$0.62	$0.58	$0.92	$0.99	$1.05	$1.14

Objective

3 *Find the Annual Premium for Fire Insurance Given Rating and Property Values.* The annual premium rate for fire insurance is expressed as a certain amount for each $100. The basic percent equation is used to find the annual insurance premium. The **replacement cost** of the building in hundreds of dollars is the base, the insurance premium per $100 of fire insurance is the rate, and the annual insurance premium is the part.

Annual premium = building replacement cost × insurance premium
(in $100s)   (per $100)

P = B × R

EXAMPLE 1 Finding the Annual Fire Insurance Premium

Flowers For You is in a building with a class B rating. The territory is rated 3. Find the annual premium to insure the building, which has a replacement cost of $378,000 and has contents with a replacement cost of $92,000.

Solution

From Table 8.1, the rates per $100 for a class B building in area 3 are $0.54 for the building and $0.60 for the contents. The premium for the building is found by solving the following formula.

Replacement cost of building = $378,000 ÷ 100 = 3780 hundreds

Rate for building = **$0.54 (from table)**

Premium for building = value (in hundreds) × rate

= 3780 × **$0.54** = $2041.20

The premium for the contents can be found in the same way.

$$\text{Replacement cost of contents} = \$92,000 \div 100 = 920 \text{ hundreds}$$
$$\text{Rate for contents} = \textbf{\$0.60 (from table)}$$
$$\text{Premium for contents} = \text{value (in hundreds)} \times \text{rate}$$
$$= 920 \times \textbf{\$0.60} = \$552$$
$$\text{Total premium} = \$2041.20 \text{ (building)} + \$552 \text{ (contents)}$$
$$= \$2593.20 \text{ (building and contents)}$$
$$= \$2593 \text{ (rounded)}$$

> **NOTE** Fire insurance preminums are rounded to the nearest dollar.

Objective

4 *Calculate Short-Term Rates and Cancellations.* Insurance is sometimes purchased for part of a year, perhaps even for just a few months. Perhaps only a short period of time remains on a lease. Also, if a business is sold or the owner wishes to change insurance carriers during the period of a policy, the existing policy must be canceled. In each of these cases, the insurance company will charge a **short-term,** or **cancellation, rate**. When the short-term rate is used, a penalty results.

As shown in Table 8.2, one month's insurance costs 18% of an annual premium while one month is only $8\frac{1}{3}\%$ of a year ($1 \div 12 = 0.083333$). The premium for a 6-month policy or a policy canceled after 6 months costs 70% of the annual premium.

Table 8.2 SHORT-TERM RATE SCHEDULE

Time in Months	Percent of Annual Premium	Time in Months	Percent of Annual Premium
1	18%	7	75%
2	35%	8	80%
3	45%	9	85%
4	55%	10	90%
5	65%	11	95%
6	70%	12	100%

EXAMPLE 2 Determining Short-Term Rates

Bob Garrett sold a building in Cleveland, Ohio. Because of the sale, he canceled his fire insurance after 4 months. The annual premium was $4680. Use the short-term rate schedule in Table 8.2 to find the amount of refund to the insured.

Solution

The short-term rate for 4 months is 55% of the annual premium.

$$\$4680 \,(\text{annual premium}) \times 0.55 = \$2574 \,(\text{premium for 4 months})$$

The refund is found by subtracting the 4-month premium from the annual premium.

$$\$4680 \,(\text{annual premium}) - \$2574 \,(\text{4-month premium})$$
$$= \$2106 \,(\text{refund})$$

Objective

5

Calculate Prorated Insurance Premium Cancellations. Occasionally, an insurance company may cancel an insurance policy. This is normally the result of fraud on the part of the insured or any violation of the insurance agreement with the insurance company.

When the insurance company initiates a policy cancellation, the insured is not penalized as with the short-term or cancellation rate. Instead, the insured is charged only for the exact amount of time that the insurance was in force. It is normal for this proration to be to the exact day. Here, we will prorate on a monthly basis, which results in the insured paying only for the number of months that the insurance was provided.

EXAMPLE **3** **Calculating Prorated Insurance Cancellations**

Your Creations Art Supplies had a fire insurance policy with an annual premium of $2832. Because the insured was in violation of fire codes, the insurance company canceled the policy after 7 months and prorated the premium. Find (a) the amount of the premium retained by the insurance company and (b) the amount of refund to the insured.

Solution

Since the cancellation is after 7 months, the insured is charged for $\frac{7}{12}$ of the year.

(a) The amount of the premium retained by the company is found by multiplying the annual premium by $\frac{7}{12}$.

$$\$2832 \text{ (annual premium)} \times \tfrac{7}{12} = \$1652 \text{ (premium for seven months)}$$

(b) The refund is found by subtracting the premium for 7 months from the annual premium.

$$\$2832 \text{ (annual premium)} - \$1652 \text{ (7-month premium)} = \$1180 \text{ (refund)}$$

The refund is equal to $\frac{5}{12}$ of the annual premium.

Objective

6

Use the Coinsurance Formula to Solve Problems. Most fires damage only a portion of a building and its contents. Since complete destruction of a building is rare, many owners try to save money by buying insurance for only a portion of the value of the building and contents. Realizing this, insurance companies place a **coinsurance clause** in fire insurance policies. With coinsurance, part of the risk of fire, under certain conditions, is assumed by the business firm taking out the insurance. For example, an 80% coinsurance clause provides that for full protection, the amount of insurance taken out must be at least 80% of the replacement cost of the building and contents insured.

If the amount of insurance is less than 80% of the replacement cost, the insurance company pays only a portion of any loss. For example, if a business firm took out insurance with a face value of only 40% of the replacement cost of the building insured and then had a loss, the insurance company would pay only half the loss, since 40% is half of 80%.

Use the following coinsurance formula to find the portion of a loss that will be paid by the insurance company.

Amount insurance companies will pay (assuming 80% coinsurance)

$$= \text{amount of loss} \times \frac{\text{amount of policy}}{80\% \text{ of replacement cost}}$$

NOTE The insurance company will never pay more than the face value of the policy, nor will the insurance company pay more than the amount of the loss.

EXAMPLE **4**   **Using The Coinsurance Formula**

Jo O'Neill owns an industrial building valued at $760,000. Her fire insurance policy has an 80% coinsurance clause and a face value of $570,000. The building suffers a fire loss of $144,000. Find the amount of the loss that the insurance company will pay and the amount that O'Neill must pay.

Solution

For full coverage, the policy should be for at least 80% of the value of the building, or

$$0.80 \times \$760,000 = \$608,000$$

Since the face value of the policy is less than 80% of the replacement cost of the building, the company will pay only a portion of the loss. Use the coinsurance formula.

$$\text{Amount insurance company pays} = \$144,000 \times \frac{\$570,000}{\$608,000} = \$135,000$$

The company will pay $135,000 towards the loss, and O'Neill must pay the additional $9000 ($144,000 − $135,000).

Scientific
Calculator
Approach

The calculator solution to Example 4 uses chain calculations and parentheses to set off the denominator. The result is then subtracted from the fire loss.

$$144000 \;\boxed{\times}\; 570000 \;\boxed{\div}\; \boxed{(}\; 80 \;\boxed{\%}\; \boxed{\times}\; 760000 \;\boxed{)}\; \boxed{=}\; 135000$$

$$144000 \;\boxed{-}\; 135000 \;\boxed{=}\; 9000$$

EXAMPLE **5**   **Finding the Amount of Loss Paid by the Insurance Company**

A Swedish investment group owns a warehouse with a replacement cost of $3,450,000. The company has a fire insurance policy with a face value of $2,950,000. The policy has an 80% coinsurance feature. If the firm has a fire loss of $233,500, find the part of the loss paid by the insurance company.

Solution

The value of the warehouse is $3,450,000. Take 80% of this value.

$$0.80 \times \$3,450,000 = \$2,760,000$$

The business has a fire insurance policy with a face value of more than 80% of the value of the warehouse. Therefore, the insurance company will pay the entire $233,500 loss.

Objective

7   *Find the Insurance Liability When There Are Multiple Carriers.*   A business may have fire insurance policies with several companies at the same time. Perhaps additional insurance coverage was purchased over a period of time, as new additions were made to a factory or building complex. Or perhaps the value of the building is so high that no one insurance company wants to take the entire risk by itself, so several companies each agree to take a portion of the insurance coverage and thereby share the risk. In either event, the insurance coverage is divided among **multiple carriers**. When an insurance claim is made against multiple carriers, each insurance company pays its fractional portion of the total claim on the property equal to its prorated share of the total coverage.

EXAMPLE 6   **Understanding Multiple Carrier Insurance**

World Recycling Conglomerate (WRC) has an insured loss of $1,800,000 while having insurance coverage greater than its coinsurance requirement. The insurance is divided among Company A with $5,900,000 coverage, Company B with $4,425,000 coverage, and Company C with $1,475,000 coverage. Find the amount of the loss paid by each of the insurance companies.

Solution

Start by finding the total face value of all three policies.

$$\$5,900,000 + \$4,425,000 + \$1,475,000 = \$11,800,000 \text{ total face value}$$

$$\$5,900,000 \qquad \text{Company A pays } \frac{\$5,900,000}{\$11,800,000} = \frac{1}{2} \text{ of the loss}$$

$$\$4,425,000 \qquad \text{Company B pays } \frac{\$4,425,000}{\$11,800,000} = \frac{3}{8} \text{ of the loss}$$

$$+\$1,475,000 \qquad \text{Company C pays } \frac{\$1,475,000}{\$11,800,000} = \frac{1}{8} \text{ of the loss}$$

$$\$11,800,000 \text{ total face value}$$

Since the insured loss is $1,800,000, the amount paid by each of the multiple carriers follows.

$$\text{Company A} \qquad \frac{1}{2} \times \$1,800,000 = \quad \$900,000$$

$$\text{Company B} \qquad \frac{3}{8} \times \$1,800,000 = \quad \$675,000$$

$$\text{Company C} \qquad \frac{1}{8} \times \$1,800,000 = \quad \underline{\$225,000}$$

$$\text{Total loss} = \$1,800,000$$

Objective

8   *Find Liability of Multiple Carriers When Coinsurance Requirement Is Not Met.* If the coinsurance requirement is not met, the total amount of the loss paid by the insurance coverage is found, and then the amount that each of the carriers pays is found by the method shown in Example 7.

EXAMPLE 7   **Finding Liability of Multiple Carriers When Coinsurance Requirements Are Not Met**

The Carpet Solution warehouse has a replacement cost of $2,000,000 and is insured under an 80% coinsurance clause for $1,200,000. The insurance consists of an $800,000 policy with Company A and a $400,000 policy with Company B. If the warehouse suffers a loss of $200,000, find (a) the part of any loss that is covered, (b) the amount of the loss the insurance companies will pay, (c) each insurance company's portion of the $200,000 loss, and (d) the amount paid by the insured.

Solution

(a) First, find the amount of insurance needed to satisfy the 80% coinsurance clause.

$$0.80 \times \$2,000,000 = \$1,600,000$$

Since the face value of the policy ($1,200,000) is less than 80% ($1,600,000), the insurance companies will pay only pay only a portion of the loss.

$$\text{Part insurance companies pay} = \frac{\$1,200,000}{\$1,600,000}$$

(b) Use the coinsurance formula to find the amount of the loss that the insurance companies will pay.

$$\text{Amount insurance companies pay} = \$200,000 \times \frac{\$1,200,000}{\$1,600,000} = \$150,000$$

(c) The total face value of the insurance is $1,200,000. Since the amount of the loss that the insurance companies will pay is $150,000, the amount paid by each of the multiple carriers is as follows.

$$\frac{\$800,000}{\$1,200,000} \times \$150,000 = \$100,000 \quad \text{Company A}$$

$$\frac{\$400,000}{\$1,200,000} \times \$150,000 = \frac{\$50,000}{\$150,000} \quad \begin{array}{l}\text{Company B}\\ \text{Amount of loss paid}\end{array}$$

(d) The Carpet Solution must pay $50,000, the difference between the loss and the amount paid by the insurance companies.

Objective

9 *List Additional Risks Against Which a Business May Be Insured.* There are many types of insurance coverage that a business might want. One of the most common is liability coverage, which protects against monetary awards from personal-injury lawsuits caused by the business. Another common coverage protects property against damage caused by windstorm, hail, or fire. Homeowners usually buy a **homeowner's policy**, which protects against these losses and many others, including losses on credit cards and automated teller cards, losses on business property brought home, and medical costs for guests who are injured. Other policies are designed for condominium owners, rental property owners, and apartment dwellers. Many types of additional coverage, such as flooding and earthquake protection, are available to give complete and comprehensive insurance coverage.

A business owner's package policy, known in the insurance industry as a **special multi-perils policy**, or **SMP**, typically includes coverage of the following:

- Replacement cost for the building and contents
- Contents coverage that provides for a 25% peak-season increase
- Business property that is in transit or temporarily away from the premises
- Money, securities, accounts receivable, and other valuable papers up to $1000
- Loss of income, including coverage for rents and interruption of business for up to 12 months
- Liability and medical coverage resulting from personal injury, advertising injury, and medical malpractice

In addition to coverage of these standard risks, a list of optional coverages is also available. The businessperson may select those that he or she feels are necessary. A few of these are

- Replacement cost coverage on exterior signs
- Replacement cost coverage for glass
- Computer coverages
- Coverages for loss of refrigeration
- Professional liability coverage for barbers, beauticians, pharmacists, hearing aid sellers, morticians, optometrists, and veterinarians
- Coverage for nonowned and hired automobiles
- Liquor liability coverage

In addition to the many coverages for business property and personal liability, the employer may be required to provide **worker's compensation insurance** for employees. This coverage provides payments to an employee who is unable to work because of a job-related injury or illness.

An employer may pay the entire premium or part of the premium for employee health insurance, **disability insurance**, dental insurance, and group life insurance. Most often these **group insurance plans** offer slightly reduced premiums to those participating in the plan. Participation in group insurance plans is sometimes an incentive for remaining with an employer, since changing jobs may eliminate participation in the group insurance plan.

8.1	Exercises

Find the total annual premium for fire insurance for each of the following. Round to the nearest dollar. Use Table 8.1.

	Territorial Rating	Building Classification	Building Replacement Cost	Contents Value	
1.	4	C	$480,000	$75,000	$4707
2.	1	C	$285,000	$152,000	$2195
3.	3	A	$596,400	$206,700	$3158
4.	3	C	$220,500	$105,000	$2229
5.	5	B	$782,600	$212,000	$9299
6.	2	B	$345,700	$174,500	$2515
7.	5	C	$583,200	$221,400	$8648
8.	4	A	$850,500	$425,800	$6467

Find the amount of refund to the insured using the Short-Term Rate Schedule in Table 8.2.

	Annual Premium	Months in Force	
9.	$2162	8	$432.40
10.	$1382	2	$898.30
11.	$4860	1	$3985.20
12.	$964	2	$626.60
13.	$1507	3	$828.85
14.	$1866	10	$186.60
15.	$4860	11	$243
16.	$13,420	6	$4026

Find (a) the amount of premium retained by the company and (b) the amount of refund to the insured using proration.

	Annual Premium	Months in Force	
17.	$2680	9	(a) $2010 (b) $670
18.	$1936	8	(a) $1290.67 (b) $645.33
19.	$4375	7	(a) $2552.08 (b) $1822.92
20.	$876	11	(a) $803 (b) $73
21.	$5308	6	(a) $2654 (b) $2654
22.	$3192	3	(a) $798 (b) $2394

Find the amount of each of the following losses that will be paid by the insurance company. Assume that each policy includes an 80% coinsurance clause.

	Replacement Cost of Building	Face Value of Policy	Amount of Loss	
23.	$277,000	$223,500	$19,850	$19,850
24.	$780,000	$585,500	$10,400	$9758.33
25.	$868,000	$650,000	$98,500	$92,201.90
26.	$750,000	$500,000	$56,000	$46,666.67
27.	$218,500	$195,000	$36,500	$36,500
28.	$124,800	$80,000	$25,000	$20,032.05
29.	$147,850	$100,000	$14,850	$12,554.95
30.	$285,000	$150,000	$18,500	$12,171.05

Find the amount paid by each insurance company in the following problems involving multiple carriers. Assume that the coinsurance requirement is met. Round all answers to the nearest dollar.

	Insurance Loss	Companies and Coverage		
31.	$80,000	Company A	$750,000	A: $60,000 B: $20,000
		Company B	$250,000	
32.	$360,000	Company 1	$1,200,000	1: $216,000; 2: $144,000
		Company 2	$800,000	
33.	$650,000	Company 1	$1,350,000	1: $292,500; 2: $260,000;
		Company 2	$1,200,000	3: $97.500
		Company 3	$450,000	
34.	$1,600,000	Company A	$4,800,000	A: $960,000; B: $160,000;
		Company B	$800,000	C: $480,000
		Company C	$2,400,000	

Find (a) the amount of the loss paid by the insurance companies, (b) each insurance company's payment, and (c) the amount paid by the insured in each of the following problems involving coinsurance and multiple carriers. Assume an 80% coinsurance clause and round all answers to the nearest dollar.

	Property Value	Insurance Loss	Companies and Coverage		
35.	$900,000	$360,000	Company A	$350,000	(a) $300,000 (b) A: $175,000
			Company B	$250,000	B: $125,000 (c) $60,000
36.	$160,000	$70,000	Company A	$90,000	(a) $65,625 (b) A: $49,219
			Company B	$30,000	B: $16,406 (c) $4375

	Property Value	Insurance Loss	Companies and Coverage		
37.	$250,000	$20,000	Company 1	$75,000	(a) $12,500 (b) 1: $7500;
			Company 2	$50,000	2: $5000 (c) $7500
38.	$480,000	$100,000	Company 1	$180,000	(a) $62,500 (b) 1: $46,875;
			Company 2	$60,000	2: $15,625 (c) $37,500

Use Table 8.1 to find the annual fire insurance premium for each of the following application problems. Round to the nearest dollar.

39. FURNITURE STORE FIRE INSURANCE   Billings Furniture owns a building with a replacement cost of $1,400,000 and with contents of $360,000. The building is class C with a territorial rating of 5. $18,804

40. INDUSTRIAL FIRE INSURANCE   Valley Crop Dusting owns a class B building with a replacement cost of $107,500. Contents are worth $39,800. The territorial rating is 2. $703

41. RESTAURANT FIRE INSURANCE   The Rocklin Grill owns a building with a replacement cost of $235,000. The contents are worth $48,500. The building is class B, with a territorial rating of 1. $1084

42. INDUSTRIAL BUILDING INSURANCE   London's Dredging Equipment is in a C-rated building with a territorial rating of 4. The building has a replacement cost of $305,000 and the contents are worth $682,000. $8700

Find the amount of refund to the insured using the Short-Term Rate Schedule in Table 8.2 for each of the following.

43. REAL ESTATE OFFICE   RE/MAX Realty pays an annual fire insurance premium of $2350. It transfers insurance companies after 4 months. $1057.50

44. PRINTERS   Postal Printers pays an annual fire insurance premium of $1960. The business is sold and insurance canceled after 6 months. $588

45. HARDWARE SUPPLY   Ace Hardware cancels its fire insurance after 8 months. The annual premium was $4650. $930

46. HORSE STABLES   Martinez Horse Stables pays an annual fire insurance premium of $3960. It changes insurance companies after 2 months. $2574

Find (a) the amount of premium retained by the company and (b) the amount of refund to the insured using proration.

47. CONSTRUCTION BUSINESS   West Construction pays an annual fire insurance premium of $2670. The insurance company cancels the policy after 5 months.   (a) $1112.50 (b) $1557.50

48. SPORTING GOODS   The Sports Center had its fire insurance canceled after 10 months. The annual premium is $3380.   (a) $2816.67 (b) $563.33

49. DRUG STORE   As the result of a recent claim, Buy-Rite Drug Store had its fire insurance policy canceled after 7 months. The annual premium is $1944.   (a) $1134 (b) $810

50. COFFEE SHOP   Java City Coffee pays an annual fire insurance premium of $4270. The insurance company cancels the policy after 3 months.   (a) $1067.50 (b) $3202.50

51. Describe three factors that determine the premium charged for fire insurance. (See Objective 2.)

52. Explain the coinsurance clause and describe how coinsurance works. (See Objective 6.)

In each of the following application problems, find the amount of the loss paid by (a) the insurance company and (b) the insured. Assume an 80% coinsurance requirement.

53. **GIFT SHOP** Indonesian Wonder Gift Shop has a building with a replacement cost of of $395,000. The shop is insured for $280,000. Fire loss is $22,500. (a) $19,936.71 (b) $2563.29

54. **WELDING SUPPLIES** Flashpoint Welding Supplies owns a building with a replacement cost of $540,000 and is insured for $308,000. Fire loss is $34,000. (a) $24,240.74 (b) $9759.26

55. **SALVATION ARMY** The main office of the Salvation Army suffers a loss from fire of $45,000. The building has a replacement cost of $550,000 and is insured for $300,000. (a) $30,681.82 (b) $14,318.18

56. **ACME MOTORS** Acme Motors owns a plant that builds electric engines for General Electric. The plant has a replacement cost of $2,850,000 and it is insured for $2,200,000. The fire loss is $185,000. $178,508.77 (b) $6491.23

57. Explain in your own words multiple carrier insurance. Give two reasons for dividing insurance among multiple carriers. (See Objective 7.)

58. Several types of insurance coverage beyond basic fire coverage are included in a home-owner's policy. List and explain three losses that would be covered. (See Objective 9.)

In each of the following, find the amount paid by each of the multiple carriers. Assume that the coinsurance requirement has been met and round to the nearest dollar.

59. **COINSURED FIRE LOSS** Camp Curry Stable had an insured fire loss of $548,000. It had insurance coverage as follows: Company A, $600,000; Company B, $400,000; and Company C, $200,000. A: $274,000 B: $182,667 C: $91,333

60. **FIRE LOSS** The Harley Shoppe had an insured fire loss of $382,000. It has insurance as follows: Company 1, $300,000; Company 2, $180,000; and Company 3, $120,000. 1: $191,000 2: $114,600 3: $76,400

In each of the following application problems, find (a) the amount that the insured would receive and (b) the amount that each of the insurance companies would pay. Round to the nearest dollar.

61. **AUTO DEALERSHIP** Sullivan Chevrolet owns a showroom with a replacement cost of $4,000,000. The fire insurance policies contain an 80% coinsurance clause. The fire policies include $1,800,000 with Company A and $600,000 with Company B. The dealership suffers a $500,000 fire loss. (a) $375,000 (b) A: $281,250; B: $93,750

62. **MANUFACTURING COMPANY** The fire insurance policies on the Global Manufacturing Company contain an 80% coinsurance clause and the warehouse has a replacement cost of $2,400,000. Fire policies on the warehouse are $900,000 with Company A and $300,000 with Company B. Global Manufacturing has a fire loss of $800,000. (a) $500,000 (b) A: $375,000; B: $125,000

63. **RESTAURANT FIRE LOSS** Jack Pritchard's Steakhouse has a replacement cost of $360,000. The fire policies are $100,000 with Company 1, $50,000 with Company 2, and $30,000 with Company 3, while each contains an 80% coinsurance clause. There is a fire at the steakhouse causing a $120,000 loss. (a) $75,000 (b) 1: $41,667; 2: $20,833; 3: $12,500

64. **HIGH-RISE CONDOMINIUMS** The Peace Lake Condo tower has a replacement cost of $5,500,000. Fire insurance policies are $1,500,000 with Company 1, $1,000,000 with Company 2, and $800,000 with Company 3. The policies contain an 80% coinsurance clause and the tower suffers a $1,200,000 fire loss. (a) $900,000 (b) 1: $409,091; 2: $272,727; 3: $218,182

| **8.2** | **Motor Vehicle Insurance** |

OBJECTIVES

1 *Describe the factors that affect the cost of motor vehicle insurance.*

2 *Define liability insurance and determine the premium.*

3 *Define property damage insurance and determine the premium.*

4 *Describe comprehensive and collision insurance and determine the premium.*

5 *Define no-fault and uninsured motorist insurance.*

6 *Apply youthful-operator factors.*

7 *Calculate a motor vehicle insurance premium.*

8 *Find the amounts paid by the insurance company and the insured.*

Objective

1 *Describe the Factors That Affect the Cost of Motor Vehicle Insurance.* There are more than 6 million car accidents in the United States each year, and many of them result in serious injuries to people. Losses due to these accidents are believed to be on the order of $230 billion. Both the high risk of loss due to an accident and the fact that states require car insurance result in almost all drivers buying car insurance.

Businesses and individuals buy motor vehicle insurance to protect against the possible large cost of an accident. The cost of this insurance, the **premium**, is determined by people called **actuaries**, who classify accidents according to location, age and sex of the drivers, and other factors. Insurance companies use these results to determine the premiums. For example, there is a higher percentage of accidents in heavily populated cities than in rural areas. Certain makes and models of automobiles are stolen more often than others. Young male drivers (16–25 years of age) are involved in many more accidents than they should be, considering their proportion of the population. The more expensive a vehicle and the newer a vehicle, the more it costs to repair. These are several of the factors that determine the cost of motor vehicle insurance.

Figure 8.2 shows where insurance companies spent their revenues. Of every $100 in premium and return on investment, $63 went to pay claims, $24 was used to pay for insurance company expenses such as employees and maintenance on buildings, $5 was spent on taxes, and $8 was company profit. The figure of 8% is called the **profit margin**. The data show that in 2010, insurance companies averaged a profit of 8% of premiums and return on investments. Of course, some insurance companies did better and others did worse.

Where the Revenue Dollar Went, 2010
(Premiums and Investments)

Source: Data from the Insurance Information Institute.

Figure 8.2

2 *Define Liability Insurance and Determine the Premium.* **Liability**, or **bodily injury, insurance** protects the insured in case he or she injures someone with a car. Many states have minimum amounts of liability insurance coverage set by law. The amount of liability insurance is expressed as two numbers with a slash between them, such as 15/30. The numbers 15/30 mean that the insurance company will pay up to $15,000 for injury to one person, and a maximum of $30,000 for all persons injured in the same accident. Table 8.3 shows typical premium rates for various amounts of liability coverage.

> **NOTE** Each year more than 5000 teenagers between the ages of 16 and 20 die due to fatal injuries caused in car accidents. An additional 400,000 drivers age 16 to 20 are seriously injured in car accidents each year.

Table 8.3 LIABILITY (BODILY INJURY) AND MEDICAL INSURANCE (PER YEAR)

	Liability and Medical Expense Limits				
Territory	15/30 $1000	25/50 $2000	50/100 $3000	100/300 $5000	250/500 $10,000
1	$268	$273	$294	$321	$368
2	269	302	341	378	392
3	310	314	375	398	459
4	320	335	349	368	389

Medical insurance is included in the cost of the liability insurance provided to the driver and passengers of a vehicle in case of injury. For example, the column of the table headed "15/30" shows that the insured can also receive reimbursement for up to $1000 of his or her own medical expenses in an accident.

For purposes of setting premiums, insurance companies divide the nation into several territories. These territories are established on the basis of population, the number of motor vehicles, and the number of accidents and other claims within the territory. Four territories are shown in Table 8.3. All tables in this section show annual premiums.

EXAMPLE 1 Finding the Liability and Medical Premium

Zallia Todd, owner of Flowers For You, is in territory 2 and wants 100/300 liability coverage. Find the amount of the premium for this coverage and the amount of medical coverage included.

Solution

Look up territory 2 in Table 8.3 and 100/300 coverage to find a premium of $378, which includes $5000 of medical coverage.

3 *Define Property Damage Insurance and Determine the Premium.* **Property damage insurance** pays for damages caused to another vehicle or other property. Table 8.4 shows the premiums for property damage insurance. The coverage amount is the maximum amount that the insurance company will pay. If a claim for damages exceeds this maximum amount, the insured must pay the excess.

EXAMPLE 2 Finding the Premium for Property Damage

Zallia Todd, in territory 2, wants property damage coverage of $50,000. Find the premium.

Solution

Property damage coverage of $50,000 in territory 2 requires a premium of $223, as Table 8.4 shows.

Table 8.4 PROPERTY DAMAGE INSURANCE (PER YEAR)

| Territory | Property Damage Limits | | | |
	$10,000	$25,000	$50,000	$100,000
1	$119	$128	$141	$162
2	168	192	223	251
3	129	134	145	158
4	154	168	189	201

Many insurance companies give discounts on insurance premiums based on good driving records, completing courses in driving safety, and insuring more than one car. Some even reduce car insurance premiums for students who make good grades. Be sure to ask for discounts—they can save you money. The graphic shows the number of states requiring discounts on automobile insurance.

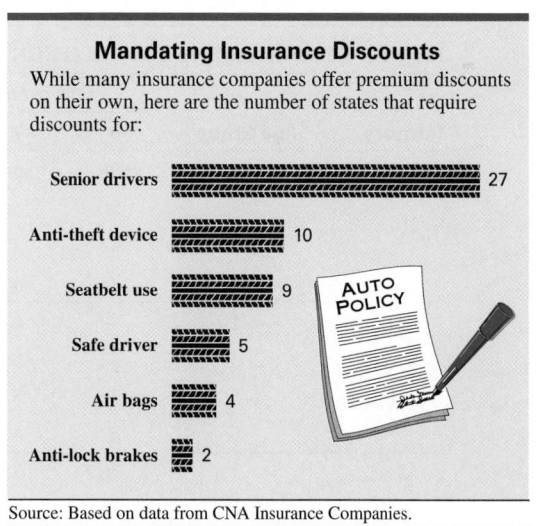

Mandating Insurance Discounts

While many insurance companies offer premium discounts on their own, here are the number of states that require discounts for:

Senior drivers — 27
Anti-theft device — 10
Seatbelt use — 9
Safe driver — 5
Air bags — 4
Anti-lock brakes — 2

AUTO POLICY

Source: Based on data from CNA Insurance Companies.

Objective

4 *Describe Comprehensive and Collision Insurance and Determine the Premium.* **Comprehensive insurance** pays for damage to the insured's vehicle caused by fire, theft, vandalism, falling trees, and other such events. **Collision insurance** pays for repairs to the insured's vehicle in case of an accident. Collision insurance often includes a **deductible**. The deductible is paid by the insured in the event of a claim, with the insurance company paying all amounts above the deductible. Common deductible amounts are $250, $500, and $1000. For example, if the cost of repairing damage caused by an accident is $2045 and the deductible amount is $500, the insured pays $500, and the insurance company pays $1545 ($2045 − $500 = $1545).

> **NOTE**   The higher the deductible amount, the lower the cost of the collision coverage. The insured shares a greater portion of the risk as the deductible amount increases.

Table 8.5 shows some typical rates for comprehensive and collision insurance. Rates are determined not only by territories but also by age group and cost category of the vehicle. Age group 1 refers to a vehicle that is 1 year old or less; age group 6 is a vehicle 6 years old or older.

> **NOTE**   Different models fall into different catagories. For example, the cost category for a Ford Escape hybrid might be a category 6 and a Lincoln Navigator might be a category 8. The collision coverage in Table 8.5 is for $500 deductible coverage.

EXAMPLE **3**   **Finding the Comprehensive and Collision Premium**

Zallia Todd, owner of Flowers For You, is in territory 2 and has a 2-year-old minivan that has a category of 8. Use Table 8.5 to find the annual premium for (a) comprehensive coverage and (b) collision coverage.

Solution

(a) The annual premium for comprehensive coverage is $74.
(b) The annual premium for collision coverage is $215.

Table 8.5 COMPREHENSIVE AND COLLISION INSURANCE

Territory	Age Group	Comprehensive			Collision ($500 Deductible)		
		6	7	8	6	7	8
1	1	$58	$64	$90	$153	$165	$184
	2–3	50	56	82	135	147	171
	4–5	44	52	76	116	128	147
	6	34	44	64	92	110	128
2	1	44	62	81	196	219	241
	2–3	42	59	74	178	194	215
	4–5	38	51	63	169	189	201
	6	33	44	58	148	154	183
3	1	70	78	108	145	157	174
	2–3	60	66	90	128	139	162
	4–5	52	64	92	111	122	139
	6	44	58	66	149	163	196
4	1	50	58	77	192	223	245
	2–3	42	46	71	187	209	233
	4–5	40	45	68	179	192	218
	6	38	42	65	165	177	201

Automobile theft is a major problem in the United States since over 1.2 million cars are stolen each year. Figure 8.3 shows the most frequently reported stolen automobiles in 2011.

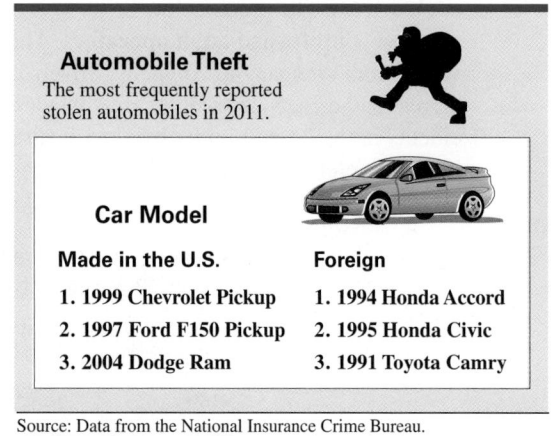

Automobile Theft
The most frequently reported stolen automobiles in 2011.

Car Model

Made in the U.S.	Foreign
1. 1999 Chevrolet Pickup	1. 1994 Honda Accord
2. 1997 Ford F150 Pickup	2. 1995 Honda Civic
3. 2004 Dodge Ram	3. 1991 Toyota Camry

Source: Data from the National Insurance Crime Bureau.

Figure 8.3

Objective

5 *Define No-Fault and Uninsured Motorist Insurance.* **No-fault insurance** refers to a state insurance program that allows an injured insured to recover financial losses from his or her own insurance company, no matter who caused the accident. An original goal of no-fault insurance was to limit lawsuits for accidents with less serious injuries. Under no fault, damages for pain and suffering are eliminated except in cases of permanent injury or death. Insurance companies argue that no-fault insurance removes lawyers and courts from the process and results in lower overall costs. Trial lawyers and some consumer groups argue that no-fault insurance leaves accident victims unable to recover all of their damages.

The New York State Insurance Department has stated that a "no-fraud industry" has emerged in which criminal rings recruit people, often immigrants, to pile into automobiles and deliberately stage accidents. As a result of this criminal activity and other issues, only about a dozen states still have no-fault insurance although many states have experimented with it.

In the states that do not have no-fault insurance a driver must be concerned about an accident with an uninsured driver. Drivers in these states need **uninsured motorist insurance**, which protects the vehicle owner in a collision with a vehicle that is not insured. Some insurance companies offer **underinsured motorist insurance**, which provides protection in the event that there is a collision with a vehicle that is underinsured. Typical costs for uninsured motorist insurance are shown in Table 8.6

Table 8.6 UNINSURED MOTORIST INSURANCE (PER YEAR)	
Territory	**Basic Limit**
1	$66
2	62
3	76
4	70

EXAMPLE 4   Determining the Premium for Uninsured Motorist Coverage

Zallia Todd, living in territory 2, wants uninsured motorist coverage. Find the premium in Table 8.6.

Solution

The annual premium for uninsured motorist coverage in territory 2 is $62.

Objective

6 *Apply Youthful-Operator Factors.* Youthful drivers are involved in more accidents than adult drivers. The graph below helps to explain why most insurance companies distinguish between **youthful** and **adult operators**. Although the age at which a driver becomes an adult varies from company to company, drivers of age 24 or less are usually considered youthful drivers and drivers 25 or older are considered adults. Owing to the higher proportion of accidents in the 24-and-under bracket, insurance companies add an additional amount to the insurance premium.

The Age of Dangerous Driving

Age	Fatal crashes per 100,000 drivers
16–20	63.4
21–24	46.1
25–34	32.0
35–44	27.0
45–54	22.6
55–64	19.9
65–69	19.1
69+	25.1

Source: National Highway Traffic Safety Administration.

In Table 8.7, there are two categories of youthful drivers, age 20 or less and age 21–24. Consideration is also given to the youthful operator who has had driver's training. Some companies give discounts to youthful drivers who are "good students" (a B average or better). To use the youthful-operator table, first determine the premium for all coverage desired and then multiply this premium by the appropriate youthful-operator factor to find the total premium.

Table 8.7 YOUTHFUL-OPERATOR FACTOR

Age	With Driver's Training	Without Driver's Training
20 or less	1.55	1.75
21–24	1.25	1.40

Objective

7 *Calculate a Motor Vehicle Insurance Premium.* The total annual insurance premium is found by adding the costs of each type of insurance coverage.

EXAMPLE 5 Using the Youthful–Operator Factor

James Ito lives in territory 4, is 22 years old, has had driver's training, and drives a 5-year-old car in category 7. He wants a 25/50 liability policy, $10,000 property damage coverage, a comprehensive and collision policy, and uninsured motorist coverage. Find his annual insurance premium.

Solution

Table	Coverage	Premium
8.3	25/50 liability	$335
8.4	$10,000 property damage	154
8.5	Comprehensive	45
8.5	Collision	192
8.6	Uninsured motorist	70
	Sum	$796

Multiply this sum by the youthful-operator factor of 1.25, found in Table 8.7.

$$\text{Total premium} = \$796 \times 1.25 = \$995$$

The calculator solution to Example 5 uses parentheses and chain calculations.

Scientific Calculator Approach

Objective

8   *Find the Amounts Paid by the Insurance Company and the Insured.* Due to deductibles and limits on the amount of insurance purchased, an accident can result in costs to the driver causing the accident. In fact, many drivers pay extra for higher coverage to limit the amount they would have to pay in the event of a serious accident. The cost of increasing coverage is usually small. For example, in Table 8.3 the additional cost of increasing liability coverage in Territory 1 from 50/100 to 100/300 is only $27 ($294−$273). Yet, doing so could save the policy holder up to $50,000 in the event of a large claim of $100,000 or more made by an individual.

EXAMPLE 6   **Finding the Amounts Paid by the Insurance Company and the Insured**

Eric Liwanag has 25/50 liability limits, $25,000 property damage limits, and $250 deductible collision insurance. While on vacation he was at fault in an accident that caused $5800 damage to his car and $3380 in damage to another car and resulted in severe injuries to the other driver and her passenger. A subsequent lawsuit for injuries resulted in a judgment of $45,000 and $35,000, respectively, to the other parties. Find the amounts that the insurance company will pay for (a) repairing Liwanag's car, (b) repairing the other car, and (c) paying the court judgment resulting from the lawsuit. (d) How much will Liwanag have to pay to the injured parties?

Solution

(a) The insurance company will pay $5550 ($5800 − $250 deductible) to repair Liwanag's car.
(b) Repairs on the other car will be paid to the property damage limits. Here, the total repairs of $3380 are paid.
(c) Since more than one person was injured, the insurance company pays the limit of $50,000 ($25,000 to each of the two injured parties).
(d) Liwanag is liable for $30,000 ($80,000 − $50,000), the amount awarded over the insurance limits.

Additional factors may affect the annual premium for motor vehicle insurance, such as whether the vehicle is used for pleasure, as transportation to and from work, or for business purposes, how far the vehicle is driven each year, whether the youthful driver is male or female, the marital status of the male youthful driver, the past driving record of the driver, and whether the driver has more than one car insured with the insurance company. Quite often, discounts are given to nonsmokers and good students. There are also discounts for automobiles equipped with air bags and antilock braking systems. Many insurance companies charge an annual policy fee, which covers the cost of processing the policy each year.

> **NOTE** Car insurance premiums often go up sharply for those who receive moving violations (tickets) from police and for those who cause accidents. Drive safely or pay the price in more ways than one!

8.2	Exercises

Find the annual premium for each of the following people.

	Name	Territory	Age	Driver's Training	Liablity	Property Damage	Comprehensive Collision Age Group	Category	Uninsured Motorist	
1.	Maxey	4	35	—	100/300	$50,000	2	8	yes	$931
2.	Morrissey	1	20	yes	25/50	$25,000	4	7	no	$900.55
3.	Shraim	3	52	—	250/500	$50,000	2	8	yes	$932
4.	Waldron	2	67	—	50/100	$100,000	1	6	yes	$894
5.	Carter	1	35	—	100/300	$25,000	5	6	no	$609
6.	Tao	2	24	yes	100/300	$50,000	5	7	yes	$1128.75
7.	Baeta	4	52	—	250/500	$50,000	1	8	yes	$970
8.	Gualco	1	31	—	250/500	$50,000	none	none	no	$509
9.	Harrison	3	44	—	50/100	$25,000	5	6	yes	$748
10.	Ballinger	2	17	yes	15/30	$10,000	4	8	yes	$1182.65
11.	Green	2	43	—	100/300	$100,000	6	6	no	$810
12.	Rodriquez	3	60	—	50/100	$100,000	5	7	yes	$795

 13. Describe four factors that determine the premium on an automobile insurance policy. (See Objective 1.)

 14. Explain the difference between comprehensive insurance and collision insurance. (See Objective 4.)

Solve each of the following application problems.

15. YOUTHFUL OPERATOR—NO DRIVER'S TRAINING   Karen Roberts's father gave her a new Honda Accord to use at college under the condition she pay her own insurance. She is 17, has not had driver's training, lives in territory 1, and her vehicle has a category of 6. She wants 50/100 liability limits, $25,000 property damage limits, comprehensive and collision insurance, and uninsured motorist coverage. Find her annual insurance premium. $1223.25

16. ADULT AUTO INSURANCE   Bill Poole is 47 years old, lives in territory 4, and drives a 2-year-old car with a category of 7. He wants 250/500 liability limits, $100,000 property damage limits, comprehensive and collision insurance, and uninsured motorist coverage. Find his annual insurance premium. $915

17. **STUDENT AUTO INSURANCE** Martha Vickers is 22, has taken driver's training, and has a 5-year-old car. She lives in territory 3 and wants the following coverage: liability 25/50, property damage $25,000, no comprehensive, no collision, and uninsured motorist. $655

18. **YOUTHFUL OPERATOR—NO DRIVER'S TRAINING** Michelle Massa is 17 years old, has not had driver's training, lives in territory 2, and (with her parents help) purchased a new Jeep Cherokee with a category of 6. She wants 50/100 liability limits, $25,000 property damage limits, comprehensive and collision insurance, and uninsured motorist coverage. Find her annual insurance premium. $1461.25

19. **BODILY INJURY INSURANCE** Suppose your bodily injury policy has limits of 25/50, and you injure a person on a bicycle. The judge awards damages of $36,500 to the cyclist. (a) How much will the company pay? (b) How much will you pay? (a) $25,000 (b) $11,500

20. **BODILY INJURY INSURANCE** Your best friend causes injury to three people and they receive damages of $50,000 each. She has a policy with bodily injury limits of 100/300. (a) How much will the company pay to each person? (b) How much must your friend pay? (a) $50,000 (b)$0

21. **INSURANCE CLAIMS PAYMENT** A reckless driver caused Leslie Silva to collide with a car in another lane. Silva had 50/100 liability limits, $25,000 property damage limits, and collision coverage with a $250 deductible. Silva's car had damage of $1878, and the other car suffered $6936 in damage. The resulting lawsuit gave injury awards of $60,000 and $55,000, respectively, to the two people in the other car. Find the amount that the insurance company will pay for (a) repairing Silva's car, (b) repairing the other car, and (c) personal injury damages. (d) How much must Silva pay beyond her insurance coverage, including the collision deductible? (a) $1628 (b) $6936 (c) $100,000 (d) $15,250

22. **INSURANCE CLAIMS PAYMENT** Driving a vehicle at excessive speed caused Bob Armstrong to crash into another car. Armstrong had 15/30 liability limits, $10,000 property damage limits, and collision coverage with a $250 deductible. Damage to Armstrong's car was $2980; the other car, with a value of $22,800, was totaled. The results of a lawsuit awarded $75,000 and $45,000, respectively, in damages for personal injury to the two people in the other car. Find the amount that the insurance company will pay for (a) repairing Armstrong's car, (b) repairing the other car, and (c) personal injury damages. (d) How much must Armstrong pay beyond his insurance coverage? (a) $2730 (b) $10,000 (c) $30,000 (d) $103,050

23. **COMPANY/INSURED LIABILITY** An employee for Safeco Security was driving to a job when a ladder fell from the truck into the path of an oncoming car. Damage to the car was $10,250. Both the driver and the passenger suffered injuries and were given court awards of $30,000 and $40,000, respectively. The security company had 25/50 liability insurance limits and $10,000 property damage limits. (a) Find the total amount paid by the insurance company for both property damage and liability and (b) find the total amount beyond the insurance limits for which the business owner was liable. (a) $60,000 (b) $20,250

24. **COMPANY/INSURED LIABILITY** A trailer-mounted concrete mixer being towed by a contractor broke loose on the beltway and caused a serious accident involving a car and three occupants. Damage to the car was $10,807. The driver and two passengers were given court awards for personal injury of $25,000, $35,000, and $38,000, respectively. The contractor had 25/50 liability insurance limits and $10,000 property damage limits. Find (a) the total amount paid by the insurance company for both property damage and liability and (b) the total amount beyond the insurance limits for which the contractor was liable. (a) $60,000 (b) $48,807

 25. Explain why insurance companies charge a higher premium on auto insurance sold to a youthful operator. Do you think that this higher premium is a good idea or not? (See Objective 6.)

 26. Property damage insurance pays for damage caused by the insured to the property of others. Since the average cost of a new car today is over $20,000, what amount of property damage coverage would you recommend to a friend who owns her own business? Why is this your recommendation? (See Objective 3.)

8.3	Life Insurance

OBJECTIVES

    1 *List reasons for purchasing life insurance.*

    2 *Define term, decreasing term, and whole-life policies.*

    3 *Understand universal life, variable life, limited payment, and endowment policies.*

    4 *Find the annual premium for life insurance.*

    5 *Use premium factors with different modes of premium payment.*

    6 *Describe discounts, conditions, and additional coverage.*

    7 *Understand nonforfeiture options.*

    8 *Calculate income under various settlement options.*

Objective

1   *List Reasons for Purchasing Life Insurance.* Individuals buy life insurance for a variety of reasons. Most often, the insured wants to provide for the needs of others in the event of early death or disability. Parents may want to guarantee that their children will have enough money for college even if the parents die. Also, some types of life insurance provide paybacks upon retirement, paybacks that allow a retired person to live better than he or she might otherwise live. Insurance money can also be used to pay off mortgages in the event of a death. According to the American Council of Life Insurers, the average amount of a life insurance policy sold in the United States today exceeds $100,000.

    Life insurance is also important for businesses, particularly for an owner or partner in a small business. A business often takes a number of years to grow and may be the owner's main asset. The unexpected death of the owner might leave the business without proper guidance and control, and the business may suffer drastically before it can be sold. Life insurance on the partners in a business supplies the surviving partner with the necessary money to buy out a deceased partner's interest in the partnership.

    The following table lists the a seven leading causes of death in the United States and things that individuals can do to reduce the risk of each. Notice that several themes occur repeatedly: quit smoking, increase physical activity, and eat more vegetables/fish/fruit. In fact, scientists believe that smoking is one of the highest health risks, but diet, exercise, and excessive weight are also very important factors.

Leading Causes of Death	To Reduce Risk:
1. Heart disease	Quit smoking, lose weight, eat more vegetables and fish but less red meat, increase physical activity
2. Cancer	Quit smoking, eat more vegetables, fish, and fruit
3. Lung disease	Quit smoking, increase physical activity
4. Stroke	Quit smoking, reduce salt in diet, increase physical activity
5. Accidents	Do not drink and drive, slow down when driving
6. Alzheimer's	Quit smoking, lose weight, eat more vegetables and fish, stay active physically, socially, and mentally
7. Diabetes	Eat more vegetables, lose weight, increase physical activity, avoid simple sugars such as candy and soda

Source: National Institute of Health Statistics, 2010.

Objective

2 *Define Term, Decreasing Term, and Whole-Life Policies.* There are several types of life insurance policies available. The most common types are term, decreasing term, and whole-life insurance.

Term insurance is the least expensive type of life insurance. It provides the most insurance per dollar spent but it does not build up any cash values for retirement. This type of insurance coverage is usually renewable until some age such as 70, when the insured is no longer allowed to renew it. As a result, most people discontinue term insurance before they die. However, term insurance is an excellent way to protect against an early death.

The premium on **renewable term** policies increases each year as the insured ages. Premiums on this type of policy become expensive by the time a person is 50 years of age or so. As a result, many people prefer **level premium term** policies. Initially, these policies require a higher premium than policies with annually increasing premiums. However, the premium on a level premium policy is constant for a period of time, such as 10 years or 20 years. Thereafter, the premiums would increase significantly.

Decreasing term insurance is a modification of term insurance where the insured pays a fixed premium until age 60 or 65, with the amount of life insurance decreasing periodically. This policy is designed to fit the ages and stages of life as life insurance needs change. For the person just starting out, it gives more protection for less money. A typical policy, costing $10 per month, is shown in Table 8.8. Decreasing term insurance is commonly available to employees of large companies as a fringe benefit, paid for by either the employee, the employer, or both. Most mortgage insurance policies are this type. The amount of life insurance coverage decreases as the amount of the mortgage is reduced.

Table 8.8 A TYPICAL DECREASING TERM INSURANCE POLICY

Age of insured	Coverage
Under 29	$80,000
30–34	70,000
35–39	60,000
40–44	50,000
45–49	40,000
50–54	30,000
55–59	20,000
60–66	10,000
67 and over	0

Whole-life insurance (also called **straight life**, **ordinary life insurance**, or **permanent**) combines life insurance protection with savings. The insured pays a constant premium until death or until retirement, whichever occurs sooner. Upon retirement, monthly payments may be made by the company to the insured until his or her death.

Whole-life insurance builds up **cash value**, which can be used to pay retirement benefits, buy **paid-up insurance**, which never requires another payment, or buy **extended term insurance**. Also, these cash values can be borrowed by the insured at favorable interest rates. Cash value accumulation is guaranteed by the company. The rate of interest used to calculate cash values by the company is very conservative. For this reason many consumer finance experts recommend the purchase of term insurance, with the difference in premiums between term insurance and whole-life insurance invested in a good no-load mutual fund or money market fund. See **Section 19.2** for a discussion of mutual funds.

> **NOTE** Many people plan to save the additional money they would have paid for whole-life insurance, but they neglect to do so. One advantage of whole-life insurance is that regular payments are required. Remember that term insurance has no cash value, whereas whole-life does.

In general, people in the United States are living longer, as shown in the graph. But many doctors are worried about an epidemic of diabetes this century due partly to poor diet and increased weights. Such an epidemic threatens to shorten the average life span.

On the Up and Up
Men and women are living longer.

Source: National Center for Health Statistics.

Objective

3 *Understand Universal Life, Variable Life, Limited Payment, and Endowment Policies.* Universal and variable life policies provide the life insurance coverage of term insurance (high coverage per premium dollar), plus a tax-deferred way to accumulate assets and earn interest at money market rates. Unlike traditional whole-life insurance policies, **universal life insurance** allows the insured to vary the amount of premium depending on the changing needs of the insured. A younger insured person with limited funds may want maximum insurance protection for the family. At a later date, the insured may want to begin actively building assets and may increase the premium to build cash value for retirement benefits. Universal life insurance is sensitive to interest rate changes. The portion of the premium going into retirement benefits receives money market interest rates and is usually guaranteed a minimum rate of return, regardless of what happens to market rates. The insured person profits from higher interest rates but is also protected if interest rates drop below the guaranteed rate. The idea is that returns will be greater than those given to ordinary life policyholders.

Variable life is the latest attempt to encourage sales of the insurance industry's main product, whole-life insurance. It allows you to allocate your premiums among one or more separate investments that offer varying degrees of risk and reward—stocks, bonds, combinations of both, or accounts that provide for guarantees of interest and principal. Typical policies available today allow the policyholder to switch investments from one fund to another twice each year. These features coupled with some tax benefits have resulted in the variable life policy accounting for 25% and 35% of the new policies sold in recent years by two of the largest life insurance companies.

Limited-payment life insurance is similar to ordinary life, except that premiums are paid for only a certain fixed number of years, such as 20 years. For this reason, this insurance is often called " 20-pay life," representing payments of 20 years. The premium for limited-payment life is higher than for ordinary life policies. Limited-payment life is commonly used by athletes, actors, and others whose income is likely to be high for several years and then decline.

An **endowment policy** is the most expensive type of policy. These policies guarantee payment of a fixed amount of money to a given individual, whether or not the insured lives. Endowment policies might be taken out by parents to guarantee a sum of money for their children's college education. Because of the high premiums, this is one of the least popular types of policies today.

It is not always easy to decide on the best type of policy. While term insurance gives the greatest amount of insurance for each premium dollar, it pays only when the insured dies. Since term insurance costs increase rapidly with age, most people buying term insurance drop it before they die. Ordinary life insurance provides less coverage for each premium dollar in the event of death; however, it does provide a return to the insured at retirement. The only certain method for determining which policy will give the best return is for the insured to know when he or she will die, and this is not possible.

The Commissioners 2001 Standard Ordinary Table of Mortality (Table 8.9) shows the number of deaths per 1000 and the remaining life expectancy in years for both males and females among the people in the United States having life insurance. Insurance companies use this **mortality table** to evaluate their life insurance reserves, from which benefits are paid. This table is updated periodically. The most recent one is shown in Table 8.9.

> **NOTE** Life expectancy for women is greater than for men, so a woman pays a lower life insurance premium than does a man of the same age. Find the insurance premium for a woman by subtracting 5 years from her age before using the table of premiums.

Table 8.9 COMMISSIONERS 2001 STANDARD ORDINARY TABLE OF MORTALITY SHOWING THE LIFE EXPECTANCY OF MEN AND WOMEN AT VARIOUS AGES

	Males		Females			Males		Females	
Age	Deaths per 1000	Expectation of Life (years)	Deaths per 1000	Expectation of Life (years)	Age	Deaths per 1000	Expectation of Life (years)	Deaths per 1000	Expectation of Life (years)
Newborn	1.0	76.6	0.5	80.8	65	16.9	16.8	11.9	20.1
5	0.2	71.8	0.2	76.0	70	25.8	13.3	17.8	16.4
10	0.2	66.9	0.2	71.0	75	41.9	10.2	27.9	13.0
15	0.6	62.0	0.4	66.1	80	70.1	7.5	43.9	9.9
20	1.0	57.2	0.5	61.3	85	116.6	5.4	74.5	7.3
25	1.1	52.5	0.5	56.4	90	187.7	3.8	121.9	5.3
30	1.1	47.8	0.7	51.6	95	269.2	2.8	193.7	3.6
35	1.2	43.1	1.0	46.8	100	363.2	2.1	275.7	2.6
40	1.7	38.3	1.3	42.0	105	459.2	1.6	410.6	1.7
45	2.7	33.7	1.9	37.3	110	589.6	1.1	581.8	1.2
50	3.8	29.2	3.1	32.7	115	765.7	0.8	763.4	0.8
55	6.2	24.8	5.1	28.3	120	1000.0	0.5	1000.0	0.5
60	9.9	20.6	8.0	24.1					

Source: American Council of Life Insurance, *Life Insurance Fact Book* (Washington, D.C, 2006).

Objective

4 *Find the Annual Premium for Life Insurance.* Calculation of life insurance rates and premiums uses complex mathematics and is done by actuaries. The results of such calculations are published in the tables of premiums. A typical table is shown in Table 8.10. The premium for a life insurance policy is found with the following formula.

$$\text{Annual premium} = \text{number of thousands} \times \text{rate per } \$1000$$

Table 8.10 ANNUAL PREMIUM RATE* PER $1000 OF LIFE INSURANCE

Age	Renewable Term	Whole Life	Universal Term	20-Pay Life
20	2.28	4.07	3.48	12.30
21	2.33	4.26	3.85	12.95
22	2.39	4.37	4.10	13.72
23	2.43	4.45	4.56	14.28
24	2.52	4.68	4.80	15.95
25	2.58	5.06	5.11	16.60
30	2.97	5.66	6.08	18.78
35	3.41	7.68	7.45	21.60
40	4.15	12.67	10.62	24.26
45	4.92	19.86	15.24	28.16
50		26.23	21.46	32.59
55		31.75	28.38	38.63
60		38.42	36.72	45.74

*For women, subtract 5 years from the actual age. For example, to find the rates for a 30-year-old woman, use the rates for age 25.

EXAMPLE 1 **Finding the Life Insurance Premium**

Judith Allen, owner of Canadian Book Sales, is 40 years old and wants to buy a life insurance policy with a face value of $50,000. Use Table 8.10 to find her annual premium for (a) a renewable term policy, (b) a whole-life policy, (c) a universal life policy, and (d) a 20-pay life plan.

Solution

Since the table gives rates per $1000 of face value, first find the number of thousands in $50,000.

$$50,000 = 50 \text{ thousands}$$

	Rate/$1000 (from Table 8.10)		Amount of Insurance (in thousands)		Annual Premium
(a) Renewable term	$3.41	×	50	=	$170.50
(b) Whole life	$7.68	×	50	=	$384.00
(c) Universal life	$7.45	×	50	=	$372.50
(d) 20-pay life	$21.60	×	50	=	$1080.00

NOTE Remember to subtract 5 years from the age of a female before using the table of premiums.

Objective

5 *Use Premium Factors with Different Modes of Premium Payment.* The annual life insurance premium is not always paid in one single payment. Many companies give the insured the option of paying the premium semiannually, quarterly, or monthly. For this convenience, the policyholder pays an additional amount, determined by a **premium factor**. Table 8.11 shows typical premium factors.

Table 8.11 PREMIUM FACTORS	
Mode of Payment	**Premium Factor**
Semiannually	0.51
Quarterly	0.26
Monthly	0.0908

EXAMPLE 2   **Using a Premium Factor**

The annual insurance premium on a $50,000 whole-life policy for Michelle Lee is $384. Use Table 8.11 to find the amount of the premium and the total annual cost if she pays at the following periods: (a) semiannually, (b) quarterly, (c) monthly.

Solution

	Annual Premium		Premium Factor		Premium Payment
(a) Semiannual	$384	×	0.51	=	$195.84 each 6 months
(b) Quarterly	$384	×	0.26	=	$99.84 each quarter
(c) Monthly	$384	×	0.0908	=	$34.87 each month

The annual costs are found as follows.

	Premium		Number of Payments/Year		Total Annual Cost
Annual payment	$384	×	1	=	$384
Semiannual	$195.84	×	2	=	$391.68
Quarterly	$99.84	×	4	=	$399.36
Monthly	$34.87	×	12	=	$418.44

Paying for the policy monthly results in a nearly 9% increase in the annual cost of the policy. Try to pay your premiums annually to save on cost.

Objective

6 *Describe Discounts, Conditions, and Additional Coverage.* Many companies today offer a **nonsmokers discount** because they feel that nonsmokers are better insurance risks. Normally, not having smoked for 12 months qualifies one as a nonsmoker. Most policies also contain a **suicide clause**. This clause states that suicide is not covered, usually for the first 2 years of the policy.

Additional coverage is often available for small increases in the premium. The **accidental death benefit** coverage will pay an additional death benefit if the insured dies as the result of an accident. An optional benefit known as **waiver of premium** allows the life insurance policy to remain in force without payment of premium when the insured becomes disabled. A **guaranteed conversion privilege** lets the insured convert term insurance to any type of whole-life or universal life insurance without physical examination. **Companion** or **spouse insurance** allows an insured to add a companion or spouse to a policy and results in both being insured on one policy.

Objective

7 *Understand Nonforfeiture Options.* Fire insurance, automobile insurance, property insurance, and term life insurance protect against specific hazards in the years during which the policy is in force. These policies rarely have any benefits remaining after premiums are no longer paid. However, whole-life, universal-life, 20-pay life, and endowment policies build up funds called **cash values** that can be withdrawn. The benefits available upon cancellation of this type of policy are called **nonforfeiture options**. The cash values that have built up in these policies can be used in any of the following ways.

1. Cancel the policy and withdraw the cash in one lump sum.
2. Leave the policy in force and borrow some of the cash value.
3. Cancel the policy and receive fixed payments during a period of time, such as 10 years.
4. Use the cash value to buy paid-up insurance that lasts for life.
5. Use the cash value to buy term insurance for a period of time after which policy is canceled.

The owner of the policy no longer has to make premium payments under the last two nonforfeiture options. Typical nonforfeiture options for a policy issued at age 25 appear in Table 8.12

Table 8.9 NONFORFEITURE OPTIONS PER $1000/POLICY ISSUED AT AGE 25

| Years in Force | Whole Life | | | | 20-Pay Life | | | | Universal Life |
| | Cash Value | Paid-up Ins. | Ext. Term | | Cash Value | Paid-up Ins. | Ext. Term | | Cash Value |
			Years	Days			Years	Days	
3*	$5	$16	1	192	$29	$93	11	18	$40
5	28	84	10	190	70	228	20	96	90
10	96	258	18	112	187	554	29	115	310
15	169	415	20	312	339	789	33	215	680
20	283	579	23	315	491	1000	Life	Life	1125
25	394	637	25	130	506	1000			1495
30	491	698	26	210	523	1000			1968

*Normally, there is no cash value accrued in the first 2 years. The cash value of universal life is an estimate, not a guarantee, of the value and will vary depending on the performance of the portfolio of investments chosen by the insured.

EXAMPLE 3 **Determining Nonforfeiture Options**

Lois Stevens purchased an $80,000 whole-life insurance policy when she was 25 years old and has paid on the policy for 20 years. Determine the following values for her policy: (a) cash value, (b) the amount of paid-up insurance that she could receive, and (c) the time period for which she could have extended-term insurance.

Solution

(a) The cash value found in Table 8.12 under whole life for 20 years is $283 per $1000 of insurance. The cash value of her policy is as follows.

$$\$283 \times 80 \,(\text{number of }\$1000\text{s}) = \$22,\!640$$

(b) Again, from Table 8.12, the amount of paid-up insurance that she could receive is $579 per $1000, or

$$\$579 \times 80 = \$46,\!320 \text{ paid-up insurance.}$$

This coverage would remain in force until her death without paying any additional premium.
(c) The time period for which she could have extended-term insurance of the same amount, $80,000, is 23 years and 315 days.

So, Lois Stevens has the option of canceling the policy and (a) taking out $22,640 in cash, (b) using the cash value to buy $46,320 in life insurance without ever having to make another payment, or (c) having $80,000 in term life insurance for 23 years and 315 days without having to make another payment. The last option would result in no insurance after the 23 years and 315 days.

There are two types of insurance companies—**mutual companies** and **stock companies**. The policyholders are the owners in a mutual company, with the policies called **participating policies**. The owners (policyholders) share in any profits of the company; the profits are paid in the form of dividends. If the company prospers, the policyholders receive a dividend or refund of premium. In a stock company, the stockholders are the owners of the company, with the policies called **nonparticipating policies**. If the company prospers, the stockholders, not the policyholders, receive a dividend. The distinction is important in determining the **net cost of insurance policies**.

Objective

8 *Calculate Income under Various Settlement Options.* At the death of a life insurance policyholder, the **beneficiary**, the individual chosen by the insured to receive benefits upon death, has several **settlement options** when choosing how the death benefits are to be received. In many cases the beneficiary elects to receive a single lump-sum payment of the face value of the policy. In other cases, the beneficiary allows the life insurance company to invest the face value and to pay the beneficiary the proceeds and interest over a period of time in the form of an **annuity**. These are the more common options available.

1. A fixed-amount annuity may be paid each month. The monthly payments continue, including interest, until all the proceeds are used up.
2. The beneficiary may prefer the payments of a fixed-period annuity. The insurance company determines the amount that may be paid monthly, for example, for 10 years. The payment continues for exactly that period of time, even if the beneficiary dies.
3. Payments for life is another option. Based upon the age and sex of the beneficiary, the insurance company calculates an amount to be paid to the beneficiary for as long as he or she lives.
4. A last option is payments for life with a guaranteed number of years. Here, if the beneficiary dies before receiving the benefits for the guaranteed time period, the payments continue to the beneficiaries' heirs until the guarantee is satisfied. The guarantees usually range from 5 to 25 years.

Table 8.13 shows the monthly income per $1000 of insurance coverage under various settlement options for one insurance company.

Table 8.13 MONTHLY PAYMENTS PER $1000 OF FACE VALUE

Options 1 and 2: Fixed Amount or Fixed Number of Year		Options 3 and 4: Income for Life				
		Age When Payments Begin		Life	Life with 10 Years	Life with 15 Years
Years	Amount	Male	Female	Annuity	Certain	Certain
10	$9.78	50	55	$4.63	$4.49	$4.38
12	8.46	55	60	5.36	5.16	4.78
14	7.63	60	65	5.94	5.73	4.91
16	6.91	65	70	6.93	6.51	5.34
18	6.07	70	75	7.86	6.93	6.28
20	5.78					

EXAMPLE 4 Finding Settlement Options

Chris Bowler is the beneficiary of a $40,000 life insurance policy. Find (a) the monthly payment if he decides to receive payments for 18 years and (b) the number of years payments will continue if he selects a monthly payment of $300.

Solution

(a) The monthly payment from Table 8.13 for 18 years is $6.07 per $1000 of face value. The monthly payment he receives is

$$\$6.07 \times 40 \text{ (thousands)} = \$242.80$$

(b) A monthly payment of $300 is equivalent to

$$\frac{\$300}{40(\text{thousands})} = \$7.50 \text{ per } \$1000 \text{ face value}$$

Reading the amount column under Options 1 and 2, find $7.63 (closest to $7.50). The $300 payment will continue for a little over 14 years.

EXAMPLE 5 Finding Settlement Options

Ron Hill, 60 years of age, is the beneficiary of a $200,000 life insurance policy. Find (a) his monthly payment from a life annuity and (b) his monthly payment from a life annuity with 15 years certain.

Solution

(a) Under Options 3 and 4 in Table 8.13, look up male, age 60. Look across to the life annuity column, to find $5.94. His monthly payment for life is

$$\$5.94 \times 200 \text{ (thousands)} = \$1188.00$$

(b) The monthly payment from a life annuity with 15 years certain is

$$\$4.91 \times 200 \text{ (thousands)} = \$982.00$$

| 8.3 | Exercises |

Find the annual premium, the semiannual premium, the quarterly premium, and the monthly premium for each of the following. (Note: Subtract 5 years for females.) Use Tables 8.10 and 8.11.

	Face Value of Policy	Age of Insured	Sex of Insured	Type of Policy	
1.	$30,000	60	F	Whole life	$952.50: $485.78: $247.65: $86.49
2.	$60,000	30	M	Whole life	$339.60: $173.20: $88.30: $30.84
3.	$35,000	40	M	20-pay life	$849.10: $433.04: $220.77: $77.10
4.	$80,000	40	F	Universal life	$596: $303.96: $154.96: $54.12
5.	$85,000	30	M	Universal life	$516.80: $263.57: $134.37: $46.93

	Face Value of Policy	Age of Insured	Sex of Insured	Type of Policy	
6.	$150,000	45	F	Renewable term	$622.50: $317.48: $161.85: $56.52
7.	$100,000	35	F	Renewable term	$297: $151.47: $77.22: $26.97
8.	$10,000	22	M	20-pay life	$137.20: $69.97: $35.67: $12.46
9.	$50,000	45	F	Universal life	$531: $270.81: $138.06: $48.21
10.	$40,000	29	F	20-pay life	$638: $325.38: $165.88: $57.93
11.	$70,000	50	M	Whole life	$1836.10: $936.41: $477.39: $166.72
12.	$60,000	35	M	Renewable term	$204.60: $104.35: $53.20: $18.58
13.	$100,000	60	F	Whole life	$3175: $1619.25: $825.50: $288.29
14.	$100,000	27	F	Universal life	$410: $209.10: $106.60: $37.23

15. Explain in your own words the advantages and disadvantages of buying renewable term life insurance. Would you buy renewable term life insurance for yourself? Why or why not? (See Objective 2.)

16. If you were the beneficiary of a $40,000 life insurance policy, what settlement option would you choose? Why? (See Objective 8.)

Find the nonforfeiture values of the following policies. The policies were issued at age 25. Use Table 8.12.

	Years in Force	Type of Policy	Face Value	Nonforfeiture Option	
17.	10	Universal life	$50,000	Cash value	$15,500
18.	15	Universal life	$75,000	Cash value	$51,000
19.	30	20-pay life	$30,000	Paid-up insurance	$30,000
20.	15	Whole life	$35,000	Extended term	20 yr. 312 days
21.	30	Universal life	$100,000	Cash value	$196,800
22.	15	20-pay life	$25,000	Paid-up insurance	$19,725
23.	20	Whole life	$100,000	Extended term	23 yr. 315 days
24.	10	Whole life	$40,000	Extended term	18 yr. 112 days

Find the monthly payment or period of payment under the following policy settlement options. Use Table 8.13.

	Beneficiary				Monthly Payment	
	Age	Sex	FaceValue	Settlement Option	Years	Amount
25.	55	M	$50,000	Fixed amount per month	20	$289
26.	65	F	$75,000	Life, 10 years certain	10	$429.75
27.	65	M	$10,000	Fixed number of years	18 years	$60.70
28.	60	M	$40,000	Fixed number of years	12 years	$338.40
29.	70	F	$30,000	Life, 15 years certain	15	$160.20
30.	60	F	$100,000	Fixed amount per month	10	$978

Solve the following application problems.

31. WHOLE-LIFE POLICY   Linda Davis buys a $50,000 whole-life policy at age 40. Her son Matthew is the beneficiary and will collect the face value of the policy. (a) Find the annual premium. (b) How much will Matthew get if his mother dies after paying premiums for 9 years?   (a) $384 (b) $50,000

32. 20-PAY LIFE POLICY   Luan Lee buys a $100,000, 20-pay life policy at age 45. Her son Bryan is the beneficiary and will collect the face value of the policy. (a) Find the annual premium. (b) How much will Bryan get if his mother dies after making payments for 12 years?   (a) $2426 (b) $100,000

33. EMPLOYEE LIFE INSURANCE   Ozark Steel Foundry feels that it would suffer considerable hardship if the firm's head moldmaker died suddenly. Therefore, the firm takes out a $280,000 policy on the moldmaker's life. The moldmaker is a 45-year-old woman, and the company buys a renewable term policy. Find the semiannual premium. $592.62

34. KEY EMPLOYEE INSURANCE   Ellen Sawyer owns the Doll Shop and has a 40-year-old key male employee whom she wants to insure for $100,000. Find the quarterly premium for a renewable term policy. $107.90

35. UNIVERSAL LIFE   Leticia Adams is a 35-year-old single mom who has a daughter with severe Down syndrome. To protect her daughter, she purchases a $200,000 universal life insurance policy on herself. Find the monthly premium. $110.41

36. WHOLE LIFE   At 25, Aaron Clinton is the primary wage earner for his family, which includes three young children. To protect his family in the event of his death and also save some funds for eventual retirement, he decides to buy $150,000 in whole-life insurance. Find the quarterly premium. $197.34

37. PREMIUM FACTORS   The annual premium for a whole-life policy is $872. Using premium factors, find (a) the semiannual premium, (b) the quarterly premium, (c) the monthly premium, and (d) the total annual cost of each of the plans.   (a) $444.72 (b) $226.72 (c) $ 79.18 (d) $889.44; $906.88; $950.16

38. UNIVERSAL LIFE   A universal life policy has an annual premium of $1806. Use premium factors to find (a) the semiannual premium, (b) the quarterly premium, (c) the monthly premium, and (d) the total annual cost for each of the plans.   (a) $921.06 (b) $469.56 (c) $163.98 (d) $1842.12; $1878.24; $1967.76

39. NONFORFEITURE OPTIONS   Catherine Konradt purchased a $20,000 whole-life policy 20 years ago when she was 25 years old. Use the table of nonforfeiture options (Table 8.12) to determine (a) the cash value, (b) the amount of paid-up insurance which she could receive, and (c) the time period for which she could have paid-up insurance.   (a) $5660 (b) $11,580 (c) 23 yr. 315 days

40. NONFORFEITURE OPTIONS   Lee Hardesty purchased a 20-pay life policy 15 years ago when he was 25 years old. The face value of the policy is $80,000. Find the following values using the nonforfeiture options table (Table 8.12): (a) cash value, (b) the amount of paid-up insurance that he could have, and (c) the time period for which he could have paid-up term insurance.   (a) $27,120 (b) $63,120 (c) 33 yr. 215 days

41. POLICY CASH VALUE The face value of a universal life policy purchased by Patty Gillette is $100,000. She purchased the policy 25 years ago when she was 25 years of age. Use the nonforfeiture options table (Table 8.12) to find the cash value of the policy today. $149,500

42. NONFORFEITURE OPTIONS When he was 25 years old, Chuck Manly purchased a $40,000 whole-life policy. Now that 30 years have passed, Manly wants to know the options available when canceling his policy. Use the nonforfeiture options table (Table 8.12) to find (a) the cash value, (b) the amount of paid-up insurance he could have, and (c) the time period for which he could have paid-up term insurance. (a) $19,640 (b) $27,920 (c) 26 yr. 210 days

43. SETTLEMENT OPTIONS Ryan Polstra is the beneficiary of a $25,000 life insurance policy. Polstra is 50 years of age and is considering the various settlement options available. Use Table 8.13 to find (a) the monthly payment if he selects payments for 12 years, (b) the number of years he will receive payments of $145 per month, (c) the monthly payment from a life annuity, and (d) the amount he would receive monthly if he chooses a life annuity with 15 years certain. (a) $211.50 (b) approx. 20 years (c) $115.75 (d) $109.50

44. SETTLEMENT OPTIONS Krista Bauer is the beneficiary of a $30,000 life insurance policy. Bauer is 65 years of age and is considering the various settlement options available. Use Table 8.13 to find (a) the monthly payment she would receive if she selects a fixed amount for 10 years, (b) the number of years she can receive $225 per month, (c) the amount she can receive per month as a life annuity, and (d) the monthly amount she could receive as a life annuity with 10 years certain. (a) $293.40 (b) approx. 14 years (c) $178.20 (d) $171.90

45. SETTLEMENT OPTIONS James Marcotte is the beneficiary of a $50,000 life insurance policy. Marcotte is 60 years of age and is considering the various settlement options available. Use Table 8.13 to find (a) the monthly payment he would receive if he selects a fixed amount for 16 years, (b) the number of years he can receive $305 per month, (c) the amount he can receive per month as a life annuity, and (d) the monthly amount he could receive as a life annuity with 10 years certain. (a) $345.50 (b) 18 yr. (c) $297 (d) $286.50

46. SETTLEMENT OPTIONS Kristen Clement is the beneficiary of a $70,000 life insurance policy. Clement is 60 years of age and is considering the various settlement options available. Use Table 8.13 to find (a) the monthly payment she would receive if she selects a fixed amount for 18 years, (b) the number of years she can receive $405 per month, (c) the amount she can receive as a life annuity, and (d) the monthly amount she could receive as a life annuity with 10 years certain. (a) $424.90 (b) approx. 20 years (c) $375.20 (d) $361.20

47. The greatest advantage of a renewable term policy is that you get the most coverage for your premium dollar. However, renewable term provides no cash value for retirement. Explain how you would provide for retirement to offset this disadvantage of a renewable term life policy. (See Objective 2.)

48. The additional charge for paying an insurance premium semiannually, quarterly, or monthly is determined by a premium factor. Would you select something other than the single premium payment? Why or why not? How could you justify the additional charge (premium factor)? (See Objective 5.)

CHAPTER TERMS

Review the following terms to test your understanding of the chapter. For each term you do not know, refer to the page number found next to that term.

accidental death benefit [p. 339]
actuaries [p. 325]
adult operator [p. 330]
annuity [p. 341]
beneficiary [p. 341]
bodily injury insurance [p. 326]
cash value [p. 335]
coinsurance clause [p. 317]
collision insurance [p. 327]
companion or spouse insurance [p. 339]
comprehensive insurance [p. 327]
decreasing term insurance [p. 335]
deductible [p. 327]
disability insurance [p. 321]
endowment policy [p. 336]
extended-term insurance [p. 335]

face value [p. 314]
group insurance plans [p. 321]
guaranteed conversion privilege [p. 339]
homeowner's policy [p. 320]
insurance [p. 313]
insured policyholder [p. 313]
insurer or carrier [p. 313]
level premium term [p. 335]
liability insurance [p. 326]
limited-payment life insurance [p. 336]
medical insurance [p. 326]
mortality table [p. 337]
multiple carriers [p. 318]
mutual companies [p. 341]
net cost of insurance policies [p. 341]
no-fault insurance [p. 329]
nonforfeiture options [p. 340]

nonparticipating policies [p. 341]
nonsmokers discount [p. 339]
ordinary life insurance [p. 335]
paid-up insurance [p. 335]
participating policies [p. 341]
peril insurance [p. 313]
permanent life insurance [p. 335]
policy [p. 314]
premium [p. 313]
premium factor [p. 338]
profit margin [p. 325]
property damage insurance [p. 326]
renewable term [p. 325]
replacement cost [p. 315]
settlement option [p. 341]
short-term or cancellation rate [p. 316]

special multiperils policy (SMP) [p. 320]
stock companies [p. 341]
straight life insurance [p. 335]
suicide clause [p. 339]
term insurance [p. 335]
territorial ratings [p. 315]
underinsured motorist insurance [p. 329]
underwriter [p. 315]
uninsured motorist insurance [p. 329]
universal life [p. 336]
variable life [p. 336]
waiver of premium [p. 339]
whole-life insurance [p. 335]
worker's compensation insurance [p. 321]
youthful operator [p. 330]

CONCEPTS

EXAMPLES

8.1 Annual premium for fire insurance

Use the building and territorial rating in Table 8.1 to find the premiums per $100 for the building and for the contents. Add the two premiums.

Building replacement cost, $160,000; contents, $35,000; territorial rating, 4; building rating, B. Find the annual premium.

Building: $1600 \times \$0.75 = \$1200$

Contents: $350 \times \$0.77 = \$269.50$

Total premium: $\$1200 + \$269.50 = \$1469.50$

8.1 Short-term rates and cancellations

Annual premium is multiplied by the short-term rate. Use Table 8.2.

Annual premium is $2320. Short-term rate for 9 months is 85%. Premium for 9 months is

$\$2320 \times 0.85 = \$1972$ Premium

$\$2320 - \$1972 = \$348$ Refund

8.1 Calculate prorated insurance premium cancellations

Multiply annual premium by a fraction with months of insurance in force as the numerator and 12 as the denominator.

Annual premium, $1620; policy canceled after 4 months. Find refund. Premium for 4 months is

$$\$1620 \times \frac{4}{12} = \$540$$

$\$1620 - \$540 = \$1080$ refund

8.1 Coinsurance formula

Part of the risk is taken by the insured. An 80% coinsurance clause is common.

Loss paid by insurance company =

$$\text{amount of loss} \times \frac{\text{policy amount}}{80\% \text{ of replacement cost}}$$

Building replacement cost, $125,000; policy amount, $75,000; loss, $40,000; 80% coinsurance clause. Find the amount of loss paid by insurance company.

$$\$40,000 \times \frac{\$75,000}{\$100,000} = \$30,000$$

Insurance company pays $30,000.

8.1 Multiple carriers

Several companies insure the same property to limit their risk; each company pays its fractional portion of any claim.

Insured loss, $500,000; insurance is Company A with $1,000,000; Company B with $750,000; Company C with $250,000. Find the amount of loss paid by each company.

Total insurance is
$$
\begin{array}{r}
\$1,000,000 \\
750,000 \\
+ \quad 250,000 \\
\hline
\$2,000,000
\end{array}
$$

Company A pays

$$\frac{\$1,000,000}{\$2,000,000} \times \$500,000 = \$250,000$$

Company B pays

$$\frac{\$750,000}{\$2,000,000} \times \$500,000 = \$187,500$$

Company C pays

$$\frac{\$250,000}{\$2,000,000} \times \$500,000 = \$62,500$$

8.2 Annual auto insurance premium

Most drivers are legally required to purchase automobile insurance. The premium is determined by the types of coverage selected, the type of car, geographic territory, past driving record, and other factors. See Tables 8.3 to Table 8.6.

Determine the premium: territory, 2; liability, 50/100: property damage, $50,000; comprehensive and collision, 3-year-old car with a category of 8; uninsured motorist coverage; driver, age 23 with driver's training.

$$
\begin{array}{rl}
\$341 & \text{Liability} \\
223 & \text{Property damage} \\
74 & \text{Comprehensive} \\
215 & \text{Collision} \\
+ \quad 62 & \text{Uninsured motorist} \\
\hline
\$915 & \times 1.25 \text{ youthful-operator factor} \\
& = \$1143.75
\end{array}
$$

8.2 Amount paid by insurance company and by insured

The company pays up to the maximum amount of insurance coverage; insured pays the balance.

Policy terms: liability, 15/30: property damage, $10,000; collision, $250 deductible. Accident caused $2850 damage to insured's car; $3850 to other car; injury liability of $20,000 and $25,000, respectively.

Company pays $2600 ($2850 − $250) to repair insured's car.

Company pays $3850 to repair other car ($10,000 limit).

Company pays $30,000 for two injured people ($15,000 each).

Insured pays $15,000 ($45,000 − $30,000), amount over limit.

8.3 Annual life insurance premium

There are several types of life policies. Use Table 8.10 and multiply by the number of $1000s of coverage. Subtract 5 years from the age for females.

Premium = number of thousands
× rate per $1000

Find the premiums on a $50,000 policy for a 30-year-old male.

Renewable term: $50 \times \$2.97 = \$148.50$

Whole life: $50 \times \$5.66 = \$283$

Universal life: $50 \times \$6.08 = \$304$

20-pay life: $50 \times \$18.78 = \$939$

8.3 Premium factors

If not paid annually, life insurance premiums may be paid semiannually, quarterly, or monthly. The annual premium is multiplied by the premium factor to determine the premium amount. Use Table 8.11.

The annual life insurance premium is $740. Find the semiannual, quarterly, and monthly premium.

Semiannual: $\$740 \times 0.51 = \$377.40$

Quarterly: $\$740 \times 0.26 = \$192.40$

Monthly: $\$740 \times 0.0908 = \$67.19$

8.3 Nonforfeiture options

Upon cancellation of a policy, the insured may receive a cash settlement, paid-up insurance, or extended-term insurance as a nonforfeiture option. Use Table 8.12.

Insurance is a $40,000, 20-pay life policy; in force for 10 years; issued at age 25.

Cash value: $\$187 \times 40 = \$7480$

Paid-up insurance: $\$554 \times 40 = \$22,160$

Extended-term insurance period is 29 years, 115 days.

8.3 Settlement options

Upon the death of the insured, the beneficiary often has choices as to how the money may be received. These range from all cash to various types of payment arrangements. Use Table 8.13.

Insurance is a $30,000 policy; female beneficiary, age 60. Find monthly payments for:

16 years: $30 \times \$6.91 = \$207.30$

Life annuity: $30 \times \$5.36 = \$160.80$

Life with 15 years certain: $30 \times \$4.78 = \$143.40$

For how many years would $200 a month be paid?

$$\frac{\$200}{30} = \$6.67 \text{ per } \$1000$$

A little more than 16 years: $6.67 is closest to $6.91.

CHAPTER 8	Review Exercises

The answer section includes answers to all Review Exercises.

Find the total annual premium for fire insurance for each of the following. Use Table 8.1. **[8.1]**

	Territorial Rating	Building Classification	Replacement Cost of Building	Contents Value	
1.	4	A	$640,000	$275,000	$4630
2.	2	C	$375,000	$198,000	$3510
3.	3	A	$80,000	$30,000	$434
4.	1	B	$193,000	$68,000	$1028

Find the amount of refund to the insured using the Short-Term Rate Schedule (Table 8.2). **[8.1]**

	Annual Premium	Months in Force	
5.	$1773	2	$1152.45
6.	$1078	6	$323.40
7.	$1486	9	$222.90
8.	$2878	5	$1007.30

Find (a) the amount of premium retained by the company and (b) the amount of refund to the insured using proration. **[8.1]**

	Annual Premium	Months in Force	
9.	$3150	5	(a) $1312.50 (b) $1837.50
10.	$1975	9	(a) $1481.25 (b) $493.75
11.	$1476	10	(a) $1230 (b) $246
12.	$2784	2	(a) $464 (b) $2320

Find the amount of each of the following losses that will be paid by the insurance company. Assume that each policy includes an 80% coinsurance clause. **[8.1]**

	Replacement Cost of Building	Face Value of Policy	Amount of Loss	
13.	$456,000	$320,000	$45,000	$39,473.68
14.	$277,500	$165,000	$97,800	$72,689.19
15.	$186,700	$120,000	$3400	$2731.66
16.	$325,000	$220,000	$42,200	$35,707.69

Find the annual motor vehicle insurance premium for the following people. **[8.2]**

	Name	Territory	Age	Driver's Training	Liablity	Property Damage	Comprehensive Collision Age Group	Category	Uninsured Motorist	
17.	Larik	1	42	—	50/100	$100,000	1	8	yes	$796
18.	Ramos	3	18	yes	13/100	$10,000	5	7	yes	$1086.55
19.	Verano	2	24	no	25/50	$25,000	2	8	yes	$1183
20.	Wilson	4	29	—	250/500	$100,000	1	6	yes	$902

Find the annual premium for each of the following life insurance policies. **[8.3]**

21. Carolyn Phelps: 20-pay life; $70,000 face value; age 55 $2281.30
22. Ralph Todd: renewable term; $50,000 face value; age 45 $246
23. Gilbert Eckern: whole life: $30,000 face value; age 23 $133.50
25. Irene Chang: universal life; $40,000 face value; age 29 $192

Solve the following application problems.

25. Dave's Body and Paint has an insurable loss of $72,000, while having insurance coverage beyond the coinsurance requirement. The insurance is divided between Company A with $250,000 coverage, Company B with $150,000 coverage, and Company C with $100,000 coverage. Find the amount of loss paid by each of the insurance companies. **[8.1]**   A: $36,000 B: $21,600 C: $14,400

26. The headquarters building of Western States Life is valued at $820,000, and the fire insurance policies contain an 80% coinsurance clause. The policies include $350,000 with Company 1 and $200,000 with Company 2. The Western building suffered a $150,000 fire loss. Find (a) the amount that Western would receive after the loss and (b) the amount of loss paid by each insurance company. Round to the nearest dollar. **[8.1]**   (a) $125,762 (b) 1: $80,030; 2: $45,732

27. Tim Martinez was late for work and driving too fast. He was unable to avoid a bicycle rider and injured her badly. He had policy liability limits of 25/50, but the judge awarded damages of $38,400 to the injured bicycle rider. Find (a) the amount that the insurance company will pay and (b) the amount that Martinez must pay. **[8.2]**   (a) $25,000 (b) $13,400

28. Three people are injured in an automobile accident and receive $15,000 each in damages. The driver has bodily injury insurance of 50/100. (a) How much will the company pay to each person and (b) how much must the driver pay? **[8.2]**   (a) $15,000 (b) $0

29. Some scaffolding falls off a truck and into the path of a car, resulting in serious damage and injury. The car had damage of $16,800, and the driver and passenger of the car were given court awards of $25,000 and $35,000, respectively. The driver of the truck had 15/30 liability insurance limits and $10,000 property damage limits. Find (a) the total amount paid by the insurance company for both property damage and liability and (b) the total amount beyond the insurance limits for which the driver was liable. **[8.2]**   (a) $40,000 (b) $36,800

30. The annual premium for a whole-life policy is $970. Use premium factors to find (a) the semiannual premium, (b) the quarterly premium, (c) the monthly premium, and (d) the total annual cost for each of the plans. **[8.3]**   (a) $494.70 (b) $252.20 (c) $88.08 (d) $989.40; $1008.80; $1056.96

31. Lori Johnson purchased a universal life policy 20 years ago when she was 25 years old. The face value of the policy is $60,000. Find the cash value of the policy using the nonforfeiture options table (Table 8.12). **[8.3]** $67,500

32. Glenn Lewis purchased a $40,000 whole-life policy 20 years ago when he was 25 years old. Use Table 8.12 to determine (a) the cash value, (b) the amount of paid-up insurance he could receive, and (c) the time period for which he could have paid-up term insurance. **[8.3]**   (a) $11,320 (b) $23,160 (c) 23 yr 315 days

33. Pete White is the beneficiary of an $80,000 life insurance policy. White is 60 years old and is considering the various settlement options available. Use Table 8.13 to find (a) the monthly payment he would receive if he selects a fixed payment for 16 years, (b) the number of years he can receive $675 per month, (c) the amount he can receive as a life annuity, and (d) the monthly amount he could receive as a life annuity with 15 years certain. **[8.3]**   (a) $552.80 (b) about 12 yr. (c) $475.20 (d) $392.80

34. Ann-Marie Sargent is the beneficiary of a $40,000 life insurance policy. Sargent is 55 years old and is considering the various settlement options available. Use Table 8.13 to find (a) the monthly payment she would receive if she selects a fixed payment for 20 years, (b) the number of years she can receive $245 per month, (c) the amount she can receive as a life annuity, and (d) the monthly amount she could receive as a life annuity with 10 years certain. **[8.3]**   (a) $231.20 (b) about 18 yr (c) $185.20 (d) $179.60

CHAPTER 8	Business Application Case #1
	Financial Planning for Insurance

Childcare Playground Toys imports parts from Thailand and Malaysia and assembles quality playground equipment and riding toys. Planning ahead, the company set aside $41,700 to pay fire insurance premiums on the company property and a semiannual life insurance premium for the president. Both were due in the same month. Find each of the following.

(a) The building occupied by the company is a class B building with a replacement cost of $1,730,000. The contents are worth $3,502,000 and the territorial rating is 4. Find the annual insurance premium. $39,940.40

(b) The president of Childcare Playground Toys is a 45-year-old woman and the company is buying a $175,000, renewable term life insurance policy on the president's life. Find the semiannual premium. $370.39

(c) Find the total amount needed to pay the fire insurance premium and the semiannual life insurance premium. $40,310.79

(d) How much more than the amount needed had the company set aside to pay these expenses? $1389.21

CHAPTER 8	Business Application Case #2
	Employee Benefits and Fire Insurance

After working for a large candy manufacturer for 19 years, Sherrie Bennett is establishing her own company to market chocolate from Europe. She plans to purchase a small commercial building and hire the following people with salaries as shown. Answer the questions that follow.

Employee	Age Sex	Duty	Annual Salary
P. Russo	30, F	Secretary	$23,500
E. Martin	45, M	Sales	$44,800
T. Hicks	50, F	Office Manager	$58,000

(a) Find the fire insurance premium for a building: replacement cost, $235,000; contents, $28,900; building rating, C; territory 5. $2796.96

(b) Bennett decides to purchase life insurance for each employee in the amount shown. Find the annual life insurance premium for renewable term coverage. Then, find the amount of the FICA and Medicare taxes for each employee for which Bennett is responsible as the employer (FICA: 6.2%; Medicare; 1.45%). Finally, find the total expenditure for each employee.

Employee	Amount of Life Insurance	Cost of Life Insurance	FICA	Medicare	Total
P. Russo	$50,000	$129	$1457	$340.75	$1926.75
E. Martin	$100,000	$492	$2777.60	$649.60	$3919.20
T. Hicks	$200,000	$984	$3596	$841	$5421

(c) Find the total annual cost of employee salaries, fire insurance, and employee benefits including life insurance, FICA, and Medicare. $140,363.91

Note that these are not all of the expenses that Bennett must pay in her first year of business. Presumably, she will pay at least part of the medical insurance, worker's compensation insurance, and unemployment insurance on her employees. She will also have to buy supplies and pay for telephone service, Internet access, travel to and from Europe, and shipping services in addition to many other costs.

PART 2	Cumulative Review: Chapters 5–8

The following credit card transactions were made at Gifts and Such. Answer Questions 1 to 5 using this information. **[5.2]**

	Sales		Credits
$93.50	$315.26	$22.51	$99.84
$117.75	$38.00	$162.15	$72.68
$173.05	$92.18		$35.63

1. Find the total amount of the sales slips. $1014.40
2. What is the total amount of the credit slips? $208.15
3. Find the total amount of the deposit. $806.25
4. Assuming that the bank charges the retailer a $2\frac{1}{4}\%$ discount charge, find the amount of the discount charge at the statement date. $18.14
5. Find the amount of the credit given to the retailer after the fee is subtracted. $788.11

Solve the following application problems

6. The bank statement of Adam Hamel Productions shows a balance of $16,298.60, a returned check amounting to $673.60, a service charge of $28.32, and an interest credit of $40.72. There were unrecorded deposits of $3631.28 and $7136.60, and checks outstanding are $2570.20, $4331.92, $293, and $1887.32. The checkbook shows a balance of $18,645.24. Use the T-account form, Figure 5.13, to find the adjusted balance of this checking account. **[5.3]** $17,984.04

7. Angela Perez worked 7 hours on Monday, 10 hours on Tuesday, 8 hours on Wednesday, 9 hours on Thursday, and 10 hours on Friday. Her regular hourly pay is $12.80. Find her gross earnings for the week if Perez is paid overtime (time-and-a-half) for all hours over 8 worked in a day. **[6.1]** $595.20

8. Laura Rogers is a commission salesperson for Education Specialties, which allows her a draw of $1200 per month. Her commision is 5% of the first $5000 in sales, 8% of the next $15,000, and 15% of all sales over $20,000. Her sales for the month were $28,400. Find (a) her total commission and (b) the earnings due at the end of the month after repaying the drawing account balance of $1200. **[6.2]**   (a) $2710 (b) $1510

9. Eric Means is paid $2.18 for each computer keyboard assembled, is charged $1.05 for each rejection, and is paid time-and-a-half for overtime production. Find his gross earnings for the week when he assembles 268 keyboards at the regular rate and 32 keyboards at the overtime rate and has 9 chargebacks. **[6.3]** $679.43

10. Greg Baker is a salesperson for Petco Wholesalers and is paid $650 per week plus a commission of 3% of all sales. His sales last week were $33,482. Find the amount of (a) his Social Security tax (6.2%), (b) his Medicare tax (1.45%), and (c) his state disability (1%) for the pay period. **[6.4]**   (a) $102.58 (b) $23.99 (c) $16.54

11. As a nurse, Connie Zhao earned $1240 one week including overtime. She is single and has two children, so she claims 3 exemptions. Her deductions include FICA (6.2%), Medicare (1.45%), federal withholding, state disability insurance (1%), state withholding of 3.2%, and a savings bond of $50. Use the percentage method of withholding to find her net pay for the week. **[6.5]** $871.02

12. The employees of Highland Farms paid a total of $968.50 in Social Security tax last month, $223.50 in Medicare tax, and $1975.38 in federal withholding tax. Find the total amount that the employer must send to the Internal Revenue Service. **[6.6]** $4359.38

13. The Custom Fireside Shop charges $286.96, including 5.5% sales tax, for a custom fireplace screen. Find the price of the fireplace screen without the tax. **[7.1]** $272

Complete the following list comparing tax rates. **[7.2]**

Percent	Per $100	Per $1000	In Mills
14. (a) 2.68%	$2.68	(b) $26.80	(c) 26.8
15. 4.62%	(a) $4.62	(b) $46.20	(c) 46.2

16. Phyllis Beaton earned $38,514.75 last year from Bel Air Supermarket as assistant manager and $675.18 in interest from her credit union. She had $1800 in IRA contributions. Find her adjusted gross income. **[7.3]** $37,389.93

17. Ben and Jane Chen are married, have one son, and file jointly. Ben is a surgeon and Jane is a stay-at-home mom. Their adjusted gross income is $234,610. Find the taxable income and tax, assuming they use the standard deduction. $211,910; $47,404.30

18. Feather's Custom Cabinets owns a class A building with a replacement cost of $179,480. The replacement cost of the contents is $83,300 and the territorial rating is 4. Find the annual fire insurance premium. **[8.1]** $1330.56

19. One restaurant has a replacement cost of $720,000. The fire policies are $200,000 with Company A, $100,000 with Company B, and $60,000 with Company C, and each contains an 80% coinsurance clause. There is a fire at the restaurant causing a $240,000 loss. Find (a) the amount that the insured would receive and (b) the amount that each of the insurance companies would pay. Round to the nearest dollar. **[8.1]** (a) $150,000 (b) A: $83,333; B: $41,667; C: $25,000

20. James Follain is 57, lives in territory 2, and wants the following automobile coverage: liability, 50/100; property damage, $50,000; comprehensive and collision (age group 3 and category 7); and uninsured motorist. Find his annual premium. **[8.2]** $879

21. Del Nelson was distracted by his cell phone as he drove along the interstate. He didn't notice that cars were braking and he crashed into the car in front of him. Nelson had 25/50 liability limits, $25,000 property damage limits, and collision coverage with a $250 deductible. Damage to Nelson's car was $6340, while the car in front of him, with a value of $34,800, was totaled. The results of a lawsuit awarded $100,000 and $65,000 in damages for personal injury to the two people in the other car. Find the amount that the insurance company will pay for (a) repairing Nelson's car, (b) repairing the other car, and (c) personal injury damages. (d) How much must Nelson pay beyond his insurance coverage? **[8.2]** (a) $6090 (b) $25,000 (c) $50,000 (d) $125,050

22. Jim Havey purchased a 20-pay life policy with a face value of $100,000. He is 50 years old. Use the premium factors to find (a) the semiannual premium, (b) the quarterly premium, (c) the monthly premium, and (d) the total annual cost of each of the plans. **[8.3]** (a) $1662.09 (b) $847.34 (c) $295.92 (d) $3324.18; $3389.36; $3551.04

CHAPTER
9

Mathematics of Buying

Managing inventories is at the heart of retailing. Look at the generalized **supply chain** below, showing **suppliers**, **manufacturer**, **wholesaler (distributor)**, and **retailer**. Prices are marked up (increased) at each step in the supply chain.

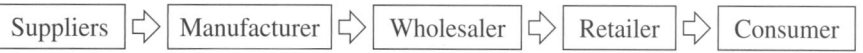

Suppliers ⇨ Manufacturer ⇨ Wholesaler ⇨ Retailer ⇨ Consumer

Think of the supply chain as a highly coordinated system that tries to deliver the right amount of inventory to the right location at the right time—and do it very cheaply. This has become very complex, yet very important, in the modern world of **global supply chains**. The goal is to have the right amount of **inventory** everywhere in the supply chain. Too much inventory results in spoilage and inventory just sitting around, whereas too little inventory results in lost sales. Imagine the complexity of managing the supply chain used by Wal-Mart Stores Inc., with its roughly 60,000 suppliers located all over the world!

Figure 9.1 shows the ratio of average inventories held by businesses to annual sales. The ratio fell from 1999 to mid 2008, which shows that managers were cutting costs by holding

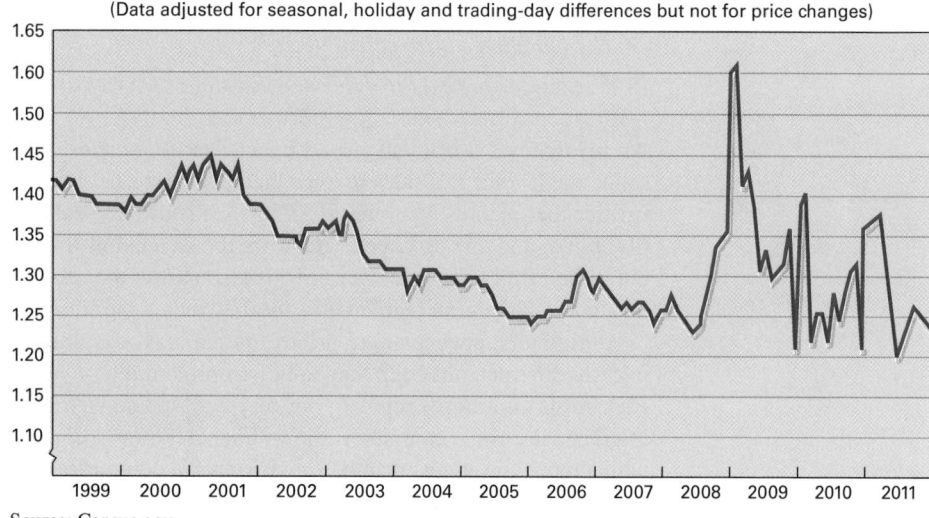

Ratio of Average Inventory to Annual Sales
(Data adjusted for seasonal, holiday and trading-day differences but not for price changes)

Source: Census.gov.

Figure 9.1

less and less inventory per dollar of sales. But what about the huge increase from late 2008 to late 2009? Inventories soared. Why? Inventory moves very rapidly in modern supply chains, based on plans that are developed a few weeks before shipments occur. Managers did not expect the sharp slowdown in purchases by **consumers** that occurred as the financial crisis began in the fall of 2008, and inventory quickly increased throughout supply chains.

Managers across the world took immediate action to reduce production and the amounts of inventory moving through the supply chains. Still, it took a year to work off the excess inventories, and many employees were laid off. You can think in terms of managers hitting the brakes on the global supply chains, but not before inventory built up. Then, companies had to work off the excess inventory.

▶STOP&THINK

> How important is it for managers to quickly detect a build up in inventories, such as at the end of 2008? What options do managers have as inventories swell to high levels? Is it reasonable for them to lay off good workers at such a time?

9.1	**Invoices and Trade Discounts**

OBJECTIVES

1 *Complete an invoice.*

2 *Understand common shipping terms.*

3 *Identify invoice abbreviations.*

4 *Calculate net cost and trade discounts.*

5 *Differentiate between single and series discounts.*

6 *Calculate each series discount separately.*

7 *Use complements to calculate series discounts.*

8 *Use a table to find the net cost equivalent of series discounts.*

An **invoice** is a document issued by a seller to a buyer as a record of a transaction. For a seller, the invoice is a **sales invoice** that records a sale. For a buyer, an invoice is a **purchase invoice** that records a purchase. An invoice shows the seller, buyer, items purchased, quantity, price, and any discounts. It shows the **extension total**, which is the number of items purchased times the price per unit. It also shows any discounts applied, the shipping and insurance charges, and the **invoice total**, which is the sum of the extension totals.

Originally, invoices were printed on paper. Today, most invoices are sent electronically over the Internet, although they are often printed out on paper for record-keeping purposes. **Electronic commerce** refers to the very widespread buying and selling of products over the Internet. Electronic commerce allows financial transactions to occur much more rapidly and with a much lower cost than before. Electronic commerce is used for much of global trade.

Objective

1 *Complete an Invoice.* The invoice in Figure 9.2 serves as a sales invoice for J. B. Sherr Company and as a purchase invoice for Kitchens Galore. The number of items shipped column multiplied by the **unit price** gives the amount or total for each item. The **total invoice amount** is the sum of the amount totals.

Trade and cash discounts, discussed later in this section, **are never applied to shipping and insurance charges**. For this reason shipping and insurance charges are often not included in the invoice total, so the purchaser must add them to the invoice total to find the total amount due. In the J. B. Sherr Company invoice, the freight (shipping) charges ($39.95) are included in the INVOICE TOTAL space.

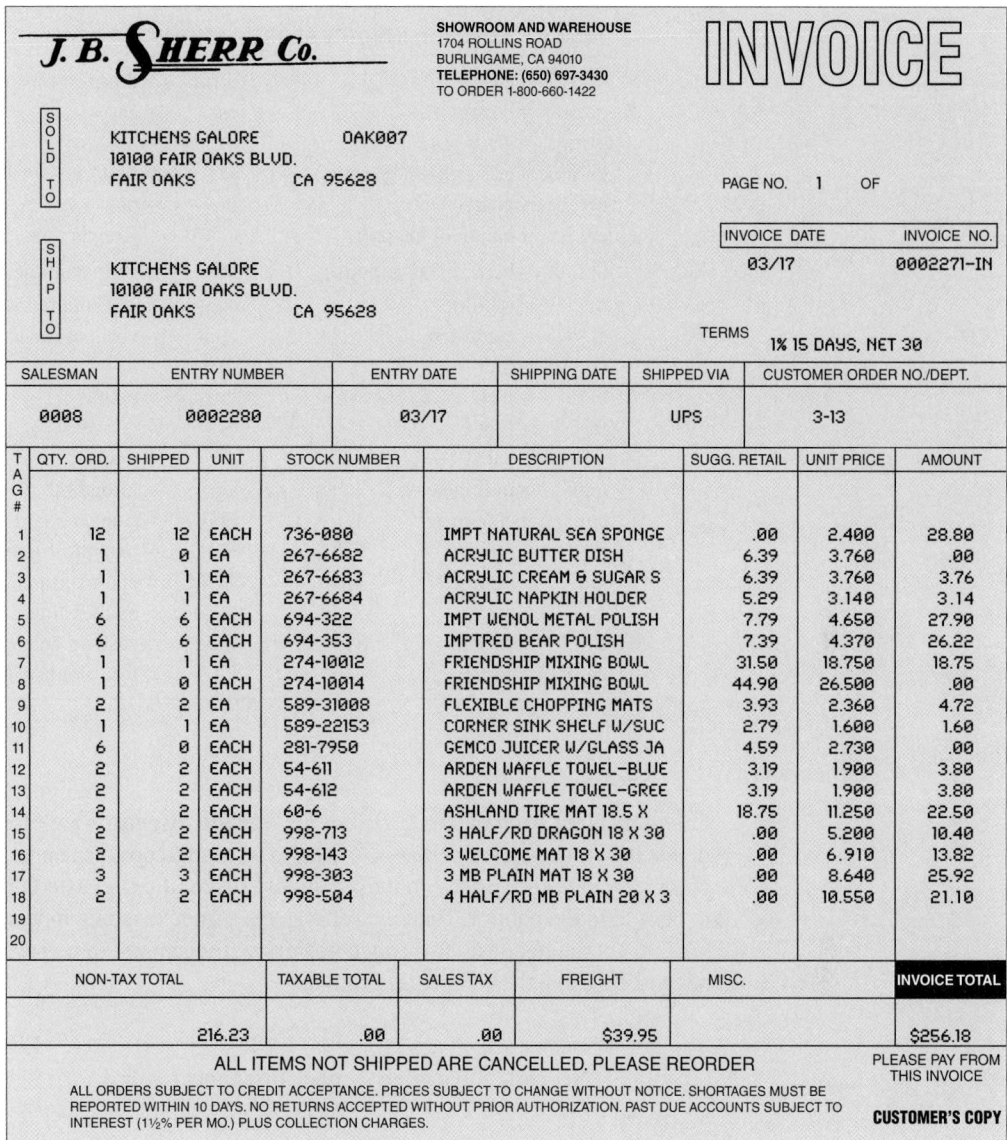

Figure 9.2

Objective

2   *Understand Common Shipping Terms.*   A common shipping term appearing on invoices is **free on board (FOB)**, followed by the words **shipping point** or **destination**. The term "FOB shipping point" means that the *buyer* pays for shipping and that ownership of the merchandise passes to the purchaser when the merchandise is given to the shipper. The term "FOB destination" means that the *seller* pays the shipping charges and retains ownership until the goods reach the destination. This distinction is important in the event that the merchandise is lost or damaged during shipment.

The shipping term **COD** means **cash on delivery**. Here, the shipper makes delivery to the purchaser on the receipt of enough cash to pay for the goods. A shipping term used when goods are moved by ship is **FAS**, which means **free alongside ship**. Here, the goods are delivered to the receiving dock with all freight charges to that point paid by the seller.

Objective

3   *Identify Invoice Abbreviations.*   A number of abbreviations are used on invoices to identify measurements, quantities of merchandise, shipping terms, and additional discounts. Those most commonly used are shown in Table 9.1. (Some of these measurements are from the metric system. These measurements often appear on invoices for imported goods.)

Table 9.1 COMMON INVOICE ABBREVIATIONS

ea.	= each	drm.	= drum
doz.	= dozen	cs.	= case
gro.	= gross (144 items)	bx.	= box
gr. gro.	= great gross (12 gross)	sk.	= sack
qt	= quart	pr.	= pair
gal	= gallon (4 quarts)	C	= Roman numeral for 100
bbl.	= barrel $\left(31\frac{1}{2} \text{ gallons}\right)$	M	= Roman numeral for 1000
mL	= milliliter	cwt.	= per hundred weight
cl	= centiliter	cpm.	= cost per thousand
L	= liter	@	= at
in.	= inch	lb	= pound
ft	= foot	oz	= ounce
yd	= yard	g	= gram
mm	= millimeter	kg	= kilogram
cm	= centimeter	FOB	= free on board
m	= meter	ROG	= receipt-of-goods
km	= kilometer	EOM	= end-of-month
ct.	= crate	ex. or x	= extra dating
cart.	= carton	COD	= cash on delivery
ctn.	= carton	FAS	= free alongside ship

Objective

4 *Calculate Net Cost and Trade Discounts.* **Trade discounts** are offered to businesses or individuals who buy an item that is to be sold or used to produce an item that will then be sold. Normally, the seller prices an item at its **list price** (the suggested price at which the item is to be sold to the public). Then the seller gives a trade discount that is subtracted from the list price to get the **net cost**, also called **net price** (the amount to be paid by the buyer). Find the net cost by using the following formula.

$$\text{Net cost} = \text{list price} - \text{trade discount} \qquad \text{or} \qquad \begin{array}{r} \textbf{List price} \\ \underline{-\ \textbf{trade discount}} \\ \textbf{net cost} \end{array}$$

NOTE The terms *net cost* and *net price* both refer to the amount paid by the buyer. However, net cost is the preferred term since this is the cost of an item to the business.

EXAMPLE 1 Calculating a Single Trade Discount

The list price to a retailer of a Shredmaster home paper shredder is $99.80, and the trade discount is 25%. Find the net cost.

Solution

First find the amount of the trade discount by taking 25% of $99.80.

$$\begin{array}{ccccc} R & \times & B & = & P \\ 25\% & \times & \$99.80 & = 0.25 \times \$99.80 = & \$24.95 \end{array}$$

Find the net cost by subtracting $24.95 from the list price of $99.80.

$$\$99.80\,(\text{list price}) - \$24.95\,(\text{trade discount}) = \$74.85\,(\text{net cost})$$

The net cost of the shredder is $74.85.

Objective

5   *Differentiate between Single and Series Discounts.* In Example 1 a **single discount** of 25% was offered. Another type of discount combines two or more discounts into a **series** or **chain discount**, also called a multiple discount. A series discount written as 20/10 means that a 20% discount is subtracted from the list price, and *from this difference* another 10% discount is subtracted.

Another discount of 15% could be attached to the series discount of 20/10, giving a new series discount of 20/10/15.

Why Trade Discounts May Change

1. *Price changes* may cause trade discounts to be raised or lowered.
2. As the *quantity purchased* increases, the discount may increase.
3. The buyer's position in *marketing channels* may determine the amount of discount offered (a wholesaler would receive a larger discount than the succeeding retailer).
4. *Geographic location* may influence the trade discount. An additional discount may be offered to increase sales in one particular area.
5. *Seasonal fluctuations* in sales may influence the trade discounts offered.
6. *Competition* from other companies may cause trade discounts to be raised or lowered.

Objective

6   *Calculate Each Series Discount Separately.* Three methods can be used to calculate a series discount and the net cost. The first of these is to *calculate each series discount separately and subtract it before finding the next discount.*

> **EXAMPLE** **2**   **Calculating Series Trade Discounts**
>
> Oaks Hardware is offered a series discount of 20/10 on a Porter-Cable cordless drill with a list price of $150. Find the net cost after the series discount.
>
> **Solution**
>
> First, find the 20% discount and subtract it from $150.
>
> $$20\% \text{ discount} = 20\% \text{ of } \$150 = \$30$$
> $$\text{Amount after } 20\% \text{ discount} = \$150 - \$30 = \$120$$
>
> Then, find the 10% discount and subtract it from the $120 amount. Notice that the 10% discount applies to the amount *after* the first discount, or to $120.
>
> $$10\% \text{ discount} = 10\% \text{ of } \$120 = \$12$$
> $$\text{Amount after both discounts} = \$120 - \$12 = \$108$$

NOTE   When finding series discounts separately, remember to apply each discount after the previous discount has been subtracted from the price.

It is important to realize that discounts in a series are never added together. For example, a series discount of 30/15 is not the same thing as a single discount of 45% (the sum of 30% and 15%). A discount of 35/15 indicates that a 35% discount is applied first. Then, a discount of 15% is applied to the amount remaining after the first discount has been subtracted.

Objective

7   *Use Complements to Calculate Series Discounts.* The second method is to *use complements.* First, find the **complement** (with respect to 1, or 100%) of each single discount. The complement with respect to 1 is found by subtracting the discount from 100%. Several examples are shown in Table 9.2. Note that you must first convert any fraction in a discount to a decimal number before subtracting from 100%. For example, $16\frac{2}{3}\%$ is first converted to 16.667 (rounded) in the table before being subtracted from 100%.

Table 9.2 TYPICAL COMPLEMENTS WITH RESPECT TO 1

Discount	Calculation	Complement	Decimal Equivalent of Complement
20%	100% − 20%	= 80%	0.80
15%	100% − 15%	= 85%	0.85
35%	100% − 35%	= 65%	0.65
$12\frac{1}{2}\%$	100% − 12.5%	= 87.5%	0.875
$16\frac{2}{3}\%$	100% − 16.667%	= 83.334%	0.833 (rounded)
$33\frac{1}{3}\%$	100% − 33.333%	= 66.667%	0.667 (rounded)

The complement of the discount is the portion actually paid. For example,

- 10% discount means 90% paid.
- 25% discount means 75% paid.
- $33\frac{1}{3}\%$ discount means $66\frac{2}{3}\%$ $\left(\frac{2}{3}\right)$ paid.
- 50% discount means 50% paid.

The **net cost equivalent**, or **percent paid**, is the product of the complements. Usually, there are only two or perhaps three complements, but there can be more.

$$\text{Net cost equivalent} = \text{first complement} \times \text{second complement} \times \cdots$$

Multiply the list price by the net cost equivalent to find the net cost.

$$\text{Net cost} = \text{list price} \times \text{net cost equivalent}$$

EXAMPLE 3 **Using Complements to Solve Series Discounts**

Kitchens Galore is offered a series discount of 20/10 on a George Foreman Grilling Machine with list price of $150. Find the net cost after the series discount.

Solution

The discounts are 20% and 10%. First, find the complement of each discount.

Discount	Complement	Decimal Form of Complement
20%	100% − 20% = 80%	0.8
10%	100% − 10% = 90%	0.9

Then, multiply *the decimal form* of the two complements to find the net cost equivalent and net cost.

$$\text{Net cost equivalent} = 0.8 \times 0.9 = 0.72$$
$$\text{Net cost} = \text{list price} \times \text{net cost equivalent}$$
$$= \$150 \quad \times \quad 0.72$$
$$= \$108$$

The discount is the difference between the list price and the net cost, or $150 − $108 = $42 in this example.

■ ■ ■ Scientific
■ ■ Calculator
　■ Approach

On many calculators you can subtract the discount percents from the list price in a series calculation. For Example 3, this would be calculated as follows:

$$150 \boxed{-} 20 \boxed{\%} \boxed{-} 10 \boxed{\%} \boxed{=} 108$$

EXAMPLE 4　Using Complements to Solve Series Discounts

The list price of a Heartland 30-inch combination gas and electric stove is $3095. Find the net cost if a series discount of 20/10/10 is offered.

Solution

Start by finding the complements with respect to 1 of each discount. Then multiply the complements to find the net cost equivalent.

20/10/10　Series discount

$$0.8 \times 0.9 \times 0.9 = \mathbf{0.648} \quad \text{Net cost equivalent}$$
$$\text{(percent paid)}$$

Complements with
respect to 1

$$\begin{aligned}
\text{Net cost} &= \text{list price} \times \text{net cost equivalent} \\
&= \$3095 \quad \times \quad \mathbf{0.648} \\
&= \$2005.56
\end{aligned}$$

$$\begin{aligned}
\text{Amount of discount} &= \text{list price} - \text{net cost} \\
&= \$3095 \quad - \$2005.56 \\
&= \$1089.44
\end{aligned}$$

NOTE　*Never round the net cost equivalent.* If a repeating decimal results, use the fraction equivalent. In Example 4, if the net cost equivalent had been rounded to 0.65, the resulting net cost would have been $2011.75 (0.65 × $3095). This error of $6.19 demonstrates the importance of not rounding the net cost equivalent.

Objective

8　*Use a Table to Find the Net Cost Equivalent of Series Discounts.* The third method is to *use a table of net cost equivalents.* For example, to use Table 9.3 for a series discount of 20/10/10, find the number located to the right of 10/10 and below 20%. The number is 0.648, the net cost equivalent for a discount of 20/10/10. Multiply this number by the list price to get the net cost.

　　The order of the discounts in the series makes no difference. A 10/20 series is the same as a 20/10 series, and a 15/10/20 series is identical to a 20/15/10 series. This is true because changing the order in which complements are multiplied does not change the net cost equivalent.

NOTE　The net cost equivalent (percent paid) found using Table 9.3 and the list price are multiplied to find the net cost.

EXAMPLE 5　Using a Table of Net Cost Equivalents

Use Table 9.3 to find the net cost equivalent for the following series discounts.

(a) 10/20　　**(b)** 10/10/40　　**(c)** 25/25/5　　**(d)** 35/20/15

Solution

(a) 0.72　　**(b)** 0.486　　**(c)** 0.534375　　**(d)** 0.442

Table 9.3 NET COST EQUIVALENTS OF SERIES DISCOUNTS

	5%	10%	15%	20%	25%	30%	35%	40%
5	0.9025	0.855	0.8075	0.76	0.7125	0.665	0.6175	0.57
10	0.855	0.81	0.765	0.72	0.675	0.63	0.585	0.54
10/5	0.81225	0.7695	0.72675	0.684	0.64125	0.5985	0.55575	0.513
10/10	0.7695	0.729	0.6885	0.648	0.6075	0.567	0.5265	0.486
15	0.8075	0.765	0.7225	0.68	0.6375	0.595	0.5525	0.51
15/10	0.72675	0.6885	0.65025	0.612	0.57375	0.5355	0.49725	0.459
20	0.76	0.72	0.68	0.64	0.6	0.56	0.52	0.48
20/15	0.646	0.612	0.578	0.544	0.51	0.476	0.442	0.408
25	0.7125	0.675	0.6375	0.6	0.5625	0.525	0.4875	0.45
25/20	0.57	0.54	0.51	0.48	0.45	0.42	0.39	0.36
25/25	0.534375	0.50625	0.478125	0.45	0.421875	0.39375	0.365625	0.3375
30	0.665	0.63	0.595	0.56	0.525	0.49	0.455	0.42
40	0.57	0.54	0.51	0.48	0.45	0.42	0.39	0.36

NOTE *Do not round any of the net cost equivalents.* Doing so will cause an error in the net cost.

9.1 | Exercises

ABBREVIATIONS ON INVOICES   What do each of the following abbreviations represent?

1. ft   foot
2. mm   millimeter
3. sk.   sack
4. qt   quart
5. gr. gro.   great gross
6. kg   kilogram
7. cs.   case
8. gro.   gross
9. drm.   drum
10. yd   yard
11. cpm.   cost per thousand
12. bbl.   barrel
13. gal   gallon
14. cwt.   per hundred weight
15. COD   cash on delivery
16. FOB   free on board

17. **USING INVOICES**   Compute each of the following extension totals, find the invoice total, and the total amount due.

HOME ACCESSORIES WHOLESALERS

Sold to: Kitchens Galore
10100 Fair Oaks Blvd.
Fair Oaks, CA 95628

Date: June 10
Order. No.: 796152
Shipped by: UPS
Terms: Net

Quantity	Order No./Description	Unit Price	Extension Total
6 doz.	pastry brush, wide	$37.80 doz.	$226.80
3 gro.	napkins, cotton	$12.60 gro.	$37.80
9 doz.	cherry pitters	$14.04 doz.	$126.36
8	food processors (3 qt.)	$106.12 ea.	$848.96
53 pr.	stainless tongs	$68.12 pr.	$3610.36
		Invoice Total	$4850.28
		Shipping and Insurance	$37.45
		Total Amount Due	$4887.73

18. USING INVOICES Compute each of the following extension totals, find the invoice total, and the total amount due.

J & K'S MUSTANG PARTS

J & K'S MUSTANG PARTS
New and Used

Sold to: Dave's Auto Body & Paint
4443-B Auburn Blvd.
Sacramento, CA 95841

Date: July 17
Order. No.: 100603
Shipped by: Emery
Terms: Net

Quantity	Order No./Description	Unit Price	Extension Total
24	filler tube gaskets	$2.25 ea.	$54.00
12 pr.	taillight lens gaskets	$4.75 pr.	$57.00
6 pr.	taillight bezels to body	$10.80 pr.	$64.80
2 gr.	door panel fasteners	$14.20 gr.	$28.40
18	bumper bolt kits	$16.50 ea.	$297.00
		Invoice Total	$501.20
		Shipping and Insurance	$23.75
		Total Amount Due	$524.95

 19. Explain the difference between "FOB shipping point" and "FOB destination." In each case, who pays for shipping? When does ownership of the merchandise transfer? (See Objective 2.)

 20. Name six items that appear on an invoice. Try to do this without looking at an invoice. (See Objective 1.)

Using complements (with respect to 1) of the single discounts, find the net cost equivalent for each of the following discounts. Use Table 9.3 for the first four problems.

21. 10/20   0.72
22. 10/10   0.81
23. 25/20/20   0.48

24. 10/15/20   0.612
25. 10/20/25   0.54
26. 40/20/10   0.432

27. 30/42$\frac{1}{2}$ 0.4025
28. 10/16$\frac{2}{3}$ 0.75
29. 20/30/5   0.532

30. 20/20/10   0.576
31. 50/10/20/5   0.342
32. 25/10/20/10   0.486

Find the net cost for each of the following. Round to the nearest cent.

33. $418 less 20/20 $267.52
34. $148 less 25/10 $99.90

35. $8.20 less 5/10 $7.01
36. $860 less 20/40 $412.80

37. $9.80 less 10/10/10 $7.14
38. $8.80 less 40/10/20 $3.80

39. $8220 less 30/5/10 $4919.67
40. $15.70 less 5/10/20 $10.74

41. $25 less 30/32$\frac{1}{2}$ $11.81
42. $590 less 10/12$\frac{1}{2}$/10 $418.16

43. $1250 less 20/20/20 $640
44. $1410 less 10/20/5 $964.44

 45. Explain the difference between a single trade discount and a series or chain trade discount. (See Objectives 4 and 5.)

 46. Identify and explain four reasons that might cause series trade discounts to change. (See Objective 5.)

 47. Explain what a complement (with respect to 1 or 100%) is. Give an example. (See Objective 7.)

 48. Using complements, explain how to find the net cost equivalent of a 25/20 series discount. Explain why a 25/10/10 series discount is not the same as a 25/20 series discount. (See Objective 7.)

Solve the following application problems in trade discount. Round to the nearest cent.

49. **DIGITAL CAMERA** The list price of a new digital camera is $399.99. If the series discount offered is 10/10/25, what is the net cost after trade discounts? $242.99

50. **ADJUSTABLE WALKERS** Roger Wheatley, a restorative nurse assistant (RNA), finds that the list price of one dozen adjustable walkers is $1680. Find the cost per walker if a series discount of 40/25 is offered. $63

51. **KITCHEN CABINETS** Modern Cabinets purchases a tile-topped wooden kitchen island list-priced at $1440. It is available at either a 10/15/10 discount or a 20/15 discount. (a) Which discount gives the lower price? (b) Find the difference in net cost. (a) 20/15 (b) $12.24

52. **TANNING SALON** Electric Beach buys a tanning gel with a list price per bottle of $17.21. Since he buys in volume for their chain of tanning salons, the purchasing manager prices the gel at two different wholesalers. One offers a 15/10/5 discount and the second offers a 15/20 discount. (a) Which discount gives the lower cost? (b) Find the difference per bottle. (a) 15/20 (b) $0.81 per bottle

53. **BULK CHEMICALS** Brazilian Chemical Supply offers a series discount of 20/20/10 on all bulk purchases. A tank (bulk) of industrial solvent is list-priced at $28,500. What is the net cost after trade discounts? $16,416

54. **KITCHEN SUPPLIES** Kitchens Galore receives a 10/5/20 series trade discount from a supplier. If it purchases 3 dozen 32-ounce smoothie makers list-priced at $468 per dozen, find the net cost. $960.34

55. **MUSIC PLAYER** This is Jennifer Rainwater's first week working as a purchaser for an electronics store. She searches for a particular portable music player and finds one priced at $107 with discounts of 20/10 at the quantity needed. She mistakenly understands 20/10 to mean a 30% discount. Find the difference in price due to this error. $2.14 for each music player

56. **BILLING ERROR** The Office Depot offers a series trade discount of 30/20 to its regular customers. Chris Hutchinson, a new man in the billing department, understood the 30/20 terms to mean 50% and computed this trade discount on a list price of $5440. How much difference did this error make in the amount of the invoice? $326.40

57. **STICKER PURCHASES** The AAA Foto and Copy Shop purchases stickers at a list price of $135 per 1000. If it receives a trade discount of $40/33\frac{1}{3}$, find the net cost of 3500 stickers. $189

58. **STATIONERY SALES** One brand of file folders is list-priced at $9.90 per dozen. A wholesale stationer offers a trade discount of 10/5/15 on the folders. Find the net cost of $5\frac{1}{2}$ dozen folders. $39.57

59. **BRASS DEADBOLTS** The list price of brass deadbolts is $9.95. A retailer has a choice of two suppliers, one offering a discount of 10/25/15 and the other offering a discount of 20/15/10. If the retailer purchases 4 dozen deadbolts, find (a) the total cost of the less expensive supplier and (b) the amount saved by selecting the lower price. (a) $274.02 (b) $18.27

60. **FIBER OPTICS** Cindy Herring has a choice of two suppliers of fiber optics for her business. Tyler Supplies offers a 20/10/25 discount on a list price of $5.70 per unit. Irving Optics offers a 30/20 series discount on a list price of $5.40 per unit. (a) Which supplier gives her the lower price? (b) How much does she save if she buys 12,500 units from the lower-priced supplier? (*Hint:* Do not round.) (a) Irving Optics (b) $750

| **9.2** | **Single Discount Equivalents** |

OBJECTIVES

1 *Express a series discount as an equivalent single discount.*

2 *Find the net cost by multiplying list price by the complements of single discounts.*

3 *Find the list price if given the series discount and the net cost.*

4 *Determine a single trade discount rate.*

5 *Find the trade discount that must be added to match a competitor's price.*

Objective

1 *Express a Series Discount as an Equivalent Single Discount.* Series or chain discounts must often be expressed as a single discount rate. Find a **single discount equivalent** to a series discount by multiplying the complements (with respect to 1 or 100%) of the individual discounts. As in the previous section, the result is the net cost equivalent. Then, subtract the net cost equivalent from 1. The result is the single discount that is equivalent to the series discount. *The single discount is expressed as a percent.*

$$\text{Single discount equivalent} = 1 - \text{net cost equivalent}$$

> **EXAMPLE 1** Finding a Single Discount Equivalent
>
> If Air Clean Manufacturing offered a 20/10 discount to wholesale accounts on all heater filters, what would be the single discount equivalent?
>
> **Solution**
>
> Find the net cost equivalent (percent paid).
>
> $$20/10$$
> $$0.8 \times 0.9 = 0.72 \quad \text{Net cost equivalent}$$
>
> Subtract the net cost equivalent from 1.
>
> $$1.00 \text{ base } (100\%) - 0.72 \text{ remains} = 0.28$$
>
> The single discount equivalent of a 20/10 series discount is 28%.

This method may also be used with the table of net cost equivalents of series discounts. For example, Table 9.3 shows 0.72 as the net cost equivalent for the series discount 20/10. The single discount is therefore 28% ($1.00 - 0.72 = 0.28 = 28\%$).

Objective

2 *Find the Net Cost by Multiplying List Price by the Complements of Single Discounts.* The net cost can also be found by multiplying the list price by the complements of each of the single discounts in a series, as shown in Example 2.

> **EXAMPLE 2** Finding the Net Cost Using Complements
>
> The list price of an oak entertainment center to a retailer is $970. Find the net cost if trade discounts of $20/15/27\frac{1}{2}$ are offered.

Solution

$$\text{Net cost} = \text{list price} \times \text{complements of individual discounts}$$

$$\text{Net cost} = \$970 \times 0.8 \times 0.85 \times 0.725$$

$$20/15/27\frac{1}{2}$$

$$= \$478.21$$

Scientific Calculator Approach

For the calculator solution to Example 2, enter the list price and multiply by the complements to find the net price.

$$970 \boxed{\times} .8 \boxed{\times} .85 \boxed{\times} .725 \boxed{=} 478.21$$

Objective

3 *Find the List Price If Given the Series Discount and the Net Cost.* Sometimes the net cost after trade discounts is known along with the series discount, and the list price must be found.

EXAMPLE 3 **Solving for List Price**

Find the list price of a Kohler kitchen sink that has a net cost of $243.20 after trade discounts of 20/20.

Solution

Use a net cost equivalent, along with knowledge of percent. Start by finding the percent paid, using complements.

$$20/20 \qquad \text{Series discount}$$

$$0.8 \times 0.8 = 0.64 \qquad \substack{\text{Net cost equivalent} \\ \text{(percent paid)}}$$

$$\substack{\text{Complements with} \\ \text{respect to 1}}$$

As the work shows, 0.64, or 64% of the list price, or $243.20, was paid. Use the basic percent equation to find the list price.

$$R \times B = P$$

$$0.64 \times \text{List price} = \$243.20$$

$$0.64 \times B = \$243.20$$

$$0.64B = \$243.20$$

$$\frac{0.64B}{0.64} = \frac{\$243.20}{0.64} = \$380 \qquad \text{List price}$$

Check the answer.

$$
\begin{array}{ll}
\$380 & \text{List price} \\
\underline{-\ 76} & (0.2 \times \$380) \\
\$304 & \\
\underline{-\ 60.80} & (0.2 \times \$304) \\
\$243.20 & \text{Net cost}
\end{array}
$$

The list price of the sink is $380.

EXAMPLE **4** **Solving for List Price**

Find the list price of a 6-foot fiberglass stepladder having a series discount of 10/30/20 and a net cost of $45.36.

Solution

Find the percent paid.

10/30/20   Series discount

$$0.9 \times 0.7 \times 0.8 = 0.504$$ Net cost equivalent (percent paid)

Complements with
respect to 1

Therefore, 0.504 of the list price is $45.36. Now use the basic percent equation.

$$R \times B = P$$

$$0.504 \times \text{List price} = \$45.36$$

$$0.504 \times B = \$45.36$$

$$0.504B = \$45.36$$

$$\frac{0.504B}{0.504} = \frac{\$45.36}{0.504} = \$90 \quad \text{List price}$$

The list price of the stepladder is $90. Check this answer as in the previous example.

NOTE Notice that Examples 3 and 4 are decrease problems similar to those shown in **Chapter 3, Section 5**. They are still base problems but may look different because the discount is now shown as a series of two or more discounts rather than a single percent decrease as in **Chapter 3**. If you need help, refer to **Section 3.5**.

Objective

4   *Determine a Single Trade Discount Rate.*

EXAMPLE **5** **Finding the Single Trade Discount Rate**

The list price of a gas-powered pressure washer is $550. If the wholesaler offers the system at a net cost of $341, find the single trade discount rate being offered.

Solution

Use the following formula.

Percent paid $\times$ list price $=$ net cost

$$P \times L = N$$

$$P \times \$550 = \$341$$

$$\$550P = \$341$$

$$\frac{550P}{550} = \frac{341}{550} = 0.62 \text{ or } 62\% \quad \text{Percent paid}$$

Since 62% is paid, the discount offered is 38% ($100\% - 62\% = 38\%$).

For an alternative approach, first find the amount of discount, or $550 - $341 = $209. Next, find the rate of discount by using the basic percent equation.

$$R \times B = P$$

$$\underline{}\% \text{ of list price is discount}$$

$$\underline{}\% \text{ of } \$550 = \$209$$

$$R \times \$550 = \$209$$

$$\$550R = \$209$$

$$\frac{550R}{550} = \frac{\$209}{550}$$

$$R = \frac{209}{550} = 0.38 = 38\%$$

By either method, the discount is 38%.

Objective

5 *Find the Trade Discount That Must Be Added to Match a Competitor's Price.*

EXAMPLE 6 **Adding a Discount to Match a Competitor's Price**

S and B Distributors offers a 20% trade discount on a good-quality digital camera list-priced at $450. What additional trade discount must be offered to match a competitor's price of $342?

Solution

First use the formula

$$P \times L = N$$

to find the single discount needed. The percent paid is found by multiplying together the complement of the 20% discount already given and the new, unknown discount.

$$0.8 \times \text{complement of additional discount} \times L = N$$

$$0.8 \times d \times \$450 = \$342$$

$$\$360d = \$342$$

$$\frac{360d}{360} = \frac{\$342}{360}$$

$$d = 0.95 \text{ or } 95\%$$

Therefore, 95% is the complement of the additional trade discount that is needed. The complement of 95% is (100% − 95%). To match the competition, S and B Distributors must give a 20/5 series discount.

9.2	**Exercises**

Find the net cost equivalent and the percent form of the single discount equivalent for each of the following series discounts.

1. 10/20   0.72; 28%

2. 10/10   0.81; 19%

3. 15/35   0.5525; 44.75%

4. 10/50   0.45; 55%

5. 20/20   0.64; 36%

6. 20/20/20   0.512; 48.8%

7. 20/20/10   0.576; 42.4%

8. 15/5/10   0.72675; 27.325%

9. 25/10   0.675; 32.5%

10. $30/37\frac{1}{2}$ 0.4375; 56.25%

11. $16\frac{2}{3}/10$ 0.75; 25%

12. 30/25   0.525; 47.5%

13. 10/10/20   0.648; 35.2%

14. 20/20/10   0.576; 42.4%

15. 55/40/10   0.243; 75.7%

16. 10/30/10   0.567; 43.3%

17. 40/25   0.45; 55%

18. 5/5/5   0.857375; 14.2625%

19. $20/12\frac{1}{2}$ 0.7; 30%

20. $10/33\frac{1}{3}$ 0.60; 40%

21. 20/10/20/10   0.5184; 48.16%

22. 10/20/25/10   0.486; 51.4%

23. 5/20/30/5   0.5054; 49.46%

24. 10/5/30/20   0.4788; 52.12%

 25. Using complements, show that the single discount equivalent of a 20/25/10 series discount is 46%. (See Objective 1.)

26. Suppose that you own a business and are offered a choice of a 10/20 trade discount or a 20/10 trade discount. Which do you prefer? Why? (See Objective 1.)

Find the list price given the net cost and the series discount.

27. Net cost, $518.40; trade discount, 20/10 $720

28. Net cost, $343.35; trade discount, 10/30 $545

29. Net cost, $279.30; trade discount, 40/5/30 $700

30. Net cost, $5250; trade discount, $25/33\frac{1}{3}$ $10,500

31. Net cost, $1313.28; trade discount, 5/10/20 $1920

32. Net cost, $2697.30; trade discount, 10/10/10 $3700

Solve the following application problems in trade discount.

33. **COMPARING DISCOUNTS**   A S'mores Maker kit has a list price of $39.95 and is offered to wholesalers with a series discount of 20/10/10. The same appliance is offered to retailers with a series discount of 20/10. (a) Find the wholesaler's price. (b) Find the retailer's price. (c) Find the difference between the two prices.   (a) $25.89 (b) $28.76 (c) $2.87

34. **COMPARING DISCOUNTS**   Kathy Miller is offered oak stair railing by The Turning Point for $1370 less 30/10. Sierra Stair Company offers the same railing for $1220 less 10/10. (a) Which offer is better? (b) How much does Miller save by taking the better offer?   (a) The Turning Point (b) $125.10

35. **PRICING POTTED PLANTS**   Irene's Plant Place paid a net price of $414.40 for a shipment of potted plants after a trade discount of 30/20 from the list price. Find the list price. $740

36. **VITAMINS, MINERALS, AND SUPPLEMENTS**   SJ's Nutrition Center received a shipment of vitamins, minerals, and diet supplements at a net cost of $1125. This cost was the result of a trade discount of 25/20 from list price. Find the list price of this shipment. $1875

37. **REFRIGERATOR**   The manufacturer's list price on an energy-saver refrigerator is $840. The manufacturer offers it to wholesalers at a series discount of 10/20/10, and directly to retailers at a series discount of 10/20. Find (a) the price to wholesalers, (b) the price to retailers, and (c) the difference between the two.   (a) $544.32 (b) $604.80 (c) $60.48

38. **VIDEOCONFERENCING DEVICE** A videoconferencing device is list-priced at $395. The manufacturer offers a series discount of 25/20/10 to wholesalers and a 25/20 series discount to retailers. (a) What is the wholesaler's price? (b) What is the retailer's price? (c) What is the difference between the prices? (a) $213.30 (b) $237 (c) $23.70

39. **SKIS** A pair of skis with a list price of $286.45 is sold by a wholesaler at a net cost of $214.84. Find the single trade discount rate being offered, rounded to the nearest tenth of a percent. 25.0%

40. **TRUCK-BED LINERS** Truck Stuff offers a fiberglass truck-bed liner at a net cost of $180. If the list price of the bed liner is $281.25, find the single trade discount rate. 36%

41. **SECURITY ALARM SYSTEMS** Capitol Alarm purchased a security alarm system at a net cost of $2733.75 and a series discount of $10/10/12\frac{1}{2}$. Find the list price. $3857.14

42. **FLAT-SCREEN TV** A 42-inch flat-screen, digital television is on sale for $447.12. Find the original list price if the series discount is 10/20/10. $690

43. **MOTOR OIL PRICING** An auto wholesaler offers a 10% trade discount on a case of oil priced at $27.60. A competitor offers the same oil at $23.60. What additional trade discount must be given to meet the competitor's price? Round to the nearest tenth of a percent. 5.0%

44. **PERSONAL COMPUTERS** A personal computer distributor has offered a computer system at a $1450 list price less a 30% trade discount. Find the additional trade discount needed to meet a competitor's net price of $933.80. 8%

9.3   Cash Discounts: Ordinary Dating Method

OBJECTIVES

1 *Calculate net cost after discounts.*

2 *Use the ordinary dating method.*

3 *Determine whether cash discounts are earned.*

4 *Use postdating when calculating cash discounts.*

5 *Determine the amount due when goods are returned.*

Objective

1 *Calculate Net Cost after Discounts.* **Cash discounts** are offered by sellers to encourage prompt payment by customers. In effect, the seller is saying, "Pay me quickly, and receive a discount." Businesses often borrow money for their day-to-day operation. Immediate cash payments from customers *decrease* the need for the seller to borrow money. However, immediate cash payments may *increase* the need for the buyer to borrow money. Still, many buyers pay in time to receive the cash discount, to lower their cost. Most businesses can *be successful only* if they control costs.

To find the net cost when a cash discount is offered, begin with the list price and subtract any trade discounts. From this amount subtract the cash discount. Use the following formula to find the net cost.

$$\text{Net cost} = (\text{list price} - \text{trade discount}) - \text{cash discount}$$

> **NOTE** If an invoice amount includes shipping and insurance charges, subtract these charges first, before a cash discount is taken. Then add them back to find net cost after the cash discount is subtracted.

The type of cash discount appears on the invoice under "Terms," which can be found in the bottom right-hand corner of the Hershey Chocolate U.S.A. invoice in Figure 9.3. Many companies using automated billing systems state the exact amount of the cash discount at the bottom of the invoice. This eliminates all calculations on the part of the buyer. The Hershey invoice is an example of an invoice stating the exact amount of the cash discount, which is found at the bottom of the invoice. However, not all businesses do this, so it is important to know how to determine cash discounts.

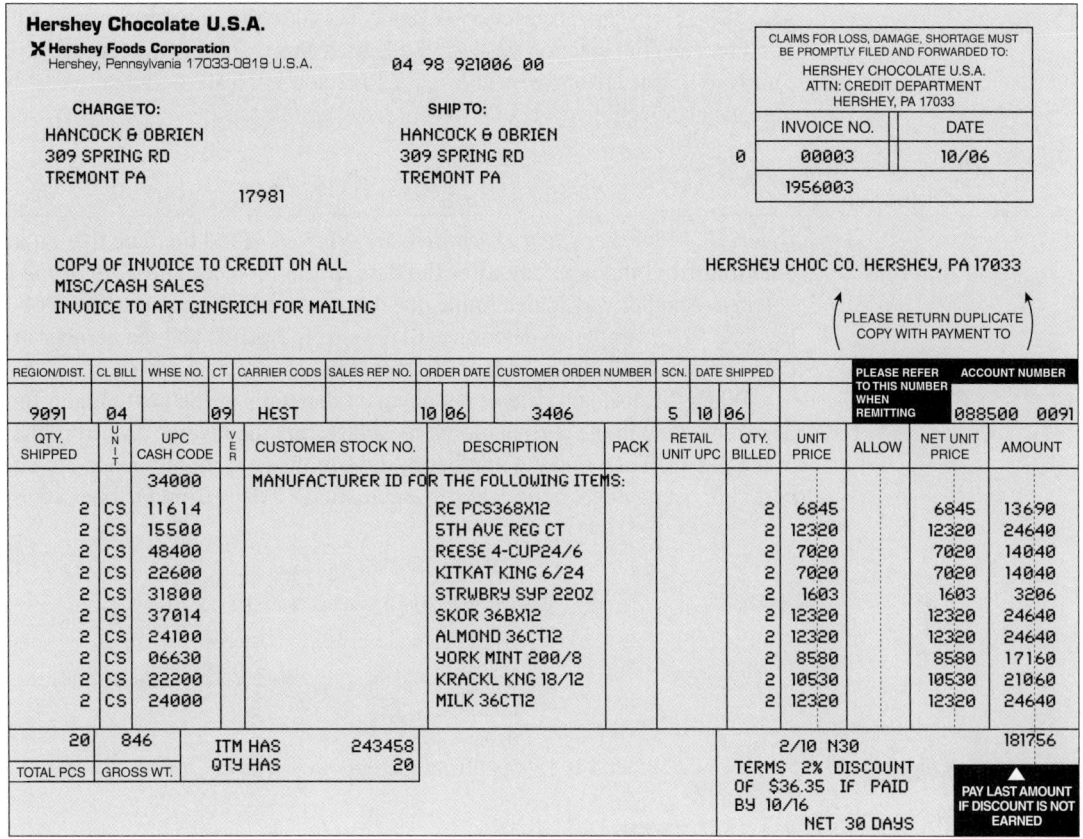

Figure 9.3

There are many methods for determining cash discounts, but nearly all these are based on the "ordinary dating method." The methods discussed in this section and the methods discussed in the next section are the ones most commonly used today.

Objective

2   *Use the Ordinary Dating Method.* The **ordinary dating method** of cash discount, for example, is expressed on an invoice as

$$2/10, \text{ n}/30 \text{ or sometimes } 2/10, \text{ net}/30$$

and is read "two ten, net thirty." The first digit is the rate of discount (2%), the second digit is the number of days allowed to take the discount (10 days), and n/30 or net/30 is the total number of days given to pay the invoice in full, if the buyer does not use the cash discount. The 2% discount may be subtracted from the amount owed if the invoice is paid within 10 days from the date of the invoice. If payment is made between the 11th and 30th days from the invoice date, the entire amount of the invoice is due. After 30 days from the date of the invoice, the invoice is considered overdue and may be subject to a late charge.

To find the due date of an invoice, use the number of days in each month given in Table 9.4.

Table 9.4 THE NUMBER OF DAYS IN EACH MONTH

30-Day Months	31-Day Months		Exception
April	January	August	February
June	March	October	(28 days normally; 29 days in leap years)
September	May	December	
November	July		

> **NOTE** Leap years occur every 4 years. They are the same as Summer Olympic years and presidential election years in the United States. If a year is evenly divisible by the number 4, it is a leap year. The years 2012 and 2016 are both leap years because they are evenly divisible by 4.

Objective

3 *Determine Whether Cash Discounts Are Earned.* Find the date that an invoice is due by counting from the next day after the date of the invoice. *The date of the invoice is never counted.* Another way to determine due dates is to add the given number of days to the starting date. For example, to determine 10 days from April 7, add the number of days to the date $(7 + 10 = 17)$. The due date, or 10 days from April 7, is April 17.

When the discount date or net payment date falls in the next month, find the number of days remaining in the current month by subtracting the invoice date from the number of days in the month. Then find the number of days in the next month needed to equal the discount period or net payment period. For example, find 15 days from October 20 as follows.

31	Days in October
$-$ 20	The beginning date, October 20
11	Days remaining in October
$+$ 4	Additional days needed in November to equal 15 days
15	Days

Finally, November 4 is 15 days from October 20.

EXAMPLE 1 **Finding Cash Discount Dates**

A Hershey Chocolate invoice is dated January 2 and offers terms of 2/10, net 30. Find (a) the last date on which the 2% discount may be taken and (b) the net payment date.

Solution

(a) Beginning with the invoice date, January 2, the last date for taking the discount is January 12 $(2 + 10)$.

(b) The net payment date is February 1 (29 days remaining in January plus 1 day in February).

EXAMPLE 2 **Finding the Amount Due on an Invoice**

An invoice received by Bass Bait Shop for $840 is dated July 1 and offers terms of 2/10, n/30. If the invoice is paid on July 8 and the FOB shipping and insurance charges are $18.70, find the total amount due.

Solution

The 2/10 means that the discount of 2% applies only if the invoice is paid within 10 days of the invoice date. The discount of 2% does apply, since the invoice date is July 1 and the invoice was paid on July 8, or only 7 days after the invoice date.

$$\text{Amount due} = \text{invoice amount} - \text{cash discount of } 2\%$$
$$= \$840 \qquad\qquad - \$840 \times 0.02$$
$$= \$823.20$$

However, shipping and insurance charges must be added to find the total amount due.

Shipping and insurance

$$\text{Total amount due} = \$823.20 + \$18.70 = \$841.90$$

Complements can also be used to work Example 2. A discount of 2% means that the complement of 2%, or 98% (100% − 2%) of the invoice amount must be paid. Find the total amount due as follows.

Invoice amount		Complement of 2%		Shipping charge		Total due
$840	×	0.98	+	$18.70	=	$841.90

> **NOTE** A cash discount is never taken on shipping and insurance charges. Be certain that shipping and insurance charges are excluded from the invoice amount before calculating the cash discount. Shipping and insurance charges must then be added back to find the total amount due.

Objective

4 *Use Postdating When Calculating Cash Discounts.* In the ordinary dating method, the cash discount date and net payment date are both counted from the date of the invoice. Occasionally, the seller places a date later than the actual invoice date, sometimes labeling it **"as of."** This is called **postdating**. Notice that the Jacob Hardware Co. invoice in Figure 9.4 is dated "07/25 as of 08/01." The cash discount period and the net payment date are counted from 08/01 (August 1). This results in giving additional time for the purchaser to pay the invoice and receive the discount. The date due (9/10) is the due date on the invoice. The phrase "terms: 8%/10 EOM" is explained in **Sections 9.4.**

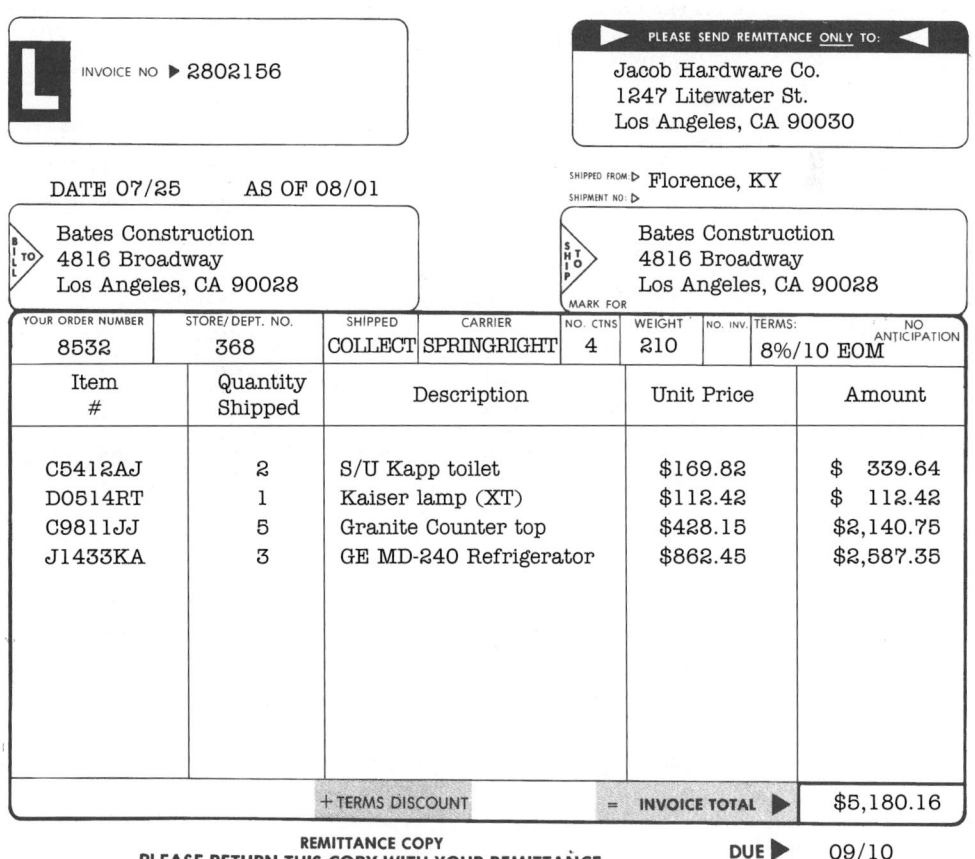

Figure 9.4

> **EXAMPLE** **3** **Using Postdating "as of" with Invoices**
>
> An invoice for some Henckles Cutlery from Germany is dated October 21 AS OF November 1 with terms of 3/15, n/30. Find (a) the last date on which the cash discount may be taken and (b) the net payment date.
>
> **Solution**
>
> **(a)** Beginning with the postdate (AS OF) of November 1, the last date for taking the discount is November 16 (1 + 15).
> **(b)** The net payment date is December 1 (29 days remaining in November and 1 day in December).

Sometimes a sliding scale of cash discounts is offered. For example, consider terms of 3/10, 2/20, 1/30, n/60. The buyer will receive only one of these discounts and then only if paid by the time required. Here is how to interpret terms of 3/10, 2/20, 1/30, n/60.

Term	Discount	If Payment Received
3/10	3%	In the first 10 days from date of invoice
2/20	2%	Between 11 days and 20 days from date of invoice
1/30	1%	Between 21 days and 30 days from date of invoice
n/60	0%	Between 31 days and 60 days from date of invoice

The full amount must be paid no later than 60 days from the date of the invoice or it will be overdue and may be subject to a penalty.

> **EXAMPLE** **4** **Determining Cash Discount Due Dates**
>
> An invoice from Cellular Products is dated May 18 and offers terms of 4/10, 3/25, 1/40, n/60. Find (a) the three final dates for cash discounts and (b) the net payment date.
>
> **Solution**
>
> **(a)** The three final cash discount dates are as follows.
>
> 4% if paid by May 28 (10 days from May 18)
> 3% if paid by June 12 (25 days from May 18)
> 1% if paid by June 27 (40 days from May 18)
>
> **(b)** The net payment date is July 17 (20 days beyond the cash discount period).

Never take more than one of the cash discounts. *With all methods of giving cash discounts, if the net payment period is not given, the net payment due date is assumed to be 20 days beyond the cash discount period.* After that date, the invoice is considered overdue. If either the final discount date or the net payment date is on a Sunday or holiday, the next business day is used. Many companies insist that payment is made when it is received. It is general practice, however, to consider payment made when it is mailed.

Objective

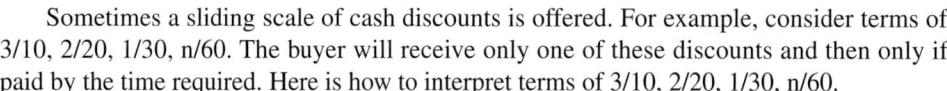

5 *Determine the Amount Due When Goods Are Returned.* A buyer receiving incorrect or damaged merchandise may return the goods to the seller. The value of the returned goods must be subtracted from the amount of the invoice before calculating the cash discount.

EXAMPLE 5 **Finding the Amount Due When Goods Are Returned**

An invoice from Homeproducts.com amounts to $380, is dated March 9, and offers terms of 4/10, net 30. If $75 of goods are returned and the invoice is paid on March 17, what amount is due?

Solution

The invoice was paid 8 days after its date ($17 - 9 = 8$), so the 4% cash discount is taken. The discount is taken on $305.

$380 (invoice amount) $-$ $75 (goods returned) $=$ $305 (goods retained)

The cash discount is subtracted from the $305. Since $305 \times 0.04 = 12.20$, the amount due is

$305 (goods retained) $-$ $12.20 (cash discount) $=$ $292.80 (amount due)

9.3	Exercises

Find the final discount date and the net payment date for each of the following problems. Assume none of these are leap years.

	Invoice Date	As of	Terms	
1.	Oct. 8		3/10, n/30	Oct. 18; Nov. 7
2.	April 12		2/10, n/30	April 22; May 12
3.	Feb. 25	Mar. 10	3/15, n/20	Mar. 25; Mar. 30
4.	Nov. 7	Nov. 18	3/10, n/30	Nov. 28; Dec. 18
5.	Sept. 11		4/10, n/60	Sept. 21; Nov. 10
6.	Mar. 23		2/10, n/30	April 2; April 22
7.	Jan. 14		2/10, n/60	Jan. 24; Mar. 15
8.	Oct. 3		3/10, n/15	Oct. 13; Oct. 18
9.	Dec. 7	Jan. 5	5/15, n/60	Jan. 20; Mar. 6
10.	July 31	Aug. 15	3/10, n/30	Aug. 25; Sept. 14

Solve for the amount of discount and the amount due on each of the following invoices.

	Invoice Amount	Invoice Date	Terms	Shipping and Insurance	Goods Returned	Date Invoice Paid	
11.	$151.35	June 6	2/10 net 30	$12.58		June 15	$3.03; $160.90
12.	$66.10	Mar. 8	6/10, n/30	$4.39		Mar. 14	$3.97; $66.52
13.	$96.06	Nov. 30	net 30	$5.22		Dec. 20	$0; $101.28
14.	$148	July 19	3/15, 1/25, n/60	$7.45		Aug. 16	$0; $155.45
15.	$724	Jan. 20	5/10, 2/20, n/30	$38.14		Feb. 5	$14.48; $747.66
16.	$1282	July 1	4/15, n/40	$21.40		July 7	$51.28; $1252.12
17.	$780.70	May 5	net 30	$3.80	$125	June 1	$0; $659.50
18.	$162	Jan. 15	2/15, net 30	$8.18	$12	Jan. 23	$3; $155.18
19.	$635	Oct. 10	5/10, n/30	$53.18	$52	Oct. 18	$29.15; $607.03
20.	$1623.08	Nov. 12	2/10, n/30	$122.14	$187	Nov. 25	$0; $1558.22

21. Describe the difference between a trade discount and a cash discount. Why are cash discounts offered? (See Objective 1.)

22. Using 2/10, n/30 as an example, explain what an ordinary cash discount means. (See Objective 2.)

Solve the following application problems.

23. HOME BAKING   Grainworks Supply offers cash discounts of 2/10, 1/15, net 30 to all customers. An invoice dated May 18 amounting to $2010.70 is paid on June 1. Find the amount needed to pay the invoice. $1990.59

24. ELECTRICAL SUPPLIES   A shipment of electrical supplies is received from the Lyskovo Electrotechnical Works located in Russia. The invoice is dated March 8, amounts to $6824.58, and has terms of 2/15, 1/20 as of March 20. Find the amount needed to pay the invoice on April 2. $6688.09

25. AGRICULTURAL PRODUCTS   Agricultural Wholesale Products offers customers a trade discount of 10/20/5 on all products, with terms of net 30. Find the customer's price for products with a total list price of $986 if the invoice was paid within 30 days. $674.42

26. FISHING EQUIPMENT   Joe Nejad received an invoice for $586.12 for fishing tackle. The invoice was dated February 21, as of March 4, with terms of 4/10, 3/30, n/60. Find the total amount necessary to pay the invoice in full on March 22. $568.54

27. COMPUTERS   A high-speed work station with dual processing chips and 10 gigabytes of memory has a list price of $2140 but sells to distributors with trade discounts of 15/10 and terms of 4/15, n/30. If the retailer receives all discounts, find the net cost to the retailer. $1571.62

28. HOME FURNACE   A manufacturer of home furnaces lists an ultra-high-efficiency model for $3900 with trade discounts to a wholesaler of 10/5 and terms of 3/20, n/60. The invoice is dated July 30 and the wholesaler pays the invoice on August 10. Find the net cost. $3234.47

29. SNOWMOBILE   The list price of a popular brand of snowmobile is $5190. If a dealer can obtain trade discounts of 10/20/30 and cash terms of 4/10, n/30, find the lowest possible net cost. $2511.13

30. TEACHING EQUIPMENT   Teacher Supplies Co. offers a trade discount to school districts that have not bought from the company previously. The discount is 10/20/5 on all products, with terms of net 30. Find the customer's price for products with a total list price of $12,342 if the invoice was paid within 30 days. $8441.93

31. NUTRITIONAL PRODUCTS   Village Nutrition offers retailers a trade discount of 10/20/10 on all purchases, with terms of 3/10, n/30. If the total list price of an order is $3215.80, find the retailers' net cost if both discounts are earned. $2021.32

32. GEORGE FOREMAN GRILL   A George Foreman Jumbo Grill plus a free Toastmaster Ultravection oven is list-priced at $140 with a trade discount of 20/5/10 and terms of 4/10, n/30. Find the cost assuming that both discounts are earned. $91.93

33. RECREATION PRODUCTS   An invoice from Tower Recreation is dated April 14 and offers terms of 6/10, 4/20, 1/30, n/50. Find (a) the three final discount dates and (b) the net payment date.   (a) April 24; May 4; May 14 (b) June 3

34. INVOICE TERMS   An invoice with terms of 4/15, 3/20, 1/30, n/60 is dated September 4. Find (a) the three final discount dates and (b) the net payment date.   (a) Sept. 19; Sept. 24; Oct. 4 (b) Nov. 3

35. INVOICE TERMS   Joe's Pizza receives an invoice dated March 28 AS OF April 5 with terms of 4/20, n/30. Find (a) the final discount date and (b) the net payment date.   (a) April 25 (b) May 5

36. AS OF DATING   An invoice is dated May 20 AS OF June 5 with terms of 2/10, n/30. Find (a) the final discount date and (b) the net payment date.   (a) June 15 (b) July 5

37. **NURSERY SUPPLIES**   Valley Nursery received an invoice for supplies amounting to $3724.40. The invoice is dated October 19 AS OF November 10 and offers terms of 2/20, n/40. Find the amount necessary to pay in full on November 28 if $104.50 worth of supplies are returned. $3547.50

38. **INTERIOR DESIGN**   Sarah Bryn Interiors received an invoice for drapery hardware amounting to $218.80. The invoice is dated July 12 AS OF July 20 and offers terms of 3/20, n/60. Find the amount necessary to pay in full on August 3 if $24.30 worth of goods are returned. $188.67

39. **APPLIANCE REPAIRS**   An invoice received by Capital Appliance for repair parts amounts to $3322.80. The invoice is dated August 22 AS OF September 10 and offers terms of 4/10, 2/20, n/30. Find the amount necessary to pay in full on September 26 if $152.80 worth of goods are returned. $3106.60

40. **CHILDREN'S RETAILER**   An invoice received by Sydney's Baby Barn amounts to $380.50. The invoice is dated October 25 AS OF November 2 and offers terms of 3/15, n/30. Find the amount necessary to pay in full on November 18 if $56.50 worth of goods are returned. $324

 41. How do you remember the number of days in each month of the year? List the months and the number of days in each.

 42. Explain how "AS OF" dating (postdating) works. Why is it used? (See Objective 4.)

9.4	**Cash Discounts: Other Dating Methods**

OBJECTIVES

 1 *Solve cash discount problems with end-of-month dating.*

 2 *Use receipt-of-goods dating to solve cash discount problems.*

 3 *Use extra dating to solve cash discount problems.*

 4 *Determine credit given for partial payment of an invoice.*

In addition to the ordinary dating method of cash discounts, there are several other cash discount methods that are in common use.

Objective

1   *Solve Cash Discount Problems with End-of-Month Dating.*   **End-of-month dating** and **proximo dating**, abbreviated **EOM** and **prox.**, are both treated the same way. For example, both "3/10 EOM" and "3/10 prox." mean that a 3% cash discount may be taken if payment is made within 10 days. *However,* the 10 days are counted from the end of the month in which the invoice is dated. For example, an invoice dated July 14 with terms of 3/10 EOM would have a discount date 10 days from the end of the month, or August 10.

Since this is a method of increasing the length of time during which a discount may be taken, it has become common business practice with EOM and prox. dating to *add a month when the date of an invoice is the 26th of the month or later.* For example, if an invoice is dated March 25 and the discount offered is 3/10 prox., the last date on which the discount may be taken is April 10. ***However, if the invoice is dated March 26 (or any later day in March) and the cash discount offered is 3/10 prox., then the last date on which the discount may be taken is May 10.***

> **NOTE** The practice of adding an extra month when the invoice is dated the 26th of a month or after is used *only* with the end-of-month (proximo) dating cash discount. It does *not* apply to any of the other cash discount methods.

EXAMPLE 1 Using End-of-Month Dating

An invoice from Harley-Davidson is dated June 10, with terms of 3/20 EOM. Find (a) the final date on which the cash discount may be taken and (b) the net payment date.

Solution

(a) Terms of 3/20 EOM mean that a 3% discount applies if payment is made within 20 days of the end of the month of the invoice date. So, the last date on which the discount applies is July 20.

(b) When no net payment due date is given, allow 20 days after the last discount date. Therefore, the net payment date is August 9, or 20 days after the last discount date of July 20.

> **NOTE** With all methods of cash discounts, if the net payment period is not given, the net payment due date is assumed to be 20 days beyond the cash discount date.

EXAMPLE 2 Understanding Proximo Dating

Find the amount due on an invoice of $8520 for several iPhones that is dated August 3 if terms are 1/10 prox. and the invoice is paid on September 4.

Solution

The last date on which the discount may be taken is September 10 (10 days after the end of August). The discount of 1% applies since September 4 is within the discount period.

$$\text{Amount due} = \text{invoice amount} - \text{cash discount of } 1\%$$
$$= \$8520 \qquad - 1\% \text{ of } \$8520$$
$$= \$8520 \qquad - 0.01 \times \$8520$$
$$= \$8434.80$$

Objective

2 *Use Receipt-of-Goods Dating to Solve Cash Discount Problems.* **Receipt-of-goods dating,** abbreviated **ROG**, offers discounts determined from the date the goods are actually received. This method is often used when shipping time is long. The invoice might arrive overnight by mail, but the goods may take several weeks. Under the ROG method of cash discount, the buyer is given time to receive and inspect the merchandise and then benefit from a cash discount. For example, the discount "3/15 ROG" allows a 3% cash discount if paid within 15 days from receipt of goods. If the invoice was dated March 5 and goods were received on April 7, the last date to take the 3% cash discount is April 22 (April 7 plus 15 days). The net payment date, since it is not stated, is 20 days after the last discount date, or May 12 (April 22 plus 20 days).

EXAMPLE 3 Using Receipt-of-Goods Dating

Java City received an invoice dated December 12, with terms of 2/10 ROG. The goods were received on January 2. Find (a) the final date on which the cash discount may be taken and (b) the net payment date.

Solution

(a) The discount date is January 12 (10 days after receipt of goods, January 2 + 10 days).
(b) The net payment date is February 1 (20 days after the last discount date).

EXAMPLE 4 Working with ROG Dating

Stabel Printing receives an invoice for $485 for printing supplies. The terms are 3/10 ROG, the invoice is dated June 8, and goods are received June 18. The invoice is paid on June 30. Find the amount due.

Solution

The last date to take the 3% cash discount is June 28, 10 days after June 18. Since the invoice is paid on June 30, 2 days after the last discount date, no cash discount may be taken. The entire amount of the invoice must be paid.

$$\text{Amount due} = \text{invoice amount} - \$0 \text{ discount}$$
$$= \$485 \quad\quad - \quad\quad \$0$$
$$= \$485$$

Objective

3 *Use Extra Dating to Solve Cash Discount Problems.* **Extra dating**, abbreviated **extra**, **ex.**, or **x**, gives the buyer additional time to take a cash discount. For example, the discount "2/10-50 extra" or "2/10-50 ex." or "2/10-50 x" allows a 2% cash discount if paid within (10 + 50) or 60 days from the date of the invoice. The discount is expressed as 2/10-50 ex. (rather than 2/60) to show that the 50 days are *extra*, or in addition to the normal 10 days offered.

There are several reasons for using extra dating. A supplier might extend the discount period during a slack season to generate more sales or perhaps to gain a competitive advantage. For example, the seller might offer Christmas merchandise with extra dating to allow the buyer to take the cash discount after the holiday selling period.

EXAMPLE 5 Using Extra Dating

An invoice for paint accessories is dated November 23 with terms 2/10–50 ex. Find (a) the final date on which the cash discount may be taken and (b) the net payment date.

Solution

(a) The discount date is January 22 (7 days remaining in November + 31 days in December = 38; thus, 22 more days are needed in January to total 60).
(b) The net payment date is February 11 (20 days after the last discount date).

EXAMPLE 6 **Understanding Extra Dating**

An invoice from KitchenAid is dated August 5, amounts to $2250, offers terms of 3/10–30 x, and is paid on September 12. Find the net payment.

Solution

The last day to take the 3% cash discount is September 14 (August 5 + 40 days = September 14). Since the invoice is paid on September 12, the 3% discount may be taken. The 3% cash discount is computed on $2250, the amount of the invoice.

$$3\% \times \$2250 = 0.03 \times \$2250 = \$67.50$$

The discount to be taken is $67.50. The cash discount is subtracted from the invoice amount to determine the amount of payment.

$$\$2250 \text{ (invoice amount)} - \$67.50 \text{ (cash discount)} = \$2182.50 \text{ (amount of payment)}$$

When customers pay invoices quickly, there is less need for a business to borrow money. In certain industries it is common to deduct interest that would have to be paid on borrowed money from the invoice amount. To do this, the company uses the current rate of interest and calculates the amount of interest over the remaining days on which the cash discount is allowable. This deduction, known as **anticipation**, is taken in addition to the cash discount earned. Anticipation involves the use of simple interest, which is discussed in **Chapter 12**.

Objective

4 *Determine Credit Given for Partial Payment of an Invoice.* Occasionally, a customer may pay only a portion of the total amount due on an invoice. If this **partial payment** is made within a discount period, the customer is entitled to a discount on the portion of the invoice that is paid.

If the terms of an invoice are 3%, 10 days, then only 97% (100% − 3%) of the invoice amount must be paid during the first 10 days. So, for each $0.97 paid, the customer is entitled to $1.00 of credit. When a partial payment is made, the credit given for the partial payment is found by dividing the partial payment by the complement of the cash discount percent. Then, to find the balance due, subtract the credit given from the invoice amount. The cash discount is found by subtracting the partial payment from the credit given.

EXAMPLE 7 **Finding Credit for Partial Payment**

Dave's Body and Paint receives an invoice for $1140, dated March 8, that offers terms of 2/10 proximo. A partial payment of $450 is made on April 5. Find (a) the amount credited for the partial payment, (b) the balance due on the invoice, and (c) the cash discount earned.

Solution

(a) The cash discount is earned on the $450 partial payment made on April 5 (April 10 was the last discount date).

$$100\% - 2\% = 98\% = 0.98$$

$$\text{Amount paid} = 0.98 \times \text{credit given}$$

$$\$450 = 0.98 \times C$$

$$\$450 = 0.98C$$

$$\frac{\$450}{0.98} = \frac{0.98C}{0.98}$$

$$\frac{\$450}{0.98} = C$$

$$= \$459.18 \quad \text{Credit given (rounded)}$$

(b) Balance due = invoice amount − credit given

= $1140 − $459.18

= $680.82

(c) Cash discount = credit given − partial payment

= $459.18 − $450

= $9.18

Scientific Calculator Approach

A calculator solution to Example 7 will include these three steps.

(a) First, find the amount of credit given.

450 ÷ 0.98 = 459.189 (rounded)

(b) Next, store the amount of credit and subtract this amount from the invoice amount to find the balance due.

STO 1140 − RCL = 680.82 (rounded)

(c) Finally, subtract the partial payment from the amount of credit given to find the cash discount.

RCL − 450 = 9.18 (rounded)

NOTE Cash discounts are important, and a business should make the effort to pay invoices early to earn the cash discounts. In many cases the money saved through cash discounts has a great effect on the profitability of a business. Often companies will borrow money to enable them to take advantage of cash discounts. The mathematics of this type of loan is discussed in **Section 12.1**, "Basics of Simple Interest."

The cash discounts discussed here are normally not used when selling to foreign customers or purchasing from foreign suppliers. Instead, other types of discounts may be offered to reduce the price of goods sold to foreign buyers. These discounts may be given as allowances for tariffs paid (import duties) by the customer, reimbursement for shipping, and insurance paid by the customer or in the form of an advertising allowance.

9.4	**Exercises**

Find the discount date and net payment date for each of the following (the net payment date is 20 days after the final discount date).

	Invoice Date	Terms	Date Goods Received	
1.	Feb. 8	3/10 EOM		Mar. 10; Mar. 30
2.	May 17	6/30 EOM		June 30; July 20
3.	July 14	2/15 ROG	Sept. 3	Sept. 18; Oct. 8
4.	Oct. 30	1/10 ROG	Dec. 12	Dec. 22; Jan. 11
5.	Nov. 22	1/10–20 x		Dec. 22; Jan. 11
6.	April 12	3/15–50 x		June 16; July 6

	Invoice Date	Terms	Date Goods Received	
7.	June 26	2/10 EOM		Aug. 10; Aug. 30
8.	Sept. 27	3/15 prox.		Nov. 15; Dec. 5
9.	July 6	2/20 ROG	Aug. 4	Aug. 24; Sept. 13
10.	Jan. 15	3/15 ROG	Feb. 5	Feb. 20; Mar. 12

Solve for the amount of discount and the amount due on each of the following.

	Invoice Amount	Invoice Date	Terms	Date Goods Received	Date Invoice Paid	
11.	$682.28	June 4	3/20 ROG	July 25	Aug. 10	$20.47; $661.81
12.	$356.20	May 17	3/15 prox.		June 12	$10.69; $345.51
13.	$194.04	Aug. 22	5/10–60 ex.		Nov. 5	$0; $194.04
14.	$9240.40	Jan. 8	1/20 ROG	Mar. 10	Mar. 23	$92.40; $9148
15.	$2960	Oct. 31	2/10 EOM		Dec. 5	$59.20; $2900.80
16.	$127.50	Feb. 17	3/20 ROG	Mar. 19	Apr. 10	$0; $127.50
17.	$4220	Oct. 4	4/15 prox.		Nov. 10	$168.80; $4051.20
18.	$256.50	July 17	3/10–40 extra		Sept. 2	$7.70; $248.80
19.	$12.38	Mar. 29	2/15 ROG	April 15	April 30	$0.25; $12.13
20.	$11,480	April 6	2/15 prox.		April 30	$229.60; $11,250.40
21.	$3250.60	Oct. 17	3/15–20 x		Oct. 20	$97.52; $3153.08
22.	$8318	June 9	3/20 EOM		July 18	$249.54; $8068.46
23.	$1708.18	Nov. 13	4/10 prox.		Dec. 10	$68.33; $1639.85
24.	$13,728.34	April 6	2/10 ROG	April 28	May 6	$274.57; $13,453.77

 25. Quite often there is no mention of a net payment date on an invoice. Explain the common business practice when no net payment date is given. (See Objective 1.)

 26. Describe why receipt-of-goods dating (ROG) is offered to customers. Use an example in your description. (See Objective 2.)

Find the credit given and the balance due on the invoice after making the following partial payments.

	Invoice Amount	Invoice Date	Terms	Date Invoice Paid	Partial Payment	
27.	$3150	Jan. 9	2/10 EOM	Feb. 8	$1862	$1900; $1250
28.	$484	June 6	5/10–30 x	July 10	$209	$220; $264
29.	$1750	Aug. 12	5/10–30 x	Sept. 15	$684	$720; $1030
30.	$920	Jan. 11	3/10, 2/15, n/30	Jan. 23	$450.80	$460; $460
31.	$160	Dec. 8	3/10, n/30	Dec. 15	$97	$100; $60
32.	$8120	Oct. 4	4/20 prox.	Nov. 15	$2016	$2100; $6020

 33. Write a short explanation of partial payment. Why would a company accept a partial payment? Why would a customer make a partial payment? (See Objective 4.)

 34. Of all the different types of cash discounts presented in this section, which type seemed most interesting to you? Explain your reasons.

Solve the following application problems in cash and trade discounts.

35. BATHROOM DECOR An invoice received by Bath and Home is dated August 18 with terms of 2/15 EOM. Find (a) the final date on which the discount may be taken and (b) the net payment date. (a) Sept. 15 (b) Oct. 5

36. RADIATOR SUPPLIES An invoice from Steamer's Radiator Supply is dated February 23 with terms of 3/20 ROG and the goods are received on March 2. Find (a) the final date on which the cash discount may be taken and (b) the net payment date. (a) Mar. 22 (b) Apr. 11

37. GLASS REPAIR SUPPLIES An invoice from Carmichael Glass is dated November 11 with terms of 3/20 ROG and the goods are received on December 3. Find (a) the final date on which the cash discount may be taken and (b) the net payment date. (a) Dec. 23 (b) Jan. 12

38. TOYOTA Find the amount due on an invoice of $283,480 for several Toyotas with terms of 1/20 ROG. The invoice is dated October 20, goods are received on December 1, and the invoice is paid on December 20. $280,645.20

39. STAINED GLASS SUPPLIES An invoice received from the Stained Glass Exchange is dated June 16 with terms of 2/10 prox. Find (a) the final date on which the cash discount may be taken and (b) the net payment date. (a) July 10 (b) July 30

40. LIGHTING SALES Lamps For Less receives an invoice amounting to $5832 with cash terms of 3/10 prox. and dated August 9. If a partial payment of $3350 is made on August 15, find (a) the credit given for the partial payment and (b) the balance due on the invoice. (a) $3453.61 (b) $2378.39

41. CERAMIC DINNERWARE Fiesta, a dinnerware manufacturer, offers terms of 2/10–30 x to stimulate slow sales in the winter months. Kitchens Galore purchased $2382.58 worth of dinnerware and was offered the above terms. If the invoice was dated November 3, find (a) the final date on which the cash discount may be taken and (b) the amount paid if the discount was earned. (a) Dec. 13 (b) $2334.93

42. RACING BIKE An ultralightweight racing bicycle has a list price of $3850. The invoice is dated September 28 and has terms of 3/10–50 x. The invoice is paid on November 25. Find the amount due. $3734.50

43. CANADIAN FOOD PRODUCTS Abigail Shellist, a wholesaler of Canadian food products, offers terms of 4/15–40 ex. to encourage the sales of her products. In a recent order, a retailer purchased $9864.18 worth of Canadian foods and was offered the above terms. If the invoice was dated March 10, find (a) the final date on which the cash discount may be taken and (b) the amount paid if the discount was earned. (a) May 4 (b) $9469.61

44. FIREFIGHTING EQUIPMENT Bacon County bought some new firefighting equipment. The invoice for the equipment shows a list price of $151,600, was dated August 20, and is offered with terms of 2/20 ROG. If the equipment was received on September 20 and the invoice was paid on October 8, find the amount due. $148,568

45. INVOICE PARTIAL PAYMENT An invoice amounting to $1920 is dated July 23 by Lexington Foot Locker and offers cash terms of 6/30–120 x. If a partial payment of $940 is made on November 28, find (a) the credit given for the partial payment and (b) the balance due on the invoice. (a) $1000 (b) $920

46. CUSTOM WHEELS Scott Ryder purchased several 19-inch and 21-inch custom wheels for his performance auto parts store and was offered a cash discount of 2/10 EOM. The invoice amounted to $7218.80 and was dated June 2. The wheels were received 7 days later, and the invoice was paid on July 7. Find the amount necessary to pay the invoice in full. $7074.42

47. **ENGLISH SOCCER EQUIPMENT** An invoice dated December 8 is received with a shipment of soccer equipment from England on April 18 of the following year. The list price of the equipment is $2538, with allowed series discounts of 25/10/10. If cash terms of sale are 3/15 ROG, find the amount necessary to pay in full on April 21. $1495.58

48. **WATERFORD CRYSTAL** William Glen receives an invoice for some Waterford Crystal from Ireland amounting to $3628.10 and dated May 17. The terms of the invoice are 5/20–90 x and the invoice is paid on September 2. Find the amount necessary to pay the invoice in full. $3446.69

49. **BEAUTY SUPPLIES** Michael Anderson Beauty Supplies offers series discounts of 15/10 with terms of 5/15–30 x. On an invoice dated June 4 for items list-priced at $128, find the amount necessary to pay the invoice in full on July 15. $93.02

50. **COPY SUPPLIES** A small college bookstore receives an invoice amounting to $388.20 with terms of 8/10, net/30 and dated August 20 AS OF September 1. If a partial payment of $225 is made on September 8, find (a) the credit given for the partial payment and (b) the balance due on the invoice.   (a) $244.57 (b) $143.63

51. **FROZEN DESSERT SHOP** The Frozen Dessert Shop receives an invoice amounting to $526.80 with terms of 2/20 prox. and dated October 5. If a partial payment of $300 is made on November 12, find (a) the credit given for the partial payment and (b) the balance due on the invoice.   (a) $306.12 (b) $220.68

52. **CUSTOM HOMES** An invoice of $7819.20 with terms of 4/10 prox. is received by Penny Carter Construction and is dated May 2. If a partial payment of $6000 is made on May 8, find (a) the credit given for the partial payment and (b) the balance due on the invoice.   (a) $6250 (b) $1569.20

53. **PARTIAL INVOICE PAYMENT** An invoice received for some precision hand tools from Germany has terms of 3/15–30 x and is dated May 20. The amount of the invoice is $1120.15, and a partial payment of $580 is made on July 1. Find (a) the credit given for the partial payment and (b) the balance due on the invoice.   (a) $597.94 (b) $522.21

54. **JEEP SUPPLIES** Jeepers Supply makes a partial payment of $660 on an invoice of $1491.54. If the invoice is dated April 14 with terms of 4/20 prox. and the partial payment is made on May 13, find (a) the credit given for the partial payment and (b) the balance due on the invoice.   (a) $687.50 (b) $804.04

55. **PARTIAL INVOICE PAYMENT** The UPS Store receives an invoice amounting to $672.30 with terms of 8/10, net 30 and dated August 20 AS OF September 1. If a partial payment of $450 is made on September 8, find (a) the credit given for the partial payment and (b) the balance due on the invoice.   (a) $489.13 (b) $183.17

56. **FROZEN YOGURT** Yogurt for You receives an invoice amounting to $263.40 with terms of 2/20 EOM and dated September 6. If a partial payment of $150 is made on October 15, find (a) the credit given for the partial payment and (b) the balance due on the invoice.   (a) $153.06 (b) $110.34

CHAPTER TERMS

Review the following terms to test your understanding of the chapter. For each term you do not know, refer to the page number found next to that term:

anticipation [p. 380]
cash discount [p. 370]
cash on delivery (COD) [p. 357]
chain discount [p. 359]
complement [p. 359]
consumer [p. 356]
distributor [p. 355]
electronic commerce (EC) [p. 356]
EOM (end of month) [p. 377]
extension total [p. 356]

extra dating (extra, ex., x) [p. 379]
free alongside ship (FAS) [p. 357]
free on board (FOB) [p. 357]
global supply chain [p. 355]
inventory [p. 355]
invoice [p. 356]
invoice total [p. 356]
list price [p. 358]
manufacturer [p. 355]

net cost [p. 358]
net cost equivalent [p. 360]
net price [p. 358]
ordinary dating method [p. 371]
partial payment [p. 380]
percent paid [p. 360]
proximo (prox.) dating [p. 377]
purchase invoice [p. 356]
receipt-of-goods dating (ROG) [p. 378]
retailer [p. 355]

sales invoice [p. 356]
series discount [p. 359]
single discount [p. 359]
single discount equivalent [p. 365]
suppliers [p. 355]
supply chain [p. 355]
total invoice amount [p. 356]
trade discounts [p. 358]
unit price [p. 356]
wholesaler [p. 355]

CONCEPTS

EXAMPLES

9.1 Trade discount and net cost

First find the amount of the trade discount. Then use the formula:

Net cost = list price − trade discount

List price, $568; trade discount, 25%. Find the net cost.

$$\text{Trade discount} = \$568 \times 0.25 = \$142$$
$$\text{Net cost} = \$568 - \$142 = \$426$$

9.1 Complements with respect to 1

The complement is the number that must be added to a given discount to get 1 or 100%.

Find the complement with respect to 1 for each of the following.

(a) $10\% + x = 100\%$
$x = 100\% - 10\%$
$x = 90\%$

(b) $12\frac{1}{2}\%$; complement = 87.5%

(c) 50%; complement = 50%

9.1 Complement and series discounts

The complement of a discount is the percent paid. Multiply the complements of the discounts in the series to get the net cost equivalent.

Series discount, 10/20/10. Find the net cost equivalent.

$$\begin{array}{ccc} 10 & / \ 20 & / \ 10 \\ \downarrow & \downarrow & \downarrow \\ 0.9 \times & 0.8 \times & 0.9 = 0.648 \end{array}$$

9.1 Net cost equivalent (percent paid) and the net cost

Multiply the net cost equivalent (percent paid) by the list price to get the net cost.

Percent paid × list price = net cost

List price, $280; series discount 10/30/20. Find the net cost.

$$\begin{array}{ccc} 10 & / \ 30 & / \ 20 \\ \downarrow & \downarrow & \downarrow \\ 0.9 \times & 0.7 \times & 0.8 = 0.504 \text{ percent paid} \end{array}$$

$$0.504 \times \$280 = \$141.12$$

9.2 Single discount equivalent to a series discount

Often needed to compare one series discount to another, the single discount equivalent is found by subtracting the net cost equivalent from 1.

$1 -$ net cost equivalent $=$ single discount equivalent

What single discount is equivalent to a 10/20/20 series discount?

10 / 20 / 20
↓   ↓   ↓
$0.9 \times 0.8 \times 0.8 = 0.576$
$1 - 0.576 = 0.424 = 42.4\%$

9.2 Finding net cost using complements of individual discounts

To find the net cost, multiply the list price by the product of the complements of the individual discounts.

List price, \$510; series discount, 30/10/5. Find the net cost.

30 / 10 / 5
↓   ↓   ↓
$\$510 \times 0.7 \times 0.9 \times 0.95 = \$305.24$

9.2 Finding list price if given the series discount and the net cost

First, find the net cost equivalent (percent paid), then use the formula to find the list price.

$$P \times L = N$$
Percent paid $\times$ list price $=$ net cost

Net cost, \$224; series discount, 20/20. Find list price.

20 / 20
↓   ↓
$0.8 \times 0.8 = 0.64$
$0.64 \times$ list price $= \$224$
$0.64L = \$224$
$L = \$350$ List price

9.2 Determining the trade discount that must be added to meet a competitor's price

First use the formula $P \times L = N$ to find the single discount needed. The answer is the complement of the discount that must be added; subtract it from 100% to get the discount.

List price \$640; trade discount 25%. Find the additional trade discount that is needed to match the competitor's price of \$432.

$$P \times L = N$$
$0.75 \times$ complement of discount $\times L = N$
$0.75 \times d \times \$640 = \$432$
$\$480d = \$432$
$d = 0.9 = 90\%$
$100\% - 90\% = 10\%$ additional discount

9.3 Determining number of days and dates

30-day months	31-day months
April	All the rest except
June	February with 28 days
September	(29 days in leap year)
November	

Date, July 24. Find 10 days from date.

July $31 - 24 = 7$ remaining in July

  10   Total number of days
$-$ 7   Days remaining in July
   3   August—future date

9.3 Ordinary dating and cash discounts

With ordinary dating, count days from the date of the invoice. Remember:

$$2 \; / \; 10, \quad n \; / \; 30$$
$$\downarrow \quad \downarrow \qquad \downarrow \quad \downarrow$$
$$\%\quad \text{days} \quad \text{net} \quad \text{days}$$

Invoice amount $182; terms 2/10, n/30. Find cash discount and amount due.

Cash discount: $182 \times 0.02 = \$3.64$

Amount due: $182 - \$3.64 = \$178.36$

9.3 Returned goods

Subtract returned goods amount from invoice before calculating the cash discount.

Invoice amount, $950; returned goods, $150; terms, 3/15, n/30. Find amount due if discount is earned.

Cash discount: $(\$950 - \$150) \times 0.03 = \$24$

Amount due: $\$950 - \$150 - \$24 = \$776$

9.4 Cash discounts with end-of-month dating (EOM or proximo)

Count the final discount date and the net date from the end of the month. If the invoice is dated the 26th or after, add the entire following month when determining the dates. If not stated, the net date is 20 days beyond the discount date.

Terms, 2/10 EOM; invoice date, Oct. 18. Find the final discount date and the net payment date.

Final discount date: November 10, which is 10 days from the end of October

Net payment date: November 30, which is 20 days beyond the discount date

9.4 Receipt-of-goods dating and cash discounts (ROG)

Time is counted from the date goods are received to determine the final cash discount date and the net payment date. If not stated, the net date is 20 days beyond the discount date.

Terms, 3/10 ROG; invoice date, March 8; goods received, May 10. Find the final discount date and the net payment date.

Final discount date: May 20 (May 10 + 10 days)

Net payment date: June 9 (May 20 + 20 days)

9.4 Extra dating and cash discounts

Extra dating adds extra days to the usual cash discount period, so 3/10–20 x is the same as 3/30. If not stated, the net date is 20 days beyond the discount date.

Terms, 3/10–20 x; invoice date, January 8. Find the final discount date and the net payment date.

Final discount date: February 7 (23 days in January + 7 days in February = 30)

Net payment date: February 27 (February 7 + 20 days)

9.4 Partial payment credit

When only a portion of an invoice amount is paid within the cash discount period, credit is given for the partial payment. Use the formula

Amount paid = $(1 - \text{discount rate}) \times \text{credit given}$

Invoice, $400; terms, 2/10, n/30; invoice date, Oct. 10; partial payment of $200 on Oct. 15. Find credit given for partial payment and the balance due on the invoice.

$200 = (1 - 0.02) \times \text{credit given}$

$200 = 0.98C$

$$C = \frac{200}{0.98} = \$204.08 \quad \text{Credit}$$

$$= \$400 - \$204.08 = \$195.92 \quad \text{Balance due}$$

The answer section includes answers to all Review Exercises.

Find the net cost (invoice amount) for the following. Round to the nearest cent. [9.1]

1. List price: $480 less 20/10 $345.60

2. List price: $276 less 10/12$\frac{1}{2}$/10 $195.62

3. List price: $2830 less 5/15/20 $1828.18

4. List price: $1620 less 20/25/15 $826.20

Find (a) the net cost equivalent and (b) the percent form of the single discount equivalent for the following series discounts. [9.2]

5. 25/15 (a) 0.6375 (b) 36.25%

6. 20/10/20 (a) 0.576 (b) 42.4%

7. 20/32$\frac{1}{2}$ (a) 0.54 (b) 46%

8. 10/20/10/30 (a) 0.4536 (b) 54.64%

Find the list price, given the net cost and the series discount. [9.2]

9. Net cost, $361.50; trade discount, 10/20 $502.08

10. Net cost, $1050.74; trade discount, 15/20 $1545.21

11. Net cost, $328.70; trade discount, 10/20/15 $537.09

12. Net cost, $1289.40; trade discount, 5/20/25 $2262.11

Find the final discount date and net payment date for the following. (The net payment date is 20 days after the final discount date.) [9.3 and 9.4]

	Invoice Date	Terms	Date Goods Received	
13.	Feb. 10	4/15 EOM	Feb. 16	Mar. 15; April 4
14.	May 8	2/10 ROG	May 20	May 30; June 19
15.	Dec. 4	3/10 prox	Dec. 8	Jan. 10; Jan. 30
16.	Oct. 20	2/20–40 extra	Oct. 31	Dec. 19; Jan. 8

Solve for the amount of discount and the amount due on the following. [9.4]

	Invoice Amount	Invoice Date	Terms	Shipping and Insurance	Date Goods Received	Date Invoice Paid	
17.	$1280.40	March 16	3/15 ROG	$76.18	April 7	April 20	$38.41; $1318.17
18.	$945.60	May 9	3/15 proximo		May 20	June 12	$28.37; $917.23
19.	$875.50	Feb. 20	4/15 EOM	$67.18	Mar. 1	Mar. 12	$35.02; $907.66
20.	$2210.60	Aug. 5	2/10–60 x		Sept. 10	Oct. 13	$44.21; $2166.39

Find the credit given and the balance due on the invoice after making the following partial payments. Round to the nearest cent. [9.4]

	Invoice Amount	Invoice Date	Terms	Date Invoice Paid	Partial Payment	
21.	$660	February 2	2/10, n/30	February 10	$300	$306.12; $353.88
22.	$5310	April 22	3/15 EOM	May 14	$2520	$2597.94; $2712.06
23.	$860	July 23	1/10 prox.	August 5	$500	$505.05; $354.95
24.	$3850	September 17	3/10–40 x	November 2	$2050	$2113.40; $1736.60

Solve the following application problems in cash and trade discounts.

25. The following invoice was paid on November 15. Find (a) the invoice total, (b) the amount that should be paid after the cash discount, and (c) the total amount due, including shipping and insurance. **[9.1 and 9.3]**   (a) $394.40 (b) $386.51 (c) $398.06

GOURMET KITCHEN WHOLESALERS			
Terms: 2/10, 1/15, n/60			November 6
Quantity	**Description**	**Unit Price**	**Extension Total**
16	tablecloths, linen	@ 17.50 ea.	$ 280.00
8	rings, napkin	@ 3.25 ea.	$ 26.00
4	cups, ceramic	@ 12.65 ea.	$ 50.60
12	bowls, 1 qt. stainless	@ 3.15 ea.	$ 37.80
		(a) Invoice Total	$ 394.40
		Cash Discount	$ 7.89
		(b) Due after Cash Discount	$ 386.51
		Shipping and Insurance	$ 11.55
		(c) Total Amount Due	$ 398.06

26. Fireside Shop offers chimney caps for $120 less 25/10. The same chimney cap is offered by Builders Supply for $111 less 25/5. Find (a) the firm that offers the lower price and (b) the difference in price. **[9.1]**   (a) Builders Supply (b) $1.91

27. Bergen Snow Tractors purchased several snowmobiles for $41,424.75 after a series discount of 10/5. Find the list price. **[9.2]** $48,450

28. Restaurant Distributing offers a commercial pasta maker for $980 with a trade discount of 25%. Find the additional trade discount needed to match a competitor's price of $661.50. **[9.2]**   10%

29. An invoice amounting to $2018 is dated September 18 and offers terms of 3/20 EOM. If $183 of goods are returned and the invoice is paid on October 18, what amount is due? **[9.4]** $1779.95

30. Subway Sandwich Shop purchased paper products list-priced at $348 less series discounts of 10/20/10 with terms of 3/10–50 extra. If the retailer paid the invoice within 60 days, find the amount paid. **[9.4]** $218.74

31. An invoice of $838 from Kara-Dolls has cash terms of 2/15 EOM and is dated March 8. Find (a) the final date on which the cash discount may be taken and (b) the amount necessary to pay the invoice in full if the cash discount is earned. **[9.4]**   (a) April 15 (b) $821.24

32. An invoice from Round Table Pizza Products amounts to $5280, was dated November 1, and offers terms of 4/15 proximo. A partial payment of $1800 is made on December 12. Find (a) the amount credited for the partial payment, (b) the balance due on the invoice, and (c) the cash discount earned. **[9.4]**   (a) $1875 (b) $3405 (c) $75

CHAPTER 9	Business Application Case #1
	Retailer Discounts

Andrew Ryan of Specialty Kitchens buys much of his merchandise from Gourmet Kitchen Wholesalers. In early September, he ordered kitchen flatware, dinnerware, and cutlery having a total list price of $9748, and appliances and cookware having a list price of $17,645. Gourmet Kitchen Wholesalers offers trade discounts of 20/10/10 on these items and charges for shipping. The invoice for this order arrived a few days later, is dated September 4, has terms of 3/15 EOM, and shows a shipping charge of $748.38. Specialty Kitchens will need to know all of the following. Round to the nearest cent.

(a) The total amount of the invoice excluding shipping. $17,750.66

(b) The final discount date. October 15

(c) The net payment date. November 4

(d) The amount necessary to pay the invoice in full on October 11 including the shipping. $17,966.52

(e) Suppose that on October 11 the invoice is not paid in full, but a partial payment of $10,000 is made instead. Find the credit given for the partial payment and the balance due on the invoice including shipping. $10,309.28; $8189.76

CHAPTER 9	Business Application Case #2
	Purchasing Decisions at a Retailer

Thomas Rugby works as a purchasing manager for a large retailer. He needs to buy 1200 vacuum cleaners with a specific power and efficiency rating. After considerable discussion with potential suppliers, he has narrowed the decision of which to use to one of the two following firms.

Company	Cost of Each Vacuum Cleaner	Trade Discount	Shipping Charge
Trident, Inc.	$117.20	5/10 net 30	$1585
Shanghai Industries	$124	2/20 ROG	$2200

(a) Assume all discounts are taken and find the total cost to purchase 1200 vacuum cleaners from each company including the shipping charges. Trident, Inc., $135,193; Shanghai Industries, $148,024

(b) Based on cost alone, which company should Thomas buy from and what would be the savings to his firm?
Trident, Inc.; Savings = $12,831

(c) However, Mr. Rugby has heard a rumor of possible quality problems with Trident Inc. products. He has been unable to verify the rumor, but he is worried about quality problems since his firm would have to handle any poor-quality vacuum cleaners returned to a store. At the same time, his boss is constantly pushing him to save costs. In this situation, which company would you choose if you had Mr. Rugby's job? Justify your choice. Answers will vary.

javier brosch / Fotolia.com

CHAPTER

10

Markup

The success of a business depends on many things. It greatly depends on managers' skills and knowledge about their customers. It also depends on keeping costs low, including the costs of borrowed money. Importantly, a firm must be able to charge a high enough price to pay operating expenses, including wages, and have some left over for profit. This chapter is about markup, which is the difference between the selling price and the purchase price.

Wal-Mart Stores Inc. is a large retailer with 2 million employees and 9000 stores in 50 countries. To manage well, managers must constantly watch financial data such as the quarterly data in Table 10.1. The data in the table shows that the cost of sales was 75% of the quarter's gross revenue of $104.2 billion, so 75% of all sales revenue at Wal-Mart is paid to suppliers. The firm paid $1,800,000,000 in income taxes and had a remaining profit of $3,400,000,000 for the quarter. After-tax profit was only 3.3% of gross revenue, meaning that the profit averaged $3.30 on every $100 in sales.

Table10.1 WAL-MART STORES (1ST QUARTER, 2011)

	(in billions)	Percent of Gross Revenue
Gross Revenue	$104.2	—
Cost of Sales	$78.2	75.0%
Selling, General, & Administrative	$20.1	19.3%
Income Tax	$1.8	1.7%
After-Tax Profit	$3.4	3.3%

Source: Wal-Mart financial statements.

▶STOP&THINK

> The percent of gross revenue that goes to profit is less than 5% at many large discount retailers and grocery stores. Estimate the amount you spend at the grocery store each week. Assume profit at the store averages 3% of gross sales and estimate the amount of profit the firm makes from you *each year*. If a grocery store experiences a theft of $850 in products during one week, how much extra must it sell to have the same profit at the end of the quarter?

10.1	**Markup on Cost**

OBJECTIVES

1. *Recognize the terms used in selling.*
2. *Use the basic markup formula.*
3. *Calculate markup based on cost.*
4. *Apply percent to markup problems.*

Objective

1   *Recognize the Terms Used in Selling.* The following terms are used in markup.

> **Cost**—The price paid to the manufacturer or supplier after trade discounts. Also called the **wholesale price.**
>
> **Markup**—The amount added to the cost to find the selling price. Also called **margin,** or **gross profit**.
>
> **Selling price**—The price at which the item is sold. Also called **retail price**.
>
> **Operating expenses**—Costs of operating the business, including salaries, rent, utilities, insurance, and advertising. Also called **overhead**.
>
> **Net profit**—The amount remaining after cost of goods and operating expenses have been paid. Also called **net earnings**.
>
> **Profit margin**—The percent of sales that remain after cost of goods sold, all operating expenses, and income taxes have been paid.

We usually think of markup in terms of products, but many of these terms apply to the U.S. Postal Service, which does not produce products. Since it is not supposed to lose money, managers at the Postal Service must carefully watch costs and price postage appropriately (see Figure 10.1). The cost to mail a 1-ounce letter has increased by more than 4% per year since 1970. In spite of these increases, the postal system is having financial problems as costs outrun revenues. It plans to shut down some small post offices, perhaps deliver mail only 5 days a week, and increase postal rates in the near future. Part of the reason the postal service is having financial problems is the Internet—people are sending less mail than in the past as they turn to the Internet instead.

U.S. Postal Rates Since 1971
Cost to Mail One Ounce

Figure 10.1

Most manufacturers, many wholesalers, and some retailers calculate markup as a percent of cost, called **markup on cost**. Manufacturers, who usually evaluate their inventories on the basis of cost, find this method to be most consistent with their business operations. Retailers, on the other hand, usually compute **markup on selling price** since retailers compare most areas of their business operations to sales revenue. Such items as sales commissions, sales taxes, advertising, and other items of expense are expressed as a percent of sales. It is reasonable, then, for the retailer to express markup as percent of sales. Wholesalers, however, use either cost or selling price, so be sure to find out which a wholesaler is using.

Objective

2 *Use the Basic Markup Formula.* Whether markup is based on cost or on selling price, the same basic **markup formula** is always used. This formula is as follows.

$$\text{Cost} + \text{markup} = \text{selling price}$$
$$C + M = S$$

The markup formula is illustrated in Figure 10.2. Most problems in markup give two of the items in the formula and ask for the third.

Figure 10.2

EXAMPLE 1 **Using the Basic Markup Formula**

Disney Books and Music received some new children's music DVDs. Use the markup formula to determine the selling price, markup, and cost of the DVDs in the following problems.

a. Cost = $10
Markup = $5
Selling price = _____

b. Cost = $10
Selling price = $15
Markup = _____

c. Markup = $5
Selling price = $15
Cost = _____

Solution

a. $C + M = S$
$\$10 + \$5 = S$
$\$15 = S$

b. $C + M = S$
$\$10 + M = \$15$
$M = \$15 - \$10$
$M = \$5$

c. $C + M = S$
$C + \$5 = \$15$
$C = \$15 - \$5$
$C = \$10$

Objective

3 *Calculate Markup Based on Cost.* **Markup based on cost** is expressed as a percent of cost. As shown in the work with percent, the base (that to which a number is being compared) is 100%, so cost will have a value of 100%. Markup and selling price will also have percent values found by comparing their dollar values to the dollar value of cost. Solve markup problems with the basic markup formula $C + M = S$.

Objective

4   *Apply Percent to Markup Problems.*

EXAMPLE **2**   **Calculating Markup on Cost**

The owner of Rose Fine Wines buys several cases of a popular wine bottled in Spain at a wholesale cost of $15 per bottle. In order to bring new customers into the store, the manager widely advertises a special promotion on this particular wine for $18.75 per bottle, or for considerably less than it can be purchased at competing stores. Find the percent of markup based on cost.

Solution

Use the markup formula

$$C + M = S$$

with $C = 15 and $S = 18.75.

$$\$15 + M = \$18.75$$
$$M = \$18.75 - \$15$$
$$M = \$3.75$$

The markup is $3.75. Now, find the percent of markup based on cost with the basic percent equation, $R \times B = P$. The base is the cost, or $15, and the markup is the part, or $3.75. Substitute these values into $R \times B = P$.

$$R \times B = P$$
$$R \times \$15 = \$3.75 \qquad \text{Base is 15.}$$
$$\$15R = \$3.75$$
$$\frac{\cancel{15}R}{\cancel{15}} = \frac{3.75}{15} \qquad \text{Divide both sides by 15.}$$
$$R = 0.25 = 25\%$$

The $3.75 markup on the wine corresponds to 25% markup on cost. For your information, wines are often marked up by more than 50% and sometimes by 100% at wine stores. So, the manager is using advertising and a lower-than-normal markup on this popular wine to bring new customers into the store. He probably anticipates that the nice selection of wines combined with the friendly and knowledgeable service will result in customers returning to the store.

NOTE   Restaurants often mark wine up by 200% or more based on cost. Many restaurants depend on the high markups on wine for income and profit.

  Scientific Calculator Approach

The calculator solution for Example 2 uses the parentheses to find the markup and then divides by the cost.

$$(\boxed{18.75} \boxed{-} \boxed{15}) \boxed{\div} \boxed{15} \boxed{=} \boxed{0.25}$$

NOTE   The markup formula and the basic percent equation can be used for solving various types of problems involving markup, as shown in the next examples.

EXAMPLE **3**   **Finding Cost When Cost Is Base**

Olympic Sports and Leisure has a markup on a Spalding microfiber composite basketball of $14, which is 50% based on cost. Find the cost and the selling price.

Solution

The markup is 50% of the cost.

$$P = R \times B$$
$$M = 50\% \times C \quad \text{Markup is part, cost is base.}$$
$$M = 0.50C$$

Since the markup is $14, substitute 14 for M.

$$\$14 = 0.50C$$
$$\frac{14}{0.50} = \frac{0.50C}{0.50}$$
$$28 = C$$

The cost of the basketball is $28. Now use the basic markup formula to find the selling price.

$$C + M = S$$
$$\$28 + \$14 = S$$
$$\$42 = S$$

The selling price of the basketball is $42.

EXAMPLE **4**   **Finding the Markup and the Selling Price**

Find the markup and selling price for a Casio solar-powered watch if the cost is $23.60 and the markup is 25% of cost.

Solution

Since the markup is 25% of cost, or $M = 0.25C$,

$$M = 0.25(\$23.60)$$
$$M = \$5.90$$

The markup is $5.90. Now use the markup formula, with $C = \$23.60$ and $M = \$5.90$.

$$C + M = S$$
$$\$23.60 + \$5.90 = S$$
$$\$29.50 = S$$

The selling price of the watch is $29.50.

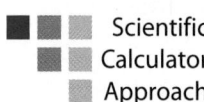
Scientific Calculator Approach

The calculator solution for Example 4 uses the percent add-on feature found on many calculators.

23.6 + 25 % = 29.5

EXAMPLE | **5** | **Finding Cost When Cost Is Base**

Olympic Sports and Leisure is selling a Wilson baseball glove for $42, which is 140% of the cost. How much did Olympic Sports and Leisure pay for the baseball glove?

Solution

If the selling price is 140% of cost, then the markup must be 40% of cost. (The cost is always 100% when markup is based on cost.)

$$M = 0.4C$$

Now use the basic formula.

$$C + M = S$$
$$C + 0.4C = \$42$$
$$1C + 0.4C = \$42$$
$$1.4C = \$42$$
$$\frac{1.4C}{1.4} = \frac{\$42}{1.4}$$
$$C = \$30$$

The cost of the glove is $30. Check: 0.40($30) = ($12) markup, and $30 + $12 = $42.

EXAMPLE | **6** | **Finding the Cost and the Markup**

The retail selling price of a Kenmore Elite 21.6-cubic-foot refrigerator is $978.75. If the markup is 35% of cost, find the cost and the markup.

Solution

Use the formula, with $M = 0.35\,C$.

$$C + M = S$$
$$C + 0.35\,C = \$978.75$$
$$1C + 0.35\,C = \$978.75$$
$$1.35\,C = \$978.75$$
$$\frac{1.35\,C}{1.35} = \frac{\$978.75}{1.35}$$
$$C = \$725$$

The cost of the refrigerator is $725. Now find the markup.

$$C + M = S$$
$$\$725 + M = \$978.75$$
$$M = \$978.75 - \$725$$
$$M = \$253.75$$

The markup is $253.75.

NOTE Remember, when calculating markup on cost, cost is *always* the base, 100%.

10.1	Exercises

Find the missing quantities. Round rates to the nearest tenth of a percent and money to the nearest cent.

	Cost	Markup	% Markup on Cost	Selling Price
1.	$12.40	$4.96	40%	$17.36
2.	$36	$7.20	20%	$43.20
3.	$23.50	$11.75	50%	$35.25
4.	$34.49	$34.49	100%	$68.98
5.	$158.70	$39.80	25.1%	$198.50
6.	$24	$14.40	60%	$38.40
7.	$67.50	$13.50	20%	$81
8.	$33.80	$8.45	25%	$42.25
9.	$210	$118	56.2%	$328
10.	$48.55	$25.25	52%	$73.80
11.	$495	$133.65	27%	$628.65
12.	$78.30	$12.53	16%	$90.83

 13. Markup may be calculated on cost or on selling price. Explain why most manufacturers prefer to use cost as base when calculating markup. (See Objective 1.)

14. Write the basic markup formula. Define each term. (See Objective 2.)

Solve the following application problems using cost as base. Round rates to the nearest tenth of a percent and money to the nearest cent.

15. HARD-TO-FIND TOOLS   The Brookstone Company sells a precision tool kit for $138. If the markup is 35% of cost, find the cost. $102.22

16. DENTAL TOOLS   The cost of a dentist's handpiece is $560 and the markup is 25% of cost. Find the markup. $140

17. GARDEN TOOLS   Orchard Supply sells garden sprayers at a price of $18.95. If markup is 38% of cost, find the cost. $13.73

18. LAWN FERTILIZER   Orchard Supply sells lawn fertilizer at a price of $12.50 per bag. If the markup is 25% of cost, find the cost. $10

19. ELECTRIC WHEELCHAIR   A retailer purchases an electric wheelchair for $2820. The firm uses a markup of 28% on cost. Find the selling price. $3609.60

20. JET SKIS   Water Sports purchases jet skis at a cost of $2880 each. If its operating expenses are 25% of its cost, and it wishes to make a net profit of 15% of its cost, find the selling price. $4032

21. HEARING AIDS   Benson Hearing pays $1540 for specialized hearing aids, which it then sells for $2450. Find the percent of markup on cost.   59.1%

22. MARKUP ON ASPIRIN   The Tower Market sells aspirin (50-tablet bottle) for $3.38 per bottle. If it pays $2.60 per bottle, find the markup percent on cost.   30%

23. OUTDOOR LIGHTING   Patios Plus sold an outdoor lighting set for $119.95. The markup on the set was $23.99. Find (a) the cost, (b) the markup percent on cost, and (c) the selling price as a percent of cost.   (a) $95.96   (b) 25%   (c) 125%

24. ATHLETIC SHOES   Fleet Feet had a markup of $23.32 on some shoes that it sold for $111.32. Find (a) the cost, (b) the markup percent on cost, and (c) the selling price as a percent of cost.   (a) $88   (b) 26.5%   (c) 126.5%

25. **FARM EQUIPMENT** Fairfield Tractor put a markup of 32% on cost on a part for which it paid $73.50. Find (a) the selling price as a percent of cost, (b) the selling price, and (c) the markup. (a) 132% (b) $97.02 (c) $23.52

26. **BRASS LAMPS** A lighting manufacturer offers brass lamps at a selling price that is 175% of the cost. The markup is $61.50. Find (a) the markup percent on cost, (b) the cost, and (c) the selling price. (a) 75% (b) $82 (c) $143.50

27. **HIKING BOOTS** Nature Trails, a manufacturer of hiking equipment, prices light-weight hiking boots at $89.04, which is 127.2% of their cost. Find (a) the cost, (b) the markup as a percent of cost, and (c) the markup. (a) $70 (b) 27.2% (c) $19.04

28. **COIN COLLECTING** North Area Coins priced a rare 1800s uncirculated silver dollar at $868, which was 112% of cost. Find (a) the cost, (b) the markup as a percent of cost, and (c) the markup. (a) $775 (b) 12% (c) $93

29. **FIRE TRUCK** A specifically outfitted model of one fire truck costs a distributor $184,630. The firm has operating expenses of 10% of cost and expects a net profit of 6% of costs. Find the selling price of each truck to the nearest dollar. $214,171

30. **MOTOR SCOOTER** Kragen Auto Supply purchases 4-stroke gas scooters at a cost of $398 each. The company's operating expenses are 16% of cost, and a net profit of 7% of cost is desired. Find the selling price of one scooter. $489.54

31. **RETAIL HARDWARE** Bell Hardware has operating expenses of 18% of cost and desires a 17% net profit on cost. The selling price of a tube of 20-year silicone caulk is $8.95. Find the cost. $6.63

32. **SLIDING GLASS DOORS** Anderson Doors sells a high-efficiency sliding glass door for $1790. Operating expenses are 21% of cost, and net profit is 9% of cost. Find the cost. $1376.92

10.2	**Markup on Selling Price**

OBJECTIVES

1 *Calculate markup based on selling price.*

2 *Solve markup problems when selling price is base.*

3 *Use the markup formula to solve variations of markup problems.*

4 *Determine percent markup on cost and the equivalent percent markup on selling price.*

5 *Convert markup percent on cost to markup percent on selling price.*

6 *Convert markup percent on selling price to markup percent on cost.*

As mentioned, wholesalers sometimes calculate markup based on cost and other times calculate **markup based on selling price**. Retailers use sales figures in almost all aspects of their business. Almost all expense and income amounts are calculated as a percent of sales. Therefore, it is common for retailers to calculate markup based on selling price. In each case, markup will be given as "on cost" or "on selling price." Remember that if markup is based on selling price, then selling price *is* the base. Since the base is 100%, selling price will have a value of 100%. This section discusses markup on selling price.

Objective

1 *Calculate Markup Based on Selling Price.* The same basic markup formula is used with markup on selling price.

$$\text{Cost } + \text{ Markup } = \text{ Selling price}$$
$$C + M \quad\quad = S$$

Objective

2 *Solve Markup Problems When Selling Price Is Base.*

EXAMPLE **1**   **Solving for Markup on Selling Price**

To compete against other discount stores, Target sells a calculator for $15 that it buys for $10. Find the markup and the percent of markup on selling price.

Solution

First, solve for markup.

$$C + M = S$$
$$\$10 + M = \$15$$
$$M = \$15 - \$10$$
$$M = \$5$$

Now solve for percent of markup on selling price. Use the basic percent equation, $R \times B = P$. In this example, P is the markup, or $5, and the base B is the selling price, or $15. Substitute these values into $R \times B = P$, and solve the equation.

$$R \times B = P$$
$$R \times \$15 = \$5$$
$$R = \frac{\$5}{\$15}$$
$$R = \frac{1}{3} = 0.333\ldots$$
$$= 33\tfrac{1}{3}\%$$

The percent of markup on selling price is $33\tfrac{1}{3}\%$.

Objective

3 *Use the Markup Formula to Solve Variations of Markup Problems.* As with problems where markup is based on cost, the basic formula $C + M = S$ may be used for all variations of markup problems when selling price is the base.

EXAMPLE **2**   **Finding Markup When Selling Price Is Given**

Find the markup on a movie in high-definition Blu-ray Disc format that sells for $22.79 if the markup is 30% of the selling price. Then find the cost paid by the retailer.

Solution

$$\text{Markup} = 30\% \text{ of selling price}$$
$$= 0.3 \times \$22.79$$
$$= \$6.84 \qquad \text{Rounded}$$

$$\textbf{Cost to retailer} = \textbf{selling price} - \textbf{markup}$$
$$= \$22.79 \quad - \quad \$6.84$$
$$= \$15.95$$

EXAMPLE **3** **Finding Cost When Selling Price Is Base**

A bookstore employee knows that one three-hole binder has a markup of $2.38, which is 40% based on selling price. Find the cost of the binder.

Solution

Start by finding selling price and then subtract markup to find cost. Here $R = 40\%$ (the rate of markup), $P = \$2.38$ (the markup), and B is the unknown (selling price). Use $R \times B = P$ as follows.

$$R \times B = P$$
$$40\% \times S = \$2.38$$
$$0.4S = \$2.38$$
$$S = \frac{\$2.38}{0.4}$$
$$S = \$5.95$$

The selling price is $5.95. Now solve for cost.

$$C + M = S$$
$$C + \$2.38 = \$5.95$$
$$C + \$2.38 - \$2.38 = \$5.95 - \$2.38$$
$$C = \$5.95 - \$2.38$$
$$C = \$3.57$$

The cost is $3.57.

EXAMPLE **4** **Finding the Selling Price and the Markup When Cost Is Given**

An employee at The Home Depot is told to calculate the selling price and markup on a 6-pack container of tomato plants if the cost is $3.16 and the markup is 40% of selling price.

Solution

Use the formula $C + M = S$. Since the markup is 40% of the selling price, $M = 0.4S$.

$$C + M = S$$
$$\$3.16 + 0.4S = S$$
$$\$3.16 + 0.4S - 0.4S = 1S - 0.4S$$
$$\$3.16 = 1S - 0.4S$$
$$\$3.16 = 0.6S$$
$$\frac{3.16}{0.6} = \frac{0.6S}{0.6}$$
$$\$5.27 = S$$

The selling price is $5.27.
    Now find the markup using the markup formula.

$$C + M = S$$
$$\$3.16 + M = \$5.27$$
$$M = \$5.27 - \$3.16$$
$$M = \$2.11$$

The markup is $2.11.

Markups vary widely from industry to industry and from business to business. This variation is a result of different costs of merchandise, operating costs, level of profit margin, and local competition. Table 10.2 shows average markups for different types of retail stores.

Table 10.2 AVERAGE MARKUPS FOR RETAIL STORES (MARKUP ON SELLING PRICE)

Type of Store	Markup	Type of Store	Markup
General merchandise	29.97%	Furniture and home furnishings	35.75%
Grocery	22.05%	Drinking places	52.49%
Other food	27.31%	Eating places	56.35%
Motor vehicle dealers (new)	12.83%	Drug and proprietary	30.81%
Gasoline service stations	14.47%	Liquor	20.19%
Other automotive dealers	29.57%	Sporting goods and bicycle	29.72%
Apparel and accessories	37.64%	Gift, novelty, and souvenir	41.86%

Source: Sole Proprietorship Income Tax Returns, U.S. Treasury Dept., Internal Revenue Service, Statistics Division.

Do not make the mistake of thinking of the markup percents in Table 10.2 as profit. Included in markup are the following costs: wages, employee benefits, transportation, taxes, maintenance, rent, utilities, insurance, etc. Profit is what remains after everything has been paid. Sometimes a firm makes a profit, but many firms also lose money in rough economic times such as a recession.

Objective

4 *Determine Percent Markup on Cost and the Equivalent Percent Markup on Selling Price.* Sometimes, a markup based on cost must be compared to a markup based on selling price. Such a conversion might be necessary for a manufacturer who thinks in terms of cost and wants to understand a wholesaler or retail customer. Or, perhaps, a retailer or wholesaler might convert markup on selling price to markup on cost to better understand the manufacturer. Make these comparisons by first computing the markup on cost, then computing the markup on selling price.

EXAMPLE **5** **Determining Equivalent Markups**

Claire Magersky sells fishing lures to both fishing-equipment wholesalers and sporting-goods stores. If the lure costs her $5.40 and she sells it for $8.64, what is the percent of markup on cost? What is the percent of markup on selling price?

Solution

To solve for markup, use the formula $C + M = S$, with $C = \$5.40$ and $S = \$8.64$.

$$C + M = S$$
$$\$5.40 + M = \$8.64$$
$$M = \$8.64 - \$5.40$$
$$M = \$3.24 \qquad \text{Markup}$$

Next, to solve for the percent of markup on cost, use the percent equation, $R \times B = P$, with $B = \$5.40$ (the cost, since markup is on cost) and $P = \$1.05$ (the markup).

$$R \times B = P$$
$$R \times \$5.40 = \$3.24$$
$$\$5.40R = \$3.24$$
$$R = \frac{3.24}{5.4}$$
$$R = 0.6 = 60\% \quad \text{Markup on cost}$$

To find the percent of markup on selling price, use the percent equation again. While P is still $3.24, B changes to $8.64 since the markup on selling price must be found. Substitute into the equation as follows.

$$R \times B = P$$
$$R \times \$8.64 = \$3.24$$
$$\$8.64R = \$3.24$$
$$R = \frac{3.24}{8.64}$$
$$R = 0.375 = 37.5\% \quad \text{Markup on selling price}$$

Example 5 shows that a 60% markup on cost is the exact same thing as a 37.5% markup on selling price. The process to convert from markup on cost to markup on selling price and vice versa is shown in the next two objectives in this section.

Objective

5 *Convert Markup Percent on Cost to Markup Percent on Selling Price.* Another method for making markup comparisons is to use **conversion formulas**. *No dollar amounts are needed to use these formulas.* Only the percent of markup is needed. If you have markup percent on cost, you can convert the markup percent on cost to markup percent on selling price with the following formula.

$$\% \text{ markup on selling price} = \frac{\% \text{ markup on cost}}{100\% + \% \text{ markup on cost}}$$

Or, if M_c represents markup on cost and M_s represents markup on selling price.

$$M_s = \frac{M_c}{100\% + M_c}$$

EXAMPLE 6 **Converting Markup on Cost to Markup on Selling Price**

Convert a markup of 25% on cost to its **equivalent percent markup** on selling price.

Solution

Use the markup on cost (M_c) of 25% in the formula to solve for markup on selling price.

$$M_s = \frac{M_c}{100\% + M_c}$$
$$= \frac{25\%}{100\% + 25\%}$$
$$= \frac{25\%}{125\%} = 20\%$$

So a 25% markup on cost is the same as a 20% markup on selling price.

Scientific Calculator Approach

The markup on cost (25%) is divided by 100% plus the markup on cost. The parentheses keys are used here.

25 % ÷ (100 % + 25 %) = 0.2

Objective

6 *Convert Markup Percent on Selling Price to Markup Percent on Cost.* Convert markup percent on selling price to markup percent on cost with the following formula.

$$\% \text{ markup on cost} = \frac{\% \text{ markup on selling price}}{100\% - \% \text{ markup on selling price}}$$

Or, if M_c represents markup on cost and M_s represents markup on selling price.

$$M_c = \frac{M_s}{100\% - M_s}$$

EXAMPLE **7** **Converting Markup on Selling Price to Markup on Cost**

Convert a markup of 30% on selling price to its **equivalent percent markup** on cost.

Solution

Use the markup on selling price (M_s) of 30% in the formula to solve for markup on cost.

$$M_c = \frac{M_s}{100\% - M_s}$$
$$= \frac{30\%}{100\% - 30\%}$$
$$= \frac{30\%}{70\%} = 42.9\% \quad \text{Rounded}$$

Therefore, a 30% markup on selling price is about the same as a 42.9% markup on cost.

Scientific Calculator Approach

For Example 7, the markup on selling price (30%) is divided by 100% minus the markup on selling price. The parentheses keys are used here.

30 % ÷ (100 % − 30 %) = 0.429 Rounded

NOTE Retailers and wholesalers commonly use both markup on cost and markup on selling price. One is not better than the other; the two simply represent different ways to talk about markup.

Table 10.3 shows common markup equivalents expressed as percents on cost and also on selling price. A table like this would be helpful to anyone using markup equivalents on a regular basis.

Table 10.3 COMMON MARKUP EQUIVALENTS

Markup on Cost	Markup on Selling Price
20%	$16\frac{2}{3}\%$
25%	20%
$33\frac{1}{3}\%$	25%
50%	$33\frac{1}{3}\%$
$66\frac{2}{3}\%$	40%
75%	$42\frac{6}{7}\%$
100%	50%

10.2 | Exercises

Find the missing quantities. Round rates to the nearest tenth of a percent and money to the nearest cent.

	Cost Price	Markup	% Markup on Selling Price	Selling Price
1.	$21	$7	25%	$28
2.	$145	$105	42%	$250
3.	$131.48	$112	46%	$243.48
4.	$117.50	$72	38.0%	$189.50
5.	$18.60	$37.20	$66\frac{2}{3}\%$	$55.80
6.	$17.28	$12.67	42.3%	$29.95
7.	$46.36	$24.96	35%	$71.32
8.	$178	$89	$33\frac{1}{3}\%$	$267
9.	$77.82	$42.18	35.2%	$120
10.	$193.15	$142.76	42.5%	$335.91

Find the missing quantities by first computing the markup on one base and then computing the markup on the other. Round rates to the nearest tenth of a percent and money to the nearest cent.

	Cost	Markup	Selling Price	% Markup on Cost	% Markup on Selling Price
11.	$230	$57.50	$287.50	25%	20%
12.	$0.50	$0.23	$0.73	46%	31.5%
13.	$13.80	$8.46	$22.26	61.3%	38%
14.	$33.75	$33.75	$67.50	100%	50%
15.	$750	$300	$1050	40%	28.6%
16.	$5.15	$10.30	$15.45	200%	$66\frac{2}{3}\%$
17.	$357.52	$78.48	$436	22%	18%
18.	$1920	$480	$2400	25%	20%

Find the equivalent markups on either cost or selling price using the appropriate formula. Round to the nearest tenth of a percent.

Markup on Cost	Markup on Selling Price
19. 25%	20%
20. 100%	50%
21. 35.1%	26%
22. 18.1%	15.3%
23. 50%	33.3%
24. $33\frac{1}{3}\%$	25%
25. 66.7%	40%
26. 20%	$16\frac{2}{3}\%$

27. Why do you suppose that grocery stores have an average markup of 22.05%, while eating places have an average markup of 56.35%?

28. To have a markup of 100% or greater, the markup must be calculated on cost. Show why this is always true. (See Objectives 5 and 6.)

Solve the following application problems. Round rates to the nearest tenth of a percent and money to the nearest cent.

29. HANDBAG   Jelica's Handbags pays $32.33 for a handbag and uses a markup of 34% on selling price. Find the selling price. $48.98

30. AUTO PARTS DEALER   An auto parts dealer pays $28.56 per dozen gallons of windshield washer fluid, and the markup is 50% on selling price. Find the selling price per gallon. $4.76

31. HOME ENTERTAINMENT SYSTEM   Fry's Electronics sells a home theater speaker package for $595 and maintains a markup of 35% on selling price. Find its cost. $386.75

32. HOT TUB   Lowe's sells a hot tub for $3522 and maintains a markup of 35% on selling price. Find the cost. $2289.30

33. CEILING FANS   The cost of a ceiling fan is $92.82 and the markup is 22% on selling price. Find the selling price. $119

34. FLY FISHING   Field and Stream Sports pays $20.80 for a child's fly rod and sells it for $32. Find the percent of markup on selling price.   35%

35. CERAMIC TILE   Ceramic tile from Belgium has a markup of 36% on the selling price. The tile has a markup of $1.62 per tile. Find (a) the selling price, (b) the cost, and (c) the cost as a percent of the selling price per tile.   (a) $4.50 (b) $2.88 (c) 64%

36. DVD RECORDER   Direct Electronics pays $196.78 for a Philips DVD recorder. The markup is 18% on selling price. Find (a) the cost as a percent of selling price, (b) the selling price, and (c) the markup.   (a) 82% (b) $239.98 (c) $43.20

37. CLOCK RADIOS   Best Products buys clock radios for $258 per dozen and has a gross profit of $7.74 per clock radio. Find the percent of gross profit based on selling price.   26.5%

38. HOME-WORKOUT EQUIPMENT   Olympics Sports has a markup of $280 on a Schwinn Bowflex. If this is a 35% markup on selling price, find (a) the selling price, (b) the cost, and (c) the cost as a percent of selling price.   (a) $800 (b) $520 (c) 65%

39. SWIMMING POOL PUMP   Leslie's Pool Supply pays $187.19 for a pool pump. If the markup is 28% on the selling price, find (a) the cost as a percent of selling price, (b) the selling price, and (c) the markup.   (a) 72% (b) $259.99 (c) $72.80

40. **LEVI'S DOCKER SHIRTS** Mervyn's Department Store priced some Levi's Docker shirts at $29.95. The cost of the shirts was 58% of the selling price. Find (a) the cost, (b) the markup, and (c) the markup as a percent of selling price.   (a) $17.37 (b) $12.58 (c) 42.0%

41. **RECYCLING ALUMINUM** Recyclable aluminum can be sold for $2880 per ton (1 ton = 2000 pounds). If Alcan Recycling wants a 50% markup on selling price, (a) how much per pound can it pay local residents for their recycled aluminum? (b) What is the equivalent markup percent on cost?   (a) $0.72 (b) 100%

42. **RETAIL SILK FLOWERS** A retailer purchases silk flowers for $31.56 per dozen and sells them for $4.78 each. (a) Find his percent of markup on selling price. (b) What is the equivalent markup on cost?   (a) 45% (b) 81.8%

43. **RIVER RAFTS** White Water Supply purchased a job lot of 380 river rafts for $7600. If it sold 158 of the rafts at $45 each, 74 at $35 each, 56 at $30 each, and the remainder at $25 each, what is (a) the total amount received for the rafts, (b) the total markup, (c) the markup percent on selling price, and (d) the equivalent markup percent on cost?   (a) $13,680 (b) $6080 (c) 44.4% (d) 80%

44. **ITALIAN SILK TIES** Dress for Success purchased 240 Italian silk ties for $2280. It sold 162 ties at $25 each, 45 ties at $15 each, 20 ties at $10 each, and the remainder at $5 each. Find (a) the total amount received for the ties, (b) the total markup, (c) the markup percent on selling price, and (d) the equivalent markup percent on cost.   (a) $4990 (b) $2710 (c) 54.3% (d) 118.9%

45. **GOLD JEWELRY** Zarrima Jewels sells a diamond necklace for $1180, which includes a markup of 60% on selling price. Find (a) the cost and (b) the percent of markup on cost.   (a) $472 (b) 150%

46. **SMOKING SUPPLIES** The Tinder Box Smoke Shop buys a special blend of pipe tobacco in 10-pound tins at a cost of $24 per tin. The shop sells the tobacco for $1.20 per ounce. Find (a) the markup percent on selling price and (b) the equivalent markup percent on cost. (*Hint:* 1 pound = 16 ounces).   (a) 87.5% (b) 700%

47. **RESTAURANT SUPPLIES** A restaurant supplier sells coffee filters for $6.90 per box. If the cost of the filters is $4.80, find (a) the percent of markup on cost and (b) the equivalent percent of markup on selling price.   (a) 43.8% (b) 30.4%

48. **ALL-PURPOSE FERTILIZER** Home Base sells a 40-pound bag of Pax All-Purpose Fertilizer for $10.98. The cost of the fertilizer is $7.32 per bag. Find (a) the percent of markup on cost and (b) the equivalent percent of markup on selling price.   (a) 50% (b) $33\frac{1}{3}\%$

49. **CORDLESS PHONES** A discount store purchased amplified cordless phones at a cost of $576 per dozen. If it needs 20% of cost to cover operating expenses and 15% of cost for net profit, what is (a) the selling price per phone and (b) the percent of markup on selling price?   (a) $64.80 (b) 25.9%

50. **BOWLING EQUIPMENT** The Bowler's ProShop determines that operating expenses are 23% of selling price and desires a net profit of 12% of selling price. If the cost of a team shirt is $29.25, what is (a) the selling price and (b) the percent of markup on cost?   (a) $45 (b) 53.8%

51. **MOUNTAIN BIKES** Cycle City advertises mountain bikes for $199.90. If its cost is $2100 per dozen, what is (a) the markup per bicycle, (b) the percent of markup on selling price, and (c) the percent of markup on cost?   (a) $24.90 (b) 12.5% (c) 14.2%

52. **APPLE IPHONE** A new iPhone that costs $1800 per dozen phones is advertised for $299. Find (a) the markup per phone, (b) the percent of markup on selling price, and (c) the percent of markup on cost.   (a) $149 (b) 49.8% (c) $99\frac{1}{3}\%$

10.3	**Markup with Spoilage**

OBJECTIVES

1 *Solve markup problems when items are unfit for sale.*

2 *Solve markup problems when a certain percent of items are unsaleable.*

3 *Calculate markup when a percent of the merchandise must be sold at a reduced price.*

Shrinkage refers to the loss of products between the point of creation (manufacturer, farmer, etc.) and the point of sale to a final customer. It includes spoilage, which we discuss in this section, but it also includes losses related to theft and breakage. Figure 10.3 shows that 77% of all shrinkage comes from either employee theft or shoplifting. Managers are well aware of this fact and work hard to establish systems designed to reduce theft. The retailing industry has worked with legislators across the country to make shoplifting a crime. Even helping a shoplifter is a crime. Shoplifters are sometimes surprised at how much trouble they are in once caught.

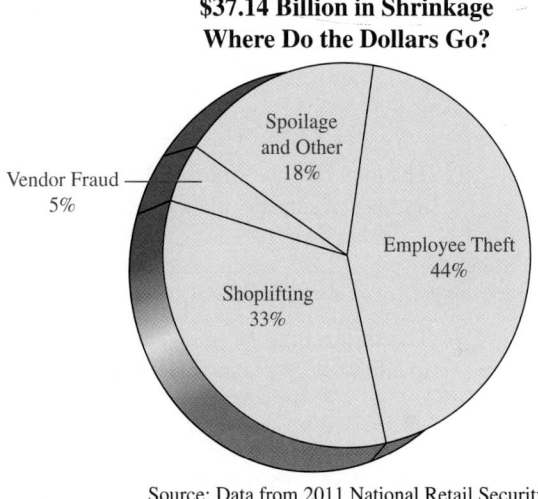

**$37.14 Billion in Shrinkage
Where Do the Dollars Go?**

Source: Data from 2011 National Retail Security
Survey, University of Florida.

Figure 10.3

Shoplifter Busted

I was caught shoplifting a hat with a price of $24.50. The police came and walked me out of the store in handcuffs—how embarrassing! Since I'm only 19 and it is my first offense, I am hoping that I can just pay something like 10 times the value of the hat, or $245.00. But I may be looking at jail time. I'm really scared. I can't eat, sleep, or do anything to get it off my mind. I have to go to court on Monday.

Objective

1 *Solve Markup Problems When Items Are Unfit for Sale.* **Spoilage** refers to products that have been damaged or blemished. Spoilage is a common problem for firms that work with fresh food such as fruit or dairy, but it also affects businesses that sell clothing, for example. Clothing items with small defects or blemishes are known as **irregulars**. A firm usually has to mark the price down to sell any product with blemishes or small defects. Any items that cannot be sold are a total loss. In either case, the markup on the good-quality items must make up for any losses on the spoiled or blemished items. The process of marking regular items at a higher price to make up for losses on damaged products is called **markup with spoilage**.

EXAMPLE **1**   **Finding Selling Price with Spoilage**

Village Nursery purchases 105 starter shrubs for $351. If a markup of 40% on selling price is necessary and 15 of the plants are unfit for sale, what is the selling price per plant?

Solution

First, find the total revenue from the sale of all the plants using a 40% markup on selling price and a cost of $351.

$$C + M = S$$
$$C + 40\%S = S$$
$$\$351 + 0.4S = S$$
$$\$351 = 1.00S - 0.4S$$
$$\$351 = 0.6S$$
$$\frac{\$351}{0.6} = S$$
$$\$585 = S$$

The total revenue from all the plants is $585. Now, divide the total selling price by the number of saleable plants to find the selling price per plant.

$$\frac{\$585}{105 \text{ purchased} - 15 \text{ unsaleable}} = \frac{\$585}{90} = \$6.50 \quad \text{Selling price per plant}$$

The shrubs must be priced at $6.50 each to realize a markup of 40% on selling price and to allow for 15 plants that cannot be sold.

NOTE   Controlling loss due to spoilage is critical in business. As spoilage increases, profits fall. These additional costs due to spoilage may be added to the price of the products sold, but the resulting higher price may be too high and no longer competitive.

Objective

2   *Solve Markup Problems When a Certain Percent of Items Are Unsaleable.*

EXAMPLE **2**   **Finding Selling Price When a Percent of Items Are Unsaleable**

The Bagel Boys bakes 60 dozen bagels at a cost of $3.24 per dozen. If a markup of 50% on selling price is needed and 5% of the bagels will not be sold and must be donated or thrown away, what is the selling price per dozen bagels?

Solution

To begin, find the total cost of the bagels.

$$\text{Cost} = 60 \text{ dozen} \times \$3.24 = \$194.40$$

Now find the selling price, using a markup of 50% of selling price.

$$C + M = S$$
$$C + 50\% = S$$
$$\$194.40 + 0.5S = S$$

$$\$194.40 = 1.00S - 0.5S$$
$$\$194.40 = 0.5S$$
$$\frac{\$194.40}{0.5} = S$$
$$\$388.80 = S$$

The total revenue from sales is $388.80.

Next, find the number of dozen bagels that will be sold. Since 5% will not be sold, 95% $(100\% - 5\%)$ will be sold.

$$95\% \times 60 \text{ dozen} = 57 \quad \text{Number of dozens sold}$$

The total revenue from sales of $388.80 must be received from 57 dozen bagels.

Find the selling price per dozen bagels by dividing the total selling price by the number of dozens to be sold.

$$\frac{\text{Total revenue from sales}}{\text{Number saleable}} = \frac{\$388.80}{57} = \$6.82 \quad \text{Selling price per dozen (rounded)}$$

A selling price of $6.82 per dozen gives the desired markup of 50% on selling price while allowing 5% of the bagels to be unsold.

Objective

3   *Calculate Markup When a Percent of the Merchandise Must Be Sold at a Reduced Price.*

> **EXAMPLE** **3**   **Finding Selling Price When Some Items Are Sold at a Reduced Price**

An athletic shoe manufacturer makes a walking shoe at a cost of $33.60 per pair. Based on past experience, 10% of the shoes will be defective and must be sold as irregulars for $48 per pair. If the manufacturer produces 1000 pairs of shoes and desires a markup of 100% on cost, what is the selling price per pair?

Solution

First, find the cost of the total production.

$$1000 \text{ pairs} \times \$33.60 = \$33,600 \quad \text{Total production cost}$$

The total revenue from sales is

$$C + M = S$$
$$C + 100\%C = S$$
$$2C = S$$

The total cost (C) is $33,600, so $S = 2C = \$67,200$, where S is the total revenue that must be earned from the sale of all shoes, irregular and regular. First, find the revenue from the sale of irregular pairs.

Revenue from sale of irregulars = number of irregulars $\times$ price per pair of irregulars

=	10% of 1000	$\times$	$48
=	100	$\times$	$48
=	$4800		

Next find the revenue that must be received from regular pairs of shoes.

Revenue needed from regulars = total amount needed − sales of irregulars

= $67,200 − $4800

= $62,400

Finally, find the price at which regular pairs must be sold.

Price per regular pair = revenue needed from regulars ÷ number of regulars

= $62,400 ÷ 900

= $69.33   Rounded

An average selling price of $69.33 per regular pair gives the manufacturer approximately 100% markup on cost when allowing the 10% that are irregulars to sell at $48 per pair.

 Scientific Calculator Approach

The calculator solution to Example 3 requires several steps.

1. Find the total revenue, and store in memory.

1000 × 33.6 × 2 = 67200 STO

2. Find the total revenue received from the sale of irregular pairs.

0.1 × 1000 × 48 =

3. Subtract the revenue from sales of irregulars from the total sales revenue.

+/− + RCL =

4. Divide by the number of regular pairs sold.

÷ 900 = 69.33   Rounded

The following bar graph lists the 10 retailers in the United States by sales. It shows both 2011 sales billions of dollars and also the profit margin, which is the percent of sales that is left after paying for the cost of goods sold, all operating expenses, and also income taxes. Multiply the profit margin by the sales to find the profit for the year. The profit margins ranged from a measly 0.3% of sales for Sears Holding to 6.1% for Kroger; many are in the 3% to 5% range. Apparently, profit at these retailing giants is often in the range of 3% to 5% of sales, or between $3 and $5 per $100 in sales. You may have thought that profits on $100 in sales would be higher; however, retailing is very competitive. Competition often drives prices and profits down.

2011 Sales of Top Ten Retailing Giants (in billions)

Retailer	Sales	Profit Margin
Walmart	$422	3.9%
CVS Caremark	$96	3.6%
Kroger	$82	6.1%
Costco	$78	1.7%
Home Depot	$68	4.9%
Target	$67	4.3%
Walgreen	$67	3.1%
Lowe's	$49	4.1%
Sears Holdings	$43	0.3%
SuperValu	$38	No profit in 2011

10.3	Exercises

Find the selling price per item.

	Total Cost	Quantity Purchased	Number Unsaleable	% Markup on Selling Price	Selling Price per Item
1.	$81	90	9	10%	$1.11
2.	$540	36	6	25%	$24
3.	$340	1 gr.	8	20%	$3.13
4.	$189	4 doz.	6	40%	$7.50
5.	$120	25	5	$33\frac{1}{3}\%$	$9
6.	$2750	120	10	50%	$50
7.	$126	8 doz.	6	15%	$1.65
8.	$2025	250	25	25%	$12

Find the missing quantities.

	Total Cost	Quantity Purchased	Percent Unsaleable	% Markup on Selling Price	Number to Sell	Selling Price per Item
9.	$161	25	4%	25%	24	$8.94
10.	$342	120	5%	20%	114	$3.75
11.	$198	2 doz.	25%	50%	18	$22
12.	$162	20 cs.	10%	30%	18	$12.86
13.	$190	80 pr.	5%	$33\frac{1}{3}\%$	76	$3.75
14.	$8750	100	30%	15%	70	$147.06
15.	$25,200	2000 gal.	5%	20%	1900	$16.58
16.	$7200	100 bbl.	10%	80%	90	$400

Find the missing quantities. Markup is based on total cost.

	Total Cost of Production	Quantity Purchased	Percent Sold at Reduced Price	% Markup on Total Cost	Number at Regular Price	Number at Reduced Price	Reduced Price	Regular Selling Price
17.	$500	200	20%	25%	160	40	$2.00	$3.41
18.	$360	120	10%	20%	108	12	$2.00	$3.78
19.	$2200	40	15%	35%	34	6	$50.00	$78.53
20.	$270	90	20%	40%	72	18	$4.00	$4.25
21.	$432	1 gr.	25%	25%	108	36	$2.50	$4.17
22.	$3000	600	10%	$33\frac{1}{3}\%$	540	60	$5.00	$6.85
23.	$2800	1000 pr.	30%	50%	700	300	$3.00	$4.71
24.	$7500	1000	50%	25%	500	500	$5.00	$13.75

25. When merchandise is unsaleable it is as if the items were not received. Explain how the price of the saleable items must be adjusted to offset this loss. (See Objective 1.)

26. Explain how we all pay for the spoiled fruit and vegetables in the produce department of the grocery store. (See Objective 1.)

Solve the following application problems.

27. **POTTERY**   The Aztec Pottery Shop finds that 15% of its production cannot be sold. It produces 100 items at a cost of $38.70 each and desires a markup of 40% on selling price. Find the selling price per item. $75.88

28. **STRAWBERRIES**   Country Produce knows that 20% of the strawberries purchased will spoil and must be thrown out. If it buys 200 baskets of strawberries for $1.20 per basket and wants a markup of 50% on selling price, find the selling price per basket of strawberries. $3.00

29. **FALL FASHIONS**   Jasmon Boutique purchased 25 mohair sweaters designed by a well-known designer for a total cost of $1200. The manager estimates that she will have to sell 5 sweaters at a discount at the end of the fall season, receiving only $225 for all. If she wants a markup of $33\frac{1}{3}\%$ on selling price, find the price for each sweater. $78.75

30. **IMPORTED CANDLES**   Cost Plus Imports purchased 30 crates of candles from Mexico for a total cost of $950.40. Each crate contains 3 dozen candles. If 4 crates of the candles are sold at the reduced price of $0.80 per candle and Cost Plus Imports wants a markup of 100% on cost, find the regular price per candle. $1.91

31. **LONG-STEMMED ROSES**   Farmers Flowers purchased 12 gross of long-stemmed roses at a cost of $1890. If 25% of the roses must be sold at $15.00 per dozen and a markup of 100% on cost is needed, find the regular selling price per dozen roses. $30

32. **CUSTOM BASEBALL CAPS**   Sports Caps Co. buys 2000 baseball hats at $7.50 per hat. If a markup of 50% on selling price is needed and 5% of the hats are unsaleable, what is the selling price of each hat? $15.79

33. **STOVE SHELL CASTINGS**   Bethel Metals finds that 20% of its stove shell castings are unsaleable. If the cost of manufacturing 55 stoves is $10,450 and Bethel Metals needs a markup of 30% on cost, what is the selling price per stove? $308.75

34. **HALLOWEEN PUMPKINS**   River Market purchased 120 small but perfect pumpkins before Halloween for $320. The manager expects 15 pumpkins to spoil. If she needs a markup of 100% on cost, find the average selling price needed. $6.10

35. **RECAPPED TRUCK TIRES**   Wheelco Tire recaps truck tires at a cost of $80.50 per tire. Past experience shows that 12% of the recaps must be sold as blemishes for $105. If it recaps 500 tires and a markup of 110% on cost is desired, what is the regular selling price per tire? $177.78

36. **ROOFING TILE**   Solano Tile manufactures roof tile at a cost of $42 per square. Past experience shows that 8% of a production run are irregulars and must be sold for $45 per square. If a production run of 10,000 squares is completed and Solano Tile desires a markup of 80% on cost, what is the regular selling price per square? $78.26

37. **BOOK PUBLISHING**   U.S. Publishing Company prints a book on sports memorabilia at a production cost of $10.80 per copy. It estimates that 20% of the production will be sold for $11.50 per copy. It prints 50,000 books and it wants a markup of 50% on selling price. Find the selling price per book. Round to the nearest cent. $24.13

38. **IMPORTED WALLPAPER**   Wallpaper Specialty Imports purchased 7000 rolls of wallpaper manufactured in France at a cost of $18.90 per roll. Past experience shows that 25% of the wallpaper will have to be sold for $20.25 per roll. Find the selling price per roll if the store wants a markup of 50% on selling price. $43.65

Supplementary Exercises: Markup

Solve the following application problems. Round rates to the nearest tenth of a percent and dollar amounts to the nearest cent.

1. **TELESCOPES**   Olympic Sports pays $74.50 for a Bushnell telescope and the markup is 30% of cost. Find the markup. $22.35

2. **BED IN A BAG**   A comforter and sheet set has a cost of $132 to the retailer and is marked up 45% on cost. Find the markup. $59.40

3. **SNOWBOARD PACKAGES**   What percent of markup on cost must be used if an Atlantis Snowboard package costing $335 is sold for $399?   19.1%

4. **LAWNMOWER**   Benson Hardware sells a self-propelled, mulching lawnmower for $399. If it pays $308 for the mower, find the markup on cost.   29.5%

5. **AUTOMOTIVE SUPPLIES**   An auto parts dealer pays $41.88 per dozen cans of fuel-injection cleaner and the markup is 50% on selling price. Find the selling price per can. $6.98

6. **GIFT SHOP SALES**   Goodies Gifts pays $26.91 for a half dozen stoneware milk jug banks. If the markup is 35% of the selling price, what is the selling price per bank? $6.90

7. **KITCHEN REMODELING**   A new kitchen range hood has a cost of $100.40 to The Home Depot. If its markup is 25% on cost, find the selling price. $125.50

8. **ART AND FRAMING**   Yen's Art and Framing pays $41.60 for a 27″ × 30″ frame and sells it for $64. Find the markup percent on cost.   53.8%

9. **PING-PONG TABLE**   Olympic Sports pays $136.79 for a Ping-Pong table. The markup is 24% on selling price. Find (a) the cost as a percent of selling price, (b) the selling price, and (c) the markup.   (a) 76% (b) $179.99 (c) $43.20

10. **DOUBLE-PANE WINDOWS**   Eastern Building Supply pays $3808 for the double-pane windows needed for a 3-bedroom, 2-bath home. If the markup on the windows is 15% on selling price, what is (a) the cost as a percent of selling price, (b) the selling price, and (c) the markup?   (a) 85% (b) $4480 (c) $672

11. **SELLING BANANAS**   The produce manager at Tom Thumb Market knows that 10% of the bananas purchased will become unsaleable and will have to be thrown out. If she buys 500 pounds of bananas for $0.32 per pound and wants a markup of 45% on the selling price, find the selling price per pound of bananas. $0.65

12. **CAKES**   Folsom Bakery finds that 12% of the cakes that it bakes do not sell, so they will be donated to the Twin Lakes Food Bank. If it bakes 150 cakes at a cost of $2.37 each and desires a markup of 70% on selling price, find the selling price per cake. $8.98

CHAPTER TERMS

Review the following terms to test your understanding of the chapter. For each term you do not know, refer to the page number found next to that term.

conversion formulas [p. 402]
cost [p. 392]
equivalent percent markup [p. 402]
gross profit [p. 392]
irregulars [p. 407]

margin [p. 392]
markup [p. 392]
markup based on cost [p. 393]
markup based on selling price [p. 398]
markup formula [p. 393]

markup on cost [p. 392]
markup on selling price [p. 392]
markup with spoilage [p. 408]
net earnings [p. 392]
net profit [p. 392]

operating expenses [p. 392]
overhead [p. 392]
retail price [p. 392]
selling price [p. 392]
shrinkage [p. 407]
spoilage [p. 407]
wholesale price [p. 392]

CONCEPTS

EXAMPLES

10.1 Markup on cost

Use rate $\times$ base = part $(R \times B = P)$, with cost as base (100%), markup % as rate, and markup as part.

Cost, $160; markup, 25% on cost. Find the markup.

$$R \times B = P$$
$$0.25 \times \$160 = \$40 \quad \text{Markup}$$

10.1 Calculating the percent of markup

Use cost + markup = selling price $(C + M = S)$ and the basic percent equation, $R \times B = P$.

Cost, $420; selling price, $546. Find the percent of markup based on cost.

$$C + M = S$$
$$\$420 + M = \$546$$
$$M = \$126$$
$$R \times B = P$$
$$R \times \$420 = \$126$$
$$R = \frac{126}{420} = 0.3 = 30\% \quad \text{Markup percent on cost}$$

10.1 Finding the cost and selling price

Use $P = R \times B$ to solve for cost. Then use $C + M = S$ to find selling price.

Markup, $56; markup on cost, 50%. Find cost and selling price.

$$P = R \times B$$
$$\$56 = 0.5C$$
$$C = \frac{56}{0.5} = \$112 \quad \text{Cost}$$
$$C + M = S$$
$$\$112 + \$56 = \$168 \quad \text{Selling price}$$

10.2 Markup on selling price

Use rate $\times$ base = part $(R \times B = P)$, with selling price as base (100%), markup % as rate, and markup as part.

Selling price, $6; markup, 25% on selling price. Find the markup.

$$P = R \times B$$
$$\text{Markup} = 25\% \times \text{selling price}$$
$$M = 0.25\,(\$6) = \$1.50 \quad \text{Markup}$$

10.2 Finding the cost

Use the formulas $R \times B = P$ and $C + M = S$.

Markup, $87.50; markup on selling price, 35%. Find the cost.

First, use $R \times B = P$ to find selling price.

$$35\% \times \text{Selling price} = \$87.50$$
$$0.35S = \$87.50$$
$$S = \$250$$

Now find cost.

$$C + M = S$$
$$C + \$87.50 = \$250 \qquad \text{Selling price}$$
$$C = \$250 - \$87.50 = \$162.50 \qquad \text{Cost}$$

10.2 Calculating the selling price and the markup

Use the formula $C + M = S$.

Cost, $150; markup, 25% of selling price. Find the selling price and the markup.

$$C + M = S$$
$$\$150 + 0.25S = S$$
$$\$150 = 0.75S$$
$$\frac{\$150}{0.75} = \frac{0.75S}{0.75}$$
$$\$200 = S \qquad \text{Selling price}$$
$$C + M = S$$
$$\$150 + M = \$200 \qquad \text{Selling price}$$
$$M = \$200 - \$150$$
$$= \$50 \qquad \text{Markup}$$

10.2 Converting markup on cost to markup on selling price

Use the following formula.

$$M_s = \frac{M_c}{100\% + M_c}$$

Markup on cost, 25%. Convert to markup on selling price.

$$M_s = \frac{25\%}{100\% + 25\%}$$
$$= \frac{0.25}{1.25} = 0.2 = 20\%$$

10.2 Converting markup on selling price to markup on cost

Use the following formula.

$$M_c = \frac{M_s}{100\% - M_s}$$

Markup on selling price, 20%. Convert to markup on cost.

$$M_c = \frac{20\%}{100\% - 20\%}$$
$$= \frac{0.2}{0.8} = 0.25 = 25\%$$

10.3 Solving markup with spoilage or unsaleable items

1. Find total cost and selling price.
2. Subtract total sales at reduced prices from total sales.
3. Divide the remaining sales amount by the number of saleable units to get selling price per unit.

60 doughnuts cost $0.15 each; 10 are not sold; 60% markup on selling price. Find selling price per doughnut.

$$\text{Cost} = 60 \times \$0.15 = \$9$$
$$C + M = S$$
$$\$9 + 0.6S = S$$
$$\$9 = 0.4S$$
$$\$22.50 = S$$
$$\$22.50 \div 50 = \$0.45 \qquad \text{Sale price per doughnut}$$

The answer section includes answers to all Review Exercises.

Find the missing quantities. Round rates to the nearest tenth of a percent and money to the nearest cent. [10.1]

	Cost Price	Markup	% Markup on Cost	Selling Price
1.	$32	$6.40	20%	$38.40
2.	$24.60	$6.15	25%	$30.75
3.	$147	$73.50	50%	$220.50
4.	$108	$45.90	42.5%	$153.90

Find the missing quantities. Round rates to the nearest tenth of a percent and money to the nearest cent. [10.2]

	Cost Price	Markup	% Markup on Selling Price	Selling Price
5.	$72.32	$18.08	20%	$90.40
6.	$105	$35	25%	$140
7.	$34.70	$17.35	$33\frac{1}{3}$%	$52.05
8.	$283.02	$177.18	38.5%	$460.20

Find the missing quantities by first computing the markup on one base and then computing the markup on the other. Round rates to the nearest tenth of a percent and money to the nearest cent. [10.2]

	Cost	Markup	Selling Price	% Markup on Cost	% Markup on Selling Price
9.	$1920	$480	$2400	25%	20%
10.	$64.50	$64.50	$129	100%	50%
11.	$8	$3.68	$11.68	46%	31.5%
12.	$474.28	$474.28	$948.56	100%	50%
13.	$44.16	$22.08	$66.24	50%	$33\frac{1}{3}$%
14.	$375.40	$150.16	$525.56	40%	28.6%

Find the equivalent markups on either cost or selling price using the appropriate formula. Round to the nearest tenth of a percent. [10.2]

	% Markup on Cost	% Markup on Selling Price
15.	25%	20%
16.	100%	50%
17.	18.1%	15.3%
18.	20%	$16\frac{2}{3}$%

Find the selling price per item. [10.3]

	Total Cost	Quantity Purchased	Number Unsaleable	% Markup on Selling Price	Selling Price per Item
19.	$324	360	36	20%	$1.25
20.	$780	52	12	40%	$32.50
21.	$970	9 doz.	6	30%	$13.59
22.	$12,650	1500 pr.	150 pr.	45%	$17.04

416

Find the missing quantities. Markup is based on total cost. **[10.3]**

	Total Cost of Production	Quantity Purchased	Percent Sold at Reduced Price	% Markup on Total Cost	Number at Regular Price	Number at Reduced Price	Reduced Price	Regular Selling Price Each
23.	$750	150	10%	25%	135	15	$2.50	$6.67
24.	$135	90 pr.	20%	40%	72	18	$1.00	$2.38
25.	$1728	2 gr.	25%	20%	216	72	$4.00	$8.27
26.	$2800	1000 pr.	30%	50%	700	300	$3.00	$4.71

Solve the following application problems on markup.

27. Premont Pools purchases chlorine tablets in 10-pound containers for $22.30 per container. Find the selling price if the markup is 35% on selling price. **[10.2]** $34.31

28. Best Buy sells a washer and dryer set for $790 while using a markup of 25% on cost. Find the cost. **[10.1]** $632

29. The Computer Service Center sells a DeskJet print cartridge for $37.50. The print cartridge costs the store $22.50. Find the markup as a percent of selling price. **[10.2]**   40%

30. Wild Rivers offers an inflatable boat for $199.95. If the boats cost $1943.52 per dozen, what is (a) the markup, (b) the percent of markup on selling price, and (c) the percent of markup on cost? Round to the nearest tenth of a percent. **[10.1 and 10.2]**   (a) $37.99 (b) 19.0% (c) 23.5%

31. Raley's Superstore bought 1820 swimming pool blow-up toys for a total cost of $10,010. The toys were sold as follows: 580 at $13.95 each, 635 at $9.95 each, 318 at $8.95 each, 122 at $7.95 each, and the balance at $5.00 each. Find (a) the total selling price of all the toys and (b) the markup as a percent of selling price (to the nearest whole percent). **[10.2]**   (a) $19,050.25 (b) 47%

32. Fan Fever purchased 200 posters at a cost of $540. If 20% of the posters must be sold at $3 each and a markup of 100% on cost is needed, find the regular selling price of each poster. **[10.3]** $6

33. Office Depot pays $3.96 for a package of 20-pound paper and sells it for $4.95. Find (a) the percent of markup on selling price and (b) the percent of markup on cost. **[10.2]**   (a) 20% (b) 25%

34. Fosters' Doughnuts bakes lemon squares at a cost of $5.79 per dozen. Markup on cost is 100% and 15% of the lemon squares will have to be sold at $7.20 per dozen. If Fosters bakes 180 dozen lemon squares, what is the regular selling price per dozen? Round to the nearest cent. **[10.3]** $12.35

CHAPTER 10	Business Application Case #1
	Discounts and Markups in Retailing

The Hallmark Shop chain buys 3400 boxes of holiday greeting cards directly from the manufacturer. The list price of the cards is $9.90 per box, there is a trade discount of 30/10/20, and a cash discount of 5/10–40x. The Hallmark Shop earns and receives both discounts.

The cards were sold as follows: 1080 boxes at $7.90, 1250 boxes at $5.90, 660 boxes at $5.00, 230 boxes at $4.00, and the remaining boxes were unsaleable. To better manage greeting card sales next year, determine each of the following.

a. The net cost of the greeting cards after trade and cash discounts. (First find total cost, then apply discounts.) $16,116.41

b. The total sales amount received from all the holiday greeting cards. $20,127

c. The amount of net profit from the sales of the cards. $4010.59

d. The markup as a percent of selling price to the nearest whole percent.   20%

e. The equivalent percent of markup on cost to the nearest whole percent.   25%

CHAPTER 10	Business Application Case #2
	Estimating Needed Markup

After a careful analysis, the manager of a retail store has estimated the following costs as a percent of the sales price, based on total annual sales. Use these figures to answer the questions that follow.

Item	Percent of Selling Price
Cost of Goods Sold Including Transportation Costs	61.2%
Wages and Benefits	19.8%
Rent, Taxes, Utilities, Maintenance, Insurance	8.3%
Theft	1.9%
Spoilage and Other	3.6%

a. Find the percent of sales that remains as profit.   5.2%

b. If annual sales at the store this year are $7,180,300, estimate the profit for the year. $373,375.60

c. Estimate the average markup on cost needed to pay all costs and leave a profit as indicated in (a) above. (*Hint:* Assume a sale of exactly $100 not including taxes. Then 61.2% of that or $61.20, is the cost of goods sold. From that you can find the markup on cost.)   63.4%

d. Use the appropriate formula in **Section 10.2** to find the markup on selling price.   38.8%

javier brosch / Fotolia.com

CHAPTER
11

Markdown and Inventory Control

Markdowns and sales are the cornerstone of many businesses today. The word "free" in advertising gets the greatest response from consumers, and the word "sale" is not far behind. While there can be many reasons for offering markdowns, the resulting increase in sales volume helps move out existing inventory to make room for new merchandise.

The global financial crisis of 2008–2012 resulted in difficult times for many individuals and business. Consumers struggled with falling home values, losses in retirement accounts as stock prices fell, loss of jobs, and difficulty obtaining loans. Unemployment rose across the country, and frightened or unemployed consumers "tightened their belts" by buying less. The slowdown in retail sales can be seen in Figure 11.1, which compares quarterly retail sales to the same quarter of the prior year. Due to a slowly growing population and inflation, the percent change in sales over the same quarter of the previous year will normally be positive, say, 3% or 4%. So, anything less than 3% to 4% shows that something negative is happening in the economy. Notice that the percent increase in sales dropped to 0% in quarter 3 of 2008 and then collapsed during 2009. Falling sales resulted in increased inventories, and managers across the world slowed production and laid off workers.

Retail Sales, Including Food, in U.S.
Quarterly Percent Change Compared to Same Quarter of the Previous Year

Source: Commerce Department.

Figure 11.1

STOP&THINK

Suppose that you are the manager of a large retail store and that demand falls sharply. What would be the first sign(s) of a sharp falloff in sales? If sales stayed low, what would happen to your inventory? What could you do as a manager to respond? How bad would things need to be before you would consider laying people off, or should layoffs ever happen?

419

Managers spend a great deal of time controlling inventory. High inventories often result in inventory sitting around (waste) that must be marked down to sell. Markdown is the topic of this chapter. Low inventories result in shortages (lost sales) when customers go elsewhere.

11.1   Markdown

OBJECTIVES

1 *Calculate markdown and reduced price.*

2 *Calculate the percent of markdown.*

3 *Find the original selling price.*

4 *Identify the terms associated with loss.*

5 *Determine the break-even point and operating loss.*

6 *Determine the amount of absolute loss and the percent of absolute loss.*

7 *Find the maximum percent of markdown to be given.*

Merchandise often does not sell at its marked price, for any of several reasons. The retailer may have ordered too much, or the merchandise may have become soiled or damaged, or perhaps only odd sizes and colors remain. Also, merchandise may not sell because of lower prices at other stores, seasonal changes, economic fluctuations, or changes in fashion.

Objective

1   *Calculate Markdown and Reduced Price.* When merchandise does not sell at its marked price, its price is often reduced. The difference between the original selling price and the reduced selling price is called the **markdown**. The selling price after the markdown is called the **reduced price**, **sale price**, or **actual selling price**. The basic **formula for markdown** is as follows.

$$\text{Reduced price} = \text{original price} - \text{markdown}$$

EXAMPLE 1   **Finding the Reduced Price**

A La-Z-Boy store has marked down a leather recliner. What is the reduced price if the original price was $960 and the markdown is 25%?

Solution

$$
\begin{aligned}
\text{Reduced price} &= \text{original price} - \text{markdown} \\
&= \$960 \quad - 25\% \text{ of } \$960 \\
&= \$960 \quad - 0.25 \times \$960 \\
&= \$720
\end{aligned}
$$

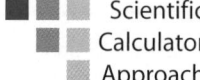 Scientific Calculator Approach

The calculator solution to Example 1 uses the complement, with respect to 1, of the 25% discount.

$$960 \;\boxed{\times}\; \boxed{(}\; 1 \;\boxed{-}\; 0.25 \;\boxed{)}\; \boxed{=}\; 720$$

Objective

2 *Calculate the Percent of Markdown.* The next example shows how to find a **percent**, or **rate of markdown**.

> **NOTE** The original selling price is always the base or 100% and the percent of markdown is always calculated on the original selling price.

EXAMPLE 2 Calculating the Percent of Markdown

A necklace and earring set with rubies has a retail value of $785. Find the percent markdown on the original price if it has been marked down to $530.

Solution

First find the markdown.

$$\text{Markdown} = \text{original price} - \text{reduced price}$$
$$= \quad \$785 \quad - \quad \$530 = \$255$$

To solve for percent of markdown on original price, use the percent equation: rate × base = part. The base is the original price of $785, the rate is unknown, and the part is the amount of markdown, or $255.

$$R \times B = P$$
$$\_\_\_\% \times \$785 = \$255$$
$$R \times \$785 = \$255$$
$$\$785R = \$255$$
$$R = \frac{255}{785}$$
$$R = 0.3248 = 32\% \quad \text{Rounded to the nearest percent}$$

The jewelry was sold at a markdown of 32%.

 Scientific Calculator Approach

In the calculator solution to Example 2, the reduced price is subtracted from the original price using parentheses. This results in the markdown, which is then divided by the original price.

(785 − 530) ÷ 785 = 0.3248

Objective

3 *Find the Original Selling Price.*

EXAMPLE 3 Finding the Original Price

Bouza's Baby News offers a child's car seat at a reduced price of $122.50 after a 30% markdown from the original price. Find the original price.

Solution

After the 30% markdown, the reduced price of $122.50 represents 70% of the original price. Find the original price, which is the base.

$$R \times B = P$$
$$70\% \times B = \$122.50$$
$$0.7B = \$122.50$$
$$B = \frac{122.50}{0.7}$$
$$B = \$175$$

The original price of the car seat was $175.

> **NOTE** In Example 3, notice that 70%, not 30%, is used in the formula. The reduced price, $122.50, is represented by 70%.

Objective

4 *Identify the Terms Associated with Loss.* The amount of markdown must be large enough to sell the merchandise while providing as much profit as possible. Merchandise that is marked down will result in either a reduced net profit, breaking even, an operating loss, or an absolute loss. Figure 11.2 illustrates the meanings of these terms.

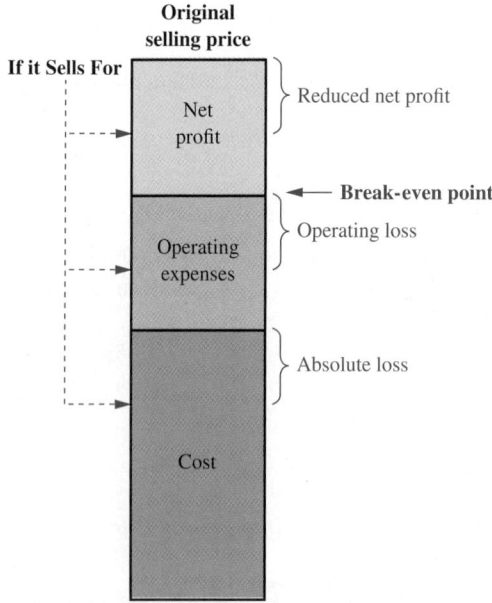

Figure 11.2

Reduced net profit results when the reduced price is still within the net profit range, that is, when it is greater than the cost plus overhead (operating expenses).

The **break-even point** is the point at which the reduced price just covers cost plus overhead (operating expenses). At this point the business neither makes money nor loses money.

An **operating loss** occurs when the reduced price is less than the break-even point. The operating loss is the difference between the break-even point and the reduced selling price.

An **absolute loss** is the result of a reduced price that not only covers none of the operating expenses but is also below the cost of the merchandise. The absolute loss is the difference between the cost and reduced selling price.

The following formulas are helpful when working with markdowns.

$$\text{Break-even point} = \text{cost} + \text{operating expenses}$$
$$\text{Operating loss} = \text{break-even point} - \text{reduced selling price}$$
$$\text{Absolute loss} = \text{cost} - \text{reduced selling price}$$

Objective

5   *Determine the Break-Even Point and Operating Loss.*

EXAMPLE **4**   **Determining a Profit or a Loss**

Cordova Appliance paid $40 for a blender. If operating expenses are 30% of cost and the blender is sold for $50, find the break-even point and the operating loss.

Solution

Use the following formula to find the break-even point.

$$\text{Cost} + \text{operating expenses} = \text{break-even point}$$
$$\$40 + (0.3 \times \$40) = \$40 + \$12 = \$52 \quad \text{Break-even point}$$

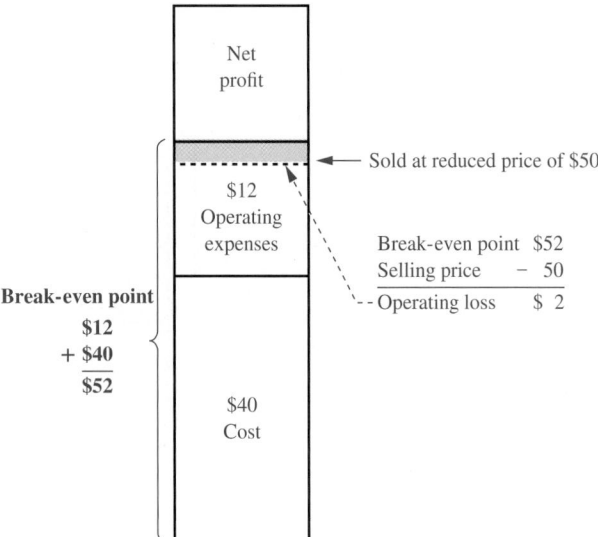

Figure 11.3

Since the break-even point is $52 and the selling price is $50, there is an operating loss of

$$\$52 - \$50 = \$2$$

This $2 loss is an operating loss since the selling price is less than the break-even point but greater than the cost. See Figure 11.3.

Scientific Calculator Approach

The calculator solution to Example 4 is as follows.

$$40 \boxed{+} 0.3 \boxed{\times} 40 \boxed{=} 52 \boxed{STO}$$
$$\boxed{RCL} \boxed{-} 50 \boxed{=} 2$$

Objective

6 *Determine the Amount of Absolute Loss and the Percent of Absolute Loss.*

EXAMPLE **5** **Determining the Operating Loss and the Absolute Loss**

A new, voice-activated GPS sells for $360. However, one retailer marks it down by 30% due to slow sales before Christmas. The unit costs the retailer $260 and the operating expenses are 20% of the cost. Find (a) the operating loss, (b) the absolute loss, and (c) the percent of absolute loss based on cost (round to the nearest percent).

Solution

(a) Break-even point $= \$260 + 0.2 \times \$260 = \$312$

Reduced price $= \$360 - (0.3 \times \$360) = \$360 - \$108 = \$252$

Operating loss $= \$312 \text{ break-even point} - \$252 \text{ reduced price} = \$60$

(b) The absolute or gross loss is the difference between the cost and the reduced price.

$$\$260 \text{ cost} - \$252 \text{ reduced price} = \$8 \text{ absolute loss}$$

Figure 11.4

(c) The percent of absolute loss is always expressed as a percent of cost, so find the percent of cost that is the absolute loss using the percent equation.

$$R \times B = P$$
$$\underline{\quad\quad}\% \times \$260 = \$8$$
$$\$260R = \$8$$
$$R = \frac{8}{260}$$
$$R = 0.0308 = 3\% \quad \text{Rounded}$$

The rate of absolute loss is approximately 3%. See Figure 11.4.

Objective

7 *Find the Maximum Percent of Markdown to Be Given.*

EXAMPLE **6** **Finding the Original Price and Maximum Percent of Markdown to Be Given**

A wood-burning pellet stove cost a retailer $1890. If the store's operating expenses are 25% of cost, and net profit is 15% of cost, what is (a) the original selling price of the stove and (b) the maximum percent of markdown that may be given without taking an operating loss (round to the nearest tenth of a percent)?

Solution

(a) The markup is 40% (25% + 15%) on cost. The selling price is found from the basic markup formula.

$$C + M = S$$
$$\$1890 + (0.4 \times \$1890) = S$$
$$\$1890 + \$756 = S$$
$$\$2646 = S$$

The oiginal selling price is $2646.

(b) Break-even point = cost + operating expenses
$$= \$1890 + 0.25 \times \$1890$$
$$= \$2362.50$$

The maximum amount of markdown that may be taken without an operating loss is as follows.

Markdown = original price − reduced price
$$= \$2646 - \$2362.50$$
$$= \$283.50$$

Since the maximum markdown is $283.50, the maximum percent of markdown can be found by asking: What percent of original selling price is markdown?

$$R \times B = P$$
$$\underline{\quad\quad}\% \times \$2646 = \$283.50$$
$$\$2646R = \$283.50$$
$$R = \frac{283.50}{2646}$$
$$R = 0.1071 = 10.7\% \quad \text{Rounded}$$

A maximum of 10.7% may be given as markdown without an operating loss.

Figure 11.5 shows the percent of adults who get an emotional high as a result of making certain purchases. Customers love buying things—they especially love buying things when they are on sale. In fact, many marketing professionals view their work as helping customers satisfy basic psychological needs versus just "selling a product."

In the Sweet Buy and Buy

Percent of adults that say they feel euphoric after shopping for the following items:

Item	Percent
Car	28%
Gift for someone	17%
House	11%
Clothes	8%
Home electronics	5%
Jewelry	4%
Vacations	4%
Furniture	4%

Source: Data from Yankelovich Partners.

Figure 11.5

11.1 | Exercises

Find the missing quantities. Round rates to the nearest whole percent and money to the nearest cent.

	Original Price	% Markdown	$ Markdown	Reduced Price
1.	$860	25%	$215	$645
2.	$240	40%	$96	$144
3.	$30.80	45%	$13.86	$16.94
4.	$1450	50%	$725	$725
5.	$6.50	20%	$1.30	$5.20
6.	$9.30	$66\frac{2}{3}$%	$6.20	$3.10
7.	$2.70	40%	$1.08	$1.62
8.	$3.85	20%	$0.77	$3.08
9.	$43.50	50%	$21.75	$21.75
10.	$2327.50	44%	$1024.10	$1303.40
11.	$857	20%	$175	$682
12.	$1538.50	18%	$276.93	$1261.57

Complete the following. If there is no operating loss or absolute loss, write "none." Use Figure 11.2 as a guide.

	Cost	Operating Expense	Break-even Point	Reduced Price	Operating Loss	Absolute Loss
13.	$48	$12	$60	$50	$10	none
14.	$25	$8	$33	$22	$11	$3
15.	$50	$16	$66	$44	$22	$6
16.	$12.50	$4	$16.50	$11	$5.50	$1.50
17.	$310	$75	$385	$250	$135	$60
18.	$78	$22	$100	$70	$30	$8
19.	$29	$10	$39	$25	$14	$4
20.	$116	$40	$156	$100	$56	$16

21. Describe five reasons why a store will reduce (mark down) the price of merchandise to get it sold.

22. As a result of a markdown, there are four possible results: reduced net profit, breaking even, operating loss, and absolute loss. As a business owner, which would concern you the most? Explain. (See Objective 4.)

Solve the following application problems. Round rates to the nearest whole percent and money to the nearest cent.

23. GAS BARBECUE   A Sunbeam Grill Master gas barbecue is marked down $76.48, a reduction of 32%. Find the original price. $239

24. RACING BICYCLE   An ultralight racing bicycle is marked down 15% to $3939.75. Find the original price. $4635

25. OAK DESK   An oak desk originally priced at $837.50 is reduced to $686.75. Find the percent of markdown on the original price.   18%

26. AUTOMOBILE SOUND SYSTEMS   Fry's Electronics prices its entire inventory of 200-watt AM/FM MP3/CD players with removable face at $133,509. If the original price of the inventory was $226,284, find the percent of markdown on the original price.   41%

27. IMPORTED RUGS   The Persian and Oriental Rug Gallery paid $2211 for an imported rug from Iran. Its operating expenses are $33\frac{1}{3}$% of cost. If it sells the rug at a clearance price of $2650, find the amount of profit or loss. $298 operating loss

28. EXERCISE BICYCLES   Exercise Equipment Co. has an end-of-season sale during which it sells a Proform Upright Bike for $265. If the cost was $198 and the operating expenses were 25% of cost, find the amount of profit or loss. $17.50 profit

29. ANTIQUES   American Antique paid $153.49 for a fern stand. Its original selling price was $208.78, but this was marked down 46% in order to make room for incoming merchandise. Operating expenses are 14.9% of cost. Find (a) the operating loss, (b) the absolute loss, and (c) the percent of absolute loss based on cost.   (a) $63.62 (b) $40.75 (c) 27%

30. TRUCK-BED LINER   Pep Boys Automotive paid $208.50 for a pickup truck–bed liner. The original selling price was $291.90, but this was marked down 35%. Operating expenses are 28% of cost. Find (a) the operating loss, (b) the absolute loss, and (c) the percent of absolute loss based on cost.   (a) $77.14 (b) $18.76 (c) 9%

31. PHOTOGRAPHIC ENLARGERS   Photo Supply, a retailer, pays $190 for an enlarger. The store's operating expenses are 20% of cost, and net profit is 15% of cost. Find (a) the selling price of the enlarger and (b) the maximum percent of markdown that may be given without taking an operating loss. Round to the nearest whole percent.   (a) $256.50 (b) 11%

32. HEAT PUMP To reduce his dependency on expensive heating oil, Julio Rodriguez bought a high-efficiency heat pump, which will cool his house in the summer and heat it in the winter. The retailer has operating expenses that are 30% of cost and net profit that is 10% of cost, and it paid $5890 for the heat pump. Find (a) the selling price of the heat pump and (b) the maximum percent of markdown that may be given without taking an operating loss.   (a) $8246 (b) 7.1% rounded.

11.2	**Average Inventory and Inventory Turnover**

OBJECTIVES

1 *Determine average inventory.*

2 *Calculate stock turnover.*

3 *Identify considerations in stock turnover.*

Many firms carry a lot of inventory. For example, Table 11.1 shows sales, inventory, and inventory as a percent of sales for Wal-Mart Stores Inc. Inventory as a percent of sales fell every year from 2006 to 2010 as managers figured out how to operate with less inventory per dollar in sales. Most retailers use **point-of-sale** computerized systems that track sales as they are made. Data is entered from the cash register directly into a database on a computer. This system allows managers to quickly see what is—and what is not—selling and to adjust the product mix being brought to the store. Computerized inventory systems place orders for products when needed, thereby freeing managers to do other things.

Table 11.1 WAL-MART STORES (FIGURES IN BILLIONS)

Year	Total Revenue	Inventory at End of Year	Inventory as a Percent of Total Revenue
2006	$315.7	$32.2	10.2%
2007	$348.7	$33.7	9.7%
2008	$378.8	$35.2	9.3%
2009	$404.2	$34.5	8.5%
2010	$408.1	$32.7	8.0%
2011	$421.8	$36.3	8.6%

Source: Wal-Mart financial statements.

One very important measure of the efficiency of a firm is **inventory turnover**, also called **stock turnover**, or just **turns**. Inventory turnover is a measure of the number of times a firm's average inventory is turned over (or sold) each year. A company with inventory turns of 52 is selling its average inventory every week, whereas a company with turns of 12 is selling its average inventory only once every month.

A higher turnover means that the firm is selling goods at a faster rate. A slower turnover may mean that the company is having difficulty selling items, or perhaps that it is poorly managed. To survive, businesses selling perishables such as fruit, dairy products, and flowers must have a high turnover since products remaining on the shelves quickly spoil. On the other hand, other businesses, such as furniture stores or hardware stores, will normally have much lower inventory turns.

Objective

1 *Determine Average Inventory.* Find stock turnover by first calculating the **average inventory**. The average inventory for a certain time period is found by adding the inventories taken during the time period and then dividing the total by the number of times that the inventory was taken.

EXAMPLE **1**   **Determining Average Inventory**

The inventory value at Medco Health Supplies was $285,672 on April 1 and $198,560 on April 30. What was the average inventory?

Solution

First, add the inventory values.

$$
\begin{array}{ll}
\$285,672 & \text{April 1} \\
+ \ \$198,560 & \text{April 30} \\
\hline
\$484,232 &
\end{array}
$$

Then divide by the number of times inventory was taken.

$$
\frac{\$484,232}{2} = \$242,116
$$

The average inventory was $242,116.

EXAMPLE **2**   **Finding Average Inventory for the Quarter**

The retail value of inventory at a small gift shop was $22,615 on January 1, $18,321 on February 1, $26,718 on March 1, and $16,228 on March 31. Find the average inventory for the first quarter of the year.

Solution

First add the inventories and then divide by the number of inventories taken.

$$
\frac{\$22,615 + \$18,321 + \$26,718 + \$16,228}{4} = \$20,970.50
$$

The average inventory for the first quarter of the year is $20,970.50.

In Example 2, inventory was taken four times to find the average inventory for the first quarter of the year. To find the average inventory for a period of time, an inventory must be taken at the beginning of the period and one final time at the end of the period. To find average inventory for a full year, it is common to find inventory on the first day of each month and on the last day of the last month. Average inventory is found by adding all these inventory amounts (13 of them) and then dividing by 13, the number of inventories taken. Methods of taking inventory and inventory valuation are discussed in the next section.

Keeping a close watch on inventory is an ongoing concern of management. Year-end sales promotions are designed to quickly reduce inventory.

MONDAY–FRIDAY 10AM–9PM SATURDAY 10AM-8PM & SUNDAY 11AM–6PM. PRICES GOOD 'TIL TUESDAY!

GET HUGE STOREWIDE SAVINGS!

YEAR-END SALE!

**No Money Down, No Interest & No Payment 'til June
...On Every Item ...On Every Room!**

Same As Cash Option. On Approved Credit With No Down Payment, Interest Accrues From Delivery Date If Not Paid in Full by June

NO DOWN PAYMENT, NO INTEREST & NO PAYMENTS 'TIL JUNE   ON 8-WAY, HAND-TIED LEATHER

Objective

2 *Calculate Stock Turnover.* Most inventories are taken at retail because products or shelf locations are marked with the retail price and not the cost. Also, statistical averages are usually shown as average turnover at retail. Many businesses, however, value inventory at cost. For this reason, stock turnover is found by either of these formulas.

$$\text{Turnover at retail} = \frac{\text{retail sales}}{\text{average inventory at retail}}$$

$$\text{Turnover at cost} = \frac{\text{cost of goods sold}}{\text{average inventory at cost}}$$

As long as there is no theft, markdowns, or unsaleable merchandise, the two turnover ratios will be equal. However, since there is usually some shrinkage, the **turnover at cost** is usually slightly higher than the **turnover at retail**. For this reason, many managers prefer to use the more conservative turnover at retail.

EXAMPLE 3 **Finding Stock Turnover at Retail**

During May, The Book Nook has sales of $38,920 and an average retail inventory of $18,600. Find the stock turnover at retail.

Solution

$$\text{Turnover at retail} = \frac{\text{retail sales}}{\text{average inventory at retail}} = \frac{\$38,920}{\$18,600} = 2.09 \text{ at retail}$$

On average, the store turned over its entire inventory 2.09 times during the month.

EXAMPLE 4 **Finding Stock Turnover at Cost**

If The Book Nook in Example 3 used a markup of 40% on selling price and if the cost of goods sold was $24,063, what is the stock turnover on cost?

Solution

Inventory at retail in the store was $18,600. Since markup is 40% on selling price, the cost is 60% of the inventory.

$$C = 0.6 \times \$18,600$$
$$= \$11,160$$

Inventory value at cost is $11,160.

$$\text{Turnover at cost} = \frac{\text{cost of goods sold}}{\text{average inventory at cost}}$$

$$= \frac{\$24,063}{\$11,160} = 2.16 \text{ at cost} \qquad \text{Rounded}$$

The turnover on cost is 2.16.

NOTE In Example 4, the average inventory at cost needed to be calculated. To do this, the rate of markup was used along with the average inventory at retail. Since the markup was 40% on selling price, the average inventory at cost was 60% of the average inventory at retail.

Objective

3 *Identify Considerations in Stock Turnover.* Stock turnover is useful only for comparison purposes. Many trade organizations publish such operating statistics to permit businesses to compare their operation with the industry as a whole. In addition to this, management uses these rates to compare turnover from period to period and from department to department.

Benefits of a Rapid Stock Turnover:

1. Capital invested in inventory is kept at a minimum. This allows additional funds to be used for special purchases and discounts.
2. Items in inventory are up-to-date and fresher and are, therefore, less likely to be sold at a reduced price or loss.
3. Costly storage space and the other expenses of handling inventory can be minimized.

Disadvantages of Rapid Stock Turnover:

1. Orders for smaller quantities of goods from wholesalers may result in losses of quantity discounts and incur additional processing, handling, and bookkeeping expenses.
2. Items can be sold out and customers may be dissatisfied.

11.2	Exercises

Find the average inventory in the following.

	Date	Average Inventory			Date	Average Inventory	
1.	April 1	$10,603		**2.**	January 1	$42,312	
	April 30	$12,757	$11,680		July 1	$38,514	$37,015
3.	July 1	$18,300			December 31	$30,219	
	October 1	$26,580	$22,673	**4.**	January 31	$69,480	
	December 31	$23,139			April 30	$55,860	
5.	January 1	$16,250			July 31	$80,715	$71,616
	March 1	$20,780			October 31	$88,050	
	May 1	$28,720			January 31	$63,975	
	July 1	$24,630	$24,500	**6.**	January 1	$65,430	
	September 1	$23,550			April 1	$58,710	
	November 1	$34,800			July 1	$53,410	$60,568
	December 31	$22,770			October 1	$78,950	
					December 31	$46,340	

Find the stock turnover at retail and turnover at cost for the following. Round to the nearest hundredth.

	Average Inventory at Cost	Average Inventory at Retail	Cost of Goods Sold	Retail Sales	
7.	$26,745	$53,085	$75,591	$149,175	2.81; 2.83
8.	$15,140	$24,080	$67,408	$106,193	4.41; 4.45
9.	$22,390	$32,730	$178,687	$259,876	7.94; 7.98
10.	$30,280	$48,160	$134,816	$212,386	4.41; 4.45
11.	$26,400	$42,660	$270,600	$437,260	10.25; 10.25
12.	$72,120	$138,460	$259,123	$487,379	3.52; 3.59
13.	$180,600	$256,700	$846,336	$1,196,222	4.66; 4.69
14.	$411,580	$780,600	$1,905,668	$3,559,536	4.56; 4.63

 15. Identify three types of businesses that you think would have a high turnover. Identify three types of businesses that you think would have a low turnover.

16. Which departments in a grocery store do you think have the highest turnover? Which ones have the lowest turnover?

Solve the following application problems. Round stock turnover to the nearest hundredth.

17. CERAMIC TILE   Bedrosian's Tile took inventory at the first of each month for the full year. The sum of these inventories was $596,428. On December 31, inventory was again taken and amounted to $49,895. Find the average inventory for the year. $49,717.15

18. PHARMACY INVENTORY   Inventory at retail at Sid's Pharmacy was $388,640 on April 1, $475,360 on May 1, and $261,280 on June 1. Find the average inventory. $375,093.33

19. GLASS SHOP   The Glass Works has an average inventory at cost of $15,730 and cost of goods sold for the same period is $85,412. Find the stock turnover at cost.   5.43

20. METAL PLATING   Capital Plating had an average inventory of $27,250 at retail. The cost of goods sold for the year was $103,400 and a markup of 40% on selling price was used. What was the turnover at cost?   6.32

21. UNDERWATER DIVING   Associated Divers uses a markup of 30% on selling price. If its average inventory is $15,650 at retail and the cost of goods sold is $53,023, what is the stock turnover at cost?   4.84

22. ELECTRICAL SUPPLIES   The cost of goods sold at Capitol Electric was $2,108,410. The following inventories were taken at cost: $208,180, $247,660, and $114,438. Find the stock turnover at cost.   11.09

23. CELL PHONES   A cell phone booth in a local mall had an average inventory of $6320 at retail. Cell phone sales for the year were $249,400. Find the stock turnover at retail.   39.46

24. HOBBY SALES   Inventory at Harbortown Hobby was taken at retail value four times and found to be at $53,820, $49,510, $60,820, and $56,380. Sales during the same period were $252,077. Find the stock turnover at retail.   4.57

25. POSTERS AND CARDS   Posters and Cards had the following inventories at retail: $33,820, $46,240, $39,830, $52,040, and $48,700. This business uses a 35% markup on cost, and the cost of goods sold during this period was $136,450. Find the turnover at cost.   4.17

26. APPLIANCE DEALER   Inventory at Standard Appliance was taken at retail four different times and found to be $98,500, $135,820, $107,420, and $124,300. The company uses a markup of 25% on cost, and the cost of goods sold for this period was $305,920. Find the inventory turnover at cost.   3.28

11.3 | Valuation of Inventory

OBJECTIVES

1 *Define perpetual inventory.*

2 *Understand universal product codes (UPC).*

3 *Use the specific-identification method to value inventory.*

4 *Use the weighted-average method to value inventory.*

5 *Use the FIFO method to value inventory.*

6 *Use the LIFO method to value inventory.*

7 *Use the gross-profit method to estimate inventory.*

8 *Use the retail method to estimate inventory.*

Objective

1

Define Perpetual Inventory. Placing a value on the merchandise that a firm has in stock is called **inventory valuation**. It is not always easy to place this value on each of the items in inventory. Many large companies keep a **perpetual inventory** by using a computer. As new items are received, the quantity, size, and cost of each are placed in the computer. Clerks enter product codes into the cash register by scanning the code attached to the item. Since inventory records are constantly updated, managers can find out the quantity on hand of any item.

Objective

2

Understand Universal Product Codes (UPC). **Universal product codes (UPC)** are the stripes known as bar codes that appear on many items sold in stores. Each product and product size is assigned its own code number. These UPCs are a great help in keeping track of inventory.

A Cracker Jack box has a UPC number (also called the *bar code*) of 0-87720-071-8. The checkout clerk or customer in a retail store passes the coded lines over an optical scanner. The numbers are picked up by a computer, which recognizes the product by its code. The computer then forwards the price of the item to the cash register. At the same time the price is being recorded, the computer is subtracting the item automatically from inventory. After all the items being purchased have passed over the scanner, the customer receives a detailed cash register receipt that gives a description of each item, the price of each item, and a total purchase price.

Most firms have programmed their systems to automatically place an order with the warehouse or supplier when the number of items on hand becomes low. This technique has allowed firms to have better control over their inventory with lower cost, compared to manually monitoring inventory and placing orders. However, computer database records are sometimes not accurate due to mistakes, spoilage, theft, etc. As a result, most businesses also take a **physical inventory** at regular intervals, such as at the end of every month. This type of inventory is called **periodic inventory** since it is done periodically or at regular time intervals. This helps detect theft and corrects mistakes that have collected in the database.

There are four major methods used for inventory valuation. They are the specific-identification method, the weighted-average method, the first-in, first-out method, and the last-in, first-out method.

Objective

3

Use the Specific-Identification Method to Value Inventory. The **specific-identification method** of inventory valuation is useful where items are easily identified and costs do not fluctuate. If the number of items is large and the exact cost of each unit is not known, then it may be difficult or impossible to use this method of inventory. With specific identification, each item is cost coded, either with numerals or a letter code. The cost may be included in a group of numbers written on the item or in a 10-letter code (where each letter is different).

For example, if a store uses the code SMALPROFIT, or

1	2	3	4	5	6	7	8	9	0
S	M	A	L	P	R	O	F	I	T

then an item bearing the cost code ARF would have a cost of

$$
\begin{array}{ccc}
A & R & F \\
\downarrow & \downarrow & \downarrow \\
3 & 6 & 8
\end{array}
$$

or $3.68. An item coded PMITT would have a cost of $529.

EXAMPLE **1** **Finding the Value of Inventory**

Hoig's Marine has four small fishing boats in stock. Cost codes indicate the following costs to the store.

Model A	$2718
Model B	$2571
Model C	$3498
Model D	$3974

Find the value of the fishing boat inventory using the specific-identification method.

Solution

The value of the inventory is found by adding the costs of the four fishing boats.

Model A	$ 2,718
Model B	2,571
Model C	3,498
Model D	+ 3,974
	$12,761 Total value of inventory

Objective

4 *Use the Weighted-Average Method to Value Inventory.* Since the cost of many items changes over time, there may be several of the same items that were purchased at different costs. Because of this variation, there are several common methods used to value an inventory. One method, the **weighted-average (average-cost) method**, values the items in an inventory at the average cost of buying them.

EXAMPLE **2** **Using Weighted-Average (Average-Cost) Inventory Valuation**

Olympic Sports and Leisure made the following purchases of the Explorer External Frame backpack during the year.

Beginning inventory	20 backpacks at $70
January	50 backpacks at $80
March	100 backpacks at $90
July	60 backpacks at $85
October	40 backpacks at $75

At the end of the year there are 75 backpacks in inventory. Use the weighted-average method to find the inventory value.

Solution

Find the total cost of all the backpacks.

Beginning inventory	$20 \times \$70 =$	$\$1,400$
January	$50 \times \$80 =$	$\$4,000$
March	$100 \times \$90 =$	$\$9,000$
July	$60 \times \$85 =$	$\$5,100$
October	$40 \times \$75 =$	$\$3,000$
Total	270	$\$22,500$

Find the average cost per backpack by dividing this total cost by the number purchased. The average cost per backpack is

$$\frac{\$22,500}{270} = \$83.33 \quad \text{Rounded}$$

Since the average cost is $83.33 and 75 backpacks remain in inventory, the weighted-average method gives the inventory value of the remaining backpacks as $83.33 \times 75 = \$6249.75$.

Scientific Calculator Approach

The calculator solution to Example 2 has several steps.

First, find the total number of backpacks purchased and place the total in memory.

$$20 \boxed{+} 50 \boxed{+} 100 \boxed{+} 60 \boxed{+} 40 \boxed{=} 270 \boxed{\text{STO}}$$

Next, find the total cost of all the backpacks purchased and divide by the number stored in memory. This gives the average cost per backpack.

$$20 \boxed{\times} 70 \boxed{+} 50 \boxed{\times} 80 \boxed{+} 100 \boxed{\times} 90 \boxed{+} 60 \boxed{\times} 85$$

$$\boxed{+} 40 \boxed{\times} 75 \boxed{=} \boxed{\div} \boxed{\text{RCL}} \boxed{=} 83.3333$$

Finally, round the average cost to the nearest cent and multiply by the number of backpacks in inventory to get the weighted-average inventory value.

$$83.33 \boxed{\times} 75 \boxed{=} 6249.75$$

Objective

5 *Use the FIFO Method to Value Inventory.* The **first-in, first-out (FIFO) method** of inventory valuation assumes a natural flow of goods through the inventory: the first goods to arrive are the first goods to be sold, so, the most recent items purchased by the company are the items remaining in inventory.

EXAMPLE 3 Using FIFO Inventory Valuation

Use the FIFO method to find the inventory value of the 75 backpacks from Olympic Sports and Leisure in Example 2.

Solution

With the FIFO method, the 75 remaining backpacks are assumed to consist of the last 75 backpacks purchased, or 40 backpacks bought in October and 35 ($75 - 40 = 35$) backpacks from the previous purchase in July.

The value of the inventory is as follows.

October	40 backpacks at $75 =	$3000	Value of last 40
July	35 backpacks at $85 =	$2975	Value of previous 35
	75 valued at	= $5975	Inventory value

The value of the backpack inventory is $5975 using the FIFO method.

Objective

6   *Use the LIFO Method to Value Inventory.* The **last-in, first-out (LIFO) method** of inventory valuation assumes a flow of goods through the inventory that is just the opposite of the FIFO method. With LIFO, the goods remaining in inventory are the first goods purchased.

EXAMPLE 4   Using LIFO Inventory Valuation

Use the LIFO method to value the 75 backpacks in inventory at Olympic Sports and Leisure (see Example 2).

Solution

The calculation starts with the beginning inventory and moves through the year's purchases, resulting in 75 backpacks. The beginning inventory and January purchases come to 70 backpacks, so the cost of 5 more ($75 - 70 = 5$) backpacks from the March purchase is needed.

Beginning inventory	20 backpacks at $70 = $1400	Value of first 20
January	50 backpacks at $80 = $4000	Value of next 50
March	5 backpacks at $90 = $450	Value of last 5
Total 75 valued	$5850	Inventory value

The value of the backpack inventory is $5850 using the LIFO method.

Depending on the method of valuing inventories that is used, Olympic Sports and Leisure may show the inventory value of the 75 backpacks as follows.

Average-cost method	$6249.75
FIFO	$5975.00
LIFO	$5850.00

The preferred inventory valuation method would be determined by Olympic Sports and Leisure, perhaps on the advice of an accountant. The comparison of inventory evaluation methods below would help them in selecting the method.

Comparing Inventory Valuation Methods

- When the market is stable, prices do not fluctuate. Since prices are not changing, all methods give the *same* inventory value.
- In a market where prices are rising and falling, each method gives a *different* inventory value.
- Weighted-average costs tend to *smooth out* inventory values that might result from price fluctuations.
- The FIFO method results in an inventory value that most closely reflects the *current* replacement cost of inventory.
- The LIFO method results in the last cost of inventory being assigned to the cost of merchandise sold. This results in a *closer matching* of current costs with sales revenues.

NOTE Accepted accounting practice insists that the method used to evaluate inventory be stated on the company financial statements.

The large quantities and varied types of items that are often in inventory make it time-consuming and expensive to take an actual physical inventory. Where this is the case, a physical inventory may be taken only once or twice a year. However, the need to monitor the performance of the business throughout the year is extremely important. To do this, methods of approximating inventory value have been developed. Two common methods for doing this are the gross-profit method and the retail method.

Objective

7   *Use the Gross-Profit Method to Estimate Inventory.* An estimate of inventory using the **gross-profit method** is found as follows.

$$\begin{array}{l} \text{Beginning inventory (at cost)} \\ + \text{ Purchase (at cost)} \\ \hline \text{Merchandise available for sale (at cost)} \\ - \text{ Cost of goods sold} \\ \hline \text{Ending inventory (at cost)} \end{array}$$

The beginning inventory and amount of purchases are taken from company records, and the cost of goods sold is normally determined by applying the rate of markup to the amount of net sales.

EXAMPLE 5 **Estimating Inventory Value Using the Gross-Profit Method**

Inventory on June 30 was $242,000. During the next 3 months, the company had purchases of $425,000 and net sales of $528,000. Use the gross-profit method to estimate the value of the inventory on September 30 if the company uses a markup of 25% on selling price.

Solution

First, find the cost of goods sold. Since markup is 25% of selling price, find cost.

$$C + M = S$$
$$C + 0.25S = S$$
$$C + 0.25S - 0.25S = S - 0.25S$$
$$C = S - 0.25S$$
$$C = 0.75S$$
$$C = 0.75 \times \$528,000$$
$$C = \$396,000$$

The cost of goods sold is $396,000. Now use the gross-profit method.

$$\begin{array}{ll} \$242,000 & \text{Beginning inventory (June 30)} \\ + \ 425,000 & \text{Purchases} \\ \hline \$667,000 & \text{Merchandise available for sale} \\ - \ 396,000 & \text{Cost of goods sold} \\ \hline \$271,000 & \text{Ending inventory (September 30)} \end{array}$$

The estimated value of the inventory on September 30 is $271,000.

8 *Use the Retail Method to Estimate Inventory.* The **retail method** of estimating inventory requires that a business keep records of all purchases at both cost and retail prices. The format for estimating inventory value at retail is the same as that used in estimating inventory using the gross-profit method. The difference, however, is that all amounts used are at retail. Inventory at retail is estimated as follows.

> Beginning inventory (at retail)
> + Purchases (at retail)
> ─────────────────────────────
> Merchandise available for sale (at retail)
> − Net sales
> ─────────────────────────────
> Ending inventory (at retail)

Notice that net sales are used in this method instead of cost of goods sold. Also, ending inventory value at retail must now be changed to an estimated value at cost. This is done by multiplying the ending inventory value at retail by a ratio determined by comparing the merchandise available for sale at cost to the merchandise available for sale at retail.

EXAMPLE 6 **Estimating Inventory Value Using the Retail Method**

At one booth in the mall, inventory on March 31 was valued at $9000 at cost and $15,000 at retail. During the next 3 months, the company made purchases of $36,000 at cost, or $60,000 at retail, and had total sales of $54,000. Use the retail method to estimate the value of inventory at cost on June 30.

Solution

At Cost	At Retail	
$9,000	$15,000	Beginning inventory
+ 36,000	+ 60,000	Purchases
$45,000	$75,000	Merchandise available for sale
	− 54,000	Net sales
	$21,000	June 30 inventory (at retail)

Now find the ratio of merchandise available for sale at cost to merchandise available for sale at retail.

$$\frac{\$45,000}{\$75,000} \quad \begin{array}{l} \text{Merchandise available for sale at cost} \\ \text{Merchandise available for sale at retail} \end{array}$$

Finally, the estimated inventory value at cost on June 30 is found by multiplying inventory at retail on June 30 by this ratio.

$$\$21,000 \times \frac{45,000}{75,000} = \$12,600 \quad \text{June 30 inventory (at cost)}$$

The retail method of estimating inventory value assumes that the ratio of the merchandise available for sale at cost to the merchandise available for sale at retail is the same as the ratio of the ending inventory at cost to ending inventory at retail. Both the gross-profit method and the retail method of estimating inventories must be updated from time to time with physical inventory counts to assure accurate record keeping.

Companies selling on the Internet are often able to have products shipped directly from a manufacturer or wholesaler to their customers. This will usually result in decreased inventory requirements in the supply chain since the Internet retailer may not hold inventory.

Humm, which one should I buy?

11.3   Exercises

Find the inventory value for the following using the specific-identification method.

	Description	Cost	
1.	Fair	$208	
	Good	$274	$827
	Excellent	$345	
3.	Good	$79	
	Excellent	$186	$560
	Mint	$295	

	Description	Cost	
2.	Economy	$1215	
	Standard	$1509	
	Luxury	$1873	$6713
	Deluxe	$2116	
4.	Incomplete	$835	
	Cheap	$972	$4337
	Improved	$1170	
	Tolerable	$1360	

Find the inventory values using (a) the weighted-average method, (b) the FIFO method, and (c) the LIFO method for each of the following. Round to the nearest dollar.

	Purchases		Now in Inventory	
5.	Beginning inventory:	10 units at $800		(a) $18,200
	June:	25 units at $900		(b) $19,500
	August:	15 units at $1000	20 units	(c) $17,000
6.	Beginning inventory:	80 units at $14.50		(a) $1316
	July:	50 units at $15.80		(b) $1289
	October:	70 units at $13.90	90 units	(c) $1318
7.	Beginning inventory:	50 units at $30.50		(a) $2352
	March:	70 units at $31.50		(b) $2385
	June:	30 units at $33.25		(c) $2313
	August:	40 units at $30.75	75 units	
8.	Beginning inventory:	700 units at $12.50		(a) $14,724
	May:	400 units at $17.50		(b) $20,700
	August:	500 units at $22.50		(c) $9100
	October:	600 units at $30.00	720 units	

Solve the following application problems. Round to the nearest dollar.

9. **SPECIFIC-IDENTIFICATION INVENTORY VALUE**   Towne Furniture had the following coffee tables in stock.

Model Number	Cost
P6251	$182
C3852	$210
PC623	$132
RW778	$921
WO335	$325

Find the inventory value using the specific-identification method. $1770

10. **HEATING AND AIR CONDITIONING**   Foothill Heat and Cool had the following refrigeration compressors in stock. Use the specific-identification method to find the inventory value. $4022

Model Number	Cost
AC129	$428
AC428	$715
AC2207	$526
AC78C	$1718
AC3107	$635

11. **BANDAGE INVENTORY**   A Rite-Aid drug store made the following purchases of elastic bandages made in Brazil.

Beginning inventory:	24 units at $1.50
June:	40 units at $1.35
August:	48 units at $1.25
November:	18 units at $1.60

Inventory at the end of the year shows that 35 units remain. Find the inventory value using (a) the weighted-average method, (b) the FIFO method, and (c) the LIFO method.   (a) $48; (b) $50; (c) $51

12. **CANDLES**   The Hobby House purchased of a variety of scented candles during the year as follows.

Beginning inventory:	200 candles at $1.10
March:	400 candles at $1.20
May:	700 candles at $1.00
August:	500 candles at $1.15
November:	300 candles at $1.30

At the end of the year, it had 450 candles in stock. Find the inventory value using (a) the weighted-average method, (b) the FIFO method, and (c) the LIFO method.   (a) $509; (b) $563; (c) $520

13. GREETING CARDS   The warehouse manager for DV Pharmacy made the following purchases of boxes of greeting cards.

Beginning inventory:	200 boxes at $3.10
July:	250 boxes at $3.50
August:	300 boxes at $4.25
October:	280 boxes at $4.50

Inventory at the end of October shows that 320 boxes remain. Find the inventory value using (a) the weighted-average method, (b) the FIFO method, and (c) the LIFO method.   **(a)** $1251; **(b)** $1430; **(c)** $1040

14. GAME BOY   Online Electronics made the following purchases of Game Boy consoles throughout the year.

Beginning inventory:	300 consoles at $21.60
March:	400 consoles at $24.00
August:	450 consoles at $24.30
November:	350 consoles at $22.50

An inventory at the end of December shows that 530 consoles remain. Find the inventory value using (a) the weighted-average method, (b) the FIFO method, and (c) the LIFO method.   **(a)** $12,328; **(b)** $12,249; **(c)** $12,000

15. PARTY SUPPLIES   Party Tyme Wholesalers made the following purchases of 11-inch paper plates.

Beginning inventory:	350 cases at $8.25
October:	300 cases at $9.50
November:	360 cases at $11.45
December:	240 cases at $10.10

The January inventory found that there were 625 cases remaining. Find the inventory value using (a) the weighted-average method, (b) the FIFO method, and (c) the LIFO method.   **(a)** $6144; **(b)** $6784; **(c)** $5500

16. LINEN SUPPLY   Industrial Linen Supply made the following purchases of shop towels.

Beginning inventory:	650 towels at $3.80
June:	500 towels at $4.20
September:	450 towels at $3.95
December:	600 towels at $4.05

In January an inventory found that there were 775 towels remaining. Find the inventory value using (a) the weighted-average method, (b) the FIFO method, and (c) the LIFO method.   **(a)** $3092; **(b)** $3121; **(c)** $2995

17. SECURITY DOORS   The inventory on December 31 at Security Doors was $136,000 at cost. During the next 3 months, the company made purchases of $148,000 (cost) and had net sales of $236,000. Use the gross-profit method to estimate the value of the inventory at cost on March 31 if the company uses a markup of 35% on selling price. $130,600

18. TOY STORE INVENTORY   Happy Toys has an inventory of $52,000 at cost on June 30. Purchases during the next 3 months were $68,000 (cost), and net sales were $126,000. If the company uses a 40% markup on selling price, use the gross-profit method to estimate the value of the inventory at cost on September 30. $44,400

19. PIANO REPAIR The September 30 inventory at Liverpool Piano Repair was $43,750 at cost and $62,500 at retail. Purchases during the next 3 months were $51,600 at cost and $73,800 at retail, and net sales were $92,500. Use the retail method to estimate the value of inventory at cost on December 31. $30,641

20. EVALUATING INVENTORY Uptown Sound had an inventory of $27,000 at cost and $45,000 at retail on March 31. During the next 3 months, it made purchases of $108,000 at cost and $180,000 at retail and had net sales of $162,000. Use the retail method to estimate the value of inventory at cost on June 30. $37,800

21. In your opinion, what are the benefits to a merchant who is using universal product codes (UPC)? (See Objective 2.)

22. List the four inventory valuation methods discussed in this section. Explain how one of these methods is used to determine inventory value.

CHAPTER TERMS

Review the following terms to test your understanding of the chapter. For each term you do not know, refer to the page number found next to that term.

absolute loss [p. 423]
actual selling price [p. 420]
average inventory [p. 428]
break-even point [p. 423]
first-in, first-out (FIFO)
  method [p. 435]
formula for markdown
  [p. 420]
gross-profit method
  [p. 437]

inventory turnover [p. 428]
inventory valuation
  [p. 433]
last-in, first-out (LIFO)
  method [p. 436]
markdown [p. 420]
operating loss [p. 423]
percent of markdown
  [p. 421]
periodic inventory [p. 433]

perpetual inventory
  [p. 433]
physical inventory [p. 433]
point-of-sale [p. 428]
rate of markdown
  [p. 421]
reduced net profit [p. 422]
reduced price [p. 420]
retail method [p. 438]
sale price [p. 420]

specific-identification
  method [p. 433]
stock turnover [p. 428]
turnover at cost [p. 430]
turnover at retail [p. 430]
turns [p. 428]
universal product code
  (UPC) [p. 433]
weighted-average (average-
  cost) method [p. 434]

CONCEPTS

EXAMPLES

11.1 Percent of markdown

Markdown is always a percent of the original price. Use the following formula.

$$\text{Markdown percent} = \frac{\text{markdown amount}}{\text{original price}}$$

Original price, $76; markdown, $19. Find the percent of markdown.

$$\text{Markdown percent} = \frac{19}{76}$$
$$= 0.25 = 25\%$$

11.1 Break-even point

Add cost to operating expenses to find the break-even point.

Cost, $54; operating expenses, $16. Find the break-even point.

$$\$54 + \$16 = \$70 \quad \text{Break-even point}$$

11.1 Operating loss

When the reduced price is below the break-even point, subtract the reduced price from the break-even point to find the operating loss.

Break-even point, $70; reduced price, $58. Find the operating loss.

$$\$70 - \$58 = \$12 \quad \text{Operating loss}$$

11.1 Absolute loss

When the reduced price is below cost, subtract the reduced price from the cost to find the absolute loss.

Cost, $54; reduced price, $48. Find the absolute loss.

$$\$54 - \$48 = \$6 \quad \text{Absolute loss}$$

11.2 Average inventory

Take inventory 2 or more times; add the totals and divide by the number of inventories to get the average.

Inventories: $22,635, $24,692, and $18,796. Find the average inventory.

$$\frac{\$22,635 + \$24,692 + \$18,796}{3} = \frac{\$66,123}{3}$$
$$= \$22,041 \quad \text{Average inventory}$$

11.2 Turnover at retail

Use the following formula.

$$\text{Turnover} = \frac{\text{retail sales}}{\text{average inventory at retail}}$$

Sales, $78,496; average inventory at retail, $18,076. Find turnover at retail.

$$\frac{\$78,496}{\$18,076} = 4.34 \text{ at retail} \quad \text{Rounded}$$

11.2 Turnover at cost

Use the following formula.

$$\text{Turnover} = \frac{\text{cost of goods sold}}{\text{average inventory at cost}}$$

Cost of goods sold, $132,710; average inventory at cost, $32,960. Find the turnover at cost.

$$\frac{\$132,710}{\$32,960} = 4.03 \text{ at cost} \quad \text{Rounded}$$

11.3 Specific-identification to value inventory

Each item is cost coded and the cost of each of the items is added to find total inventory.

Costs: item 1, $593; item 2, $614; item 3, $498. Find total value of inventory.

$$\$593 + \$614 + \$498 = \$1705 \quad \text{Total value of inventory}$$

11.3 Weighted-average method of inventory valuation

This method values items in an inventory at the average cost of buying them.

Beginning inventory of 20 at $75; purchases of 15 at $80; 25 at $65; 18 at $70; 22 remain in inventory. Find the inventory value.

$$20 \times \$75 = \$1500$$
$$15 \times \$80 = \$1200$$
$$25 \times \$65 = \$1625$$
$$18 \times \$70 = \$1260$$

Totals 78 $5585

$$\frac{\$5585}{78} = \$71.60 \text{ Rounded} \times 22 = \$1575.20 \quad \text{Value of inventory}$$

11.3 First-in, first-out (FIFO) method of inventory valuation

First items in are first sold. Inventory is based on cost of most recent items purchased.

Beginning inventory of 25 items at $40; purchase on Aug. 7, 30 items at $35; 35 remain in inventory. Find the inventory value.

$$30 \times \$35 = \$1050 \quad \text{Value of last 30}$$
$$5 \times \$40 = \$200 \quad \text{Value of previous 5}$$

Totals 35 $1250   Value of inventory

11.3 Last-in, first-out (LIFO) method of inventory valuation

The goods remaining in inventory are the first goods purchased.

Beginning inventory of 48 items at $20 each; purchase on May 9, 40 items at $25 each; 55 remain in inventory. Find the inventory value.

$$48 \times \$20 = \$960 \quad \text{Value of first 48}$$
$$7 \times \$25 = \$175 \quad \text{Value of last 7}$$

Totals 55 $1135   Value of inventory

11.3 Estimating inventory value using the gross-profit method

Beginning inventory (at cost)

\+ Purchases (at cost)

Merchandise available for sale (at cost)

− Cost of goods sold

Ending inventory (at cost)

Find cost using $C + M = S$; $C = \$198,000$

$121,000	Beginning inventory
+ 212,500	Purchases
$333,500	Merchandise available for sale
− 198,000	Cost of goods sold
$135,500	Ending inventory (at cost)

11.3 Estimating inventory value using the retail method

$$\frac{\text{Goods available for sale at cost}}{\text{Goods available for sale at retail}} = \%(\text{cost ratio})$$

$$\begin{matrix}\text{Ending inventory} \\ \text{at retail}\end{matrix} \times \%(\text{cost ratio}) = \begin{matrix}\text{inventory} \\ \text{at cost}\end{matrix}$$

	At Cost	At Retail
Beginning inventory	$7,000	$10,000
Purchases	+21,000	+30,000
Goods available for sale	$28,000	$40,000
Net sales		−25,000
Ending inventory		$15,000

$28,000   Goods available for sale at cost

$40,000   Goods available for sale at retail

$$= 0.7 = 70\%$$

$\$15,000 \times 0.7 = \$10,500$ Inventory value at cost

CHAPTER 11 | Review Exercises

The answer section includes answers to all Review Exercises.

Find the missing quantities. Round rates to the nearest whole percent and money to the nearest cent. [11.1]

	Original Price	% Markdown	$ Markdown	Reduced Price
1.	$96	30%	$28.80	$67.20
2.	$15	$33\frac{1}{3}\%$	$5	$10
3.	$5.40	50%	$2.70	$2.70
4.	$2340	25%	$585	$1755

Complete the following. If there is no operating loss or absolute loss, write "none." Use Figure 11.2 as a guide. [11.1]

	Cost	Operating Expense	Break-even Point	Reduced Price	Operating Loss	Absolute Loss
5.	$150	$48	$198	$132	$66	$18
6.	$80	$20	$100	$93	$7	none
7.	$78	$22	$100	$70	$30	$8
8.	$5	$1.25	$6.25	$5.50	$0.75	none

Find the average inventory in each of the following. **[11.2]**

Date	Inventory Amount at Retail	
9. Beginning inventory	$44,398	
March 31	$37,704	$41,051
11. Beginning inventory	$77,159	
April 1	$67,305	
July 1	$80,664	$76,411.80
October 1	$95,229	
December 31	$61,702	

Date	Inventory Amount at Retail	
10. Beginning inventory	$316,481	
July 1	$432,185	$348,468
December 31	$296,738	
12. Beginning inventory	$36,502	
April 1	$27,331	
July 1	$28,709	$32,859.80
October 1	$32,153	
December 31	$39,604	

Find the stock turnover at retail and at cost in each of the following. Round to the nearest hundredth. **[11.2]**

	Average Inventory at Cost	Average Inventory at Retail	Cost of Goods Sold	Retail Sales	
13.	$14,120	$25,572	$81,312	$146,528	5.73; 5.76
14.	$11,195	$16,365	$89,343	$129,938	7.94; 7.98
15.	$90,300	$128,350	$423,168	$598,111	4.66; 4.69
16.	$102,895	$195,150	$476,417	$889,884	4.56; 4.63

Find the inventory value in each of the following using the specific-identification method. **[11.2]**

Description	Cost	
17. Small	$122	
Medium	$199	$556
Large	$235	
19. Economy	$795	
Standard	$850	$3640
Luxury	$915	
Deluxe	$1080	

Description	Cost	
18. Poor	$314	
Fair	$422	$1242
Good	$506	
20. Good	$1283	
Better	$1398	$6017
Best	$1564	
Designer	$1772	

Solving the following application problems.

21. A one-year-old Harley-Davidson motorcycle originally priced at $13,875 is marked down to $9990. Find the percent of markdown on the original price. **[11.1]**   28%

22. A cordless telephone costs a retailer $56. The store's operating expenses are 30% of cost, and net profit is 10% of cost. Find (a) the selling price of the cordless telephone and (b) the maximum percent of markdown that may be given without taking an operating loss. Round to the nearest whole percent. **[11.1]**   **(a)** $78.40; **(b)** 7%

23. Party Supplies had an inventory of $29,332 on January 1, $36,908 on July 1, and $31,464 on December 31. Find the average inventory. **[11.2]** $32,568

24. The Natural Grocer has an average inventory of $25,380 at cost. If the cost of goods sold for the year was $273,375, find the stock turnover at cost. Round to the nearest hundredth. **[11.2]**   10.77

25. Western Boots sells cowboy hats and boots. Inventory at retail value at the end of each quarter of the past year was $78,230, $46,590, $63,980, and $104,125. Sales during the same period were $925,370. Find the stock turnover at retail rounded to the nearest hundredth. **[11.3]**   12.64

26. Thunder Manufacturing made the following purchases of rivet drums during the year: 25 at $135 each, 40 at $165 each, 15 at $108.50 each, and 30 at $142 each. An inventory shows that 45 rivet drums remain. Find the inventory value using (a) the weighted-average method, (b) the FIFO method, and (c) the LIFO method. **[11.3]** (a) $6489 (b) $5887.50 (c) $6675

27. The inventory on December 31 at Modern Clothiers was $118,000 at cost. During the next 3 months, the company made purchases of $186,000 (cost) and had net sales of $378,000. Use the gross-profit method to estimate the value of the inventory at cost on March 31 if the company uses a markup of 50% on selling price. **[11.3]** $115,000

28. Tap Plastics had an inventory of $54,000 at cost and $90,000 at retail on June 30. During the next 3 months, it made purchases of $216,000 at cost and $360,000 at retail and had net sales of $324,000. Use the retail method to estimate the value of the inventory at cost on September 30. **[11.3]** $75,600

CHAPTER 11	Business Application Case #1
	Reducing Prices to Move Merchandise

Surf and Skate purchased two dozen pairs of Roces adults' inline skates at a cost of $2925. Markup on this type of product is 35% of selling price, while operating expenses for the store are 25% of cost. Only 6 pairs of the skates sell at the original price and the manager decides to mark down the remaining skates. The price is reduced 25% and 6 more pairs sell. The remaining 12 pairs of skates are marked down 50% of the original selling price and are finally sold.

(a) Find the original selling price of each pair of skates. **(b)** Find the total sales of all the skates.

(c) Find the operating loss. **(d)** Find the absolute loss.

(a) $187.50; **(b)** $3093.75; **(c)** $562.50; **(d)** $0

CHAPTER 11	Business Application Case #2
	Going Out of Business

Jetson Boats is going out of business. The company has a long history of selling and servicing boats, but debts piled up during Mr. Jetson's long illness and inventories fell as he stopped purchasing from manufacturers. Since no one wants to buy the business, Mr. Jetson's son has temporarily taken over, and he must mark down the following in order to close the business.

Item	Total Cost	Original Selling Price
Small boats	$92,350	$117,500
Mid-sized boats	$127,900	$172,400
Parts	$32,900	$52,640
Miscellaneous	$18,740	$28,280

(a) Find the average markup on cost Mr. Jetson used for each. Round to the nearest tenth of a percent. Small boats, 27.2%; Mid-sized boats, 34.8%; Parts, 60%; Misc., 50.9%

(b) Sum the Total Cost and Original Selling Prices columns in the table above and then find the average markup on total cost to the nearest tenth. Total Cost, $271,890; Original Selling Price, $370,820; 36.4%

(c) Assume the son marks down the total of the original selling prices found in (b) above by 15% and sells one-half of the inventory. Further assume he marks the remaining inventory down an additional 20% from that already reduced price, and then sells it. Find the total revenue received. $283,677.30

(d) Find the total revenue received from (c) as a percent of total cost from (b) to determine the final markup actually received. Round to the nearest tenth of a percent. 4.3%

PART 3 | Cumulative Review: Chapters 9–11

Find the net cost (invoice amount) for each of the following. **[9.1]**

1. List price $280, less 10/20 $201.60

2. List price $375, less 25/10/5 $240.47

Find the net cost equivalent and the percent form of the single discount equivalent for the following series discounts. **[9.2]**

3. 10/20   0.72; 28%   4. 20/20   0.64; 36%   5. 20/30/5   0.532; 46.8   6. 50/40/10   0.27; 73%

Solve for the amount of discount and the amount due on each of the following. **[9.4]**

	Invoice Amount	Invoice Date	Terms	Shipping and Insurance	Date Goods Received	Date Invoice Paid	
7.	$740.58	Mar. 20	2/10/ROG	$36.80	April 6	Apr. 14	$14.81; $762.57
8.	$874.22	Feb. 12	4/15 proximo		Feb. 22	Mar. 12	$34.97; $839.25
9.	$3788.20	Jul. 19	3/15 EOM	$71.18	Aug. 7	Aug. 9	$113.65; $3745.73
10.	$4692.50	Nov. 5	2/15-50x		Nov. 10	Jan. 6	$93.85; $4598.65

Find the missing quantities by first computing the markup on one base and then computing the markup on the other. Round rates to the nearest tenth of a percent and money to the nearest cent. **[10.2]**

	Cost	Markup	Selling Price	% Markup on Cost	% Markup on Selling Price
11.	$288.14	$288.14	$576.28	100%	50%
12.	$114.66	$38.22	$152.88	$33\frac{1}{3}$%	25%

Find the missing quantities. Markup is based on total cost. **[10.3]**

	Total Cost	Quantity Purchased	Percent Sold at Reduced Price	% Markup on Total Cost	Number at Regular Price	Number at Reduced Price	Reduced Price	Regular Selling Price Each
13.	$1400	1000 pr.	30%	50%	700 pr.	300 pr.	$1.50	$2.36
14.	$2250	150	10%	25%	135	15	$7.50	$20

Complete the following. If there is no operating loss or absolute loss, write "none." Use Figure 11.2 as a guide. **[11.1]**

	Cost	Operating Expense	Break-even Point	Reduced Price	Operating Loss	Absolute Loss
15.	$150	$48	$198	$132	$66	$18
16.	$39	$11	$50	$35	$15	$4

Find the average inventory in each of the following. **[11.2]**

Date	Inventory Amount at Retail	
17. Beginning inventory	$74,422	
July 1	$58,320	$64,877
December 31	$61,889	
18. Beginning inventory	$218,143	
April 1	$186,326	
July 1	$275,637	$211,981
October 1	$207,448	
December 31	$172,351	

Find the stock turnover at retail and at cost in each of the following. Round to the nearest hundredth. **[11.2]**

Average Inventory at Cost	Average Inventory at Retail	Cost of Goods Sold	Retail Sales	
19. $14,120	$25,572	$81,312	$146,528	5.73 at retail; 5.76 at cost
20. $45,150	$64,175	$211,584	$299,056	4.66 at retail; 4.69 at cost

Solve the following application problems.

21. A home-security system is list-priced at $2995. The manufacturer offers a series discount of 20/20/20 to wholesalers and a 20/20 series discount to retailers. (a) What is the wholesaler's price? (b) What is the retailer's price? (c) What is the difference between the prices? **[9.2]**   (a) $1533.44 (b) $1916.80 (c) $383.36

22. Pet Supply Wholesalers receives an invoice dated June 22 for $3578 with terms of 2/10 EOM. The invoice is paid on July 8. Find the amount necessary to pay the invoice in full. **[9.4]** $3506.44

23. An appliance store sells a dishwasher for $949 while using a 30% markup on cost. Find the cost. **[10.1]** $730

24. Office Max sells a Texas Instruments financial calculator for $19.95. The calculator costs the store $15.96. Find the markup as a percent of selling price. **[10.2]**   20%

25. Area Rugs Galore offers an 8- by10-foot Persian rug for $499.95. If the rugs cost $4499.55 per dozen, find (a) the markup, (b) the percent of markup on selling price, and (c) the percent of markup on cost. Round to the nearest tenth of a percent. **[10.1 and 10.2]**   (a) $124.99 (b) 25% (c) $33\frac{1}{3}$%

26. A commercial riding lawn mower, originally priced at $9250, is marked down to $6660. Find the percent of mark-down on the original price. **[11.1]**   28%

27. John Cross Pool Supply, a retailer, pays $285 for a diving board. The original selling price was $399, but it was marked down 40%. If operating expenses are 30% of cost, find (a) the operating loss and (b) the absolute loss. **[11.1]**   (a) $131.10 operating loss (b) $45.60 absolute loss

28. Boise Medical Supplies had an inventory of $58,664 on January 1, $73,815 on July 1, and $62,938 on December 31. Find the average inventory. **[11.2]** $65,139 average inventory

Round to the nearest dollar amount.

29. Craighead Riding Tractors made the following purchases of fuel tanks during the year: 25 at $270 each, 40 at $330 each, 15 at $217 each, and 30 at $284 each. An inventory shows that 45 fuel tanks remain. Find the inventory value, using the weighted-average method. **[11.3]** $12,978 weighted-average method

30. Find the inventory value listed in Exercise 29 using (a) the FIFO method and (b) the LIFO method. **[11.3]**
(a) $11,775 FIFO (b) $13,350 LIFO

javier brosch / Fotolia.com

Simple Interest

Loans are fundamental to modern business. Businesses borrow to make payroll, build a new building, develop a new product, expand internationally, or buy another company. However, the interest on loans can be costly. When an individual, family, or company files for **bankruptcy,** it is usually because their income is not large enough to handle the amount of debt owed. Interestingly, the Koran forbids Muslims from charging interest. Instead, Islamic banks take an ownership interest in firms until they are repaid through profits.

The **prime rate** is the interest rate at which our strongest corporations (e.g., Microsoft) can borrow. Interest rates such as the prime rate continually change, and many other rates move up and down more or less parallel to the prime rate. So, for example, the cost of borrowing to buy a car or a house usually goes up as the prime rate increases.

Figure 12.1 shows prime rate and housing start data for the United States. The high prime rate of the 1980s corresponded to high interest rates on homes. The high interest rate drove the cost of buying a home up to the point where fewer people bought homes and new housing starts fell to low levels. At the opposite extreme, the prime rate was very low around 2003, making homes cheaper. The low interest rate contributed to the frenzied level of new home construction at the time.

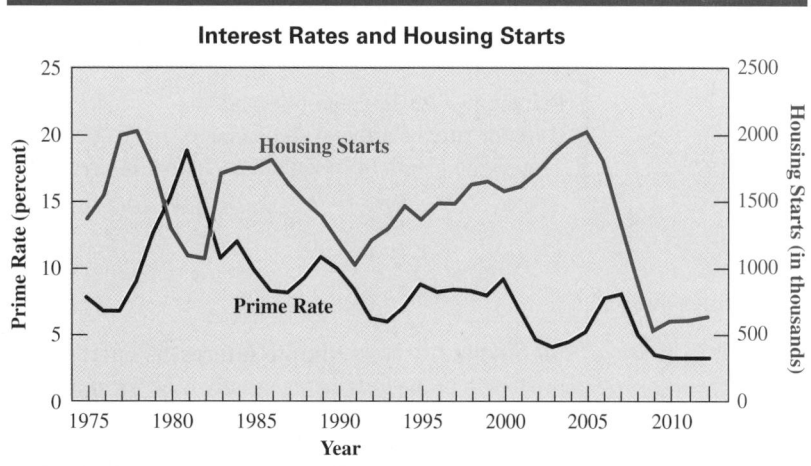

Source: U.S. Bureau of Census.

Figure 12.1

However, something odd happened in 2008 and 2009—namely, new house starts collapsed even as the prime rate was very low and falling. Why? The answer lies in the severe financial crisis that began in 2008 as home prices fell from very high levels, unemployment increased rapidly, and people became worried about the economy. Actually, interest rates fell because (1) the demand for loans fell sharply, and (2) the government tried to lessen the pain of the recession by working to keep interest rates low. The uncertain times caused people to spend less, causing inventories to soar in global supply chains. Managers responded by laying off people and working to reduce inventories, which made the problems even worse for housing.

▶ STOP&THINK

> The financial crisis that began in 2008 was originally centered around subprime home loans made in the United States to individuals or families without good credit. Why did it spread so quickly around the world? What does "global economy" really mean? How can rapidly falling home values in the United States result in the near bankruptcy of the small city of Norvik, Norway, as happened in 2008?

Two basic types of interest are in common use today: **simple interest** and **compound interest**. Simple interest is interest paid on only the principal. Compound interest is interest paid on *both principal and past interest.* This chapter discusses simple interest, and **Chapter 14** covers compound interest.

12.1	**Basics of Simple Interest**

OBJECTIVES

1 *Find simple interest.*
2 *Find interest for less than a year.*
3 *Find principal if given rate and time.*
4 *Find rate if given principal and time.*
5 *Find time if given principal and rate.*

Interest is the price paid for borrowing money. Interest rates are usually expressed as a percent of the amount borrowed. For example, in some states, retail companies such as Sears, The Home Depot, and J.C. Penney charge up to 21% interest per year on money owed to them on credit cards. Here are three very important terms!

> **Principal**—the amount borrowed.
> **Rate** (or **rate of interest**)—percent of interest charged by lender.
> **Time**—the length of time in years before repayment is due.

Objective

1 *Find Simple Interest.* **Simple interest** is interest charged on the entire principal for the entire length of the loan and is usually used for short-term loans that last less than a year. It is found using a modification of the basic percent formula.

$$\text{Simple interest} = \text{principal} \times \text{rate} \times \text{time}$$
$$I = P \times R \times T \quad \text{or}$$
$$I = PRT$$

The rate, R, is expressed as a decimal or fraction, and time, T, is expressed as the number of years, or the fraction of a year.

> **NOTE** It is important to remember that time is in years. This means that a time period given in months or days *must* be converted to a fraction of a year before being substituted into the formula for T.

EXAMPLE **1**   **Finding Simple Interest**

In addition to using some of their own money, Gilbert Construction Company must borrow $120,000 to build an 1800-square-foot home. The owner, Susan Gilbert, is considering whether she should borrow the funds at (a) 8% per year for 1 year or (b) $8\frac{1}{2}\%$ per year for $1\frac{1}{2}$ years. Find the simple interest on both loans and (c) the difference between the two.

Solution

(a) Use the formula $I = PRT$. Substitute $120,000 for P, 0.08 (the decimal form of 8%) for R, and 1 for T.

$$I = PRT$$
$$= \$120,000 \times 0.08 \times 1$$
$$= \$9600 \qquad \text{Simple interest}$$

Check the answer by dividing $9600 by $120,000 to find 0.08, or 8% interest.

(b) Again use the simple interest formula. However, now use $R = 0.085$ ($8\frac{1}{2}\%$) and $T = 1.5$ ($1\frac{1}{2}$ years).

$$I = PRT$$
$$= \$120,000 \times 0.085 \times 1.5$$
$$= \$15,300 \qquad \text{Simple interest}$$

(c) Difference $= \$15,300 - \$9600 = \$5700$

The second loan has a higher interest rate and a longer time. It adds $5700 to the cost of building the house and, therefore, reduces any profit on the house by that amount. Gilbert chooses the 1-year loan since she already has a contract with the individual who will buy the home and she can build and deliver the home within 1 year. To make a profit, Gilbert must constantly keep costs low.

Objective

2   *Find Interest for Less Than a Year.* Notice in part (a) of the next example how 9 months is written as $\frac{9}{12}$ of a year and in part (b) that 13 months (obviously more than 1 year) is written as $\frac{13}{12}$ or $1\frac{1}{12}$ of a year. Also notice that sometimes it is necessary to round interest to the nearest cent, as shown next in part (b) of Example 2.

EXAMPLE **2**   **Finding Simple Interest Using Months**

Jodie Luk needs to borrow $5600 to finish her last semester in college. Her uncle offers to lend her the money either at (a) 8% simple interest for 9 months or (b) $8\frac{1}{2}\%$ simple interest for 13 months. Find the interest on both options and (c) the difference between the two.

Solution

(a) Since there are 12 months in a year, 9 months is $\frac{9}{12}$, or 0.75, of a year. Find the interest as follows.

$$I = PRT$$
$$= \$5600 \times 0.08 \times \frac{9}{12}$$
$$= \$336$$

(b) Use $\frac{13}{12}$ to represent 13 months in terms of number of years.

$$I = PRT$$
$$= \$5600 \times 0.085 \times \frac{13}{12}$$
$$= \$515.67 \qquad \text{Rounded}$$

(c) Difference $= \$515.67 - \$336 = \$179.67$

Scientific Calculator Approach

The calculator solution to Example 2 follows.

$$5600 \boxed{\times} 0.08 \boxed{\times} 9 \boxed{\div} 12 \boxed{=} 336 \boxed{\text{STO}}$$

$$5600 \boxed{\times} 0.085 \boxed{\times} 13 \boxed{\div} 12 \boxed{=} 515.67 \text{ (rounded)}$$

$$515.67 \boxed{-} \boxed{\text{RCL}} \boxed{=} 179.67 \text{ difference}$$

Objective

3 *Find Principal If Given Rate and Time.* Sometimes the amount of interest is known, but the principal, rate, or time must be found. Do this with the following modifications of the formula for simple interest.

$$I = PRT$$
$$\frac{I}{RT} = \frac{P\cancel{R}\cancel{T}}{\cancel{R}\cancel{T}} \qquad \text{Divide both sides by } RT$$
$$\frac{I}{RT} = P \quad \text{or} \quad P = \frac{I}{RT}$$

Similarly, dividing both sides of $I = PRT$ by PT gives the formula for R.

$$R = \frac{I}{PT}$$

And dividing both sides of $I = PRT$ by PR gives the formula for T.

$$T = \frac{I}{PR}$$

> **NOTE** You do not have to remember all the formulas above. Just remember $I = PRT$ and use algebra to solve for the unknown **(Section 2.3)**. Do not forget that the *rate must be a decimal or fraction* and *time must be in years.*

EXAMPLE 3 **Finding the Principal**

Ajax Coal borrows funds at 10.5% for 10 months to buy a tractor that will be used to keep the roads in the firm's coal mine in good condition. Find the principal that results in interest of $13,125.

Solution

Find the principal by dividing both sides of $I = PRT$ by RT.

$$P = \frac{I}{RT}$$

$$= \frac{\$13,125}{0.105 \times \frac{10}{12}} \quad \text{Substitute values for variables.}$$

$$= \$150,000$$

The principal or loan amount is $150,000.

Scientific
Calculator
Approach

For the calculator solution to Example 3, divide using the chain calculation.

13125 ÷ (0.105 × 10 ÷ 12) = 150000

Objective

4 *Find Rate If Given Principal and Time.* The next example shows how to find the interest rate if the principal and time are given.

EXAMPLE 4 Finding the Rate

After a large down payment, Jessica Warren borrowed $9000 from her credit union to purchase a previously owned Toyota Camry. Find the interest rate if the loan was for 9 months and the interest was $540.

Solution

Divide both sides of $I = PRT$ by PT to get the following.

$$R = \frac{I}{PT}$$

$$= \frac{\$540}{\$9000 \times \frac{9}{12}} \quad \text{Substitute values for variables.}$$

$$= 0.08$$

The rate was 8%.

NOTE In order to avoid rounding errors, it is important not to round off any calculations until the very end when solving these types of problems.

Objective

5 *Find Time If Given Principal and Rate.* The simple interest formula can also be used to find the time of a loan.

EXAMPLE 5 Finding the Time

Jennifer Wells, a loan officer at Midwest Bank, made a loan of $19,200 at 10%. How many months will it take to produce $1120 in interest?

Solution

Use $I = PRT$ and divide both sides by PR to get

$$T \text{ (in years)} = \frac{I}{PR}$$

We included "(in years)" to emphasize this important point—time of the loan is measured in years. Now substitute $1120 for I, $19,200 for P, and 0.10 for R.

$$T \text{ (in years)} = \frac{\$1120}{\$19,200 \times 0.10} \quad \text{Substitute values for variables.}$$

$$= \frac{\$1120}{\$1920}$$

Reduced to lowest terms

$$T \text{ (in years)} = \frac{\$1120}{\$1920} = \frac{7}{12} \text{ year} = 7 \text{ months}$$

NOTE In all the examples of this section, time has been expressed in years or months. **Section 12.2** will deal with interest problems in which the time is expressed in days.

12.1	**Exercises**

Find the simple interest for each of the following. Round to the nearest cent.

1. $6800 at 10% for $1\frac{1}{4}$ years $850

2. $9500 at 12% for $1\frac{1}{2}$ years $1710

3. $12,400 at $9\frac{1}{2}$% for 8 months $785.33

4. $4800 at 8% for 8 months $256

5. $8250 at 13% for 15 months $1340.63

6. $2830 at 15% for 6 months $212.25

7. $9874 at $7\frac{1}{8}$% for 11 months $644.90

8. $10,745 at $4\frac{5}{8}$% for 9 months $372.72

9. $74,986.15 at 12.23% for 5 months
$3821.17

10. $39,072.76 at 11.23% for 7 months
$2559.59

Complete this chart. Round money to the nearest cent, rate to the nearest tenth of a percent, and time to the nearest month.

	Principal	Interest	Rate	Time in Months
11.	$10,000	$500	10%	6
12.	$15,000	$1562.50	$12\frac{1}{2}$%	10
13.	$4062.50	$162.50	8%	6
14.	$1440	$84	10%	7
15.	$3800	$199.50	7%	9
16.	$2600	$144.08	$9\frac{1}{2}$%	7
17.	$5350	$749	12%	14
18.	$24,800	$3534	$9\frac{1}{2}$%	18 months, or 1.5 years

Solve the following application problems. Round money to the nearest cent, rate to the nearest tenth of a percent, and time to the nearest month.

19. Find the time, in years, necessary for an $8200 loan to produce $1353 in interest at 11%.   1.5 years

20. Interest charges of $1642.50 were due on a 9% loan of $18,250. Find the time in years.
1 year

21. Find the principal if $245 in interest is due after 10 months at 7%. $4200

22. What amount of principal produces $55 in interest after 1 month at 11%? $6000

23. What time (in months) is necessary for a principal of $8400 to produce $770 in interest at 10%?   11 months

24. How many months are necessary for $4800 to produce $44 in interest at 11%?   1 month

25. Find the rate if a principal of $1890 produces $138.60 in interest after 11 months.   8%

26. A loan of $8500 produces interest of $595 in 7 months. Find the rate.   12%

27. LATE-PAYMENT PENALTY   Casey Watkins is 3 months late on a car payment to a finance company. Her contract included a penalty rate of 10% per year on the loan balance of $5850. Find the penalty. $146.25

28. CONSTRUCTION   Denver Construction, Inc. is 2 months late on a payment. The penalty is based on a loan amount of $682,500 and a rate of 14%. Find the penalty.
$15,925

29. LOAN TO BUY TIMBER   Georgia Plantations borrows funds to buy land and agrees to pay interest of $114,375 in 9 months at 10% interest. Find the principal. $1,525,000

30. AUTOMOBILE LOAN   Michael George borrows money to replace his Chevrolet. He agrees to pay $1170 in interest at 9% in 10 months. Find the principal (loan amount).
$15,600

31. LAWN MOWERS   The Green Care Company needs to borrow $7000 to buy new lawn mowers. The firm wants to pay no more than $560 in interest. If the interest rate is 12%, what is the longest time for which the money may be borrowed?   8 months

32. NEW STORE   Max Perry wants to borrow $50,000 to move his vitamin store to a better location. However, his credit history is poor. His bank will lend him only $30,000 and then only at a high interest rate of 14%. If Perry cannot pay more than $3500 in interest, find the longest period of time the money may be borrowed.   10 months

33. SAVINGS   June Peters deposits $6400 in a savings account at her bank. When she withdraws the money 8 months later, she receives a check for $6453.33. Assume simple interest and find the rate of interest paid by the bank.   1.25%

34. SAVINGS   Latoya Johnson deposited $5000 in a certificate of deposit for 6 months and will receive interest of $50. Find the simple interest rate.   2.0%

 35. A $6000 loan was made for 3 months at 7% simple interest. A student calculates the interest due on the loan as follows.

$$I = \$6000 \times 0.07 \times 3 = \$1260$$

Is this correct? If not, explain why not and state the correct answer. (See Objective 1.)

 36. Are you willing to invest your own funds in an account paying 1% per year for several years? Why or why not? What interest rate should a bank charge you when you borrow? Why?

37. DENTAL WORK   Lupe Garcia needs to borrow $3200 for 8 months for dental work that she needs this month. She can choose between a credit union charging 10% or a loan company charging 18%. How much will she save by using the credit union? $170.67

38. CAR REPAIR   Tomas Rodriguez needs to borrow $3900 so he can repair damages to his car. He plans to pay the loan back in full in 5 months using his income tax refund. He can go to a finance company that will charge him 18% or to his uncle, who has agreed to charge him 9%. Find the difference in the interest charges. $146.25

39. SPORTING GOODS   A sporting goods store needs to borrow $30,000 to purchase several bikes made of a new, lightweight alloy after a recent Tour de France bike race stimulated interest for the bike. The manager wants to pay back no more than $32,500 in 9 months. What is the highest interest rate the manager can accept?   11.1%

40. STUDY ABROAD A student needs to borrow $3500 for living expenses for a study-abroad program in Hong Kong. She feels that she will be able to pay back only $3750 in 7 months after she works in the summer. What is the highest interest rate she is able to pay? 12.2%

41. DRESS SHOP Gladys's Dress Shop received an invoice for $2543, with terms of 2/15, n/60 (see Section 9.3). The store can borrow money at the bank at 9.5%. How much would be saved by borrowing money for 60 − 15 = 45 days to take advantage of the cash discount? (*Hint:* If discount is earned, firm does not need to borrow full amount of invoice.) $21.27

42. PET SUPPLIES Westside Pet Supplies received an invoice of $1796, with terms 1/10, n/30 (see Section 9.3). Due to a poor credit history, the store must pay 14.5% interest. How much would the store save by borrowing money for 30 − 10 = 20 days to take advantage of the cash discount? (*Hint:* If discount is earned, firm does not need to borrow full amount of invoice.) $3.64

43. HOME ADDITION Ricky and Gina Hardin borrow $49,800 to add a den with a fireplace to their home. They finance the loan at 10% simple interest for 4 months. They hope to pay the loan off then, using proceeds from the sale of a rental house. Find the interest. $1660

12.2 Simple Interest for a Given Number of Days

OBJECTIVES

1 *Find the number of days from one date to another using a table.*

2 *Find the number of days from one date to another using the actual number of days.*

3 *Find exact and ordinary interest.*

The previous section showed how to find simple interest for loans of a given number of months or years. In this section, *loans for a given number of days* are discussed. In business, it is common for loans to be for a given number of days, such as "due in 90 days," or else to be due at some fixed date in the future, such as "due on April 17."

Objective

1 *Find the Number of Days from One Date to Another Using a Table.* There are two ways to find the number of days from one date to another. One way is by the use of Table 12.1. This table assigns a different number to each day of the year. For example, the number for June 11 is found by locating 11 at the left, and June across the top. You will find that June 11 is day 162. Also, December 29 is day 363. The number of days from June 11 to December 29 is found by subtracting.

December 29 is day   363
June 11 is day   − 162   Subtract.
           201

There are 201 days from June 11 to December 29. (Throughout this book, ignore leap years unless otherwise stated.)

> **NOTE** When counting the number of days of a loan, do not count the day the loan is made, but do count its due date.

Table 12.1 THE NUMBER OF EACH OF THE DAYS OF THE YEAR (ADD 1 TO EACH DATE AFTER FEBRUARY 29 FOR A LEAP YEAR)

Day of Month	Jan.	Feb.	March	April	May	June	July	Aug.	Sept.	Oct.	Nov.	Dec.	Day of Month
1	1	32	60	91	121	152	182	213	244	274	305	335	1
2	2	33	61	92	122	153	183	214	245	275	306	336	2
3	3	34	62	93	123	154	184	215	246	276	307	337	3
4	4	35	63	94	124	155	185	216	247	277	308	338	4
5	5	36	64	95	125	156	186	217	248	278	309	339	5
6	6	37	65	96	126	157	187	218	249	279	310	340	6
7	7	38	66	97	127	158	188	219	250	280	311	341	7
8	8	39	67	98	128	159	189	220	251	281	312	342	8
9	9	40	68	99	129	160	190	221	252	282	313	343	9
10	10	41	69	100	130	161	191	222	253	283	314	344	10
11	11	42	70	101	131	162	192	223	254	284	315	345	11
12	12	43	71	102	132	163	193	224	255	285	316	346	12
13	13	44	72	103	133	164	194	225	256	286	317	347	13
14	14	45	73	104	134	165	195	226	257	287	318	348	14
15	15	46	74	105	135	166	196	227	258	288	319	349	15
16	16	47	75	106	136	167	197	228	259	289	320	350	16
17	17	48	76	107	137	168	198	229	260	290	321	351	17
18	18	49	77	108	138	169	199	230	261	291	322	352	18
19	19	50	78	109	139	170	200	231	262	292	323	353	19
20	20	51	79	110	140	171	201	232	263	293	324	354	20
21	21	52	80	111	141	172	202	233	264	294	325	355	21
22	22	53	81	112	142	173	203	234	265	295	326	356	22
23	23	54	82	113	143	174	204	235	266	296	327	357	23
24	24	55	83	114	144	175	205	236	267	297	328	358	24
25	25	56	84	115	145	176	206	237	268	298	329	359	25
26	26	57	85	116	146	177	207	238	269	299	330	360	26
27	27	58	86	117	147	178	208	239	270	300	331	361	27
28	28	59	87	118	148	179	209	240	271	301	332	362	28
29	29		88	119	149	180	210	241	272	302	333	363	29
30	30		89	120	150	181	211	242	273	303	334	364	30
31	31		90		151		212	243		304		365	31

EXAMPLE 1 **Finding the Number of Days**

Find the number of days from (a) March 24 to July 22 and (b) November 8 to February 17 of the next year.

Solution

(a) The number of days can be estimated. There are about 4 months from March 24 to July 22. Assume 30 days per month and multiply to find about 120 days. Now to find the exact number of days, note that March 24 is day 83 and July 22 is day 203.

$$
\begin{array}{ll}
\text{July 22 is day} & 203 \\
\text{March 24 is day} & -\ 83 \\
\hline
& 120
\end{array}
$$

There are 120 days from March 24 to July 22. It turns out that our estimate was the exact number of days. Estimates rarely provide the exact answer, but they can help minimize errors by providing approximate values.

(b) Since November 8 is in one year and February 17 is in the next year, first find the number of days from November 8 to the end of the year.

$$
\begin{array}{lr}
\text{Last day of the year is number} & 365 \\
\text{November 8 is day} & -\ 312 \\
\hline
& 53
\end{array}
$$

There are 53 days from November 8 to the end of the year.

Then find the number of days from the beginning of the next year to February 17. According to the chart, February 17 is the 48th day of the year. The total number of days is found as follows.

$$
\begin{array}{lr}
\text{November 8 to end of year} & 53 \\
\text{January 1 to February 17} & +\ 48 \\
\hline
& 101
\end{array}
$$

There are 101 days from November 8 to February 17 of the next year.

Objective

2   *Find the Number of Days from One Date to Another Using the Actual Number of Days.*
The number of days from one date to another can also be found using the number of days in each month of the year, as shown in Table 12.2.

Table 12.2 THE NUMBER OF DAYS IN EACH MONTH

31 Days		30 Days	28 Days
January	August	April	February
March	October	June	(29 days in leap year)
May	December	September	
July		November	

EXAMPLE 2   **Finding the Number of Days from One Date to Another Using Actual Days**

Find the number of days from (a) March 12 to June 7 and (b) November 4 to February 21.

Solution

(a) Since March has 31 days, there are $31 - 12 = 19$ days left in March, then 30 days in April, 31 in May, and an additional 7 days in June, for a total as follows.

$$
\begin{array}{rl}
19 & \text{Remaining in March} \\
30 & \text{April} \\
31 & \text{May} \\
+\ \ 7 & \text{June} \\
\hline
87 & \text{Days from March 12 to June 7}
\end{array}
$$

(b) Add the days in each of the months.

$$
\begin{array}{rl}
26 & \text{Remaining in November} \\
31 & \text{December} \\
31 & \text{January} \\
+\ 21 & \text{February} \\
\hline
109 &
\end{array}
$$

There are 109 days from November 4 to February 21.

Two other ways of remembering the number of days in each month are the rhyme method and the knuckle method, as seen below.

Rhyme Method:

30 days hath September
April, June, and November.
All the rest have 31, except February,
which has 28 and in a leap year 29.

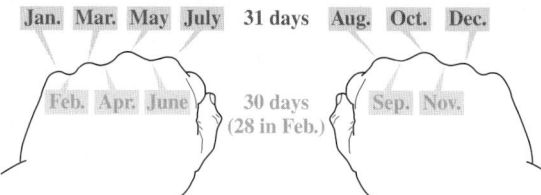

Knuckle Method

EXAMPLE **3** **Finding Specific Dates**

Find the date that is 90 days from (a) March 25 and (b) November 7.

Solution

(a) From Table 12.1, March 25 is day 84. Add 90.

$$
\begin{array}{r}
\text{March 25 is day} \quad 84 \\
+ \quad 90 \text{ days} \\
\hline
174
\end{array}
$$

As shown in Table 12.1, day 174 is June 23, so 90 days from March 25 is June 23. Alternatively, work as follows.

$$
\begin{array}{lr}
\text{March 25 to end of month} & 6 \\
\text{April} & 30 \\
\text{May} & + \ 31 \\
\hline
& 67
\end{array}
$$

Since $90 - 67 = 23$, an additional 23 days in June are needed, giving June 23.

(b) November 7 is day 311. Add 90 days to get the following.

$$
\begin{array}{r}
311 \\
+ \ 90 \\
\hline
401
\end{array}
$$

Since there are only 365 days in a year, subtract 365.

$$
\begin{array}{r}
401 \\
- \ 365 \\
\hline
36 \quad \text{Day of the following year}
\end{array}
$$

Day 36 of the following year is February 5, so that 90 days from November 7 is February 5 of the following year.

Objective

3   *Find Exact and Ordinary Interest.* In the formula for simple interest, time is always measured in years or parts of years. In the examples of the previous section, time was in months, with *T* in the formula $I = PRT$ written as follows.

$$
T = \frac{\text{given number of months}}{12}
$$

Things are not so simple when the loan is given in days. There are two common methods for calculating simple interest for a given number of days: **exact interest** and **ordinary** (or **banker's interest**).

In the formula $I = PRT$, the fraction for time is found using one of these.

$$\text{Exact interest} \quad T = \frac{\text{exact number of days in the loan}}{365}$$

$$\text{Ordinary or banker's interest} \quad T = \frac{\text{exact number of days in the loan}}{360}$$

Government agencies and the Federal Reserve Bank use exact interest, as do many credit unions and banks. However, there are still many banks that use ordinary interest for loans. Exact interest is used for savings accounts. Ordinary interest may have been used originally because it was easier to calculate than exact interest. With the modern use of calculators and computers, however, ordinary interest is probably used today out of tradition and because it produces a *greater dollar amount* of interest than does exact interest, as shown in the next example.

EXAMPLE 4 **Finding Exact and Ordinary Interest**

Alameda Printing borrowed \$35,300 on May 12. The loan, at an interest rate of 10%, is due on August 27. Find the interest on the loan using (a) exact interest and (b) ordinary interest.

Solution

Use Table 12.1 or calculate the number of days in each month to find that there are 107 days from May 12 to August 27. In both situations, $P = \$35,300$, $R = 0.10$, and the loan is for 107 days. The only difference between the two situations is the number of days in the denominator of the fraction for time. *Exact interest* uses 365 days, and *ordinary interest* uses 360 days.

(a) Exact Interest

$$I = PRT$$
$$I = \$35,300 \times 0.10 \times \frac{107}{365}$$
$$I = \$1034.82 \qquad \text{Rounded}$$

(b) Ordinary Interest

$$I = PRT$$
$$I = \$35,300 \times 0.10 \times \frac{107}{\mathbf{360}}$$
$$I = \$1049.19 \qquad \text{Rounded}$$

Difference between the two $= \$1049.19 - \$1034.82 = \$14.37$

Ordinary interest results in an additional \$14.37 in interest.

NOTE If P and R are the same, more interest is generated using ordinary interest than using exact interest.

The formulas from **Sections 12.1** and **12.2** are repeated here for your convenience.

Interest $I = PRT$

Principal $P = \dfrac{I}{RT}$ $\left.\right\}$ T is in years.

Rate $R = \dfrac{I}{PT}$

Time T (in years) $T = \dfrac{I}{PR}$

Time T (in months) $T = \dfrac{I}{PR} \times 12$ T is a fraction of a year.

Time T (in days) $T = \dfrac{I}{PR} \times 360$ Use 360 days for banker's (ordinary) interest.

Time T (in days) $T = \dfrac{I}{PR} \times 365$ Use 365 days for exact interest.

NOTE   Throughout the balance of this book, assume ordinary (or banker's) interest unless stated otherwise.

12.2	**Exercises**

Find the exact number of days from the first date to the second. (In Exercises 5–6, assume that the second month given is in the following year.)

1. May 7 to December 2   209 days   **2.** April 24 to July 7   74 days

3. October 27 to December 2   36 days   **4.** July 12 to October 29   109 days

5. September 2 to March 17   196 days   **6.** July 24 to March 30   249 days

Find the date that is the indicated number of days from the given date.

7. 120 days from June 14   October 12   **8.** 45 days from July 28   September 11

9. 30 days from February 8   March 10   **10.** 90 days from November 18   February 16

11. 120 days from December 12   April 11   **12.** 150 days from November 1   March 31

Find the amount of ordinary interest you would pay for each of the following. Round to the nearest cent.

13. $18,000 at 10% for 90 days $450   **14.** $11,400 at $8\frac{1}{4}$ for 200 days $522.50

15. $87,500 at 9% for 150 days $3281.25   **16.** $8620 at 11.25% for 120 days $323.25

17. A loan of $8500 at 9.5% made on June 3 and due October 31 $336.46

18. A loan of $6800 at 12% made on June 20 and due December 26 $428.40

19. A loan of $322,000 at 9.25% made on February 27 and due August 5 $13,155.04

20. A loan of $3600 at 11% made on December 2 and due February 20 $88

Find the exact interest for each of the following. Round to the nearest cent.

21. $3800 at 10% for 100 days $104.11   **22.** $41,500 at 8.5% for 200 days $1932.88

23. $7400 at 9.5% for 60 days $115.56   **24.** $5000 at 8% for 90 days $98.63

25. A loan of $6500 at 7% made on July 12 and due on October 12 $114.68

26. A loan of $8120 at 9% made on January 30 and due May 20 $220.24

27. A loan of $4100 at 12% made on June 24 and due February 12 of the next year $314.07

28. A loan of $14,000 at 8% made on August 12 and due March 19 of the next year $672

29. Explain the difference between exact and ordinary interest. (See Objective 3.)

30. As a borrower, would you prefer exact or ordinary interest? Why? (See Objective 3.)

Solve the following application problems using exact interest. Round to the nearest cent.

31. IRS PENALTY   Nguyen Le started a new construction business but failed to withhold taxes from her employees at first. She owes the IRS $8327, on which the IRS also assesses a 40% per-year penalty rate. Find the penalty given that she is paying 100 days late. $912.55

32. MISSED TAX PAYMENT   Bella Steinem missed an income tax payment. The payment was due June 15 and was paid September 7. The penalty was 14% simple interest on the unpaid tax of $4600. Find the penalty. $148.21

33. PLAYGROUND EQUIPMENT   The manager of a franchised kindergarten borrowed $46,800 on October 30 at 12% simple interest. Find the interest due on March 15. $2092.54

34. GRAPHIC ARTS   Ben Peterson borrowed $38,500 on November 7 for a digital printer and some other equipment. He agreed to repay the 10.5% rate loan on March 30 of the following year. Find the interest. $1583.77

Solve the following application problems using ordinary interest. Round to the nearest cent.

35. PHOTOGRAPHY STUDIO   Nolan Brinkman borrowed $48,000 on June 10 to open a photography studio. Given a rate of $12\frac{1}{4}$,% find the interest due on Christmas (December 25). $3234

36. WESTERN WEAR   On May 18, the Wilson Dude Ranch bought a supply of assorted Western wear and saddles for $16,905. The ranch agreed to pay for it on August 30, with $10\frac{1}{2}$% interest. Find the interest owed. $512.79

37. PLUMBING   Suarez Plumbing can borrow $1,250,000 for 300 days at $10\frac{1}{2}$% interest. A few years ago when interest rates were low, the same loan would have had an interest rate of $8\frac{3}{4}$%. Find the difference in the interest charges. $18,229.17

38. CONSTRUCTION IN MEXICO   A construction company in Mexico City borrows 300,000 pesos for 90 days at an interest rate of 8%. The same loan would have been at a rate of 35% several years ago. Find the difference in the interest charges based on the two rates.   20,250 pesos

In Exercises 39–42 find the (a) exact interest and (b) ordinary interest for the following, rounded to the nearest cent. Then (c) find the amount by which the ordinary interest is larger.

39. $18,000 at 9% for 120 days   (a) $532.60; (b) $540; (c) $7.40

40. $75,000 at 11% for 120 days   (a) $2712.33; (b) $2750; (c) $37.67

41. $145,000 at $9\frac{1}{2}$% for 240 days   (a) $9057.53; (b) $9183.33; (c) $125.80

42. $250,000 at $12\frac{1}{8}$% for 180 days   (a) $14,948.63; (b) $15,156.25; (c) $207.62

Solve the following application problems. Round to the nearest cent.

43. FIRE TRUCK   Bergen County borrows $385,000 to purchase a new pumper. The loan must be repaid once property taxes are paid for the year, or in 200 days, at a rate of 6%. How much more interest would be required to pay using ordinary interest compared to exact interest? $175.80

44. SKI EQUIPMENT   Ski Apache borrows $120,000 for extra inventory for the coming ski season. The owners expect to repay the loan after the ski season is over, in 140 days, at a rate of $10\frac{1}{2}$%. How much more would the firm pay using ordinary interest compared to exact interest? $67.12

45. NEW TRUCKS   Blaine Trucking wishes to borrow $880,000 for new trucks on September 20 and plans to pay off the loan on May 1 of the following year. State Bank will lend it the funds at 9% based on exact interest calculations. First Bank will lend it the funds at $8\frac{7}{8}$% interest based on ordinary interest calculations. Which bank is asking for less interest? How much less?   First Bank; $9.34

46. INTERNATIONAL CONSTRUCTION   A Canadian construction firm needs to borrow an additional $3,500,000 for 150 days to build a bridge linking Mexico to the United States. National Bank will lend it the funds at $10\frac{1}{2}$% simple interest based on exact interest calculations, and Laredo Bank will lend it the funds at $10\frac{5}{8}$% simple interest based on ordinary interest calculations. Which bank is asking for less interest? How much less? National Bank; $3920.52

12.3	**Maturity Value**

OBJECTIVES

1 *Find maturity value.*

2 *Find principal if given maturity value, time, and rate.*

3 *Find rate if given principal, maturity value, and time.*

4 *Find time if given maturity value, principal, and rate.*

The amount borrowed is called the **principal**, or **present value**, since it is the amount today. The amount that must be repaid at the **maturity date** of the loan is called the **maturity value**, or **future value**, since it is the amount that must be repaid when the loan matures on a specific day in the future. The maturity value is the principal plus the interest: $M = P + I$.

Objective

1   *Find Maturity Value.* Jim Bacon gets his uncle to **cosign** on a ten month, $9000 loan from a bank so that Jim can finish his last year of college. By cosigning, the uncle agrees to repay the bank in the event that Jim does not. The interest rate on the 10-month loan is 8.5%. The maturity value is found as follows.

$$\text{Interest} = PRT$$

$$= \$9000 \times 0.085 \times \frac{10}{12} = \$637.50$$

$$\text{Maturity value} = P + I$$

$$= \$9000 + \$637.50 = \$9637.50$$

Thus, the maturity value of $9637.50 must be repaid in 10 months from September 1, or on July 1 of the following year.

NOTE   Since the maturity value includes both the principal and the interest, it will always be larger than the principal, which is the amount borrowed.

EXAMPLE 1   Finding Interest and Maturity Value

Jim Wilcox would like to remodel his gift kiosk at the mall. To remodel the kiosk, he borrows $7200 for 21 months at 9.25% interest. Find the interest due on the loan and the maturity value.

Solution

Interest due is found using $I = PRT$, where T is in years $\left(21\,\text{months} = \frac{21}{12}\,\text{years}\right)$.

$$I = PRT$$
$$= \$7200 \times 0.0925 \times \frac{21}{12} = \$1165.50$$

Find the maturity value using $M = P + I$, where $P = \$7200$ and $I = \$1165.50$.

$$M = P + I$$
$$= \$7200 + \$1165.50 = \$8365.50$$

The formula for maturity value, $M = P + I$, can be written in a different way if I is replaced with PRT $(\text{since } I = PRT)$.

$$M = P + I$$
$$= P + PRT \qquad \text{Substitute } PRT \text{ for } I.$$
$$= P(1 + RT) \qquad \text{Use the distributive property.}$$

Therefore, the maturity value M of a principal of P dollars at a rate of interest R for T years can be written in either of the following forms.

$$M = P + I \qquad \text{or} \qquad M = P(1 + RT)$$

NOTE Do not round values too soon when using a formula to do interest rate problems. Round *after* finding the final value.

EXAMPLE 2   Finding Maturity Value

Use the formula $M = P(1 + RT)$ to find the maturity value for a loan of $60,000 for 120 days at 9% interest.

Solution

Substitute $60,000 for P, 9% or 0.09 for R, and $\frac{120}{360}$ for T (since 120 days is $\frac{120}{360}$ of a year). The maturity value is as follows.

$$M = P(1 + RT)$$
$$= \$60,000 \times \left[1 + \left(0.09 \times \frac{120}{360}\right)\right]$$

NOTE Parentheses were placed around $0.09 \times \frac{120}{360}$ to emphasize that these numbers are multiplied as a first step.

$$M = \$60,000 \times (1 + 0.03)$$
$$= \$60,000 \times 1.03$$
$$= \$61,800$$

The interest can be found by subtracting the principal from the maturity value.

$$I = \$61,800 - \$60,000 = \$1800$$

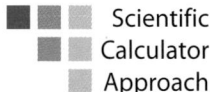
Scientific
Calculator
Approach

The calculator solution to this example uses parentheses on the calculator in place of the brackets.

$$60000 \boxed{\times} \boxed{(} \boxed{1} \boxed{+} \boxed{0.09} \boxed{\times} \boxed{120} \boxed{\div} \boxed{360} \boxed{)} \boxed{=} 61800 \boxed{STO}$$

Subtract the principal from $61,800 to obtain the interest.

$$\boxed{RCL} \boxed{-} \boxed{60000} \boxed{=} 18000$$

Objective

2   *Find Principal If Given Maturity Value, Time, and Rate.* Sometimes the maturity value is given, and either the principal, rate, or time must be found. For example, given the maturity value, rate, and time, find principal as follows.

$$M = P(1 + RT)$$

$$\frac{M}{(1 + RT)} = \frac{P(1 + RT)}{(1 + RT)} \qquad \text{Divide both sides by } (1 + RT).$$

$$\frac{M}{(1 + RT)} = \frac{P\cancel{(1 + RT)}}{\cancel{(1 + RT)}} \qquad \text{Divide out common factors.}$$

$$\boxed{\frac{M}{1 + RT} = P \qquad \text{or} \qquad P = \frac{M}{1 + RT}}$$

Principal is also called the *present value* of the loan.

EXAMPLE **3**   **Finding Principal Given Time, Rate, and Maturity Value**

Find the principal that would produce a maturity value of $45,900 in 4 months at 6% interest.

Solution

Use the formula above and substitute $45,900 for M, 0.06 for R, and $\frac{4}{12}$ for T.

$$P = \frac{M}{1 + RT}$$

$$= \frac{\$45,900}{1 + \left(0.06 \times \frac{4}{12}\right)}$$

As shown by the parentheses, first multiply 0.06 and $\frac{4}{12}$, and then add 1.

$$P = \frac{\$45,900}{1 + 0.02}$$

$$= \frac{\$45,900}{1.02}$$

$$= \$45,000$$

$$
\begin{array}{lll}
\text{Principal} & = \text{present value} = \$45,000 \\
\text{Maturity value} & = \text{future value} = \$45,900 \\
\text{Interest} & = \text{maturity value} - \text{present value} \\
& = \quad M \qquad\quad - \qquad P \\
& = \$45,900 \quad - \$45,000 \\
& = \$900
\end{array}
$$

■■■ Scientific
■■ Calculator
■ Approach

First, find the denominator of the equation in Example 3.

$$1 \; \boxed{+} \; \boxed{(} \; \boxed{0.06} \; \boxed{\times} \; \boxed{4} \; \boxed{\div} \; \boxed{12} \; \boxed{)} \; \boxed{=} \; 1.02 \; \boxed{STO}$$

Then divide the numerator by the denominator.

$$45900 \; \boxed{\div} \; \boxed{RCL} \; 1.02 \; \boxed{=} \; 45000$$

Objective

3 *Find Rate If Given Principal, Maturity Value, and Time.* If principal, maturity value, and time are given, rate can be found as follows.

$$M = P(1 + RT)$$

$$M = P + PRT \quad \text{Use the distributive property.}$$

$$M - P = PRT \quad \text{Subtract } P \text{ from both sides.}$$

$$\frac{M - P}{PT} = \frac{\cancel{P}R\cancel{T}}{\cancel{P}\cancel{T}} \quad \text{Divide both sides by } PT.$$

$$\boxed{\frac{M - P}{PT} = R \quad \text{or} \quad R = \frac{M - P}{PT}}$$

EXAMPLE **4** **Finding Rate Given Principal, Maturity Value, and Time**

Lin Pao invests a principal of $14,400 and receives a maturity value of $15,080 in 200 days. Find the interest rate.

Solution

Use the formula above and substitute values.

$$R = \frac{M - P}{PT}$$

$$= \frac{\$15{,}080 - \$14{,}400}{\$14{,}400 \times \frac{200}{360}}$$

$$= 0.085, \quad \text{or} \quad 8.5\%$$

■■■ Scientific
■■ Calculator
■ Approach

The calculator solution to Example 4 uses parentheses to separate the numerator ($15,080 − $14,400) and the denominator $\left(\$14{,}400 \times \frac{200}{360}\right)$.

$$\underbrace{\boxed{(} \; \boxed{15080} \; \boxed{-} \; \boxed{14400} \; \boxed{)}}_{\text{Numerator}} \; \boxed{\div} \; \underbrace{\boxed{(} \; \boxed{14400} \; \boxed{\times} \; \boxed{200} \; \boxed{\div} \; \boxed{360} \; \boxed{)}}_{\text{Denominator}} \; \boxed{=} \; 0.085, \quad \text{or} \quad 8.5\%$$

Notice that maturity value minus principal ($M - P$) is interest I. Therefore,

$$R = \frac{M - P}{PT} = \frac{I}{PT}$$

Example 4 can be solved using this formula.

$$\text{Interest} = \$15,080 - \$14,400 = \$680$$

$$R = \frac{I}{PT}$$

$$= \frac{\$680}{\$14,400 \times \frac{200}{360}}$$

$$= 0.085, \quad \text{or} \quad 8.5\%$$

Objective

4 *Find Time If Given Maturity Value, Principal, and Rate.* Given maturity value, principal, and rate, time can be found as follows.

$$M = P(1 + RT)$$

$M = P + PRT$ Use the distributive property.

$M - P = PRT$ Subtract P from both sides.

$\dfrac{M - P}{PR} = \dfrac{PRT}{PR}$ Divide both sides by PR

$$\frac{M - P}{PR} = T \,(\text{in years}) \quad \text{or} \quad T = \frac{M - P}{PR}$$

This gives a value for time T in *years*. To convert to *days* multiply by 360. For example, $\frac{1}{2}$ of a year is $\frac{1}{2} \times 360 = 180$ days.

$$T(\text{in days}) = \frac{M - P}{PR} \times 360$$

Since $I = M - P$, this is the same as

$$T(\text{in days}) = \frac{I}{PR} \times 360$$

EXAMPLE 5 **Finding the Time in Days**

Mustang Signs borrowed $18,250 at $10\frac{1}{8}\%$ interest for the construction of two new signs and agreed to repay $19,687.19. Find the time in days and round to the nearest day if necessary.

Solution

Use the formula above and substitute values.

$$T = \frac{M - P}{PR} \times 360$$

$$= \frac{\$19,687.19 - \$18,250}{\$18,250 \times 0.10125} \times 360$$

$$= \frac{1437.19}{1847.81} \times 360$$

$$= 280 \text{ days} \quad \text{Rounded}$$

 Scientific Calculator Approach

The calculator solution to Example 5 uses parentheses to set off both the numerator and the denominator.

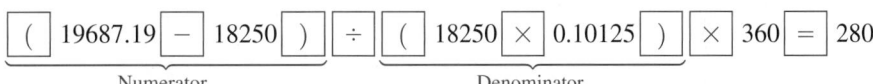

The formulas from Section 12.3 are repeated here for your convenience.

Interest	$I = PRT$
Maturity Value	$M = P(1 + RT)$
Principal	$P = \dfrac{I}{RT} = \dfrac{M - P}{RT} = \dfrac{M}{1 + RT}$
Rate	$R = \dfrac{I}{PT} = \dfrac{M - P}{PT}$
Time (in years)	$T = \dfrac{I}{PR} = \dfrac{M - P}{PR}$
Time (in days)	$T = \dfrac{I}{PR} \times 360 = \dfrac{M - P}{PR} \times 360$

12.3 | Exercises

Find the interest and the maturity value for the following loans. Round to the nearest cent.

1. $8500 at 10% for 9 months $637.50; $9137.50
2. $12,200 at $9\frac{1}{2}$% for 10 months $965.83; $13,165.83
3. $5800 at 8.5% for 140 days $191.72; $5991.72
4. $10,800 at $7\frac{3}{4}$% for 220 days $511.50; $11,311.50
5. $8640 at 10% for $1\frac{1}{4}$ years $1080; $9720
6. $34,600 at 13% for $1\frac{1}{2}$ years $6747; $41,347

Complete this chart. Round money to the nearest cent, rate to the nearest tenth of a percent, and time to the nearest day.

	Principal	Interest	Rate	Time in Days	Maturity Value
7.	$4800	$133.33	10%	100	$4933.33
8.	$7500	$300	12%	120	$7800
9.	$8600	$133.78	8%	70	$8733.78
10.	$7400	$292.92	$9\frac{1}{2}$%	150	$7692.92
11.	$14,000	$490	$10\frac{1}{2}$%	120	$14,490
12.	$12,800	$544	$8\frac{1}{2}$%	180	$13,344
13.	$16,400	$717.50	$7\frac{7}{8}$%	200	$17,117.50
14.	$28,600	$2002	$10\frac{1}{2}$%	240	$30,602
15.	$14,800	$666	9%	180	$15,466
16.	$81,000	$8086.05	9.1%	395	$89,086.05
17.	$1800	$126	14%	180	$1926
18.	$11,250	$460	12.8%	115	$11,710
19.	$42,459.44	$3272.92	15%	185	$45,732.36
20.	$75,000	$1187.50	7.5%	76	$76,187.50

Solve the following application problems. Round to the nearest cent.

21. **HOT TUB**   José Garcia borrowed $12,000 for 140 days at $10\frac{1}{2}\%$ to add a hot tub and enclosure to his home. Find the interest and the maturity value. $490; $12,490

22. **FUNERAL EXPENSES**   Jessica Singleton's grandfather had been ill for several years, so everything he owned was used for medical expenses. At his death, Singleton had to borrow $12,000 for 120 days at 11% to pay for the balance of her grandfather's funeral and for related attorney expenses and court costs. Find the interest and maturity value on the loan. $440; $12,440

23. **WEDDING COSTS**   Joey Patrick and Lori Hooten borrowed $12,400 at $10\frac{5}{8}\%$ interest for wedding expenses and a honeymoon to Hawaii. Given that they must repay $12,912.36, find the time in days and the amount of interest. Round to the nearest day.   140 days; $512.36

24. **BOAT DEALERSHIP**   James Wilson borrows $845,000 at 9% interest to expand his inventory of fishing boats. He agrees to repay $904,150 on the maturity date of the loan. Find the amount of interest paid and time in days. $59,150; 280 days

25. **PERSONAL TRAINER**   James Wicker borrowed $12,000 for equipment so that he could do some of his personal training work in his garage. He agreed to repay $13,200 after 300 days. Find the amount of interest and the interest rate. $1200; 12%

26. **BURGLAR ALARMS**   Belinda Tate received a contract to install burglar alarms in an apartment house and needed to borrow $28,000 for related equipment and supplies. Since she used a certificate of deposit for collateral for the loan, she was required to repay only $29,166.67 in 250 days. Find the amount of interest and the interest rate rounded to the nearest tenth of a percent. $1166.67; 6%

27. **AUTO MECHANIC**   Mona Melton likes to work on cars. She signs a simple interest note with a maturity value of $65,000 at 11.5% for 300 days to open a small auto repair shop. Find the principal and the interest. $59,315.59; $5684.41

28. **SETTLING A LAWSUIT**   Jill Phan borrowed some money to settle a lawsuit against her restaurant—a customer slipped on a puddle of water from the icemaker and fell. The 180-day loan was at 9% interest and Phan must repay $44,412.50. Find the principal and the interest. $42,500; $1912.50

 29. List the two basic equations from which all of the other equations in this section can be derived. Use the two equations to derive the equation for time given maturity value, principal, and rate. (See Objectives 1 and 3.)

 30. Using $I = PRT$ and $M = P + I$, explain the steps to derive the equation for principal given maturity value, rate, and time. (See Objective 2.)

12.4   Inflation and the Time Value of Money

OBJECTIVES

1 *Define inflation and the consumer price index.*

2 *Understand the time value of money.*

3 *Define present value and future value.*

4 *Calculate present and future values using simple interest.*

5 *Find present value for a given maturity value.*

6 *Find present value after a loan is made.*

Believe it or not, in 1960 a family of four would have done well with an income of only $500 per month. Today, it costs $500 or more a month just to rent a small apartment. Five hundred dollars will not buy nearly as much today as it did in 1960. Why? The answer is inflation.

Think about the last raise you or someone you know received. Was it enough to cover the increased costs associated with inflation? It doesn't mean much if your raise is 2% in a year when prices of the things you buy go up by, say, 4.3%. Even though inflation usually increases prices slightly in any one year, in the long run it has a very large effect on purchasing power.

Objective

1 *Define Inflation and the Consumer Price Index.* **Inflation** is the rise in the overall price of goods and services. Let's look at the cost of a basic hamburger to illustrate the effects of inflation. The bar chart below shows the historic cost of a hamburger at McDonald's, which increased from 15 cents in 1960 to $1.00 in 2011. Are we getting more for our money when paying $1.00 in 2011 versus $0.15 nearly 50 years ago? No! We are buying the same thing. In reality, the value of a dollar has gone down, so that $1.00 in today's money is about the same as $0.15 in 1960 money, at least for hamburgers. It is very important to increase your pay in order to maintain the same purchasing power, especially if inflation is high.

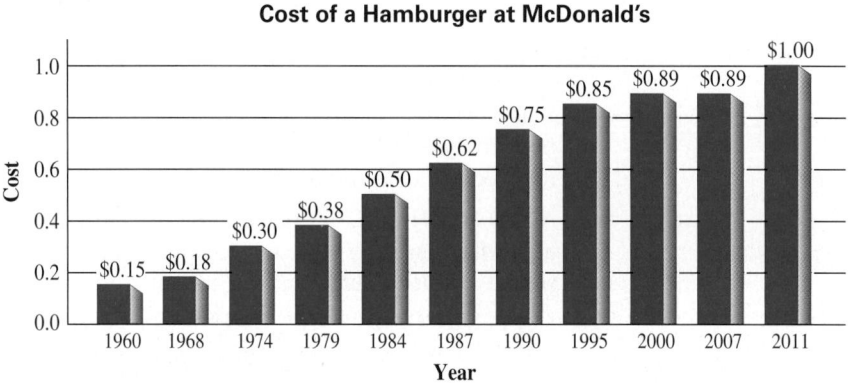

Cost of a Hamburger at McDonald's

Source: Based on data from http://www.foodtimeline.org/foodfaq5.html#mcdonalds.

The **consumer price index (CPI)** is calculated by the government annually in the United States and is often referred to as the "cost-of-living index." The CPI can be used to track inflation. It measures the average change in prices from one year to the next for a common bundle of goods and services bought by the average consumer on a regular basis. Figure 12.2 shows yearly inflation for the past few years. Note that inflation was very high in 1980—prices were increasing at more than 10% per year. However, inflation has continued to decrease and was at a record low during 2009.

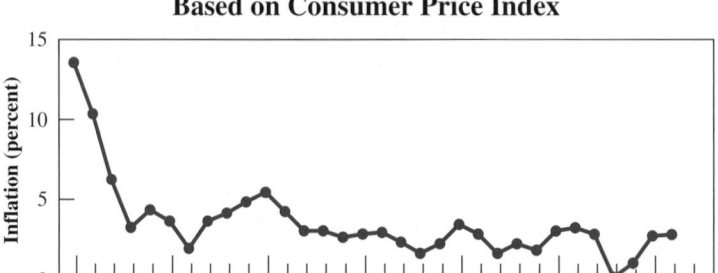

Annual Inflation Rate Based on Consumer Price Index

Source: U.S. Bureau of Census.

Figure 12.2

EXAMPLE 1 Estimating the Effect of Inflation

Inflation from one year to the next was 4.8% as measured by the CPI. (a) Find the effect of the increase on a family with an annual income and budget of $39,600 (after taxes). (b) What is the overall effect if the family receives only a 2% after-tax increase in pay for the year?

Solution

(a) First, estimate the increase in the costs of the goods and services that the family buys. Then find the total cost of buying those items next year.

$$\text{Increase in costs} = 0.048 \times \$39{,}600 = \$1900.80$$
$$\text{Cost of goods and services next year} = \$39{,}600 + \$1900.80 = \$41{,}500.80$$

(b) Find the increase in income, then find the new income.

$$\text{After-tax increase in income} = 0.02 \times \$39{,}600 = \$792$$
$$\text{Family's new after-tax income} = \$39{,}600 + \$792 = \$40{,}392$$

So the amount the family has to spend increased from $39,600 to $40,392, but an estimate of the cost of the goods and services the family buys increased from $39,600 to $41,500.80. The loss in purchasing power is the difference between the two numbers.

$$\text{Loss of purchasing power} = \$41{,}500.80 - \$40{,}392 = \$1108.80$$

The family will have to buy less or go into debt in order to buy the same goods and services.

Retired people are particularly concerned with inflation since they must live off Social Security checks and the assets they have accumulated during their lifetime. Some retired people do not have ways of increasing their income to keep pace with inflation and therefore must lower their standards of living substantially during retirement. Other retired people have investments such as stocks that help them stay ahead of inflation.

The federal government works to keep inflation at moderate levels since high inflation can be so harmful. When the economy becomes overheated and inflationary pressures increase, the Federal Reserve nudges interest rates upward. This reduces borrowing slightly, slows the economy, and reduces inflationary pressures. Conversely, if inflation is low and the economy is growing very slowly or not at all, the Federal Reserve nudges interest rates downward, thereby stimulating the economy and creating more jobs. The Federal Reserve has the very difficult task of maintaining a growing and healthy economy with low levels of inflation.

NOTE For the past 20 years, inflation rates have been relatively low. However, some experts believe that the recent, large government expenditures will cause inflation to increase sharply in the future. Watch for inflation—it affects you!

Objective

2 *Understand the Time Value of Money.* Would you deposit $1000 with your bank for 2 years and expect only $1000 back when the money is returned? Probably not! You would expect interest in addition to the return of your principal. The **time value of money** is the idea that the loaning of money to someone or to a firm has value, and that value is typically repaid by returning interest in addition to principal.

The time value of money is an important concept. Regular investments of relatively small sums of money can result in large sums at later dates. For example, how would you like to turn $54,000 into over $150,000? Simply invest $150 per month for 30 years, say from age 30 to age 60, at 6% interest compounded monthly. This topic is discussed in **Chapters 14** and **15**.

Application of the time value of money will help you send your children to college, purchase a home, and prepare for your own retirement. The time value of money is equally important to firms that invest to build factories, develop new technologies, or need capital for many other reasons.

Objective

3 *Define Present Value and Future Value.* The principal amount that must be invested today to produce a given future amount is called the **present value**. The amount that this sum grows to at some future date is called the **future value**.

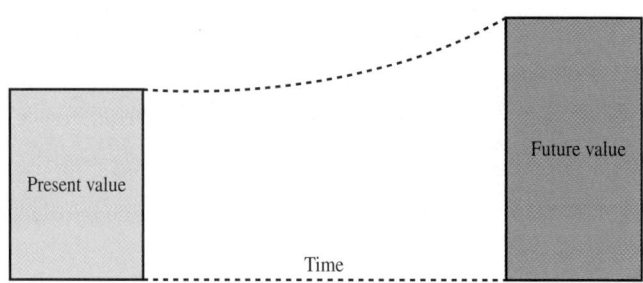

We calculated the future value in the earlier sections of this chapter when we were calculating the maturity amount.

$$\text{Future value} = M = P(1 + RT)$$

We have also been calculating the present value in the earlier sections of this chapter when we were calculating the principal with the following form of the above equation.

$$\text{Present value} = P = \frac{M}{(1 + RT)}$$

Objective

4 *Calculate Present and Future Values Using Simple Interest.*

EXAMPLE **2** **Finding Future Value**

Joan Waters loans part of her inheritance of $28,500 to a cousin at $6\frac{1}{2}$% simple interest on May 30. Find the future value of this amount on February 4 of the following year. Round to the nearest cent.

Solution

First find the number of days from May 30 to February 4 by finding the number of days from May 30 to the end of the year. Then find the number of days from the beginning of the year to February 4.

The end of the year is day	365
May 30 is day	− 150
May 30 to end of year	215

February 4 is day 35 of the next year. The total number of days is $215 + 35 = 250$ days. Now use the formula for the maturity value (future value) using simple interest.

$$M = P(1 + RT)$$

$$= \$28,500\left(1 + 0.065 \times \frac{250}{360}\right)$$

$$= \$29,786.46 \qquad \text{Rounded}$$

The future value on February 4 is $29,786.46.

EXAMPLE **3**   **Finding Present Value**

KLTV Television plans to spend $280,000 for a new satellite dish and associated electronic equipment in 18 months. What present value must be invested today at 6% simple interest so that the firm will have the needed future value?

Solution

Use the following form of the simple interest formula.

$$P = \frac{M}{(1 + RT)}$$

$$= \frac{\$280,000}{\left(1 + 0.06 \times \frac{18}{12}\right)}$$

$$= \frac{\$280,000}{(1 + 0.09)}$$

$$= \frac{\$280,000}{1.09}$$

$$= \$256,880.73$$

KLTV Television must invest a present value of $256,880.73 today at 6% simple interest in order to have a future value of $280,000 in 18 months.

Scientific Calculator Approach

For the calculator solution to Example 3, the denominator $\left(1 + 0.06 \times \frac{18}{12}\right)$ should be considered a single number. Set it apart using parentheses.

$280000 \boxed{\div} \underbrace{\boxed{(} \boxed{1} \boxed{+} \boxed{.06} \boxed{\times} \boxed{18} \boxed{\div} \boxed{12} \boxed{)}}_{\text{Denominator}} \boxed{=} 256880.73$

Objective

5   *Find Present Value for a Given Maturity Value.* Example 3 showed how to find the present value of an amount needed at a specific future date. Sometimes a company needs cash, so it sells a loan it has made rather than continuing to receive payments. Notes are sold for their present value on the date sold. The amount they are sold for depends on the interest rate on the date sold. The market interest rate often differs from the interest rate on the original note.

Finding the Present Value of a Loan

> **Step 1** Find the future value (maturity value) of the loan using the original terms of the loan. Use $M = P(1 + RT)$.
>
> **Step 2** Find the present value of this amount using the market interest rate and the time remaining until maturity. Use $P = \dfrac{M}{(1 + RT)}$.

EXAMPLE 4   **Finding Present Value of a Loan**

Joplin Laugherty borrowed $365,000 for 10 months from Bank USA at 9% simple interest to remodel his seafood restaurant. Later that day, the largest employer in the area declared bankruptcy and told the managers of the bank that they would not be able to repay the loans from the bank. Managers at the bank decide to immediately sell the loan made to Joplin Laugherty to raise much-needed cash. The investment company buying the note sees that the economy is slowing and requires a higher interest rate on the loan of 12% since the risk of repayment has increased. Find (**a**) the present value received by the bank and (**b**) the loss the bank took on the loan.

Solution

First, find the maturity value of the loan to Laugherty's using the terms of the loan.

$$M = P(1 + RT)$$
$$= \$365,000\left(1 + 0.09 \times \frac{10}{12}\right)$$
$$= \$392,375$$

The investment company is buying the right to receive $392,375 from Laugherty's in 10 months. Find the present value using the market rate of 12%.

$$P = \frac{M}{1 + RT}$$
$$= \frac{\$392,375}{1 + 0.12 \times \frac{10}{12}}$$
$$= \frac{\$392,375}{1 + 0.1}$$
$$= \frac{\$392,375}{1.1}$$
$$= \$356,704.55 \qquad \text{Rounded}$$

Here are the numbers:

Amount loaned by bank	$= \$365,000$
Maturity value that must be paid	$= \$392,375$
Amount bank receives for loan	$= \$356,704.55$

The loss the bank took is found as follows.

$$\text{Loss to bank} = \$365,000 - \$356,704.55 = \$8295.45$$

Normally, a bank would not make a loan and then sell it immediately at a loss. However, in this case the bank needed the cash and was forced to sell the loan at a loss.

NOTE In Example 4, the money was lent to the restaurant owner at 9% simple interest. However, since the slowing economy increased the risk of a default on the loan, the market interest rate went up to 12%. If the interest rate had remained at 9%, the bank would not have lost any money when selling the loan.

 Scientific Calculator Approach

The calculator solution to Example 4 follows.

$$365000 \boxed{\times} \boxed{(} \boxed{1} \boxed{+} \boxed{0.09} \boxed{\times} \boxed{10} \boxed{\div} \boxed{12} \boxed{)} \boxed{=} 392375$$

$$392375 \boxed{\div} \boxed{(} \boxed{1} \boxed{+} \boxed{0.12} \boxed{\times} \boxed{10} \boxed{\div} \boxed{12} \boxed{)} \boxed{=} 356704.55$$

Objective

6 *Find Present Value after a Loan Is Made.* Sometimes the present value of a loan is needed when the amount currently owed is not known. In that event, you must still find the maturity value of the loan and then find the present value of this amount on the date the loan is to be sold using the market interest rate at that time.

EXAMPLE 5 **Finding Present Value on a Date After Loan Is Made**

An Argentinean made a loan of $26,000 to a business partner on May 13 for 90 days. The interest rate on the loan is 8%. After the loan is made, the general level of interest rates in Argentina rises quickly to 12%. Find the present value of the loan on June 26.

Solution

First find the maturity value of the loan. The principal is $26,000, the rate is 8%, and the time is 90 days, or $\frac{90}{360}$ year.

$$M = P(1 + RT)$$
$$= \$26{,}000\left[1 + \left(0.08 \times \frac{90}{360}\right)\right]$$
$$= \$26{,}000(1 + 0.02)$$
$$= \$26{,}520$$

The loan was made on May 13, for 90 days. The loan is due on August 11. As shown in Figure 12.3, the number of days from June 26 (the day for which the present value is desired) to August 11 is as follows.

4	Days in June
31	Days in July
+ 11	Days in August
46	Total days

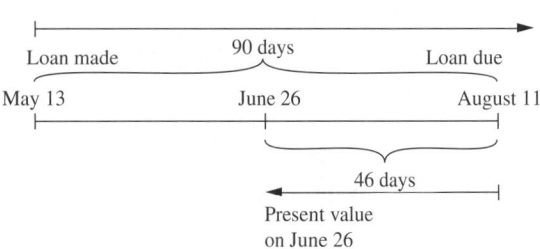

Figure 12.3

The total number of days could also be found by using Table 12.1.

To find the present value 46 days before the loan is paid off, use the formula for present value, with $M = \$26{,}520$, $R = 12\%$, and $T = \frac{46}{360}$ year.

$$P = \frac{M}{1 + RT}$$

$$= \frac{\$26{,}520}{1 + \left(0.12 \times \frac{46}{360}\right)}$$

$$= \$26{,}119.50 \qquad \text{Rounded}$$

The businessman should be willing to accept $26,119.50 on June 26 in full payment of the loan, both principal and interest. This amount would grow to $26,520 at 12% by August 11.

NOTE Since $\frac{46}{360}$ in the example results in a number with digits that go on forever, it is important that it not be rounded at an intermediate step. Wait and round the final answer.

12.4 Exercises

In the following problems, find the present value or future value, as indicated, to the nearest cent.

	Present Value	Interest Rate	Time	Future Value
1.	$4800	9%	110 days	$4932
2.	$8000	$8\frac{1}{2}\%$	140 days	$8264.44
3.	$10,500	11%	10 months	$11,462.50
4.	$6800	$12\frac{1}{2}\%$	9 months	$7437.50
5.	$4100	$8\frac{3}{8}\%$	$1\frac{1}{4}$ years	$4529.22
6.	$7400	$10\frac{1}{4}\%$	$1\frac{1}{2}$ years	$8537.75
7.	$2400	6%	100 days	$2440.00
8.	$1900	9%	180 days	$1985.50
9.	$8400	$11\frac{1}{8}\%$	6 months	$8867.25
10.	$9300	12%	11 months	$10,323.00
11.	$8700	$5\frac{7}{8}\%$	$1\frac{1}{8}$ years	$9275.02
12.	$6400	$7\frac{1}{4}\%$	$1\frac{1}{2}$ years	$7096.00

 13. Explain the difference between the interest rate on a loan and the time value of money. (See Objective 4.)

14. Explain the meaning of inflation and the CPI. (See Objective 1.)

Solve the following application problems. Round to the nearest cent.

15. **AUTO DEALERSHIPS** General Motors loaned one of its auto dealers $6,500,000 on August 4 at $9\frac{1}{2}\%$ simple interest. Find the future value as of December 31. $6,755,576.39

16. **LOAN TO A SUPPLIER** Karl's Kameras loaned a supplier $28,300 on July 14 at 8% simple interest. Find the future value of the loan on March 15 of the following year. $29,834.49

17. **BANK LOANS** Chase Bank loaned a large Canadian company $85 million at 8.78% simple interest for 90 days, even as the bank was paying an average of 2.135% on the same funds to depositors. Find the difference between the interest earned by the bank and the interest paid to depositors. $1,412,062.50

18. **FINANCE COMPANY** A finance company borrows $250,000 at $9\frac{1}{2}\%$ interest per year. It lends the money to many different small borrowers with poor credit history at $16\frac{1}{2}\%$ per year. Find the difference in interest earned and interest paid out assuming all loans are for 1 year. $17,500

19. **CREDIT RISK** Ben Aflack made a loan of $80,000 at 8% for 200 days. Due to severe injuries received in a car accident on the same day the loan was made, Aflack immediately had to sell the loan to an investor. The investor believes the credit risk of the borrower is high and requires 12% simple interest. Find the present value of the loan. $78,333.34

20. **PRESENT VALUE** Find the present value, on the date it was made, of a loan of $14,700 at 12% for 210 days if money is worth 10%. $14,862.05

21. **PRESENT VALUE** A loan of $6980 was made on May 24, for 214 days, at 11%. Find the present value of the loan on July 9, if the time value of money is 10%. $7104.85

22. **PRESENT VALUE** On February 24, an 89-day loan of $980 at 12% is made. Find the present value of the loan on March 10, if the time value of money is 10%. $988.48

23. **COLLEGE LOAN** Worried about looming college expenses for her 16-year-old daughter, Lupe Martinez invested $5400 at 2.25% simple interest for 10 months. Find the future value. $5501.25

24. **LAWSUIT AWARD** A marketing company misrepresented a product, was sued by a plaintiff, and the judge awarded the plaintiff $280,000. The plaintiff received this amount on July 17 and deposited it in an investment earning 3.5% simple interest on the same day. Find the future value on November 30. $283,702.22

25. **INFLATION AND PURCHASING POWER** A family with a spending budget of $26,500 receives an increase in wages of 3% in a year in which inflation was 4.5%. Find the net gain or loss in its purchasing power, ignoring taxes. $397.50 loss

26. **GAIN IN PURCHASING POWER** Ben Thomas spends $34,300 and receives a 6% raise in a year in which inflation was 2.5%. Ignoring taxes, find the net gain in his purchasing power. $1200.50

Three different bids are given in each of the following two exercises. For each, find the lowest bid using the concept of present value. Assume that the time value of money is 10%.

27. $16,800 today, $17,400 in 150 days, $18,000 in 210 days $17,400 in 150 days

28. $41,250 today, $41,102 in 210 days, $45,000 in 300 days $41,102 in 210 days

29. Describe some possible effects of inflation on people earning minimum wage.

30. What effects can you foresee of a rapid increase in inflation from 6% to 10%?

CHAPTER TERMS

Review the following terms to test your understanding of the chapter. For each term you do not know, refer to the page number found next to that term.

banker's interest [p. 462]
bankruptcy [p. 451]
compound interest [p. 452]
consumer price index
 (CPI) [p. 472]

cosign [p. 465]
exact interest [p. 462]
future value [p. 474]
inflation [p. 472]
interest [p. 452]

maturity date [p. 465]
maturity value [p. 465]
ordinary interest [p. 462]
present value [p. 474]
prime rate [p. 451]

principal [p. 452]
rate of interest [p. 452]
simple interest [p. 452]
time [p. 452]
time value of money [p. 473]

CONCEPTS	EXAMPLES

12.1 Finding simple interest given time expressed in years

Use the formula $I = PRT$ with R in decimal form and time in years.

Find the simple interest on $65,000 for 2 years at 8% per year.

$$I = PRT$$
$$= \$65,000 \times 0.08 \times 2$$
$$= \$10,400$$

12.1 Finding simple interest given time expressed in months

Use $I = PRT$. Express time in years by dividing time in months by 12.

Find the simple interest on $8600 for 14 months at $6\frac{1}{2}\%$ per year.

$$I = PRT$$
$$= \$8600 \times 0.065 \times \frac{14}{12}$$
$$= \$652.17 \qquad \text{Rounded}$$

12.1 Determining principal given interest, rate, and time

Use the formula

$$P = \frac{I}{RT}$$

with R in decimal form and time in years.

Find the principal that would produce an interest of $1500 in 8 months at 6%.

$$P = \frac{I}{RT}$$
$$= \frac{\$1500}{0.06 \times \frac{8}{12}}$$
$$= \$37,500$$

12.1 Finding rate given interest, principal, and time

Use the formula

$$R = \frac{I}{PT}$$

with T in years.

Find the rate on a $15,000 loan for 60 months if the interest was $6750.

$$R = \frac{I}{PT}$$
$$= \frac{\$6750}{\$15,000 \times \frac{60}{12}}$$
$$= 0.09, \text{ or } 9\%$$

12.1 Determining time given interest, principal, and rate	Find the time for a loan of \$12,000 at 10% to produce \$2400 in interest.
Use the formula $$T = \frac{I}{PR}$$ with R in decimal form.	$$T = \frac{I}{PR}$$ $$= \frac{\$2400}{\$12,000 \times 0.10}$$ $$= 2 \text{ years}$$

12.2 Finding the number of days from one date to another using a table	Find the number of days from February 15 to July 28.
Find the day corresponding to each date and subtract.	July 28 is day ⎯ 209 Feb. 15 is day ⎯ − 46 ⎯⎯⎯⎯⎯⎯ 163 days

12.2 Determining the number of days from one date to another using the actual number of days in a month	Find the number of days from January 17 to April 15.
Add the actual number of days in each month or partial month from one date to the next.	14 Remaining in January 28 February 31 March + 15 April ⎯⎯⎯⎯⎯ 88 days

12.2 Finding exact interest	Find the exact interest on \$14,600 at 7% for 100 days.
Use the formula $I = PRT$ with $$T = \frac{\text{time in days}}{365}$$	$$I = PRT$$ $$= \$14,600 \times 0.07 \times \frac{100}{365}$$ $$= \$280$$

12.2 Finding ordinary interest (bankers' interest)	Find the ordinary interest on \$11,000 at 7% for 90 days.
Use the formula $I = PRT$ with $$T = \frac{\text{time in days}}{360}$$	$$I = PRT$$ $$= \$11,000 \times 0.07 \times \frac{90}{360}$$ $$= \$192.50$$

12.3 Determining the maturity value of a loan when principal, rate, and time are known	Find the maturity value of a \$25,000 loan that is made for 2 years at 6%.
Use the formula $$M = P(1 + RT)$$ with R in decimal form and T in years.	$$M = P(1 + RT)$$ $$= \$25,000[1 + (0.06 \times 2)]$$ $$= \$28,000$$

12.3 Finding the principal when maturity value, rate, and time are known	Find the principal that would produce a maturity value of \$15,000 in 9 months at 7%.

Use the formula

$$P = \frac{M}{1 + RT}$$

with R in decimal form and T in years.

$$P = \frac{M}{1 + RT}$$

$$= \frac{\$15,000}{1 + \left(0.07 \times \frac{9}{12}\right)}$$

$$= \$14,251.78 \qquad \text{Rounded}$$

12.3 Determining the time in days when maturity value, rate, and principal are known

Use the formula

$$T = \frac{M - P}{PR} \times 360$$

to find time in days.

A principal of \$12,000 produces a maturity value of \$12,540 at a 6% rate. Find the time of the loan in days.

$$T = \frac{M - P}{PR} \times 360$$

$$= \frac{\$12,540 - \$12,000}{\$12,000 \times 0.06} \times 360$$

$$= 0.75 \times 360$$

$$= 270 \text{ days}$$

12.3 Finding rate given principal, maturity value, and time

Use the formula

$$R = \frac{M - P}{PT}$$

with time expressed in years.

A principal of \$8400 produces a maturity value of \$8718.50 in 210 days. Find the rate of interest.

$$R = \frac{M - P}{PT}$$

$$= \frac{\$8718.50 - \$8400}{\$8400 \times \frac{210}{360}}$$

$$= 0.065, \text{ or } 6.5\%$$

12.3 Finding time in days when principal, rate, and interest are known

Use the formula

$$T = \frac{I}{PR} \times 360$$

with R in decimal form.

\$8500 was invested at 8% and \$141.67 interest was earned. Find the time in days.

$$T = \frac{I}{PR} \times 360$$

$$= \frac{\$141.67}{\$8500 \times 0.08} \times 360$$

$$= 75 \text{ days}$$

12.4 Finding the effect of inflation on the cost of living

Use the percent formula.

Find the increase in the cost of living for a family with a budget of \$24,600 after taxes in a year with $3\frac{1}{2}\%$ inflation.

$$0.035 \times \$24,600 = \$861$$

They experience an \$861 increase in the cost of living.

12.4 Determining present value given maturity or future value, rate, and time

Use the formula

$$P = \frac{M}{1 + RT}$$

with R in decimal form and T in years.

A debt of $8000 must be paid in 9 months. Find the amount that could be deposited today at 5% interest so that enough money will be available.

$$P = \frac{M}{1 + RT}$$

$$= \frac{\$8000}{1 + \left(0.05 \times \frac{9}{12}\right)}$$

$$= \$7710.84 \qquad \text{Rounded}$$

12.4 Finding present value of a loan

Use the formula

$$M = P(1 + RT)$$

with R in decimal form and time in years. Then use the formula

$$P = \frac{M}{1 + RT}$$

with $R =$ time value of money and T in years.

A loan of $7500 at 12% is due in 15 months. Find the present value of the loan if the time value of money is 9%.

$$M = P(1 + RT)$$

$$= \$7500 \times \left[1 + \left(0.12 \times \frac{15}{12}\right)\right]$$

$$= \$8625$$

$$P = \frac{M}{1 + RT}$$

$$= \frac{\$8625}{1 + \left(0.09 \times \frac{15}{12}\right)}$$

$$= \$7752.81$$

12.4 Finding present value of a loan after it is made

Use the formula $M = P(1 + RT)$ with R in decimal form and T in years. Next, use the formula

$$P = \frac{M}{1 + RT}$$

with $R =$ time value of money, and $T =$ fraction of a year using days from present value date to due date.

An $8000 loan is made on June 5 for 90 days at 9%. The time value of money is 11%. Find the present value of the loan on August 10. First find maturity value of the loan.

$$M = P(1 + RT)$$

$$= \$8000 \times \left[1 + \left(0.09 \times \frac{90}{360}\right)\right]$$

$$= \$8180$$

Now, find time in days from Aug. 10 to maturity date.

Loan made	90 days		Loan due
June 5		August 10	Sept. 3

24 days

$$P = \frac{M}{1 + RT}$$

$$= \frac{\$8180}{1 + \left(0.11 \times \frac{24}{360}\right)}$$

$$= \$8120.45$$

CHAPTER 12 | Review Exercises

The answer section includes answers to all Review Exercises.

Complete this table. Round money to the nearest cent, rate to the nearest tenth of a percent, and time to the nearest month. [12.1]

	Interest	Principal	Rate	Time
1.	$840	$8400	5%	2 years
2.	$840	$9600	$10\frac{1}{2}\%$	10 months
3.	$696.80	$8710	12%	8 months
4.	$144	$2400	8%	9 months
5.	$810	$12,000	9%	9 months
6.	$750	$8000	7.5%	15 months
7.	$540	$12,000	6%	9 months
8.	$1600	$8000	8%	30 months

Find the number of days from the first date to the second. [12.2]

9. April 15 to August 7   114 days
10. July 12 to November 4   115 days

Find the exact interest for the following. Round to the nearest cent. [12.2]

	Interest	Principal	Rate	Time
11.	$258.90	$10,500	$7\frac{1}{2}\%$	120 days
12.	$336.58	$8400	$9\frac{3}{4}\%$	150 days
13.	$222.51	$7200	8%	From July 12 to November 30
14.	$867.95	$16,500	10%	From February 4 to August 15

Find ordinary interest for the following. Round to the nearest cent. [12.2]

	Interest	Principal	Rate	Time
15.	$43.17	$7400	7%	30 days
16.	$3241.33	$52,000	10.2%	220 days

Complete the following table. Round money to the nearest cent, rate to the nearest tenth of a percent, and time to the nearest day. Use ordinary interest. [12.3]

	Principal	Rate	Time	Interest
17.	$12,199.80	$7\frac{1}{2}\%$	80 days	$203.33
18.	$6181.82	11%	180 days	$340
19.	$6000	7%	60 days	$70
20.	$8400	$8\frac{1}{4}\%$	120 days	$231
21.	$7800	9%	40 days	$78
22.	$4900	$10\frac{1}{8}\%$	90 days	$124.03

Complete the following table. Round money to the nearest cent and rate to the nearest tenth of a percent. [12.3]

	Maturity Value	Principal	Rate	Time
23.	$6270	$5500	8%	$1\frac{3}{4}$ years
24.	$7272.60	$6900	7.2%	9 months
25.	$12,180.00	$12,000	9%	60 days

	Maturity Value	Principal	Rate	Time
26.	$6752.78	_$6500_	10%	140 days
27.	$8120.00	$8000	_9%_	60 days
28.	$17,537.50	$15,250	_12%_	15 months

Find the present value of each of the following. Round to the nearest cent. [12.4]

	Present Value	Maturity Value	Rate	Time
29.	_$6418.15_	$6600	$8\frac{1}{2}\%$	120 days
30.	_$11,612.90_	$12,000	12%	100 days

Find the present value of the following loans on the day they are made. Round to the nearest cent. [12.4]

	Present Value	Principal Amount	Interest Rate of Loan	Length of Loan	Time Value of Money
31.	_$8093.75_	$8000	$9\frac{1}{2}\%$	10 months	8%
32.	_$19,550.56_	$20,000	7%	15 months	9%

Find the present value for the following loans on the indicated dates. Assume that the time value of money is 9%. Round to the nearest cent. [12.4]

	Present Value	Amount	Interest Rate of Loan	Length of Loan	Loan Made	Find Present Value On
33.	_$8096.89_	$8000	10%	60 days	Feb. 1	March 15
34.	_$15,598.34_	$15,000	8%	300 days	Apr. 1	October 15

Solve the following application problems. Round money to the nearest cent, rate to the nearest tenth of a percent, and time to the nearest day.

35. Christina Barrett borrowed $4500 at $7\frac{1}{2}\%$ for 90 days to go on an exchange trip to Seoul, Korea. Find the simple interest. [12.1] $84.38

36. CenterStage Music borrowed $18,600 at 9% simple interest for 150 days to obtain a trade discount on guitars purchased from Martin. Find the maturity value. [12.3] $19,297.50

37. A loan to an auto shop of $34,200 at $7\frac{1}{2}\%$ has a maturity value of $35,981.25. Find the time in days. [12.3]   250 days

38. An 8-month, 9% loan had a maturity value of $3816. Find the amount originally borrowed. [12.3] $3600

39. Collins Dairy just bought new milking machines. The machines must be paid for with a single payment of $12,000 in 270 days. The firm has $11,200 that it can invest today. What rate of interest must it earn on this deposit to have the necessary $12,000? [12.2]   9.5%

40. Quik Print is ordering a new $27,500 printing press. The seller of the press wants payment in 120 days. The print shop has $26,000 available for investment today. What rate of interest must it earn on this deposit to have the needed $27,500? Is it reasonable to earn this rate? [12.2]   17.3%; no

41. Angela Rueben needs $14,000 but has only $13,400. How many days will it take to get the needed amount if she can earn 5% per year? [12.3]   322 days

42. Find the present value of a loan on the day it was made if the loan is for $9100 at 11% for 85 days. Assume that money has a time value of 9.7% [12.4] $9127.31

43. A loan of $19,250 is made on October 15, at 12%. The loan is for 75 days. Find the present value of the loan on November 27 if money has a time value of 11.7%. [12.4] $19,528.16

44. Suppose a loan of $11,800 is made on July 12, for 153 days, at 9%. Find the present value of the loan on September 20, if money has a time value of 11%. [12.4] $11,948.33

45. Sherri Woods makes and spends $28,400 per year. She receives an increase in her annual salary of 6% during a ye in which inflation is 3%. Ignoring taxes, find her net gain or loss in purchasing power. [12.4] $852 gain

46. Bob and Jane Shaw have been spending their entire after-tax income of $46,850. Assume they receive no increase in their after-tax salary for a particular year during which inflation was 6%. Find the net gain or loss in their purchasing power. **[12.4]** $2811 loss

47. Explain the possible effects of inflation on individuals who are retired. **[12.4]**

48. Use intuition to decide which of the following you would prefer: (a) a salary of $35,000 per year with no raises for 10 years or (b) a salary of $32,000 per year with annual raises of 3% per year for each of the next 10 years. Explain the reason for your choice. **[12.4]**

CHAPTER 12	Business Application Case #1
	Financing a Startup

Wes Whitmeyer started an appraisal company to estimate the value of homes and commercial real estate. During the first few months of operation of his new business, he received the following simple-interest loans.

Loan Number	Date Loan Made	Principal	Length of Loan	Interest Rate	Purpose of Loan
1	March 3	$12,000	6 months	10%	Used truck
2	April 17	$6200	90 days	12%	Computer equipment
3	July 9	$18,400	200 days	$9\frac{1}{2}\%$	Remodel the office

Complete the following table. Round to the nearest cent if needed.

Loan Number	Maturity Date	Simple Interest	Maturity Value
1	_____	_____	_____
2	_____	_____	_____
3	_____	_____	_____
Totals:		_____	_____

September 3; $600; $12,600

July 16; $186; $6386

January 25 of the following year; $971.11; $19,371.11

Totals: $1757.11; $38,357.11

CHAPTER 12	Business Application Case #2
	Financing a Tanker to Ship Chemicals

...istar Shipping needs another tanker (ship) to be used to carry chemicals from the Middle East to North America. ...rm needs to borrow $12,800,000 to purchase the ship, and managers are debating the following three simple- ...loans.

Lender	Interest Rate	Length
Shanghai Bank	8.72%	6 months
Bacon Funds	9.6%	12 months
Jidlaka Investments	9.47%	7 months

(a) Find the interest and maturity value of each loan. **(b)** Then decide on the best loan if the firm believes it will take some time to make enough money to pay off the loan.

(a)

	Interest	Maturity Value
Shanghai Bank	$558,080	$13,358,080
Bacon Funds	$1,228,800	$14,028,800
Jidlaka Investments	$707,093.33	$13,507,093.33

(b) The loan from Jidlaka Investments is only for 1 more month than the one from Shanghai Bank, but the interest rate is quite a bit higher. So that does not appear to be a good choice. The loan from Shanghai Bank looks best unless Navistar Shipping needs the longer term of 12 months from Bacon Funds.

Notes and Bank Discount

javier brosch / Fotolia.com

The ability to borrow money is at the foundation of modern society. For example, most people would not be able to buy a car or house without the ability to borrow. Figure 13.1 shows the median debt that students have accrued when in college, so students also clearly need to borrow. Businesses borrow extensively to finance operating costs or to build something such as a dam or a new factory.

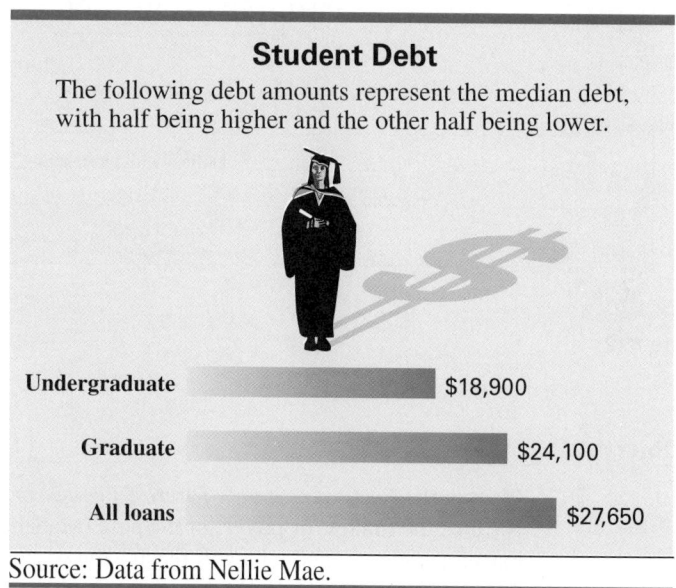

Student Debt

The following debt amounts represent the median debt, with half being higher and the other half being lower.

Undergraduate	$18,900
Graduate	$24,100
All loans	$27,650

Source: Data from Nellie Mae.

Figure 13.1

▶STOP & THINK

> Think about your own situation or that of a student friend. First, estimate your total debt today including student loans, automobile loans, charge card balances, and any other loans you may have. Then, try to estimate how much you will need to borrow each semester for the remainder of your degree program. Approximately how much will you owe when you graduate? What salary do you expect when you graduate? How long do you think it will it take you to pay off that debt?

When an individual or business borrows money, written proof of the loan often takes the form of a **promissory note**, which documents a loan. A promissory note is a legal and, frequently, a transferable document in which one person or firm agrees to pay a stated amount of money, at a stated date and interest rate, to another. Banks typically require business owners to sign promissory notes when lending them money. Sometimes, simple interest notes are used, while at other times, simple discount notes are used. Both types of notes are discussed in this chapter.

> **NOTE** A year is assumed to have 360 days for all calculations in this chapter.

13.1 Simple Interest Notes

OBJECTIVES

1 *Identify the parts of a simple interest promissory note.*
2 *Find the due date of a note.*
3 *Find the face value, time, and rate of a note.*

An example of a promissory note is shown in Figure 13.2.

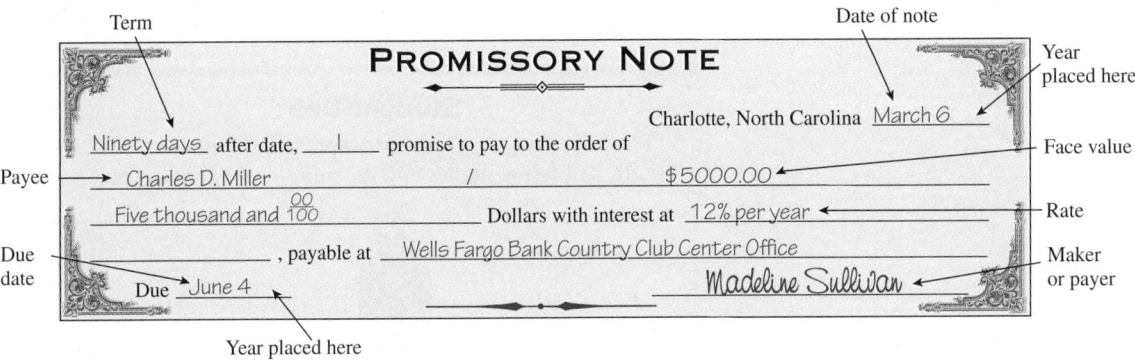

Figure 13.2

Objective

1 *Identify the Parts of a Simple Interest Promissory Note.* The person borrowing the money is called the **maker**, or **payer**, of the note (Madeline Sullivan for this note). The person who loaned the money, and who will receive the payment, is called the **payee** (Charles D. Miller for this note). The length of time until the note is due is called the **term of the note** (90 days for this note). The **face value**, or principal, of the note ($5000 for this note) is the amount written on the line in front of *dollars*. The interest rate on the note is 12% per year.

The **maturity value** of the loan is the face value plus any interest that is due. Since the interest for this note is found by using formulas for simple interest, this note is a **simple interest note**. When using the formulas for simple interest, the face value of the note is used as the value for the principal, P. Find the interest on the note shown in Figure 13.2 as follows.

$$\text{Interest} = \text{face value} \times \text{rate} \times \text{time}$$
$$= \$5000 \times 0.12 \times \frac{90}{360}$$
$$= \$150$$

$$\text{Maturity value} = \text{face value} + \text{interest}$$
$$= \$5000 + \$150$$
$$= \$5150$$

Madeline Sullivan must pay $5150 to Charles D. Miller on the maturity date of the note, or June 4, which is 90 days after March 6.

The promissory note shown in Figure 13.2 contains all the information needed to calculate interest owed and maturity value. However, banks and other financial institutions use a more comprehensive note containing very detailed listings of necessary payment dates and amounts, as well as paragraphs describing the bank's rights in case of nonpayment of the note. A typical promissory note from a large bank is shown in Figure 13.3.

BORROWER	FIXED RATE

Joan Waters

ADDRESS
2705 4Th ST., Kansas City, MO

TELEPHONE NO.   IDENTIFICATION NO.
HA69724

FIXED RATE CONSUMER NOTE, DISCLOSURE AND SECURITY AGREEMENT

OFFICER INITIALS	INTEREST RATE	PRINCIPAL AMOUNT	FUNDING DATE	MATURITY DATE	CUSTOMER NUMBER	LOAN NUMBER
GWS	12%	$10,000	4/1	8/1	3627014	HA69724

** ANNUAL PERCENTAGE RATE **	** FINANCE CHARGE **	AMOUNT FINANCED	TOTAL OF PAYMENTS
THE COST OF THE CREDIT AS A YEARLY RATE.	THE DOLLAR AMOUNT THE CREDIT WILL COST.	THE AMOUNT OF CREDIT PROVIDED TO THE BORROWER OR ON BORROWER'S BEHALF.	THE AMOUNT BORROWER WILL HAVE PAID AFTER PAYMENTS HAVE BEEN MADE AS SCHEDULED.
12%	$1957.04	$10,000	$11,957.04

NUMBER OF PAYMENTS	AMOUNT OF PAYMENTS	WHEN PAYMENTS ARE DUE
36	$332.14 monThly	beginning April 11

DEMAND FEATURE: ☐ This Note has a demand feature.

REQUIRED DEPOSIT ACCOUNT: ☐ If checked, the Lender requires that Borrower maintain a deposit balance with Lender. The Annual Percentage Rate does not take into account required deposits.

SECURITY: A security interest has been granted in: ☐ Collateral securing other loans with Lender may also secure this loan; ☐ Any deposit accounts of Borrower with Lender; ☒ The goods or property being purchased; ☐ Other (describe): LOT 167, BILL MORRIS SURVEY

FILING FEES: $ NONE in fees are being paid to public officials in order to research, perfect or release a security interest in the Collateral.

PREPAYMENT: If Borrower pays off early, Borrower ☐ may ☐ will not have to pay a penalty; ☐ may ☐ will not be charged a minimum finance charge; ☐ may ☐ will not be entitled to a refund of part of the finance charge.

ITEMIZATION: Borrower has the right to receive at this time an itemization of the Amount Financed. Borrower ☐ does ☐ does not want an itemization.

LATE CHARGES: If an installment is received more than 10 days late, Borrower will be charged a late payment charge of: ☐ _____ % of the unpaid late installment; ☒ 5 % of the unpaid late installment or $ 15.00, whichever is ☒ greater ☐ less; as permitted by law.

ASSUMPTION: ☐ This loan may not be assumed on its original terms. ☐ This loan may be assumed on its original terms, subject to certain conditions.

See your contract documents for additional information about nonpayment, default, prepayment penalties and refunds and acceleration.

e means an estimate

Figure 13.3

Most notes written by banks are secured by **collateral**. That is, the person borrowing the money *must pledge assets* such as cars, stock, or real estate that are of equal value or greater value than the amount of the loan. The collateral for the note in Figure 13.3 is Lot 167 located in the Bill Morris Survey. In the event of nonpayment, the bank will take the collateral and sell or liquidate it. The bank then uses the proceeds to pay off the note. Any excess is returned to the maker of the note.

Objective

2 *Find the Due Date of a Note.* When a promissory note is given in months, the loan is due on the same day of the month, after the given number of months has passed. For example, a 4-month note made on May 25 would be due 4 months in the future on September 25. Other examples follow.

A loan made on January 31 for 3 months would normally be due on April 31. However, there are only 30 days in April, so the loan is due on April 30. Whenever a due date does not exist, such as February 30 or November 31, use the last day of the month (February 28 or November 30 in these examples). February 29 must be used if it is a leap year.

Date Made	Length of Loan	Date Due
March 12	5 months	August 12
April 24	7 months	November 24
October 7	9 months	July 7
January 31	3 months	April 30

EXAMPLE **1** **Finding Due Date, Interest, and Maturity Value**

Fred Romero needs to borrow money to purchase equipment needed to start his own graphic arts company. He signs a note with a face value of $15,000, a term of 10 months, and a rate of $11\frac{1}{2}\%$ on April 30. Find the due date, interest, and maturity value.

Solution

Ten months from April 30 is February 30 of the following year, which does not exist. So the due date is the last day of February, or February 28. It would be due February 29 if it is a leap year.

$$\text{Interest} = \$15,000 \times 0.115 \times \frac{10}{12} = \$1437.50$$

$$\text{Maturity value} = \$15,000 + \$1437.50 = \$16,437.50$$

NOTE   When the length of the loan is given in months, do *not* convert the time to days in order to find the date due.

The term of a promissory note is often given as a number of days. For example, a loan might be signed on March 12, and be due in 90 days. To find the date due, use the exact number of days in a month. This can be done in either of two ways, as shown in **Chapter 12**.

One way is to look back at Table 12.1, which shows the number of each day. From the table, March 12 is the 71st day of the year. The loan is due 90 days after March 12. The number of the day on which the loan is due is found as follows.

$$\begin{array}{r} 71 \\ +\ 90 \\ \hline 161 \end{array}$$ Number of the day loan is made.
Number of days until due.
Number of the day loan is due is 161.

From Table 12.1, day 161 is June 10. A 90-day loan made on March 12 is due on June 10.

As an alternative method, use the actual number of days in each month. The loan is made on March 12. Since March has 31 days, there are 19 more days in March.

$$\begin{array}{r} 31 \\ -\ 12 \\ \hline 19 \end{array}$$

There are 30 days in April, and 31 in May. Find the total as follows.

19	Rest of days in March
30	Days in April
+ 31	Days in May
80	

The loan is for 90 days, which is 10 more than 80, making the loan due on June 10. The following table shows several more examples.

Date Made	Length of Loan	Due Date
January 9	60 days	March 10
May 28	120 days	September 25
November 21	100 days	March 1
October 9	180 days	April 7

Objective

3   *Find the Face Value, Time, and Rate of a Note.*   The next examples show how to find the face value, time, or rate for a note. Each of these examples uses formulas from **Chapter 12**.

> **NOTE**   Face value for simple interest notes is the same as the principal, P, as used in **Chapter 12**.

EXAMPLE 2   **Finding Face Value and Interest**

Sheila Walker signed a 120-day note at 9% for funds she used to pay off several old bills. A single payment of $7725 paid off her note when it was due. Find the face value and interest for the note.

Solution

The payment of $7725 is the maturity value of the note. The maturity value is found with the following formula from **Chapter 12**.

$$M = P(1 + RT)$$

Since P is not known in this example, solve for P by dividing both sides by $1 + RT$.

$$P = \frac{M}{1 + RT}$$

Now substitute $7725 for M, 0.09 for R, and $\frac{120}{360}$ for T.

$$P = \frac{\$7725}{1 + \left(0.09 \times \frac{120}{360}\right)}$$

$$= \frac{\$7725}{1 + 0.03}$$

$$= \frac{\$7725}{1.03}$$

$$= \$7500$$

The face value of the note was $7500. The interest charge was $7725 − $7500 = $225.

EXAMPLE 3 **Finding the Time of a Note**

The owner of Jay's Country Music in Nashville signed a note with a face value of $45,000 to buy digital recording equipment. The interest rate is 10% and the maturity value is $47,250. Find the time of the note, in days.

Solution

Recall the formula for time in days using banker's interest from **Chapter 12**.

$$T \text{ (in days)} = \frac{M - P}{PR} \times 360$$

Find the time by substituting $47,250 for M, $45,000 for P, and 10%, or 0.10, for R.

$$T \text{ (in days)} = \frac{\$47,250 - \$45,000}{\$45,000 \times 0.10} \times 360$$

$$= \frac{\$2250}{\$4500} \times 360$$

$$= 0.125 \times 360$$

$$= 180 \text{ days}$$

The loan was for 180 days. Since $M - P = I$, the same time in days can also be found using the equation from **Chapter 12**.

$$T \text{ (in days)} = \frac{I}{PR} \times 360$$

NOTE A common error when solving for time T (in days) is forgetting to multiply by 360.

EXAMPLE 4 **Finding the Rate of a Note**

Leslie Graham, owner of Graham's Fine Wines, signed a note with a face value of $12,500 on April 12. She needed the funds to remodel the store. On August 30, a maturity value of $12,961.81 is to be repaid. Find the rate on the note.

Solution

Find the rate by starting with the formula for simple interest, $I = PRT$, and dividing both sides by PT.

$$R = \frac{I}{PT}$$

Interest (I) = $12,961.81 - $12,500 = $461.81

Principal (P) = $12,500

Time (T) = $\frac{140}{360}$ since there are 140 days from April 12 to August 30.

$$R = \frac{\$461.81}{\$12,500 \times \frac{140}{360}}$$

$$= 9.5 \qquad \text{Rounded}$$

The rate is 9.5%. The same rate can be found using the alternative form of the equation $R = \dfrac{M - P}{PT}$ found in **Chapter 12**.

NOTE Do not round before the final answer in problems such as Example 4.

13.1	**Exercises**

Identify each of the following from the promissory note that follows.

1. maker   Helen Spence

2. payer   Helen Spence

3. payee   Leta Clendenen

4. face value $7500

5. term of loan   90 days

6. day loan made   October 27

7. day loan due   January 25

8. maturity value $7631.25

PROMISSORY NOTE

Jackson, Mississippi October 27

Ninety days after date, ___I___ promise to pay to the order of

Leta Clendenen / $7500.00

Seven thousand five hundred and 00/100 Dollars with interest at _7% per year_

_____, payable at ___Crocker–Citizens Bank, Oak Park Branch___

Due _January 25_   _Helen Spence_

Find the due date of each of the following.

	Date Made	Term of Loan	
9.	April 20	5 months	September 20
10.	July 12	3 months	October 12
11.	December 31	6 months	June 30
12.	May 31	4 months	September 30
13.	January 6	70 days	March 17
14.	September 14	125 days	January 17
15.	November 24	150 days	April 23
16.	December 8	160 days	May 17

Find the date due and the maturity value for each of the following. Use Table 12.1 on page 459 in your textbook. Round money to the nearest cent.

	Date Made	Face Value	Term of Loan	Rate	
17.	June 12	$6000	150 days	9%	November 9; $6225
18.	March 18	$9500	200 days	10%	October 4; $10,027.78
19.	August 14	$5000	300 days	$8\frac{1}{2}\%$	June 10; $5354.17
20.	October 20	$4500	180 days	12%	April 18; $4770

Complete the following table. Round money to the nearest cent, time to the nearest day, and rate to the nearest tenth of a percent.

	Principal	Rate	Time	Maturity Value
21.	$8400	10%	180 days	$8820
22.	$7200	9%	240 days	$7632
23.	$3600	8%	120 days	$3696
24.	$8500	7.5%	250 days	$8942.71
25.	$8400	11%	140 days	$8759.33
26.	$6800	12.5%	180 days	$7225
27.	$12,240	$10\frac{1}{2}$%	200 days	$12,954
28.	$15,000	9%	150 days	$15,562.50

29. State and explain the different parts of a simple interest promissory note. (See Objective 1.)

30. Name at least five reasons why a small firm such as a bicycle or boat shop might need to borrow money. List three reasons you might need to borrow money.

Solve the following application problems. Round to the nearest cent.

31. WEDDING SUPPLIES On October 7, Janet Nastor signed a 200-day note with a face value of $18,400 for an inventory of wedding dresses and other supplies for her store. If the rate on the note was $9\frac{3}{4}$%, find (a) the due date and (b) the maturity value. **(a)** April 25 **(b)** $19,396.67

32. SKI PURCHASE Jill Sample's Ski House bought $15,900 worth of skis from Rossignol on September 19. The firm signed a 200-day, $11\frac{1}{2}$% note for the skis. Find (a) the due date and (b) the maturity value of the note. **(a)** April 7 **(b)** $16,915.83

33. FITNESS GYM On April 15, Bobby and Jill Watson signed a 7-month note with a face value of $85,000 for equipment to start a small fitness gym. If the rate on the note was $10\frac{1}{2}$%, find (a) the due date and (b) the maturity value. **(a)** November 15 **(b)** $90,206.25

34. HOBBY STORE Ted Jenson borrowed $49,000 for 9 months at 8.5% to purchase numerous remote-control race cars and helicopters and also a few high-tech robots made in Japan. If he signed the note with the bank on July 5, find (a) the due date and (b) the maturity value. **(a)** April 5 **(b)** $52,123.75

35. NOOK COLOR™ Staples Office Supplies borrowed funds to buy NOOK Color electronic book and magazine readers to stock all its stores in one district. The 320-day note is at 7.8% with a maturity value of $304,000. Find the face value. $284,289.28

36. START-UP COMPANY A 15-year-old computer whiz needs two computers and some software to start a home business. His parents help him by signing a note with a maturity value of $5400, rate of 12%, and time of 240 days. Find the face value. $5000

37. FLOWER SHOP Marie's Flowers uses the proceeds from an 11%, 7-month note with a maturity value of $30,222.33 to build a garden area with a fountain in front of her store. If the note is due on November 7, find (a) the date the loan was made and (b) the face value. **(a)** April 7 **(b)** $28,400

38. PHYSICAL THERAPIST A physical therapist signed an 11-month, $9\frac{1}{2}$% note with a maturity value of $92,836.92 due on March 30. Find (a) the date the loan was made and (b) the face value. **(a)** April 30 **(b)** $85,400

39. STATIONERY SHOP West Stationery is getting ready to pay a note that is due. The interest rate is 12%, the face value is $12,000, and the interest is $360. Find the time (in days) of the note. 90 days

40. SCUBA SHOP Ocean Scuba just paid the $15,072 maturity value on a note with a face value of $14,400. The interest rate was 8%. Find the time (in days) of the note. 210 days

41. **SECURITY SYSTEM PURCHASE** The manager of the local electronics plant bought a security system for $12,000, paying for it with a 120-day note with a maturity value of $12,320. Find the interest rate she paid on the note. 8%

42. **COFFEE SHIPMENT** Dunn Brothers Coffee Company signed a $17,000, 90-day note for a shipment of coffee. The maturity value of the note was $17,382.50. Find the interest rate paid. 9%

43. **ALASKA CRUISE** Bob and Sheryl Robinson sign a $6800 note at 12% simple interest for 90 days and use the funds to help pay for a 2-week cruise to Alaska. If Sheryl receives an after-tax year-end bonus of $5000 in 90 days, how much additional money will they need to pay off the note? $2004

44. **INCOME TAX REFUND** The owner of Ben's Package Goods expects a $7400 refund on his taxes from the government in 100 days. He signs a 100-day note for $8600 at 9% to purchase extra inventory in order to get large-quantity discounts. How much additional money beyond his tax refund will he need at maturity? $1415

13.2 | Simple Discount Notes

OBJECTIVES

1 *Define simple discount notes.*

2 *Find bank discount and proceeds.*

3 *Calculate proceeds if given face value, discount rate, and time.*

4 *Distinguish between discount rates and simple interest rates.*

5 *Find effective interest rates.*

6 *Understand T-bills.*

7 *Find the face value that produces the desired proceeds.*

8 *Find discount rate, face value, or time.*

Banks can write a note as either a simple interest note, as seen in Section 13.1, or as a simple discount note, as discussed in this section. One type of note is not better than the other type—they are simply two different ways to make a loan. A simple interest note can be set up by the bank as a simple discount note, and vice versa. We discuss both types of notes since both are in common use.

Objective

1 *Define Simple Discount Notes.* Simple interest and **simple discount notes** have the same components: amount loaned to the borrower, interest rate, time, interest, and amount to be repaid by the borrower when the note matures. However, the two different types of notes use different names for these components. Also, simple discount notes are sometimes called **interest-in-advance notes** since the interest is subtracted from the face value to find the amount loaned to the borrower. The following may help you see the difference between the two types of notes.

	Simple Interest Note	Simple Discount Note
Amount loaned to borrower	face value	proceeds
+ Interest	+ interest	+ discount
Amount to be repaid	maturity value	face value

So, the **proceeds** to the borrower in a simple discount note is the same thing as face value (or principal) in a simple interest note. The **discount** in a simple discount note is the same thing as interest in a simple interest note. Finally, **face value** in a simple discount note is the same thing as maturity value in a simple interest note. However, here is a subtle difference in terms of what the interest rate and discount rates are multiplied by.

> **NOTE** For *simple interest*, the interest rate must be multiplied by the amount loaned to a borrower.

> **NOTE** For a *simple discount*, the discount rate must be multiplied *by the amount to be repaid by the borrower.*

As an example of a simple discount note, suppose a borrower signs a note with a face value of $2000 and a discount of $150 as follows. Then,

$2000   Face value or maturity value of the note

− $150   Discount or interest that must be paid at maturity

$1850   Proceeds that the borrower actually receives at the time loan is made

> **NOTE** Simple *interest* is calculated on the *principal*, while simple *discount* is calculated on the *maturity value.*

Objective

2 *Find Bank Discount and Proceeds.* The formula for finding the bank discount is similar to the formula for calculating simple interest. Different letters are used to emphasize that the loan is a *discount loan* and that interest charges are computed based on maturity value rather than on the amount received by the borrower.

Calculating Bank Discount

> $$B \qquad M \times D \times T$$
> Bank discount = face value × discount rate × time
>
> where B = bank discount
>
> M = face value (maturity value)
>
> D = discount rate
>
> T = time (in years)
>
> Then, if P is the proceeds:
>
> Proceeds received (loan amount) = face value − bank discount
>
> or $P = M - B$
>
> The maturity value, or face value, M, is the sum of the discount and the proceeds.
>
> $$M = P + B$$

> **EXAMPLE** **1** **Finding Discount and Proceeds**
>
> Marie Gostowski borrowed $12,000 for 10 months from Bank of America so that she could buy a new, larger commercial oven for her bakery. The banker discounted the note at 9%. Find the amount of the discount and the proceeds.

Solution

Find the discount with the formula $B = MDT$, with $M = \$12{,}000$, $D = 9\%$, and $T = \frac{10}{12}$, or $\frac{5}{6}$.

$$B = MDT$$

$$= \$12{,}000 \times 0.09 \times \frac{5}{6} = \$900$$

The discount of $900 is the interest charge on the loan. The value of the proceeds that Gostowski actually received when making the loan is found using $P = M - B$.

$$P = M - B$$
$$= \$12,000 - \$900 = \$11,100$$

After signing the note for $12,000, Gostowski will be given $11,100. Then, 10 months later, she must make a single payment of $12,000 to the bank.

■

NOTE In Example 1, the value of the proceeds of $11,100 is the present value, and the maturity value of $12,000 is the future value.

Objective

3 *Calculate Proceeds If Given Face Value, Discount Rate, and Time.* The value of the proceeds of a simple discount note is the face value (maturity value) *minus* the discount $(M - B)$. The discount equals maturity value × discount rate × the time in years. Look at the following.

$$P = M - B$$
$$= M - MDT \qquad \text{Substitute } MDT \text{ for } B.$$
$$= M(1 - DT) \qquad \text{Use the distributive property.}$$

NOTE Time must be in years or a fraction of a year for simple discount notes, just as it was for simple interest notes.

EXAMPLE **2** **Finding Proceeds**

Josh Crandall borrows $25,000 (in U.S. currency) from a bank in Cameroon to purchase a used Land Rover for his African safari company. Find the proceeds if the loan is for 90 days and has a discount rate of $10\frac{1}{2}\%$.

Solution

There are two ways to find the proceeds. One way would be to use the formula $B = MDT$ to find the discount and then subtract the discount from the face value to find the proceeds.

$$B = MDT$$
$$= \$25,000 \times 0.105 \times \frac{90}{360} = \$656.25$$

The proceeds are then

$$P = M - D$$
$$= \$25,000 - \$656.25 = \$24,343.75$$

As a second method and a check for finding the proceeds, use the formula $P = M(1 - DT)$. Here, $M = \$25,000$, $D = 10\frac{1}{2}\%$, and $T = \frac{90}{360}$.

$$P = M(1 - DT)$$
$$= \$25,000\left[1 - \left(0.105 \times \frac{90}{360}\right)\right]$$

Inside the brackets, be sure to first multiply $0.105 \times \frac{90}{360}$, and then subtract from 0.105.

$$P = \$25,000(1 - 0.02625)$$
$$= \$25,000(0.97375)$$
$$= \$24,343.75$$

The proceeds of a simple discount note can be found using either method.

■

> **NOTE** Do not round when making calculations within any one formula. Round only after all calculations in the formula have been made.

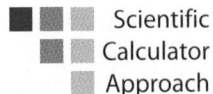 **Scientific Calculator Approach**

For the calculator solution to Example 2, think of the problem as

$$\$25{,}000\left(1 - 0.105 \times \frac{90}{360}\right)$$

and enter the parentheses accordingly.

25000 $\boxed{\times}$ $\boxed{(}$ 1 $\boxed{-}$ 0.105 $\boxed{\times}$ 90 $\boxed{\div}$ 360 $\boxed{)}$ $\boxed{=}$ 24343.75

Objective

4 **_Distinguish Between Discount Rates and Simple Interest Rates._** A discount rate of 12% is not the same as a simple interest rate of 12%. The next example shows why.

EXAMPLE 3 **Comparing Discount Rates and Simple Interest Rates**

Two different notes each have a face value of $7500 and a time of 90 days. One has a simple interest rate of 12%, and the other has a discount rate of 12%.

(a) Find the interest owed on each.

Solution

For the Simple Interest Note	For the Simple Discount Note
$I = PRT$	$B = MDT$
$= \$7500 \times 0.12 \times \dfrac{90}{360}$	$= \$7500 \times 0.12 \times \dfrac{90}{360}$
$= \$225$	$= \$225$

In each case, the interest is $225.

(b) Find the amount _actually received_ by the borrower in each case.

Solution

For the Simple Interest Note	For the Simple Discount Note
Principal = face value	Proceeds = $M - B$
$= \$7500$	$= \$7500 - \$225$
	$= \$7275$

With the simple interest note, the borrower has the use of $7500, but only $7275 is available with the simple discount note. In each case, the interest charge is the same, $225, but _more money is available to the borrower with the simple interest note._

(c) Find the maturity value of each note.

Solution

For the Simple Interest Note	For the Simple Discount Note
$M = P + I$ $= \$7500 + \$225$ $= \$7725$	Maturity value = face value $= \$7500$

The differences between these two notes is summarized as follows.

	Simple Interest	Simple Discount
Face value	$7500	$7500
Interest	$225	$225
Amount available to borrower	$7500	$7275
Maturity value	$7725	$7500

The borrower in the 12% simple interest note uses $7500 for 90 days and pays $225 in interest. The borrower in the 12% simple discount note is able to use only $7275 for 90 days and must pay the same interest. Therefore, in this particular case, the 12% simple interest note is better than the 12% discount note.

Objective

5

Find Effective Interest Rates. Interest rates can be given in different ways. The interest rate that is written on the note is the **stated**, or **nominal, interest rate**. It may or may not be the same rate as the **true interest rate**, which also called the **effective interest rate** and the **annual percentage rate**. The true interest rate is based on the actual interest charge, amount loaned to the borrower, and the length of the loan.

The **Federal Truth in Lending Act** was passed in 1969 because of the confusion resulting from the different ways of calculating interest charges. This act requires that all interest rates be given in a standard way, so that they can quickly and easily be compared to one another. The next example shows how to find the effective interest rate corresponding to the discount rate given in Example 3.

EXAMPLE 4 **Finding Rate of Interest for Discount Notes**

Find the rate of simple interest for the simple discount note in Example 3.

Solution

The discount rate of 12% in the simple discount note in Example 3 is the nominal rate for that note and not the effective rate. This is because the 12% applies to the maturity value of $7500 and *not* to the proceeds of $7275 actually received by the borrower. Find the effective interest rate using the formula for simple interest, $I = PRT$, with $I = \$225$, $P = \$7275$, and $T = \frac{90}{360}$.

Start with $I = PRT$, and divide both sides by PT.

$$R = \frac{I}{PT}$$

Then substitute the given numbers.

$$R = \frac{\$225}{\$7275 \times \frac{90}{360}}$$

$$= \frac{\$225}{\$1818.75}$$

$$= 0.1237, \quad \text{or} \quad 12.37\% \quad \text{Rounded}$$

The effective rate of interest is 12.37%, and not 12%, which is the nominal rate written on the note. Federal regulations require that a borrower be told the effective rate of interest. However, the regulations allow the rate to be rounded to the nearest quarter of a percent, so 12.37% could be reported as 12.25% in this case. In Example 3, we were comparing a simple interest loan with an effective rate of 12.00%, so it becomes obvious which is better from the borrower's perspective.

■

NOTE The nominal (stated) interest rate may be different than the true (effective) interest rate.

Objective

6 *Understand T-Bills.* **U.S. Treasury bills (T-bills)** are one common use of discount notes. The U.S. government uses T-bills to borrow money from investors. These financial instruments are available with 13-week, 26-week, or 52-week maturities. Rather than paying the face value for a T-bill, investors pay the face value minus the discount, which is based on the current interest rate and length to maturity of the bill. The investor receives the face amount of the T-bill when it matures. T-bills are considered to be very safe investments since they are loans to the U.S. government. A T-bill may be bought and sold many times during its lifetime.

NOTE Treasury bills can be purchased by individuals directly or through mutual funds or exchange-traded funds that buy Treasury bills.

EXAMPLE 5 Finding Facts about T-Bills

Managers at a bank in Brazil are worried about devaluation of the Brazilian currency. They purchase $1 million in 26-week U.S. T-bills with a stated rate of 4%, so that this money is in a safe place for a short period of time. Find (a) the total purchase price, (b) the total maturity value, (c) the interest earned, and (d) the effective rate of interest.

Solution

$$M = \$1,000,000; D = 0.04; T = \tfrac{26}{52} \quad \text{(The denominator is 52 when time is in weeks.)}$$

(a) Bank discount = face value × discount rate × time

$$= \$1,000,000 \times 0.04 \times \tfrac{26}{52} = \$20,000$$

Purchase price = face value − bank discount

$$= \$1,000,000 - \$20,000 = \$980,000$$

(b) Maturity value = face value

$$= \$1,000,000$$

Maturity value
$1,000,000

Bank discount

Purchase price
$980,000

(c) Interest = bank discount

= $20,000

(d) Effective rate $= \dfrac{\text{interest earned}}{\text{purchase price (proceeds)} \times \text{time}}$

$= \dfrac{\$20,000}{\$980,000 \times \frac{26}{52}} = 0.04081 = 4.08$ Rounded

The T-bills have a stated rate of 4% but an effective rate of 4.08%.

Objective

7

Find the Face Value That Produces the Desired Proceeds. Normally, a borrower has in mind a certain amount of money needed. The next example shows how to use the amount needed by a borrower to find the face value of the discount note.

EXAMPLE **6**   **Find the Face Value That Produces the Desired Proceeds**

Mike Collins needs $4000 to repair his roof. Find the value of a note that will provide the $4000 in proceeds if he plans to repay the note in 180 days and the bank charges a 10% discount rate.

Solution

Start with the formula $P = M(1 - DT)$. Since M is not known, find a formula for M by dividing both sides by $1 - DT$.

$$M = \frac{P}{1 - DT}$$

Replace P with $4000, D with 10%, or 0.1, and T with $\frac{180}{360}$.

$$M = \frac{\$4000}{\left(1 - 0.1 \times \frac{180}{360}\right)}$$

$$= \frac{\$4000}{1 - 0.05} = \$4210.53 \quad \text{Rounded}$$

Collins must sign a discount note with a face value of $4210.53 to get the $4000 that he needs.

 Scientific
Calculator
Approach

The calculator solution to Example 6 follows.

Objective

8

Find Discount Rate, Face Value, or Time. The formula for simple interest, $I = PRT$, can be solved for P, R, or T. Similarly, the formula for simple discount, $B = MDT$, can be solved for M, D, or T. Do this as shown in the next example.

EXAMPLE **7** **Finding Discount**

Sheila Watts borrowed proceeds of $4480 on a discount note to help with college expenses. Her 240-day note had a maturity value of $4800. Find the discount rate.

Solution

To find the discount rate, start with the formula $B = MDT$ and divide both sides by MT.

$$D = \frac{B}{MT}$$

Discount: $B = \$4800 - \$4480 = \$320$

Also, $M = \$4800$ and $T = \frac{240}{360}$. Now find D.

$$D = \frac{\$320}{\$4800 \times \frac{240}{360}} = 0.10$$

The discount rate is 10%.

13.2	**Exercises**

Find the discount and the proceeds. Round money to the nearest cent.

	Maturity Value	Discount Rate	Time in Days	
1.	$4600	9%	90	$103.50; $4496.50
2.	$6800	10%	180	$340; $6460
3.	$8500	11%	300	$779.17; $7720.83
4.	$15,500	12%	200	$1033.33; $14,466.67
5.	$8400	6%	30	$42; $8358
6.	$9800	$8\frac{3}{4}$%	50	$119.10; $9680.90

Find the due date and the proceeds for the following. Round to the nearest cent.

	Maturity Value	Discount Rate	Date Made	Time in Days	
7.	$8400	11%	January 3	100	April 13; $8143.33
8.	$5400	12%	March 25	90	June 23; $5238
9.	$12,000	$9\frac{1}{2}$%	August 21	180	February 17; $11,430
10.	$9750	$7\frac{1}{2}$%	December 9	200	June 27; $9343.75

Complete this table.

	Maturity Value	Discount Rate	Date Made	Due Date	Time in Days	Discount	Proceeds
11.	$24,000	$9\frac{1}{2}$%	2/4	8/3	180	$1140	$22,860
12.	$8275	7%	5/13	9/10	120	$193.08	$8081.92
13.	$14,400	11%	8/7	1/4	150	$660	$13,740
14.	$8200	10%	2/9	5/10	90	$205	$7995
15.	$7200	6%	11/12	2/10	90	$108	$7092
16.	$19,600	10%	12/2	8/11	252	$1372	$18,228

Solve the following application problems. Round rates to the nearest tenth of a percent and money to the nearest cent.

17. **BOAT PURCHASE** A Chevron employee bought a small boat with funds borrowed from First National Bank. He intends to repay the note with a Christmas bonus of $6000 to be paid to him in 120 days. Given an 11% discount, find the discount and the proceeds. $220; $5780

18. **INCOME TAX PAYMENT** LaTonya Barker must make a quarterly tax payment to the Internal Revenue Service. She decides to borrow money from her company (Bicycles Unlimited) and repay the loan in 100 days using an $8500 bonus she will receive at that time. Given an 8.5% discount rate, find the discount and the proceeds. $200.69; $8299.31

19. **BUSINESS TRIP TO ALASKA** Walter Bates needed funds to go on a business trip to Alaska, and he signed a note for $6000. At a $10\frac{1}{2}$% discount rate, the discount on the note was $210. Find the length of the loan in days.   120 days

20. **DIVORCE SETTLEMENT** Will and Juliet Ramapo divorced. As part of the divorce settlement, the judge required Will to sign a $12,500 note at 8.5% simple discount in favor of his wife, who will have custody of their two children. Find the length of the loan in days if the discount is $737.85.   250 days

21. **SUBWAY** Charles River signed a 300-day note for $98,500 to open a Subway franchise. Find the discount rate if the discount is $5951.04.   7.2%

22. **TRADE WITH MEXICO** Juan Ramirez borrows $380,000 in U.S. dollars to construct a warehouse in Juarez, Mexico, near the border with Texas. He signed the 250-day note with proceeds of $354,930.56 for a warehouse to store U.S.-made medical equipment before distributing it throughout Mexico. Find the discount rate.   9.5%

23. **LAPTOP** Jane Peters frequently travels to Hong Kong and needs to purchase a special laptop for the visually impaired costing $3200. If the discount rate is 10% and the term is 140 days, find the maturity value of the loan. $3329.48

24. **LAST YEAR AT COLLEGE** Mary Gibb estimates that she needs $10,000 to finish her last year at college. She borrows the funds from her uncle for 12 months at a favorable 4% discount rate. Find the face value of the loan. $10,416.67

25. **HOME REMODELING** Faith Daigle signs an 8.5% discount note with a maturity value of $7800 and a term of 8 months so that she can remodel her kitchen. Find the proceeds and the effective interest rate. $7358; 9.0%

26. **PERSONAL DISCOUNT NOTE** Ed Foust goes to the bank and signs a note for $8400. The bank charges a 7% discount rate. Find the proceeds and the effective rate charged by the bank if the note is for 8 months. $8008; 7.3%

27. **JAPANESE FISHING** A Japanese contractor needed proceeds of $410,000 to finish construction of a ship specially designed to catch, harvest, and freeze fish on long voyages such as to the coast of South America. A Japanese bank loaned the contractor the funds at a 4.25% discount rate for 120 days. Find the face value of the note and the effective interest rate. $415,891.80; 4.3%

28. **INTERNATIONAL FINANCE** A Canadian pipeline company requires proceeds of $720,000 (local currency) and borrows from a bank in Hong Kong at a 12% discount for 45 days. Find the face value of the note and the effective interest rate. $730,964.47; 12.2%

The following exercises apply to U.S. Treasury bills. (Assume 52 weeks per year for each exercise, and round to the nearest hundredth of a percent.)

29. **PURCHASE OF T-BILLS** A large Brazilian investment firm purchases $25,000,000 in U.S. T-bills at a 3% discount for 13 weeks. Find (a) the purchase price of the T-bills, (b) the maturity value of the T-bills, (c) the interest earned, and (d) the effective rate.   (a) $24,812,500 (b) $25,000,000 (c) $187,500 (d) 3.02%

30. **T-BILLS** Nina Horn buys a $50,000 T-bill at a 5.8% discount for 26 weeks. Find (a) the purchase price of the T-bill, (b) the maturity value, (c) the interest earned, and (d) the effective rate of interest.   (a) $48,550 (b) $50,000 (c) $1450 (d) 5.97%

31. Explain the difference between simple interest notes and simple discount notes.

32. Compare the formulas for simple interest rate and simple discount rate. Define all variables for both, and explain the difference between simple interest rate and simple discount rate. (See Objective 4.)

 33. As a borrower, would you prefer a simple interest note with a rate of 11% or a simple discount note with a rate of 11%? Explain using an example. (See Objective 4.)

 34. Explain why individuals or companies from other parts of the world invest in U.S. T-bills from time to time.

13.3   Comparing Simple Interest and Simple Discount

OBJECTIVES

1 *Compare the differences between simple interest and simple discount notes.*

2 *Convert between simple interest and simple discount rates.*

People in business use both simple interest notes (**Section 13.1**) and simple discount notes (**Section 13.2**). In this section, the two types of notes are compared. First, here are the similarities between the two types of notes.

1. The borrower receives a lump sum of money at the beginning of each type of note.

2. Both types of notes are repaid with a single payment at the end of a stated period of time.

3. This length of time is generally one year or less.

Objective

1 *Compare the Differences between Simple Interest and Simple Discount Notes.* Table 13.1 compares these two types of notes.

Table 13.1 A COMPARISON OF SIMPLE INTEREST AND SIMPLE DISCOUNT NOTES

Variables Used for Simple Interest	Variables Used for Simple Discount
I = Interest	B = Discount
P = Principal (face value)	P = Proceeds (amount received)
R = Rate of interest	D = Discount rate
T = Time in years, or fraction of a year	T = Time in years, or fraction of a year
M = Maturity value	M = Maturity value (face value)

	Formulas	
Elements	**Simple Interest**	**Simple Discount**
Face value	Stated on note, or $$P = \frac{M}{1 + RT}$$	Same as maturity value, or $$M = \frac{P}{1 - DT}$$
Interest charge	$I = PRT$	$B = MDT$
Maturity value	$M = P + I$ or $M = P(1 + RT)$	Same as face value, or $$M = \frac{P}{1 - DT}$$
Amount received by borrower	Face value or principal	Proceeds $P = M - B$ or $P = M(1 - DT)$
Identifying phrases	Interest at a certain rate	Discounted at a certain rate
	Maturity value greater than face value	Proceeds (less than face)
		Maturity value equal to face value
	Simple interest	Simple discount rate
True annual interest rate	Same as stated rate, R	Greater than stated rate, D

Objective

2 *Convert between Simple Interest and Simple Discount Rates.* As shown earlier, a 12% simple interest rate is *not* the same as a 12% simple discount rate. This section shows formulas to convert between simple interest rates and simple discount rates. To find these formulas, start with the basic formulas for simple interest and simple discount.

<table>
<tr><td align="center">**Simple Interest**</td><td></td><td align="center">**Simple Discount**</td></tr>
<tr><td align="center">$M = P(1 + RT)$</td><td align="center">and</td><td align="center">$P = M(1 - DT)$</td></tr>
<tr><td align="center">↳ Principal</td><td></td><td align="center">↳ Proceeds</td></tr>
</table>

Solve both the simple interest formula and the simple discount formula for P, the principal or proceeds received by the borrower.

<table>
<tr><td align="center">**Simple Interest**</td><td align="center">**Simple Discount**</td></tr>
<tr><td align="center">$P = \dfrac{M}{1 + RT}$</td><td align="center">$P = M(1 - DT)$</td></tr>
</table>

Since the right-hand side of each equation is P, then the two right-hand sides must equal one another.

$$\frac{M}{1 + RT} = M(1 - DT)$$

Divide both sides by M to get

$$\frac{1}{1 + RT} = 1 - DT$$

By going through several more algebraic steps, this equation can be solved for either R or D, giving the results in the box.

The simple interest rate R and the simple discount rate D are calculated by the formulas

$$R = \frac{D}{1 - DT} \quad \text{and} \quad D = \frac{R}{1 + RT}$$

where T is time in years.

NOTE These two formulas show that neither proceeds nor maturity value is needed to convert between the two types of rates; only rate and time are needed.

EXAMPLE 1 **Converting Interest and Discount Rates**

John Patterson's lawn care business has two outstanding notes. (a) The first note is a 180-day simple discount note with a face value of $16,800 and a discount rate of 10%. Convert this rate to a simple interest (effective interest) rate. (b) The second note is a 140-day simple interest note with a face value of $24,600 and an interest rate of 11%. Find the corresponding simple discount rate.

Solution

(a) Find R with the following formula.

$$R = \frac{D}{1 - DT}$$

Again, notice that no dollar amounts, not even face value, are needed. Here $D = 0.10$ and $T = \frac{180}{360}$.

$$R = \frac{0.10}{1 - \left(0.10 \times \frac{180}{360}\right)} = \frac{0.1}{1 - 0.05} = \frac{0.1}{0.95} = 0.105263 \text{ or } 10.53\%$$

The answer can be checked by first finding the interest on the simple discount loan.

$$B = MDT$$

$$= \$16,800 \times 0.10 \times \frac{180}{360}$$

$$= \$840$$

Then find the loan proceeds.

$$P = M - B$$

$$= \$16,800 - \$840$$

$$= \$15,960$$

Finally, use the formula for a simple interest calculation to find the simple interest rate:

$$R = \frac{I}{PT}$$

$$= \frac{\$840}{\$15,960 \times \frac{180}{360}}$$

$$= 10.53\% \qquad \text{Rounded}$$

(b) Find the simple discount rate that corresponds to a simple interest rate of 11% for 140 days. Use the following formula.

$$D = \frac{R}{1 + RT}$$

Replace R with 0.11 and T with $\frac{140}{360}$. Then,

$$D = \frac{0.11}{1 + \left(0.11 \times \frac{140}{360}\right)}$$

$$= \frac{0.11}{1 + 0.042777778}$$

$$= 0.1055 \qquad \text{Rounded}$$

or 10.55%, rounded to the nearest hundredth of a percent.

NOTE   In Example 1, the simple interest rate is greater than the equivalent simple discount rate. This is always the case. The simple interest rate is always greater than the equivalent simple discount rate.

■■□ Scientific
■□ Calculator
□ Approach

The calculator approach to Example 1 uses parentheses to group each denominator.

(a) 0.10 ÷ (1 − 0.10 × 180 ÷ 360) = 0.1053 Rounded

(b) 0.11 ÷ (1 + 0.11 × 140 ÷ 360) = 0.1055 Rounded

Denominator

13.3	**Exercises**

Find the simple interest rate that corresponds to the given discount rate for the given time. Round to the nearest hundredth of a percent.

1. 9%, 120 days   9.28%

2. 12%, 180 days   12.77%

3. 10.5%, 200 days   11.15%

4. 7%, 100 days   7.14%

5. 8%, 120 days   8.22%

6. 9.5%, 300 days   10.32%

Find the simple discount rate that corresponds to the given simple interest rate for the given time. Round to the nearest hundredth of a percent.

7. 8.5%, 120 days   8.27%

8. 10.5%, 200 days   9.92%

9. 12%, 220 days   11.18%

10. 8%, 240 days   7.59%

11. 10%, 100 days   9.73%

12. 9%, 180 days   8.61%

 13. Is the rate associated with simple discount notes the true annual interest rate? If not, explain why not and show how to calculate the true rate.

14. Use an example to show that a simple interest note at 10% results in less than a simple discount note at 10%.

Solve the following application problems.

15. SURGERY   Sherri Johnson needs to borrow money for an operation. She can borrow at a 13% simple interest rate or at a 12.8% simple discount rate. If she needs the money for 90 days, which loan should she take?   13% simple interest

16. WEDDING   Reann Kiang needs to borrow $8600 to pay for her only daughter's wedding. One bank charges 12% simple interest and a second bank charges 11% simple discount. If she needs the money for 120 days, which loan should she take?   11% simple discount

17. MOTORCYCLE   Sean McTuff wants to borrow $6000 for 180 days to purchase a used Harley-Davidson motorcycle with a "lotta chrome" on it. How much less interest is paid with a 12% simple interest note compared to a 12% simple discount note? $22.98

18. VET CLINIC   Dr. Jensen needs a 9-month construction loan with proceeds of $280,000 to construct a clinic. How much less interest is paid with a 9.5% simple interest note compared to a 9.5% simple discount note? $1530.48

19. REGISTERED BREEDER   Samantha Spade needs $12,000 to purchase several registered poodles and set up cages so she can start a business breeding dogs. She approaches two banks for a 1-year loan. Regions Financial offers her 10% simple discount and First Financial offers her 9.5% simple interest. Identify the better loan and find the difference in interest.   First Financial; $193.33

20. eBAY SALES   Nesta Yumong needs to borrow $8500 for 90 days to start a business on eBay buying and selling silver coins and other memorabilia. She has a choice of a 9% simple discount note or a 9.25% simple interest note. Identify the loan with the lower interest amount and find the difference in interest.   simple discount note; $0.91

 21. Explain the similarities and differences between simple interest notes and simple discount notes. (See Objective 1.)

 22. Assume a simple discount rate of 12% and explore the effect of time on the simple interest rate. Do this by substituting three different times, each less than 1 year, into the appropriate formula. (See Objective 2.)

13.4	**Discounting a Note**

OBJECTIVES

1 *Find the discount and the proceeds of a note.*

2 *Find the proceeds of a rediscounted note.*

Businesses often accept either simple interest or simple discount notes in place of immediate payment for goods or services. For example, a company that manufactures skis, a retailer that sells the skis, and a bank may do business as follows.

1. Ski manufacturer sells skis to a retailer and accepts a promissory note instead of cash.
2. Ski manufacturer needs cash and sells the note to a bank before it matures.
3. Retailer pays the maturity value of the note to the bank when due.

Selling the note to a bank allows the manufacturing company to get cash earlier, but of course the firm gives up the interest, which the bank will earn instead. The maturity value of the note less a fee charged by the bank is called the **bank discount**, or **discount**. The process of receiving cash for a note or selling a note is called **discounting a note**.

The amount of cash actually received by the manufacturer from the bank is called the **proceeds**. The bank then collects the maturity value from the maker of each note when it becomes due. Normally, such notes are sold with **recourse**. This means that if the maker of the note does not pay for some reason, the bank collects from the seller of the note. This protects the bank against loss. You may have noticed that banks do not like to lose money!

Objective

1 *Find the Discount and the Proceeds of a Note.* Use the following procedure to discount a note.

> **Step 1** Find the maturity value of the original note (if necessary). Use $M = P(1 + RT)$.
> **Step 2** Find the discount period.
> **Step 3** Find the discount using the formula $B = MDT$.
> **Step 4** The proceeds are found by $P = M - B$.
>
> This method is shown in the next examples.

EXAMPLE **1** **Finding Proceeds**

Destination Mad is a rock-and-roll band that wants to record an album and produce 1500 CDs both to promote the band and to sell to fans. They sign a 200-day simple interest note with Blues Recording Studio dated March 24. It has a face value of $9600 and simple interest of 12%. On August 15, Blues Recording Studio sells the note to a bank at a discount rate of 12.5%. Find the proceeds to the recording studio.

Solution

Go through the four steps of discounting a note.

STEP 1 First find the maturity value of the simple interest note.

$$M = P(1 + RT)$$

$$= \$9600\left(1 + 0.12 \times \frac{200}{360}\right) = \$10,240$$

STEP 2 Find the **discount period**, or the number of days from August 15 until the note is due. As shown in Figure 13.4, the note is due 200 days after March 24, or October 10. The number of days from August 15 to October 10 is found as follows.

$$\begin{array}{rl} 16 & \text{Days left in August} \\ 30 & \text{Days in September} \\ + 10 & \text{Days until note is due in October} \\ \hline 56 & \text{Days of discount period} \end{array}$$

Figure 13.4

STEP 3 Find the *bank discount* using $B = MDT$ with $M = \$10,240$ and $T = \frac{56}{360}$.

$$B = \$10,240 \times 0.125 \times \frac{56}{360} = \$199.11 \quad \text{Rounded}$$

STEP 4 Find the *proceeds* using the formula $P = M - B$.

$$P = \$10,240 - \$199.11 = \$10,040.89$$

The bank purchases the note on August 15 for $10,040.89 in cash paid to Blues Recording Studio. Then, on the maturity date of October 10, the bank will collect $10,240 from Destination Mad, shown as follows.

Date	Transaction
March 24	The band signs 200-day simple interest note for $9600.
August 15	Blues Recording Studio sells note to bank for $10,040.89.
October 10	The bank receives $10,240 from the payer (band).

In 141 (200 − 56) days, the recording studio in Example 1 earned the following interest.

$$\text{Interest earned} = \$10,040.89 - \$9600 = \$440.89$$

The effective rate of interest is found as follows.

$$R = \frac{I}{PT}$$

$$= \frac{\$440.89}{\$9600 \times \frac{144}{360}}$$

$$= 11.48\% \quad \text{Rounded}$$

Their effective interest rate was a little less than the 12% rate stated on the note.

> **NOTE** In discounting a note, the business receives less money than if it held the note to maturity, but it will receive the money sooner.

EXAMPLE **2** **Finding Proceeds and Discount**

On February 27, Andrews Hyundai receives a 150-day simple interest note with a face value of $35,000 at 8% interest per year. On March 27, the firm discounts the note at the bank. Find the proceeds if the discount rate is 12%.

Solution

Again, go through the four steps to discount a note.

STEP 1 First find the maturity value of the simple interest note.

$$M = P(1 + RT)$$

$$= \$35,000\left(1 + 0.08 \times \frac{150}{360}\right) = \$36,166.67 \quad \text{Rounded}$$

STEP 2 One hundred fifty days from February 27 is July 27. The discount period from March 27 to July 27 is 122 days as shown in Figure 13.5.

Figure 13.5

> **NOTE** Remember, the discount period is calculated *from the date of sale* to the *due date* of the loan, not from the date the loan was made.

STEP 3 Use $B = MDT$ with the discount rate of 12% to find the discount.

$$B = \$36,166.67 \times 0.12 \times \frac{122}{360} = \$1470.78 \quad \text{Rounded}$$

STEP 4 Use $P = M - B$ to find the proceeds.

$$P = \$36,166.67 - \$1470.78 = \$34,695.89$$

The Hyundai delearship receives $34,695.89 from the bank on March 27.

Objective

2 ***Find the Proceeds of a Rediscounted Note.*** In the next example, a company borrows money from a bank by signing a *simple discount note*. The bank making the loan then sells the note to a finance company. In this case, with the same note being discounted twice, the note is said to have been **rediscounted**. Notice in the example that the rate charged by the finance company to the bank is lower than the rate charged to the public. This is very common in transactions between large financial institutions, with the lower rate a sort of "wholesale" rate.

Even though the note in Example 3 is rediscounted, the steps used are basically the same as those used in earlier examples. The only difference is that since the original note was a simple discount note instead of a simple interest note, it is not necessary to solve for maturity value. The face value *is* the maturity value.

EXAMPLE 3 **Finding Proceeds of a Rediscounted Note**

The chief financial officer of Communication Networks signed a 180-day note with a discount rate of 12% and a face value of $140,000 with a bank. Fifty-four days after the note was signed, the bank rediscounted the note to Century Finance at 10% for cash. Find the proceeds Century Finance must pay the bank.

Solution

Go through the steps given for discounting a note.
STEP 1 The maturity value of the note is $140,000.

NOTE The fact that the bank charged a 12% discount rate plays no part in the problem since only the maturity value of the note is needed.

STEP 2 The discount period is $180 - 54 = 126$ days.
STEP 3 The discount (to Century Finance) is

$$\text{Discount} = \$140,000 \times 0.10 \times \frac{126}{360} = \$4900$$

STEP 4 The proceeds are

$$\$140,000 - \$4900 = \$135,100$$

This example can be summarized as follows.

1. Communication Networks signs a note with a maturity value of $140,000. The original proceeds to Communication Networks is found as follows.

$$P = M - MDT$$

$$= \$140,000 - \$140,000 \times 0.12 \times \frac{180}{360}$$

$$= \$131,600$$

Then, 54 days after the note is signed, the bank rediscounts the note to Century Finance, receiving proceeds of $135,100. Finally, 180 days after signing the note (and 126 days after the note was discounted), Communication Networks pays $140,000 to Century Finance.

2. The bank lends $131,600 for 54 days and makes $135,100 - $131,600 = $3500 in interest. The effective interest rate earned by the bank is found as follows.

$$R = \frac{I}{PT}$$

$$= \frac{\$3500}{\$131,600 \times \frac{54}{360}}$$

$$= 17.73\% \qquad \text{Rounded}$$

Not only notes are discounted. It is very common for a business to sell part of its accounts receivable (money owed to the business—see **Section 18.3**) to a financial institution. This process is called **factoring**, and the people who buy the accounts receivable are called **factors**. The calculations involved with factoring are the same as those discussed in this section.

13.4   Exercises

Find the discount period for each of the following.

	Loan Made	Length of Loan	Date of Discount	
1.	June 28	120 days	August 4	83 days
2.	March 13	180 days	June 1	100 days
3.	August 4	220 days	January 12	59 days
4.	November 5	60 days	December 18	17 days

Find the proceeds when each of the following simple discount notes are discounted. Round to the nearest cent.

	Maturity Value	Discount Period	Discount Rate	
5.	$8200	120 days	8%	$7981.33
6.	$8000	200 days	9%	$7600
7.	$15,000	180 days	12%	$14,100
8.	$18,200	240 days	11%	$16,865.33

Each of the following simple interest notes was discounted at 12%. Find the discount period, the discount, and the proceeds for each. Round money to the nearest cent.

	Loan Made	Face Value	Length of Loan	Simple Interest Rate	Discounted	
9.	January 9	$3500	120 days	9%	March 9	61 days; $73.30; $3531.70
10.	April 23	$4000	150 days	7%	June 11	101 days; $138.59; $3978.08
11.	May 5	$6800	130 days	$10\frac{1}{2}$%	July 6	68 days; $159.98; $6897.85
12.	May 29	$4500	80 days	8%	July 8	40 days; $61.07; $4518.93
13.	September 18	$10,000	220 days	10%	February 4	81 days; $286.50; $10,324.61
14.	October 11	$17,500	100 days	11%	January 2	17 days; $102.20; $17,932.52

Solve the following application problems. Round money to the nearest cent and interest rates to the nearest hundredth of a percent.

15. AIR CONDITIONER   On June 7, Capital Air, Inc. accepted a 150-day simple interest note for $8500 at 10% when it installed an air-conditioning unit on a commercial building. The note is discounted on August 3 at 12%. Find (a) the discount period, (b) the discount, and (c) the proceeds to Capital Air.   **(a)** 93 days **(b)** $274.48 **(c)** $8579.69

16. ELECTRONIC EQUIPMENT   On October 1, Home Health signed a $90,000 note at $11\frac{1}{2}$% simple interest for 180 days for electronic equipment. On February 18, the note was sold to another firm at a discount rate of $12\frac{1}{2}$%. Find (a) the discount period, (b) the discount, and (c) the proceeds.   **(a)** 40 days **(b)** $1321.88 **(c)** $93,853.12

17. CEMENT FOUNDATION On April 20, Hendrix Foundations accepts a $18,500 note for work done on the cement foundation for a commercial building. The note is for 180 days at 7.5% simple interest. If Hendrix sells the note at a 9% discount rate 30 days after receipt, find (a) the bank discount and (b) the proceeds. **(a)** $719.77 **(b)** $18,473.98

18. ELECTRONIC GAMES Warrior Games accepted a $420,800 note from a large retailer for several thousand copies of electronic games. The note is for 200 days at 7% simple interest. If the firm sells the note at an 8% discount rate 90 days after receipt for funds to make payroll, find (a) the bank discount and (b) the proceeds. **(a)** $10,686.24 **(b)** $426,478.20

19. REDISCOUNTING A NOTE Citizen's First Bank accepted a $24,000 simple discount note from a customer at a discount rate of $10\frac{1}{2}$% for 150 days. They rediscounted the note to Northside Bank at 11% exactly 90 days before its maturity date. Find (a) the proceeds to the customer, (b) the proceeds to Citizen's First Bank, and (c) the actual amount of interest earned by Citizen's First Bank on the note. **(a)** $22,950 **(b)** $23,340 **(c)** $390

20. SIMPLE DISCOUNT NOTE Farmer's Bank accepted a $17,000 simple discount note from a customer. The note was for 120 days at an 11% discount rate. The bank then rediscounted the note at a second bank, at 8%, 15 days before the maturity date of the note. Find each of the following: (a) the proceeds to the customer of Farmer's Bank, (b) the proceeds to Farmer's Bank when it rediscounted the note, and (c) the actual amount of interest earned by Farmer's Bank on the note. **(a)** $16,376.67 **(b)** $16,943.33 **(c)** $566.66

21. DISCOUNT NOTE State Bank accepts a simple discount note at 12% for 280 days on December 3, with a maturity value of $36,500. It rediscounts the note at 10% on May 4 of the following year. Find (a) the proceeds to the maker of the note, (b) the proceeds to State Bank, and (c) the actual interest earned by State Bank. **(a)** $33,093.33 **(b)** $35,202.22 **(c)** $2108.89

22. DISCOUNT NOTE On March 13, First Bank accepted a note due in 180 days with a face value of $45,000 and a discount rate of 9.8%. The bank discounts the note on July 15 at a rate of 10.5%. Find (a) the proceeds to the customer of the bank, (b) the proceeds to the bank when it rediscounts the note, and (c) the actual amount of interest earned by the bank. **(a)** $42,795 **(b)** $44,265 **(c)** $1470

23. T-BILLS On behalf of the bank where he works, Jim Jackson purchased $100,000 in 52-week T-bills at a discount rate of 4.8% and sold them 32 weeks later at a discount rate of 5%. Find (a) the total purchase price, (b) the discount at the time of sale, (c) the proceeds to the bank, and (d) the effective interest rate to Jim Jackson. (*Hint:* Treat T-bills as a discount note.) **(a)** $95,200 **(b)** $1923.08 **(c)** $98,076.92 **(d)** 4.91%

24. T-BILLS On June 1, the finance ministry of Saudi Arabia purchased $10,000,000 in 26-week T-bills at a discount rate of 3.9% and then sold them 15 weeks later at a discount rate of 3.74%. Find (a) the total purchase price, (b) the discount at the time of sale, (c) the proceeds to the Saudi finance ministry, and (d) the effective interest rate. (*Hint:* Treat T-bills as a discount note.) **(a)** $9,805,000 **(b)** $79,115.38 **(c)** $9,920,884.62 **(d)** 4.10%

 25. Explain the purpose of discounting a note.

26. Explain why banks or other financial institutions may need to rediscount notes. (See Objective 2.)

CHAPTER TERMS

Review the following terms to test your understanding of the chapter. For any terms you do not know, refer to the page number found next to that term.

annual percentage rate [p. 501]
collateral [p. 491]
discount [p. 498]
discount period [p. 511]
discounting a note [p. 510]
effective interest rate [p. 501]
face value [p. 498]
factors [p. 514]
factoring [p. 514]

Federal Truth in Lending Act [p. 501]
interest-in-advance notes [p. 497]
maker [p. 490]
maturity value [p. 490]
nominal interest rate [p. 501]
payee [p. 490]
payer [p. 490]
proceeds [p. 498]
promissory note [p. 489]

recourse [p. 510]
rediscounted [p. 512]
simple discount note [p. 497]
simple interest note [p. 490]
stated rate [p. 501]
term of the note [p. 490]
true interest rate [p. 501]
U.S. Treasury bills (T-bills) [p. 502]

CONCEPTS

EXAMPLES

13.1 Maturity value of a loan

Interest $I = PRT$

Maturity value $M = P + I = P(1 + RT)$

A note with a face value of $12,000 is due in 60 days. The rate is 8%. Find the maturity value.

$$I = PRT$$
$$= \$12{,}000 \times 0.08 \times \frac{60}{360} = \$160$$
$$M = P + I$$
$$= \$12{,}000 + \$160 = \$12{,}160$$

13.1 Finding the due date, interest, and maturity value of a note with the term in months

1. Add the number of months to date of note to find due date.
2. Use $I = PRT$ to find interest.
3. Use $M = P + I$ to find maturity value.

Find the due date, interest, and maturity value of a $4800 loan made on May 12 for 9 months at 9%. The due date is 9 months from May 12, which is February 12 of the following year.

$$I = PRT$$
$$= \$4800 \times 0.09 \times \frac{9}{12} = \$324$$
$$M = P + I$$
$$= \$4800 + \$324 = \$5124$$

13.1 Determining the face value of a note, given rate, time, and maturity value

Use the formula

$$P = \frac{M}{1 + RT}$$

A 90-day note has an interest rate of 9% and a maturity value of $5726. Find the face value.

$$P = \frac{M}{1 + RT}$$
$$= \frac{\$5726}{1 + \left(0.09 \times \frac{90}{360}\right)} = \$5600$$

13.1 Finding the time of a note in days given maturity value, face value, and interest rate

Use $T = \dfrac{M - P}{PR} \times 360$ to find time in days.

Alternatively, since $I = M - P$, use

$T = \dfrac{I}{PR} \times 360$.

A note has a face value of $4800, an interest rate of 6%, and a maturity value of $5000. Find the time of the note in days.

$$T = \frac{\$5000 - \$4800}{\$4800 \times 0.06} \times 360$$

$$= 250 \text{ days}$$

13.1 Determining the rate of a note given the face value, time, and maturity value

Use $R = \dfrac{M - P}{PT}$ to find the rate. Alternatively,

since $I = M - P$, use $R = \dfrac{I}{PT}$.

A 240-day note has a face value of $9000 and a maturity value of $9300. Find the interest rate.

$$R = \frac{\$9300 - \$9000}{\$9000 \times \frac{240}{360}} = 0.05$$

The rate is 5%.

13.2 Finding the discount and proceeds of a simple discount note

1. Calculate bank discount B using the formula $B = MDT$ with $D =$ discount rate.
2. Calculate proceeds using the formula $P = M - B$.

Tom Jones borrows $15,000 for 60 days at a discount rate of 9%. Find the bank discount and proceeds.

$B = MDT$

$$= \$15,000 \times 0.09 \times \frac{60}{360} = \$225$$

$P = M - B$

$$= \$15,000 - \$225 = \$14,775$$

13.2 Determining the effective rate or true rate of interest given face value, time, and discount rate

First, find the discount (B) using the formula $B = MDT$. Find the proceeds using the formula $P = M - B$. Calculate the true rate of interest from either

$$R = \frac{M - P}{PT} \quad \text{or} \quad R = \frac{I}{PT}$$

A note has a face value of $9000, a time of 120 days, and a discount rate of 12%. Find the true rate of interest.

$B = MDT$

$$= \$9000 \times 0.12 \times \frac{120}{360} = \$360$$

$P = M - B$

$$= \$9000 - \$360 = \$8640$$

$$R = \frac{I}{PT}$$

$$= \frac{\$360}{\$8640 \times \frac{120}{360}} = 0.125$$

The effective rate is 12.5%.

13.2 Finding the face value of a simple discount note

Use the formula $M = \dfrac{P}{1 - DT}$ to find the face value M.

Find the face value of a note that will provide $38,000 in proceeds if the note is repaid in 220 days and the bank charges an 8% discount rate.

$$M = \frac{P}{1 - DT}$$

$$= \frac{\$38,000}{1 - \left(0.08 \times \frac{220}{360}\right)}$$

$$= \$39,953.27 \qquad \text{Rounded}$$

13.2 Determining the discount rate of a note given face value and proceeds

Find the discount B from the formula $B = M - P$.

Find the rate from the formula $D = \dfrac{B}{MT}$.

A 90-day note has a face value of $15,000 and proceeds of $14,568.75. Find the discount rate.

$$B = M - P$$
$$= \$15,000 - \$14,568.75$$
$$= \$431.25$$

$$D = \frac{B}{MT}$$

$$= \frac{\$431.25}{\$15,000 \times \frac{90}{360}} = 0.115$$

The discount rate is 11.5%.

13.3 Finding the simple interest rate that equates to a given discount rate

Find the simple interest rate using the formula

$$R = \frac{D}{1 - DT}$$

A 180-day simple discount note is at 10%. Find the equivalent simple interest rate.

$$R = \frac{D}{1 - DT}$$

$$= \frac{0.10}{1 - 0.10 \times \frac{180}{360}} = 10.53\% \quad \text{Rounded}$$

13.3 Find the simple discount rate that equates to a given simple interest rate

Find the discount rate using the formula

$$D = \frac{R}{1 + RT}$$

A 240-day simple interest note is at $10\frac{3}{4}\%$. Find the equivalent simple discount rate.

$$D = \frac{R}{1 + RT}$$

$$= \frac{0.1075}{1 + 0.1075 \times \frac{240}{360}} = 10.03\% \quad \text{Rounded}$$

13.4 Finding the proceeds, to an individual or firm, after discounting a note

Step 1 Find the maturity value of the original note (if necessary). Use $M = P(1 + RT)$.

Step 2 Find the discount period.

Step 3 Find the discount using the formula $B = MDT$.

Step 4 The proceeds are found by $P = M - B$.

Moe's Ice Cream converts a 9%, 150-day simple interest note dated March 1 with a face value of $15,000 to cash on June 1. Assume a discount rate of 11%.

1. Find the proceeds.

$$M = P(1 + RT)$$

$$= \$15,000 \times \left(1 + 0.09 \times \frac{150}{360}\right)$$

$$= \$15,562.50$$

2. Find the discount period.

Discount Period = 58 days

Date Made	Discount Date	Due Date
March 1	June 1	July 29

150 Days

3. Find the bank discount.

$$B = \$15,562.50 \times 0.11 \times \frac{58}{360}$$

$$= \$275.80 \qquad \text{Rounded}$$

4. Find the proceeds.

$$P = \$15,562.50 - \$275.80$$

$$= \$15,286.70$$

The bank will pay $15,286.70 to Moe on June 1 and collect $15,562.50 on July 29 from the maker of the note.

CHAPTER 13 | Review Exercises

The answer section includes answers to all Review Exercises.

Complete the following table for simple interest notes. Round money to the nearest cent. **[13.1]**

	Face Value	Rate	Time	Interest	Maturity Value
1.	$9800	$8\frac{1}{2}\%$	200 days	$462.78	$10,262.78
2.	$3000	$10\frac{1}{2}\%$	90 days	$78.75	$3078.75
3.	$8000	12%	240 days	$640	$8640
4.	$14,500	9.25%	180 days	$670.63	$15,170.63

In the following, find the due date and the maturity value. **[13.1]**

	Date Made	Face Value	Term of Loan	Simple Interest Rate	Date Due	Maturity Value
5.	January 8	$12,000	120 days	9%	May 8	$12,360
6.	June 19	$6000	200 days	9.75%	January 5	$6325

Find the discount and the proceeds for the following discounted notes. **[13.2]**

	Face Value	Discount Rate	Time	Discount	Proceeds
7.	$18,000	12%	80 days	$480	$17,520
8.	$26,000	$10\frac{1}{2}$%	180 days	$1365	$24,635

Each of the following simple interest notes was discounted 12%. Find the (a) discount period, (b) discount, and (c) proceeds for the following discounted notes. **[13.4]**

	Loan Made	Face Value	Length of Loan	Rate	Date of Discount	
9.	September 4	$12,000	150 days	9%	October 25	(a) 99 days (b) $410.85 (c) $12,039.15
10.	December 20	$8500	120 days	$11\frac{1}{8}$%	February 28	(a) 50 days (b) $146.92 (c) $8668.29

Find the true simple interest rate corresponding to each of the following simple discount rates. Round to the nearest hundredth of a percent. **[13.3]**

	Time	Discount Rate	
11.	150 days	11%	11.53%
12.	170 days	9%	9.40%

Solve the following application problems. Round rates to the nearest hundredth of a percent, time to the nearest day, and money to the nearest cent.

13. What simple discount rate corresponds to a simple interest rate of 12% on a 180-day note? **[13.3]**   11.32%

14. Ben's Ice Cream borrowed $23,500 for 200 days at $8\frac{3}{4}$% simple interest. Find the maturity value. **[13.1]** $24,642.36

15. The note in Exercise 14 was discounted 80 days before maturity at 10%. Find the discount. **[13.2]** $547.61

16. Benito Maintenance signed a $45,000 simple interest note for 200 days and was charged $2250 in interest. Find the rate. **[13.1]**   9%

17. Walter Bates borrowed $23,000 at 10% simple interest to start a cabinet-making business. Find the term of the loan if the interest is $1150. **[13.1]**   180 days

18. A borrower signed a note with a face value of $50,000 at a $9\frac{1}{2}$% discount rate and received $47,361.11. Find the term of the note. **[13.2]**   200 days

19. To expand his saw-sharpening business, Chuck Giles signed a note with a face value of $18,500 for 150 days that had proceeds of $17,671.35. Find the discount rate. **[13.2]**   10.75%

20. A 90-day note has a loan amount of $12,000 and a maturity value of $12,330. Find the simple interest rate and simple discount rate of this note. **[13.3]**   11%; 10.71%

21. Bill Barton needed money for a new automobile and signed a note for $15,000 at a simple discount rate of 8% and a term of 240 days. Find the effective rate of interest. **[13.2]**   8.45%

22. On December 8, Joan Jones signed a 100-day, 10% discount note at First Bank for $14,000. First Bank sold the note to a finance company on February 12 at a $9\frac{1}{2}$% discount. Find the proceeds to First Bank. **[13.4]** $13,874.39

23. West Stables must pay a note given to one of its suppliers. The interest rate on the note is 8%, the face value is $12,300, and the simple interest is $410. Find the time of the note. **[13.1]**   150 days

24. Martinez Cleaners borrows $42,000 for 200 days at $9\frac{1}{2}$% simple interest. Find the interest. **[13.1]** $2216.67

25. A company with bad credit signed a $79,000, 120-day note for a shipment of goods. The maturity value of the note is $83,187. Find the rate of interest paid on the note. **[13.1]**   15.9%

26. Christina Barrett borrowed funds at an 11% discount rate for 180 days. Find the maturity value if the discount was $1012. **[13.2]** $18,400

27. Tom Watson Insurance accepted a 270-day, $8000 note on May 25. The simple interest rate on the note is 15%. The note was then discounted at 12% on August 7. Find the proceeds. **[13.4]** $8318.53

28. An architect sells a note at a 9% discount. The note has a face value of $18,400 and a discount of $782. Find the length in days. **[13.4]**   170 days

29. Yami's Kennels signed a 288-day note with a face value of $25,000 and a discount rate of 9.5%. Find the bank discount and proceeds. **[13.2]** $1900; $23,100

30. The owner of Scarino's Pizza signed a note with a discount of $2880 and proceeds of $33,120. Find the maturity value. **[13.2]** $36,000

31. On March 3, National Bank accepted a $25,000, 180-day note at a discount rate of 9%. It rediscounts the note on May 26 at $9\frac{1}{2}$%. Find the proceeds to National Bank. **[13.4]** $24,366.67

32. Linda Youngman accepted a $16,000, 120-day note from a customer. The note had a discount rate of 9% and was accepted on May 12. The note was then discounted at 11% on July 20. Find the proceeds to Youngman. **[13.4]** $15,750.67

33. Colonial Bank accepted a 200-day note at 10% simple interest with a face value of $83,000. It discounted the note at a 10% simple discount rate 90 days before it matured. Find the proceeds to Colonial Bank. **[13.2]** $85,420.83

34. Marilyn Neault needs to borrow $35,264 for equipment to set up an optometrist office. She signs a 12% simple discount note at the bank for 216 days. Find the face value of the note. **[13.3]** $38,000

35. On November 16, the Wedding Shoppe accepted a 9.5% simple interest 200-day note with a face value of $11,200 for a wedding at Clear Lake. Find the proceeds if the note was discounted at 11% on January 13. **[13.4]** $11,279.51

36. Find the simple interest rate that corresponds to an $11\frac{3}{4}$% simple discount rate on a 220-day note. Then find the discount rate that corresponds to a 9.5% simple interest rate on a 220-day note. **[13.3]**   12.66%; 8.98%

37. Would you prefer a $15,000 note at 12% simple interest or one at 12% discount interest? Explain. **[13.3]**

38. Explain the differences between a simple interest note and a simple discount note. Which type of note (if either) is preferred by a borrower? Explain. **[13.3]**

CHAPTER 13	**Business Application Case #1**
	How Do Global Banks Make Money?

Bank of America borrowed $80,000,000 at 5% simple interest for 180 days from a Chinese investment house. At the same time, the bank made the following loans, each for the exact same 180-day period.

1. A 7% simple interest note for $38,000,000 to a Canadian firm that extracts oil from Canadian tar sands;

2. An 8.2% simple discount note for $27,500,000 to a British contractor building a factory in South Africa; and

3. An 8% simple discount note for $14,500,000 to a Louisiana company building minesweepers in New Orleans for the Mexican government.

   (a) Find the difference between interest received and interest paid by the bank on these funds.   (a) $1,037,500

   Interest to be paid to the Chinese investment house:

   $$I = \$80,000,000 \times 0.05 \times \frac{180}{360} = \$2,000,000$$

   Interest from the Canadian firm:

   $$I = \$38,000,000 \times 0.07 \times \frac{180}{360} = \$1,330,000$$

   Interest from the British contractor:

   $$B = \$27,500,000 \times 0.082 \times \frac{180}{360} = \$1,127,500$$

   Interest from the Louisiana company:

   $$B = \$14,500,000 \times 0.08 \times \frac{180}{360} = \$580,000$$

Interest received by Bank of America

$1,330,000
1,127,500
580,000
——————
$3,037,500

Interest received by Bank of America	$3,037,500
Interest paid by Bank of America	− 2,000,000
Difference	$1,037,500

(b) The bank did not loan out all $80,000,000. Find the amount it actually loaned out.   (b) $78,292,500

Loan		Amount Loaned Out
First		$38,000,000
Second	$27,500,000 − $1,127,500 =	$26,372,500
Third	$14,500,000 − $580,000 =	$13,920,000
	Total loaned out	$78,292,500

(c) Find the effective rate of interest earned by the bank.   (c) 2.65%

$$\frac{\$1,037,500}{\$78,292,500 \times \frac{1}{2}} = 2.65\%$$

CHAPTER 13	Business Application Case #2
	Financing a Refinery

In addition to using cash on hand, Pinston Refining needs to borrow $185,000,000 for 1 year while constructing the first phase of a new refinery. Managers have approached three banks and have been offered the following loans. In each loan, the proceeds to Pinston Refining are $185,000,000.

Lender	Type of Note	Interest or Discount Rate
Bank U.S.	Discount	9.5%
Japan FundCo	Simple	9.8%
Niacin Strong	Discount	10.4%

(a) Find the maturity value for each and determine the best loan.

(b) Find the difference in interest between the worst and best loans.

(a)

	Interest (or Discount)	Maturity Value
Bank U.S.	$19,419,889.50	$204,419,889.50
Japan FundCo	$18,130,000.00	$203,130,000.00
Niacin Strong	$21,473,214.29	$206,473,214.29

The best loan is the one with the lowest total interest for the one-year loan, or the loan offered by Japan FundCo.

(b) The most expensive loan is the one offered by Niacin Strong. Difference in interest = $3,343,214.29

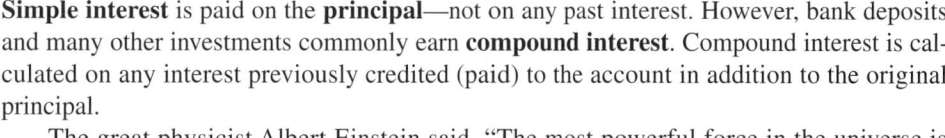

javier brosch / Fotolia.com

Compound Interest

Albert Einstein

Simple interest is paid on the **principal**—not on any past interest. However, bank deposits and many other investments commonly earn **compound interest**. Compound interest is calculated on any interest previously credited (paid) to the account in addition to the original principal.

The great physicist Albert Einstein said, "The most powerful force in the universe is compound interest." This amazing "powerful force" is something that you can use throughout your life if you choose to do so. To show what can be done using compound interest, assume your parent(s) had invested on your behalf $1000 earning 6% per year on the day you were born. As Figure 14.1 shows, the $1000 would grow to over $18,000 by age 50 and nearly $106,000 by age 80. Note that this $106,000 could be used to give you $6360 in interest *each year for the remainder of your life* and that the entire $106,000 would still be in your estate. All of this with only a $1000 initial investment!

> **NOTE** Nearly every wealthy individual has used compounding.

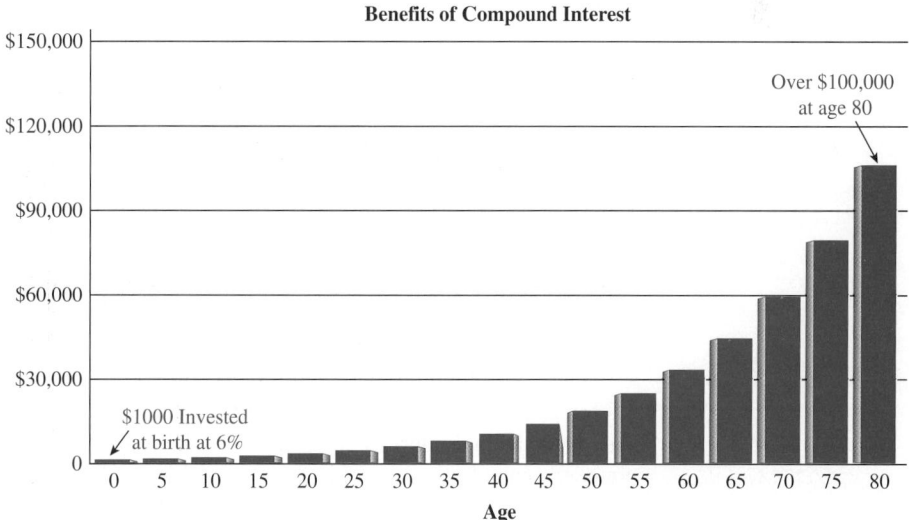

Figure 14.1

▶STOP&THINK

> Why are most wealthy people older? Is it possible to accumulate $1,000,000 in your life-time? What are some things you would need to do to accomplish that goal?

14.1	**Compound Interest**

OBJECTIVES

1 *Find compound interest and compound amount.*

2 *Determine the number of periods and rate per period.*

3 *Find values in the interest table.*

4 *Use the formula for compound interest to find the compound amount.*

5 *Find the effective rate of interest.*

Objective

1 *Find Compound Interest and Compound Amount.* Compound interest includes interest on principal and also interest on interest already paid. Assume that $1000 is deposited into a mutual fund paying 8% per year. Use the formula for simple interest at the end of each year for 3 years to find the compound amount in 3 years.

Year 1:   Interest at end of year 1 $= \$1000 \times 0.08 \times 1 = \$80$

Principal at end of year 1 $= \$1000 + \$80 = \$1080$

This principal plus interest will earn interest for year 2. Do these same calculations for years 2 and 3.

Year 2:   Interest at end of year 2 $= \$1080 \times 0.08 \times 1 = \$86.40$

Principal at end of year 2 $= \$1080 + \$86.40 = \$1166.40$

Year 3:   Interest at end of year 3 $= \$1166.40 \times 0.08 \times 1 = \$93.31$

Principal at end of year 3 $= \$1166.40 + \$93.31 = \$1259.71$

The final amount of $1259.71 is the **compound amount**, **future amount**, or **future value**. The interest earned during the 3 years is found as follows.

$$\text{Interest} = \text{compound amount} - \text{original principal}$$

$$\text{Interest} = \$1259.71 - \$1000 = \$259.71$$

Simple interest on $1000 for 3 years at 8% would be: $\$1000 \times 0.08 \times 3 = \$240$. So, compound interest resulted in an extra $19.71 ($259.71 − $240) interest in 3 years. Figure 14.2 shows the advantage of compound interest over simple interest for a $1000 investment as the number of years increases.

> **NOTE** Compound interest earns interest on principal and it also earns interest on any interest already earned.

The future amount using compound interest can be found by multiplying the principal times the quantity (1 + rate) once for each period the investment is to be compounded. Rate is the annual interest rate. Therefore, the future amount of $1000 invested at 8% compounded annually for 3 years is shown as follows.

Multiply by (1 + 0.08) 3 times.

$$\text{Future value} = \$1000 \times (1 + 0.08) \times (1 + 0.08) \times (1 + 0.08)$$

$$= \$1000 \times 1.08 \times 1.08 \times 1.08$$

$$= \$1259.71$$

Note that $1.08 \times 1.08 \times 1.08$ can be written as $(1.08)^3$, or 1.08^3, using an **exponent** for the number of times 1.08 is multiplied times itself. Thus, the future amount of $1000 invested at 8% compounded annually for 3 years can also be shown as follows.

Exponent

$$\text{Future value} = \$1000 \times 1.08^3 = \$1259.71 \quad \text{(Rounded)}$$

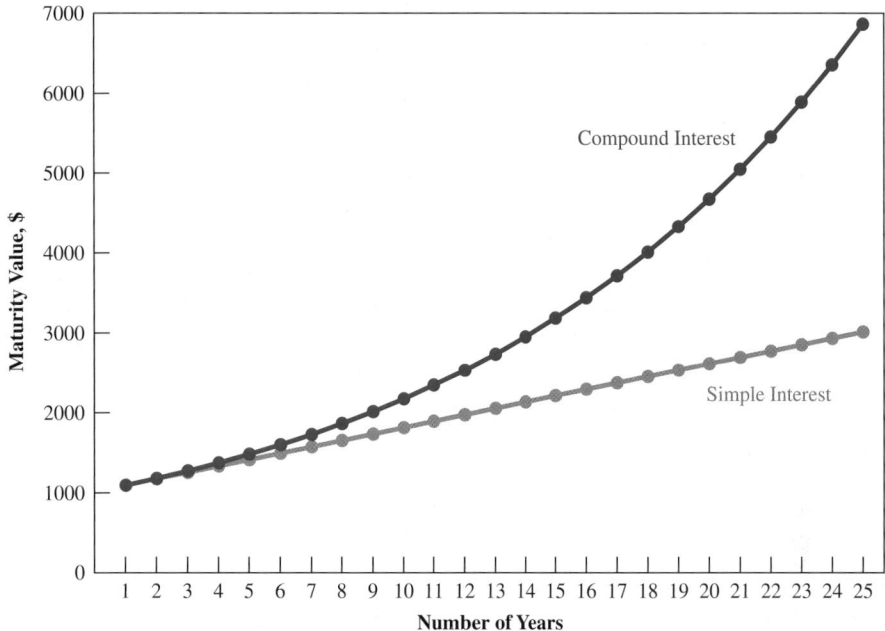

Compound Interest Versus Simple Interest
$1000 Invested at 10%

Figure 14.2

The number 3 is the exponent and is the number of years this investment is compounded. The future value of an investment of $2000 at 8.5% for several different annual periods is shown.

Number of Years	Future Value at 8.5%
5	$2000 \times 1.085^5 = \$3007.31$
10	$2000 \times 1.085^{10} = \$4521.97$
30	$2000 \times 1.085^{30} = \$23{,}116.50$

NOTE The future value of an investment depends on the amount of the initial investment, the interest rate, and the length of time the funds remain invested. The last of these, time, is why many of the wealthy are older. They have had many years to accumulate money and let compound interest work.

EXAMPLE **1** **Finding Compound Interest**

In 4 years, Tony and Lynn Jameson will need $8000 for a down payment on a manufactured home. They have $5500 that they put in an investment earning 5% per year compounded annually. Find (a) the future amount in 4 years, (b) the amount of compound interest earned, (c) the excess of compound interest over simple interest for the 4 years, and (d) the additional amount needed to achieve their goal.

Solution

(a) Future amount $= \$5500 \times 1.05^4 = \$6685.28$ Rounded

(b) Compound interest $=$ future amount $-$ original investment

$$= \$6685.28 - \$5500 = \$1185.28$$

(c) Simple interest = $5500 × 0.05 × 4 = $1100

    Compound interest − simple interest = $1185.28 − $1100

                                    = $85.28

(d) Amount still needed = $8000 − $6685.28

                        = $1314.72

Objective

2

Determine the Number of Periods and Rate per Period. Interest is often credited to an account more than once a year when calculating compound interest. For example, interest on an investment may be compounded monthly. This means that interest is calculated and credited to the account each month. That interest will then earn interest in future months. Compound interest, unlike simple interest, pays interest on principal plus any previously credited interest.

The interest rate given or advertised is normally the annual rate, such as 6% compounded monthly or 8% compounded annually. These are the **nominal**, or **stated**, rates. Divide the annual rate by the number of computing periods in a year to find the interest rate per compounding period, as shown in the table.

Compounding Period	Interest Credited at the End of Each	Number of Times Interest Is Credited per Year	Number of Times Interest Would Be Credited over 5 Years	Rate per Compounding Period if R Is Rate per Year
Annual	Year	1	$5 \times 1 = 5$	R
Semiannual	6 months	2	$5 \times 2 = 10$	$\frac{R}{2}$
Quarterly	Quarter	4	$5 \times 4 = 20$	$\frac{R}{4}$
Monthly	Month	12	$5 \times 12 = 60$	$\frac{R}{12}$

EXAMPLE **2** **Finding Number of Periods and Rate per Period**

(a) A bond pays interest of 8%, compounded semiannually. This means that semiannually, or twice a year, interest of 8% ÷ 2 = 4% is added to all money that has been on deposit for 6 months or more.

(b) An interest rate of 6% per year, compounded quarterly, means that every 3 months (quarterly), interest of 6% ÷ 4 = 1.5% is added to all money that has been on deposit for at least a quarter.

NOTE In Example 2(a), the **period of compounding** is semiannual (every 6 months), while it is quarterly (every 3 months) in Example 2(b).

The formula for compound interest is often written using algebraic notation. If P dollars are deposited at a rate of interest i per period for n periods, then the compound amount and interest earned are found as follows.

$$\text{Compound amount} = M = P(1 + i)^n$$
$$\text{Interest earned} = I = M - P$$

NOTE It is important to keep in mind that i is the interest rate *per compounding period,* and not per year, and n is the total number of *compounding periods,* not the number of years.

EXAMPLE **3** **Finding Compound Interest**

Jonathan Simons invests $2500 in an investment paying 4% compounded semiannually for 5 years. (a) Estimate the future value using simple interest. Then find (b) the compound amount, (c) the compound interest, and (d) the amount by which simple interest calculations underestimate the compound interest that is earned.

Solution

(a) Simple interest calculations can be used to estimate the compound amount but they will always underestimate the actual amount. Use 4% ÷ 2 = 2% per period and 5 years × 2 = 10 periods for the calculations.

$$\text{Simple interest} = PRT$$
$$= \$2500 \times 0.02 \times 10 = \$500$$
$$\text{Estimate of future amount} = P + I = \$2500 + \$500 = \$3000$$

(b) Compound amount $= P(1 + i)^n$
$$= \$2500 \times (1 + 0.02)^{10}$$
$$= \$2500 \times 1.02^{10}$$
$$= \$3047.49 \quad \text{Rounded}$$

(c) Compound interest $= M - P$
$$= \$3047.49 - \$2500 = \$547.49$$

(d) Underestimation when simple interest is used $=$ compound interest $-$ simple interest
$$= \$547.49 - \$500 = \$47.49$$

Objective

3 *Find Values in the Interest Table.* The value of $(1 + i)^n$ can be found by direct calculation using scientific calculators or from tables. One such table is given in the compound interest column (column A) of the interest table in **Appendix C**. The interest rate per compounding period is on the upper left-hand corner of each page.

EXAMPLE **4** **Using the Interest Table**

Find the following values in the compound interest table in **Appendix C**.

Number of compounding periods

(a) $(1 + 5\%)^{12}$ or $(1 + 0.05)^{12} = (1.05)^{12}$

Interest rate per compounding period

Find the 5% page of the interest table. Look in column A, for compound interest, and find 12 (or 12 periods) at the left side. You should find 1.79585633.

Number of compounding periods

(b) $(1 + 8\%)^{27} = (1.08)^{27} = 7.98806147$

Interest rate per compounding period

Find the 8% page. Then look in column A and find 27 at the left.

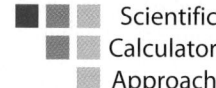

Scientific
Calculator
Approach

For the calculator solution to Example 4,

(a) The value of $(1.05)^{12}$ can be found as follows.

$$1.05 \boxed{y^x} 12 \boxed{=} 1.795856326$$

(b) The value of $(1.08)^{27}$ is found as follows.

$$1.08 \boxed{y^x} 27 \boxed{=} 7.988061469$$

NOTE Some calculators have an $\boxed{a^x}$ or $\boxed{x^y}$ key instead of a $\boxed{y^x}$ key. All of these keys are used in the same way.

Objective

4 *Use the Formula for Compound Interest to Find the Compound Amount.* The evaluation of $(1 + i)^n$ using tables or calculators can now be used to find the compound amount and interest.

EXAMPLE 5 **Finding Compound Interest**

John Smith inherits $15,000, which he deposits in a retirement account that pays interest compounded semiannually. How much will he have after 25 years if the funds grow (a) at 6%, (b) at 8%, and (c) at 10%? Round to the nearest cent.

Solution

In 25 years, there are $2 \times 25 = 50$ semiannual periods. The semiannual interest rates are (a) $\frac{6\%}{2} = 3\%$, (b) $\frac{8\%}{2} = 4\%$, and (c) $\frac{10\%}{2} = 5\%$. Use the formula $M = P(1 + i)^n$ and your calculator to find the following. Alternatively, the compound interest table in Appendix C can be used to find the value of $(1 + i)^n$.

(a) $\$15,000(1.03)^{50} = \$15,000 \times 4.383906019 = \$65,758.59$
(b) $\$15,000(1.04)^{50} = \$15,000 \times 7.106683346 = \$106,600.25$
(c) $\$15,000(1.05)^{50} = \$15,000 \times 11.46739979 = \$172,011.00$

The $15,000 that John Smith inherits is the present value he has today. The future value is the amount he will have in 25 years.

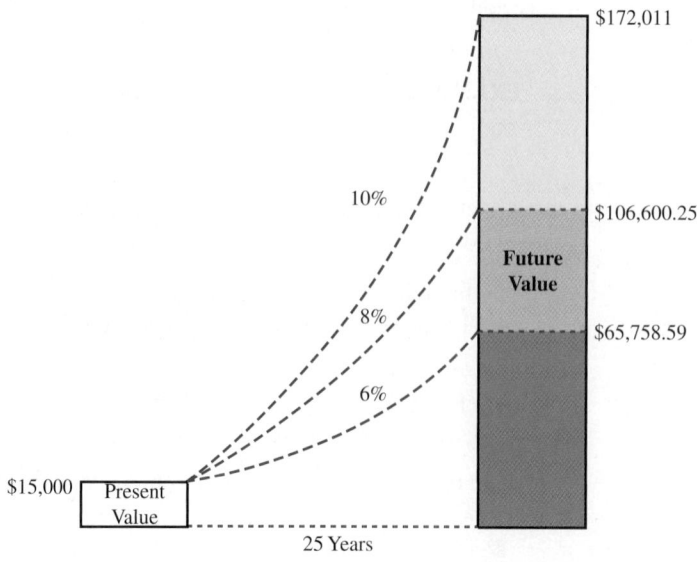

■ ■ ▨ Financial
▨ ■ ▨ Calculator
▨ Approach

Present value, interest per compounding period, and number of compound periods are known. Future value is the unknown. See **Appendix A.2.**

(a) -15000 $\boxed{PV}$ 3 $\boxed{i}$ 50 $\boxed{n}$ $\boxed{FV}$ 65758.59

(b) -15000 $\boxed{PV}$ 4 $\boxed{i}$ 50 $\boxed{n}$ $\boxed{FV}$ 106600.25

(c) -15000 $\boxed{PV}$ 5 $\boxed{i}$ 50 $\boxed{n}$ $\boxed{FV}$ 172011

Answers will vary by a few cents, depending on the specific calculator used.

> **NOTE** Simple interest rate calculations are usually indicated by phrases such as *simple interest, simple interest note,* or *discount rate.* Compound interest rate calculations are usually indicated by phrases such as *compounded annually, 6% per quarter,* or *compounded daily.*

The more often interest is compounded, *the more interest is earned.* Use a financial calculator or a compound interest table more complete than the one in this text and use the compound interest formula to get the results shown in Table 14.1. (Leap years were ignored in finding daily interest.)

Table 14.1 INTEREST ON $1000 AT 6% PER YEAR FOR 10 YEARS

Frequency of Compounding	Interest per Compounding Period	Number of Compounding Periods	Interest
Not at all (simple interest)	—	—	$600.00
Annually	6%	10	$1790.85
Semiannually	6%/2	20	$1806.11
Quarterly	6%/4	40	$1814.02
Monthly	6%/12	120	$1819.40
Daily	6%/365	3650	$1822.03
Hourly	6%/8760	87,600	$1822.12
Every Minute	6%/525,600	5,256,000	$1822.12

Table 14.1 shows that compounding produces significantly more interest than does simple interest. However, increasing the frequency of compounding makes smaller and smaller differences in the amount of interest earned with an increasing number of compounding periods.

EXAMPLE 6 Finding Compound Amount

Ben Fitzgerald is comparing two different investment options. Find the compound amount on a deposit of $8000 for 3 years at (a) 6% compounded quarterly and (b) 6% compounded monthly.

Solution

(a) Number of compounding periods = 3 years × 4 quarters per year = 12 and interest of 6% ÷ 4 = 1.5% is credited at the end of each quarter.

$$\$8000(1.015)^{12} = \$9564.95 \quad \text{Rounded}$$

(b) Number of compounding periods = 3 years × 12 months per year = 36 and interest of 6% ÷ 12 = 0.5% is credited at the end of each quarter

$$\$8000(1.005)^{36} = \$9573.44 \quad \text{Rounded}$$

■ ■ ■ Scientific
■ ■ Calculator
■ Approach

Solve Example 6 using a scientific calculator as follows.

(a) $8000 \boxed{\times} 1.015 \boxed{y^x} 12 \boxed{=} 9564.95$

(b) $8000 \boxed{\times} 1.005 \boxed{y^x} 36 \boxed{=} 9573.44$

■ ■ ■ Financial
■ ■ Calculator
■ Approach

Example 6 can also be solved using a financial calculator, as follows.

(a) $-8000 \boxed{PV} 1.5 \boxed{i} 12 \boxed{n} \boxed{FV} 9564.95$

(b) $-8000 \boxed{PV} 0.5 \boxed{i} 36 \boxed{n} \boxed{FV} 9573.44$

Although these values are exactly the same as those found using the Scientific Calculator Approach, values sometimes differ slightly when using different calculators. The difference is usually very small.

Another use of compound interest calculations is to find the effect of **inflation** on real estate values.

EXAMPLE **7** **Finding the Effect of Inflation on Real Estate Values**

Bill and Joy Lopez purchase a home for $167,200. If the house increases in value by 3% per year, find its value at the end of 4 years.

Solution

The value of the house compounds at 3% for 4 years. Use the table in Appendix C to find 1.12550881. You can also use your calculator to work this problem.

$$\text{Future value of home} = \$167,200 \times 1.12550881$$
$$= \$188,185 \qquad \text{Rounded}$$

The home is expected to increase in value by $188,185 − $167,200 = $20,985 during the 4 years.

Objective

5 *Find the Effective Rate of Interest.* The nominal, or stated, interest rate is the annual rate of interest. If interest is compounded more often than once a year, then the actual rate of interest earned *will be greater than* the nominal rate. The rate actually earned is called the **effective rate of interest**. It is necessary to understand effective rate of interest to compare one loan to another, in order to identify which is better.

Consider a $1000 investment for 1 year that grows at 8% compounded quarterly. There are 4 compounding periods, and the interest rate per compounding period is $\frac{8\%}{4} = 2\%$. Find the maturity value and interest as follows.

$$M = \$1000 \times (1 + 0.02)^4 = \$1082.43$$
$$\text{Interest} = \$1082.43 - \$1000 = \$82.43$$

The $1000 investment earns $82.43 in interest during the year. Find the corresponding effective interest rate by dividing the interest by the original investment at the beginning of the year.

$$\frac{\$82.43}{\$1000} = 8.243\%$$

Alternatively, the effective rate of interest can be found from the stated rate of interest using the following.

$$(1 + i)^n - 1$$

where i = the rate per compounding period and n = the number of compounding periods in 1 year. The value of $(1 + i)^n$ can be calculated using a calculator, but it can also be found in column A of Appendix C.

EXAMPLE | **8** | **Finding the Effective Rate of Interest**

James Suhr plans to start his own business as a graphic artist, and he has been offered two different 1-year loans.

    Loan A: nominal rate of 10% compounded quarterly
    Loan B: nominal rate of 9% compounded monthly

Find the effective rate of interest for each and decide on the better deal.

Solution

Loan A: $\dfrac{10\%}{4}$ = 2.5% per quarter for 4 compounding periods

$$
\begin{aligned}
\text{Effective rate} &= (1 + i)^n - 1 \\
&= (1 + 0.025)^4 - 1 \\
&= 10.38\%
\end{aligned}
$$

Loan B: $\dfrac{9\%}{12}$ = 0.75% per month for 12 months

$$
\begin{aligned}
\text{Effective rate} &= (1 + i)^n - 1 \\
&= (1 + 0.0075)^{12} - 1 \\
&= 9.38\%
\end{aligned}
$$

Loan B has the lower effective interest rate, so it will result in less interest, assuming that the amount borrowed and the time of the loans are the same.

14.1 | Exercises

Find the compound amount and the amount of interest earned for the following. Round to the nearest cent. Use your calculator, rather than the tables, in Exercises 1–4.

1. $12,000 at 8% compounded annually for 3 years $15,116.54; $3116.54
2. $8500 at 6% compounded semiannually for $4\frac{1}{2}$ years $11,090.57; $2590.57
3. $6000 at 5% compounded quarterly for 2 years $6626.92; $626.92
4. $10,500 at 10% compounded quarterly for 4 years $15,587.31; $5087.31

Find the compound amount when the following deposits are made. Round to the nearest cent.

5. $1000 at 8% compounded annually for 40 years $21,724.52
6. $925 at 5% compounded annually for 12 years $1661.17
7. $10,000 at 6% compounded semiannually for 9 years $17,024.33
8. $8765.72 at 12% compounded monthly for 4 years $14,132.32

Find the amount of interest earned by the following deposits. Round to the nearest cent.

9. $8400 at 7% compounded annually for 8 years $6032.76
10. $6200 at 11% compounded annually for 5 years $4247.36

11. $12,600 at 8% compounded quarterly for $4\frac{3}{4}$ years $5755.82

12. $23,000 at 12% compounded monthly for $2\frac{1}{2}$ years $8000.53

Find simple interest; then use column A of the interest table and the same interest rate to find the interest compounded annually. Find the amount by which the compound interest is larger. Round to the nearest cent.

	Principal	Rate	Number of Years	
13.	$1000	6%	5	$300; $338.23; $38.23
14.	$800	7%	6	$336; $400.58; $64.58
15.	$7908.42	5%	8	$3163.37; $3775.92; $612.55
16.	$10,240	10%	11	$11,264; $18,975.92; $7711.92

Find the effective rate corresponding to the following nominal rates. Round to the nearest hundredth of a percent.

17. 8% compounded quarterly   8.24%

18. 10% compounded quarterly   10.38%

19. 9% compounded monthly   9.38%

20. 12% compounded monthly   12.68%

Solve the following application problems. Round to the nearest cent.

21. FINDING COMPOUND AMOUNT   William Gates invested $5000 at 6% for 3 years. Find the compound amount if the compound period is (a) quarterly and (b) monthly. (a) $5978.09 (b) $5983.40

22. FINDING COMPOUND AMOUNT   Bertha James invested $10,000 in a bond mutual fund that pays 8% interest. She plans to leave the money invested for 3 years. Find the compound amount if the compounding period is (a) semiannually and (b) quarterly. (a) $12,653.19 (b) $12,682.42

23. COMPOUNDING PERIODS   Find the interest earned on $10,000 for 4 years at 6% compounded (a) yearly, (b) semiannually, (c) quarterly, and (d) monthly. (e) Find the simple interest.   (a) $2624.77 (b) $2667.70 (c) $2689.86 (d) $2704.89 (e) $2400

24. COMPOUNDING PERIODS   Suppose $32,000 is invested for 2 years at 10% interest. Find the interest earned on the deposit if the interest is compounded (a) yearly, (b) semiannually, (c) quarterly, and (d) monthly. (e) Find the simple interest.   (a) $6720 (b) $6896.20 (c) $6988.89 (d) $7052.51 (e) $6400

25. LOAN TO A RESTAURANT   Benjamin Moore loans $8800 to the owner of a new restaurant. He will be repaid at the end of 4 years, with interest at 8% compounded semiannually. Find how much he will be repaid. $12,043.41

26. BANK CD   Brenda Gilliam deposits $8000, earned from testing elementary school students for learning disabilities, in a bank CD paying 4% compounded semiannually. Find the future value in 3 years. $9009.30

27. COMPARING BANKS   There are two banks in Citrus Heights. One pays interest of 4% compounded annually, and the other pays 4% compounded quarterly. If Stan deposits $10,000 in each bank, (a) how much will he have in each bank at the end of 3 years? (b) How much more would he have in the bank that paid more interest? (a) $11,248.64; $11,268.25 (b) $19.61

28. COMPARING YIELDS   Barbara Mason is considering two investments. One yields 8% compounded quarterly and a second yields 9% compounded monthly. She deposits $6000 in each for a period of 2 years. (a) Find the amount she will have in each at the end of 2 years. Then (b) find the additional amount in the higher-yielding investment.   (a) $7029.96; $7178.48 (b) $148.52

29. GUARANTEED PENSION   One of the pension funds that Jessica Walters manages must have $3,450,000 in 2 years. The fund currently has $2,600,000 and it earns 5% compounded monthly. Find the expected shortage in the pension in 2 years. $577,152.52

30. PENSION SHORTAGE   The government is requiring Ace Plumbing to have $4.2 million in its pension plan in 18 months. It currently has $3.2 million earning 6% compounded semiannually. Find the expected shortage in the pension in 18 months. $703,273.60

31. COMPARING INVESTMENTS   Joan Getz is comparing two investment opportunities, the first at 6% compounded semiannually and the second at 5% compounded monthly. Find the effective interest rates for each. Which would produce more income for Getz?   6.09%; 5.12%; the first option

32. RAISING FUNDS   A church plans to raise funds by selling bonds to individuals and businesses in the community. It is considering two options, the first at 8% compounded annually and the second at 6% compounded monthly. Find the effective interest rate for both. Which would produce the lower cost for the church?   8%; 6.17%; the second option

Use either a scientific or financial calculator to solve the following for compound amount.

33. $15,000 at 6.5% compounded annually for 3 years $18,119.24

34. $24,500 at 8.9% compounded semiannually for 2 years $29,160.83

35. $9500 at 10.3% compounded quarterly for $2\frac{1}{2}$ years $12,250.08

36. $18,000 at 6% compounded monthly for $2\frac{1}{4}$ years $20,594.73

 37. Explain the basic difference between simple interest and compound interest. (See Objective 1.)

 38. Do long-term investments grow more using simple interest or compound interest? Why is this type of interest to your advantage when saving for events several years in the future? (See Objective 1.)

39. COMPARING YIELDS   Jess Cockrell has $20,000 to invest for 1 year. He can lend it to his brother, who has agreed to pay 7% simple interest, or to a bank paying 4% compounded quarterly. Find the extra interest earned if he lends the funds to his brother. $587.92

40. COMPARING YIELDS   Benson Automotive has $400,000 to invest for 9 months. The firm has the choice of lending it to a local contractor at 8% simple interest or to a bank that will pay 4% compounded monthly. Find the additional interest that would be generated by the simple interest note in this situation. $11,838.75

41. RETIREMENT INVESTMENT   Peter and Betsy Mueller inherit $12,000 from Peter's aunt. Although they are only in their early thirties, the Muellers decide to set the money aside for their eventual retirement. They invest the funds in a Roth IRA account so that they will not have to pay any taxes on the earnings. Find the amount they will have in 25 years if the funds are invested in a fund that grows at 8% compounded semiannually for 25 years. $85,280.20

14.2   **Daily and Continuous Compounding**

OBJECTIVES

1 *Define savings account and money market account.*

2 *Calculate interest compounded daily.*

3 *Find compound interest for time deposit accounts.*

4 *Determine the penalty for early withdrawal.*

5 *Find compound amount with continuous compounding.*

One positive result of the financial crisis that began in 2008 was increased levels of household savings. Figure 14.3 shows that household savings as a percent of income fell rapidly from 1982 to 2007. People tended to save less and less during those years. However, savings picked up again beginning in 2008 as discussions about the world's financial problems were in the news and people became worried about debt and whether they had saved enough.

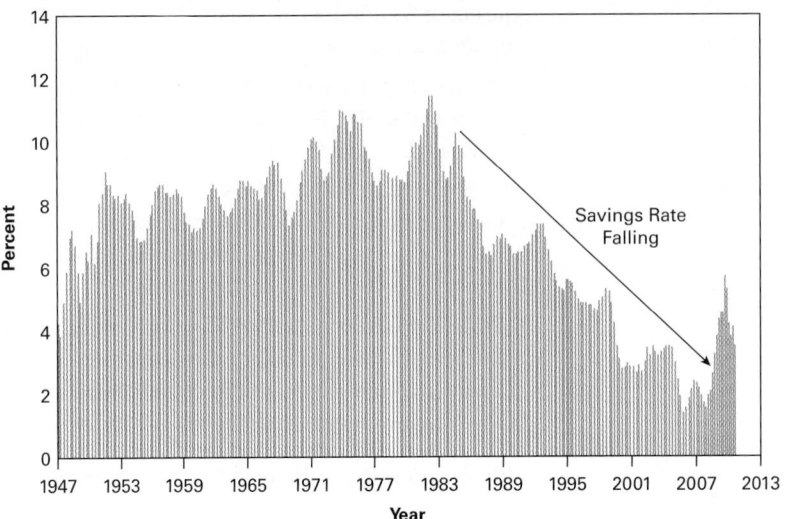

Source: Bureau of Economic Analysis.

Figure 14.3

Economists agree that families should try to save more than they did in the low-savings years of 2006–2008. However, additional saving by households is initially painful for the economy. This is because higher household savings means less household spending. In turn, less household spending means less demand for goods and services and therefore, lower retail sales.

Objective

1   *Define Savings Account and Money Market Account.* A **savings account**, or **passbook account**, is an account at a bank or other financial institution that normally requires no minimum balance, no minimum term, and no notice or penalty for withdrawals. Passbook accounts generally show transactions in a small book. They have mostly been replaced by savings accounts that provide monthly statements. Both of these accounts pay interest at a rate stated periodically by the bank.

In contrast, **money market accounts** pay interest rates that change frequently but that are maintained only as long as the balance in the account does not fall below a predetermined minimum, often between $1000 and $2500. These accounts offer interest rates almost as high as those of time deposits, while permitting funds to be withdrawn at any time. These accounts were set up to compete with the money market funds offered by many stock brokerage and mutual funds firms.

Both savings accounts and money market accounts are used to meet the day-to-day money needs of a person or business. Money can be deposited in, or withdrawn from, savings accounts and money market accounts with no penalty, although most money market funds limit the number of withdrawals per month. Historically, interest rates on both savings accounts and money market accounts have varied widely. Many checking accounts now also pay a small amount of interest, but the banks charge a fee if the balance falls below a specific amount. The Truth in Savings Act of 1991 resulted in **Regulation DD**, which requires that interest on savings accounts be *paid based on the exact number of days*.

Savings accounts and money markets are one of the safest places to place money. These accounts at most, but not all, institutions are insured by either the **Federal Deposit Insurance Corporation (FDIC)** or **Federal Savings and Loan Insurance Corporation (FSLIC)** on deposits up to a specified limit. Deposits up to $250,000 are insured. Call your bank and ask if your funds are federally insured—you have a right to know.

Interest rates on savings accounts have ranged widely from close to 0% currently to as high as 5% in the past. Since most economists expect interest rates to increase from current levels at some point, we arbitrarily choose to use $3\frac{1}{2}\%$ in Table 14.2 and for all of the interest rate calculations in this section.

Table 14.2 VALUES OF $(1 + i)^n$ FOR $3\frac{1}{2}$% COMPOUNDED DAILY

Number of Days n	Value of $(1 + i)^n$	n	Value of $(1 + i)^n$	n	Value of $(1 + i)^n$	n	Value of $(1 + i)^n$	n	Value of $(1 + i)^n$
1	1.000095890	19	1.001823491	37	1.003554076	55	1.005287650	73	1.007024219
2	1.000191790	20	1.001919556	38	1.003650307	56	1.005384048	74	1.007120783
3	1.000287699	21	1.002015631	39	1.003746548	57	1.005480454	75	1.007217357
4	1.000383617	22	1.002111714	40	1.003842797	58	1.005576870	76	1.007313939
5	1.000479544	23	1.002207807	41	1.003939056	59	1.005673296	77	1.007410531
6	1.000575480	24	1.002303909	42	1.004035324	60	1.005769730	78	1.007507132
7	1.000671426	25	1.002400021	43	1.004131602	61	1.005866174	79	1.007603742
8	1.000767381	26	1.002496141	44	1.004227888	62	1.005962627	80	1.007700362
9	1.000863345	27	1.002592271	45	1.004324184	63	1.006059089	81	1.007796990
10	1.000959318	28	1.002688410	46	1.004420489	64	1.006155560	82	1.007893628
11	1.001055300	29	1.002784558	47	1.004516803	65	1.006252041	83	1.007990276
12	1.001151292	30	1.002880716	48	1.004613127	66	1.006348531	84	1.008086932
13	1.001247293	31	1.002976882	49	1.004709460	67	1.006445030	85	1.008183598
14	1.001343303	32	1.003073058	50	1.004805802	68	1.006541538	86	1.008280273
15	1.001439322	33	1.003169243	51	1.004902153	69	1.006638056	87	1.008376958
16	1.001535350	34	1.003265438	52	1.004998513	70	1.006734583	88	1.008473651
17	1.001631388	35	1.003361641	53	1.005094883	71	1.006831119	89	1.008570354
18	1.001727435	36	1.003457854	54	1.005191262	72	1.006927665	90	1.008667067

Note: The value of $(1 + i)^n$ for $3\frac{1}{2}$% compounded daily for a quarter with 91 days is 1.008763788 and for a quarter with 92 days is 1.008860519.

Objective

INTEREST BY QUARTER FOR $3\frac{1}{2}$% COMPOUNDED DAILY ASSUMING 90-DAY QUARTERS

Number of Quarters	Value of $(1 + i)^n$
1	1.008667067
2	1.017409251
3	1.026227205
4	1.035121585

2 *Calculate Interest Compounded Daily.* Interest on savings accounts is found using compound interest. It is common for banks to pay interest **compounded daily** so that interest is credited for every day that the money is on deposit.

The formula used for daily compounding is the same one given in the previous section:

$$M = P \cdot (1 + i)^n$$

However, some calculators do not keep track of enough decimal places to maintain accuracy when working with such small interest rates on a daily basis. For example, 1.2% ÷ 365 is on the order of 0.000032877, which could be shown as 0.0000329 on some calculators. As a result, Table 14.2 provides the necessary numbers for 1 to 92 days and for 1 to 4 quarters, assuming 3.5% interest. The table goes to only 92 days since interest is normally credited to the depositor's account only quarterly, even with daily compounding. The four quarters in a year begin on January 1, April 1, July 1, and October 1. Although some quarters have 91 or 92 days in them, we assume 90-day quarters for convenience in calculation.

NOTE See **Appendix A.2** for financial calculators that do not require the use of a table.

EXAMPLE 1 Finding Interest Using Daily Compounding

Mr. Watson wants his 6-year-old son Billy to learn about savings and interest. He took Billy to a bank on September 12 and opened a savings account with $500, to which Billy added $23.50 he had received from doing chores. Find the amount of interest Billy has earned by his birthday, November 20, if he earns $3\frac{1}{2}\%$ compounded daily.

Solution

There are 18 days remaining in September, 31 days in October, and 20 days in November. The money was on deposit for $18 + 31 + 20 = 69$ days. The table value for 69 days is 1.006638056, so the compound amount is

$$\$523.50 \times 1.006638056 = \$526.98 \quad \text{Rounded}$$

and the interest earned is $\$526.98 - \$523.50 = \$3.48$.

Even Billy is old enough that he isn't impressed with $3.48. Mr. Watson, knowing the power of compound interest over the long term, insists that Billy continue to save part of his earnings. He wants Billy to learn to be a saver.

 Scientific Calculator Approach

Using a scientific calculator, Example 1 can be solved as follows.

523.50 $\boxed{\times}$ $\boxed{(}$ 1 $\boxed{+}$ 0.035 $\boxed{\div}$ 365 $\boxed{)}$ $\boxed{y^x}$ 69 $\boxed{=}$ 526.98

 Financial Calculator Approach

Solve for the unknown future value using a financial calculator as follows.

−523.50 $\boxed{PV}$ 0.009589041 $\boxed{i}$ 69 $\boxed{n}$ $\boxed{FV}$ 526.98

⌐→ 3.5 $\boxed{\div}$ 365

Interest rates on savings accounts change often. If the rate is other than $3\frac{1}{2}\%$, use the formula for compound amount from **Section 14.1**, that is,

$$M = P(1 + i)^n$$

where $i = $ *annual rate* and $n = $ number of days.

EXAMPLE 2 Finding Quarterly Interest

Tom Blackmore is a private investigator. On January 10, he deposited $2463 in a savings account paying $3\frac{1}{2}\%$ compounded daily. He deposits an additional $1320 on February 18 and $840 on March 3. Find the interest earned through April 10.

Solution

Treat each of the three amounts separately. The $2463 was in the account for 21 days in January, 28 days in February, 31 days in March, and 10 days in April for a total of 90 days. The compound amount is found using 1.008667067 from the table.

Compound amount $= \$2463 \times 1.008667067 = \$2484.35$ First deposit plus interest

A deposit of $1320 was made on February 18. This amount was on deposit for 10 days in February, 31 days in March and 10 days in April for a total of 51 days.

Compound amount $= \$1320 \times 1.004902153 = \$1326.47$ Second deposit plus interest

The final deposit of $840 was on deposit for 28 days in March and 10 days in April for a total of 38 days.

Compound amount = $840 × 1.003650307 = $843.07   Final deposit plus interest

The total amount in the account is found by adding the three compound amounts together, and the interest earned is the total amount in the account minus deposits.

Total in account = $2484.35 + $1326.47 + $843.07 = $4653.89

Interest earned = $4653.89 − ($2463 + $1320 + $840) = $30.89

The interest earned is $30.89.

EXAMPLE 3 **Finding Quarterly Interest**

Beth Gardner owns Blacktop Paving Inc. She needs a place to keep extra cash, a place that will earn interest but that will allow her to get funds when needed. She opened a savings account on July 20 with a $24,800 deposit. She then withdrew $3800 on August 29 for an unexpected truck repair, and she made another withdrawal for $8200 on September 29 for payroll. Find the interest earned through October 1, if the interest rate is $3\frac{1}{2}$% compounded daily.

Solution

Of the original $24,800, a total of $24,800 − $3800 − $8200 = $12,800 earned interest from July 20 to October 1, or for 274 − 201 = 73 days. Find the factor 1.007024219 from the table.

Compound amount = $12,800 × 1.007024219 = $12,889.91

Interest = $12,889.91 − $12,800 = $89.91

The withdrawn $3800 earned interest from July 20 to August 29, or for 241 − 201 = 40 days.

Compound amount = $3800 × 1.003842797 = $3814.60

Interest = $3814.60 − $3800 = $14.60

Finally, the withdrawn $8200 earned interest from July 20 to September 29 or for 272 − 201 = 71 days.

Compound amount = $8200 × 1.006831119 = $8256.02

Interest = $8256.02 − $8200 = $56.02

The total interest earned is ($89.91 + $14.60 + $56.02) = $160.53. The total in the account on October 1 is found as follows.

Deposits + interest − withdrawals = balance on October 1

$24,800 + $160.53 − ($3800 + $8200) = $12,960.53

Objective

3 *Find Compound Interest for Time Deposit Accounts.* Savings accounts and money market accounts are handy for funds needed on a day-to-day basis but time deposits are better for larger sums that are not needed in the near future. **Time deposits** are deposits that must be left at a bank for a specific period of time such as 6 months, 1 year, or 3 years. Importantly, they pay a higher interest rate than savings accounts. Time deposits often require a minimum investment of $500 or more. There is no law that requires a bank to issue a certificate with a time deposit, but most do issue an accompanying certificate and they refer to it as a **certificate of deposit**, or **CD**. A typical CD is shown in Figure 14.4.

Scenic River Federal Savings Bank

Certificate of Deposit

1. Account Summary

Accountholder(s)	JOHN DOE	Account Number	123-45670
		Date of Issuance	JANUARY 23
		Maturity Date	JULY 23

Principal Amount	Term	Nominal Rate / APR	Additional Deposits
$ 3000	12 MONTHS	2.5%/2.52%	None

2. General

This is a Certificate of Deposit in the amount set forth above issued to the Accountholder(s) named above, by Scenic River Federal Savings Bank.

Scenic River

3. Account Renewal

Unless the Accountholder(s) has instructed the Bank not to renew this certificate of deposit, it will automatically and repeatedly be renewed at its maturity for an identical term and at the interest rate the Bank is then offering. Notice of maturity will be mailed to the Accountholder(s) at least 15 days prior to each maturity. The Bank reserves the right not to renew this certificate of deposit, but it must mail notice of such intention to the Accountholder(s) at least 15 days prior to maturity.

4. Interest

This certificate of deposit shall earn interest at the rate set forth above. Such interest shall be compounded daily and credited monthly. During renewal terms, this certificate of deposit will earn interest at the rate the Bank is then offering. Interest earned during any term may be withdrawn during that term without penalty. Upon renewal, principal shall include interest earned (but not paid) during the prior term.

5. Interest Checks N/A

The Accountholder(s) has authorized the Bank to pay interest on the following basis:
☐ Monthly   ☐ Quarterly   ☐ Semi Annually

6. Withdrawal Penalty

In the event of any withdrawal of principal at any time prior to the maturity of this or any renewal term, the Accountholder(s) shall pay a penalty equal to three months' interest, (if the term of this certificate of deposit is equal to or less than one year), or six months' interest, (if the term of this certificate of deposit is greater than one year), on the amount withdrawn, at the rate being paid on this certificate of deposit at the time of withdrawal. If the Accountholder withdraws part or all of the balance of this certificate of deposit during the seven calendar days subsequent to the maturity of this or any renewal term, there will be no withdrawal penalty.

Any withdrawal which reduces the balance of this certificate of deposit below $1,000 will be treated as a withdrawal of the remaining balance.

No penalty will be charged for withdrawal following the death or adjudicated incompetence of the Accountholder.

SCENIC RIVER FEDERAL SAVINGS BANK

By _Sue Smith_

Authorized Representative

Figure 14.4

It is not a good idea to invest all of one's money in a certificate of deposit, since a penalty is charged for early withdrawal. At least some cash should be left in a savings or money market account for daily needs. Additionally, many financial planners recommend that some portion of liquid assets be placed in mutual funds containing stocks or bonds.

The higher interest paid by some certificates of deposit can be found using Table 14.3 on the next page. This table assumes daily compounding and 365 days per year.

Table 14.3 COMPOUND INTEREST FOR TIME DEPOSIT ACCOUNTS (DAILY COMPOUNDING)

Number of Years	Interest Rate			
	4%	**5%**	**6%**	**7%**
1	1.04080849	1.05126750	1.06183131	1.07250098
2	1.08328232	1.10516335	1.12748573	1.15025836
3	1.12748944	1.16182231	1.19719965	1.23365322
4	1.17350058	1.22138603	1.27122407	1.32309429
5	1.22138937	1.28400343	1.34982552	1.41901993
10	1.49179200	1.64866481	1.82202895	2.01361755

EXAMPLE **4**   **Finding Compound Amount and Interest on Time Deposits**

Vivek Pandey deposits $4000 into each of two separate CDs. The first CD pays 4% compounded daily and matures in 3 years. The second CD pays 5% compounded daily and matures in 4 years. Find the maturity value of each.

Solution

Look in Table 14.3 for 4% and 3 years to find 1.12748944.

$$\text{Maturity value} = \$4000 \times 1.12748944 = \$4509.96$$

Look in Table 14.3 for 5% and 4 years to find 1.22138603.

$$\text{Maturity value} = \$4000 \times 1.22138603 = \$4885.54$$

Alternatively, you can find these values using $M = P(1 + i)^n$ and your calculator, although the results might differ a bit from the preceding ones due to rounding.

NOTE   Many time deposits earn interest compounded monthly or quarterly rather than daily. In that event, calculate interest using the techniques of **Section 14.1**.

Objective

4   *Determine the Penalty for Early Withdrawal.*   A penalty is incurred if a depositor withdraws funds from a time deposit, such as a CD, before the maturity date. The procedure for calculating this early withdrawal penalty is not standard. However, many financial institutions use the following rules for calculating the **early withdrawal penalty**.

Calculating the Early Withdrawal Penalty on a Time Deposit

1. If money is withdrawn within 3 months of the deposit, no interest will be paid at all on the money withdrawn.
2. If money is withdrawn after 3 months but before the end of the term, then 3 months interest is deducted from the time the account has been open and regular passbook interest is paid on the account.

EXAMPLE 5 **Finding Interest When Early Withdrawal Occurs**

Use the rules listed above to find the amount of interest earned on each of the following.

(a) On January 5, Raymond Hoyle deposited $5000 in a 1-year certificate of deposit paying 4% compounded daily. He withdrew the money on March 12 of the same year.
(b) Bob Kashir deposited $6000 in a 4-year certificate of deposit paying 5% compounded daily. He withdrew the money 15 months later. The passbook rate at his bank is $3\frac{1}{2}\%$ compounded daily.

Solution

(a) Since March 12 is within 3 months of January 5, no interest at all is earned. The bank will simply return the $5000.
(b) The money is withdrawn early, so 3 months' interest is lost. The money was on deposit for 15 months' but only $15 - 3 = 12$ months' interest will be paid. Also, interest will be paid at the passbook rates, $3\frac{1}{2}\%$ compounded daily, instead of the more generous 5% compounded daily. The compound amount is found using the factor for four 90-day quarters (assume it is not a leap year) at $3\frac{1}{2}\%$. From Table 14.2, this is 1.035121585.

$$\$6000(1.035121585) = \$6210.73$$

The interest is found by subtracting the initial deposit of $6000 from $6210.73.

$$\text{Interest} = \$6210.73 - \$6000 = \$210.73$$

Objective

5 *Find Compound Amount with Continuous Compounding.* In this chapter, we have discussed annual, semiannual, quarterly, monthly, and daily compounding. Table 14.1 shows that more frequent compounding results in more interest, although the additional interest becomes smaller and smaller with more frequent compounding. It is possible to extend Table 14.1 to include compounding every hour, or second, or even every instant in time. Compounding every instant is called **continuous compounding**, and it is commonly used by various institutions, including banks. The formula for continuous compounding requires a number coded into your calculator as e^x. The number is approximately equal to 2.718281828. See **Appendix A** to learn how to use this function.

Continuous Compounding

$$M = Pe^{rt}$$

where
M is the maturity value
P is the original investment
e is a number that is coded into your calculator
r is the annual interest rate
t is the number of the years, or the fraction of a year, that the investment is held

EXAMPLE 6 **Finding the Compound Amount for Continuous Compounding**

Find the compound amount for the following deposits.

(a) $1000 at 6% compounded continuously for 10 years
(b) $45,000 at 5% compounded continuously for 3 years

Solution

(a) $1000 at 6% compounded continuously for 10 years

Use the formula in the box with $P = \$1000$, $r = 0.06$, and $t = 10$. The compound amount is as follows.

$$M = Pe^{rt}$$
$$M = \$1000e^{0.06 \cdot 10}$$
$$= \$1000e^{0.6}$$
$$= \$1000 \cdot 1.8221188$$
$$= \$1822.12 \qquad \text{Rounded}$$

Of this amount,

$$\$1822.12 - \$1000 = \$822.12$$

is interest, the same as when interest is compounded every minute, as shown in Table 14.1.

(b) $45,000 at 5% compounded continuously for 3 years.

$$M = \$45,000e^{0.05 \cdot 3}$$
$$= \$45,000e^{0.15}$$
$$= \$45,000 \times 1.16183424 = \$52,282.54$$

Scientific Calculator Approach

Example 6(b) can be solved as follows. Recall that $r \cdot t = 0.05 \times 3 = 0.15$.

$$45000 \;\boxed{\times}\; 0.15 \;\boxed{e^x}\; \boxed{=}\; 52282.54$$

NOTE The interest rates paid by banks in some years are quite low compared to the returns from other investments such as stocks. However, in other years, the returns from banks may equal or even exceed returns from stocks.

EXAMPLE 7 Finding the Compound Amount for Continuous Compounding

Find the compound amount for the following deposits in which time is not in an even number of years.

(a) $15,000 at 4.5% compounded continuously for 6 months

(b) $8200 at 4% compounded continuously for 216 days

Solution

(a) Use the formula with $P = \$15,000$, $r = 4.5\% = 0.045$, and $t = \frac{6}{12} = 0.5$.

$$M = Pe^{rt}$$
$$= \$15,000 \cdot e^{0.045 \cdot 0.5}$$
$$= \$15,000 \cdot e^{0.0225}$$
$$= \$15,341.33 \qquad \text{Rounded}$$

(b) Use the formula with $P = \$8200$, $r = 4\% = 0.04$, and $t = \frac{216}{360} = 0.6$.

$$M = Pe^{rt}$$
$$= \$8200 \cdot e^{0.04 \cdot 0.6}$$
$$= \$8200 \cdot e^{0.024}$$
$$= \$8399.18 \qquad \text{Rounded}$$

14.2	**Exercises**

Find the interest earned by the following. Assume $3\frac{1}{2}\%$ interest compounded daily, and use the exact number of days.

	Amount	Date Deposited	Date Withdrawn	
1.	$6200	October 7	December 10	$38.16
2.	$3850	January 5	February 9	$12.94
3.	$6500	February 17	April 15	$35.62
4.	$2830	May 4	June 23	$13.60

Find the amount on deposit on the first day of the next quarter when the following sums are deposited as indicated. Assume $3\frac{1}{2}\%$ interest compounded daily.

	Amount	Date Deposited	
5.	$7235.82	February 14	$7267.81
6.	$3018.25	April 7	$3042.95
7.	$2965.72	July 1	$2992.00
8.	$4031.46	April 1	$4066.79

Find the compound amount for the following investments. Assume daily compounding and use Table 14.3.

	Amount Deposited	Interest Rate	Time in Years	
9.	$5000	6%	2	$5637.43
10.	$2900	5%	10	$4781.13
11.	$14,000	7%	3	$17,271.15
12.	$7500	4%	5	$9160.42

Find the amount of interest earned by the following investments. Assume daily compounding and use Table 14.3.

	Amount Deposited	Interest Rate	Time in Years	
13.	$20,000	7%	3	$4673.06
14.	$6800	5%	5	$1931.22
15.	$5000	4%	4	$867.50
16.	$1000	6%	1	$61.83

17. Explain the difference between passbook accounts, time deposit accounts, certificates of deposit, and insured money market accounts.

18. Use an example to show that continuous compounding is better for a saver than semiannual compounding.

Solve each of the following application problems. Assume $3\frac{1}{2}\%$ interest compounded daily. Round to the nearest cent at each step.

19. SAVINGS ACCOUNT   Teresa Tabor had $4300 in her savings account on July 1. She then deposited $1000 on July 30 and $500 on September 5. Find the balance in the account on October 1. $5845.41

20. SAVINGS ACCOUNT   Vicki Phelps had $8600 in her savings account on April 1. She then deposited $800 on May 5 and an additional $350 on June 20. Find the balance in the account on July 1. $9830.12

21. EXTRA CASH   On April 1, Action Sports opened a savings account with a deposit of $17,500. A withdrawal of $5000 was made 21 days later and another withdrawal of $980 was made 12 days before July 1. Find (a) the interest earned through July 1 and (b) the balance on July 1.   (a) $118.49 (b) $11,638.49

22. EXCESS CASH   The owner of Rondo's Magic Shop opened a savings account for the extra cash in the firm. The initial deposit of $7800 was made on July 7. A withdrawal of $1500 was made 46 days later, with an additional withdrawal of $1000 made 30 days before October 1. Find (a) the interest earned through October 1 and (b) the balance on October 1.   (a) $55.90 (b) $5355.90

For the following application problems on investments, use the rules for finding the early withdrawal penalty as given in the text. Assume daily compounding of interest and use Table 14.2.

23. TIME DEPOSIT   Alyssa Datolli deposited $8500 in a 4-year time deposit account paying 3.5% interest. She withdrew the funds after 30 days to purchase a car. Find the interest. $0

24. TIME DEPOSIT   Jana Box deposited $6000 in a 3-year account paying 4% interest but needed the money 2 months later and withdrew it. How much interest did she receive? $0

25. TIME DEPOSIT   Emma Gilger placed $20,000 in a 10-year account paying 5% interest. The savings and loan where she placed her money pays a passbook rate of $3\frac{1}{2}\%$ compounded daily. She withdrew $5000 of her money after 15 months. Find the interest that she earned on the $5000. $175.61

26. TIME DEPOSIT   Trish Hardison deposited $18,680 in a 4-year account paying 4% interest. The bank where she put the money pays a passbook rate of $3\frac{1}{2}\%$ compounded daily. She withdrew $2000 after 15 months. Find the interest that she earned on the $2000. $70.24

Use the formula for continuous compounding to find the compound amount and interest for each of the following. Assume there are 360 days a year in Exercises 33 and 34.

	Amount	Interest Rate	Time	
27.	$8000	6%	2 years	$9019.97; $1019.97
28.	$4500	4.5%	6 years	$5894.84; $1394.84
29.	$18,200	5.5%	10 months	$19,053.58; $853.58
30.	$8008.43	6%	6 months	$8252.32; $243.89
31.	$6800	4.5%	3 quarters	$7033.42; $233.42
32.	$9400	7%	2 quarters	$9734.83; $334.83
33.	$12,800	3%	250 days	$13,069.46; $269.46
34.	$25,000	4.5%	324 days	$26,033.28; $1033.28

Solve the following application problems. Round to the nearest cent.

35. PARTIAL COLLATERAL FOR A LOAN An Italian engineering firm deposited $800,000 in a 2-year time deposit earning 6% compounded daily as partial collateral for a loan. At maturity, find (a) the compound amount and (b) the interest earned. (a) $901,988.58 (b) $101,988.58

36. WELDING SHOP Joni Perez needs to borrow $20,000 to extend a welding shop, but the bank will not lend her the money. Joni's uncle agrees to put up collateral for the loan with a $20,000, 4-year certificate of deposit paying 4% compounded daily. This means that the bank will take all or part of his deposit if Joni should fail to repay the loan. Find (a) the compound amount earned by her uncle and (b) the interest earned if the funds remain at the bank for the full 4 years.   (a) $23,470.01 (b) $3470.01

37. RETIREMENT Tara Nolan has worked for the same company for 15 years and on retirement has the option of investing her retirement money in either of two funds. One fund pays 6% compounded continuously and the other pays 7% compounded semiannually. If she has $286,000 to deposit for 2 years, which investment should she choose? Find the extra interest earned by making the better choice. (*Hint:* $e^{0.12} = 1.1275$.)   7% compounded semiannually; $5726.58

38. IRA INVESTMENT Lee Stringer has just retired and rolls $145,000 from one of his pension plans into an Individual Retirement Account. One investment choice yields 8% compounded quarterly and the other yields 7.5% compounded continuously. Given a term for each investment of 3 years, find the amount of extra interest that will be earned with the better choice.   8% compounded quarterly; $2308.27

 39. Is it important to you for your bank to have insurance on your savings account? Why or why not?

 40. Go to your bank and find the current interest rates it pays on savings accounts, IMMAs, and CDs.

14.3	**Finding Time and Rate**

OBJECTIVES

1 *Find time given principal, maturity value, and rate.*

2 *Find rate given time, principal, and maturity value.*

3 *Use more than one table to solve interest problems.*

In **Chapter 12**, we saw how to work with the formula for simple interest, $I = PRT$, to find any one of the variables given the other three. In this section, we do the same thing using the formula for compound interest, $M = P(1 + i)^n$. However, we will wait until the next section, when we discuss present value and future value, to solve this equation for the principal, P.

Objective

1 *Find Time Given Principal, Maturity Value, and Rate.* The next two examples show how to find time.

> | **EXAMPLE** **1** **Finding Time** |
> |---|
>
> James Thompson needs $45,000 to start a small music store but has only $29,000. How long must he wait to start the business if he believes he can earn 10% compounded annually?

Solution

Use the formula $M = P(1 + i)^n$, with $M = \$45,000$, $P = \$29,000$, and $i = 0.10$. The value of n is unknown.

$$M = P(1 + i)^n$$

$$\$45,000 = \$29,000(1 + 0.10)^n$$

$$\$45,000 = \$29,000(1.1)^n$$

$$\frac{\$45,000}{\$29,000} = (1.1)^n \qquad \text{Divide by \$29,000.}$$

$$1.551724138 = (1.1)^n$$

Solving this equation would require advanced algebra. However, a good approximation can be found by looking down column A of the 10% page of the interest table in **Appendix C**. The number 1.61051000 in row 5 is very close to the number on the left side of the equation above. Since interest is compounded annually, he must wait about 5 years.

EXAMPLE **2** **Finding Time to Double**

Suppose the general level of inflation in the economy averages 4% per year. Find the number of years it would take for the general level of prices to double.

Solution

To find the number of years it will take for $1 worth of goods and services to cost $2, solve for n in the following equation.

$$2 = 1(1 + 4\%)^n$$

or

$$2 = 1(1 + 0.04)^n$$

where $M = 2$, $P = 1$, and $i = 4\%$. This equation simplifies as follows.

$$2 = (1.04)^n$$

As in the previous examples, look down column A of the 4% page of the interest table to find the number closest to 2. The closest number is 2.02581652. This number corresponds to 18 periods, so to the nearest year, the general level of prices would double in 18 years.

NOTE   Prices would double about every $7\frac{1}{2}$ years if inflation were 10%.

Objective

2   *Find Rate Given Time, Principal, and Maturity Value.*   The same method we used to find time can be used to find rate, although you must look at several pages in **Appendix C**. This is because only one interest rate is shown on each page. The method is to look on a page for any interest rate and find the value in column A and the row for the number of periods. Go to pages with higher or lower interest rates as needed to get as close to the rate as possible.

EXAMPLE 3 **Finding Rate**

Kaj Songram needs to borrow $8000 for 1 year. He has been offered a loan with interest compounded monthly and a compound amount of $8493.42. Find the rate.

Solution

Use the equation $M = P(1 + i)^n$, with i unknown. Notice that n is the number of compounding periods, which is 12.

$$\$8493.42 = \$8000(1 + i)^{12}$$

Divide both sides by $8000.

$$1.0616775 = (1 + i)^{12}$$

Find the row for 12 periods in column A of the interest tables in **Appendix C**. Check this number in column A under different rates as necessary until you find the number closest to 1.0616775. The closest number is 1.06167781, corresponding to an interest rate of $\frac{1}{2}\%$ per month, or

$$\frac{1}{2} \times 12 = 6\% \text{ per year}$$

Objective

3 *Use More Than One Table to Solve Interest Problems.* Some problems require the use of more than one table, as in the next example.

EXAMPLE 4 **Using More Than One Table**

Jean King deposits $2500 in a fund paying 6% compounded quarterly. After 4 years, the rate drops to 5% compounded semiannually. Find the amount in her account at the end of 7 years.

Solution

First find the future value after 4 years using $\frac{6\%}{4} = 1.5\%$ per quarter for 16 quarters.

$$\text{Future value at end of 4 years} = P(1 + i)^n$$
$$= \$2500 \cdot (1 + 0.015)^{16}$$
$$= \$3172.46$$

Use this as the present value at the beginning of year 5, and use a rate of $\frac{5\%}{2} = 2.5\%$ per semiannual period for 6 semiannual periods.

$$\text{Future value at end of 7 years} = P(1 + i)^n$$
$$= \$3172.46 \cdot (1 + 0.025)^6$$
$$= \$3679.08$$

Jean King will have $3679.08 in her account at the end of 7 years.

Scientific
Calculator
Approach

Here are the steps for solving Example 4 using a calculator.

End of 4 years: 2500 $\times$ (1 + .015) y^x 16 = 3172.46

End of 7 years: 3172.46 $\times$ (1 + .025) y^x 6 = 3679.08

Notice the future value is exactly the same as the value obtained using the tables.

NOTE Keep the formulas for periodic versus continuous compounding separate in your mind. Periodic compounding refers to compounded monthly, compounded quarterly, etc.

For periodic compounding: $M = P(1 + i)^n$

For continuous compounding: $M = Pe^{rt}$

14.3 Exercises

Complete this table. Round time to the nearest period, interest to the nearest whole percent per year, and money to the nearest cent. (As a review, some of these problems do not require the methods of this section.)

	Principal	Compound Amount	Interest Rate	Compounded	Time in Years
1.	$6200	$7384.30	6%	annually	3
2.	$12,000	$17,631.94	8%	annually	5
3.	$3600	$4824.34	10%	semiannually	3
4.	$2500	$2760.20	4%	semiannually	$2\frac{1}{2}$
5.	$12,000	$15,149.72	6%	annually	4
6.	$13,200	$22,680.06	7%	annually	8
7.	$8500	$13,403.64	8%	quarterly	$5\frac{3}{4}$
8.	$3100	$3765.63	6%	monthly	$3\frac{1}{4}$

 9. During your working career of 40 years, approximately how many times can you double an investment at 6% interest and at 8% interest? (*Hint:* Use column A in **Appendix C.**) What does this mean to you? (See Objective 2.)

 10. Explain how to find the interest rate given principal, compound amount, compounding period, and time in years. (See Objective 2.)

Solve the following application problems. Round as in Exercises 1–10.

11. HOTEL MANAGEMENT Management wants to remodel the dining room of a hotel and signs a note with proceeds of $344,546.29, a maturity value of $420,000, and a rate of 8% compounded quarterly. Find the length of the loan.   about $2\frac{1}{2}$ years

12. NEW POLICE CARS The Otero County Police Department borrows $220,287.35 to purchase several new police cars equipped with sophisticated radar to detect speeders. Find the length of the loan if the maturity value is $252,000 and the rate is 9% compounded monthly.   18 months

13. NEW AUTO Gladys Ford will need a new car and invests $12,000 in a mutual fund containing corporate bonds paying about 6% per year compounded quarterly. Find the compound amount in (a) 3 years and (b) 5 years.   (a) $14,347.42 (b) $16,162.26

14. **TRUST FUND**   Elton Scallion invests the $95,000 he inherited in a trust for his mentally ill son, who cannot work. If the investments yield 5% compounded semiannually, find the compound amount (a) in 10 years and (b) in 25 years.   (a) $155,668.56 (b) $326,525.33

15. **UNKNOWN INTEREST RATE**   Roy Bledsoe deposits $46,000 in an account that has interest compounded semiannually. In $2\frac{1}{2}$ years the account contains $58,708.95. Find the interest rate paid.   10%

16. **UNKNOWN INTEREST RATE**   Jim Pierce invests $12,500 and expects to receive $13,945.85 in $2\frac{3}{4}$ years. Assume interest is compounded quarterly and find the interest rate.   4%

17. **STUDENT LOAN**   By the time she received her college degree, Samantha Blackstone had borrowed $28,300 in loans. Her father agreed to assume the loans for her and re-financed the loans into one simple interest note. Due to his good credit history, the note has a low interest rate of 7% compounded semiannually and a maturity value of $34,787.93. Find the length of the loan.   3 years

18. **HOME CONSTRUCTION LOAN**   A home construction loan of $80,000 at 12% compounded monthly resulted in a maturity value of $92,877.52. Find the term or length of the loan. $1\frac{1}{4}$ years

Use the ideas of Example 2 in the text to answer the following questions. Find the time, to the nearest year, that it would take for the general level of prices in the economy to double if the average annual inflation rate is as follows.

19. $2\frac{1}{2}$%   28 years   20. 6%   12 years

21. $3\frac{1}{2}$%   20 years   22. 4%   18 years

23. **GASOLINE DEMAND**   Worldwide, demand for gasoline is increasing at a rate of about 2% per year. If it continues to increase at this rate indefinitely, find the number of years before the oil companies would need to double the supply of gasoline.   35 years

24. **POPULATION GROWTH**   The rate of growth of world population appears to be further slowing due to (1) the large number of deaths caused by AIDS and (2) women having fewer children. Assume that world population grows at 1.5% per year (Figure 14.5). Use column A in **Appendix C** estimate the number of years it would require for world population to double.   approximately 47 years

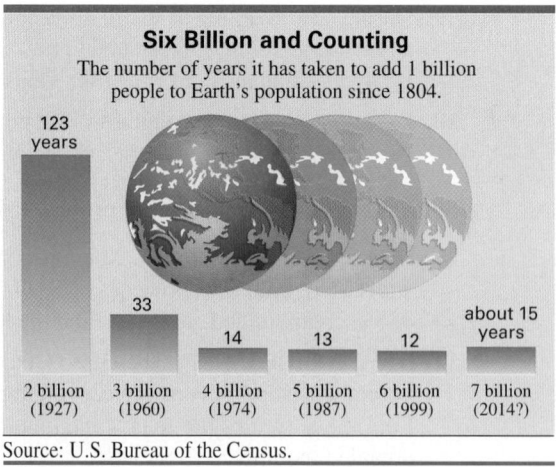

Source: U.S. Bureau of the Census.

Figure 14.5

The remainder of these exercises may require the use of any of the tables presented in this chapter.

25. INVESTING Dawn Young deposits $10,000 at 8% compounded quarterly. Two years after she makes the first deposit, she adds another $20,000, also at 8%, compounded quarterly. What total amount will she have 5 years after her first deposit? $40,224.31

26. SAVING FOR COLLEGE Holly Crabtree has decided to help her young grandson pay for college. In 2004, she deposited $5000 in an account paying 6% compounded semiannually. Exactly 2 years later, she deposits another $2000 in a different account paying 5% compounded quarterly. Find the account balance after an additional 5 years (in 2011). $10,127.02

For Exercises 27–30 use Table 14.3 for the certificates of deposit.

27. SAVING FOR COLLEGE Khy Luk wants to save to help a grandchild through college. He deposits $5000 into an account paying 8% per year compounded quarterly. After $3\frac{3}{4}$ years, the compound amount is used to purchase a 4-year CD paying 5% compounded daily. Find the account balance after $7\frac{3}{4}$ years. $8219.12

28. LONG-TERM SAVINGS Lupe Gonzales puts $4000 in a fund for 5 years that pays 6% compounded annually. After 5 years, she hopes to take the future value and invest it in a mutual fund yielding 8% per year compounded annually for 20 years. Find the final amount that Gonzales will have after 25 years. $24,949.64

29. COMPOUND INTEREST Jean Sides has $11,000 in a mutual fund that pays 10% compounded semiannually. After the money has been on deposit for 4 years, $5000 is invested in a fund that pays 7% compounded daily for 3 years. (The remaining money stays at 10% compounded semiannually.) Find the total amount on deposit in both accounts, both principal and interest, after the 7 years. $21,247.04

30. COMPOUND INTEREST Frank Sabas has $45,000 in an account paying 8% compounded quarterly. After $2\frac{1}{4}$ years, Sabas removes $20,000 and invests for 5 years in a fund paying 6% compounded daily. (The remaining money continues to earn 8% compounded quarterly.) Find the total amount on deposit in both accounts, both principal and interest, after the $7\frac{1}{4}$ years. $77,190.58

14.4	**Present Value at Compound Interest**

OBJECTIVES

> 1 *Review the meaning of future value and present value.*
>
> 2 *Find the present value.*

Objective

1 *Review the Meaning of Future Value and Present Value.* In **Sections 14.1** and **14.2**, the principal, interest rate, and time were given and **future value** was found using $M = P(1 + i)^n$ or using **Appendix C**. In **Section 14.3**, the interest rate and time were found given the other values in the formula. In this section, we look at how to find the **present value**, or the amount that must be deposited today in order to accumulate the needed future value at the needed time. Figure 14.6 shows the idea of present value and future value.

Figure 14.6

Objective

2 *Find the Present Value.* Earlier, P was used for principal or amount borrowed or deposited at the beginning of a term. The phrase *present value* is often used, instead of the word *principal*, if the value is unknown. Thus P also represents present value and it can be found as follows.

$$M = P(1 + i)^n$$

$$\frac{M}{(1 + i)^n} = \frac{P(1 + i)^n}{(1 + i)^n} \quad \text{Divide by } (1 + i)^n.$$

$$P = \frac{M}{(1 + i)^n} \quad \text{Use this formula for present value.}$$

The present value, P, is found by dividing the compound amount, M, by $(1 + i)^n$. The value of $(1 + i)^n$ can be found using your calculator, or it can be read from column A in **Appendix C**. Alternatively, the fraction $\frac{1}{(1 + i)^n}$ is found in column B in **Appendix C**.

$$P = \frac{M}{(1 + i)^n} = M \cdot \frac{1}{(1 + i)^n}$$

From column B in Appendix C

From column A in Appendix C

EXAMPLE 1 **Finding Present Value**

Eric Long signs a note with an interest maturity value of $17,291.52 to purchase 0.5 acres located on a small creek. The note has an interest rate of 9% compounded semiannually and a period of 2 years. Find the present value, or the amount of proceeds that he receives.

Solution

The interest rate is 9% $\div$ 2 or 4.5% per semiannual period, and the number of compounding periods is 2 years $\times$ 2 semiannual periods per year or 4. The present value can be found in one of three ways: (1) using a calculator, (2) using column A in **Appendix C**, and (3) using column B in **Appendix C**.

(1) $P = \dfrac{M}{(1 + i)^n}$

$P = \dfrac{\$17,291.52}{1.1925186} \quad \text{Use the calculator to find } (1 + 0.045)^4$

$P = \$14,500$

(2) $P = M \cdot \dfrac{1}{(1 + i)^n}$

$P = \$17,291.52 \times 0.83856134 \quad \text{Value of } (1 + 0.045)^4 \text{ from column A, Appendix C}$

$P = \$14,500$

(3) $P = \dfrac{\$17,291.52}{(1 + 0.045)^4}$

$P = \dfrac{\$17,291.52}{1.192518601} \quad \text{Value of } \dfrac{1}{(1 + 0.045)^4} \text{ from column B, Appendix C}$

$P = \$14,500$

NOTE In this case, all three methods produce the same answer. In some situations, answers may differ by a few cents due to rounding.

Financial Calculator Approach

Future value, interest rate per compounding period, and number of compounding periods are known in this problem. Present value is the unknown.

$$17291.52 \boxed{FV}\ 4.5\ \boxed{i}\ 4\ \boxed{n}\ \boxed{PV}\ -14500$$

The minus sign indicates that Eric Long must pay out $14,500 now to obtain the needed future value.

EXAMPLE 2 **Finding Present Value**

Green Acres Sprinklers, Inc. will receive $185,000 in 3 years as part of a lawsuit settlement. Find the present value if money can be invested at 5% compounded quarterly.

Solution

The original investment will grow at a rate of $\frac{5\%}{4} = 1.25\%$ per quarter for 12 quarters. Enter these values in the formula as required and solve.

$$P = \frac{M}{(1+i)^n} \qquad \text{Formula for present value}$$

$$= \frac{\$185,000}{(1+0.0125)^{12}} \qquad \text{Substitute values into formula.}$$

$$= \$159,379.09$$

A deposit of $159,379.09 at 5% compounded quarterly for 3 years will result in the desired amount of $185,000.

Scientific Calculator Approach

Example 2 can be solved as follows.

$$185000 \boxed{\div} \boxed{(}\ 1\ \boxed{+}\ 0.0125\ \boxed{)}\ \boxed{y^x}\ 12\ \boxed{=}\ 159379.09$$

EXAMPLE 3 **Finding the Value of a Business**

Tom Fredrickson owns a men's clothing store worth $125,000. The business is in a great location and is growing rapidly. Fredrickson is confident that the value of the business will increase at the rate of 16% per year, compounded semiannually, for the next 4 years. If he sells the business, he will invest the proceeds at 8% compounded quarterly. What sale price should he insist on?

Solution

This problem requires two steps. First, decide on the future value of the business. This is done with the formula for compound amount, $M = P(1+i)^n$. Here, $P = \$125,000$, $i = 16\% \div 2 = 8\%$, and $n = 4 \times 2 = 8$ periods.

$$M = \$125,000(1+0.08)^8$$
$$= \$125,000(1.85093021)$$
$$= \$231,366.28$$

Now find the present value of this sum, assuming that money can be invested at 8% compounded quarterly. Use the formula

$$P = M \cdot \frac{1}{(1 + i)^n}$$

with $M = \$231{,}366.28$, $i = 8\% \div 4 = 2\%$, and $n = 4 \times 4 = 16$ periods.

$$P = \$231{,}366.28 \cdot \frac{1}{(1 + 0.02)^{16}}$$

$$= \$231{,}366.28(0.72844581)$$

$$= \$168{,}537.80$$

Fredrickson should not sell the business for less than $168,537.80. An investment of this amount at 8% compounded quarterly for 4 years will produce the same future amount as the growth in the value of the business.

14.4	**Exercises**

Find the present value and the amount of interest earned for the following deposits. Round to the nearest cent.

	Amount Needed	Time	Interest	Compounded	
1.	$4800	3 years	8%	annually	$3810.39; $989.61
2.	$3300	4 years	11%	annually	$2173.81; $1126.19
3.	$12,200	$2\frac{1}{2}$ years	12%	quarterly	$9077.95; $3122.05
4.	$7000	$3\frac{1}{4}$ years	10%	quarterly	$5077.94; $1922.06
5.	$8500	1 year	12%	monthly	$7543.32; $956.68
6.	$18,000	$1\frac{1}{2}$ years	9%	monthly	$15,734.81; $2265.19

7. Explain the difference between present value and future value. (See Objective 1.)

8. List three reasons why a business owner may need to place a value on a business. (See Objective 2.)

Solve the following application problems.

9. **PACK MULES** David Fontana Backpackers will need to buy some new pack mules in 5 years. These mules will cost a total of $10,000. What lump sum should the firm invest today at 7%, compounded annually, in order to be able to buy the mules? How much interest will be earned? $7129.86; $2870.14

10. **CANDY STORE** A candy store owner needs $85,000 in 1 year to open a branch in a mall. Find the lump sum that could be invested today at 5% compounded monthly to produce the needed funds. Find the interest earned. $80,862.90; $4137.10

11. **ECOTOUR** The Datons' accountant told them they will get a refund of $8500 on their income taxes. They are excited and decide to borrow as much as possible now to go on a lifelong dream tour of 1 month in the Amazon in South America. They do not want to borrow more than can be repaid with their income tax refund. Find the proceeds if their accountant agrees to lend them the funds at 7% compounded monthly for 2 months. $8401.69

12. **HOME REMODEL** Daisy Wadsworth knows she will receive a bonus of $12,000 in 3 months and decides to remodel her home. She does not want to borrow more than she can repay using her bonus. Although the bank usually does not make short, small loans, she has a good relationship with her banker and he lends her the funds at 9% compounded monthly. Find the proceeds. $11,734.00

13. **SMALL GROCERY STORE** José Martinez, an immigrant from Mexico, estimates that he needs $9000 to start a (very) small grocery store in 3 years. How much must he deposit today if his credit union will pay 4% compounded quarterly? $7987.04

14. **BUILDING A SCHOOL** Ebbertson County needs an additional $8,000,000 in 4 years to build an elementary school. Assume it can earn 6% compounded quarterly, and determine the amount that must be deposited today to satisfy this future need. $6,304,248.32

15. **TIME VALUE OF MONEY** Assume that money can be invested at 8% compounded quarterly. Which is larger, $2500 now or $3800 in 5 years? (*Hint:* First find the present value of $3800; then compare present values.) $3800 in 5 years

16. **TIME VALUE OF MONEY** Assume that money can be invested at 10% compounded semiannually. Which is larger, $3000 now or $7500 in 10 years? (*Hint:* First find the present value of $7500; then compare present values.) $3000 now is larger

17. **FUTURE VALUE** An investment of $30,000 earns interest of 10% compounded semiannually for $2\frac{1}{2}$ years. Find the future value of the investment. If money can be deposited elsewhere for $2\frac{1}{2}$ years at 8% compounded quarterly, find the present value of this future value. $38,288.45; $31,409.86

18. **SELLING AN ESTATE** Judith McGrath sold her deceased grandfather's home and accepted a note for $65,000 with interest of 9% compounded semiannually for 3 years. Find the future value. Then find the present value of this future value if funds can be invested elsewhere for 3 years at 6% compounded monthly. $84,646.91; $70,734.76

19. **CAFE OF MODERN ART** The owner of Cafe of Modern Art signs a note for $16,800 at 10% simple interest for 4 years. Find the maturity value of the note. What should the holder of the note be willing to accept in payment for the note today if funds can be invested for 4 years at 6% per year compounded quarterly? $23,520; $18,534.49

20. **MATURITY VALUE** In 6 years, Susan Hessney must pay off a note with a face value of $12,000 and simple interest of 9% per year. Find the maturity value of the note. What should the holder of the note be willing to accept in complete payment today, if money can be invested for 6 years at 6% per year compounded quarterly? $18,480; $12,927.57

21. **VALUING A HAIR SALON** Jessie Jones believes her hair salon is worth $20,000 and estimates that its value will grow at 10% per year compounded annually for the next 3 years. If she sells the business, the funds will be invested at 8% compounded quarterly. (a) Find the future value if she holds onto the business. (b) What price should she insist on now if she sells the business? (a) $26,620 (b) $20,989.69

22. **BIKE SHOP** Andy Sargent figures his bike shop is worth $88,000 if sold today and that it will grow in value at 8% per year compounded annually for the next 6 years. If he sells the business, the funds will be invested at 5% compounded semiannually. (a) Find the future value of the shop. (b) What price should he insist on at this time if he sells the business? (a) $139,644.94 (b) $103,833.82

CHAPTER TERMS

Review the following terms to test your understanding of the chapter. For any terms you do not know, refer to the page number found next to that term.

certificate of deposit (CD) [p. 537]
compound amount [p. 524]
compound interest [p. 523]
compounded daily [p. 535]
continuous compounding [p. 540]
early withdrawal penalty [p. 539]

effective rate of interest [p. 530]
exponent [p. 524]
Federal Deposit Insurance Corporation (FDIC) [p. 534]
Federal Savings and Loan Insurance Corporation (FSLIC) [p. 534]

future amount [p. 524]
future value [p. 524]
inflation [p. 530]
money market account [p. 534]
nominal rate [p. 526]
passbook account [p. 534]
period of compounding [p. 526]

present value [p. 549]
principal [p. 523]
Regulation DD [p. 534]
savings account [p. 534]
simple interest [p. 523]
stated rate [p. 526]
time deposit [p. 537]

CONCEPTS

EXAMPLES

14.1 Finding the compound amount and the interest

Determine the interest rate per period and the number of compounding periods. Use the formula $M = P(1 + i)^n$ to calculate the compound amount. Then subtract the principal from the compound amount to obtain interest.

Find the compound amount and the interest if $7200 is deposited at 9% compounded monthly for 4 years.

$$i = \frac{0.09}{12} = 0.0075$$

$$n = 4 \times 12 = 48$$

$$M = P(1 + i)^n$$
$$= \$7200(1.0075)^{48}$$
$$= \$7200(1.43140533) = \$10,306.12$$

$$I = M - P$$
$$= \$10,306.12 - \$7200 = \$3106.12$$

14.1 Determining the effective rate of interest

Divide the interest earned during the year by the amount invested at the beginning of the year.

Find the effective rate of interest if a $1200 investment grows to $1295 by the end of the year.

$$\text{Interest} = \$1295 - \$1200 = \$95$$

$$\text{Effective rate of interest} = \frac{\$95}{\$1200} = 7.92\% \quad \text{Rounded}$$

14.1 Determining the effective rate of interest given a nominal rate

Use the formula $(1 + i)^n - 1$, where i is the interest rate per compounding period and n is the number of compounding periods.

Find the effective rate to the nearest hundredth if the annual rate is 9% compounded quarterly.

$$\frac{9\%}{4} = 2.25\% \text{ per quarter for 4 quarters}$$

$$\text{Effective rate} = (1 + i)^n - 1$$
$$= (1 + 0.0225)^4 - 1$$
$$= 9.31\%$$

14.2 Interest compounded daily

Determine the number of days and then find the value of $(1 + i)^n$ using Table 14.2. Multiply this value by the principal to obtain compound amount. Subtract principal from compound amount to obtain interest. A calculator can also be used to find $(1 + i)^n$.

Janice deposited $1535 on September 5 in an account paying $3\frac{1}{2}\%$ compounded daily and withdrew everything on December 5. How much interest was earned?

There are 25 additional days in September, 31 days in October, 30 days in November, and 5 days in December.

$$25 + 31 + 30 + 5 = 91 \text{ days}$$

$$\text{Compound amount} = \$1535(1.008763788)$$
$$= \$1548.45 \quad \uparrow \quad \text{From table}$$
$$\text{Interest} = \$1548.45 - \$1535$$
$$= \$13.45$$

14.2 Finding the interest and balance when withdrawals are made

Find the amount that earns interest for the entire quarter and determine compound amount and interest on this sum using Table 14.2. Then, find compound amount and interest for the amount withdrawn. Find the final balance by adding the total interest to the original balance and subtracting the withdrawal.

Tom had $1500 in his $3\frac{1}{2}\%$ compounded daily savings account on October 1. He withdrew $450 on October 15. How much interest had he earned by January 1 and what was his final balance?

$$\$1500 - \$450 = \$1050 \text{ earns interest for the}$$
$$\text{entire 92-day quarter.}$$

$$\text{Compound amount} = \$1050 \times 1.008860519$$
$$= \$1059.30 \quad \uparrow \text{From table}$$
$$\text{Interest} = \$1059.30 - \$1050 = \$9.30$$

The withdrawn $450 earns interest for 14 days.

$$\text{Compound amount} = \$450 \times 1.001343303$$
$$= \$450.60 \quad \uparrow \text{From table}$$
$$\text{Interest} = \$450.60 - \$450 = \$0.60$$
$$\text{Total interest} = \$9.30 + \$0.60 = \$9.90$$
$$\text{Final balance} = \$1500 + \$9.90 - \$450$$
$$= \$1059.90$$

14.2 Finding the compound amount and interest earned on time deposits

Use Table 14.3 to find the value corresponding to the rate and number of years. Next, multiply the table value by the initial amount to obtain compound amount. Then subtract initial investment from compound amount to obtain interest.

Mike invests $15,000 in a certificate of deposit paying 5% compounded daily. Find the compound amount and interest after 4 years.

$$\text{Table value} = 1.22138603$$
$$\text{Compound amount} = \$15,000 \times 1.22138603$$
$$= \$18,320.79$$
$$\text{Interest} = \$18,320.79 - \$15,000$$
$$= \$3320.79$$

14.2 Finding the penalty for early withdrawal of funds from a time deposit account

If money is withdrawn within 3 months, no interest is paid. Otherwise, determine the number of months for which interest will be paid. Find value in Table 14.2 for rate and time. Then multiply this by initial deposit to obtain compound amount. Find the interest by subtracting initial deposit from compound amount.

Tom deposited $5000 in a 3-year CD paying 7% compounded daily. He withdrew the money 15 months later. The passbook rate at his bank is $3\frac{1}{2}\%$ compounded daily. Find the amount of interest earned. Tom will get the passbook rate for $15 - 3 = 12$ months, or 4 quarters. Passbook rate of $3\frac{1}{2}\%$ for 4 quarters gives a table value of 1.035121585.

$$\text{Compound amount} = \$5000 \times 1.035121585$$
$$= \$5175.61$$
$$\text{Interest} = \$5175.61 - \$5000 = \$175.61$$

14.2	Determining the interest and compound amount for continuous compounding	Find the interest and compound amount for $2000 at 6% compounded continuously for 8 years.

14.2 Determining the interest and compound amount for continuous compounding

Use the formula

$$M = Pe^{rt}$$
$$\text{Interest} = M - P$$

Find the interest and compound amount for $2000 at 6% compounded continuously for 8 years.

$$M = Pe^{rt}$$
$$M = \$2000e^{0.06 \cdot 8}$$
$$= \$2000e^{0.48}$$
$$= \$2000(1.6160744) = \$3232.15$$
$$I = M - P$$
$$I = \$3232.15 - \$2000 = \$1232.15$$

14.3 Finding the time given interest rate, compound amount, and principal

Substitute values for M, P, and i in the formula $M = P(1 + i)^n$; then divide both sides by the value of P. Find the value in column A of the interest table (**Appendix C**), closest to the left-hand side of the equation, for the correct value of i. The corresponding value of n is the number of periods required to obtain the compound amount.

How long would it take for $1800 at 6% compounded semiannually to become $7361.97?

$$i = 6\% \div 2 = 3\%$$
$$M = P(1 + i)^n$$
$$\$7361.97 = \$1800(1.03)^n$$
$$4.0899833 = (1.03)^n$$

In column A of the 3% page, the number 4.13225188 is *close* to 4.0899833, so $n = 48$. It would take 48 6-month periods, or 24 years.

14.3 Finding the rate, given principal, compound amount, and time

Divide the compound amount by the principal. Use the row of the interest table that corresponds to the number of interest periods and find the value of column A in **Appendix C**, closest to the quotient obtained above. You may need to examine several pages. Then find the interest rate per year.

A principal of $7000 is deposited for 18 months with interest compounded monthly. Find the rate if the compound amount is $7657.50.

$$M = P(1 + i)^n$$
$$\$7657.50 = \$7000(1 + i)^{18}$$
$$1.09392857 = (1 + i)^{18}$$

Find the row for 18 periods in the interest table. Check row 18 across the different interest rates (pages) in the table to find the closest entry to 1.09392857. The closest number is 1.09392894 on the 0.5% interest rate page. So the rate is 0.5% × 12, or 6% per year compounded monthly.

14.4 Finding the present value of a future amount

Use the formula

$$P = \frac{M}{(1 + i)^n}$$

where M = future value
i = interest rate per compounding period
n = number of periods.

What amount deposited today at 5% compounded monthly will produce $8000 in 3 years?

$$M = \$8000$$
$$i = \frac{5\%}{12} = 0.4167\% \qquad \text{Rounded}$$
$$n = 3 \times 12 = 36$$
$$P = \frac{M}{(1 + i)^n}$$
$$= \frac{\$8000}{(1 + 0.004167)^{36}}$$
$$= \$6887.73$$

The answer section includes answers to all Review Exercises.

Find the compound amount and the interest earned for the following deposits. Round to the nearest cent. [14.1]

1. $12,400 at $6\frac{1}{2}$% compounded annually for 6 years $18,093.36; $5693.36

2. $7000 at 6% compounded semiannually for 4 years $8867.39; $1867.39

3. $22,500 at 4% compounded quarterly for 5 years $27,454.28; $4954.28

4. $18,000 at 7% compounded quarterly for 4 years $23,758.73; $5758.73

5. $9000 at 9% compounded monthly for $2\frac{1}{2}$ years $11,261.45; $2261.45

6. $12,000 at 6% compounded monthly for $3\frac{1}{4}$ years $14,576.65; $2576.65

Find the effective rate of interest corresponding to the following nominal rates. Round to the nearest hundredth of a percent. [14.1]

7. 7% compounded quarterly   7.19%

8. 8% compounded quarterly   8.24%

9. 4% compounded semiannually   4.04%

10. 9% compounded monthly   9.38%

Find the interest earned by the following deposits. Assume $3\frac{1}{2}$% interest compounded daily. Round to the nearest cent. [14.2]

	Interest	Amount	Date Deposited	Date Withdrawn
11.	$24.29	$2900	March 4	May 30
12.	$24.21	$6000	May 20	July 1
13.	$22.68	$3020.80	July 15	October 1

Find the amount on deposit on the first day of the next quarter when the following sums are deposited as indicated. Assume $3\frac{1}{2}$% compounded daily. Round to the nearest cent. [14.2]

	Amount at End of Quarter	Amount	Date Deposited
14.	$3523.23	$3500	January 22
15.	$7248.84	$7200.35	April 22
16.	$9648.39	$9600.40	August 10

Use Table 14.3 to find the compound amount for each of the following certificates of deposit. Assume daily compounding. Round to the nearest cent. [14.2]

	Compound Amount	Amount Deposited	Interest Rate	Time in Years
17.	$4647.29	$4000	5%	3
18.	$7328.66	$6500	6%	2
19.	$12,213.89	$10,000	4%	5

Find the compound amount and the interest for the following deposits. Assume continuous compounding. Round to the nearest cent. [14.2]

	Compound Amount	Interest	Amount	Interest Rate	Time
20.	$22,058.47	$9458.47	$12,600	8%	7 years
21.	$5809.17	$809.17	$5000	3%	5 years

Complete the following table. Round time to the nearest period, interest to the nearest whole percent per year, and money to the nearest cent. **[14.3]**

	Principal	Amount	Interest Rate	Compounded	Time in Years
22.	$4300	$5754.37	<u>6%</u>	Annually	5
23.	$8600	$11,566.04	<u>10%</u>	Quarterly	3
24.	$7500	<u>$9896.09</u>	8%	Quarterly	$3\frac{1}{2}$
25.	$6000	$6749.18	4%	Annually	<u>3</u>
26.	$8400	$10,357.20	6%	Monthly	<u>$3\frac{1}{2}$</u>

Find the present value for the following future amounts. Round to the nearest cent. Also find the interest earned. **[14.4]**

	Amount Needed	Time	Interest Rate	Compounded	Present Value	Interest Earned
27.	$14,300	3 years	$5\frac{1}{2}\%$	Annually	<u>$12,178.08</u>	<u>$2121.92</u>
28.	$4000	3 years	4%	Semiannually	<u>$3551.89</u>	<u>$448.11</u>
29.	$6000	5 years	10%	Quarterly	<u>$3661.63</u>	<u>$2338.37</u>
30.	$3000	4 years	6%	Monthly	<u>$2361.30</u>	<u>$638.70</u>

Solve the following application problems.

31. Discount Auto Insurance deposited $1800 in a savings account paying $3\frac{1}{2}\%$ compounded daily on January 1 and deposited an additional $2300 in the account on March 12. Find the balance on April 1. **[14.2]** $4120.01

32. Susan Chu opens a savings account on June 10 with a deposit of $4000 and makes an additional deposit of $1200 on July 6. Find the balance on September 1 assuming an interest rate of $3\frac{1}{2}\%$ compounded daily. **[14.2]** $5238.54

33. Kerry Craton deposited $2000 in a 10-year CD earning 4% compounded daily. Find the compound amount and interest at the end of 10 years. **[14.2]** $2983.58; $983.58

34. Elizabeth Daigle put $4000 of her divorce settlement in a 5-year CD that paid 6% compounded daily. Find the compound amount and interest at the end of 5 years. **[14.2]** $5399.30; $1399.30

35. Elegant Interiors needs $65,000 in 3 years for capital improvements at the retail store. What lump sum should be invested today at 9% compounded monthly to generate this amount? **[14.4]** $49,669.68

36. Computers Inc. accepted a 2-year note for $12,540 in lieu of immediate payment for computer equipment sold to a local firm. Find (a) the maturity value given a rate of 10% compounded annually and (b) the present value of the note at 6% per year compounded semiannually for 2 years. **[14.4]** (a) $15,173.40 (b) $13,481.37

37. Jack Taylor invests $15,000 in an account paying 6% per year compounded annually. In how many years will the compound amount become $18,937.15? **[14.3]** 4 years

38. The consumption of electricity in one area has increased historically at 6% per year. If it continues to increase at this rate indefinitely, find the number of years before the electric utility would need to double the amount of generating capacity. **[14.3]** approximately 12 years

CHAPTER 14	Business Application Case #1
	Valuing a Chain of McDonald's Restaurants

James and Mary Watson own a small chain of McDonald's restaurants that is valued at $2,300,000. They believe that the chain will grow in value at 12% per year compounded annually for the next 5 years. If they sell the chain, the funds will be invested for 5 years at a rate of 6% compounded semiannually. They expect inflation to be 4% per year for the next 5 years. Ignore taxes and answer the following. Round answers to the nearest dollar.

(a) Find the future value of the chain after 5 years. Then find the price they should sell the chain for if they wish to have the same future value at the end of 5 years. $4,053,386; $3,016,100

(b) Find the future value of the chain if it only grows at 2% per year for 5 years. Then find the price they should ask for the chain given a 2% growth rate per year. $2,539,386; $1,889,542

(c) What future value would the chain be worth if it grew at their expected rate of inflation? Find the price they should ask for the chain if it grows at the rate of inflation. $2,798,302; $2,082,199

(d) Complete the following table.

Growth Rate	Future Value	Value Today
2%	$2,539,386	$1,889,542
4% (inflation)	$2,798,302	$2,082,199
12%	$4,053,386	$3,016,100

NOTE   The value of the chain varies by more than $1 million dollars depending on the rate of growth assumed for the business for the next 5 years.

CHAPTER 14	Business Application Case #2
	Replacing a Coal-Fired Power Plant

PowerCo needs to replace an aging coal-fired power plant in 8 years. Managers hope to replace it with a high-efficiency plant that will sequester carbon emissions rather than allowing carbon to be released into the atmosphere. Managers plan to borrow most of the money needed, but they plan to accumulate at least $50,000,000 of the cost.

(a) If managers invest $32,000,000 now at an estimated 5% compounded semi-annually after income taxes, find the amount it will grow to in 8 years. $47,504,179.84

(b) How much more will they need in 8 years? $2,495,820.16

(c) Find the present value of the shortage identified in (b) using 5% compounded semiannually. This is the additional amount managers need to set aside today to have the $50,000,000 in 5 years. $1,949,730.72

javier brosch / Fotolia.com

Annuities and Sinking Funds

Chapters **12, 13,** and **14** involved **lump sums** of cash. However, few people can afford to pay cash for a house or for college expenses. Rather, most people save using regular contributions such as those to a retirement plan.

It is amazing to see what regular investments will do in time. Figure 15.1 shows (1) the future value of $25,000 (Chapter 14) and the future value of an investment of $5000 each year (Chapter 15), both at 7% compounded annually. The future value based on the annual payments quickly overtakes that from the one-time investment. The annual investments of $5000 grow to $1,000,000 during a working career. What a powerful saving tool you have available to you!

Figure 15.1

▶ STOP&THINK

> No doubt, retirement seems very far in the future to you. However, everyone who does not die young will retire if financially able to do so. Those without enough income must continue to work even into their seventies. Furthermore, having money in a retirement account makes you feel more secure and in control of your own destiny. First, talk to someone over 60 years old about retirement then answer these questions: Should you think about retirement planning before age 50? How important is it to you that your employer offers a retirement plan?

| 15.1 | **Amount of an Annuity** |

OBJECTIVES

1 *Identify the types of annuities.*

2 *Find the amount of an annuity.*

3 *Find the amount of an annuity payment.*

4 *Find the number of payments.*

5 *Find the amount of an annuity due.*

6 *Find the value of an individual retirement account (IRA).*

An **annuity** is a *sequence of equal payments*. It can be used to accumulate money for the future or to pay off a debt. Examples of annuities include car payments, mortgage payments on a home, and a regular contribution to a retirement plan. Another example of an annuity is the regular payments of the life insurance benefits from an insurance company to the spouse of the deceased person. In this chapter, you will see that an annuity is a very effective way to accumulate funds for future needs such as a wedding, a new car, or future college expenses.

The time between the payments of an annuity is the **payment period**, with the time from the beginning of the first payment period to the end of the last called the **term of the annuity**. The **amount of the annuity**, also called the **future value of the annuity**, is the total amount accumulated at the end of the annuity. It is the sum of all payments along with compound interest on each payment to the end of the term.

Objective

1 *Identify the Types of Annuities.* There are several different kinds of annuities.

Contingent annuity—An annuity that has variable beginning or ending dates. For example, a person who leaves a fixed annual sum to the surviving spouse for a fixed number of years creates a contingent annuity because the beginning date, which is the death of the person, is uncertain, or variable.

Annuity certain—An annuity that has a specified beginning and ending date. An example is the 48 payments needed to pay off a car loan. Payments in an **ordinary annuity** are made at *the end of each period,* whereas payments in an **annuity due** are made at *the beginning of each period.*

Simple annuity—An annuity in which the payment dates match the compounding period. An example is an annuity in which the interest is compounded quarterly and a payment is made at the end of each quarter.

Consider an annuity with payments of $2500 at the *end of each year* for 6 years into an investment account paying 8% per year compounded annually. The definitions above can be used to identify this annuity as *certain, ordinary,* and *simple.* Find the future value at the end of 6 years by adding the future values of the deposits made at the end of each of the years. The payment of $2500 at the end of the first year will be invested for 5 years. The payment at the end of the second year will be invested for 4 years, etc.

Figure 15.2 shows each payment, the calculation to find the compound amount of that payment, the compound amount of each payment, and the *future value of the annuity of* $18,339.82.

How an Annuity Works

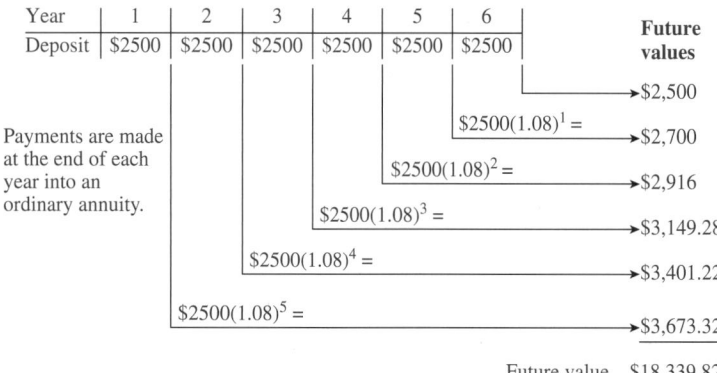

Figure 15.2

The future value of the annuity at the end of year 6 is \$18,339.82.

 Scientific Calculator Approach

The value of \$2500 invested for 5 years, or $\$2500(1.08)^5$, is found as follows.

$$1.08 \boxed{y^x} 5 \boxed{\times} 2500 \boxed{=} 3673.32$$

The other values on the right-hand side of Figure 15.2 can be found in a similar fashion.

 Financial Calculator Approach

This future value of the annuity can easily be found using a financial calculator.

$$6 \boxed{n} 8 \boxed{i} -2500 \boxed{PMT} \boxed{FV} 18339.82$$

Objective

2 *Find the Amount of an Annuity.* This method for finding the amount of the annuity of \$2500 at the end of each year for 6 years was tedious, so we use a formula.

Finding the Future Value of an Annuity

A simple annuity is made up of payments of R dollars at the end of each period for n periods, at a rate of interest i per period. The amount or future value of the annuity, S, is given by this equation.

$$S = R\left[\frac{(1 + i)^n - 1}{i}\right]$$

The expression in brackets is commonly written $s_{\overline{n}|i}$ (read "*s-angle-n-at-i*") or

$$S = R \cdot s_{\overline{n}|i}$$

where the value of $s_{\overline{n}|i}$ for a specific n and i is found in column C of **Appendix C**.

For our annuity, $R = \$2500$, $n = 6$, and $i = 0.08$. By the formula, the amount of the annuity is as follows.

$$S = R \cdot s_{\overline{n}|i}$$

$$S = \$2500 \cdot s_{\overline{6}|0.08}$$

$$= \$2500\left[\frac{(1 + 0.08)^6 - 1}{0.08}\right] \quad \text{Definition of } s_{\overline{6}|0.08}$$

$$= \$2500\left[\frac{(1.08)^6 - 1}{0.08}\right]$$

$$= \$2500\left(\frac{1.586874323 - 1}{0.08}\right)$$

$$= \$2500(7.335929037)$$

$$= \$18,339.82 \quad \text{Rounded}$$

This is exactly the same result found earlier.

Scientific
Calculator
Approach

The expression $S = \$2500\left[\frac{(1 + 0.08)^6 - 1}{0.08}\right]$ above can be evaluated using a calculator as follows.

2500 $\times$ ((1 + 0.08) y^x 6 $-$ 1) $\div$ 0.08 $=$ 18339.82

Notice that the numerator in the brackets is entered as $((1 + 0.08)^6 - 1)$ in order to maintain the order of operations.

To save time, tables of values of $s_{\overline{n}|i}$ have been calculated for the amount of an annuity for different values of n and i. They appear in column C of the interest table in **Appendix C**. Look in this table for 8% and 6 periods to find the following.

$$s_{\overline{6}|0.08} = 7.33592904$$

NOTE The number from the table is slightly different than the result found using the formula. This tiny difference is due to rounding.

EXAMPLE **1** **Finding the Amount of an Ordinary Annuity**

The hospital where Tish Baker works as an aide pays \$800 at the end of each quarter into her retirement plan. If she chooses an investment that yields 6% per year compounded quarterly, how much will she have in 10 years? How much interest will she have earned?

Solution

Baker's payments form an ordinary annuity, with $R = \$800, n = 10 \times 4 = 40$ compounding periods (quarters), and $i = 6\% \div 4 = 1.5\%$ per compounding period (per quarter). The amount, or future value, of the annuity is found as follows.

$$S = \$800(54.26789391) \quad \text{Using column C of table}$$

$$= \$43,414.32$$

The interest earned is the future amount less all payments.

$$I = \$43,414.32 - 40 \times \$800 = \$11,414.32$$

The future amount can be checked using the formula for calculating the amount of an annuity.

$$S = R\left[\frac{(1 + i)^n - 1}{i}\right]$$

$$S = \$800\left[\frac{(1 + 0.015)^{40} - 1}{0.015}\right]$$

$$= \$800\left(\frac{1.814018409 - 1}{0.015}\right)$$

$$= \$800(54.26789391)$$

$$= \$43,414.32$$

Notice that the factor 54.26789391 found using a scientific calculator is exactly the same as the factor from the table in **Appendix C**.

Scientific Calculator Approach

To solve for *S* in the preceding problem, first find the fraction.

$$(\;(\;1 + 0.015 \;) \;\boxed{y^x} \;40 \;- \;1 \;) \;\div \;0.015 \;\boxed{STO}$$

Then multiply: $800 \;\boxed{\times} \;\boxed{RCL} \;\boxed{=} \;43414.32$

Financial Calculator Approach

Payment, number of compounding periods, and interest rate per compounding period are known. Future value is the unknown. Be sure to set your calculator to an ordinary annuity with payments at the end of each period, before keying in the following.

$$-800 \;\boxed{PMT} \;40 \;\boxed{n} \;1.5 \;\boxed{i} \;\boxed{FV} \;43414.32$$

EXAMPLE **2** **Finding the Amount of an Ordinary Annuity**

At the birth of her grandson, Junella Smith decides to help pay for his college education. She commits to making deposits of $600 into an account *at the end of each 6 months for 18 years*. Smith has narrowed her choices to an annuity at an insurance company paying 6% compounded semiannually, a CD at a bank paying 5% compounded semiannually, or a savings account at a credit union paying $3\frac{1}{2}$% compounded semiannually. (a) Find the amount of the annuity in each case. (b) Which is preferred if all three options are safe?

Solution

(a) There are $2 \times 18 = 36$ semiannual periods in 18 years. The semiannual interest, value from **Appendix C**, and future amount are shown in the table that follows.

In each case, the future amount is found using either $S = R\left[\frac{(1 + i)^n - 1}{i}\right]$ or

$S = R \cdot s_{\overline{n}|i}$ and table values, where $R = \$600$, $n = 36$, and i is the semiannual interest.

	Semiannual Interest	Value from Appendix C	Future Amount
Annuity	$\frac{6\%}{2} = 3\%$	63.27594427	$37,965.57
CD	$\frac{5\%}{2} = 2.5\%$	57.30141263	$34,380.85
Savings account	$\frac{3\frac{1}{2}\%}{2} = 1.75\%$	49.56612949	$29,739.68

The future values of the investments over time are shown in the graph.

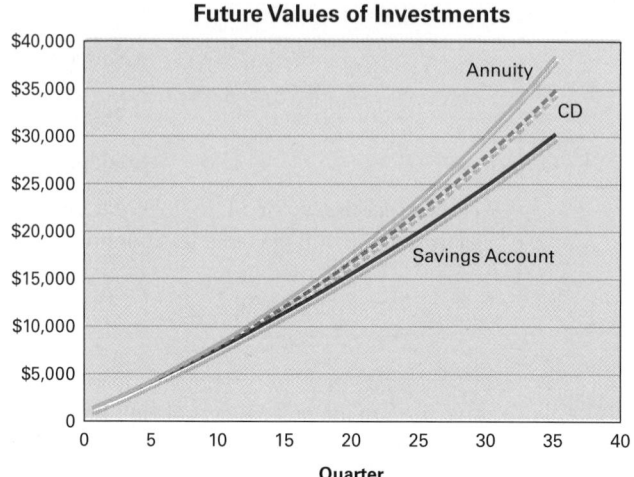

Future Values of Investments

(b) The amount in the account grows more rapidly with the higher interest rate paid by the annuity. So, as long as all of the investment choices have equal risk in terms of losing money, then the annuity is the best investment of the three choices. Junella Smith might make a different choice if the risk associated with the different alternatives were not equal, since she may not want to take any risk of losing money.

NOTE Example 2 in **Appendix A.2** shows how a financial calculator can be used to solve this same type of problem.

Objective

3 *Find the Amount of an Annuity Payment.* Sometimes the lump sum that will be needed at some time in the future is known, and the amount of each payment into an annuity that will result in the required amount must be found.

EXAMPLE **3** **Finding the Amount of an Annuity Payment**

Fast Copy, Inc. will need several new commercial printers in 3 years and the owner wants to make end-of-quarter payments now toward that goal. She estimates that the equipment will cost $70,000. If funds earn 6% compounded quarterly, find the payment of the annuity needed to accumulate this amount.

Solution

This is an ordinary annuity with $S = \$70,000$, $i = 1\frac{1}{2}\%$ (6% ÷ 4), and $n = 12$ (3 years × 4 quarters per year). The unknown in the formula for the amount of an annuity is the size of each payment, or R.

$$\$70,000 = R \cdot s_{\overline{12}|0.015}$$
$$\$70,000 = R \cdot 13.04121143 \qquad \text{From column C, \textbf{Appendix C}}$$
$$R = \$70,000 \div 13.04121143$$
$$R = \$5367.60$$

Each end-of-quarter payment must be $5367.60.

Financial Calculator Approach

Future value, number of compounding periods, and interest rate per compounding period are known. Payment is the unknown.

$$70{,}000 \;\boxed{FV}\; 12 \;\boxed{n}\; 1.5 \;\boxed{i}\; \boxed{PMT}\; -5367.60$$

The negative sign in front of the payment indicates that the company must make payments into a fund to accumulate the desired future value.

NOTE The value of n is the number of compounding periods (*not years*), and i is the interest per compounding period (*not interest per year*).

Objective

4 *Find the Number of Payments.* The next example shows how to find the number of periods necessary to accumulate a certain amount of money.

EXAMPLE **4** **Finding the Number of Payments**

The Dunlaps want to purchase their first home and need $12,000 for a down payment. They can save $825 per quarter. If they deposit this amount in an account paying 3% interest compounded quarterly, how long will it be before they can purchase a home?

Solution

Here the amount of the annuity (S), the amount of each payment (R), and the interest rate per period (i) are known. The unknown is n, the number of quarters for which deposits must be made. Start with the formula for the amount of an annuity and substitute $12,000 for S, $825 for R, and $\frac{3}{4}\%$ (3% $\div$ 4) for i.

$$S = R \cdot s_{\overline{n}|i}$$

$$\$12{,}000 = \$825 \cdot s_{\overline{n}|0.0075}$$

$$14.54545455 = s_{\overline{n}|0.0075} \qquad \text{Divide both sides by \$825.}$$

Go to the $\frac{3}{4}\%$ page in the interest table. Look down column C for the first number *larger* than 14.54545455. The first number that is *larger* is 14.70340370, which corresponds to 14 quarters in the n column of the table. The family must save for 14 quarters, or $3\frac{1}{2}$ years. At the end of this period of time they will have a little more than the $12,000 needed.

$$\$825(14.70340370) = \$12{,}130.31$$

NOTE The table value used is the one *larger* than the calculated value, not closed to it.

Financial Calculator Approach

Future value, quarterly payment, and interest rate per quarter are known in Example 4. The unknown is n, the number of quarters.

$$-12000 \;\boxed{FV}\; 825 \;\boxed{PMT}\; 0.75 \;\boxed{i}\; \boxed{n}\; 14$$

Objective

5 *Find the Amount of an Annuity Due.* As mentioned earlier, with ordinary annuities, payments are made at the *end of each time period.* With **annuities due** the payments are made at the *beginning of the time period.* The difference between an ordinary annuity and an annuity due is subtle, but both are used in the financial services industry. The following charts may help you understand the difference between an ordinary annuity and an annuity due.

In an *ordinary annuity,* payments are made at the *end of each time period,* as shown below. Think of the payments as being made *on the last second of the last day* of each period.

Ordinary annuity payments are at the end of each year.

In an *annuity due,* payments are made at the *beginning of each period.* Think of payments as being made *on the first second of the first day* of each period.

Annuity due payments are at the beginning of each year.

Now look at the following diagrams. The one on top is the annuity due just discussed. Note that the payment is at the first of each period. The one on the bottom is an ordinary annuity with one additional period added—payments are at the end of each period. Notice the alignment of the arrows representing the payments in both. They are exactly the same, although the ordinary annuity has one extra payment at the end of year 5. We use this similarity to find the amount of an annuity due below.

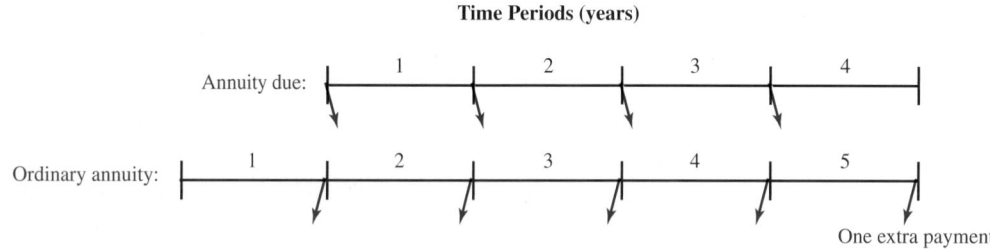

Finding the Amount of an Annuity Due

To find the amount of an annuity due, treat each payment as if it were made at the end of the preceding period. Then follow these steps.

Step 1 Add 1 to the number of periods.
Step 2 Use this number of periods in column C of the interest table to find the amount of the annuity.
Step 3 Subtract one payment from the amount found in Step 2.

EXAMPLE 5 **Finding the Amount of an Annuity Due**

Mr. and Mrs. Thompson set up an investment program using an *annuity due* with payments of $500 *at the beginning of each quarter.* Find the amount of the annuity if they make payments for 7 years in a mutual fund paying 6% compounded quarterly.

Solution

There are $7 \times 4 = 28$ compounding periods.

STEP 1 Add 1 to the number of periods: $28 + 1 = 29$.

STEP 2 Use the $\frac{6\%}{4} = 1.5\%$ interest table with 29 periods in column C of **Appendix C** to find the following number: 35.99870085.

$$\text{Amount} = \$500 \times 35.99870085 = \$17,999.35$$

STEP 3 Subtract one payment.

$$\text{Future value} = \$17,999.35 - \$500 = \$17,499.35$$

Financial Calculator Approach

First change the calculator settings to annuity due (payments at the beginning of each period). Then enter known values for payment, number of periods, and interest rate per period. Finally, press the future value key to find the unknown.

$$-500 \;\boxed{PMT}\; 28 \;\boxed{n}\; 1.5 \;\boxed{i}\; \boxed{FV}\; 17499.35$$

> **NOTE** When solving for the amount of an annuity due, be sure to
>
> 1. add one period to the total number of annuity periods, and
> 2. subtract one payment from the amount found.

Objective

6 *Find the Value of an Individual Retirement Account (IRA).* A really great investment vehicle that working people can often use to save for retirement is an **individual retirement account**, also called an **IRA**. There are two common types of IRA accounts, regular IRAs and Roth IRAs.

Deposits to a **regular IRA** account are often excluded from federal income taxes in the current year. Therefore, a contribution to a regular IRA may reduce the amount of income taxes *that you must pay this year*. Interest earned in a regular IRA is not subject to income taxes in the year earned. At retirement, the account holder withdraws funds from the regular IRA and pays taxes at that time. As a result, a regular IRA may allow you to save for retirement *without having to pay taxes* on the savings for years or even decades!

WHICH IRA IS BEST FOR YOU?		
If you've been contributing to a nondeductible, traditional IRA, the new Roth IRA, where earnings grow tax-free, may be the better option. If you're trying to decide between a deductible IRA and a Roth, here are some facts that may help.		
	DEDUCTIBLE IRA	**ROTH IRA**
Tax deductible?	If you qualify	No
Taxable at withdrawal?	Yes	No
Penalty for early withdrawal?	Yes, prior to age 59.5	Yes*
Mandatory withdrawal age?	70.5	None
Penalty-free withdrawals?	$10,000 for first-time home buyers; unlimited for education	$10,000 for first-time home buyers, after 5 year wait; unlimited for education
*Never any penalty for withdrawing your own contributions, but a penalty applies to withdrawal of any gains within 5 years of opening the account and/or before turning 59.5.		

Deposits to a **Roth IRA** are not excluded from federal taxes in the year paid, so they *do not* reduce current income taxes. However, the deposit and interest do grow tax-free. In addition, one huge advantage is that the withdrawals from the Roth IRA at retirement are *not* subject to income taxes. This offers you a great opportunity to save money for retirement without having to pay taxes when you withdraw the funds.

> **NOTE**   Early withdrawal from either a regular IRA or a Roth IRA may result in a penalty.

EXAMPLE 6   Finding the Value of an IRA

At 27, Joann Gretz sets up an IRA with Merrill Lynch where she plans to deposit $2000 at the end of each year until age 60. Find the amount of the annuity if she invests in (a) a corporate bond fund, which has historically yielded 6% compounded annually, versus (b) a stock fund, which has historically yielded 10% compounded annually. Although past performance is no guarantee of the future, assume that future yields equal historical yields.

Solution

It is 33 years from age 27 to age 60.

(a) Corporate bond fund: Look in column C of **Appendix C** with $n = 33$ and $i = 6\%$ to find 97.34316471.

$$\text{Amount} = \$2000 \times 97.34316471 = \$194{,}686.33$$

(b) Stock fund: Look in column C of **Appendix C** with $n = 33$ and $i = 10\%$ to find 222.25154420.

$$\text{Amount} = \$2000 \times 222.25154420 = \$444{,}503.09$$

Gretz can see the projected difference in the results of the corporate bond fund and the stock fund using the graph in Figure 15.3. On this basis, she decides to try to maximize return on investment in the future. However, she plans to do so without taking too much risk and decides to use both funds.

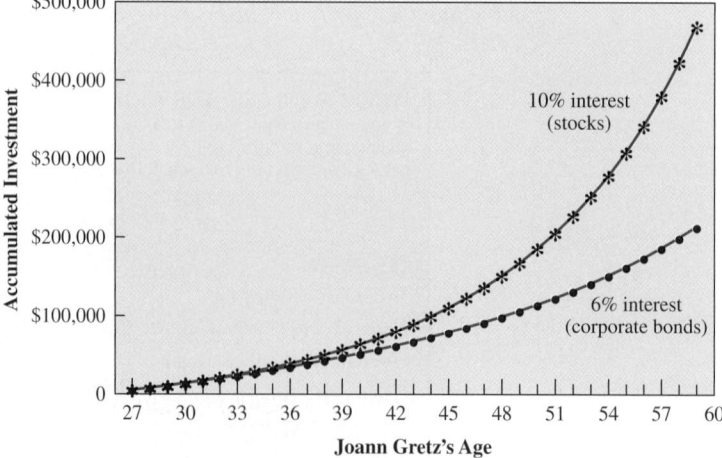

Projected Value of IRA for Joann Gretz

Figure 15.3

EXAMPLE **7**   **Saving for Retirement**

At age 20, Tom Jones begins saving for retirement by making end-of-year payments of $400 into an IRA account, until age 65 (a total of 45 years). Becky Smith doesn't begin saving for retirement until age 40, at which time she deposits $1000 at the end of each year until age 65 (a total of 25 years). Assume that each account earns 7% compounded annually and find the amount available at age 65 to each individual.

Solution

Tom Jones saves $400 at the end of each year for 45 years at 7% compounded annually.

$$\text{Future amount} = \$400 \cdot s_{\overline{45}|0.07} = \$400 \times 285.74931084$$
$$= \$114,299.72$$

Becky Smith saves $1000 at the end of each year for 25 years also earning 7% compounded annually.

$$\text{Future amount} = \$1000 \cdot s_{\overline{25}|0.07} = \$1000 \times 63.24903772$$
$$= \$63,249.04$$

Even though Becky Smith deposits much more each year than Tom Jones, Jones ends up with a lot more money at age 65. Why? Tom Jones saved for 45 years, giving compound interest a lot of time to work for him. Becky Smith has made it a harder for herself by not starting to save until age 40, but it is still a good idea for her to save. The important idea is to start saving early so that compound interest can also work for you!

NOTE   The last example shows that it is very important to begin saving early in life, but it is never too late to begin saving.

15.1   **Exercises**

Find the following values using column C of the table in Appendix C.

1. $s_{\overline{15}|0.03}$ 18.59891389

2. $s_{\overline{30}|0.08}$ 113.28321111

3. $s_{\overline{10}|0.09}$ 15.19292972

4. $s_{\overline{50}|0.12}$ 2400.01824858

Find the value of the following ordinary annuities if interest is compounded annually. Find the total amount of interest earned.

5. $R = \$850, i = 0.06, n = 28$ $58,248.89; $34,448.89

6. $R = \$200, i = 0.10, n = 20$ $11,455.00; $7455.00

7. $R = \$1000, i = 0.08, n = 25$ $73,105.94; $48,105.94

8. $R = \$2000, i = 0.065, n = 50$ $686,359.34; $586,359.34

Find the value of the following ordinary annuities and then find the total amount of interest earned.

9. $R = \$1400$, 10% per year compounded quarterly for 8 years $67,410.39; $22,610.39

10. $R = \$250$, 8% per year compounded quarterly for 10 years $15,100.50; $5100.50

11. $R = \$800$, 9% per year compounded monthly for 4 years $46,016.57; $7616.57

12. $R = \$500$, 6% per year compounded monthly for 3 years $19,668.05; $1668.05

Find the amount of the following annuities due if interest is compounded annually. Find the amount of interest earned.

13. $R = \$1200, i = 0.075, n = 8$ $13,475.82; \$3875.82

14. $R = \$1400, i = 0.08, n = 10$ $21,903.68; \$7903.68

15. $R = \$17,544, i = 0.08, n = 6$ $138,997.66; \$33,733.66

16. $R = \$64,715, i = 0.06, n = 12$ $1,157,242.54; \$380,662.54

Assume that you are able to invest \$900 per year in an ordinary annuity where interest is not taxed. Complete the following table by finding the amount of the annuity for each interest rate and time period given.

	Annual Compounding Rate				
	5%	**7%**	**9%**	**11%**	**13%**
10 years	**17.** $11,320.10	**18.** $12,434.80	**19.** $13,673.64	**20.** $15,049.81	**21.** $16,577.77
20 years	**22.** $29,759.36	**23.** $36,895.94	**24.** $46,044.11	**25.** $57,782.55	**26.** $72,852.15
30 years	**27.** $59,794.96	**28.** $85,014.71	**29.** $122,676.78	**30.** $179,118.79	**31.** $263,879.29

 32. Explain the difference in the methods used to calculate the amount of an ordinary annuity and the amount of an annuity due. (See Objectives 2 and 5.)

 33. Explain the difference between a regular IRA and a Roth IRA. Which is better for a young person? (See Objective 6.)

 34. **MILLIONAIRE BY CHOICE**   Ben Watson, 22, recently graduated from college and started work at his first professional job. He has set a goal for himself to become a millionaire. Watson's employer invests \$2800 at the end of each year into a retirement plan. Is this enough for Watson to be a millionaire in time? If not, what else can he do?

First, find the amount of the following annuities due; then find the amount of interest earned.

35. Payments of \$500 made at the beginning of each quarter for 10 years at 4% compounded quarterly $24,687.62; \$4687.62

36. \$50 deposited at the beginning of each month for 4 years at 6% compounded monthly $2718.42; \$318.42

37. \$100 deposited at the beginning of each quarter for 9 years at 8% compounded quarterly $5303.43; \$1703.43

38. \$1500 deposited at the beginning of each semiannual period for 11 years at 9% compounded semiannually $56,905.54; \$23,905.54

Find the periodic payment that will amount to the following sums under the given conditions.

39. $S = \$20,000$, interest at $7\frac{1}{2}\%$ compounded annually, payments made at the end of each year for 10 years $1413.72

40. $S = \$30,000$, interest is 5% compounded semiannually, payments made at the end of each 6-month period for 8 years $1547.97

41. $S = \$50,000$, interest is 12% compounded quarterly, payments made at the end of each quarter for 8 years $952.33

42. $S = \$24,000$, interest is 9% compounded monthly, payments are made at the end of each month for $3\frac{1}{4}$ years $532.05

Find the minimum number of payments that must be made to accumulate the given amount of money at the stated interest rate. Also, find the amount of the annuity.

43. $15,000 needed, payments of $450 are made at the end of each quarter at 6% compounded quarterly   28 quarterly payments; $15,516.67

44. $21,000 needed, payments of $1500 are made at the end of each 6-month period at 10% compounded semiannually   11 semiannual payments; $21,310.18

45. $35,000 needed, payments of $825 are made at the end of each month at 9% compounded monthly   37 monthly payments; $35,030.62

46. $37,500 needed, payments of $1250 are made at the end of each month at 12% compounded monthly   27 monthly payments; $38,526.11

Solve the following application problems.

47. INVESTING IN AN IRA   At the end of each quarter, the Rodriguez family invests $450 in an IRA earning 8% compounded quarterly. Find the amount of their annuity at the end of $3\frac{1}{2}$ years. $7188.27

48. RETIREMENT ACCOUNT   An employer deposits $1200 at the end of each quarter into Natasha Kimskey's retirement account. Kimskey chooses to put the money into a fund that invests in real estate mortgages that has historically paid 8% compounded quarterly. Find the amount of the annuity in 10 years, assuming the yield remains constant. $72,482.38

49. CHILD-SUPPORT PAYMENTS   Becky Smith decides to put the child support payments from her previous husband into an annuity for the education of her two children. At the end of each month for 4 years, she puts $300 into a mutual fund that has yielded 9% compounded monthly. Find (a) the amount of the annuity and (b) the interest earned.   (a) $17,256.21 (b) $2856.21

50. EXCESS CASH   Digital Electronics Inc. decides to accumulate funds in order to build a building in 4 years. It deposits $20,000 at the end of every month in an account earning 6% compounded monthly. Find the future value. $1,081,956.64

51. FUTURE VALUE   Pam Parker deposits $2435 at the beginning of each year for 8 years in an account paying 6% compounded annually. She then leaves that money alone, with no further deposits, for an additional 5 years. Find the final amount on deposit after the entire 13-year period. Find the total amount of interest earned. $34,186.78; $14,706.78

52. ANNUITY DUE   Tim Bessner invests $500 at the *beginning* of each quarter for 10 years in an account paying 7% compounded quarterly. He then leaves the money alone, with no further deposits, for an additional 6 years. Find the amount on deposit after the 16 years and find total interest earned. $44,155.58; $24,155.58

53. RECREATIONAL VEHICLE   Tom and Sandra Kip are trying to save $4000 as the down payment on a new recreational vehicle. If they can deposit $125 at the end of each month in an account paying 4% compounded monthly, how long will it take them to accumulate the necessary amount? How much will they actually accumulate?   31 months; $4075.14

54. NEW SHOWROOM   Western Motors needs $120,000 as a down payment on a new showroom. If the company deposits $10,000 at the end of each quarter at 5% compounded quarterly, how long will it take to get the needed money? How much will the company actually have?   12 quarters; $128,603.61

55. AFFORDING COLLEGE   In order to help his daughter go to college, Bill Thomas plans to invest $250 per quarter for 10 years in either (a) an ordinary annuity paying 8% compounded quarterly or (b) a CD yielding 6% compounded quarterly. Find the amount of the annuity for both choices.   (a) $15,100.50 (b) $13,566.97

56. COLLEGE FUND   The Crockers have decided to invest $1500 at the end of each year for 12 years in a college fund for their twin grandsons. They can choose either (a) a mutual fund of domestic stocks expected to yield 10% per year or (b) a savings account expected to yield about 4% per year. Find the amount of the annuity in both cases.   (a) $32,076.43 (b) $22,538.71

| 15.2 | **Present Value of an Annuity** |

1 *Calculate the present value of an annuity.*

2 *Use the formula for the present value of an annuity.*

3 *Find the equivalent cash price.*

The previous section discussed how to find the amount of an annuity after a series of equal, periodic payments. This section considers the present value of such an annuity. There are two ways to think of the **present value of an annuity**.

1. The *present value of an annuity* is a lump sum that can be deposited today that will amount to the same future amount as would the periodic *payments into an annuity* (see Example 1 on page 564).
2. The present value of an annuity is a lump sum that can be deposited today that is needed to generate the *payments from an annuity* (see Example 2 on page 565).

Objective

1 *Calculate the Present Value of an Annuity.* As an example of this second way of looking at the present value of an annuity, let us find the amount that *must be deposited today,* at 10% compounded annually, so that $1500 could be removed *at the end of each year for 6 years.*

The amount that must be deposited today is the sum of the present values of each of the separate withdrawals. In other words, today's deposit must include the present value of the withdrawal made at the end of year 1 plus the present value of the withdrawal at the end of year 2 and so forth, all the way to the present value of the withdrawal at the end of year 6.

Use column B of **Appendix C** to find the present value of the payment at the end of the first year with one compounding period and a rate of 10% per year.

$$\text{Present value of 1st payment} = \$1500(0.90909091) = \$1363.64$$

Find the present values for payments at the end of years 2 through 6 in a similar fashion to see the values in Figure 15.4.

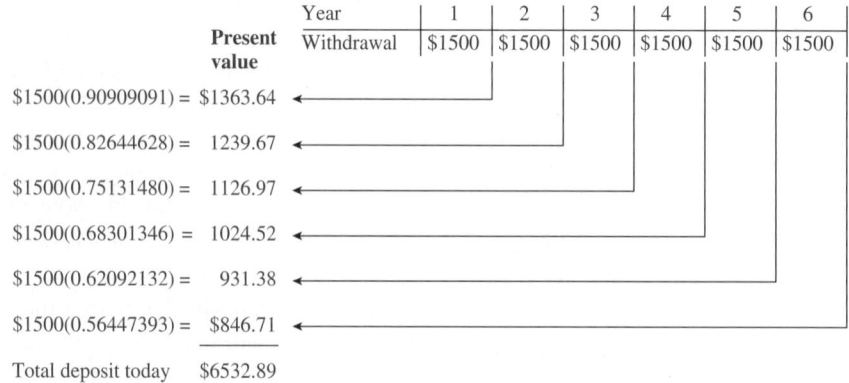

Figure 15.4

A lump sum deposit today of $6532.89 at 10% compounded annually would permit withdrawals of $1500 at the end of each year for 6 years. Also, a lump sum deposit today of $6532.89 left in an account for 6 years would produce *the same final total* as deposits of $1500 at the end of each year for 6 years, with all deposits at 10% compounded annually.

Objective

2   *Use the Formula for the Present Value of an Annuity.*

Finding the Present Value of an Annuity

> Here is the formula for the present value A of an annuity with a payment of R dollars at the end of each period. The term is n periods and i is the rate of interest per compounding period. The lump sum deposit must be made at the beginning of year 1.
>
> $$A = R\left[\frac{(1+i)^n - 1}{i(1+i)^n}\right]$$
>
> The expression in brackets is abbreviated $a_{\overline{n}|i}$.
>
> $$A = R \cdot a_{\overline{n}|i}$$
>
> $a_{\overline{n}|i}$ is read as "*a*-angle-*n*-at-*i*."

Values of $a_{\overline{n}|i}$ are given in column D of the interest table. We can use the table to check the problem given on the preceding page. Look on the 10% page, for 6 payments at 10%, finding the number 4.35526070. Then multiply, which gives the following.

$$A = \$1500(4.35526070) = \$6532.89$$

This is the same answer found earlier.

EXAMPLE 1   Finding the Present Value of an Annuity

Dion Martinez has decided to make annual payments of $1200 at the end of each year for 15 years into an investment that she thinks will yield 8% compounded annually. What lump sum deposited today at 8% compounded annually will result in the same future value?

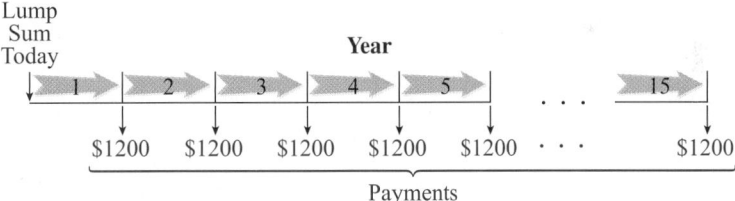

Solution

Column D of the interest tables in **Appendix C** shows that $a_{\overline{15}|0.08} = 8.55947869$.

Present value is $A = R \cdot a_{\overline{n}|i}$

$$A = \$1200 \cdot 8.55947869 = \$10{,}271.37$$

A lump sum of $10,271.37 deposited today at 8% compounded annually will result in the same total after 15 years as year-end deposits of $1200 for 15 years at 8%.

This result can be checked by finding the future value of $10,271.37 for 15 years at 8%. Use column A of **Appendix C** and the formula from **Chapter 14** for compound amount M.

$$M = P(1+i)^n$$
$$M = \$10{,}271.37 \cdot 3.17216911 = \$32{,}582.52$$

On the other hand, using the amount of an annuity that is column C of **Appendix C**, deposits of $1200 at the end of each year for 15 years, at 8% produces the following.

$$S = R \cdot s_{\overline{n}|i}$$
$$S = R \cdot s_{\overline{15}|0.08}$$
$$= \$1200 \cdot 27.15211393 = \$32{,}582.54$$

The difference of 2 cents is due to rounding.

Financial Calculator Approach

Set your calculator to an ordinary annuity (payments at the end of each period). Payment, number of compounding periods, and interest rate per compounding period are known. Present value is the unknown.

$$-1200 \;\boxed{PMT}\; 15 \;\boxed{n}\; 8 \;\boxed{i}\; \boxed{PV}\; 10271.37$$

NOTE There are two ways to produce $32,582.54 in 15 years at 8% compounded annually:

1. a single deposit of $10,271.37 today, or
2. payments of $1200 at the end of each year for 15 years.

EXAMPLE 2   Finding the Present Value

Fred and Sara Zhao recently divorced. As one part of the divorce settlement, Sara must pay Fred $2000 at the end of each year for 10 years. If money can be deposited at 6% compounded annually, find the lump sum she could deposit today to have enough money, with principal and interest, to make the payments.

Solution

Look under $n = 10$ and $i = 0.06$ in column D of the interest tables to find $a_{\overline{10}|0.06} = 7.36008705$.

$$A = R \cdot a_{\overline{10}|0.06}$$
$$= \$2000 \cdot 7.36008705$$
$$= \$14{,}720.17$$

A deposit of $14,720.17 today at 6% compounded annually is sufficient to make the 10 year-end payments of $2000 each. The difference between the sum of all payments, $10 \times \$2000 = \$20{,}000$, and the amount deposited today is the interest.

$$\text{Interest} = 10 \times \$2000 - \$14{,}720.17 = \$5279.83$$

NOTE Although the $2000 withdrawals are at the end of each year, the original lump-sum deposit must be made at the beginning of year 1.

EXAMPLE 3   Finding the Present Value

An Australian engineering firm hires a new manager for its North American operations. The contract states that if the new manager works for 5 years, then he will receive a benefit of $15,000 at the end of each semiannual period for 8 years. Find the lump sum the firm could deposit today to satisfy the retirement contract if funds can be invested at 10% compounded semiannually. Ignore taxes.

Payments of $15,000 each

Solution

First find the present value of an annuity with $2 \times 8 = 16$ periods at 5% per compounding period. Use column D of the interest tables to find $a_{\overline{16}|0.05} = 10.83776956$.

$$A = R \cdot a_{\overline{16}|0.05}$$
$$A = \$15,000 \cdot 10.83776956$$
$$= \$162,566.54$$

The firm needs $162,566.54 at the end of the 5-year work period to satisfy the retirement benefits.

It can meet this liability today by depositing the present value of $162,566.54 assuming 10% compounded semiannually over 5 years. Use column B of the interest tables with $n = 5 \times 2 = 10$ and $i = \frac{10\%}{2} = 5\%$ and the formula from **Chapter 14** to find the following.

$$P = \frac{M}{(1 + i)^n} = M\frac{1}{(1 + i)^n}$$
$$P = \$162,566.54 \cdot 0.61391325$$
$$= \$99,801.75$$

A lump sum of $99,801.75 deposited today will grow to $162,566.54 in 5 years which, with interest, is enough to make all 16 retirement payments of $15,000 each.

EXAMPLE 4 **Determining Retirement Income**

Bill Jones wishes to retire at age 65 and withdraw $25,000 at the end of each year until age 90. (a) If money earns 8% per year compounded annually, how much will he need at age 65? (b) If Jones starts an IRA at age 32 by depositing $2000 per year in an account paying 8% per year compounded annually, will the IRA account contain enough money?

Solution

(a) The amount needed at age 65 is the present value of an annuity of $25,000 per year for $90 - 65 = 25$ years, with interest of 8% compounded annually. Use column D of the interest tables to find $a_{\overline{25}|0.08} = 10.67477619$.

$$A = R \cdot a_{\overline{n}|i}$$
$$A = \$25,000 \cdot 10.67477619$$
$$= \$266,869.40$$

Assuming Jones continues to earn 8% compounded annually, he will need $266,869.40 at age 65 to generate the needed $25,000 at the end of each year until age 90.

(b) Jones makes payments of $2000 at the end of each year for $65 - 32 = 33$ years, at 8% compounded annually. These payments form a regular annuity with $n = 33$ and $i = 0.08$. Use column C of the interest tables to find $s_{\overline{33}|0.08} = 145.95062044$.

$$S = R \cdot s_{\overline{n}|i}$$
$$S = \$2000 \cdot 145.95062044$$
$$= \$291,901.24$$

The value in the IRA account at age 65 ($291,901.24) exceeds the amount needed to fund 25 yearly withdrawals of $25,000 each ($266,869.40). Therefore, $2000 invested at the end of each year for 33 years is enough to generate $25,000 at the end of each year for $90 - 65 = 25$ years as long as he earns 8%.

> **NOTE** We have ignored the effect of income taxes in our examples. Funds in retirement accounts grow free of income tax, but income taxes must be paid on retirement funds in most accounts when withdrawn. An exception is funds from Roth IRA accounts, which are not subject to income tax when withdrawn.

> **NOTE** Example 7 in **Appendix A.2** shows how a financial calculator can be used to solve a similar problem.

Objective

3 *Find the Equivalent Cash Price.* One thousand dollars in your hands today is better than $1000 to be paid to you in 8 years. This is true since $1000 in your hands today could earn interest for 8 years, so it would be more than $1000 in 8 years. Thus, the timing of any payment(s) is important when comparing different situations. The next example shows how to convert two different payment situations into present values so that the better of the two becomes clear.

EXAMPLE **5** **Finding Equivalent Cash Price**

Julia Smithers is an attorney trying to settle an estate that owns a piece of property desired by two different developers. Delton Properties offers $140,000 in cash, today, for the land. Stoneybrook offers $50,000 now as a down payment, with payments of $8000 at the end of each quarter for 4 years. Money may be invested at 8% compounded quarterly. Stoneybrook offers a bank guarantee that the payment will be made, making each offer equally safe. Which bid should the attorney accept?

Solution

The bids are best compared using the present value of the two offers. The offer from Delton Properties is $140,000 cash today, so $140,000 is the present value for that offer.

However, Stoneybrook's offer includes payments and cash. Find the present value of Stoneybrook's offer by adding the present value of the annuity payments to the cash to be paid today. Use column D of the interest table to find the present value of the annuity payments of $8000 at the end of each quarter. Use $n = 4 \times 4 = 16$ periods and $i = 8\% \div 4 = 2\%$ per compounding period.

$$A = R \cdot a_{\overline{n}|i}$$
$$A = \$8000 \cdot a_{\overline{16}|0.02}$$
$$= \$8000(13.57770931)$$
$$= \$108,621.67$$

Present value of Stoneybrook's offer $=$ cash $+$ present value of annuity payments
$$= \$50,000 + \$108,621.67$$
$$= \$158,621.67$$

This amount, $158,621.67, is called the **equivalent cash price**. This exceeds the $140,000 in cash offered by Delton Properties, so the attorney should accept Stoneybrook's bid as long as the company has good credit.

15.2 Exercises

Find the following values.

1. $a_{\overline{15}|0.075}$ 8.82711975

2. $a_{\overline{20}|0.09}$ 9.12854567

3. $a_{\overline{15}|0.12}$ 6.81086449

4. $a_{\overline{40}|0.06}$ 15.04629687

Find the present value of each of the following annuities. Round to the nearest cent.

	Amount per Payment	Payment at End of Each	No. of Years	Money Invested at	
5.	$3000	year	8	10% compounded annually	$16,004.78
6.	$1500	year	10	$7\frac{1}{2}$% compounded annually	$10,296.12
7.	$800	6 months	10	6% compounded semiannually	$11,901.98
8.	$650	6 months	8	7% compounded semiannually	$7861.18
9.	$400	quarter	5	8% compounded quarterly	$6540.57
10.	$200	month	$3\frac{1}{2}$	5% compounded monthly	$7691.41

 11. Explain the difference between the future value and present value of an annuity. Illustrate the difference with an example.

12. An individual wins a state lottery that pays $50,000 a year for 20 years. Must the state have $1 million to pay for this prize? If not, how can the state ensure that it has the necessary funds? (See Objective 1.)

Solve the following application problems. Round to the nearest cent.

13. LOTTERY   Wei Long was elated when she won a state lottery paying $85,480 at the end of each year for 20 years. Find the amount the state must set aside today to satisfy this annuity at 8% compounded annually. $839,255.24

14. DIVORCE SETTLEMENT   Tom and Kitty Wysong recently divorced. Ms. Wysong agreed to pay Mr. Wysong $8000 every 6 months for 12 years since he had helped her through medical school. What amount should Ms. Wysong set aside today in an account earning 10% per year compounded semiannually in order to satisfy this obligation? $110,389.13

15. CARE OF DISABLED CHILD   Mr. Roberts is retired and wishes to set up a 10-year annuity with quarterly payments of $8000 for the care of his disabled son. Find the amount he should deposit today at 6% interest compounded quarterly. $239,326.76

16. EQUIPMENT REPLACEMENT   Physician's Pain Management plans to set aside an annual payment of $18,000 per year for 4 years for replacement of physical therapy equipment. Assuming 8% compounded annually, what lump sum deposited today would result in the same future value? $59,618.28

17. WITHDRAWALS   What lump sum deposited today at 8% compounded semiannually would permit withdrawals of $1200 at the end of each 6-month period for 7 years? How much interest is earned? $12,675.75; $4124.25

18. TRUST FUND   Henry Worthington sets up a trust fund for his grandson. He wants his grandson to be able to make withdrawals from the trust fund of $3000 at the end of each quarter for 10 years. Find the amount needed in the trust fund, if money will earn 6% compounded quarterly. $89,747.54

19. RETIREMENT INCOME   In addition to his income from Social Security and two rental houses that he owns, Chandra Lach needs $18,000 at the end of each year for 25 years at retirement. Find the amount he must accumulate if he earns (a) 5% per year and (b) 7% per year.   (a) $253,691.00 (b) $209,764.50

20. RETIREMENT INCOME   In addition to income from Social Security and a pension, Fernando Martinez needs $12,000 per year for 30 years at retirement. Find the amount he must accumulate if he earns (a) 4% per year and (b) $7\frac{1}{2}$% per year.   (a) $207,504.40 (b) $141,724.64

21. **PAYING FOR COLLEGE**   Tom Potter estimates that his daughter's college needs, beginning in 8 years, will be $3600 at the end of each quarter for 4 years. (a) Find the total amount needed in 8 years assuming 8% compounded quarterly. (b) Will he have enough money available in 8 years if he invests $700 at the end of each quarter for the next 8 years at 8% compounded quarterly?   (a) $48,879.75 (b) No

22. **VAN PURCHASE**   In 4 years, Jennifer Videtto will need a delivery van for her office-supply store, that will require a down payment of $10,000 with payments of $1200 per month for 36 months. (a) Find the total amount needed in 4 years assuming 9% compounded monthly. (b) Will she have enough money available if she invests $1000 at the end of each month for the next 4 years at 9% compounded monthly?   (a) $47,736.17 (b) Yes

23. **COMMERCIAL BUILDING**   A small commercial building sells for a down payment of $25,000 and payments of $4000 at the end of each semiannual period for 20 years. Find the equivalent cash price of the building, if money may be invested at 10% compounded semiannually. $93,636.35

24. **FISHING BOAT**   A fishing boat is sold with a down payment of $21,000 and payments of $3500 at the end of each quarter for $7\frac{1}{2}$ years. Find the equivalent cash price of the boat if money may be invested at 12% compounded quarterly. $89,601.54

Based only on present value, which of the following bids should be accepted?

25. $100,000 today, or $51,000 down and $8000 at the end of each year for 12 years; assume money may be invested at 10% compounded annually $51,000 down and $8000 per year

26. $140,000 today, or $86,000 down and $2000 at the end of each month for 3 years; assume money may be invested at 12% compounded monthly $86,000 down with $2000 per month

27. $335,000 today, or $175,000 down and $9500 at the end of each quarter for $4\frac{1}{2}$ years; assume money may be invested at 7% compounded quarterly $335,000 today

28. $4,000,000 today, or $600,000 down and $300,000 at the end of each 6-month period for 8 years; assume money may be invested at 10% compounded semiannually $4,000,000 today

Solve the following application problems.

29. **COMMERCIAL FARMING**   A manager for a commercial farmer plans to retire in 5 years and is to receive $10,000 at the end of each semiannual period for 15 years. Find the shortage in 5 years if the farmer deposits $12,000 at the end of each semiannual period. Assume his deposits earn 8% compounded semiannually. $28,847.04

30. **SEVERANCE PAY**   A large manufacturer plans to move an operation from Texas to India in 2 years, resulting in layoffs in the United States. Management anticipates a severance pay for the laid-off workers of $330,000 per month for 6 months. Find the shortage in 2 years if they deposit $65,000 per month in an account. Assume 6% compounded monthly. $292,729.77

31. **PLANNING AHEAD**   George Joyce is terminally ill and expects to live 5 years. He has a daughter who will need $12,000 at the end of each year for 4 years beginning at the time of his death. Assume 8% per year and find the amount that must be deposited today to satisfy his daughter's needs. $27,050.13

32. **LIVE IN EUROPE**   Beatrice Rice plans to live in Europe for 3 years beginning in 10 years. Assume an interest rate of 9% per year and assume she needs $35,000 at the end of each year while in Europe. Find the lump sum that must be deposited today to satisfy this need. $37,423.62

| 15.3 | **Sinking Funds** |

OBJECTIVES

1 *Find the amount of a sinking fund payment.*

2 *Set up a sinking fund table.*

Section 1 of this chapter showed how to find the amount of an annuity—the sum of money that will be in an account after making a series of equal periodic payments. Businesses often have a need to raise a certain amount of money at some fixed time in the future. In such a case, the problem is turned around. The businessperson knows how much money is needed in the future and must find the amount of each periodic payment.

A **sinking fund** is a fund that is set up to receive these periodic payments. The periodic payments plus the interest produce the necessary lump sum needed in the future.

Sinking funds are set up to provide money to build new factories, buy equipment, and purchase other companies. Also, many corporations and governmental agencies set up sinking funds to cover the face value of **bonds** or other debt that must be paid off at some time in the future. This section discusses the mechanics of setting up a sinking fund to pay off a bond when it is due.

Objective

1 *Find the Amount of a Sinking Fund Payment.* The payments into a sinking fund are just the payments of an annuity. If S is the amount to be accumulated, R is the amount of each periodic payment, n is the number of periods, and i is the interest rate per period, then

$$S = R \cdot s_{\overline{n}|i}$$

The symbol for future amount needed is S and it is the known quantity in sinking fund problems. The unknown is the amount of each periodic payment, or R. Divide both sides of the formula by $s_{\overline{n}|i}$ to solve for R.

$$R = \frac{S}{s_{\overline{n}|i}}$$

Finding the Amount of Each Payment

The amount of each payment R, into a *sinking fund* that must contain S dollars after n payments, with interest of i per period, follows.

$$R = S \cdot \left(\frac{1}{s_{\overline{n}|i}}\right)$$

The right-hand side is read as capital S times 1 divided by s-angle-n-at-i.

Values of $1 \div s_{\overline{n}|i}$ are given in column E of the interest table. These values also can be found by dividing the corresponding numbers from column C into 1.

EXAMPLE 1 Finding Periodic Payments

Arctic Drilling Inc. borrowed money by selling bonds with a maturity value in 15 years totaling $10,000,000. Find the amount of each payment into a sinking fund needed to build the required amount in 15 years to pay off the bonds. Assume 9% compounded annually.

Solution

Look in column E of the interest table for 9% and 15 years to find 0.03405888. The amount of each payment is calculated as follows:

$$R = S \cdot \left(\frac{1}{s_{\overline{n}i}}\right)$$

$$R = \$10,000,000\left(\frac{1}{s_{\overline{15}0.09}}\right)$$

$$= \$10,000,000(0.03405888)$$

$$= \$340,588.80$$

If the corporation deposits $340,588.80 at the end of each year for 15 years, it will have the $10,000,000 needed to pay off the bonds.

■

> **NOTE** The 9% interest rate in Example 1 is what the corporation *earns* on money it has deposited. The *interest that the corporation pays* to the people who bought the $10,000,000 in bonds plays no part in this calculation.

Objective

2 *Set Up a Sinking Fund Table.* To keep track of the various payments into a sinking fund, accountants often make up a sinking fund table, as shown in Example 2.

EXAMPLE **2** **Setting Up a Sinking Fund Table**

Arctic Drilling, Inc. in Example 1 deposited $340,588.80 at the end of each year in a sinking fund earning 9% compounded annually. Set up a sinking fund table for the first 8 years.

Solution

The sinking fund contains no money until the end of year 1 when a single deposit of $340,588.80 is made. This payment earns no interest in the first year since it is made at the end of the year. The balance at the end of the first year is $340,588.80. This amount earns interest at 9% during the second year and a payment is also made at the end of the second year.

End of second year = (1st payment + interest) + 2nd payment

= ($340,588.80 + $340,588.80 × 0.09) + $340,588.80

= $711,830.59

Continue in this fashion to find the values in the table. Be sure to round interest to the nearest cent each time before completing each row of the table. This is an excellent application for computer spreadsheet use.

SINKING FUND TABLE

	Beginning of Period		End of Period	
Period	Accumulated Amount	Periodic Deposit	Interest Earned	Accumulated Amount
1	0	$340,588.80	0	$340,588.80
2	$340,588.80	$340,588.80	$30,652.99	$711,830.59
3	$711,830.59	$340,588.80	$64,064.75	$1,116,484.14
4	$1,116,484.14	$340,588.80	$100,483.57	$1,557,556.51
5	$1,557,556.51	$340,588.80	$140,180.09	$2,038,325.40
6	$2,038,325.40	$340,588.80	$183,449.29	$2,562,363.49
7	$2,562,363.49	$340,588.80	$230,612.71	$3,133,565.00
8	$3,133,565.00	$340,588.80	$282,020.85	$3,756,174.65

NOTE Rounding of the payment to the nearest dollar may cause the final result in Example 2 to differ slightly from the future amount needed.

The exact amount of debt at a future date was known in Examples 1 and 2. Example 3 shows how to estimate future debt before setting up the needed sinking fund.

EXAMPLE **3** **Finding Periodic Payments**

Children's Hospital plans to purchase a new MRI machine in 3 years. The machine currently sells for $2,100,000, but the price is expected to increase at 8% per year compounded semiannually. The hospital decides to set up a sinking fund to purchase the machine. Find the amount of each year-end payment into the fund if annual payments are made and the money is expected to earn 6% compounded annually. Round each to the nearest dollar.

Solution

First, find the future price of the MRI machine using $\frac{8\%}{2} = 4\%$ interest for $3 \times 2 = 6$ periods using column A in **Appendix C**.

$$\text{Future price} = \$2,100,000 \times 1.26531902 = \$2,657,170 \quad \text{Rounded}$$

This is the total amount that the sinking fund must accumulate. The required payment to a sinking fund is found using column E in **Appendix C** with 3 periods and 6% interest to find 0.31410981.

$$\text{Payment} = \$2,657,170 \times 0.31410981 = \$834,643 \quad \text{Rounded}$$

Payments of $834,643 at the end of each year into a sinking fund paying 6% per year compounded annually will produce enough to pay cash for the MRI machine in 3 years.

Two different interest rates are involved in Example 3. The price is increasing at 8% per year compounded semiannually, but deposits in the sinking fund earn 6% compounded annually. **Interest rate spreads** such as this are common in business. For example, banks use an interest rate spread between what they pay for funds on deposit and what they charge on loans to customers.

| **15.3** | **Exercises** |

Find each of the following values.

1. $\dfrac{1}{s_{\overline{12}|0.075}}$ 0.05427783

2. $\dfrac{1}{s_{\overline{20}|0.035}}$ 0.03536108

3. $\dfrac{1}{s_{\overline{40}|0.09}}$ 0.00295961

4. $\dfrac{1}{s_{\overline{30}|0.045}}$ 0.01639154

Find the amount of payment to be made into a sinking fund so that the indicated amount will be there when needed. Round to the nearest cent.

5. $8500 in 4 years, money earns $5\frac{1}{2}$% compounded annually, 4 annual payments $1957.50

6. $4850 in $7\frac{1}{2}$ years, money earns 7% compounded semiannually, 15 semiannual payments $251.35

7. $14,000 in 5 years, money earns 8% compounded quarterly, 20 quarterly payments $576.19

8. $28,000 in 10 years, money earns 10% compounded quarterly, 40 quarterly payments $415.41

9. Explain the purpose of a sinking fund. Why is it given a name other than annuity?

10. Define the phrase *interest rate spread*. Why do interest rate spreads exist? (See Objective 2.)

In Exercises 11–14, do the following. Find (a) the present value needed to fund the end-of-period retirement benefit using the interest rate given, and find (b) the end-of-period semiannual payment needed to accumulate the value found in part (a) assuming regular investments for 25 years in an account yielding 8% compounded semiannually.

11. $10,000 per year for 25 years, 8% per year   (a) $106,747.76 (b) $699.22

12. $12,000 every 6 months for 25 years, 7% compounded semiannually   (a) $281,467.41 (b) $1843.67

13. $12,000 per quarter for 9 years, 8% compounded quarterly   (a) $305,866.11 (b) $2003.48

14. $10,000 per quarter for 12 years, 12% compounded quarterly   (a) $252,667.07 (b) $1655.02

Solve the following application problems. Round to the nearest cent.

15. **CATTLE FEED LOT**   The owner of Bainbridge Cattle sets up a sinking fund to accumulate $1,800,000 needed in 3 years to purchase land and construct a cattle feed lot. Find (a) the amount of each end-of-6-month payment assuming 7% compounded semiannually and (b) the total amount of interest earned.   (a) $274,802.78 (b) $151,183.32

16. **ALLIGATOR HUNTING**   Cajun Jack needs $45,000 in 4 years for a boat used to hunt alligators that are used both for leather and for the meat. (a) Find the amount of each payment if payments are made at the end of each quarter into a fund earning 6% compounded quarterly. (b) Find the total amount of interest earned.   (a) $2509.43 (b) $4849.12

17. **CLEANING MACHINE**   Smith Dry Cleaning must buy a new cleaning machine in 9 years for $110,000. The firm desires to set up a sinking fund for this purpose. Find the payment into the fund at the end of each year if money in the fund earns 6% compounded annually. $9572.45

18. **TALENT AGENCY**   Catriona Kaplan's Baby Beautiful Talent Agency needs $79,000 in 6 years. To accumulate the necessary funds, the company sets up a sinking fund with payments made into the fund quarterly. Find the payment into this fund if money in the fund earns 5% compounded quarterly. $2842.95

19. **JAIL**   A city sold $4,000,000 worth of bonds to finish paying for a new jail. To pay off the bonds when they mature in 8 years, the city sets up a sinking fund. Find the amount of each payment into the fund if the city makes annual payments and the money earns 6% compounded annually. Find the amount of interest earned by the deposits. $404,143.76; $766,849.92

20. **CHURCH FUND-RAISING**   A small church-related college sold $1,480,000 in bonds to pay for an addition to the administration building. The bonds must be paid off in 15 years. To accumulate the money to pay off the bonds, the college sets up a sinking fund. If the college makes payments at the end of each 6 months and the money earns 10% compounded semiannually, find the amount of each payment into the fund. Find the amount of interest earned by the deposits. $22,276.13; $811,716.10

21. COAL MINING   Pennsylvania Coal Co. has contracted to pay $960,211.72 in 4 years to purchase a huge Caterpillar tractor used to scoop up chunks of dirt, rock, and coal. Assume funds on deposit earn 8% interest compounded annually and complete the following sinking fund table.

| | Beginning of Period | | End of Period | |
Period	Accumulated Amount	Periodic Deposit	Interest Earned	Accumulated Amount
1	$0	$213,090.95	$0	$213,090.95
2	$213,090.95	$213,090.95	$17,047.28	$443,229.18
3	$443,229.18	$213,090.95	$35,458.33	$691,778.46
4	$691,778.46	$213,090.98	$55,342.28	$960,211.72

22. CASINO BOAT PURCHASE   Riverside Gambling, Inc. needs $4,000,000 in 8 years to purchase a replacement casino boat. Assume annual payments earn 6% compounded annually, and complete the sinking fund table.

| | Beginning of Period | | End of Period | |
Period	Accumulated Amount	Periodic Deposit	Interest Earned	Accumulated Amount
1	$0	$404,143.76	$0	$404,143.76
2	$404,143.76	$404,143.76	$24,248.63	$832,536.15
3	$832,536.15	$404,143.76	$49,952.17	$1,286,632.08
4	$1,286,632.08	$404,143.76	$77,197.92	$1,767,973.76
5	$1,767,973.76	$404,143.76	$106,078.43	$2,278,195.95
6	$2,278,195.95	$404,143.76	$136,691.76	$2,819,031.47
7	$2,819,031.47	$404,143.76	$169,141.89	$3,392,317.12
8	$3,392,317.12	$404,143.85	$203,539.03	$4,000,000.00

23. FOOTBALL STADIUM   A school district needs to build a new football stadium at a cost of $8,000,000. It sets up a sinking fund with end-of-quarter payments in an account earning 7% compounded quarterly. Find the amount that needs to be deposited each quarter if it wishes to build the stadium (a) in 3 years and (b) in 4 years. (a) $604,910.16 (b) $437,596.64

24. AIRPORT IMPROVEMENTS   A city near Chicago sold $9,000,000 in bonds to pay for improvements to an airport. It set up a sinking fund with end-of-quarter payments in an account earning 8% compounded quarterly. Find the amount that should be deposited in this fund each quarter if it wishes to pay off the bonds in (a) 7 years and (b) 12 years.   (a) $242,907.03 (b) $113,416.56

CHAPTER TERMS

Review the following terms to test your understanding of the chapter. For each term you do not know, refer to the page number found next to the term.

amount of an annuity [p. 562]
annuity [p. 562]
annuity certain [p. 562]
annuity due [p. 562 or 568]
bonds [p. 581]
contingent annuity [p. 562]

corporate bond fund [p. 570]
equivalent cash price [p. 578]
future value of an annuity [p. 562]
individual retirement account (IRA) [p. 569]

interest rate spread [p. 583]
lump sums [p. 561]
ordinary annuity [p. 562]
payment period [p. 562]
present value of an annuity [p. 574]

regular IRA [p. 569]
Roth IRA [p. 570]
simple annuity [p. 562]
sinking fund [p. 581]
stock fund [p. 570]
term of an annuity [p. 562]

CONCEPTS

EXAMPLES

15.1 Finding the amount of an annuity

Use n, the number of periods, and i, the interest rate per period, to find $s_{\overline{n}|i}$ in column C of the interest table in **Appendix C**. Find the amount S from the formula $S = R \cdot s_{\overline{n}|i}$ with R the periodic payment into the annuity, or use the formula.

$$S = R\left[\frac{(1+i)^n - 1}{i}\right]$$

Bill Thomas deposits $4500 at the end of each year at 6% compounded annually. How much will Thomas have at the end of 40 years?

$$n = 40; i = 6\%$$

From the table

$$s_{\overline{40}|0.06} = 154.76196562$$

and

$$S = (\$4500)(154.76196562) = \$696,428.85$$

15.1 Finding the amount of each payment into an annuity

Determine the amount needed in the future S, the interest rate per period i, and the number of periods n. Use the interest table in **Appendix C** to find $s_{\overline{n}|i}$, then find R from the formula $S = R \cdot s_{\overline{n}|i}$.

Find the amount of the periodic payment that will produce $18,000 if the interest is 6% compounded monthly and monthly payments are made for 4 years.

$$S = \$18,000$$
$$n = 4 \times 12 = 48$$
$$i = 0.06 \div 12 = 0.005$$
$$s_{\overline{48}|0.005} = 54.09783222$$
$$S = R \cdot s_{\overline{n}|i}$$
$$\$18,000 = R(54.09783222)$$
$$\$332.73 = R$$

15.1 Finding the number of payments

Divide the amount of the annuity S by the amount of the payment R to find $s_{\overline{n}|i}$. Find the page in **Appendix C** corresponding to the interest rate i. Look in column C using the value found for $s_{\overline{n}|i}$ (or the first larger number) to find n.

George Gleine needs $5000. He can put $210 per quarter into an account paying 4% compounded quarterly. How long will it take to accumulate the money?

$$s_{\overline{n}|0.01} = \frac{S}{R} = \frac{\$5000}{\$210}$$
$$s_{\overline{n}|0.01} = 23.80952381$$

Closest table value is 24.47158598, so $n = 22$ quarters; $22 \div 4 = 5\frac{1}{2}$ years.

15.1 Finding the amount of an annuity due

Add 1 to the number of periods and use this as the value of n. Use n and i, the interest rate per period, to find $s_{\overline{n}|i}$ in the interest table. To find the amount, use the formula.

$$S = R \cdot s_{\overline{n}|i} - 1 \text{ payment}$$

Find the amount of an annuity due if payments of $700 are made at the beginning of each month for 3 years into an account paying 5% compounded monthly.

$$n = (12 \times 3) + 1 = 37$$

$$i = 5\% \div 12 = \frac{5}{12}\%$$

$$s_{\overline{37}|0.467} = 39.91480775$$

$$S = \$700(39.91480775) - \$700$$

$$= \$27,240.37$$

15.1 Finding the amount of an IRA

Use n, the number of periods, and i, the interest rate per period, to find $s_{\overline{n}|i}$ in column C of the interest table in **Appendix C**. Find the amount S from the formula $S = R \cdot s_{\overline{n}|i}$ with R the periodic payment into the annuity.

Deposits of $1500 at the end of each year are made into an IRA account paying 10% per year. Find the accumulated amount in 30 years.

$$n = 30; i = 10\%$$

From the table, we have the following.

$$s_{\overline{30}|0.10} = 164.49402269$$

$$S = \$1500 \cdot 164.49402269$$

$$= \$246,741.03$$

15.2 Finding the present value of an annuity

Use the number of periods n, interest rate per period i, and column D of the interest table to find $a_{\overline{n}|i}$. Find the present value of the annuity A, using the formula

$$A = R \cdot a_{\overline{n}|i}$$

with R the payment per period.

What lump sum deposited today at 9% compounded annually will yield the same total as payments of $2500 at the end of each year for 8 years?

$$R = \$2500; n = 8; i = 9\%$$

$$a_{\overline{8}|0.09} = 5.53481911$$

$$A = \$2500(5.53481911)$$

$$= \$13,837.05$$

15.2 Finding equivalent cash price

Use the number of periods n, interest rate per period i, and column D of the interest table to find $a_{\overline{n}|i}$. Find the present value using the formula

$$A = R \cdot a_{\overline{n}|i}$$

Add the value of A to the down payment to obtain the equivalent cash value.

A buyer offers to purchase a business for $75,000 down and quarterly payments of $4000 for 5 years. If money may be invested at 8% compounded quarterly, how much is the buyer actually offering?

$$R = \$4000$$

$$n = 4 \times 5 = 20; i = 8\% \div 4 = 2\%$$

$$a_{\overline{20}|0.02} = 16.3514334$$

$$A = \$4000 \times 16.3514334$$

$$= \$65,405.73$$

Equivalent cash value $= \$75,000 + \$65,405.73$

$$= \$140,405.73$$

15.3 Determining the payment into a sinking fund

Use the number of payments n, the interest rate per period i, and column E of the interest table to find the value of $1 \div s_{\overline{n}|i}$. Use the formula

$$R = S \cdot \frac{1}{s_{\overline{n}|i}}$$

to calculate the payment.

A company must set up a sinking fund to accumulate $50,000 in 5 years. Find the amount of the payments if they are made at the end of each year and the fund earns 8%.

$$n = 5; i = 0.08$$

$$\frac{1}{s_{\overline{n}|i}} = 0.17045645$$

$$R = \$50,000(0.17045645)$$
$$= \$8522.82$$

15.3 Setting up a sinking fund table

Determine the payment R and the interest at the end of each payment. Then add the previous total, next payment, and interest to find the accumulated amount. Repeat for each period.

Managers want to set up a sinking fund to accumulate $10,000 in 4 years. They plan to make annual payments into the account, which pays 8% compounded annually. Set up a table.

$$n = 4; i = 0.08$$

$$\frac{1}{s_{\overline{4}|0.08}} = 0.22192080$$

$$R = \$10,000(0.22192080)$$
$$= \$2219.21$$

| | Beginning of Period | | End of Period | |
Period	Accumulated Amount	Periodic Deposit	Interest Earned	Accumulated Amount
1	$0	$2219.21	$0	$2219.21
2	2219.21	2219.21	177.54	4615.96
3	4615.96	2219.21	369.28	7204.45
4	7204.45	2219.19	576.36	10,000.00

CHAPTER 15 | Review Exercises

The answer section includes answers to all Review Exercises.

Find the amount of the following annuities. [15.1]

1. $1500 is deposited at the end of each year for 22 years, money earns $6\frac{1}{2}$% compounded annually. $69,152.45

2. $1000 is deposited at the end of each semiannual period for 12 years, money earns 6% compounded semiannually. $34,426.47

3. $3000 is deposited at the end of each quarter for $6\frac{3}{4}$ years, money earns 10% compounded quarterly. $113,736.00

4. $1000 is deposited at the end of each month for $3\frac{1}{2}$ years, money earns 9% compounded monthly. $49,153.29

5. $18,000 is deposited at the beginning of each year for 7 years, money earns $6\frac{1}{2}$% compounded annually. $163,383.42

6. $3500 is deposited at the beginning of each quarter for $5\frac{1}{2}$ years, money earns 8% compounded quarterly. $97,457.37

7. Fatima Burke deposits $800 at the end of each quarter for $5\frac{1}{2}$ years in an account she expects to earn 5% compounded quarterly. Find the future value and amount of interest. $20,114.46; $2514.46

8. A firm of attorneys deposits $7500 of profit-sharing money at the end of each semiannual period for $7\frac{1}{2}$ years. Find the final amount in the account if the deposit earns 5% compounded semiannually. Find the amount of interest earned. $134,489.45; $21,989.45

Find the present value of the following ordinary annuities. [15.2]

9. Payments of $4200 are made annually at 7% compounded annually for 15 years. $38,253.24

10. Payments of $800 are made semiannually at 8% compounded semiannually for $4\frac{1}{2}$ years. $5948.27

11. Payments of $450 are made quarterly for $5\frac{1}{4}$ years at 6% compounded quarterly. $8055.06

12. Payments of $125 are made monthly for $4\frac{1}{6}$ years at 10% compounded monthly. $5094.30

Find the amount of each payment to be made to a sinking fund so that enough money will be available to pay off the indicated loan. [15.3]

13. $85,000 loan, money earns 9% compounded annually, 6 annual payments $11,298.18

14. $42,000 loan, money earns 6% compounded quarterly, 26 quarterly payments $1332.74

15. $240,000 loan, money earns 9% compounded semiannually, 9 semiannual payments $22,217.87

16. $35,000 loan, money earns 9% compounded monthly, 47 monthly payments $623.89

Solve the following application problems.

17. Jaime Bickers invests $4000 at the end of each semiannual period for 8 years. His financial advisor told him the funds should earn about 6% compounded semiannually. Find the amount of the annuity. **[15.1]** $80,627.53

18. Bill Wild can save $600 at the end of each year in an account earning 10% per year. How many years are required for him to accumulate $100,000? **[15.1]**   31 years

19. Jessica Savage purchased her father's home when he went to an assisted-living center. She owes her father $85,000 and plans to pay it off in 3 years. Find the required end-of-quarter payments into a sinking fund if she earns 7% compounded quarterly. **[15.3]** $6427.17

20. Moira Roberts has promised to give $25,000 to her church in 3 years. If she can earn 6% compounded monthly, find the lump sum she can deposit today to accumulate the necessary funds. **[15.2]** $20,891.12

21. According to the terms of a divorce settlement, one spouse must pay the other $28,000 in 17 months. What lump sum can be invested today, at 6% compounded monthly, so that enough will be available for the payment? **[15.2]** $25,723.79

22. A-1 Plumbing needs $48,000 in 4 years to replace two trucks. Find the amount it must deposit at the end of each quarter in a fund earning 6% compounded quarterly. **[15.3]** $2676.72

23. A power company needs to replace some large generators at an estimated cost of $680,000 in $5\frac{1}{2}$ years. It expects to receive a payment of $240,000 from another source at that time. Find the payment required at the end of each semiannual period to accumulate the remaining funds needed to purchase the generators. Assume the company can earn 8% compounded semiannually. **[15.3]** $32,625.58

24. Hilda Worth invests $500 at the *beginning* of each semiannual period into an IRA account paying 10% compounded semiannually. Given that she is 30 years old, find the amount she will have accumulated at age 54. **[15.1]** $98,713.33

25. In 3 years, Aqua Inc. plans to expand operations with the purchase of equipment for a fish farm on the coast of Florida. At that time, the firm expects to begin 5 years of end-of-quarter payments of $54,239.82 assuming 8% compounded quarterly. (a) Find the present value of the payments when they are scheduled to begin in 3 years. (b) Then find the lump sum the firm must deposit today in an account earning $7\frac{1}{2}$% compounded annually to satisfy the debt payments. **[15.1]**   (a) $886,898.80 (b) $713,918.56

Prepare a sinking fund table for the following. [15.3]

26. A firm sets up a sinking fund to pay off a $100,000 note due in 4 years. The firm makes annual payments into an account earning 9% compounded annually.

| | Beginning of Period | | End of Period | |
Period	Accumulated Amount	Periodic Deposit	Interest Earned	Accumulated Amount
1	$0	$21,866.87	$0	$21,866.87
2	$21,866.87	$21,866.87	$1968.02	$45,701.76
3	$45,701.76	$21,866.87	$4113.16	$71,681.79
4	$71,681.79	$21,866.85	$6451.36	$100,000.00

CHAPTER 15	Business Application Case #1
	Financial Planning

At age 32, Tish Baker has decided to invest $3600 per year for 33 years until she is 65, in her retirement plan. She has also decided to place one-half of the funds in a stock index fund that roughly tracks the return on the Standard and Poor's index. The other half of the funds will be placed in a mutual fund containing bonds.

(a) Find the amount she will have at 65 assuming the stock fund averages 9% per year compounded annually and the bond fund averages $6\frac{1}{2}$% per year compounded annually. $517,204.85

(b) The amount found in part (a) seems like a lot of money. But Baker knows that inflation will increase her cost of living. She wants to see the effect of 3% annual inflation on her financial goals. Find the income she needs at age 65 to have the same purchasing power as an income of $20,000 today. (*Hint:* Look at the section on inflation in **Section 12.4** and use column A of the tables.) $53,046.70

(c) Baker wishes to fund her retirement for 20 years (to age 85). Find the present value at the time of her retirement of the annual income found in part (b) assuming that the funds earn 8% per year compounded annually. $520,820.32

(d) Will her expected savings from part (a) fund her retirement at a purchasing power of $20,000 per year in today's dollars?   Almost, but not quite.

Baker will also receive a monthly check from Social Security during her retirement. The bar chart below shows the importance of Social Security to Americans. If Baker saves as much as she plans and she has correctly estimated her needs at retirement, she will not have to rely on Social Security for more than one-half of her income. This may allow her to travel or do other things she enjoys during retirement.

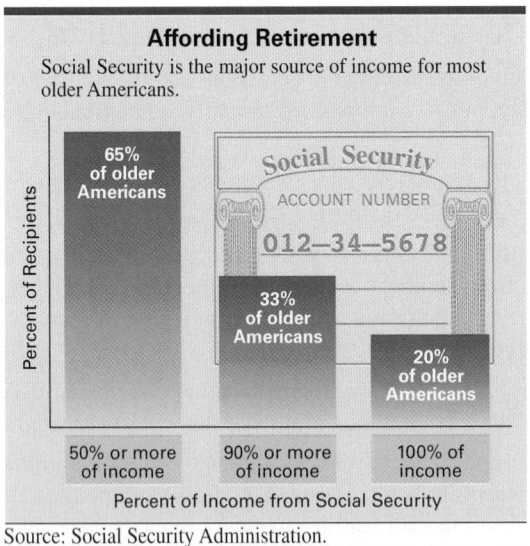

Affording Retirement
Source: Social Security Administration.

CHAPTER 15	Business Application Case #2
	Financing the Cost of a New Building

Administrators at Bacon College are debating the construction of a new building to house the School of Business Administration. They have estimated the total amount needed at the time construction starts in 5 years to be $21,300,000. The college already has $4,500,000 earning $6\frac{1}{2}$% per year that can be used to meet that goal.

(a) Find the future value of the $4,500,000. $6,165,389.97

(b) Find the shortage in 5 years. $15,134,610.03

(c) Find the amount that must be placed into a sinking fund earning $6\frac{1}{2}$% per year, to accumulate the additional funds needed. $2,658,160.27

Each year, the president of the college hopes to get donors to contribute the amount just calculated in part (c), but he knows it will be difficult.

Business and Consumer Loans

javier brosch / Fotolia.com

It is nearly impossible to pay cash for everything. Credit is used by individuals for cell phones, lights, running water, charge cards, automobile loans, and home loans. Credit is used by businesses that borrow directly from banks and other corporations or through markets using bonds. Banks even borrow money from individuals making deposits in savings accounts or time deposits, businesses, and other banks. The market for debt is global today, with money often crossing the boundaries of countries. The entity doing the lending is the **lender**, **debtor**, or **creditor**. The entity doing the borrowing is the **borrower**, or **debtor**.

Local, state, and federal governments also borrow. A **budget surplus** refers to income from taxes and other sources that exceeds spending. A **budget deficit** refers to government spending that exceeds income. Figure 16.1 shows that the U.S. government has run deficits every year since 2002, with particularly large deficits since the financial crisis began in 2008. Deficit spending in the United States results in higher levels of debt. The goverment finances the increasing debt by borrowing and/or by creating money. As a result, record amounts of both borrowing and money creation is occurring.

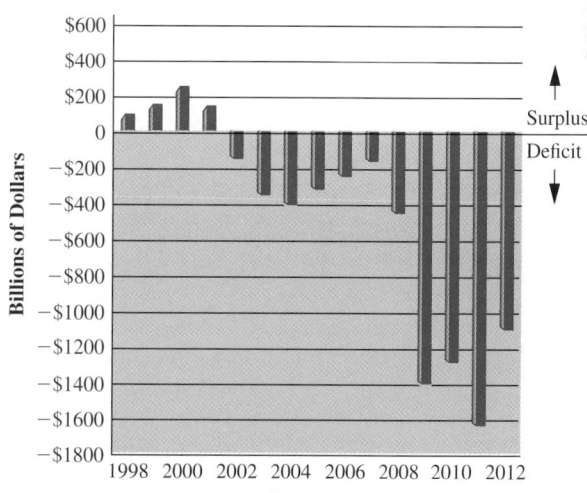

Massive Federal Budget Deficits

Note: Fiscal year ends Sept. 30

Figure 16.1

▶ STOP&THINK

From whom does the U.S. government borrow money? Do you think that individuals and businesses may have had enough cash to lend the government $1.6 trillion in 2011? If not, then who? Could it be other countries? If so, what countries might have excess money? Who must pay the interest on money borrowed by the government?

Originally, businesses offered credit as an additional service to customers. Today, the interest on loans to customers represents a significant portion of the total profit at many firms. The simple interest and simple discount notes discussed in an earlier chapter required a lump-sum payment at maturity. In this chapter, the principal and interest are paid back in periodic payments, e.g., monthly or quarterly payments.

A law passed in 2005 affected a borrower's ability to declare Chapter 7 and Chapter 13 bankruptcies. A **Chapter 7 bankruptcy** results in the liquidation of all assets with funds going to creditors even as other debts are canceled resulting in a fresh start for the borrower. A **Chapter 13 bankruptcy** requires a borrower to enter into a repayment plan and make payments until all debt is paid. It has become more difficult to declare bankruptcy because the new law has made it more difficult to file under Chapter 7, thereby requiring more troubled borrowers to file under Chapter 13.

Be careful how much you borrow. You could end up weighted down by debt, as shown in the cartoon for students, home owners, the United States, and Europe. Many believe these groups have far too much debt. In contrast, China and many of the large banks have record levels of cash and investments.

Debt can be crushing!

16.1	**Open-End Credit**

OBJECTIVES

1 *Define open-end credit.*

2 *Understand revolving charge accounts and credit accounts.*

3 *Use the average daily balance method to calculate finance charges.*

4 *Define loan consolidation.*

Objective

1 *Define Open-End Credit.* A common way of buying on credit, called **open-end credit**, has no fixed payments. The customer continues making payments until no outstanding balance is owed. With open-end credit, additional credit is often extended before the initial amount is paid off. Examples of open-end credit include most department store credit accounts and credit cards, as well as MasterCard and Visa. Individuals are given a **credit limit** on these accounts based on their income and other factors. They are then allowed to charge up to this amount.

Objective

2 *Understand Revolving Charge Accounts and Credit Accounts.* Individuals may open **credit accounts** at certain stores. This allows the customer to make frequent purchases from that store during the month without having to pay cash or write a check. Such accounts are often never paid off, although a minimum amount must be paid each month. Since the account may never be paid off, it is called a **revolving charge account**.

Credit cards such as MasterCard and Visa are accepted by most stores and restaurants worldwide. Sometimes there is an annual membership fee or a minimum monthly charge for the use of this service. Credit cards are a convenient way to make purchases and track expenses since they provide a monthly statement. Part of their convenience is due to the fact that they are so widely accepted and can also be used at ATM machines for cash. Figure 16.2 shows the share of the huge U.S. credit-card market by type of card. Figure 16.3 shows a copy of a receipt for a customer using a credit card.

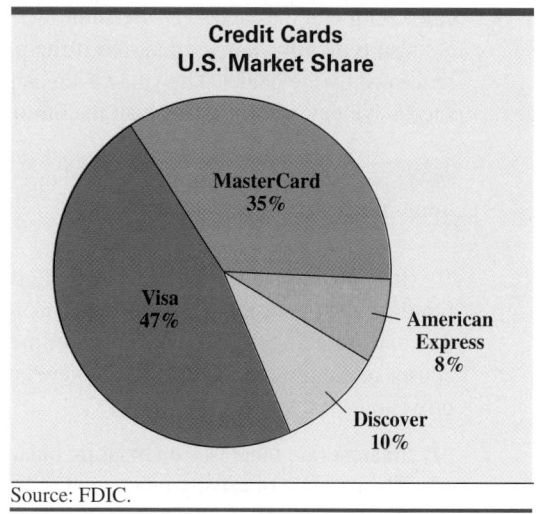

Figure 16.2

> **NOTE** Debit cards do not create debt. When a debit card is swiped, the funds are immediately transferred out of the account.

Figure 16.3

At the end of a monthly billing period, the customer receives an **itemized billing** similar to that shown in Figure 16.4. Charges over and above the combined cost of the various charges are called **finance charges**. They include interest, credit life insurance, and international transaction fees.

Many lenders charge **late fees** for payments that are received after the due date and **over-the-limit fees** in the event the debt exceeds the amount authorized by the issuer of the card. Both late fees and over-the-limit fees tend to be high, so avoid them if you can. Lenders also typically charge a late fee if the payment made is *less than the minimum payment* requested by the lender. They may even cancel the account or increase the interest rate if two successive payments are less than the minimum requested.

> **NOTE** Lenders may simply deny charges to an account that cause the debt to exceed previously established credit limits.

It is not unusual in our society for credit to be so easy to obtain that individuals and families end up having a lot of problems related too much credit-card debt. It did not help that many credit-card companies sometimes took advantage of people. There were so many abuses related to credit cards that a new law was passed in 2009. Here are just a few of the provisions of the new law:

1. Interest rate increases on existing balances were restricted.
2. The practice of raising rates on existing balances based on payment records was ended.
3. Credit-card holders can decide to close accounts and pay off balances.

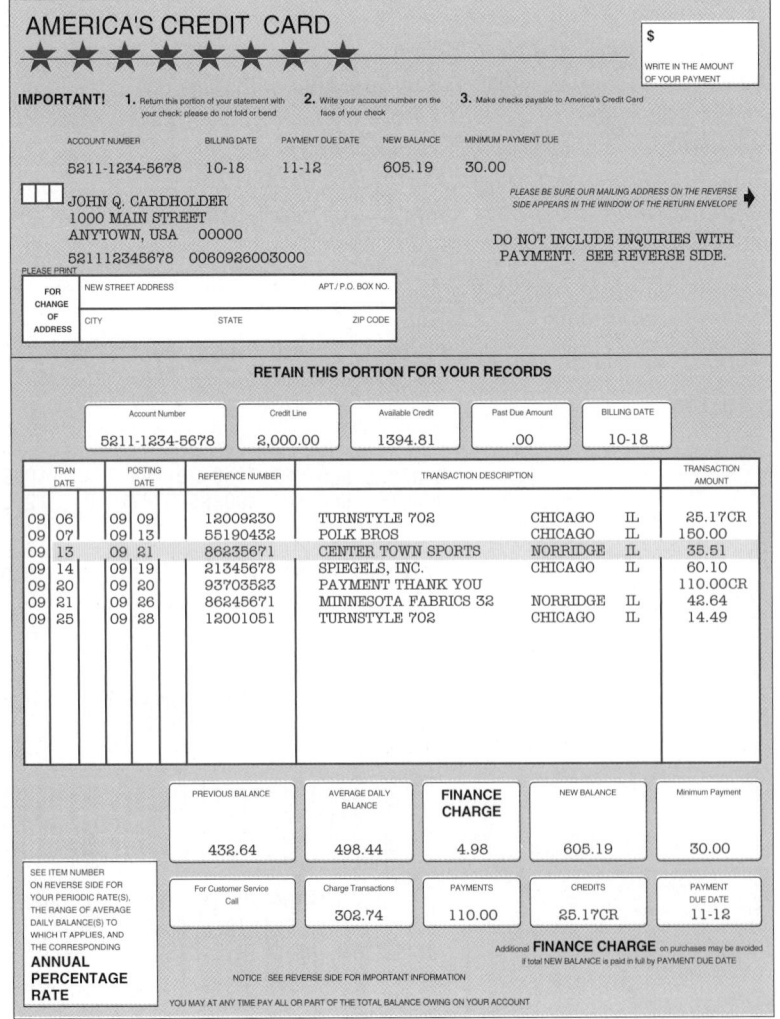

Figure 16.4

4. Some limits on the issuance of credit cards to anyone under 21 were created.
5. More time was given to pay monthly credit-card bills.
6. Limits were placed on over-the-limit fees (fees charged when the balance goes over approved level).

The new law helped millions of people, but some still end up in trouble due to too much credit-card and other debt.

Objective

3 *Use the Average Daily Balance Method to Calculate Finance Charges.* Finance charges on many open-ended accounts are zero as long as the borrower *pays the full amount owed each month.* An exception is on cash advances, which result in a finance charge even if the balance is paid in full at the end of the month. Finance charges apply if balances are not paid in full, and they are usually calculated using the **average daily balance** method.

First, the balance owed on the account is found at the end of each day during a month or billing period. All of these ending daily balance amounts are added and the total is divided by the number of days during the billing period. The result is the average daily balance of the account. The finance charge is then calculated on this amount.

EXAMPLE 1 **Finding Average Daily Balance**

The activity in the MasterCard account of Kay Chamberlin for one billing period is shown in the following table. (a) Find the average daily balance on the next billing date of April 3 if the previous balance was $209.46. (b) Find the finance charge for the month if the monthly charge is $1\frac{1}{2}\%$ of the average daily balance. (c) Find the total amount due at the end of the billing period.

Transaction Description		Transaction Amount
Previous balance, $209.46		
March 3	Billing date	
March 12	Payment	$50.00CR*
March 17	Drug store	$28.46
March 20	Mail order	$31.22
April 1	Auto parts	$59.10
April 3	End of billing cycle	

*CR represents "credit."

Solution

(a) Using the transaction data above, the following table shows the beginning date, end date, and number of days at each specific unpaid balance. Note that March 3 is the first day and April 3 is the last day of the billing month. Each payment or charge results in a separate row in the table.

Beg. Date	End Date	Number of Days		Unpaid Balance
Mar. 3	Mar. 12	9	Previous balance carried forward is	$209.46
Mar. 12	Mar. 17	5	On March 12, subtract $50 to get	$159.46
Mar. 17	Mar. 20	3	On Mar. 17, add $28.46 to get	$187.92
Mar. 20	Apr. 1	12	On Mar. 20, add $31.22 to get	$219.14
Apr. 1	Apr. 3	2	On Apr. 1, add $59.10 to get	$278.24
		31 days in the billing period		

Next find a weighted average of the unpaid balances for the month. Multiply each unpaid balance by the number of days outstanding, total the products, and divide by the 31 days in this billing cycle. Some months will have fewer than 31 days in the cycle.

$$\$209.46 \times 9 = \$1885.14$$
$$\$159.46 \times 5 = 797.30$$
$$\$187.92 \times 3 = 563.76$$
$$\$219.14 \times 12 = 2629.68$$
$$\$278.24 \times 2 = \underline{556.48}$$
$$\$6432.36$$

Now divide the total by 31, since there are 31 days in this billing cycle.

Average daily balance $= \$6432.36 \div 31 = \$207.50$ Rounded

Chamberlin will pay a finance charge based on the average daily balance of $207.50.

Scientific Calculator Approach

The calculator solution to part (a) of Example 1 is as follows: Multiply each unpaid balance by the respective number of days until the balance changes. Add these values together and divide by the number of days in the month (31 days).

(209.46 $\times$ 9 + 159.46 $\times$ 5 + 187.92 $\times$ 3 + 219.14 $\times$ 12

+ 278.24 $\times$ 2) $\div$ 31 = 207.5

(b) Find the finance charge for the month by multiplying the monthly rate of $1\frac{1}{2}\%$ by the average daily balance.

Finance charge $= 0.015 \times \$207.50 = \$3.11$

The finance charge would be different for a month with a different average daily balance.

(c) The amount due at the end of the billing period is the previous balance minus any payments and credits, plus any new charges, including the finance charge.

Previous balance	− payment	+ drug store	mail + order	auto + parts	finance + charge	
$209.46	− $50	+ $28.46	+ $31.22	+ $59.10	+ $3.11	= $281.35

Ending balance

The amount due on April 3 is $281.35, but the credit-card issuer usually gives card holders a couple of weeks to pay without incurring any penalty charges or additional interest.

NOTE The billing period in Example 1 is 31 days. Some billing periods are 30 days or less. Be sure to use the correct number of days.

NOTE Not all billings for open-end accounts occur on the same day of the month.

If finance charges are expressed on a per month basis, find the **annual percentage rate** by multiplying the monthly rate by 12, the number of months in a year. Table 16.1 shows typical monthly rates and the corresponding annual percentage rates. Notice that the interest rates charged by some credit-card companies are extremely high!

Table 16.1 MONTHLY FINANCE CHARGES AND CORRESPONDING ANNUAL PERCENTAGE RATES

Quoted Monthly Finance Charge	Annual Percentage Rate
$\frac{1}{2}$ of 1%	6%
$\frac{2}{3}$ of 1%	8%
$\frac{3}{4}$ of 1%	9%
$\frac{5}{6}$ of 1%	10%
1%	12%
$1\frac{1}{4}$%	15%
$1\frac{1}{2}$%	18%
$1\frac{2}{3}$%	20%
$1\frac{3}{4}$%	21%
2%	24%

NOTE The monthly finance charge percent is used only to calculate the finance charge, not the minimum payment.

Figure 16.5 shows the results of a recent survey of working adults. The highest-ranking recommendation by working adults to college graduates is to avoid credit-card debt. Presumably, the working adults know that credit-card debt can accumulate faster than you might imagine and also that the interest rate on that debt is very high. Once credit-card debt has accumulated, it is very difficult to get rid of it.

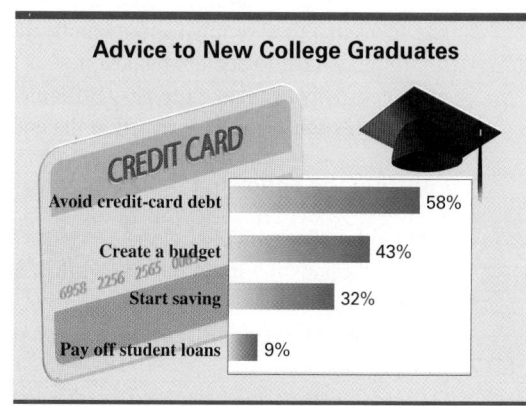

Source: Survey of 2000 working adults.

Figure 16.5

Objective

4 *Define Loan Consolidation.* Credit has historically been *so easy to obtain* for individuals in our society *that it has sometimes become problematic*. Individuals with many high-interest revolving-account loans sometimes **consolidate their loans** into one lower-interest loan, frequently with a longer term. It may cost to consolidate loans, but it allows people to handle their bills without defaulting on debt and ruining their credit history. Consolidating a loan may help someone afford the payments, but it does not extend the life of the items purchased that created the loans in the first place.

EXAMPLE 2 **Loan Consolidation**

Between auto loans, a home loan, and the revolving account loans shown below, teachers Bill and Cynthia Taylor have more short-term debt than they can handle. They have gone to George Willis at Glaston Credit Union for help.

Revolving Account	Debt	Annual Percentage Rate	Minimum Payment
Sears	$3880.54	18%	$150
Dillards	1620.13	16%	75
MasterCard	3140.65	14%	100
Visa	8940.60	20%	270
Totals	$17,581.92		$595

Solution

George Willis (1) put the Taylors on a *strict budget,* (2) consolidated the revolving account debts into one *longer-term,* low-interest loan at the credit union, and (3) decreased the payment on one auto by refinancing it at a lower rate. In all, Willis reduced the Taylors' monthly payments by about $225 per month.

NOTE Families such as the Taylors in Example 2 who consolidate their debts and then take additional loans can develop serious financial problems and may end up with more debt than they can handle. In this event, the only option may be a very stressful experience referred to as bankruptcy.

Unfortunately, families sometimes owe so much on high-interest credit cards and automobile loans that they simply cannot handle the debt even by consolidating loans. In that event the family may have to declare bankruptcy or get second jobs, pushing workloads up to 60 hours per week. This can make life *very* difficult. It is best to avoid high-interest credit-card debt by buying only what you can pay off at the end of the month. Look at the following ideas.

Consider the Following before Buying

1. Do I really need the item *now*, or can I delay the purchase until I have the cash to buy it? Perhaps it will go on sale while I'm waiting.
2. Can I get along with a less expensive used one rather than a new one?
3. What is the real cost, including cash price, sales tax, and finance charges, of purchasing this item?
4. Am I getting the best price for the item and best loan terms (such as interest rate and term of loan) possible or should I shop around on the Internet for a better deal?
5. Can I truly afford the payments?
6. If I buy this item, can I still save every month?

| 16.1 | Exercises |

Find the finance charge for the following revolving credit accounts. Assume interest is calculated on the average daily balance of the account. (See Example 1.)

	Average Daily Balance	Monthly Interest Rate	
1.	$836.15	1.2%	$10.03
2.	$8431.10	1.4%	$118.04
3.	$389.95	$1\frac{1}{4}$%	$4.87
4.	$2235.46	1.6%	$35.77

Find the average daily balance for the following credit-card accounts. Assume the billing date is the same day in each month, and use the number of days in each month. Then find the finance charge if interest is 1.5% per month on the average daily balance. (See Example 1.) Finally, find the balance at the end of the billing cycle.

5. Previous balance $139.56

September 12	Billing date		
September 20	Payment CR	$45	$132.64; $1.99; $133.80
September 21	CDs	$37.25	

6. Previous balance $412.48

November 5	Billing date		
November 18	Payment CR	$150	$341.56; $5.12; $352.10
November 30	Dinner and play	$84.50	

7. Previous balance $2737.28

May 4	Billing date		
May 15	Payment CR	$200	$2764.63; $41.47; $2881.75
May 19	Airline ticket	$303	

8. Previous balance $228.95

January 27	Billing date		
February 9	Cheese	$11.08	
February 13	Returns CR	$26.54	$221.44; $3.32; $259
February 20	Payment CR	$29	
February 25	Repairs	$71.19	

9. Previous balance $938.34

June 11	Billing date		
June 15	Returns CR	$319.35	
June 20	Jewelry	$347.19	$938.73; $14.08; $857.83
June 24	Car rental	$222.57	
July 3	Payment CR	$345	

10. Previous balance $355.72

March 29	Billing date		
March 31	Returns CR	$209.53	
April 2	Cleaning supplies	$28.76	
April 10	Gasoline	$14.80	
April 12	Returns CR	$63.54	$139.71; $2.10; $74.32
April 13	Returns CR	$11.71	
April 20	Payment CR	$72	
April 21	Flowers	$29.72	

11. Previous balance $714.58

August 17	Billing date	
August 21	Mail order	$26.94
August 23	Returns CR	$25.41
August 27	Wine	$31.82
August 31	Payment CR	$128
September 9	Returns CR	$71.14
September 11	Birthday gift	$110
September 14	Donation	$100

$681.52; $10.22; $769.01

12. Previous balance $412.42

March 10	Billing date	
March 13	Returns CR	$28.18
March 15	School supplies	$16
March 20	Payment CR	$200
April 3	Gasoline	$28.45
April 5	Clothing	$86.80

$285.33; $4.28; $319.77

Solve the following application problems.

13. **CREDIT-CARD DEBT**   Jerry Jasper has an average daily balance of $2800.35 for the month on a credit card that charges 1.5% on the average daily balance. (a) Find the monthly finance charge. (b) Find the finance charge if he can change the loan to a credit card that charges 1% on the average unpaid balance. (c) Find the savings.   (a) $42.01 (b) $28 (c) $14.01

14. **REDUCING FINANCE CHARGES**   Maria Estefan has an average daily balance of $4509.66 for the month on a credit card that charges 1.8% on the average daily balance. (a) Find the monthly finance charge. (b) Find the finance charge if she can change the loan to a credit card that charges 1% on the average unpaid balance. (c) Find the savings.   (a) $81.17 (b) $45.10 (c) $36.07

15. **DREAM VACATION**   After taking his dream vacation to Europe, Benjamin Thompson has an average daily balance of $4850.39 on a credit card that charges 1.5% per month. (a) Find the interest charges. (b) Find the interest charges if he can change the loan to a credit card that charges 0.8% per month. (c) Find the savings.   (a) $72.76 (b) $38.80 (c) $33.96

16. **CREDIT-CARD DEBT**   Jerry Johnson has been ill and has an average daily balance of $16,432.51 on a credit card charging 1.6% interest. (a) Find the monthly finance charge. (b) Find the finance charge if he can change the loan to a credit card that charges 0.5% on the average daily balance. (c) Find the savings.   (a) $262.92 (b) $82.16 (c) $180.76

 17. Explain how the average daily balance is determined. (See Objective 3.)

 18. Explain how consolidating loans may be of some advantage to a credit-card holder. What disadvantages can you think of? (See Objective 4.)

 19. Suppose your brother owes $1200, $1500, and $2380 on credit cards charging 15%, 18%, and 24%, respectively. What would you recommend to your brother? Why? (See Objective 4.)

20. Make a table listing all your debts, showing the amount owed, monthly payment, and interest rate on each. Compare your debt payments to your monthly income. Try to move any significant credit-card debt to another card with a lower interest rate.

21. Victor Barton crushed his foot in a car accident. His insurance paid only a portion of his medical bills and he was left with $18,400 in related debt, which he ended up charging to a credit card that charges 1.5% per month on the average daily balance. Find the amount he can save each month if he can move the debt to a credit card that charges no interest for 1 year on balances transferred. $276

22. Ben Fuller has a debt of $13,850 from his years as a college student and he currently pays 1.25% per month in interest charges. Find the savings if he can move the debt to a credit card that charges no interest for 1 year on balances transferred. $173.13

16.2	Installment Loans

OBJECTIVES

1 *Define installment loan and annual percentage rate.*

2 *Find the total installment cost and finance charge.*

3 *Use a table to find the APR.*

Objective

1 *Define Installment Loan and Annual Percentage Rate.* A loan is **amortized** if both principal and interest are paid off by a sequence of periodic payments. An example is a payment of $440 per month for 48 months on a car loan. This type of loan is called an **installment loan**. Installment loans are used for cars, boats, home improvements, furniture, and even for consolidating several smaller loans into one affordable payment.

Since the enactment of the **Federal Truth-in-Lending Act (Regulation Z)** in 1969, lenders must report their **finance charge** (the charge for credit) and their **annual percentage rate (APR)** on installment loans. The Truth-in-Lending Act does *not* regulate interest rates or credit charges, but merely requires a standardized and truthful report of what they are to within one-eighth of a percent of the actual APR. In practice, many institutions round to the nearest one-quarter of a percent. Each state sets the allowable interest rates and charges. Lenders normally give borrowers a document such as the one in Figure 16.6, showing all credit charges.

The **nominal**, or **stated**, interest rate can differ from the APR. The APR is the *true effective annual interest rate* for a loan. For example, consider a 1-year loan of $1000 with a maturity value of $1120. The interest is $120. Look in the table below at the effect of time on the effective interest rate. Clearly not all loans with $1000 in proceeds and $120 in interest are equivalent.

TIME	CALCULATIONS	EFFECTIVE RATE
1 year	$R = \dfrac{\$120}{(\$1000 \times 1)}$	12%
$\frac{3}{4}$ year	$R = \dfrac{\$120}{\left(\$1000 \times \frac{3}{4}\right)}$	16%
$\frac{1}{2}$ year	$R = \dfrac{\$120}{\left(\$1000 \times \frac{1}{2}\right)}$	24%

Note and
Disclosure Statement

BORROWER NAME (Last – First – Middle Initial) AND ADDRESS (Street – City – State – Zip Code)	DATE	MEMBER NUMBER	NOTE NUMBER
Smith, John Q. 10123 Fair Oaks Blvd. Fair Oaks, CA 95628			

	CONTRACT NUMBER	REFERENCE NUMBER	MATURITY DATE
	012-2719-6	XXXXXXXXX	XXXXXXX

In this agreement "you" and "your" mean each person who signs this agreement. The "credit union" means the credit union whose name appears above and anyone to whom the credit union transfers its rights under this agreement. The terms on the reverse side are part of this agreement. Boxes checked below apply to this agreement.

TRUTH IN LENDING DISCLOSURE

ANNUAL PERCENTAGE RATE The cost of your credit as a yearly rate.	FINANCE CHARGE The dollar amount the credit will cost you.	Amount Financed The amount of credit provided to you or on your behalf.	Total of Payments The amount you will have paid when you have made all payments as scheduled.	Prepayment: If you pay off early you will not have to pay a penalty. e means an estimate
13.99%	$ 1,605.64	$ 6,800.00	$ 8,405.64	

	Number of Payments	Amount of Payments	When Payments Are Due	Property Insurance: You may obtain property insurance from anyone you want that is acceptable to the credit union.
Your Payment Schedule will be:	36	$233.49	monthly beginning May 15	XXXXXXXXXXXXXXXXXXXXXXXXXXXXXXXXXXXX $

Security: Collateral securing other loans with the credit union will also secure this loan. You are giving a security interest in your shares and/or deposits in the credit union; and **X** the goods/property being purchased; ☐ Other (Describe)

Late Charge: N/A	Filing Fees	Non-Filing Insurance
	$ N/A	$ N/A

See your contract documents for any additional information about nonpayment, default, and any required repayment in full before the scheduled date.

ITEMIZATION OF THE AMOUNT FINANCED

ITEMIZATION OF AMOUNT FINANCED OF $	AMOUNT GIVEN TO YOU DIRECTLY $	AMOUNT PAID ON YOUR ACCOUNT $	PREPAID FINANCE CHARGE $
AMOUNT PAID TO OTHERS $ ON YOUR BEHALF $	To To	$ $	To To

NOTE AND SECURITY AGREEMENT   CONTINUED ON REVERSE SIDE

Promise to Pay: You promise to pay $ _____ to the credit union plus interest on the unpaid balance at _____ % per year until what you owe has been repaid.

Collection Costs: You promise to pay all costs of collecting the amount you owe under this agreement including court costs and reasonable attorney fees.

Security Offered:	MODEL	YEAR	I.D. NUMBER	TYPE	VALUE
	Chevrolet Caprice		1NA1G1H96XE6811		

Other (Describe):

You Pledge Shares and/or Deposits of $ _____ in account number _____ Key No. _____ This Note is governed by the laws of **Illinois**

SIGNATURE: If you agree to make and be bound by the terms of this Note and Security Agreement sign below. *If you are not a borrower but an owner of the collateral for this loan, sign below and check the box for "Owner of Collateral". By doing so you agree only to the terms of the Security Agreement.*
CAUTION: IT IS IMPORTANT THAT YOU THOROUGHLY READ THIS CONTRACT BEFORE YOU SIGN IT.

Borrower **X** (SEAL)	Date	Borrower ☐ Owner of Collateral (other than a Borrower) **X** (SEAL)	Date
Borrower ☐ Owner of Collateral (other than a Borrower) **X** (SEAL)	Date	Witness **X**	Date

CREDIT INSURANCE APPLICATION

"You" or "Your" means the member and the joint insured (if applicable).

Credit insurance **is voluntary and not required in order to obtain this loan.** You may select any insurer of your choice. You can get this insurance only if you check the "yes" box below and sign your name and write in the date. The rate you are charged for the insurance is subject to change. You will receive written notice before any increase goes into effect. You have the right to stop this insurance by notifying your credit union in writing. Your signature below means you agree that:

- If you elect insurance, you authorize the credit union to add the charges for insurance to your loan each month.
- You are eligible for disability insurance only if you are working for wages or profit for 25 hours a

week or more on the date of any advance. If you are not, that particular advance will not be insured until you return to work. If you are off work because of temporary layoff, strike or vacation, but soon to resume, you will be considered at work. Are you working for wages or profit for 25 hours a week or more? ☐ Yes ☐ No

- You are eligible for insurance up to the Maximum Age for Insurance. Insurance will stop when you reach that age.

NOTE: THE LIFE AND DISABILITY INSURANCE CONTAINS CERTAIN BENEFIT EXCLUSIONS, INCLUDING A PRE-EXISTING CONDITION EXCLUSION. PLEASE REFER TO YOUR CERTIFICATE FOR DETAILS.

YOU ELECT THE FOLLOWING INSURANCE COVERAGE(S)	YES	NO	PREMIUM SCHEDULE	INSURANCE MAXIMUMS		DISABILITY	LIFE
CREDIT DISABILITY		X	$	e	MONTHLY TOTAL BENEFIT	$ 600	N/A
					INSURABLE BALANCE PER LOAN ACCOUNT	$50,000	N/A
					MAXIMUM AGE FOR INSURANCE	66	N/A

If you are totally disabled for more than **30** days, then the Disability Benefit will begin with the **31st** day of disability. | **SECONDARY** (If you desire to name one) **BENEFICIARY**

DATE April 3	DATE OF BIRTH	DATE	DATE OF BIRTH

SIGNATURE OF BORROWER ELIGIBLE TO BE INSURED (Be sure to check the boxes above.)	SIGNATURE OF JOINT INSURED (CO-BORROWER) (Only required if JOINT CREDIT LIFE coverage is selected)
X John Q. Smith	X N/A

Figure 16.6

Interest charges vary significantly from one loan to another and can be quite high. Look at Figure 16.7, which shows the added interest cost to finance a well-equipped automobile. The finance charge for a loan depends on the borrower's past credit record, income, down payment, and other factors. *It pays to shop and make comparisons based on APR figures before borrowing.*

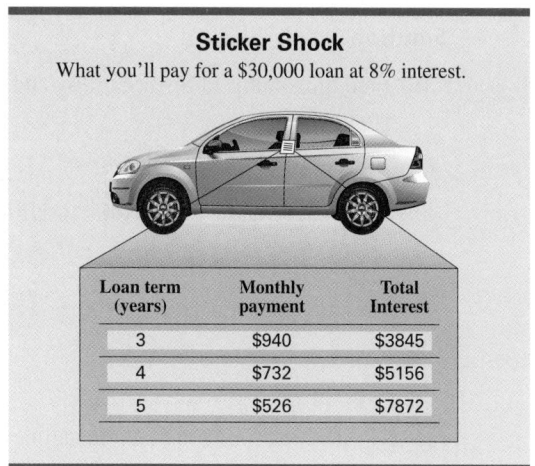

Sticker Shock
What you'll pay for a $30,000 loan at 8% interest.

Loan term (years)	Monthly payment	Total Interest
3	$940	$3845
4	$732	$5156
5	$526	$7872

Figure 16.7

Objective

2   *Find the Total Installment Cost and Finance Charge.* In order to find the annual percentage rate on a loan, it is necessary to first find the **total installment cost (deferred payment price)**, the **finance charge**, and the **amount financed**. We will then show how to find the annual percentage rate for an installment loan in Objective 3.

Finding Amount Financed

Step 1 Find the total installment cost.

Total installment cost = down payment
+ (amount of each payment × number of payments)

Step 2 Find the finance charge.

Finance charge = total installment cost − cash price

Step 3 Finally, find the amount financed.

Amount financed = cash price − down payment

NOTE Lenders frequently *allow the borrower to choose the day of the month* that installment payments are due. This allows the borrower to pay the bill after a payday for example.

EXAMPLE 1 **Finding Total Installment Cost, Amount Financed, and Finance Charge**

Ed Chamski makes his living by teaching piano both at home and at a nearby community college where he is a professor of music. He purchased a new baby grand piano for $8500 with $1500 down and 48 monthly payments of $184.34 each. Find (a) the total installment cost, (b) the finance charge, and (c) the amount financed.

Solution

(a) Find the total installment cost by adding the down payment to the total amount of all payments.

$$\text{Total installment cost} = \$1500 + 48 \times \$184.34 = \$10{,}348.32$$

(b) The finance charge is the total installment cost less the cash price.

$$\text{Finance charge} = \$10{,}348.32 - \$8500 = \$1848.32$$

(c) The amount financed is $8500 - $1500 = $7000.

NOTE In determining the total installment cost, the down payment is added to the total of the monthly payments.

Students frequently borrow money using a **Stafford loan**, which is a type of installment loan. The government pays the interest on a *subsidized* Stafford loan while the student borrower is in school on at least a half-time basis. On the other hand, the student is responsible for interest on *unsubsidized* Stafford loans. Repayment of a loan begins 6 months after the borrower ceases at least half-time enrollment. You can find information about Stafford loans at the financial aid office of your college or at a bank.

Objective

3 *Use a Table to Find the APR.* Annual percentage rate tables, available from the nearest federal reserve bank or the Board of Governors of the Federal Reserve System, Washington, D.C. 20551, are used for APR rates that *are accurate enough* to satisfy federal law. Table 16.2 shows a small portion of these tables.

The APR is found using the annual percentage rate table as follows.

Finding Annual Percentage Rate Using a Table

Step 1 Divide the finance charge by the amount financed, and multiply by $100.

$$\frac{\text{Finance charge}}{\text{Amount financed}} \times \$100$$

The result is the finance charge per $100 of the amount financed.

Step 2 Read down the left column of Table 16.2 to the proper number of payments. Go across to the number closest to the number found in Step 1. Read up the column to find the annual percentage rate.

NOTE Interest rates on installment loans are often higher than home mortgage rates and certainly much higher than the rates paid by banks on deposits.

Table 16.2 ANNUAL PERCENTAGE RATE TABLE FOR MONTHLY PAYMENT PLANS

Annual Percentage Rate (Finance Charge per $100 of Amount Financed)

Number of Payments	10.00%	10.25%	10.50%	10.75%	11.00%	11.25%	11.50%	11.75%	12.00%	12.25%	12.50%	12.75%	13.00%	13.25%	13.50%	13.75%
1	0.83	0.85	0.87	0.90	0.92	0.94	0.96	0.98	1.00	1.02	1.04	1.06	1.08	1.10	1.12	1.15
2	1.25	1.28	1.31	1.35	1.38	1.41	1.44	1.47	1.50	1.53	1.57	1.60	1.63	1.66	1.69	1.72
3	1.67	1.71	1.76	1.80	1.84	1.88	1.92	1.96	2.01	2.05	2.09	2.13	2.17	2.22	2.26	2.30
4	2.09	2.14	2.20	2.25	2.30	2.35	2.41	2.46	2.51	2.57	2.62	2.67	2.72	2.78	2.83	2.88
5	2.51	2.58	2.64	2.70	2.77	2.83	2.89	2.96	3.02	3.08	3.15	3.21	3.27	3.34	3.40	3.46
6	2.94	3.01	3.08	3.16	3.23	3.31	3.38	3.45	3.53	3.60	3.68	3.75	3.83	3.90	3.97	4.05
7	3.36	3.45	3.53	3.62	3.70	3.78	3.87	3.95	4.04	4.12	4.21	4.29	4.38	4.47	4.55	4.64
8	3.79	3.88	3.98	4.07	4.17	4.26	4.36	4.46	4.55	4.65	4.74	4.84	4.94	5.03	5.13	5.22
9	4.21	4.32	4.43	4.53	4.64	4.75	4.85	4.96	5.07	5.17	5.28	5.39	5.49	5.60	5.71	5.82
10	4.64	4.76	4.88	4.99	5.11	5.23	5.35	5.46	5.58	5.70	5.82	5.94	6.05	6.17	6.29	6.41
11	5.07	5.20	5.33	5.45	5.58	5.71	5.84	5.97	6.10	6.23	6.36	6.49	6.62	6.75	6.88	7.01
12	5.50	5.64	5.78	5.92	6.06	6.20	6.34	6.48	6.62	6.76	6.90	7.04	7.18	7.32	7.46	7.60
13	5.93	6.08	6.23	6.38	6.53	6.68	6.84	6.99	7.14	7.29	7.44	7.59	7.75	7.90	8.05	8.20
14	6.36	6.52	6.69	6.85	7.01	7.17	7.34	7.50	7.65	7.82	7.99	8.15	8.31	8.48	8.64	8.81
15	6.80	6.97	7.14	7.32	7.49	7.66	7.84	8.01	8.19	8.36	8.53	8.71	8.88	9.06	9.23	9.41
16	7.23	7.41	7.60	7.78	7.97	8.15	8.34	8.53	8.71	8.90	9.08	9.27	9.46	9.64	9.83	10.02
17	7.67	7.86	8.06	8.25	8.45	8.65	8.84	9.04	9.24	9.44	9.63	9.83	10.03	10.23	10.43	10.63
18	8.10	8.31	8.52	8.73	8.93	9.14	9.35	9.56	9.77	9.98	10.19	10.40	10.61	10.82	11.03	11.24
19	8.54	8.76	8.98	9.20	9.42	9.64	9.86	10.08	10.30	10.52	10.74	10.96	11.18	11.41	11.63	11.85
20	8.98	9.21	9.44	9.67	9.90	10.13	10.37	10.60	10.83	11.06	11.30	11.53	11.76	12.00	12.23	12.46
21	9.42	9.66	9.90	10.15	10.39	10.63	10.88	11.12	11.36	11.61	11.85	12.10	12.34	12.59	12.84	13.08
22	9.86	10.12	10.37	10.62	10.88	11.13	11.39	11.64	11.90	12.16	12.41	12.67	12.93	13.19	13.44	13.70
23	10.30	10.57	10.84	11.10	11.37	11.63	11.90	12.17	12.44	12.71	12.97	13.24	13.51	13.78	14.05	14.32
24	10.75	11.02	11.30	11.58	11.86	12.14	12.42	12.70	12.98	13.26	13.54	13.82	14.10	14.38	14.66	14.95
25	11.19	11.48	11.77	12.06	12.35	12.64	12.93	13.22	13.52	13.81	14.10	14.40	14.69	14.98	15.28	15.57
26	11.64	11.94	12.24	12.54	12.85	13.15	13.45	13.75	14.06	14.36	14.67	14.97	15.28	15.59	15.89	16.20
27	12.09	12.40	12.71	13.03	13.34	13.66	13.97	14.29	14.60	14.92	15.24	15.56	15.87	16.19	16.51	16.83
28	12.53	12.86	13.18	13.51	13.84	14.16	14.49	14.82	15.15	15.48	15.81	16.14	16.47	16.80	17.13	17.46
29	12.98	13.32	13.66	14.00	14.33	14.67	15.01	15.35	15.70	16.04	16.38	16.72	17.07	17.41	17.75	18.10
30	13.43	13.78	14.13	14.48	14.83	15.19	15.54	15.89	16.24	16.60	16.95	17.31	17.66	18.02	18.38	18.74

Table 16.2 (CONTINUED) ANNUAL PERCENTAGE RATE TABLE FOR MONTHLY PAYMENT PLANS

Annual Percentage Rate (Finance Charge per $100 of Amount Financed)

Number of Payments	10.00%	10.25%	10.50%	10.75%	11.00%	11.25%	11.50%	11.75%	12.00%	12.25%	12.50%	12.75%	13.00%	13.25%	13.50%	13.75%
31	13.89	14.25	14.61	14.97	15.33	15.70	16.06	16.43	16.79	17.16	17.53	17.90	18.27	18.63	19.00	19.38
32	14.34	14.71	15.09	15.46	15.84	16.21	16.59	16.97	17.35	17.73	18.11	18.49	18.87	19.25	19.63	20.02
33	14.79	15.18	15.57	15.95	16.34	16.73	17.12	17.51	17.90	18.29	18.69	19.08	19.47	19.87	20.26	20.66
34	15.25	15.65	16.05	16.44	16.85	17.25	17.65	18.05	18.46	18.86	19.27	19.67	20.08	20.49	20.90	21.31
35	15.70	16.11	16.53	16.94	17.35	17.77	18.18	18.60	19.01	19.43	19.85	20.27	20.69	21.11	21.53	21.95
36	16.16	16.58	17.01	17.43	17.86	18.29	18.71	19.14	19.57	20.00	20.43	20.87	21.30	21.73	22.17	22.60
37	16.62	17.06	17.49	17.93	18.37	18.81	19.25	19.69	20.13	20.58	21.02	21.46	21.91	22.36	22.81	23.25
38	17.08	17.53	17.98	18.43	18.88	19.33	19.78	20.24	20.69	21.15	21.61	22.07	22.52	22.99	23.45	23.91
39	17.54	18.00	18.46	18.93	19.39	19.86	20.32	20.79	21.26	21.73	22.20	22.67	23.14	23.61	24.09	24.56
40	18.00	18.48	18.95	19.43	19.90	20.38	20.86	21.34	21.82	22.30	22.79	23.27	23.76	24.25	24.73	25.22
41	18.47	18.95	19.44	19.93	20.42	20.91	21.40	21.89	22.39	22.88	23.38	23.88	24.38	24.88	25.38	25.88
42	18.93	19.43	19.93	20.43	20.93	21.44	21.94	22.45	22.96	23.47	23.98	24.49	25.00	25.51	26.03	26.55
43	19.40	19.91	20.42	20.94	21.45	21.97	22.49	23.01	23.53	24.05	24.57	25.10	25.62	26.15	26.68	27.21
44	19.86	20.39	20.91	21.44	21.97	22.50	23.03	23.57	24.10	24.64	25.17	25.71	26.25	26.79	27.33	27.88
45	20.33	20.87	21.41	21.95	22.49	23.03	23.58	24.12	24.67	25.22	25.77	26.32	26.88	27.43	27.99	28.55
46	20.80	21.35	21.90	22.46	23.01	23.57	24.13	24.69	25.25	25.81	26.37	26.94	27.51	28.08	28.65	29.22
47	21.27	21.83	22.40	22.97	23.53	24.10	24.68	25.25	25.82	26.40	26.98	27.56	28.14	28.72	29.31	29.89
48	21.74	22.32	22.90	23.48	24.06	24.64	25.23	25.81	26.40	26.99	27.58	28.18	28.77	29.37	29.97	30.57
49	22.21	22.80	23.39	23.99	24.58	25.18	25.78	26.38	26.98	27.59	28.19	28.80	29.41	30.02	30.63	31.24
50	22.69	23.29	23.89	24.50	25.11	25.72	26.33	26.95	27.56	28.18	28.80	29.42	30.04	30.67	31.29	31.92
51	23.16	23.78	24.40	25.02	25.64	26.26	26.89	27.52	28.15	28.78	29.41	30.05	30.68	31.32	31.96	32.60
52	23.64	24.27	24.90	25.53	26.17	26.81	27.45	28.09	28.73	29.38	30.02	30.67	31.32	31.98	32.63	33.29
53	24.11	24.76	25.40	26.05	26.70	27.35	28.00	28.66	29.32	29.98	30.64	31.30	31.97	32.63	33.30	33.97
54	24.59	25.25	25.91	26.57	27.23	27.90	28.56	29.23	29.91	30.58	31.25	31.93	32.61	33.29	33.98	34.66
55	25.07	25.74	26.41	27.09	27.77	28.44	29.13	29.81	30.50	31.18	31.87	32.56	33.26	33.95	34.65	35.35
56	25.55	26.23	26.92	27.61	28.30	28.99	29.69	30.39	31.09	31.79	32.49	33.20	33.91	34.62	35.33	36.04
57	26.03	26.73	27.43	28.13	28.84	29.54	30.25	30.97	31.68	32.39	33.11	33.83	34.56	35.28	36.01	36.74
58	26.51	27.23	27.94	28.66	29.37	30.10	30.82	31.55	32.27	33.00	33.74	34.47	35.21	35.95	36.69	37.43
59	27.00	27.72	28.45	29.18	29.91	30.65	31.39	32.13	32.87	33.61	34.36	35.11	35.86	36.62	37.37	38.13
60	27.48	28.22	28.96	29.71	30.45	31.20	31.96	32.71	33.47	34.23	34.99	35.75	36.52	37.29	38.06	38.83

EXAMPLE 2 Finding Annual Percentage Rate

Toots McGee placed a $2400 down payment on a new Subaru Outback with a total cost of $25,400. She needed the all-wheel drive (AWD) of the Subaru for the snowy conditions in Minnesota where she lives. She signed a note with payments of $494.40 for 60 months. Find the annual percentage rate.

Solution

$$\text{Total installment cost} = \text{down payment} + \text{sum of all payments}$$
$$= \$2400 + 60 \times \$494.40 = \$32,064$$
$$\text{Finance charge} = \text{total installment cost} - \text{cash price}$$
$$= \$32,064 - \$25,400 = \$6664$$
$$\text{Amount financed} = \text{cash price} - \text{down payment}$$
$$= \$25,400 - \$2400 = \$23,000$$

Now find the annual percentage rate.

$$\frac{\text{Finance charge}}{\text{Amount financed}} \times \$100 = \frac{\$6664}{\$23,000} \times \$100$$
$$= \$28.97 \text{ in finance charges per } \$100 \text{ financed}$$

The nearest value in the table on the 60 payment row is $28.96 which corresponds to an interest rate of 10.50%. The APR is 10.50%.

Financial Calculator Approach

In Example 2, a more precise value of the APR can be found using a financial calculator. Payment, number of compounding periods, and present value (loan amount) are known. The interest rate per compounding period is unknown.

$$-494.40 \boxed{PMT}\ 60 \boxed{n}\ 23000 \boxed{PV}\ \boxed{i}\ 0.87529468$$

Multiply this rate per month by 12 months to get an annual rate of $0.87529468 \times 12 = 10.50\%$ (rounded).

16.2 | Exercises

Find the finance charge and the total installment cost for the following. (See Example 1.)

	Amount Financed	Down Payment	Cash Price	Number of Payments	Amount of Payment	Total Installment Cost	Finance Charge
1.	$12,400	$5000	$17,400	60	$264.94	$20,896.40	$3496.40
2.	$650	$125	$775	24	$32	$893	$118
3.	$150	None	$150	12	$15	$180	$30
4.	$1200	None	$1200	20	$70	$1400	$200
5.	$780	$300	$1080	10	$90	$1200	$120
6.	$490	None	$490	12	$43.30	$519.60	$29.60

Find the annual percentage rate using Table 16.2. (See Example 2.)

	Amount Financed	Finance Charge	No. of Monthly Payments	APR
7.	$1850	$157.30	15	12.50%
8.	$345	$24.62	12	13%
9.	$442	$28.68	14	10.25%
10.	$4690	$1237.22	48	12%
11.	$145	$13.25	18	11.25%
12.	$650	$73.45	24	10.50%

 13. Explain the difference between open-end credit and installment loans. (See **Section 16.1** and Objective 1 of this section.)

14. Find the APR on one of your personal loans. (See Objective 3.)

Solve the following application problems. Express annual percentage rate to the nearest one hundredth of a percent.

15. FLAT-SCREEN TV Rudolf Heston bought a flat-screen TV with special sound speakers for $1800 so that he and his friends could watch sports together. He paid $200 down and agreed to payments of $142.16 per month for 12 months. Find the annual percentage rate. 12.00%

16. REFRIGERATOR PURCHASE Sears offers a refrigerator for $960 with no down payment, $176.44 in interest charges, and 30 equal payments. Find the annual percentage rate. 13.50%

17. LIVING ROOM SET Judy and Charles Bitters purchased a complete living room set for $2725. They paid $500 down and financed the balance with payments of $258.69 for 9 months. Find the annual percentage rate. 11.00%

18. SOFA ON SALE A department store has a sofa on sale for $900. A buyer paying 20% down finances the balance by paying $34.30 per month for 2 years. Find the annual percentage rate that the store must include in its advertising. 13.25%

19. COMPUTER SYSTEM PURCHASE A contractor in Mexico City purchases a computer system for 650,000 pesos. After making a down payment of 100,000 pesos, he agrees to payments of 26,342.18 pesos per month for 24 months. Find (a) the total installment cost and (b) the annual percentage rate. (a) 732,212.32 pesos (b) 13.75%

20. TRUCK PURCHASE An electrical contractor in Hiroshima, Japan, purchases a truck costing 2,700,000 yen. He makes a down payment of 1,000,000 yen and agrees to monthly payments of 54,855 yen for 36 months. Find (a) the total installment cost and (b) the annual percentage rate. (a) 2,974,780 yen (b) 10.00%

21. STORE EXPANSION Dillon Sporting Goods borrows $180,000 to expand its store to include winter sporting supplies such as skis and snowmobiles. It makes no down payment but agrees to monthly payments of $6974.66 for 30 months. Find (a) the total installment cost and (b) the annual percentage rate. (a) $209,239.80 (b) 12.00%

22. ENGINE REPLACEMENT Jose Yaki purchased a new 505-horsepower engine for his 2006 Corvette for $11,450. He made a down payment of $5000 and agreed to make 24 payments of $305.15. Find the annual percentage rate. 12.50%

 23. When are people more likely to use installment loans rather than open-end credit? (*Hint:* Search your local newspaper for examples.)

 24. Which type of loan tends to have higher interest rates—installment loans or credit loans? Document this with several examples of each type of loan.

16.3	**Early Payoffs of Loans**

OBJECTIVES

1 *Use the United States Rule when prepaying a loan.*
2 *Find the amount due on the maturity date using the United States Rule.*
3 *Find the balance due after missing a payment.*
4 *Use the Rule of 78 when prepaying a loan.*

Objective

1 *Use the United States Rule When Prepaying a Loan.* It is common for a payment to be made on a loan *before it is due*. This may occur when a person receives extra money or when a debt is refinanced elsewhere. Prepayments of loans are discussed in this section.

The first method for calculating the effect of an early loan payment is the **United States Rule**, which is used by the U.S. government as well as most states and financial institutions. Under the United States Rule, any payment is first applied to any interest owed. The balance of the payment is then used to reduce the principal amount of the loan.

The United States Rule

Step 1 Find the simple interest due from the date the loan was made until the date the partial payment is made. Use the formula $I = PRT$.
Step 2 Subtract this interest from the amount of the payment.
Step 3 Any difference is used to reduce the principal.
Step 4 Treat additional partial payments in the same way, always finding interest on *only* the unpaid balance after the last partial payment.

The remaining unpaid principal plus interest on this unpaid principal is then due on the maturity date of the loan.

Objective

2 *Find the Amount Due on the Maturity Date Using the United States Rule.* If the partial payment is not large enough to pay the interest due, the payment is either held in suspension until enough money is available to pay the interest due or the payment is rejected and returned. Either way, the borrower is contacted. This means that making a partial payment smaller than the interest due *offers no advantage* to the borrower—the lender just holds the partial payment until enough money is available to pay the interest owed.

EXAMPLE 1	Finding the Amount Due

On August 14, Jane Ficker signed a 180-day note for $28,500 for an X-ray machine for her dental office. The note has an interest rate of 10%. On October 25, a payment of $8500 is made. (a) Find the balance owed on the principal. (b) If no additional payments are made, find the amount due at maturity of the loan.

Solution

(a) First, find that there are 72 days from August 14 to October 25. Then find simple interest using $I = PRT$.

$$\text{Interest} = \$28{,}500 \times 0.10 \times \frac{72}{360} = \$570$$

Subtract the interest from the October 25 payment to find the amount of the payment to be applied to principal. Then reduce the original principal by this amount.

$$\text{Applied to principal} = \$8500 - \$570 = \$7930$$
$$\text{New principal} = \$28{,}500 - \$7930 = \$20{,}570$$

(b) The note was originally for 180 days with the partial payment made after 72 days. Thus, interest on the new principal of \$20,570 will be charged for $180 - 72 = 108$ days.

$$\text{Interest} = \$20{,}570 \times 0.10 \times \frac{108}{360} = \$617.10$$

If no additional partial payments are made, the amount due at the maturity date is the remaining principal plus interest on that remaining principal.

$$\text{Amount due at maturity} = \$20{,}570 + \$617.10 = \$21{,}187.10$$

In order to find the total interest paid when partial payments are made, the individual interest payments are added.

EXAMPLE **2** **Finding Total Interest Paid**

A lawn furniture manufacturer signs a 140-day note on February 5. The note, for \$45,600, is to a supplier of aluminum tubing for the furniture and carries a simple interest rate of 12%. On March 19, the manufacturer receives an unexpected payment from one of its customers and applies \$16,000 toward the note. A further early payment permits a second \$13,250 partial payment on April 23. Find the interest paid on the note and the amount paid on the due date of the note.

Solution

The first partial payment was made on March 19, which is 42 days after the loan was made. In 42 days, the interest on the note is found using $I = PRT$.

$$I = \$45{,}600 \times 0.12 \times \frac{42}{360} = \$638.40$$

A partial payment of \$16,000 was made on March 19. Of this amount, \$638.40 is applied to interest.

\$16,000.00	Amount of payment
− 638.40	Interest owed
\$15,361.60	Applied to principal

After the partial payment on March 19, the balance on the loan is found as follows.

\$45,600.00	Original amount of loan
− 15,361.60	Applied to principal
\$30,238.40	New amount owed

A second partial payment is made on April 23, which is $12 + 23 = 35$ days later. Find interest on \$30,238.40 for 35 days.

$$I = \$30{,}238.40 \times 0.12 \times \frac{35}{360} = \$352.78$$

A payment of \$13,250 is made on April 23. Of this, \$352.78 applies to interest, leaving

$$\$13{,}250 - \$352.78 = \$12{,}897.22$$

to reduce the principal. After the partial payment on April 23, the principal is as follows.

$$
\begin{array}{ll}
\$30,238.40 & \text{Previous balance} \\
-\ 12,897.22 & \text{Applied to principal} \\
\hline
\$17,341.18 & \text{New principal}
\end{array}
$$

The first partial payment was made 42 days after the note was signed, with the second payment made 35 days after that. The second payment was made $42 + 35 = 77$ days after the note was signed. Since the note was for 140 days, the note is due

$$140 - 77 = 63$$

days after the second partial payment. Interest on the new balance of $17,341.18 for 63 days is

$$I = \$17,341.18 \times 0.12 \times \frac{63}{360} = \$364.16$$

On the date the loan matures, a total of

$$\$17,341.18 + \$364.16 = \$17,705.34$$

must be paid. The total interest paid over the life of the loan is

$$\$638.40 + \$352.78 + \$364.16 = \$1355.34$$

All this work is summarized in the following table.

Date Payment Made	Amount of Payment	Applied to Interest	Applied to Principal	Remaining Balance
March 19	$16,000	$638.40	$15,361.60	$30,238.40
April 23	13,250	352.78	12,897.22	17,341.18
Date of maturity (June 25)	17,705.34	364.16	17,341.18	0
Totals		$1355.34	$45,600.00	

Objective

3

Find the Balance Due after Missing a Payment. The next example shows what happens when a payment is missed.

EXAMPLE 3 **Finding Balance Due After a Missed Payment**

On March 5, Susan Richter bought $\frac{1}{2}$ acre of land with a 3-year-old mobile home for $49,900 from an elderly couple. She paid $2000 down and signed a promissory note with monthly payments of $887.39 for 6 years at 10% interest. She made the first payment on April 1, but missed the May 1 payment due to expenses related to a car accident. Richter called the couple and discussed her situation. They agreed not to charge her a penalty for the missed payment, but interest charges would continue to apply. Find the loan balance if Richter makes a regular payment on June 1 if interest is based on the number of days since the last payment.

Solution

$$\text{Amount financed} = \$49,900 - \$2000 = \$47,900$$

1ST PAYMENT MADE ON APRIL 1:

Number of days from March 5 to April 1 is 27.

Interest from March 5 to April 1 $= \$47,900 \times 0.10 \times \dfrac{27}{360} = \$359.25$

Amount applied to principal $= \$887.39 - \$359.25 = \$528.14$
Balance after 1st payment $= \$47,900 - \$528.14 = \$47,371.86$

2ND PAYMENT WAS NOT MADE:

Lender agreed not to charge a penalty.
Interest continues to accrue.

3RD PAYMENT WAS MADE ON JUNE 1:

Number of days from April 1 to June 1 is 61.

Interest from April 1 to June 1 $= \$47,371.86 \times 0.10 \times \dfrac{61}{360} = \$802.69$

Payment of \$887.39 on June 1 is larger than interest due of \$802.69.
Amount applied to principal $= \$887.39 - \$802.69 = \$84.70$
Principal after June 1 payment $= \$47,371.86 - \$84.70 = \$47,287.16$

Her loan balance will go down as long as she makes the regular payments. Many lenders would have charged Richter a penalty for a missed or late payment. If the elderly couple had charged Richter a penalty, it would have been taken out of the June 1 payment before interest. Thus, a payment is used first to pay a penalty and to then pay interest. Finally, anything remaining is used to reduce the principal.

NOTE A good discussion question relates to whether it is ethical for a lending bank to charge a penalty for one missed payment by a borrower who has always made payments in a timely way, but who was seriously injured in a car accident.

Objective

4 *Use the Rule of 78 When Prepaying a Loan.* A variation of the United States Rule, called the **Rule of 78**, is still used by many lenders. The rule of 78 is sometimes called the **sum-of-the-balances method** when the length of the contract is other than 1 year. This rule allows a lender to earn more of the finance charge during the early months of the loan compared to the United States Rule. Lenders typically use this rule to protect against early payoffs on *small loans*. Effectively, the lender will earn a higher rate of interest in the event of an early payoff under the Rule of 78 than under the United States Rule. The Rule of 78 *favors the lender* in the event of an early payoff.

NOTE Some individuals suggest that the Rule of 78 should be banned, believing that it gives lenders unfair advantage. On the other hand, some lenders support the rule, saying that it compensates them for the costs of setting up loans for borrowers who repay a loan quickly.

The Rule of 78 gets its name from a loan of 12 months—the sum of the months $1 + 2 + 3 + \cdots + 12 = 78$. The finance charge for the first month is $\frac{12}{78}$ of the total finance charge, with $\frac{11}{78}$ in the second month, $\frac{10}{78}$ in the third month, and $\frac{1}{78}$ in the final month. The Rule of 78 can be applied to loans with terms other than 12 months. For example, the sum of the months in a 6-month contract is $1 + 2 + 3 + 4 + 5 + 6 = 21$. The finance charge for the first month would be $\frac{6}{21}$, $\frac{5}{21}$ for the second month, and so on.

The **unearned interest**, or interest not earned by the lender under the Rule of 78 for a loan of 12 months, depends on the month in which the loan is paid off. The unearned interest is returned to the borrower. If the loan is paid off at the end of 2 months, then the interest earned by the lender is $\frac{12}{78} + \frac{11}{78} = \frac{23}{78}$ of the finance charge. Thus, the interest not earned by the lender is

$$1 - \frac{23}{78} \qquad \text{or, equivalently,} \qquad \frac{1}{78} + \frac{2}{78} + \cdots + \frac{10}{78}$$

which is $\frac{55}{78}$ of the finance charges. The process is similar for loans of lengths other than 12 months.

Finding Unearned Interest

The unearned interest is given by

$$U = F\left(\frac{N}{P}\right)\left(\frac{1 + N}{1 + P}\right)$$

where U = unearned interest, F = finance charge, N = number of payments remaining, and P = total number of payments.

EXAMPLE 4 **Finding Payoff Value**

Richard Buck borrowed $1800 that he is paying back in 24 monthly payments of $88.50 each. With 9 payments remaining, he decides to repay the loan in full. Find (a) the amount of unearned finance charge and (b) the amount necessary to repay the loan in full.

Solution

(a) Total installment cost = 24 × $88.50 = $2124

   Finance charge   = $2124 − $1800 = $324

   The amount of unearned interest is found as follows. The finance charge is $324, the scheduled number of payments is 24, and the loan is paid off with 9 payments left. Use the formula.

$$\text{Unearned interest} = \$324 \times \left(\frac{9}{24}\right) \times \frac{(1 + 9)}{(1 + 24)}$$

$$= \$324 \times \left(\frac{9 \times 10}{24 \times 25}\right)$$

$$= \$48.60$$

Paying off the loan 9 months early produces a savings of $48.60 in interest.

(b) When Buck decides to pay off the loan, he has 9 payments of $88.50 left. These payments total as follows.

$$9 \times \$88.50 = \$796.50$$

By paying the loan early, Buck saves the unearned interest of $48.60, so

$$\$796.50 - \$48.60 = \$747.90$$

is needed to pay the loan in full.

Scientific
Calculator
Approach

The calculator solution to Example 4 is as follows.

(a) First think of the problem as $\dfrac{(324 \times 9 \times (1 + 9))}{(24 \times (1 + 24))}$ or as $\dfrac{324 \times 9 \times 10}{24 \times 25}$, then solve.

$$(\boxed{324} \times \boxed{9} \times (\boxed{1} + \boxed{9})) \div$$

$$(\boxed{24} \times (\boxed{1} + \boxed{24})) = \boxed{48.6} \text{ STO}$$

(b) $9 \times \boxed{88.5} - \text{RCL} = \boxed{747.9}$

16.3 | Exercises

Find the balance due on the maturity date of the following notes. Find the total amount of interest paid on the note. Use the United States Rule.

	Principal	Interest	Time in Days	Partial Payments	
1.	$6500	8%	100	$1500 on day 56	$5130.57; $130.57
2.	$5800	10%	120	$2500 on day 60	$3453.28; $153.28
3.	$8500	12%	150	$5000 on day 45	$3754.46; $254.46
4.	$6000	$10\frac{1}{2}$%	130	$3000 on day 100	$3202.78; $202.78
5.	$10,000	$8\frac{1}{4}$%	180	$6000 on day 120	$4333.78; $333.78
6.	$12,600	$11\frac{1}{2}$%	140	$8000 on day 100	$5066.42; $466.42

Each of the following loans is paid in full before its date of maturity. Find the amount of unearned interest. Use the Rule of 78.

	Finance Charge	Total Number of Payments	Remaining Number of Payments When Paid in Full	
7.	$975	48	30	$385.52
8.	$325	36	6	$10.25
9.	$460	20	4	$21.90
10.	$325	24	22	$274.08
11.	$3653.82	48	9	$139.81
12.	$3085.54	60	15	$202.33

 13. Explain the concept of the United States Rule. When is the United States Rule likely to be applied? (See Objective 1.)

 14. Explain the concept of the Rule of 78. When is the Rule of 78 likely to be applied? (See Objective 4.)

 15. Why is it of no advantage to the borrower to make a partial payment smaller than the amount of interest due? What would the lender do with this payment? (See Objective 2.)

 16. List some advantages of paying loans off faster than required.

Solve the following application problems.

17. COMPUTER CONSULTANT   The computer system at Genome Therapy crashed several times last year. On January 10, the company borrows $125,000 at 11% for 250 days to pay a consultant for some equipment and work on their Novell network. However, managers decide to pay the loan in full on July 1. Find (a) the interest due and (b) the total amount due using the United States Rule.   (a) $6569.44 (b) $131,569.44

18. **LOAN REPAYMENT**   Titus Czech signed a 100-day note for $2800 at 15% compounded annually but repaid the loan in full in 80 days instead. Find (a) the interest paid and (b) the amount due in 80 days using the United States Rule.   (a) $93.33 (b) $2893.33

19. **HOME REMODELING**   Freida Batherson signed a note with proceeds of $8400 and a monthly payment of $383.75 for 24 months to remodel her kitchen. Find the amount of unearned interest using the Rule of 78 if she uses her income tax refund to pay off the loan in month 14. $148.50

20. **EARLY PAYOFF**   George Duda has decided that making the small monthly payment on a 6-month loan is a nuisance. The total finance charge is only $34, and the loan is paid in full with 3 months remaining. Find the unearned interest using the Rule of 78. $9.71

21. **EASY PAYMENT PLAN**   Anne Kelly purchased a refrigerator on the "easy payment plan" with only $100 down and 18 equal monthly payments of $45.20. The total cash price of the refrigerator was $800. After making 6 monthly payments, she decided to pay the loan in full. Use the Rule of 78 and find (a) the amount of unearned interest and (b) the amount necessary to pay the loan in full.   (a) $51.82 (b) $490.58

22. **FINANCING A USED CAR**   A used car costs $8850. After a down payment of $2000, the balance is financed with 48 payments of $194.25 each. The loan is paid off with 15 payments left. Use the Rule of 78 to find (a) the amount of unearned interest and (b) the amount necessary to pay the loan in full.   (a) $252.45 (b) $2661.30

23. **PAPER GOODS INVENTORY**   To save on freight charges, Wholesale Paper orders large quantities of basic paper goods every 4 months. For its last order, the firm signed a note on February 18 that matures on May 15. The face value of the note was $104,500, with interest of 11%. The firm made a partial payment of $38,000 on March 20, with a second partial payment of $27,200 on April 16. Find the amount due on the maturity date of the note and the amount of interest paid on the note using the United States Rule. $41,176.11; $1876.11

24. **TESTING EQUIPMENT**   Mid-City Electronics bought new testing equipment, paying for it with a note for $32,000. The note was made on July 26 and is due on November 20. The interest rate is 13%. The firm made a partial payment of $6000 on August 31, with a second partial payment of $11,700 on October 4. Find the amount due on the maturity date of the note and the amount of interest paid on the note using the United States Rule. $15,295.60; $995.60

25. **MISSED PAYMENT**   James Thompson's loan balance after his May 3 payment was $11,832.20. He missed the June 3 payment but made a payment of $463.12 on July 8. No penalty was charged and the loan has an interest rate of 9% simple interest. Find (a) the number of days from May 3 to July 8 and (b) the loan balance on July 8.   (a) 66 days (b) $11,564.31

26. **MISSED PAYMENT**   Pam Cunningham borrowed money to start up a pet store and owed $14,940.87 on November 7. She missed the December payment but she was able to make a larger-than-usual payment of $800 on January 4. No penalty was charged and the loan has an interest rate of 12% simple interest. Find (a) the number of days from November 7 to January 4 and (b) the loan balance on January 4.   (a) 58 days (b) $14,429.73

16.4	**Personal Property Loans**

OBJECTIVES

1 *Define personal property and real estate.*

2 *Use the formula for amortization to find payment.*

3 *Set up an amortization table.*

4 *Find monthly payments.*

1 *Define Personal Property and Real Estate.* Items that can be moved from one location to another, such as an automobile, a boat, or a stereo, are called **personal property**. In contrast, buildings, land, and homes cannot be moved and are called **real estate**, or **real property**. Personal property loans are discussed in this section and real estate loans are discussed in the next section. Both types are installment loans.

As the following headline suggests, people can end up with more debt than they can afford. In that event, individuals are sometimes forced to return personal property such as an automobile to the lender. When this happens, the property is said to be **repossessed** by the lender.

Students Cautioned about
Too Much Debt . . .

2 *Use the Formula for Amortization to Find Payment.* Paying for something in full up front means that no loan is needed. But usually more expensive items are purchased on credit and require a series of regular payments. A loan is said to be **amortized** if both principal and interest are paid off in a *sequence of equal payments made at regular intervals.*

The amount of each payment can be calculated using the formula, given in **Section 15.2**, for the present value A of an annuity with payment R, interest rate per period i, and n periods. The formula is repeated here for convenience.

$$A = R\left[\frac{(1 + i)^n - 1}{i(1 + i)^n}\right]$$

The unknown in **Section 15.2** was the present value A. Now the present value (loan amount) is known along with the interest rate per compounding period and number of periods—the payment R is the unknown. The equation above can be solved for R and a scientific calculator can be used to calculate payments. Alternatively, you can use the tables in **Appendix C** and solve the equation $A = R \cdot a_{\overline{n}|i}$ for R.

The periodic payment R needed to amortize a loan of A dollars with interest of i per period for n periods follows.

$$R = A\left(\frac{1}{a_{\overline{n}|i}}\right)$$

The notation $a_{\overline{n}|i}$ is read "*a*-angle–*n*-at-*i*." Values of $\frac{1}{a_{\overline{n}|i}}$ for different n's and i's can be found in column F of **Appendix C**. Thus, the periodic payment R is found by multiplying the loan amount A by a number taken from the table in **Appendix C**.

EXAMPLE **1** **Finding Amortization Information**

Pablo Valdez recently accepted a job as a designer of World Wide Web pages. Valdez and his spouse, a teacher and avid water skier, decide to borrow $15,000 to purchase a new ski boat. They borrow the funds for 36 months at 12% per year. Find (a) the monthly payment, (b) the portion of the first payment that is interest, (c) the balance due after one payment, (d) the interest owed for the second month, and (e) the balance after the second payment.

Solution

(a) Use $\dfrac{12\%}{12} = 1\%$ per period for i and 36 periods for n in the amortization table in **Appendix C** to find 0.03321431.

$$\text{Monthly payment} = \$15,000 \times 0.03321431 = \$498.21 \quad \text{\small Rounded}$$

(b) Interest for the month is found using the simple interest formula $I = PRT$.

$$I = \$15,000 \times 0.12 \times \frac{1}{12} = \$150$$

$$\text{Amount used to reduce principal} = \$498.21 - \$150$$
$$= \$348.21$$

(c) Balance after 1st payment $= \$15,000 - \$348.21$
$$= \$14,651.79$$

(d) Interest for 2nd month $= \$14,651.79 \times 0.12 \times \dfrac{1}{12}$
$$= \$146.52$$

$$\text{Amount used to reduce principal} = \$498.21 - \$146.52$$
$$= \$351.69$$

(e) Balance after 2nd payment $= \$14,651.79 - \$351.69$
$$= \$14,300.10$$

 Financial Calculator Approach

The unknown payment in Example 1 can also be found using a financial calculator. Enter the known values for present value, number of compounding periods, and interest rate per compounding period.

$$15000 \boxed{PV}\ 36 \boxed{n}\ 1 \boxed{i}\ \boxed{PMT}\ -498.21$$

$$12\% \div 12 \text{ months} = 1\% \text{ per month}$$

Objective

3 *Set up an Amortization Table.* An **amortization table**, or **schedule**, shows the amount of each payment that goes to interest and to principal. It also shows the debt remaining after each payment. One excellent way to calculate an amortization table is to use spreadsheet software. Sometimes, amortization tables are referred to as **loan repayment tables**.

> **NOTE** Be sure to round interest to the nearest cent each time before proceeding.

EXAMPLE 2 Finding Payments, Interest, and Loan Balances

A contractor agrees to pay $15,000 for a new computer system. This amount will be repaid in 3 years with semiannual payments at an interest rate of 8% compounded semiannually. Set up an amortization schedule for this loan.

Solution

The interest rate per 6-month compounding period is $\frac{8\%}{2} = 4\%$. Use 4% and 6 periods in column F in **Appendix C** to find 0.1907619.

$$\text{Payment} = \$15,000 \times 0.1907619 = \$2861.43$$

This is the payment for all periods other than the last one. To complete the amortization table, follow these steps.

> 1. Calculate interest at 4% of the balance at end of previous period using $I = PRT$ and round to the nearest cent.
> 2. Portion applied to principal = amount of payment − interest for period
> 3. Balance at end of period = balance at end of prior period − portion applied to principal

The payment for the last period sometimes differs slightly since it is whatever is required to pay the loan off in full. It usually differs by only a few cents from the regular payment.

Payment Number	Amount of Payment	Interest for Period	Portion Applied to Principal	Balance at End of Period
0	—	—	—	$15,000.00
1	$2861.43	$600.00	$2261.43	12,738.57
2	2861.43	509.54	2351.89	10,386.68
3	2861.43	415.47	2445.96	7,940.72
4	2861.43	317.63	2543.80	5,396.92
5	2861.43	215.88	2645.55	2,751.37
6	2861.42	110.05	2751.37	0

Objective

4 *Find Monthly Payments.* Table 16.3 can also be used to find the monthly payment. Determine the table value corresponding to the annual percentage rate (APR) and the number of monthly payments. Then find the monthly payment by multiplying the number from the table by the amount to be financed.

Table 16.3 LOAN PAYOFF TABLE

APR \ Months	18	24	30	36	42	48	54	60
8%	0.059138	0.045229	0.036887	0.031336	0.027376	0.024413	0.022113	0.020277
9%	0.0596	0.045683	0.037347	0.0318	0.027845	0.024885	0.022589	0.020758
10%	0.060056	0.046146	0.03781	0.032267	0.028317	0.025363	0.023072	0.021247
11%	0.060516	0.046608	0.038277	0.032739	0.028793	0.025846	0.023561	0.021742
12%	0.060984	0.047075	0.038747	0.033214	0.029276	0.026333	0.024057	0.022245
13%	0.06145	0.047542	0.03922	0.033694	0.029762	0.026827	0.024557	0.022753
14%	0.061917	0.048013	0.0397	0.034178	0.030252	0.027327	0.025065	0.023268
15%	0.062383	0.048488	0.04018	0.034667	0.03075	0.027831	0.025578	0.02379
16%	0.062855	0.048963	0.040663	0.035159	0.03125	0.02834	0.026096	0.024318
17%	0.063328	0.049442	0.04115	0.035653	0.031755	0.028854	0.026620	0.024853
18%	0.063806	0.049925	0.04164	0.036153	0.032264	0.029369	0.027152	0.025393
19%	0.064283	0.050408	0.042133	0.036656	0.032779	0.0299	0.027687	0.02594
20%	0.064761	0.050896	0.04263	0.037164	0.033298	0.030431	0.02823	0.026493
21%	0.065244	0.051388	0.04313	0.037675	0.033821	0.030967	0.028776	0.027053

EXAMPLE 3 Finding Monthly Payments

After a down payment, Linda Dean owes $8700 on a 1-year-old Toyota Prius. She wishes to pay the loan off in 60 monthly payments. Find the amount of each payment and the finance charge, if the APR on her loan is 18%. Her interest rate is high because she has a poor credit history.

Solution

Multiply the amount to be financed of $8700 by the number from Table 16.3 for 60 months and 18%, which is 0.025393.

$$\text{Payment} = \$8700 \times 0.025393 = \$220.92$$
$$\text{Total of payments} = 60 \times \$220.92 = \$13{,}255.20$$
$$\text{Finance charge} = \$13{,}255.20 - \$8700 = \$4555.20$$

16.4	Exercises

Find each of the following.

1. $\dfrac{1}{a_{\overline{15}|0.075}}$ 0.11328724

2. $\dfrac{1}{a_{\overline{40}|0.075}}$ 0.07940031

3. $\dfrac{1}{a_{\overline{36}|0.10}}$ 0.10334306

4. $\dfrac{1}{a_{\overline{48}|0.12}}$ 0.12052312

Find the payment necessary to amortize the following loans. Use column F of the interest table in Appendix C and the formula of this section.

	Amount of Loan	Interest Rate	Payments Made	Number of Years	Payment
5.	$3000	$7\frac{1}{2}\%$	annually	3	$1153.61
6.	$3500	9%	annually	4	$1080.34
7.	$4500	8%	semiannually	$7\frac{1}{2}$	$404.73
8.	$7200	14%	semiannually	$3\frac{1}{2}$	$1335.98
9.	$96,000	8%	quarterly	$7\frac{3}{4}$	$4185.25
10.	$210,000	12%	quarterly	8	$10,299.79
11.	$4876	12%	monthly	3	$161.95
12.	$6400	9%	monthly	$3\frac{1}{2}$	$178.20

Use Table 16.3 to find the monthly payment and then find the finance charge for each loan.

	Amount Financed	Number of Months	APR	Monthly Payment	Finance Charge
13.	$4800	36	9%	$152.64	$695.04
14.	$4800	24	12%	$225.96	$623.04
15.	$12,000	48	13%	$321.92	$3452.16
16.	$8102	48	8%	$197.79	$1391.92

Solve the following application problems. Use column F of the interest table in Appendix C.

17. **OPENING A RESTAURANT** Chuck and Judy Nielson agreed to buy a restaurant for $340,000. They paid $40,000 down and agreed to pay the remainder in quarterly payments over 7 years at 12% compounded quarterly. Find the quarterly payment and the total amount of interest paid over 7 years. $15,987.97; $147,663.16

18. **NEW LIMOUSINE** Midtown Limousine Service bought a new Lincoln limousine for $57,000. The company agreed to pay 10% down and pay off the rest with monthly payments for 36 months at 9%. Find the amount of each monthly payment necessary to amortize the loan. Find the total amount of interest paid over 3 years. $1631.33; $7427.88

19. **DIGITIZER** Grants Graphics buys a commercial digitizer and high-speed printer for $4000 and finances the entire amount. It amortizes the loan using 4 annual payments at 8% per year. Prepare an amortization schedule for this equipment.

Payment Number	Amount of Payment	Interest for Period	Portion to Principal	Principal at End of Period
0	—	—	—	$4000.00
1	$1207.68	$320.00	$887.68	3112.32
2	1207.68	248.99	958.69	2153.63
3	1207.68	172.29	1035.39	1118.24
4	1207.70	89.46	1118.24	0

20. **TRUCK FINANCING** Long Haul Trucking purchases a used tractor for pulling large trailers on interstate highways at a cost of $72,000. It agrees to pay for it with a loan that will be amortized over 9 annual payments at 8% interest. Prepare an amortization schedule for the truck.

Payment Number	Amount of Payment	Interest for Period	Portion to Principal	Principal at End of Period
0	—	—	—	$72,000.00
1	$11,525.74	$5760.00	$5765.74	66,234.26
2	11,525.74	5298.74	6227.00	60,007.26
3	11,525.74	4800.58	6725.16	53,282.10
4	11,525.74	4262.57	7263.17	46,018.93
5	11,525.74	3681.51	7844.23	38,174.70
6	11,525.74	3053.98	8471.76	29,702.94
7	11,525.74	2376.24	9149.50	20,553.44
8	11,525.74	1644.28	9881.46	10,671.98
9	11,525.74	853.76	10,671.98	0

Solve the following application problems. Use Table 16.3.

21. **ENGINEERING WORK STATIONS** An engineering firm purchases seven new work stations for $3500 each. It makes a down payment of $10,000 and amortizes the balance with monthly payments at 11% for 4 years. Prepare an amortization schedule showing the first 5 payments.

Payment Number	Amount of Payment	Interest for Period	Portion to Principal	Principal at End of Period
0	—	—	—	$14,500.00
1	$374.77	$132.92	$241.85	14,258.15
2	374.77	130.70	244.07	14,014.08
3	374.77	128.46	246.31	13,767.77
4	374.77	126.20	248.57	13,519.20
5	374.77	123.93	250.84	13,268.36

22. TAVERN REMODEL Becky Johanson needed $25,000 to remodel the entrance to her small tavern. She had $5000 and borrowed the remaining $20,000. She agreed to amortize the balance with monthly payments for 5 years at 12% compounded monthly. Prepare an amortization schedule for the first 5 payments.

Payment Number	Amount of Payment	Interest for Period	Portion to Principal	Principal at End of Period
0	—	—	—	$20,000.00
1	$444.90	$200.00	$244.90	19,755.10
2	444.90	197.55	247.35	19,507.75
3	444.90	195.08	249.82	19,257.93
4	444.90	192.58	252.32	19,005.61
5	444.90	190.06	254.84	18,750.77

 23. Identify and explain three important items that you will see in an installment loan. (See Objectives 2 and 3.)

 24. Explain how people can get in over their heads in terms of monthly payments. How can this be avoided?

Prepare an amortization schedule for the following loans. Use a spreadsheet package on a computer if you have one available. Do not forget to round interest to the nearest cent each month before finding the portion of each payment that goes to principal.

25. Tim Gates financed $8000 on a used car at 12% for 15 months.

Payment Number	Amount of Payment	Interest for Period	Portion to Principal	Principal at End of Period
0	—	—	—	$8000.00
1	$576.99	$80.00	$496.99	7503.01
2	576.99	75.03	501.96	7001.05
3	576.99	70.01	506.98	6494.07
⋮	⋮	⋮	⋮	⋮
14	576.99	11.37	565.62	571.28
15	576.99	5.71	571.28	0

26. NETWORK LINK Caribbean Tours Inc. financed $108,000 to set up a network link between its offices in the United States and Mexico. It agrees to repay the 10% loan with 16 quarterly payments.

Payment Number	Amount of Payment	Interest for Period	Portion to Principal	Principal at End of Period
0	—	—	—	$108,000.00
1	$8272.69	$2700.00	$5572.69	102,427.31
2	8272.69	2560.68	5712.01	96,715.30
3	8272.69	2417.88	5854.81	90,860.49
⋮	⋮	⋮	⋮	⋮
15	8272.69	398.62	7874.07	8,070.92
16	8272.69	201.77	8070.92	0

16.5 Real Estate Loans

OBJECTIVES

1 *Determine monthly payments on a home.*

2 *Prepare a repayment schedule.*

3 *Understand the benefit of paying more than the minimum.*

4 *Define escrow accounts.*

5 *Define fixed- and variable-rate loans.*

A home is *one of the most expensive purchases* made by the average person. The amount of the monthly payment is *a major concern* for prospective buyers. The size of this payment is found by the exact same methods and formulas used in **Section 16.4**, but because of the many different interest rates and repayment periods, special tables are often used.

Figure 16.8 shows that there have been two major trends in home mortgage rates during the past 50 years. Rates generally went up during the period 1965–1980, and rates generally fell during the period 1981–2011. The highest rate of over 15% in 1980 resulted in very high payments on homes. The lowest rates were in 1965 and again in 2012. Part of the reason for the very low rates in 2012 was federal government action to stabilize home prices by lowering the interest rates to offset falling home prices during the financial crisis. Use the World Wide Web to find current mortgage rates for your area.

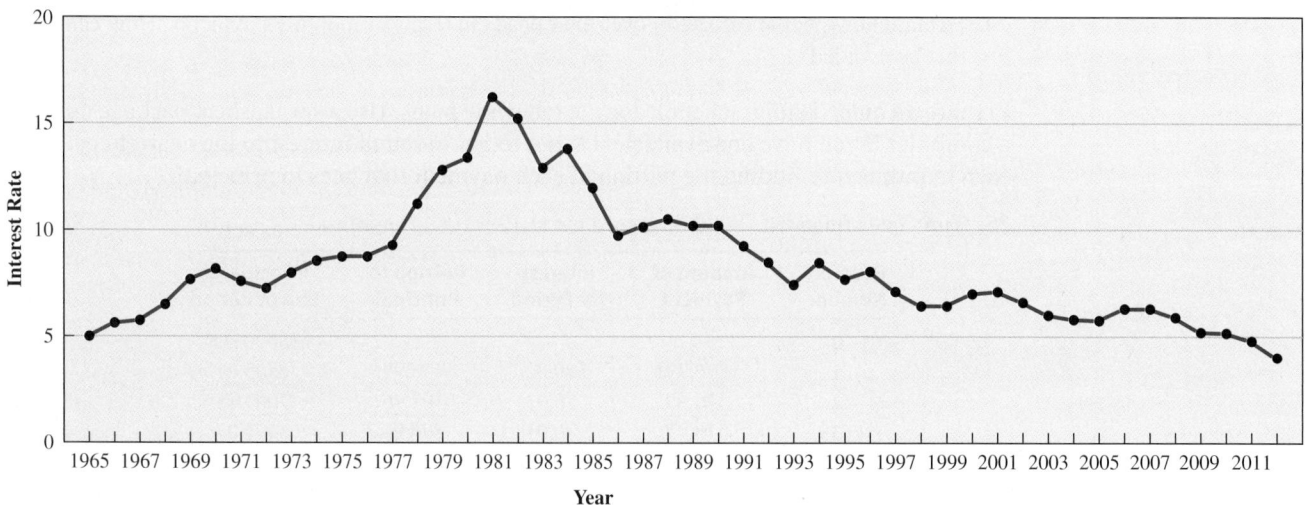

Mortgage Interest Rates
30-Year Fixed-Rate Mortgages

Source: Board of Governors of the Federal Reserve System, Federal Reserve Bulletin, 2012.

Figure 16.8

Objective

1   *Determine Monthly Payments on a Home.* The real estate amortization table (Table 16.4) shows the monthly payment necessary to repay a $1000 loan for differing interest rates and lengths of repayment. This table is used to find the monthly payment by multiplying the loan amount, in thousands of dollars, by the correct factor from the table. Higher interest rates mean higher borrowing costs, as you can clearly see from the next example.

Table 16.4 AMORTIZATION (PRINCIPAL AND INTEREST PER THOUSAND DOLLARS)

Term in Years	4.00%	5.00%	6.00%	7.00%	8.00%	9.00%	10.00%
10	$10.12	$10.61	$11.10	$11.61	$12.13	$12.67	$13.22
15	$7.40	$7.91	$8.44	$8.99	$9.56	$10.14	$10.75
20	$6.06	$6.60	$7.16	$7.75	$8.36	$9.00	$9.65
25	$5.28	$5.85	$6.44	$7.07	$7.72	$8.39	$9.09
30	$4.77	$5.37	$6.00	$6.65	$7.34	$8.05	$8.78

| **EXAMPLE** **1** | **Finding Payments to Amortize a Loan** |

After a small down payment, Bill and Judy Able need to borrow $115,000 to purchase a home and are debating whether they should use a 20-year or 30-year mortgage. They also want to know the effect of two different rates, 6% and 8%, on payments and costs. Find (a) the monthly payment for both rates at 20 years and at 30 years. Then find (b) the installment cost for each of the four combinations.

Solution

(a) The amount to be financed is $115,000 ÷ 1000 = $115 in thousands. The factor from Table 16.4 for 6% and 20 years is $7.16. The corresponding monthly payment is $115 × $7.16 = $823.40. Find the other payments in the same manner.

MONTHLY PAYMENTS

| Term of | Interest Rate | |
Mortgage	6%	8%
20 years	$823.40	$961.40
30 years	$690.00	$844.10

The payment varies from a low of $690 to a high of $961.40 depending on term and rate.

(b) The installment cost is the sum of all payments. The sum of payments at 6% for 20 years is 20 years × 12 months × $823.40, or $197,616. Find the other sums in a similar manner.

SUM OF PAYMENTS

| Term of | Interest Rate | |
Mortgage	6%	8%
20 years	$197,616	$230,736
30 years	$248,400	$303,876

To the nearest thousand, the installment costs range from a low of about $198,000 to a high of roughly $304,000, which is quite a difference for a mortgage of $115,000. The above tables show that keeping the interest rate constant, while shortening the term, results in a higher monthly payment but a lower installment cost.

However, short-term mortgages generally have slightly lower interest rates than a 30-year mortgage. It is to your advantage to use a shorter term if you wish to pay off your home loan more quickly and you can afford the monthly payments.

NOTE Be sure to divide the loan amount by $1000 before calculating the monthly payment.

For many years, mortgage payoffs of 25 or 30 years have been the most common. The last few years, however, have seen **accelerated mortgages**, with payoffs of 15 or 20 years. As you can see from the last example, an accelerated mortgage results in the payment of significantly less interest over the life of the loan.

EXAMPLE 2 **Finding Loan Amount**

The Mocks wish to purchase the largest, nicest home they can afford, but they are limited to a monthly payment of $900 not including insurance and taxes. If the current mortgage rate is 6% and they would like a 30-year mortgage, what is the most they can finance?

Solution

The concept described in the first part of this section is

$$\text{Number of thousands of debt} \times \text{factor from Table 16.4} = \text{monthly payment}$$

Previously, the monthly payment was unknown. Now the payment ($900) and the factor from Table 16.4 (30 years, 6% interest yields a factor of 6.00) are known, but the debt is unknown. Using algebra, the equation above can be solved for debt.

$$\text{Number of thousands of debt} = \frac{\text{monthly payment}}{\text{factor from Table 16.4}}$$

$$= \frac{\$900}{\$6.00}$$

$$= 150$$

Therefore, they can afford a mortgage of $150,000.

■

Objective

2 *Prepare a Repayment Schedule.* The interest on real estate loans is computed on *the decreasing balance* of the loan. Each monthly payment is first applied toward the interest for the previous month. The balance is then applied toward reduction of the amount owed. Payments in the *early years* of a real estate loan are mostly interest; only a small amount goes toward reducing the principal. The amount of interest gradually decreases each month, so that larger and larger amounts of the payment apply to the principal. During the last years of the loan, most of the monthly payment is applied toward the principal.

Many lenders supply an **amortization schedule**, also called a **repayment schedule** or **loan reduction schedule**, showing the amount of payments for interest, the amount for principal, and the principal balance for each month over the entire life of the loan. These calculations can be done by hand, as shown in the next example, but they are commonly done on computers.

EXAMPLE 3 **Preparing a Repayment Schedule**

Julie Kern borrows $120,000 at 7% interest for 30 years. Find the monthly payment and calculate a repayment schedule.

Solution

$$\text{Monthly payment} = \$120 \times \$6.65 = \$798.00$$

Find the interest for the first month using the formula for simple interest, $I = PRT$.

1ST PAYMENT:

$$\text{Interest} = \$120,000 \times 0.07 \times \frac{1}{12} = \$700$$

$$\text{Amt. used to reduce debt} = \$798 - \$700 = \$98.00$$

$$\text{Debt after payment} = \$120,000 - \$98.00 = \$119,902$$

2ND PAYMENT:

$$\text{Interest} = \$119{,}902 \times 0.07 \times \frac{1}{12} = \$699.43$$

$$\text{Amt. used to reduce debt} = \$798 - \$699.43 = \$98.57$$

$$\text{Debt after payment} = \$119{,}902 - \$98.57 = \$119{,}803.43$$

The data is shown in the table.

REPAYMENT SCHEDULE

Payment Number	Monthly Payment	Interest Payment	Principal Payment	Loan Balance
0	—	—	—	$120,000.00
1	$798	$700.00	$98.00	$119,902.00
2	$798	$699.43	$98.57	$119,803.43

Table 16.5 shows payments 1–20, 256–263, and 352–360 for the loan in Example 3. During the first 20 years, the debt is large and most of each payment is used to pay interest. In fact, the 242nd payment, which occurs in year 20, is the first payment in which more than one-half of the monthly $798 payment is used to reduce principal. The debt is reduced to one-half of the original debt after the 262nd payment, or in the 21st year of payments. However, most of the last several years of payments are applied to reduce principal. The final payment is larger than $798 due to rounding, since it is the amount needed to reduce the balance to zero.

Table 16.5 LOAN REDUCTION SCHEDULE

Payment Number	Interest Payment	Principal Payment	Remaining Balance	Payment Number	Interest Payment	Principal Payment	Remaining Balance
1	$700.00	$98.00	$119,902.00	256	$366.12	$431.88	$62,331.73
2	$699.43	$98.57	$119,803.43	257	$363.60	$434.40	$61,897.33
3	$698.85	$99.15	$119,704.28	258	$361.07	$436.93	$61,460.40
4	$698.27	$99.73	$119,604.55	259	$358.52	$439.48	$61,020.92
5	$697.69	$100.31	$119,504.24	260	$355.96	$442.04	$60,578.88
6	$697.11	$100.89	$119,403.35	261	$353.38	$444.62	$60,134.26
7	$696.52	$101.48	$119,301.87	262	$350.78	$447.22	$59,687.04
8	$695.93	$102.07	$119,199.80	263	$348.17	$449.83	$59,237.21
9	$695.33	$102.67	$119,097.13	⋮	⋮	⋮	⋮
10	$694.73	$103.27	$118,993.86	352	$43.15	$754.85	$6,642.40
11	$694.13	$103.87	$118,889.99	353	$38.75	$759.25	$5,883.15
12	$693.52	$104.48	$118,785.51	354	$34.32	$763.68	$5,119.47
13	$692.92	$105.08	$118,680.43	355	$29.86	$768.14	$4,351.33
14	$692.30	$105.70	$118,574.73	356	$25.38	$772.62	$3,578.71
15	$691.69	$106.31	$118,468.42	357	$20.88	$777.12	$2,801.59
16	$691.07	$106.93	$118,361.49	358	$16.34	$781.66	$2,019.93
17	$690.44	$107.56	$118,253.93	359	$11.78	$786.22	$1,233.71
18	$689.81	$108.19	$118,145.74	360	$7.20	$1,233.71	$0.00
19	$689.18	$108.82	$118,036.92				
20	$688.55	$109.45	$117,927.47				
⋮							

Objective

3   *Understand the Benefit of Paying More than the Minimum.* Any extra payment beyond the minimum monthly payment is used to immediately reduce debt. As a result, paying extra each month reduces debt faster as shown in the next example.

EXAMPLE 4   **Paying Extra Each Month**

Joe and Mia Li just purchased a house. They owe $182,800 on a 30-year mortgage at 5% interest. A friend told Joe that he should pay extra each month. Set up an amortization table that compares making the minimum payment versus paying an extra $100 per month.

Solution

First, find the monthly payment on a $182,800 loan for 30 years at 5% interest.

Number of thousands in loan amount: $182,800 ÷ $1000 = 182.8

Monthly payment for 30-year loan at 5%: 182.8 × $5.37 = $981.64

Monthly payment if extra $100 is paid each month: $981.64 + $100 = $1081.64

The extra amount paid each month goes immediately to reduce debt. Here are the calculations for the first month for both.

Payments of $981.64

Interest $\quad$ $182,800 \times 0.05 \times \dfrac{1}{12} = 761.67

Applied to
principal $\qquad$ $981.64 - $761.67 = 219.97

Remaining
balance $\qquad$ $182,800 - $219.97 = $182,580.03$

Payments of $1081.64

$182,800 \times 0.05 \times \dfrac{1}{12} = 761.67

$1081.64 - $761.67 = 319.97

$182,800 - $319.97 = $182,480.03$

This data is shown in Table 16.6.

Table 16.6 LOAN AMORTIZATION TABLE

Payments of $981.64				Payments of $1081.64			
Payment Number	Interest	Principal	Remaining Balance	Payment Number	Interest	Principal	Remaining Balance
0	—	—	$182,800	0	—	—	$182,800
1	$761.67	$219.97	$182,580.03	1	$761.67	$319.97	$182,480.03
2	$760.75	$220.89	$182,359.14	2	$760.33	$321.31	$182,158.72
3	$759.83	$221.81	$182,137.33	3	$758.99	$322.65	$181,836.07
⋮	⋮	⋮	⋮	⋮	⋮	⋮	⋮
100	$649.64	$332.00	$155,580.43	100	$598.71	$482.93	$143,206.46
⋮	⋮	⋮	⋮	⋮	⋮	⋮	⋮
200	$478.46	$503.18	$114,326.99	200	$349.71	$731.93	$83,199.11
⋮	⋮	⋮	⋮	⋮	⋮	⋮	⋮
293	$240.90	$740.74	$57,076.15	293	$4.16	$999.43	$0.00
⋮	⋮	⋮	⋮				
300	$219.03	$762.61	$51,803.86		No more payments		
⋮	⋮	⋮	⋮				
360	$2.93	$704.20	$0.00	Totals	$134,042.47	$182,800.00	
Totals	$170,315.89	$182,800.00					

Paying an extra $100 per month results in lower debt and, therefore, less interest. The total interest paid over the life of the loan falls from $170,315.89 when paying $981.64 per month to $134,042.37 when paying $1081.64 per month. The extra $100 per month reduces total interest cost over the life of the loan by $36,273.52. It also shortens the life of the loan from 30 years (360 monthly payments) to 293 payments, or to 24 years and 5 months. The advantages occur because the extra payment results in less debt and the life of the loan ends up being much shorter. The following table shows the advantages of making extra payments.

Extra Payment	Total Monthly Payment	Total Interest Paid	Time to Pay Off Loan
$0.00	$981.64	$170,315.89	30 years, 0 months
$100.00	$1,081.64	$134,042.47	24 years, 5 months
$200.00	$1,181.64	$111,179.50	20 years, 9 months
$500.00	$1,481.64	$74,363.67	14 years, 6 months
$981.64	$1,963.28[1]	$49,011.97	9 years, 11 months

[1]Double the 30-year payment

Paying extra every month can (1) reduce the total Interest paid over the life of the loan and (2) shorten the period of time during which payments must be made. The results are amazing!

Objective

4   *Define Escrow Accounts.* Many lenders require **escrow accounts** (also called **impound accounts**) for people taking out a mortgage. With an escrow account, buyers pay $\frac{1}{12}$ of the total estimated property tax and insurance each month. The lender holds these funds until the taxes and insurance fall due and then pays the bills for the borrower. Many consumer groups oppose this practice, since the lender earns interest on the money while waiting for payments to come due. In fact, a few states require that interest be paid to the homeowner on escrow accounts on any homes located in those states.

EXAMPLE **5**   **Finding Total Monthly Payment**

Bob Jones used a $75,000 loan for 25 years at 8% to purchase a small summer cabin. Annual insurance and taxes on the property are $654 and $1329, respectively. Find the monthly payment.

Solution

Use Table 16.4 to find 7.72. Add monthly insurance and taxes to the loan payment.

$$\text{Payment} = 75 \times 7.72 + \frac{\$654 + \$1329}{12}$$
$$= \$579 + \$165.25$$
$$= \$744.25$$

Scientific Calculator Approach

The calculator solution to Example 5 is to first find the monthly payment on the principal by multiplying the number of thousands (75) by the number from the table. Add to this the monthly payment due to insurance and taxes.

75 × 7.72 + (654 + 1329) ÷ 12 = 744.25

Objective

5   *Define Fixed- and Variable-Rate Loans.* Home loans with fixed, stated interest rates are called **fixed-rate loans**. Fixed-rate loans keep payments from going up when interest rates go up, which helps consumers and hurts lenders. On the other hand, fixed-rate loans keep payments from going down when interest rates fall, which hurts consumers and helps lenders.

   Variable-interest-rate loans, also called **adjustable-rate mortgages (ARM)**, have become popular and are offered by most mortgage lenders. These types of mortgages have interest rates that periodically move up or down as market rates move up or down. However, they usually have a **cap** so that rates do not go beyond some maximum number. Also, rates often have a cap on how much they can change at one time. In 2012, one lender offered the following mortgages.

30-year fixed	3.75% rate, payments are fixed for 30 years
15-year fixed	3.00% rate, payments are fixed for 15 years
1-year ARM	2.50% rate, it changes at the end of each year

> **NOTE** No one knows where interest rates will be in the future. Many families lock in the interest rate on their mortgage for 15 to 30 years because of risk. The risk to a family of not locking in interest rates is that the mortgage payment might increase significantly after a few years.

   Home ownership potentially offers benefits above and beyond a good place to live. For example, interest on home mortgages may be deductible on your income tax return and well-maintained homes in good areas have usually gone up in value with time. On the other hand, homeowners must pay for new roofs or other repairs to keep their homes in good condition.

> **NOTE** In some countries, interest rates vary widely because inflation rates in those countries vary a lot. As a result, it is not possible to get 30-year fixed-rate mortgages in some countries.

16.5	**Exercises**

Use Table 16.4 to find the monthly payment for the following loans.

	Amount of Loan	Interest Rate	Term of Loan	Monthly Payment
1.	$98,000	7%	30 years	$651.70
2.	$169,500	5%	25 years	$991.58
3.	$162,000	6%	15 years	$1367.28
4.	$132,000	9%	25 years	$1107.48
5.	$223,000	7%	20 years	$1728.25
6.	$147,000	4%	30 years	$701.19

 7. Explain how different interest rates can make a large difference in interest charges over a 30-year loan. (See Objective 1.)

 8. Explain how changing the term of a loan can result in significantly different interest charges over the life of the loan. (See Objective 2.)

Find the total monthly payment including taxes and insurance for the following loans. Round to the nearest cent.

	Amount of Loan	Interest Rate	Term of Loan	Annual Taxes	Annual Insurance	Monthly Payment
9.	$119,000	6%	30 years	$2050	$520	$928.17
10.	$154,000	5%	20 years	$3600	$840	$1386.40
11.	$135,000	8%	20 years	$3200	$680	$1451.93
12.	$68,400	9%	30 years	$1256	$350	$684.45
13.	$162,400	4%	25 years	$4350	$740	$1281.64
14.	$210,000	7%	15 years	$4700	$980	$2361.23

Solve the following application problems.

15. HOME PURCHASE Peter and Betsy Mueller hope to buy a home costing $145,000 with annual insurance and taxes of $780 and $2950, respectively. They have $20,000 saved for a down payment and their real estate agent has told them that they can get a 7% rate for a 15-year mortgage. They are qualified for a home loan as long as the total monthly payment does not exceed $1500. Are they qualified for the loan? Yes, they are qualified. The payment would be $1434.58.

16. CONDOMINIUM PURCHASE The Appletons wish to buy a condo for $148,000 with annual insurance and taxes of $680 and $2270 respectively. They have $8000 to pay down, plan to amortize the balance at 4% for 30 years, and qualify for the loan if the total monthly payment does not exceed $1000. Are they qualified? Yes. The payment would be $913.63.

17. REPAYMENT SCHEDULE Eric and Beth Eddy purchase a home and finance a debt of $212,000 for 20 years at 9%. Complete a repayment schedule for the first two monthly payments.

Payment Number	Total Payment	Interest Payment	Principal Payment	Balance of Principal
0	—	—	—	$212,000.00
1	$1908	$1590.00	$318.00	$211,682.00
2	$1908	$1587.62	$320.38	$211,361.62

18. REPAYMENT SCHEDULE Charlotte Cumings purchases a townhouse for her mother that cost $164,000. Charlotte has $25,000 and her mother has $10,000 that they use for a down payment. They finance the balance at 7% for 10 years. Prepare a repayment schedule for the first two payments.

Payment Number	Total Payment	Interest Payment	Principal Payment	Remaining Balance
0	—	—	—	$129,000
1	$1497.69	$752.50	$745.19	$128,254.81
2	$1497.69	$748.15	$749.54	$127,505.27

19. DUPLEX Adam Vort purchases a duplex needing work for $108,000 and agrees to pay 20% down. Find (a) the monthly payment if the loan is financed at 10% for 25 years, and if insurance and taxes are $560 and $1432, respectively. Then find (b) the interest portion of the second monthly payment and (c) the remaining debt after that payment. **(a)** $951.38 **(b)** $719.46 **(c)** $86,268.70

20. BORROWING PESOS Lety and Roberto Jaramillo borrowed 2,000,000 pesos to build a house on a mountain overlooking Guadalajara, Mexico. The loan was for 10 years and the rate was 10%. Find (a) the monthly payment. Then find (b) the interest portion of the second monthly payment and (c) the remaining debt after that payment. Round each answer to the nearest peso.   (a) 26,440 pesos (b) 16,446 pesos (c) 1,957,114 pesos

21. **AFFORDABLE MORTGAGE PAYMENT**   Paul Shingle can afford a mortgage payment of $980 per month not including insurance and taxes. Given a 30-year loan with a rate of 9%, find the maximum mortgage (to the nearest thousand) that he can afford. $122,000

22. **AFFORDABLE MORTGAGE PAYMENT**   Jessie Baker can spend $1100 per month not including insurance and taxes. Given a 20-year loan with a rate of 5%, find the maximum mortgage (to the nearest thousand) that she can afford. $167,000

23. **FOR RENTERS**   Take the amount either you or a friend currently pays for rent. Subtract $300 from that number as a rough estimate of insurance and taxes. Use this amount to estimate the home loan you or your friend can afford to buy, assuming a 4%, 30-year mortgage. Are there homes selling for this amount in your area? (See Example 2.)

24. **FOR HOMEOWNERS**   Interest rates might have increased or decreased significantly since you financed your home. Find your loan balance and then use the World Wide Web to find mortgage rates in your area. Calculate the monthly payment on your existing debt for a 30-year fixed-rate mortgage at the new rate and compare to your current payment. In the event that the payment would be lower, it may be worth refinancing your mortgage, but you need to look carefully at the monthly savings, the length of time you expect to be in the home, and the cost of refinancing.

25. **EXTRA PAYMENT ON MORTGAGE**   Joan Barker owes $134,852 on her home at a rate of 6% and has a regular monthly payment of $869.35, not including taxes and insurance. Her new job has given her additional income, and she is now thinking about paying an extra $400 per month on her mortgage payment. Prepare a repayment schedule for the first five payments for both payment amounts.

Payments of $869.35				Payments of $1269.35			
Payment Number	Interest	Principal	Remaining Balance	Payment Number	Interest	Principal	Remaining Balance
0	—	—	$134,852	0	—	—	$134,852
1	$674.26	$195.09	$134,656.91	1	$674.26	$595.09	$134,256.91
2	$673.28	$196.07	$134,460.84	2	$671.28	$598.07	$133,658.84
3	$672.30	$197.05	$134,263.79	3	$668.29	$601.06	$133,057.78
4	$671.32	$198.03	$134,065.76	4	$665.29	$604.06	$132,453.72
5	$670.33	$199.02	$133,866.74	5	$662.27	$607.08	$131,846.64

26. **EXTRA PAYMENT ON MORTGAGE**   Adolf and Isla Jimenez are buying a nice condominium near a lake in Wisconsin and will have a mortgage of $285,080. The interest rate on the 30-year loan is 7%, with a payment of $1895.78, excluding insurance and taxes. They are thinking of paying $4000 per month for the first 6 months since Adolf has extra income during those months from book royalties. Prepare a repayment schedule for the first six payments for both payment amounts.

Payments of $1895.78				Payments of $4000			
Payment Number	Interest	Principal	Remaining Balance	Payment Number	Interest	Principal	Remaining Balance
0	—	—	$285,080	0	—	—	$285,080
1	$1,662.97	$232.81	$284,847.19	1	$1,662.97	$2,337.03	$282,742.97
2	$1,661.61	$234.17	$284,613.02	2	$1,649.33	$2,350.67	$280,392.30
3	$1,660.24	$235.54	$284,377.48	3	$1,635.62	$2,364.38	$278,027.92
4	$1,658.87	$236.91	$284,140.57	4	$1,621.83	$2,378.17	$275,649.75
5	$1,657.49	$238.29	$283,902.28	5	$1,607.96	$2,392.04	$273,257.71
6	$1,656.10	$239.68	$283,662.60	6	$1,594.00	$2,406.00	$270,851.71

CHAPTER TERMS

Review the following terms to test your understanding of the chapter. For any terms you do not know, refer to the page number found next to that term.

accelerated mortgages [p. 623]
adjustable-rate mortgages (ARM) [p. 628]
amortization schedule [pp. 617, 624]
amortization table [p. 617]
amortized [pp. 601, 616]
amount financed [p. 603]
annual percentage rate (APR) [pp. 597, 601]
average daily balance [p. 595]
borrower [p. 591]
budget deficit [p. 591]
budget surplus [p. 591]
cap [p. 628]

Chapter 7 bankruptcy [p. 592]
Chapter 13 bankruptcy [p. 592]
credit accounts [p. 592]
consolidate loans [p. 598]
credit card [p. 592]
credit limit [p. 592]
creditor [p. 591]
debtor [p. 591]
deferred payment price [p. 603]
escrow accounts [p. 627]
Federal Truth-in-Lending Act [p. 601]
finance charges [pp. 593, 601, 603]

fixed-rate loans [p. 628]
impound accounts [p. 627]
installment loan [p. 601]
itemized billing [p. 593]
late fees [p. 593]
lender [p. 591]
loan reduction schedule [p. 624]
loan repayment tables [p. 617]
nominal rate [p. 601]
open-end credit [p. 592]
over-the-limit fees [p. 593]
personal property [p. 616]
real estate [p. 616]
real property [p. 616]
Regulation Z [p. 601]

repayment schedule [p. 624]
repossessed [p. 616]
revolving charge account [p. 592]
Rule of 78 [p. 612]
Stafford loan [p. 604]
stated rate [p. 601]
sum-of-the-balances method [p. 612]
total installment cost [p. 603]
unearned interest [p. 613]
United States Rule [p. 609]
variable-interest-rate loans [p. 628]

CONCEPTS

EXAMPLES

16.1 Finding the finance charge on a revolving charge account using the average daily balance method

1. Find the unpaid balance on each day.
2. Add the daily unpaid balances and divide by the number of days in the billing period.
3. Calculate the finance charge by multiplying the average daily balance by the interest rate.

Previous balance, $115.45; November 1, Billing date; November 15, Payment of $35; November 22, Jacket $45. Find the finance charge if interest is 1% per month on the average daily balance.

1. 14 days at $115.45 = $1616.30
   7 days at ($115.45 − $35 = $80.45) = $563.15
   9 days at ($80.45 + $45 = $125.45) = $1129.05

2. 14 + 7 + 9 = 30 days
   $1616.30 + $563.15 + $1129.05 = $3308.50
   Average daily balance = $\dfrac{\$3308.50}{30}$ = $110.28

3. Finance charge = $110.28 × 0.01 = $1.10

16.2 Finding the total installment cost, finance charge, and amount financed

Total installment cost = down payment + (amount of each payment × number of payments)

Finance charge = total installment cost − cash price

Amount financed = cash price − down payment

Joan Taylor bought a gold necklace for $1580. She put $350 down and then made 12 payments of $115 each. Find the total installment cost, the finance charge, and the amount financed.

Total installment cost = $350 + (12 × $115) = $1730

Finance charge = $1730 − $1580 = $150

Amount financed = $1580 − $350 = $1230

16.2 Finding APR using a table

1. Determine the finance charge per $100.

$$\frac{\text{Finance charge}}{\text{Amount financed}} \times \$100$$

2. Find the number of payments in the leftmost column of Table 16.2; then go across to the number closest to the number found in Step 1 and read up to find APR.

Use the table to find the APR for the following example.

$$\text{Finance charge} = \$992$$
$$\text{Amount financed} = \$8200$$

$$\text{Finance charge per }\$100 = \frac{992}{8200} \times \$100 = \$12.10$$

Number of payments = 24; table value closest to $12.10 is $12.14; APR = 11.25%.

16.3 United States Rule for repayment of loans

1. Find interest from date of loan to date of partial payment.
2. Subtract interest from partial payment.
3. Reduce principal by any difference.
4. Find additional interest from date of partial payment to next partial payment or maturity date and add this interest to unpaid principal.

Sam Spade signed a 120-day note for $3000 at 11% on February 1. Spade made a partial payment of $1200 on March 18. What is the amount due at maturity?

1. There are $27 + 18 = 45$ days from February 1 to March 18.

$$I = PRT$$

$$I = \$3000\,(0.11)\left(\frac{45}{360}\right) = \$41.25$$

2. $\$1200 - \$41.25 = \$1158.75$ is applied to reduction of principal.
3. $\$3000 - \$1158.75 = \$1841.25$ is balance owed.
4. There are $120 - 45 = 75$ days until maturity, so additional interest is

$$I = \$1841.25\,(0.11)\left(\frac{75}{360}\right) = \$42.20$$

Then $\$1841.25 + \$42.20 = \$1883.45$ is due at maturity.

16.3 Finding the unearned interest using the Rule of 78

Find the unearned interest:

$$U = F\left(\frac{N}{P}\right)\left(\frac{1+N}{1+P}\right)$$

where U = unearned interest,
F = finance charge,
N = number of payments remaining, and
P = total number of payments

Then find the amount left to pay and subtract the unearned interest to find balance remaining.

Tom Fish borrows $1500 to buy a big-screen TV, which he is paying back in 36 monthly installments of $52.75 each. With 10 payments remaining, he decides to pay the loan in full. Find the amount of unearned interest and the amount necessary to pay the loan in full.

$$\text{Installment cost} = 36 \times \$52.75 = \$1899$$
$$\text{Finance charge} = \$1899 - \$1500 = \$399$$

$$\text{Unearned interest} = \$399 \times \frac{10}{36} \times \frac{(1+10)}{(1+36)} = \$32.95$$

The 10 payments of $52.75 that are left amount to $52.75 \times 10 = \$527.50$.

$$\text{Balance} = \$527.50 - \$32.95 = \$494.55$$

16.4 Finding the periodic payment to amortize a loan

Use the number of periods for the loan n, interest rate per period i, and column F of the interest table to find $1 \div a_{\overline{n}|i}$. Then use the formula

$$R = A \cdot \left(\frac{1}{a_{\overline{n}|i}}\right)$$

to calculate the payment.

Bob agrees to pay \$18,600 for a car. The amount will be repaid in monthly payments over 4 years at an interest rate of 9%. Find the amount of each payment.

$$n = 12 \times 4 = 48$$

$$i = \frac{9\%}{12} = \frac{3\%}{4}$$

$$\frac{1}{a_{\overline{48}|0.0075}} = 0.02488504$$

$$R = \$18{,}600 \times 0.02488504$$

$$= \$462.86$$

16.4 Setting up an amortization schedule

Find the periodic payment; then find the interest for the first period using $I = PRT$ (R in this formula is rate). Subtract I from R and reduce the original debt by this amount, D. Find the balance by subtracting the debt reduction D from the original amount A. Repeat until the original debt is amortized.

Teri Meyer borrows \$1800 for 2 years at 10%. She will repay this amount with semiannual payments. Set up an amortization schedule.

$$n = 4 \qquad i = \frac{10\%}{2} = 5\%$$

$$\frac{1}{a_{\overline{4}|0.05}} = 0.28201183$$

$$\text{Periodic payment} = \$1800 \times 0.28201183$$

$$\text{Periodic payment} = \$507.62$$

$$I = PRT$$

$$I = \$1800 \times 0.10 \times \frac{1}{2}$$

$$= \$90$$

$$\text{Apply to principal} = \$507.62 - \$90$$

$$= \$417.62$$

$$\text{Balance} = \$1800 - \$417.62$$

$$= \$1382.38$$

Continue to get table shown below.

Payment Number	Amount of Payment	Interest for Period	Portion Applied to Principal	Principal at End of Period
0	—	—	—	\$1800.00
1	\$507.62	\$90.00	\$417.62	1382.38
2	507.62	69.12	438.50	943.88
3	507.62	47.19	460.43	483.45
4	507.62	24.17	483.45	0

16.4 Finding monthly payments, total amount paid, and finance charge

Multiply the amount to be financed by the number from Table 16.3. This is the periodic payment. Find the total amount repaid by multiplying the periodic payment by the number of payments. Subtract the amount financed from the total amount repaid to obtain the finance charge.

Nick owes $9600 on a Ford Taurus. He wishes to pay the car off in 48 monthly payments. Find the amount of each payment and the finance charge if the APR on his loan is 12%.

$$\text{Amount financed} = \$9600$$

Table value (Table 16.3) for 48 payments and 12% is 0.026333.

$$\text{Payment} = \$9600 \times 0.026333 = \$252.80$$

$$\text{Total amount repaid} = \$252.80 \times 48 = \$12{,}134.40$$

$$\text{Finance charge} = \$12{,}134.40 - \$9600 = \$2534.40$$

16.5 Finding the amount of the monthly mortgage payments and total interest charges over the life of a mortgage

Use the number of years and the interest rate to find the amortization value per thousand dollars from Table 16.4. Then multiply the table value by the number of thousands in the principal to obtain the monthly payment. Find the total amount of payments and subtract the original amount owed from total payments to obtain interest paid.

Lou and Rose Peacock buy a small house. After a down payment, they owe $75,000. Find the monthly payment at 7% and the total charges over the life of a 25-year mortgage.

$$n = 25 \qquad i = 7\%$$

Table value (Table 16.4) = $7.07.

There are $\dfrac{\$75{,}000}{1000} = 75$ thousands in $75,000.

$$\text{Monthly payment} = 75 \times \$7.07$$
$$= \$530.25$$
$$\text{Total payments} = 25 \times 12 \times \$530.25$$
$$= \$159{,}075$$
$$\text{Interest paid} = \$159{,}075 - \$75{,}000$$
$$= \$84{,}075$$

16.5 Paying extra each month

The calculations are the same as above, although the principal will be larger.

Assume Lou and Rose Peacock from above decide to pay an extra $300 every month. Construct an amortization table for the first five payments for both payment amounts.

Payments of $530.25				Payments of $830.25			
Payment Number	Interest	Principal	Remaining Balance	Payment Number	Interest	Principal	Remaining Balance
0	—	—	$75,000	0	—	—	$75,000
1	$437.50	$92.75	$74,907.25	1	$437.50	$392.75	$74,607.25
2	$436.96	$93.29	$74,813.96	2	$435.21	$395.04	$74,212.21
3	$436.41	$93.84	$74,720.12	3	$432.90	$397.35	$73,814.86
4	$435.87	$94.38	$74,625.74	4	$430.59	$399.66	$73,415.20
5	$435.32	$94.93	$74,530.81	5	$428.26	$401.99	$73,013.21

The answer section includes answers to all Review Exercises.

Find the finance charge for each of the following revolving charge accounts. Assume interest is calculated on the average daily balance of the account. [16.1]

	Average Daily Balance	Monthly Interest Rate	
1.	$8463.22	$1\frac{1}{2}\%$	$126.95
2.	$3240.60	$1\frac{1}{4}\%$	$40.51
3.	$875.12	1.62%	$14.18

Find the average daily balance for the following credit-card accounts. Assume the billing date is the same day of each month, and use the number of days in each month. Then find the finance charge if interest is $1\frac{1}{2}\%$ per month on the average daily balance. Finally, find the amount due at the end of the billing cycle. [16.1]

4. Previous balance $634.25

March 9	Billing date		
March 17	Payment CR	$125	$552.56; $8.29; $551.80
March 30	Lunch	$34.26	

5. Previous balance $236.26

July 10	Billing date		
July 15	Athletic shoes	$28.25	
July 20	Payment CR	$75	$216.51; $3.25; $203.40
July 31	Pillow cases	$35	
August 5	Returns CR	$24.36	

Find the cash price, total installment cost, and the finance charge for each of the following. [16.2]

	Amount Financed	Down Payment	Cash Price	Number of Payments	Amount of Payment	Total Installment Cost	Finance Charge
6.	$2300	$400	$2700	18	$139.73	$2915.14	$215.14
7.	$3800	$800	$4600	20	$212	$5040	$440
8.	$6500	$1500	$8000	36	$225	$9600	$1600

Find the annual percentage rate using Table 16.2. [16.2]

	Amount Financed	Finance Charge	Number of Monthly Payments	
9.	$4100	$435	18	13%
10.	$11,200	$1008	20	10.00%
11.	$8800	$766.48	15	12.75%
12.	$10,270	$1065	20	11.5%

Find the balance due on the maturity date and the total amount of interest on the following notes. Use the United States Rule. [16.3]

	Principal	Interest	Time in Days	Partial Payments	
13.	$12,400	$8\frac{1}{2}\%$	180 days	$2000 on day 62	$10,876.33; $476.33
14.	$9000	12%	120 days	$2000 on day 40	$7309.87; $309.87
15.	$6000	11%	120 days	$3200 on day 30 $2000 on day 90	$915.66; $115.66
16.	$9000	9%	90 days	$3000 on day 30 $1500 on day 45	$4641.89; $141.89

Find the amount of each payment needed to amortize the following loans. Round to the nearest cent. **[16.4]**

17. $24,000 loan; repaid at 9% in 8 semiannual payments $3638.63

18. $18,500 loan; repaid at 10% in 10 semiannual payments $2395.83

19. $12,400 loan; repaid at 10% in 20 quarterly payments $795.42

20. $8600 loan; repaid at 9% in 24 monthly payments $392.89

Find the monthly payment and finance charge for the following loans using Table 16.3. Round to the nearest cent. **[16.4]**

21. $9400 financed for 24 months at 12% $442.51; $1220.24

22. $12,000 financed for 42 months at 10% $339.80; $2271.60

23. $9000 financed for 48 months at 8% $219.72; $1546.56

24. $15,000 financed for 30 months at 11% $574.16; $2224.80

Find the monthly payment for the following real estate loans using Table 16.4. **[16.5]**

25. $180,000 loan at 4% for 30 years $858.60

26. $112,800 loan at 6% for 20 years $807.65

27. $100,000 loan at 8% for 15 years $956

28. $235,400 loan at 5% for 25 years $1377.09

Solve the following application problems.

29. Sandmeyer Concrete Company signed an 11% note for $5600 dated June 20 for 150 days. The firm made partial payments of $1330 on July 20 and $1655 on September 3. (a) What payment is required when the note is due? (b) What was the total interest paid on the note? **[16.3]**   (a) $2788.22 (b) $173.22

30. Debbie Blaisdell has a revolving charge at a department store. Her monthly statement contained the following information. **[16.1]**

6-10	Billing date; previous balance	$157.35
6-20	Payment	$45 CR
6-25	Craft department	$52.20
7-2	Shoe department	$69

Find the average daily balance on the next billing date of July 10. Then, find the finance charge if the interest is 1.5% per month on the average daily balance. $171.85; $2.58

31. Ben Franklin purchased a 2-year-old Honda Accord with a cash price of $15,780 with a down payment of $2780 and agreed to make 48 monthly payments of $332.84. Find the total installment cost and the annual percentage rate. **[16.2]** $18,756.32; 10.50%

32. ABC Plumbing borrows $28,100 to buy a new truck. The firm agrees to make quarterly payments for 3 years at 12% per year. Find the amount of the quarterly payment. **[16.4]** $2822.98

33. Mr. and Mrs. Zagorin plan to buy a home costing $198,000, paying 20% down and financing the balance at 7% for 30 years. The taxes are $3400 per year and fire insurance costs $760 per year. Find the monthly payment (including taxes and insurance). **[16.5]** $1400.03

34. Jerome Watson, owner of Watson Welding, purchases a building for his business and makes a $25,000 down payment. He finances the balance of $122,500 for 20 years at 8%. (a) Find the total monthly payment given taxes of $3200 per year and insurance of $1275 per year. (b) Assume that insurance and taxes do not increase and find the total cost of owning the building for 20 years (include the down payment). **[16.5]**   (a) $1397.02 (b) $360,284.80

35. After his August 15 payment, Tony Garza's loan balance was $8432.18. He missed the September 15 monthly payment but made a payment of $500 on October 14. He did not make any charges during this time. No penalty was charged and the loan has a simple interest rate of 12%. Find (a) the number of days from August 15 to October 14 and (b) the loan balance after the October 14 payment. **[16.3]**   (a) 60 days (b) $8100.82

CHAPTER 16	Business Application Case #1
	Consolidating Loans

John and Kathy MacGruder have had credit problems in the past, so they were able to get loans only by paying higher-than-market interest rates. They are struggling to make their current payments, but they have done so regularly for more than a year. Now they are trying to reduce their monthly payments by refinancing at lower rates where possible and also by extending the terms on loans where possible.

(a) Find the monthly payments on each of the following purchases and the total monthly payment. Use column F in the interest tables in **Appendix C** and Table 16.4.

Purchase	Original Loan Amount	Interest Rate	Term of Loan	Monthly Payment
Honda Accord	$18,800	12%	4 years	$495.08
Ford truck	$14,300	18%	4 years	420.06
Home	$96,500	9%	15 years	$978.51
2nd mortgage on home	$4500	12%	3 years	149.46
Total				$2043.11

(b) These monthly expenses do not include car insurance ($215 per month), health insurance ($120 per month), or taxes on their home ($3540 per year), among other expenses. Find their total monthly outlay for all of these bills.

Expense	Monthly Outlay
Payments on debt from (a)	$2043.11
Car insurance	215.00
Health insurance	120.00
Taxes on home	$295.00
Total	$2673.11

(c) The MacGruders learn that they can (1) refinance the remaining $14,900 debt on the Honda Accord at 12% over 4 years, (2) refinance the remaining $8600 loan amount on the Ford truck at 12% over 3 years, (3) refinance the remaining $94,800 loan amount on their home at 8% over 30 years, and (4) reduce their car insurance payments by $28 per month. Complete the table below. Use column F in the interest tables in **Appendix C** and Table 16.4.

Item	New Loan Amount	New Interest Rate	New Term of Loan	New Monthly Payment
Honda Accord	$14,900	12%	4 years	$392.37
Ford truck	8600	12%	3 years	285.64
Home	94,800	8%	30 years	695.83
2nd mortgage on home	4500	12%	3 years	149.46
Car insurance				187.00
Health insurance				120.00
Taxes on home				$295.00
Total				$2125.30

(d) Find the reduction in their monthly payments. $547.81

NOTE   Part of the savings in the monthly payment came from reducing the interest rates. The remainder of the savings came from extending the loans further into the future.

CHAPTER 16	Business Application Case #2
	Starting out after College

Jessica Simms and Ben Waller met in the last year of college. Jessica received her degree in architecture at the same time that Ben received his in accounting. They married later that year and both found good jobs earning $78,640 per year between the two of them. However, they had accumulated a lot of student loans, credit-card debt, and car payments, as shown. Now they have a baby.

(a) Find the total of debt payments.

Debt	Loan Balance	Interest Rate	Minimum Monthly Payment
Her student loans	$12,380	8%	$251.02
His student loans	$28,600	9%	$419.00
Credit cards	$14,860	15%	$225.00
Her car	$18,230	9%	$453.65
His car	$6,350	12%	$298.92
		Total	$1647.59

(b) Find the monthly FICA and Medicare taxes they must pay. **(c)** Then add the FICA and Medicare taxes to the other expenses shown below.

FICA and Medicare taxes (7.65% of monthly salary)	$ 501.33
Income tax withholding	$820.45
Rent	$985.00
Utilities, cable TV, cell phones	$358.00
Auto, medical, and life insurance	$236.00
Food, entertainment, and child expenses	$1100.00
Professional, clothing, miscellaneous	$380.00
Total	$4380.78

(d) Find the sum of (a) and (c). $6028.37

(e) Find the amount left over each month. $524.96

(f) Assume the Wallers apply the extra left over at the end of each month from (e) and also their monthly rent to pay a mortgage. If interest rates are 5% on 30-year fixed-rate loans, estimate the largest debt they can finance to the nearest thousand. $281,000

(g) The mortgage broker has told the Wallers that they must make a 10% down payment in order to borrow the full amount calculated in (f). Find the amount of the down payment needed if they borrow this full amount. Then estimate the number of months it will take to save the down payment needed if they save the cash left over each month from (e) and they earn 4% compounded monthly. $22,888.89, 41 months

| **PART 4** | Cumulative Review: Chapters 12–16 |

Round money amounts to the nearest cent, time to the nearest day, and rates to the nearest tenth of a percent.

Find the value of the unknown quantity using simple interest. Use banker's interest. [12.1–12.2]

	Interest	Principal	Rate	Time
1.	$150	$4500	8%	5 months
2.	$417.64	$6200	9.7%	250 days
3.	$46.67	$2400.17	7%	100 days
4.	$302.60	$12,449.83	12.5%	70 days
5.	$50.93	$2100	9.7%	90 days
6.	$306	$6800	13.5%	120 days
7.	$202.22	$9100	10%	80 days
8.	$915	$18,300	12%	150 days

Find the discount and the proceeds. [13.2]

	Face Value	Discount Rate	Time (Days)	
9.	$9000	12%	90	$270; $8730
10.	$875	$6\frac{1}{2}$%	210	$33.18; $841.82

11. Convert a simple discount rate of 10% for 90 days to a simple interest rate and round to the nearest tenth of a percent. [13.3]   10.3%

12. Convert a simple interest rate of 12% for 180 days to a simple discount rate and round to the nearest tenth of a percent. [13.3]   11.3%

Find the compound amounts for the following deposits. [14.1]

13. $1000 at 4% compounded annually for 17 years $1947.90

14. $3520 at 8% compounded annually for 10 years $7599.42

Find the compound amounts and interest earned for the following deposits. Assume $3\frac{1}{2}$% interest compounded daily. [14.2]

	Amount	Date Deposited	Date Withdrawn	
15.	$12,600	March 24	June 3	$12,686.07; $86.07
16.	$7500	November 20	February 14	$7562.10; $62.10

Find the present value and the amount of interest earned for the following. Round to the nearest cent. [14.4]

	Amount Needed	Time (Years)	Interest	Compounded	
17.	$1000	7	8%	Annually	$583.49; $416.51
18.	$19,000	9	5%	Semiannually	$12,182.15; $6817.85

Find the amount of the following ordinary annuities. [15.1]

	Amount of Each Deposit	Deposited	Rate	Time (Years)	
19.	$1000	Annually	4%	8	$9214.23
20.	$3500	Semiannually	6%	4	$31,123.18

Find the present value of the following annuities. **[15.2]**

	Amount per Payment	Payment at End of Each	Time (Years)	Rate of Investment	Compounded	
21.	$925	6 months	11	8%	Semiannually	$13,367.28
22.	$27,235	Quarter	8	8%	Quarterly	$639,160.10

Find the required payment into a sinking fund. **[15.3]**

	Future Value	Interest Rate	Compounded	Time (Years)	
23.	$3600	8%	Annually	7	$403.46
24.	$4500	10%	Quarterly	7	$112.90

Solve the following application problems. Use 360-day years where applicable.

25. Walter Bates sets aside $5000 today to help pay his son's college expenses, which will begin in 9 years. Given a rate of 8% compounded semiannually, find the future value of this investment. **[14.1]** $10,129.08

26. A divorce settlement calls for one spouse to pay the other a lump sum of $12,000 in 18 months. Assume funds earn 7% compounded semiannually. Find the lump sum that must be deposited today to satisfy this payment. **[14.4]** $10,823.31

27. Bill Jones borrowed $12,000 using a simple interest note at 8% for 40 days. Find (a) the maturity value and (b) the interest. **[13.1]**   (a) $12,106.67 (b) $106.67

28. Sherie Whatly borrowed $15,000 on a simple discount note at 10% for 100 days. Find (a) the interest and (b) the proceeds. **[13.2]**   (a) $416.67 (b) $14,583.33

29. Tom Davis owes $7850 to a relative. He has agreed to pay the money in 5 months, at a simple interest rate of 6%. One month before the loan is due, the relative discounts the loan at the bank. The bank charges a 7.92% discount rate. How much money does the relative receive? **[13.4]** $7993.14

30. James Pool earned $23,500 last year. Find the gain in purchasing power for a year in which he receives a raise of 4.1% but inflation as measured by the CPI was 3.7%. **[12.4]** $94

31. Thomas Wood has an average daily balance of $6327.12 on a credit card that charges 1.5% per month. Find (a) the monthly finance charge, (b) the finance charge if he could change the loan to a credit card that charges 0.8% on the average daily balance, and (c) the savings. **[16.1]**   (a) $94.91 (b) $50.62 (c) $44.29

32. A used automobile costing $10,500 was purchased with $1000 down and payments of $315 per month for 36 months. Find (a) the total installment cost, (b) the finance charge, (c) the amount financed, and (d) the annual percentage rate. **[16.2]**   (a) $12,340 (b) $1840 (c) $9500 (d) 12%

33. On July 7, Gene Harper borrows $3000 at 9% interest to pay for surgery to correct his nearsightedness. Find the balance owed immediately after a partial payment on September 30 of $720. Assume the United States Rule applies for partial payments. **[16.3]** $2343.75

34. A public utility needs $60 million in 5 years for a major capital expansion. What annual payment must it place in a sinking fund earning 10% per year in order to accumulate the required funds? **[15.3]** $9.828 million (rounded)

35. At 58, Thomas Jones knows that he must start saving for his retirement. He decides to invest $300 per quarter in an account paying 6% compounded quarterly. Find the accumulated amount (a) at age 65 and (b) at age 70. **[15.1]** (a) $10,344.44 (b) $20,869.57

36. Ben Torres borrows $18,500 at 10% compounded monthly for 48 months to purchase a farm tractor. Find the monthly payment using Table 16.3. **[16.4]** $469.22

37. The owner of Jessica's Cookies has an extra $3200 that she puts into a savings account paying $3\frac{1}{2}\%$ per year compounded daily. Find the interest if the funds are left there for 65 days. **[14.2]** $20.01

38. Jonah Goldratt wants to borrow $189,000 at 7% for 30 years to purchase a home. Insurance and taxes combined are $3250 per year. Can he afford the home if he can only afford payments of $1300 per month at the maximum? **[16.5]**   No, the monthly payment would be $1527.68.

javier brosch / Fotolia.com

CHAPTER

17

Depreciation

Businesses are allowed to take certain deductions from gross income before income taxes are calculated, including the following.

Cost of goods sold

Operating expenses (salaries, rent, utilities, etc.)

Research and development

Selling, general, and administrative expenses

Interest expenses

Another expense that businesses are allowed to deduct is the cost of assets such as machines, vehicles, equipment, buildings and fixtures. Since these assets often last for years, the income of the business would be distorted if these items were considered to be an expense and deducted in the year purchased. Instead, a method called **depreciation** is used to spread the cost of the asset over the length of its useful life. The depreciation of assets is another deduction used by most businesses.

Depreciation is used with assets having a useful life of more than 1 year. The asset to be depreciated must have a predictable life: a truck can be depreciated because its useful life can be estimated, but land cannot be depreciated because its life is indefinite. Figure 17.1 shows the remaining value of a Kenworth truck as it is depreciated over its useful life. The truck in this example has a 5-year life.

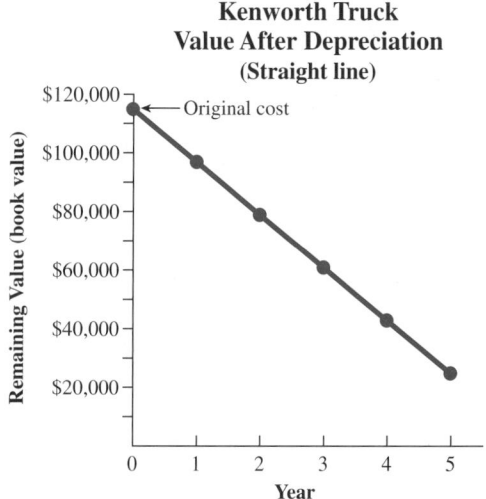

Figure 17.1

▶ STOP&THINK

> Employee salaries, rents, utilities, and other daily operating expenses are deducted on business income tax returns in the year paid, resulting in an immediate savings in taxes. However, only a small percent of the value of a long-term asset such as a building may be deducted in the year purchased. Why the difference? If laws were changed to allow an immediate, full deduction of the cost of a building or other asset, would managers spend money differently? Explain.

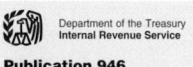

Department of the Treasury
Internal Revenue Service

Publication 946
Cat. No. 13081F

How To Depreciate Property

- **Section 179 Deduction**
- **Special Depreciation Allowance**
- **MACRS**
- **Listed Property**

Over the years, several methods of computing depreciation have been used, including *straight-line, declining-balance, sum-of-the-years'-digits,* and *units-of-production.* These methods are used in keeping company accounting records, and, in some states, for preparing state income tax returns. Assets purchased after 1981 are depreciated for federal tax returns with the accelerated cost recovery system or the modified accelerated cost recovery system discussed in **Section 17.5**. The use of depreciation for federal income tax purposes is detailed in an Internal Revenue Service Publication 946.

A company need not use the same method of depreciation for all its various assets. For example, the straight-line method of depreciation might be used on some assets and the declining-balance method on other assets. Furthermore, the depreciation method used in preparing a company's financial statements may be different from the method used in preparing income tax returns. Management goals for financial statements often differ from those for tax returns.

17.1	Straight-Line Method

OBJECTIVES

1 *Understand the terms used in depreciation.*

2 *Use the straight-line method to find the annual depreciation.*

3 *Use the straight-line method to find the book value of an asset.*

4 *Determine the book value of an asset after several years.*

5 *Calculate the accumulated depreciation.*

6 *Use the straight-line method to prepare a depreciation schedule.*

Objective

1 *Understand the Terms Used in Depreciation.* Physical assets such as machinery, cars, or buildings are **tangible assets**. A tangible asset may be depreciated as long as its useful life can be estimated. The key terms used in depreciation are summarized below.

Cost is the basis for determining depreciation. It is the total amount paid for the asset.

Useful life is the period of time during which the asset will be used. The Internal Revenue Service (IRS) has guidelines as to the estimated life of assets used in a particular trade or business. However, useful life depends on the use of the asset, repair policy, replacement policy, obsolescence, and other factors.

Salvage value or **scrap value** (sometimes called **residual value**) is the estimated value of an asset when it is retired from service, traded in, disposed of, or exhausted. An asset may have a salvage value of zero or **no salvage value**.

Accumulated depreciation is the amount of depreciation taken so far, a running balance of depreciation to date.

Book value is the cost of an asset minus the total depreciation to date (cost minus accumulated depreciation). The book value at the end of an asset's life is equal to the salvage value. Book value can never be less than salvage value.

Objective

2

Use the Straight-Line Method to Find the Annual Depreciation. The simplest method of depreciation, **straight-line depreciation**, assumes that assets lose an equal amount of value during each year of life. For example, suppose a heavy-equipment trailer is purchased by Village Nursery and Landscaping at a cost of $14,100. The trailer has an estimated useful life of 8 years and a salvage value of $2100. Find the amount to be depreciated (**depreciable amount**) using the following formula.

$$\text{Amount to be depreciated} = \text{cost} - \text{salvage value}$$

Here, the amount to be depreciated over the 8-year period is figured as follows.

$14,100	Cost
− 2,100	Salvage value
$12,000	Amount to be depreciated

With the straight-line method, an equal amount of depreciation is taken each year of the 8-year life of the trailer.

$$\text{Annual depreciation} = \$12,000 \div 8 = \$1500$$

Or, use the following formula. The annual depreciation by the *straight-line method* for an item having a cost of c, a salvage value s, and a life of n years, is d, where

$$\text{Annual depreciation} = d = \frac{c - s}{n}$$

Use the formula for the example by substituting $14,100 for c, $2100 for s, and 8 for n.

$$d = \frac{\$14,100 - \$2100}{8} = \$1500$$

The annual straight-line depreciation is $1500. Each year during the 8-year life of the trailer, $1500 will be treated as an expense by the company owning the trailer. The annual depreciation of $1500 is $\frac{1}{8}$ of the depreciable amount. The annual rate of depreciation is often given as a percent, in this case, $12\frac{1}{2}\% \left(\frac{1}{8} = 12\frac{1}{2}\%\right)$ per year.

Objective

3

Use the Straight-Line Method to Find the Book Value of an Asset. The **book value**, or remaining value of an asset at the end of a year, is the original cost minus the depreciation up to and including that year (the **accumulated depreciation**). In the example, the book value at the end of the first year is $12,600.

$14,100	Cost
− 1,500	First-year's depreciation
$12,600	Book value at the end of the first year

Book value is found with the following formula.

$$\text{Book value} = \text{cost} - \text{accumulated depreciation}$$

EXAMPLE 1   **Finding First-Year Depreciation and Book Value**

Commercial Fisheries purchased some navigation equipment at a cost of $2650. The estimated life of the equipment is 5 years, with a salvage value of $350. Find the (a) annual rate of depreciation, (b) annual amount of depreciation, and (c) book value at the end of each of the 5 years.

Solution

(a) The annual rate of depreciation is 20%, since a 5-year life means $\frac{1}{5}$, or 20%, per year.

(b) First find the depreciable amount.

$$
\begin{array}{ll}
\$2650 & \text{Cost} \\
\underline{-\ 350} & \text{Salvage value} \\
\$2300 & \text{Depreciable amount}
\end{array}
$$

This $2300 will be depreciated evenly over the 5-year life for an annual depreciation of $460 ($2300 × 20% = $460, or $2300 ÷ 5 = $460). The annual depreciation can also be found by the following formula.

$$ d = \frac{c - s}{n} $$

Substitute $2650 for c, $350 for s, and 5 for n.

$$ d = \frac{\$2650 - \$350}{5} = \$460 $$

The annual depreciation by the straight-line method is $460.

(c) The book value at the end of a year can be found by subtracting the depreciation amount of $460 from the book value at the end of the prior year. Year 0 is included to show the initial cost of the equipment.

Year	Depreciation	Book Value at End of Year	
0	$0	$2650	
1	$460	$2650 − $460 = $2190	
2	$460	$2190 − $460 = $1730	
3	$460	$1730 − $460 = $1270	
4	$460	$1270 − $460 = $810	
5	$460	$810 − $460 = $350	Salvage value

No further depreciation is allowed after year 5.

■

If an asset has **no salvage value** at the end of the expected life, then the entire cost will be depreciated over the life of the asset. In Example 1, if the navigation equipment was expected to have no salvage value at the end of 5 years, the annual amount of depreciation would have been $530 (since $2650 ÷ 5 = $530).

> **NOTE** Find the book value at the end of any year by multiplying the annual amount of straight-line depreciation by the number of years and subtract this result, the accumulated depreciation to date, from the cost.

Objective

4 *Determine the Book Value of an Asset after Several Years.*

EXAMPLE 2 **Finding the Book Value at the End of Any Year**

A lighted display case at the Bead Works costs $3400 and has an estimated life of 10 years and a salvage value of $800. Find the book value at the end of 6 years.

Solution

The annual rate of depreciation is 10% (10-year life leads to $\frac{1}{10}$, or 10%).

$$
\begin{array}{ll}
\$3400 & \text{Cost} \\
\underline{-\ 800} & \text{Salvage value} \\
\$2600 & \text{Depreciable amount}
\end{array}
$$

Since $2600 is depreciated evenly over the 10-year life of the case, the annual depreciation is $260 ($2600 $\times$ 10% = $260, or $2600 $\div$ 10 = $260).

Objective

5 *Calculate the Accumulated Depreciation.* The accumulated depreciation over the 6-year period follows.

$$\$260 \times 6 \text{ (years)} = \$1560 \quad \text{Accumulated depreciation (6 years)}$$

Find the book value at the end of 6 years by subtracting the accumulated depreciation from the cost.

$3400	Cost
− 1560	Accumulated depreciation (6 years)
$1840	Book value at the end of 6 years

After 6 years, this display case would be carried on the books with a value of $1840.

NOTE The book value helps the owner of a business estimate the value of the business, which is important when the owner is borrowing money or trying to sell the business.

Objective

6 *Use the Straight-Line Method to Prepare a Depreciation Schedule.* A **depreciation schedule** is often used to show the annual depreciation, accumulated depreciation, and book value over the useful life of an asset. As an aid in comparing the three methods of depreciation, the depreciation schedule of Example 3 and the schedules shown in the double-declining-balance method (see **Section 17.2**) and the sum-of-years'-digits method (see **Section 17.3**) use the same asset. The following example will be used in several places in this chapter so that you can better compare depreciation methods.

EXAMPLE 3   Preparing a Depreciation Schedule

Village Nursery and Landscaping bought a small pickup truck for $21,500. It is estimated that the truck will have a useful life of 5 years, at which time it will have a salvage value (trade-in value) of $3500. Prepare a depreciation schedule using the straight-line method of depreciation.

Solution

The annual rate of depreciation is 20% (5-year life $= \frac{1}{5}$ per year $=$ 20%). Find the depreciable amount as follows.

$21,500	Cost
− 3,500	Salvage value
$18,000	Depreciable amount

This $18,000 will be depreciated evenly over the 5-year life, giving an annual depreciation of $3600 ($18,000 $\times$ 20% = $3600).

Year	Computation	Amount of Depreciation	Accumulated Depreciation	Book Value	
0	—	—	—	$21,500	
1	(20% × $18,000)	$3600	$3,600	$17,900	
2	(20% × $18,000)	$3600	$7,200	$14,300	
3	(20% × $18,000)	$3600	$10,800	$10,700	
4	(20% × $18,000)	$3600	$14,400	$7,100	
5	(20% × $18,000)	$3600	$18,000	$3,500	Salvage value

The depreciation is $3600 each year. The accumulated depreciation at the end of 5 years is equal to the depreciable amount, and the book value at the end of 5 years is equal to the salvage value.

■

NOTE If the depreciation rate is a repeating decimal, use the fraction that is equivalent to the decimal. Instead of 33.3%, use the fraction $\frac{1}{3}$; instead of 16.7%, use the fraction $\frac{1}{6}$.

| 17.1 | **Exercises** |

Find the annual straight-line rate of depreciation, given each of the following estimated lives.

1. 5 years   20%   **2.** 4 years   25%   **3.** 8 years   12.5%   **4.** 10 years   10%

5. 20 years   5%   **6.** 25 years   4%   **7.** 15 years $6\frac{2}{3}\%$ **8.** 30 years $3\frac{1}{3}\%$

9. 80 years   1.25%   **10.** 40 years   2.5%   **11.** 50 years   2%   **12.** 100 years   1%

Find the annual amount of depreciation for each of the following, using the straight-line method.

13. Cost:	$9000	**14.** Cost:	$3400
Estimated life:	20 years $450	Estimated life:	4 years $650
Estimated scrap value: None		Estimated scrap value: $800	

15. Cost:	$68,280	**16.** Cost:	$8100
Estimated life:	4 years $16,020	Estimated life:	6 years $1225
Estimated scrap value: $4200		Estimated scrap value: $750	

17. Cost:	$4200	**18.** Cost:	$12,200
Estimated life:	5 years $840	Estimated life:	10 years $900
Estimated scrap value: None		Estimated scrap value: $3200	

Find the book value at the end of the first year for the following, using the straight-line method.

19. Cost:	$3200	**20.** Cost:	$35,000
Estimated life:	8 years $2850	Estimated life:	10 years $31,750
Estimated scrap value: $400		Estimated scrap value: $2500	

21. Cost:	$5400	**22.** Cost:	$4500
Estimated life:	12 years $5000	Estimated life:	5 years $3600
Estimated scrap value: $600		Estimated scrap value: None	

Find the book value at the end of 5 years for the following, using the straight-line method.

23. Cost:	$4800	**24.** Cost:	$16,000
Estimated life:	10 years $2775	Estimated life:	20 years $12,500
Estimated scrap value: $750		Estimated scrap value: $2000	

25. Cost:	$80,000	**26.** Cost:	$37,100
Estimated life:	50 years $73,000	Estimated life:	10 years $18,550
Estimated scrap value: $10,000		Estimated scrap value: None	

27. Develop a single formula that will show how to find annual depreciation using the straight-line method of depreciation. (See Objective 2.)

 28. Explain the procedure used to calculate depreciation when there is no salvage value. Why will the book value always be zero at the end of the asset's life?

Solve the following application problems.

29. MACHINERY DEPRECIATION   Dallas Tool and Diecasting Company selects the straight-line method of depreciation for a lathe costing $12,000 with a 3-year life and an expected scrap value of $3000. Prepare a depreciation schedule.

Year	Computation	Amount of Depreciation	Accumulated Depreciation	Book Value
0	—	—	—	$12,000
1	$\left(33\frac{1}{3}\% \times \$9000\right)$	$3000	$3000	$9000
2	$\left(33\frac{1}{3}\% \times \$9000\right)$	$3000	$6000	$6000
3	$\left(33\frac{1}{3}\% \times \$9000\right)$	$3000	$9000	$3000

30. TRUCK DEPRECIATION   Village Nursery and Landscaping paid $25,600 for a 1-ton, dual-axle flatbed truck with an estimated life of 6 years and a salvage value of $7000. Prepare a depreciation schedule using the straight-line method of depreciation.

Year	Computation	Amount of Depreciation	Accumulated Depreciation	Book Value
0	—	—	—	$25,600
1	$\left(16\frac{2}{3}\% \times \$18,600\right)$	$3100	$3100	$22,500
2	$\left(16\frac{2}{3}\% \times \$18,600\right)$	$3100	$6200	$19,400
3	$\left(16\frac{2}{3}\% \times \$18,600\right)$	$3100	$9300	$16,300
4	$\left(16\frac{2}{3}\% \times \$18,600\right)$	$3100	$12,400	$13,200
5	$\left(16\frac{2}{3}\% \times \$18,600\right)$	$3100	$15,500	$10,100
6	$\left(16\frac{2}{3}\% \times \$18,600\right)$	$3100	$18,600	$7000

31. OFFICE EQUIPMENT DEPRECIATION   Shippers' Express paid $9400 for office equipment with an estimated life of 6 years and a salvage value of $2200. Prepare a depreciation schedule using the straight-line method of depreciation.   Book values: $8200; $7000; $5800; $4600; $3400; $2200

32. BUSINESS FIXTURES   Dorothy Sargent buys fixtures for her shop at a cost of $7800 and estimates the life of the fixtures as 10 years, after which they will have no salvage value. Prepare a depreciation schedule, calculating depreciation by the straight-line method.   Book values: $7020; $6240; $5460; $4680; $3900; $3120; $2340; $1560; $780; $0

33. TUGBOAT   A Dutch petroleum company purchased a tugboat for $1,300,000. The estimated life is 20 years, at which time it will have a salvage value of $200,000. (a) Use the straight-line method of depreciation to find the annual amount of depreciation. (b) Find the book value at the end of 5 years.   (a) $55,000 depreciation (b) $1,025,000 book value

34. DEPRECIATING COMPUTER EQUIPMENT   The new computer equipment at Leisure Travel has a cost of $14,500, an estimated life of 8 years, and scrap value of $2100. Find (a) the annual depreciation and (b) the book value at the end of 4 years using the straight-line method of depreciation.   (a) $1550 depreciation (b) $8300 book value

35. **BOAT RAMP** A freshwater boat ramp has an estimated life of 15 years and no scrap value. If the boat ramp cost $37,900 and the straight-line method is used, find (a) the annual depreciation and (b) the book value after 7 years. Round depreciation to the nearest dollar. (a) $2527 depreciation (b) $20,211 book value

36. **PACKAGING EQUIPMENT** The packaging equipment at Rainbow Bakery has a cost of $132,400, an estimated life of 10 years, and a salvage value of $35,000. Find the book value of the packaging equipment after 8 years using the straight-line method of depreciation. $54,480

37. **HUMAN TRANSPORTER** A firm purchased several two-wheel Segway human transporters, which allow the human rider to direct movement by simply leaning. Managers believe that the transporters will save employees time as they move around the factory. The total cost of the transporters $19,830, the scrap value is $1200, and useful life is 5 years. Use the straight-line method of depreciation to find (a) the annual rate of depreciation, (b) the annual amount of depreciation, and (c) the book value at the end of the first year. (a) 20% (b) $3726 (c) $16,104

38. **WAREHOUSE SHELVING** Compu-Tech purchased new warehouse shelving for $37,500. The estimated life is 10 years, with a salvage value of $7500. Use the straight-line method of depreciation to find (a) the annual rate of depreciation, (b) the annual amount of depreciation, (c) the book value at the end of 5 years, and (d) the accumulated depreciation at the end of 8 years. (a) 10% (b) $3000 (c) $22,500 (d) $24,000

17.2   Declining-Balance Method

OBJECTIVES

1 *List the declining-balance methods.*

2 *Find the declining-balance rate.*

3 *Find depreciation and book value using the double-declining-balance method.*

4 *Use the formula to find depreciation by the double-declining-balance method.*

5 *Prepare a depreciation schedule using the double-declining-balance method.*

The straight-line method of depreciation assumes that the cost of an asset is spread equally and evenly over each year of its life. This is not realistic for many assets. For example, a new work van loses much more value during its first year of life than during its fifth year. Using straight-line depreciation for such assets would give a book value higher than the actual value of the asset during the early years.

Methods of accelerated depreciation are used to more accurately reflect the rate at which many assets actually lose value. **Accelerated depreciation** produces larger amounts of depreciation in the earlier years of the life of an asset and smaller amounts in the later years. The total amount of depreciation taken over the life of an asset is the same as with the straight-line method (the difference of cost and salvage value), but the distribution of the annual amounts is different. The effect of accelerating depreciation on an income tax return is to reduce current income taxes now, at the expense of reducing taxes less in future years.

One of the more common accelerated methods of depreciation is the **declining-balance method**. This method requires that a *declining-balance rate* be first established. The rate is multiplied by last year's book value to get this year's depreciation. *Since the book value declines from year to year, the annual depreciation from year to year also declines.* This explains the method's name of declining balance.

Objective

1   *List the Declining-Balance Methods.*

Three Common Declining-Balance Methods

200%, or double-declining-balance, method. With this method, 200% of the straight-line rate, or twice the straight-line rate, is used.

150% declining-balance method. With this method, $1\frac{1}{2}$ times the straight-line rate is used.

125% declining-balance method. With this method, $1\frac{1}{4}$ times the straight-line rate is used.

When using the declining-balance method of depreciation, *do not subtract salvage value* before calculating the depreciation. Also, stop subtracting depreciation once the book value has reached the salvage value. The book value of the asset *never* goes below the salvage value.

Objective

2   *Find the Declining-Balance Rate.* Calculate depreciation using the declining-balance method by first finding the straight-line rate of depreciation. Then adjust the straight-line rate to the desired declining-balance rate (200%, 150%, or 125% as desired). The following examples of declining-balance depreciation show the **200% method**, or **double-declining-balance method**.

EXAMPLE **1**   **Finding the 200% Declining-Balance Rate**

Find the straight-line rate and the double-declining-balance (200%) rate for each of the following years of life.

Solution

Years of Life	Straight-Line Rate	Double-Declining-Balance Rate
3	33.33% $\left(\frac{1}{3}\right)$	$\times 2 = 66.67\%$ $\left(\frac{2}{3}\right)$
4	25%	$\times 2 = 50\%$
5	20%	$\times 2 = 40\%$
8	12.5%	$\times 2 = 25\%$
10	10%	$\times 2 = 20\%$
20	5%	$\times 2 = 10\%$
25	4%	$\times 2 = 8\%$
50	2%	$\times 2 = 4\%$

NOTE   Throughout the remainder of this chapter, money amounts will be rounded to the nearest dollar, a common practice when dealing with depreciation. The rounded value is then used in further calculations.

Objective

3 *Find Depreciation and Book Value Using the Double-Declining-Balance Method.*

EXAMPLE **2** **Finding Depreciation and Book Value Using Double-Declining-Balance**

Northridge Golf and Country Club purchased a portable storage building for $8100. It is expected to have a life of 10 years, at which time it will have a salvage value of $1000. Using the double-declining-balance method of depreciation, find the first and second years' depreciation and the book value at the end of the first and second year.

Solution

First, find the double-declining-balance rate. Ignore salvage value when doing so. The straight-line rate for a useful life of 10 years is $\frac{1}{10}$, or 10% So, the double-declining-balance rate for a life of 10 years is twice that, or $2 \times 10\% = 20\%$.

$$
\begin{aligned}
\text{Depreciation in year 1} &= \text{original cost} \times \text{double-declining rate} \\
&= \quad \$8100 \quad \times \quad\quad 0.20 \\
&= \$1620
\end{aligned}
$$

$$
\begin{aligned}
\text{Book value end year 1} &= \text{cost} \quad - \text{depreciation in year 1} \\
&= \$8100 - \quad\quad \$1620 \\
&= \$6480
\end{aligned}
$$

- -

$$
\begin{aligned}
\text{Depreciation in year 2} &= \text{book value at end of year 1} \times \text{double-declining rate} \\
&= \quad\quad \$6480 \quad\quad \times \quad\quad 0.20 \\
&= \$1296
\end{aligned}
$$

$$
\begin{aligned}
\text{Book value end year 2} &= \text{book value at end of year 1} - \text{depreciation in year 2} \\
&= \quad\quad \$6480 \quad\quad - \quad\quad \$1296 \\
&= \$5184
\end{aligned}
$$

Objective

4 *Use the Formula to Find Depreciation by the Double-Declining-Balance Method.*
Declining-balance depreciation can also be found with the following formula.

Finding Annual Depreciation Using Declining Balance

The annual depreciation, d, by the declining-balance method, is given by

$$d = r \times b$$

where r is the declining-balance rate and b is the book value in the previous year. (In year 1, b is the original cost of the asset.)

EXAMPLE **3** **Using a Formula to Find Depreciation and Book Value**

Pioneer Beverage buys a small bottling machine for $59,400. The expected life of the bottling machine is 5 years, at which time it will have a salvage value of $3800. Using the double-declining-balance method of depreciation, find the first and second years' depreciation and the book value at the end of the first and second year.

Solution

The straight-line depreciation rate for a 5-year life is 20%. The double-declining rate is 40% (20% times 2). The first year's depreciation is 40% of the declining balance or, in the first year, 40% of the cost. Use the formula, substituting 0.40 for r and $59,400 for b.

$$d = r \times b$$
$$d = 0.40 \times \$59,400 = \$23,760$$

The depreciation in the first year is $23,760. The book value at the end of the first year is as follows.

$59,400   Cost
$- 23,760$ Depreciation to date
$35,640   Book value at the end of the first year

The second year's depreciation is 40% of $35,640 (last year's book value, or declining balance).

$$d = r \times b$$
$$d = 0.40 \times \$35,640 = \$14,256$$

The depreciation in the second year is $14,256. At the end of the second year the book value is figured as shown.

$59,400   Cost
$- 38,016$ Depreciation to date ($23,760 + $14,256)
$21,384   Book value at the end of the second year

NOTE The total amount of depreciation taken over the life of the asset is the same using either the straight-line or the double-declining-balance method of depreciation, but the distribution of the annual amounts is different.

Objective

5 *Prepare a Depreciation Schedule Using the Double-Declining-Balance Method.* The next example shows a depreciation schedule for the same pickup truck used in Example 3 of **Section 17.1**. Here, the declining-balance method is used, where the same rate is used each year, and the rate is multiplied by the declining balance (last year's book value). This example shows that the amount of depreciation in a given year may have to be adjusted so that book value is never less than salvage value.

EXAMPLE 4   Preparing a Depreciation Schedule

Village Nursery and Landscaping bought a new pickup truck at a cost of $21,500. It is estimated that the truck will have a useful life of 5 years, at which time it will have a salvage value (trade-in value) of $3500. Prepare a depreciation schedule using the double-declining-balance method of depreciation.

Solution

The annual rate of depreciation is 40% (20% straight-line $\times$ 2 = 40%). Do not subtract salvage value from cost before calculating depreciation. In year 1, the full cost is used to calculate depreciation.

Year	Computation	Amount of Depreciation	Accumulated Depreciation	Book Value
0	—	—	—	$21,500
1	(40% × $21,500)	$8600	$8,600	$12,900
2	(40% × $12,900)	$5160	$13,760	$7,740
3	(40% × $7740)	$3096	$16,856	$4,644
4		$1144	$18,000	$3,500
5		$0	$18,000	$3,500 Salvage value

In year 4, 40% of $4644 is $1858. If this amount were subtracted from $4644, the book value would drop below the salvage value of $3500. Since book value may *never be less than salvage value*, depreciation of $1144 ($4644 − $3500) is taken in year 4, so that book value equals salvage value. No further depreciation remains for year 5 or subsequent years.

17.2 Exercises

Find the annual double-declining-balance (200% method) rate of depreciation, given each of the following estimated lives.

1. 5 years   40%
2. 20 years   10%
3. 8 years   25%
4. 25 years   8%
5. 15 years $13\frac{1}{3}$%
6. 4 years   50%
7. 10 years   20%
8. 30 years $6\frac{2}{3}$%
9. 6 years $33\frac{1}{3}$%
10. 40 years   5%
11. 50 years   4%
12. 100 years   2%

Find the first year's depreciation for each of the following by using the double-declining-balance method of depreciation.

13. Cost: $18,000
Estimated life: 10 years $3600
Estimated scrap value: $3000

14. Cost: $4950
Estimated life: 20 years $495
Estimated scrap value: None

15. Cost: $12,500
Estimated life: 5 years $5000
Estimated scrap value: $500

16. Cost: $38,000
Estimated life: 40 years $1900
Estimated scrap value: $5000

17. Cost: $3800
Estimated life: 4 years $1900
Estimated scrap value: None

18. Cost: $1140
Estimated life: 6 years $380
Estimated scrap value: $350

Find the book value at the end of the first year for each of the following by using the double-declining-balance method of depreciation. Round to the nearest dollar.

19. Cost: $4200
Estimated life: 10 years $3360
Estimated scrap value: $1000

20. Cost: $2500
Estimated life: 6 years $1667
Estimated scrap value: $400

21. Cost: $1620
Estimated life: 8 years $1215
Estimated scrap value: None

22. Cost: $5640
Estimated life: 5 years $3384
Estimated scrap value: $800

Find the book value at the end of 3 years for each of the following by using the double-declining-balance method of depreciation. Round to the nearest dollar.

23. Cost: $16,200
Estimated life: 8 years $6834
Estimated scrap value: $1500

24. Cost: $8500
Estimated life: 10 years $4352
Estimated scrap value: $1100

25. Cost: $6000
    Estimated life: 3 years $750
    Estimated scrap value: $750

26. Cost: $75,000
    Estimated life: 50 years $66,355
    Estimated scrap value: None

27. Another name for the double-declining-balance method of depreciation is the 200% method. Explain why the straight-line method of depreciation is often called the 100% method.

28. Explain why the amount of depreciation taken in the last year of an asset's life may be zero when using the double-declining-balance method of depreciation.

Solve the following application problems. Round to the nearest dollar.

29. WEIGHT-TRAINING EQUIPMENT   Gold's Gym selects the double-declining-balance method of depreciation for some weight-training equipment costing $14,400. If the estimated life of the equipment is 4 years and the salvage value is zero, prepare a depreciation schedule.

Year	Computation	Amount of Depreciation	Accumulated Depreciation	Book Value
0	—	—	—	$14,400
1	(50% × $14,400)	$7200	$7200	$7200
2	(50% × $7200)	$3600	$10,800	$3600
3	(50% × $3600)	$1800	$12,600	$1800
4	—	$1800*	$14,400	$0

*To depreciate to $0 scrap value

30. STUDIO SOUND SYSTEM   A studio sound system costing $11,760 has a 3-year life and a scrap value of $1400. Prepare a depreciation schedule using the double-declining-balance method of depreciation.

Year	Computation	Amount of Depreciation	Accumulated Depreciation	Book Value
0	—	—	—	$11,760
1	$\left(66\frac{2}{3}\%\right) \times \$11{,}760$	$7840	$7840	$3920
2	—	$2520*	$10,360	$1400
3	—	$0	$10,360	$1400

*To depreciate to $1400 scrap value

31. ELECTRONIC ANALYZER   Neilo Lincoln-Mercury decides to use the double-declining-balance method of depreciation on a Barnes Electronic Analyzer that was acquired at a cost of $25,500. If the estimated life of the analyzer is 8 years and the estimated scrap value is $3500, prepare a depreciation schedule.   Book values: $19,125; $14,344; $10,758; $8068; $6051; $4538; $3500; $3500

32. CONVEYOR SYSTEM   Prepare a depreciation schedule for the installation of a conveyor system using the double-declining-balance method of depreciation. Cost = $14,000; estimated life = 5 years; estimated scrap value = $2500.   Book values: $8400; $5040; $3024; $2500; $2500

33. **CARPET-CLEANING EQUIPMENT**   John Walker, owner of the Carpet Solution, purchased some truck-mounted carpet-cleaning equipment at a cost of $8200. The estimated life of the equipment is 8 years and the expected salvage value is $1250. Use the double-declining-balance method of depreciation to find the depreciation in the third year. $1153

34. **CHOCOLATE YUMS**   Hiram Chocolates purchased two brass containers to hold a chocolate mix before pouring the candy. The total cost is $6800, and they have a useful life of 8 years with a salvage value of $1200. Find the depreciation in the second year using the double-declining-balance method of depreciation. $1275

35. **CONSTRUCTION EQUIPMENT**   Cool Pools purchased a backhoe at a cost of $39,240. It is estimated that the backhoe will have a life of 5 years and no salvage value. Use the double-declining-balance method of depreciation to find the book value at the end of the third year. $8476

36. **COMMUNICATION EQUIPMENT**   Caroline Fell purchased some communication equipment for her public relations firm at a cost of $19,700. She estimates the life of the equipment to be 8 years, at which time the salvage value will be $1000. Use the double-declining-balance method of depreciation to find the book value at the end of 5 years. $4675

37. **POWER TOOLS**   West Construction purchased some power tools for the shop at a cost of $5800. They have a life of 8 years and a scrap value of $1000. Use the double-declining-balance method of depreciation to find (a) the annual rate of depreciation, (b) the amount of depreciation in the first year, (c) the accumulated depreciation at the end of the fifth year, and (d) the book value at the end of the fifth year.   (a) 25% (b) $1450 (c) $4425 (d) $1375

38. **SCHOOL EQUIPMENT**   Gale Klein bought some whiteboards for her reading clinic at a cost of $3620. The estimated life of the whiteboards is 5 years, with a salvage value of $400. Use the double-declining-balance method of depreciation to find (a) the annual rate of depreciation, (b) the amount of depreciation in the first year, (c) the accumulated depreciation at the end of the third year, and (d) the book value at the end of the third year.   (a) 40% (b) $1448 (c) $2838 (d) $782

17.3   Sum-of-the-Years'-Digits Method

OBJECTIVES

1 *Understand the sum-of-the-years'-digits method.*

2 *Find the depreciation fractions for the sum-of-the-years'-digits method.*

3 *Use the formula to calculate the sum-of-the-years'-digits depreciation.*

4 *Prepare a depreciation schedule using the sum-of-the-years'-digits method.*

Objective

1   *Understand the Sum-of-the-Years'-Digits Method.* The **sum-of-the-years'-digits method** of depreciation is another accelerated depreciation method. The double-declining-balance method of depreciation produces more depreciation than the straight-line method in the early years of an asset's life and less in the later years. The sum-of-the-years'-digits method, however, produces results in between the straight-line and the double-declining-balance method—more depreciation than straight-line at the beginning and more depreciation than double-declining at the end.

Objective

2   *Find the Depreciation Fractions for the Sum-of-the-Years'-Digits Method.* The use of the sum-of-the-years'-digits method requires a **depreciation fraction** instead of the depreciation rate used earlier. The annual depreciation is this depreciation fraction multiplied by the depreciable amount (cost minus salvage value). The depreciation fraction decreases annually, as does the depreciation.

To find the depreciation fraction, first find the denominator, which remains constant for every year of the life of the asset. The denominator is the sum of all the years of the estimated life of the asset (sum of the years' digits). For example, if the life is 6 years, the denominator is 21 (since $1 + 2 + 3 + 4 + 5 + 6 = 21$). The numerator of the fraction decreases each year and represents the years of life remaining at the beginning of that year.

EXAMPLE **1**   **Finding the Depreciation Fraction**

Find the depreciation fraction for each year if the sum-of-the-years'-digits method of depreciation is to be used for an asset with a useful life of 6 years.

Solution

First determine the denominator of the depreciation fraction. The denominator is 21 ($1 + 2 + 3 + 4 + 5 + 6 = 21$). Next determine the numerator for each year. The number of years of life remaining at the beginning of any year is the numerator.

Year	Depreciation Fraction
1	$\frac{6}{21}$
2	$\frac{5}{21}$
3	$\frac{4}{21}$
4	$\frac{3}{21}$
5	$\frac{2}{21}$
6	$\frac{1}{21}$
21 Sum of the year's digits	$\frac{21}{21}$ Sum of the fractions

Under the sum-of-the-years'-digits method, an asset having a life of 6 years is assumed to lose $\frac{6}{21}$ of its value the first year, $\frac{5}{21}$ the second year, $\frac{4}{21}$ the third year, and so on. The sum of the six fractions in the table is $\frac{21}{21}$, or 1, so that the entire depreciable amount is used over the 6-year life.

NOTE   It is common to not write these fractions in lowest terms so that the year in question can be seen.

A quick method of finding the sum of the years' digits is to use the formula

$$\text{Sum of the years' digits} = \frac{n(n + 1)}{2}$$

where n is the estimated life of the asset.

For example, if the life is 6 years, 6 is multiplied by 6 plus 1, resulting in 6×7, or 42. Then 42 is divided by 2, giving 21, the same denominator used in Example 1. This method eliminates adding digits and is especially useful when the life of an asset is long.

Objective

3 *Use the Formula to Calculate the Sum-of-the-Years'-Digits Depreciation.* The depreciation fraction in any year is multiplied by the depreciable amount (as in the straight-line method) to calculate the amount of depreciation in any one year.

The formula for sum-of-the-years'-digits depreciation is

$$d = r \times (c - s)$$

where r is the depreciation fraction, c is the cost of the asset, and s is the salvage value.

EXAMPLE **2** **Finding Depreciation Using the Sum-of-the-Years'-Digits Method**

A Ditch Witch 1220 Trencher is purchased by Village Nursery and Landscaping at a cost of $8940. It has a useful life of 8 years and an estimated salvage value of $1200. Find the first and second years' depreciation using the sum-of-the-years'-digits method.

Solution

The depreciation fraction has a denominator of 36 (or $1 + 2 + 3 + 4 + 5 + 6 + 7 + 8$). The numerator for the first year of useful life is 8. The first-year fraction, $\frac{8}{36}$, is multiplied by the depreciable amount, 7740 ($8940 cost $-$ $1200 salvage value).

$$d = r \times (c - s)$$
$$= \frac{8}{36} \times (\$8940 - \$1200)$$
$$= \frac{8}{36} \times \$7740 = \$1720$$

The first year's depreciation is $1720.

The book value at the end of the first year is $8940 (original cost) $-$ $1720 (first year's depreciation) $=$ $7220. For the second and succeeding years, always go back to the *original* depreciable amount and not to book value, as in the declining-balance method. The depreciation fraction for the second year, $\frac{7}{36}$, is multiplied by the original depreciable amount, $7740 ($8940 cost $-$ $1200 salvage value). This gives

$$\frac{7}{36} \times \$7740 = \$1505$$

The second year's depreciation is $1505. In this example, the depreciation for any year is always found by multiplying the appropriate fraction by $7740.

 Scientific Calculator Approach

The calculator solution to Example 2 finds $\frac{1}{36}$ of the depreciation amount and stores the result ┃STO┃ in memory. This amount is then recalled ┃RCL┃ to find future depreciation amounts.

8940 ┃−┃ 1200 ┃=┃ ┃÷┃ 36 ┃=┃ ┃STO┃ ┃×┃ 8 ┃=┃ 1720

┃RCL┃ ┃×┃ 7 ┃=┃ 1505

EXAMPLE **3** **Finding Depreciation When There Is No Salvage Value**

City Saturn purchased an electronic smog analyzer for $9000. Using the sum-of-the-years'-digits method of depreciation, find the first and second years' depreciation if the analyzer has an estimated life of 4 years and no salvage value.

Solution

The depreciation fraction has a denominator of 10 (or $1 + 2 + 3 + 4$). The numerator in the first year is 4. The first-year depreciation fraction is $\frac{4}{10}$, which is multiplied by the amount to be depreciated, or $9000 ($9000 cost because there is no salvage value).

$$d = r \times (c - s)$$

$$= \frac{4}{10} \times (\$9000 - \$0)$$

$$= \frac{4}{10} \times \$9000$$

$$= \$3600$$

The first year's depreciation is $3600.

The fraction for finding the depreciation in the second year is $\frac{3}{10}$, which is multiplied by the depreciable amount, or $9000.

$$\frac{3}{10} \times \$9000 = \$2700$$

The second year's depreciation is $2700.

Objective

4   *Prepare a Depreciation Schedule Using the Sum-of-the-Years'-Digits Method.* For comparison, the next example uses the same pickup truck discussed in **Sections 17.1** and **17.2**.

EXAMPLE 4   Preparing a Depreciation Schedule

Village Nursery and Landscaping bought a new pickup truck for $21,500. It is estimated that the truck will have a useful life of 5 years, at which time it will have a salvage value (trade-in value) of $3500. Prepare a depreciation schedule using the sum-of-the-years'-digits method of depreciation.

Solution

Using the formula on page 655, the depreciation fraction has a denominator found as follows.

$$\frac{5 \times 6}{2} = 15$$

Year	Computation	Amount of Depreciation	Accumulated Depreciation	Book Value	
0	—	—	—	$21,500	
1	$\left(\frac{5}{15} \times \$18,000\right)$	$6000	$6,000	$15,500	
2	$\left(\frac{4}{15} \times \$18,000\right)$	$4800	$10,800	$10,700	
3	$\left(\frac{3}{15} \times \$18,000\right)$	$3600	$14,400	$7,100	
4	$\left(\frac{2}{15} \times \$18,000\right)$	$2400	$16,800	$4,700	
5	$\left(\frac{1}{15} \times \$18,000\right)$	$1200	$18,000	$3,500	Salvage value

NOTE The sum-of-the-years'-digits method of depreciation allows rapid depreciation in the early years of the asset's life and also provides some depreciation during the last years.

The three methods of depreciation can be compared visually by graphing the amounts of depreciation in each year and the book values at the end of each year. Figure 17.2 shows the depreciation using each of the three methods for the truck used by Village Nursery and Landscaping. Figure 17.3 shows the book value after depreciation for each of the three methods.

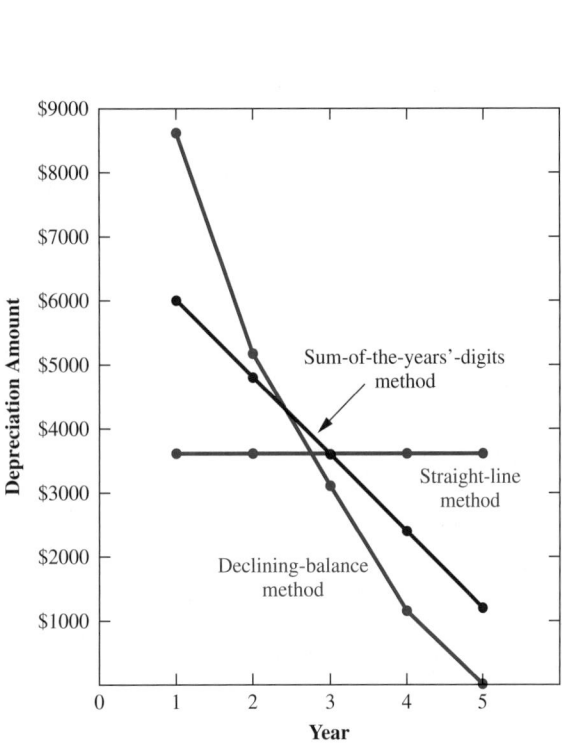

Figure 17.2 Comparing Methods of Depreciation

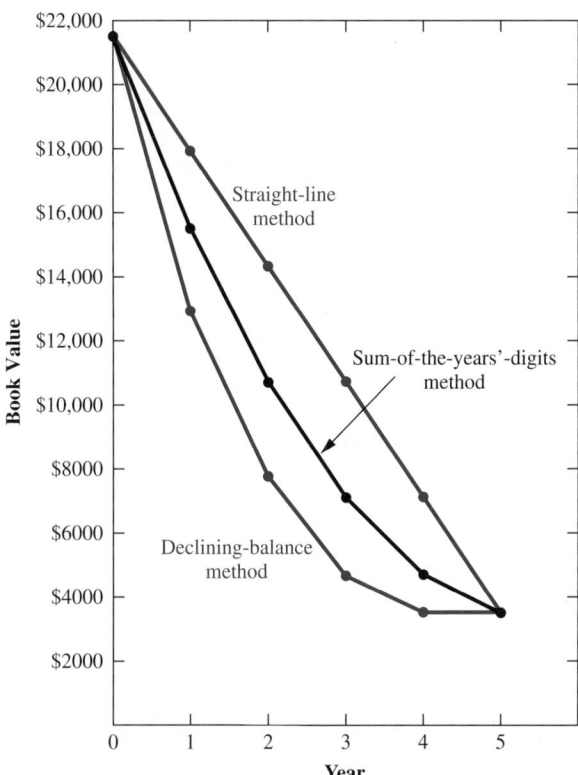

Figure 17.3 Comparison of Book Value Amounts

When used in preparing income tax returns, accelerated depreciation methods with higher, up-front depreciation result in lower income taxes in the early years compared to higher income taxes in later years. Remember *never to depreciate* the value of an asset below its salvage value.

Choosing a Method of Depreciation

Although there is no simple way to decide which method of depreciation is preferable in a given case, the following considerations may help to arrive at an answer.

- Will a larger deduction in the first year or years help pay for the asset with the tax dollars saved?
- Is it expected that earnings during the first years will be larger than in the following years? Larger depreciation deductions help to reduce taxes.
- Will a steady deduction over the life of the asset be advantageous?
- Accelerated deductions in early years mean little or no deductions in later years.
- Is profit expected to increase in the coming years during the life of the asset? If this is the case, a steady deduction over the life of the asset will allow depreciation in later years.
- Will repair bills be higher in later years? If so, these higher repair bills may offset the lower depreciation in later years that occurs with the declining-balance and the sum-of-the-years'-digits depreciation methods.

17.3	**Exercises**

Find the sum-of-the-years'-digits depreciation fraction for the first year given the following estimated lives.

1. 4 years $\frac{4}{10}$ **2.** 3 years $\frac{3}{6}$ **3.** 6 years $\frac{6}{21}$ **4.** 5 years $\frac{5}{15}$

5. 7 years $\frac{7}{28}$ **6.** 8 years $\frac{8}{36}$ **7.** 10 years $\frac{10}{55}$ **8.** 20 years $\frac{20}{210}$

Find the first year's depreciation for the following using the sum-of-the-years'-digits method of depreciation.

9. Cost: $4800
    Estimated life: 4 years $1640
    Estimated scrap value: $700

10. Cost: $5600
    Estimated life: 5 years $1600
    Estimated scrap value: $800

11. Cost: $60,000
    Estimated life: 10 years $10,000
    Estimated scrap value: $5000

12. Cost: $1440
    Estimated life: 8 years $320
    Estimated scrap value: None

13. Cost: $1350
    Estimated life: 3 years $600
    Estimated scrap value: $150

14. Cost: $9500
    Estimated life: 8 years $1800
    Estimated scrap value: $1400

Find the book value at the end of the first year for the following using the sum-of-the-years'-digits method of depreciation. Round to the nearest dollar.

15. Cost: $9500
    Estimated life: 8 years $7700
    Estimated scrap value: $1400

16. Cost: $25,000
    Estimated life: 10 years $20,455
    Estimated scrap value: None

17. Cost: $3800
    Estimated life: 5 years $2700
    Estimated scrap value: $500

18. Cost: $15,650
    Estimated life: 6 years $11,750
    Estimated scrap value: $2000

Find the book value at the end of 3 years for the following using the sum-of-the-years'-digits method of depreciation.

19. Cost: $2240
    Estimated life: 6 years $890
    Estimated scrap value: $350

20. Cost: $27,500
    Estimated life: 10 years $14,000
    Estimated scrap value: None

21. Cost: $4500
    Estimated life: 8 years $2400
    Estimated scrap value: $900

22. Cost: $6600
    Estimated life: 5 years $2520
    Estimated scrap value: $1500

 23. Write a description of how the depreciation fraction is determined in any year of an asset's life when using the sum-of-the-years'-digits method of depreciation. (See Objective 2.)

24. If you were starting your own business, what type of business would it be? Which of the three depreciation methods, straight line, double declining balance, or sum of the years' digits, would you decide to use? Why?

Solve the following application problems. Round to the nearest dollar.

25. COMMERCIAL FREEZER Town Market has purchased a new freezer at a cost of $10,800. The estimated life of the freezer is 6 years, at which time the salvage value is estimated to be $2400. Complete a depreciation schedule using the sum-of-the-years'-digits method of depreciation.

Year	Computation	Amount of Depreciation	Accumulated Depreciation	Book Value
0	—	—	—	$10,800
1	$\left(\frac{6}{21} \times \$8400\right)$	$2400	$2400	$8400
2	$\left(\frac{5}{21} \times \$8400\right)$	$2000	$4400	$6400
3	$\left(\frac{4}{21} \times \$8400\right)$	$1600	$6000	$4800
4	$\left(\frac{3}{21} \times \$8400\right)$	$1200	$7200	$3600
5	$\left(\frac{2}{21} \times \$8400\right)$	$800	$8000	$2800
6	$\left(\frac{1}{21} \times \$8400\right)$	$400	$8400	$2400

26. **RESTAURANT EQUIPMENT**   Old South Restaurant has purchased a new steam table for $14,400. The expected life of the unit is 4 years, at which time the salvage value is estimated to be $2400. Complete a depreciation schedule using the sum-of-the-years'-digits method of depreciation.

Year	Computation	Amount of Depreciation	Accumulated Depreciation	Book Value
0	—	—	—	$14,400
1	$\left(\frac{4}{10} \times \$12,000\right)$	$4800	$4800	$9600
2	$\left(\frac{3}{10} \times \$12,000\right)$	$3600	$8400	$6000
3	$\left(\frac{2}{10} \times \$12,000\right)$	$2400	$10,800	$3600
4	$\left(\frac{1}{10} \times \$12,000\right)$	$1200	$12,000	$2400

27. **OFFICE FURNITURE**   Sunset Real Estate Company has purchased office desks at a cost of $2700. The estimated life of the furniture is 6 years, at which time the salvage value is estimated to be $600. Complete a depreciation schedule using the sum-of-the-years'-digits method of depreciation.   Book values: $2100; $1600; $1200; $900; $700; $600

28. **FORKLIFT**   Prepare a depreciation schedule for the following forklift using the sum-of-the-years'-digits method of depreciation. Cost is $15,000, estimated life is 10 years, and estimated scrap value is $4000.   Book values: $13,000; $11,200; $9600; $8200; $7000; $6000; $5200; $4600; $4200; $4000

29. **WATER TAXI**   Find the depreciation in the third year for a water taxi using the sum-of-the years'-digits method of depreciation. Cost is $60,400, estimated life is 8 years, and estimated scrap value is $4600. $9300

30. **HOSPITAL EQUIPMENT**   Orangevale Rents uses the sum-of-the-years'-digits method of depreciation on all hospital rental equipment. If it purchases new hospital beds at a cost of $12,800 and estimates the life of the beds to be 10 years with no scrap value, find the book value at the end of the fourth year. $4887

31. **LIGHT-RAIL TOOLING**   Electro-car, a light-rail manufacturer, purchased a power-wheel and axle jig from a German manufacturer for $31,880. The jig has an expected life of 20 years and an estimated salvage value of $5000. Find the book value at the end of the third year. $24,584

32. **SOLAR COLLECTOR**   Find the depreciation in the third year for a solar collector using the sum-of-the-years'-digits method of depreciation. The cost is $23,000, estimated life is 8 years, and the estimated scrap value is $5000. $3000

33. **COMMERCIAL CARPET**   Mercury Savings Bank has installed new floor covering at a cost of $25,200. It has a useful life of 6 years and no salvage value. Find (a) the first and (b) the second year's depreciation using the sum-of-the-years'-digits method.   (a) $7200 (b) $6000

34. **ASSET DEPRECIATION**   Using the sum-of-the-years'-digits method of depreciation, find (a) the first and (b) the second year's depreciation for an asset that has a cost of $3375, an estimated life of 5 years and no salvage value.   (a) $1125 (b) $900

35. **FAST-FOOD RESTAURANTS**   In-N-Out Burgers purchased a new deep-fry unit at a cost of $12,420. The expected life of the unit is 8 years, with a scrap value of $1800. Use the sum-of-the-years'-digits method of depreciation to find (a) the first year's depreciation fraction, (b) the amount of depreciation in the first year, (c) the accumulated depreciation at the end of the eighth year, and (d) the book value at the end of the fourth year.   (a) $\frac{8}{36}$ (b) $2360 (c) $10,620 (d) $4750

36. **SEWER DEROOTER**   Armour Drain bought a new sewer derooter for $6725. The life of the machine is 10 years and the scrap value is $1500. Use the sum-of-the-years'-digits method of depreciation to find (a) the first year's depreciation fraction, (b) the amount of depreciation in the first year, (c) the accumulated depreciation at the end of the tenth year, and (d) the book value at the end of the sixth year.   (a) $\frac{10}{55}$ (b) $950 (c) $5225 (d) $2450

17.4   Units-of-Production Method and Partial-Year Depreciation

OBJECTIVES

1 *Describe the units-of-production method of depreciation.*

2 *Use the units-of-production method to find the depreciation per unit.*

3 *Calculate annual depreciation by the units-of-production method.*

4 *Prepare a depreciation schedule using the units-of-production method.*

5 *Calculate partial-year depreciation by the straight-line method.*

6 *Calculate partial-year depreciation by the double-declining-balance method.*

7 *Calculate partial-year depreciation by the sum-of-the-years'-digits method.*

Objective

1 *Describe the Units-of-Production Method of Depreciation.*   An asset often has a useful life given in terms of *units of production* or *units of output,* such as hours of use or miles of service. For example, an airliner or truck may have a useful life given as hours of air time or miles of travel. A steel press or stamping machine may have a life given as the total number of units that it can produce. With these assets, the **units-of-production method** of depreciation is used. Just as with the straight-line method of depreciation, a constant amount of depreciation is taken with the units-of-production method. With the straight-line method a constant amount of depreciation is taken each year. The units-of-production method depreciates a constant amount per unit of use or production.

Objective

2 *Use the Units-of-Production Method to Find the Depreciation per Unit.*   Find the depreciation per unit with the following formula.

$$\text{Depreciation per unit} = \frac{\text{depreciable amount}}{\text{units of life}}$$

For example, suppose a stump chipper owned by Brent's Tree Service costs $15,000, has a salvage value of $3000, and is expected to operate 700 hours. Find the depreciation per hour of operation by dividing the depreciable amount by the number of hours of life.

The depreciable amount is $15,000 - $3000 = $12,000. Use the formula to find the depreciation per unit.

$$\frac{\$12,000 \text{ depreciable amount}}{700 \text{ hours of life}} = \$17.14 \quad \text{Depreciation per hour (rounded)}$$

Objective

3 *Calculate Annual Depreciation by the Units-of-Production Method.* Use the following formula and multiply the number of hours the machine was used during the year by the depreciation per unit to find the annual depreciation.

$$\text{Depreciation} = \text{number of units (hours)} \times \text{depreciation per unit (hour)}$$

EXAMPLE 1 **Using Units-of-Production Depreciation**

North American Trucking purchased a Kenworth truck for $115,000. The truck has a salvage value of $25,000 and an estimated life of 500,000 miles. Find the depreciation for a year in which the truck is driven 128,000 miles.

Solution

First find the depreciable amount.

$$
\begin{array}{ll}
\$115,000 & \text{Cost} \\
- 25,000 & \text{Scrap value} \\
\hline
\$90,000 & \text{Depreciable amount}
\end{array}
$$

Next find the depreciation per unit.

$$\frac{\$90,000 \text{ depreciable amount}}{500,000 \text{ miles of life}} = \$0.18 \text{ depreciation per mile}$$

Multiply to find the depreciation for the year.

$$128,000 \text{ miles} \times \$0.18 = \$23,040 \text{ depreciation for the year}$$

 Scientific Calculator Approach

The calculator solution to Example 2 uses parentheses to find the depreciable amount and then chain calculations to find the depreciation amount.

$$\boxed{(} \; 115000 \; \boxed{-} \; 25000 \; \boxed{)} \; \boxed{\div} \; 500000 \; \boxed{=} \; 0.18 \; \boxed{\text{STO}}$$

$$\boxed{\text{RCL}} \; \boxed{\times} \; 128000 \; \boxed{=} \; 23040$$

EXAMPLE 2 **Preparing a Depreciation Schedule**

Global Electronics purchased a shrink-wrapping machine that costs $52,300, has an estimated salvage value of $4000, and has an expected life of 690,000 units. Prepare a depreciation schedule using the units-of-production method of depreciation. Use the following packaging schedule.

Year 1	240,000 units
Year 2	150,000 units
Year 3	90,000 units
Year 4	120,000 units
Year 5	90,000 units

Solution

The depreciable amount is $48,300 ($52,300 − $4000). The depreciation per unit is found as follows.

$$\frac{\$48,300}{690,000 \text{ units}} = \$0.07 \text{ per unit}$$

The annual depreciation is found by multiplying the number of units packaged each year by the depreciation per unit.

Year 1 240,000 units × $0.07 = $16,800
Year 2 150,000 units × $0.07 = $10,500
Year 3 90,000 units × $0.07 = $6,300
Year 4 120,000 units × $0.07 = $8,400
Year 5 90,000 units × $0.07 = $6,300
Total: 690,000 units $48,300 *depreciable amount*

Objective

4 *Prepare a Depreciation Schedule Using the Units-of-Production Method.* These results were used to help prepare the following depreciation schedule.

Year	Computation	Depreciation	Accumulated Depreciation	Book Value
0	—	—	—	$52,300
1	(240,000 × $0.07)	$16,800	$16,800	35,500
2	(150,000 × $0.07)	10,500	27,300	25,000
3	(90,000 × $0.07)	6,300	33,600	18,700
4	(120,000 × $0.07)	8,400	42,000	10,300
5	(90,000 × $0.07)	6,300	48,300	4,000

NOTE Depreciation spreads out the depreciable cost of an asset over its useful life. Once the salvage value is reached, no further depreciation is allowed, even if assest is still in use.

Objective

5 *Calculate Partial-Year Depreciation by the Straight-Line Method.* So far, each of the examples in depreciation assumed that the depreciable asset was purchased at the beginning of a year. If the asset is purchased during the year, only a fraction of the first year's depreciation may be taken. For example, if an asset is acquired on June 1, only $\frac{7}{12}$ (since 7 months remain) of the first year's depreciation may be taken. For an asset acquired on April 1, only $\frac{9}{12}$, or $\frac{3}{4}$, of the first year's depreciation may be taken. If the asset is purchased at a date other than the first of the month, then count that month for depreciation if purchased on or before the 15th of the month. This **partial-year depreciation** is explained in the following examples.

Each of the methods of depreciation studied so far (except the units-of-production method) is affected differently by a partial year. The units-of-production method is not affected by the partial first year since actual use determines depreciation.

EXAMPLE **3** **Finding Partial-Year Depreciation by the Straight-Line Method**

A jewelry display rack purchased on October 1 at a cost of $6750 has an estimated salvage value of $750 and an expected life of 5 years. Using the straight-line method of depreciation, find the depreciation in the year of purchase.

Solution

The depreciation for a full year is

$$\frac{\$6750 - \$750}{5 \text{ years}} = \frac{\$6000}{5} = \$1200$$

Since the purchase date is October 1, 3 months remain in the year. This means that only $\frac{3}{12}$, or $\frac{1}{4}$, of the $1200 may be taken in the year of purchase.

$$\$1200 \times \frac{1}{4} = \$300 \quad \text{Depreciation allowed in the year of purchase}$$

The next 4 years are depreciated at the full $1200 per year and the last 9 months $\left(\frac{3}{4}\right)$ of depreciation, figured as follows, are reported in the sixth calendar year.

$$\$1200 \times \frac{3}{4} = \$900 \quad \text{Partial-year depreciation}$$

As before, the total depreciation over all the years is the depreciable amount, or $6000.

Objective

6 *Calculate Partial-Year Depreciation by the Double-Declining-Balance Method.*

EXAMPLE **4** **Finding Partial-Year Depreciation with Double Declining Balance**

A boat dock with a life of 10 years is installed on April 12 at a cost of $72,000. If the double-declining-balance method is used, find the depreciation for the first partial year and the next full year.

Solution

The double-declining-balance rate is 20% $\left(\frac{1}{10} \times 2 = \frac{2}{10} = \frac{1}{5} = 20\%\right)$. Calculate the first year's depreciation.

$$\$72,000 \times 0.2 = \$14,400 \quad \text{Depreciation first full year}$$

Now find the depreciation for 9 months, or $\frac{3}{4}$ year. (Since April 12 is on or before April 15, count all of April.)

$$\$14,400 \times \frac{3}{4} = \$10,800 \quad \text{Partial-year depreciation}$$

The book value (declining balance) is $61,200 ($72,000 − $10,800). Use this book value to find the first full-year depreciation.

$$\$61,200 \text{ declining balance} \times 0.2 = \$12,240$$

The depreciation for the first full year is $12,240. Depreciation for the following years would be calculated as usual.

Objective

7 *Calculate Partial-Year Depreciation by the Sum-of-the-Years'-Digits Method.*

EXAMPLE 5 **Finding Partial-Year Depreciation with Sum of the Years' Digits**

An industrial air-conditioning compressor is purchased on July 1 at a cost of $3800. It is estimated that the compressor will have a life of 4 years and a scrap value of $600. Use the sum-of-the-years'-digits method to find the depreciation for each year of the life of the asset.

Solution

The partial year here is $\frac{1}{2}$ (6 months). The depreciation fraction in year 1 is $\frac{4}{10}$ and the depreciable amount is $3200 ($3800 − $600).

$$\frac{4}{10} \times \$3200 = \$1280 \quad \text{Depreciation year 1}$$

$$\$1280 \times \frac{1}{2} = \$640 \quad \text{Partial-year depreciation}$$

Partial-year depreciation in the sum-of-the-years'-digits method requires depreciation in the first full year (year 2) to be the sum of the second half of depreciation in year 1 and the first half of depreciation in year 2. Depreciation in year 3 will be the sum of the second half of year 2 and the first half of year 3 and so on for the remaining life. See Figure 17.4.

Figure 17.4

NOTE If an asset is purchased on or before the 15th of the month, then count that month for depreciation. However, if an asset is purchased on the 16th of the month or after, begin depreciation with the following month.

17.4	Exercises

Find the depreciation per unit in each of the following. Round to the nearest thousandth of a dollar.

	Cost	Salvage Value	Estimated Life	
1.	$22,500	$1500	60,000 units	$0.35
2.	$5000	$400	10,000 units	$0.46
3.	$3750	$250	120,000 units	$0.029
4.	$7500	$500	15,000 units	$0.467
5.	$300,000	$25,000	4000 hours	$68.75
6.	$600,000	$50,000	2000 hours	$275
7.	$175,000	$25,000	5000 hours	$30
8.	$125,000	$20,000	500,000 miles	$0.21

Find the amount of depreciation in each of the following.

	Depreciation per Unit	Units Produced			Depreciation per Unit	Units Produced	
9.	$0.23	78,000	$17,940	10.	$0.15	380,000	$57,000
11.	$0.54	32,000	$17,280	12.	$0.73	16,500	$12,045
13.	$0.185	15,000	$2775	14.	$0.032	73,000	$2336
15.	$0.40	17,400	$6960	16.	$0.015	180,000	$2700

 17. In your own words, describe the conditions under which the units-of-production method of depreciation is most applicable. (See Objective 1.)

 18. Explain salvage value. Discuss how salvage value is used in all four depreciation methods described in this chapter: straight-line, declining-balance, sum-of-the-years'-digits, and units-of-production methods.

Find the depreciation in the first partial year and the next full year for each of the following. Round to the nearest dollar.

	Cost	Salvage Value	Life	Depreciation Method	Date Acquired	
19.	$9700	$700	4 years	Straight line	June 1	$1313; $2250
20.	$5600	$1000	10 years	Straight line	Oct. 1	$115; $460
21.	$20,000	$1000	20 years	Double declining	Mar. 1	$1667; $1833
22.	$5250	$550	10 years	Double declining	May 1	$700; $910
23.	$3150	None	6 years	Sum of years' digits	July 12	$450; $825
24.	$9600	$600	5 years	Sum of years' digits	Sept. 10	$1000; $2800
25.	$6300	$900	8 years	Sum of years' digits	Mar. 28	$900; $1088
26.	$14,375	$2000	10 years	Sum of years' digits	Apr. 19	$1500; $2100

Solve the following application problems. Round to the nearest dollar.

27. **GARBAGE COMPACTOR** Cajun Catfish purchased a garbage compactor at a cost of $6800. The expected life is 5000 hours of production, at which time it will have a salvage value of $500. Prepare a depreciation schedule, using the units-of-production method, given the following production: year 1: 1350 hours; year 2: 1820 hours; year 3: 730 hours; year 4: 1100 hours.

Year	Computation	Amount of Depreciation	Accumulated Depreciation	Book Value
0	—	—	—	$6800
1	(1350 × $1.26)	$1701	$1701	$5099
2	(1820 × $1.26)	$2293	$3994	$2806
3	(730 × $1.26)	$920	$4914	$1886
4	(1100 × $1.26)	$1386	$6300	$500

28. **TRUCKING BUSINESS**   Jack Armstrong purchased a dump truck at a cost of $87,000. He estimates that it is good for 300,000 miles and will have a salvage value of $15,000. Use the units-of-production method to prepare a depreciation schedule given the following production: year 1: 108,000 miles; year 2: 75,000 miles; year 3: 117,000 miles.

Year	Computation	Amount of Depreciation	Accumulated Depreciation	Book Value
0	—	—	—	$87,000
1	(108,000 × $0.24)	$25,920	$25,920	$61,080
2	(75,000 × $0.24)	$18,000	$43,920	$43,080
3	(117,000 × $0.24)	$28,080	$72,000	$15,000

29. **SOFT-DRINK BOTTLING**   A small soft-drink bottler purchased an automatic filling and capping machine for $185,000. The machine has a scrap value of $30,000 and an estimated life of 20,000 hours. Find the depreciation for a year in which the machine was in operation 3400 hours. $26,350

30. **CARDBOARD RECYCLING**   A cardboard crusher costs $13,800, has an estimated salvage value of $2400, and has an expected life of 300,000 units. Find (a) the amount of depreciation each year and (b) the book value at the end of each year. Use the units-of-production method of depreciation given the following production schedule. (a) $1368; $1596; $1482 (b) $12,432; $10,836; $9354

    Year 1   36,000 units
    Year 2   42,000 units
    Year 3   39,000 units

31. **LOADER**   Ajax Construction purchased a small loader for $156,000 and estimates the life of the machine to be 10 years with a salvage value of $10,000. If the straight-line method of depreciation is used and the system is purchased on October 1, find the first partial-year depreciation and the following full-year's depreciation. $3650; $14,600

32. **GRANITE COUNTERTOPS**   The Copley Square Hotel had new granite countertops installed in the lobby at a cost of $64,400. The countertops have a useful life of 8 years and no salvage value. If the straight-line method of depreciation is used and the granite countertops were installed on March 11, find the first partial-year depreciation and the following full-year's depreciation. $6708; $8050

33. **iPHONES**   Tri-State Insurance Company purchased iPhones for all outside salespeople at a cost of $4500. The phones were purchased on October 8, the estimated life of the phones is 5 years, and they are expected to have no salvage value. Use the double-declining-balance method of depreciation to find the first partial-year depreciation and the following full-year's depreciation. $450; $1620

34. **AUTOMATED TELEPHONES**   Tele-Mation Services purchased a $14,200 auto-dial system on June 25. The estimated life of the system is 8 years and the salvage value is $3000. Use the double-declining-balance method of depreciation to find the first partial-year's depreciation and the following full-year's depreciation. $1775; $3106

35. **COMMERCIAL REROOFING** A warehouse had a new roof installed on June 27 at a cost of $44,400. The estimated life is 15 years and there is no scrap value. Use the sum-of-the-years'-digits method to find the first partial-year's depreciation and the following full-year's depreciation. $2775; $5365

36. **WAITING ROOM FURNITURE** On September 14, Dr. Patel purchased new furniture for his office. The cost of the furniture was $7850, the salvage value is $500, and expected life is 6 years. Use the sum-of-the-years'-digits method to find the first partial-year's depreciation and the following full-year's depreciation. $700; $1983

17.5	Modified Accelerated Cost Recovery System

OBJECTIVES

1 *Understand the modified accelerated cost recovery system (MACRS).*

2 *Determine the recovery period of different types of property.*

3 *Find the depreciation rate given the recovery period and recovery year.*

4 *Use the MACRS method to find the amount of depreciation.*

5 *Prepare a depreciation schedule using the MACRS.*

Objective

1 *Understand the Modified Accelerated Cost Recovery System (MACRS).* A depreciation method known as the **accelerated cost recovery system (ACRS)** originated as part of the Economic Recovery Tax Act of 1981. It was later modified by the Tax Equity and Fiscal Responsibility Act of 1982 and again by the Tax Reform Act of 1984. The Tax Reform Act of 1986 brought the most recent and significant overhaul to the accelerated cost recovery system (ACRS) and applies to all property placed in service after 1986. This most recent method is known as the **modified accelerated cost recovery system (MACRS)**. The result is that there are now three systems for computing depreciation for *federal tax purposes.*

Federal Tax Depreciation Methods

1. The MACRS method of depreciation is used for all property placed in service after 1986.
2. The ACRS method of depreciation will continue to be used for all property placed in service from 1981 through 1986.
3. The straight-line, declining-balance, and sum-of-the-years'-digits methods continue to be used if the property was placed in service before 1981.

NOTE The units-of-production method of depreciation is still allowed under the MACRS.

Keep two things in mind about MACRS. First, the system is designed, really, for tax purposes (it is sometimes called the **income tax method**). Businesses often use some alternative method of depreciation (in addition to MACRS) for financial accounting purposes. Second, some states do not allow the modified accelerated cost recovery system of depreciation for finding state income tax liability. This means businesses must use the MACRS on the federal tax return and one of the previous methods on the state tax return.

Objective

2

Determine the Recovery Period of Different Types of Property. Under the modified accelerated cost recovery system, assets are placed in one of nine **recovery classes**, depending on whether the law assumes a 3-, 5-, 7-, 10-, 15-, 20-, 27.5-, 31.5-, or 39-year life for the asset. These lives, or **recovery periods**, are determined as follows.

MACRS Recovery Classes

3-year property	Tractor units for over-the-road use, any racehorse that is over 2 years old, or any other horse that is over 12 years old
5-year property	Automobiles, taxis, buses, trucks, computers, office machinery, any property used in research and experimentation, breeding cattle and dairy cattle, appliances, carpets, and furniture used in a residential rental real estate activity, and certain geothermal, solar, and wind energy property
7-year property	Office furniture and fixtures, agricultural machinery and equipment, any property that does not have a class life and has not been designated by law as being in any other class, and any natural gas gathering line placed in service after April 11, 2005
10-year property	Vessels, barges, tugs, any single-purpose agricultural or horticultural structure, any tree or vine bearing fruits or nuts, and qualified small electric meter and qualified smart electric grid system
15-year property	Improvements made to land, such as shrubbery, fences, roads, and bridges, any tree or vine bearing fruits or nuts, any retail motor fuels outlet, any municipal wastewater treatment plant, any qualified leasehold improvement property, and any qualified restaurant property
20-year property	Certain farm buildings and municipal sewers
25-year property	Property that is an integral part of the gathering, treatment, or commercial distribution of water and municipal sewers
27.5-year property	Residential rental real estate, such as rental houses, apartment complexes, and mobile homes, not including land
31.5-year property	Nonresidential real estate, such as office buildings, stores, and warehouses if placed in service before May 13, 1993, not including land
39-year property	Nonresidential property placed in service after May 12, 1993, not including land

NOTE Land may not be depreciated. Only the cost of buildings and other improvements may be depreciated.

EXAMPLE 1 **Finding the Recovery Period for Property**

Rancher's Supply owns the following assets. Determine the recovery period for each of them.

(a) Computer equipment   **(d)** Office furniture
(b) An industrial warehouse (after May 12, 1993)   **(e)** A farm building (storage shed)
(c) A pickup truck

Solution

Use the list just given.

(a) 5 years   **(d)** 7 years
(b) 39 years   **(e)** 20 years
(c) 5 years

Objective

3   *Find the Depreciation Rate Given the Recovery Period and Recovery Year.* With MACRS, salvage value is ignored so that *depreciation is based on the original cost of the asset.* The depreciation rates are determined by applying the double-declining-balance (200%) method to the 3-, 5-, 7-, and 10-year class properties, the 150% declining-balance method to the 15- and 20-year class properties, and the straight-line (100%) method to the 27.5-, 31.5-, and 39-year class properties. Since these calculations are repetitive and require additional knowledge, the Internal Revenue Service provides tables that show the depreciation rates expressed as percents. The rates are shown in Table 17.1. To determine the rate of depreciation for any year of life, find the recovery year in the left-hand column and then read across to the allowable recovery period.

Table 17.1 MACRS DEPRECIATION RATES

Recovery Year	Applicable Percent for the Class of Property								
	3-year	5-year	7-year	10-year	15-year	20-year	27.5-year	31.5-year	39-year
1	33.33	20.00	14.29	10.00	5.00	3.750	1.818	1.587	2.568
2	44.45	32.00	24.49	18.00	9.50	7.219	3.636	3.175	2.564
3	14.81	19.20	17.49	14.40	8.55	6.677	3.636	3.175	2.564
4	7.41	11.52	12.49	11.52	7.70	6.177	3.636	3.175	2.564
5		11.52	8.93	9.22	6.93	5.713	3.636	3.175	2.564
6		5.76	8.92	7.37	6.23	5.285	3.636	3.175	2.564
7			8.93	6.55	5.90	4.888	3.636	3.175	2.564
8			4.46	6.55	5.90	4.522	3.636	3.175	2.564
9				6.56	5.91	4.462	3.637	3.175	2.564
10				6.55	5.90	4.461	3.636	3.174	2.564
11				3.28	5.91	4.462	3.637	3.175	2.564
12					5.90	4.461	3.636	3.174	2.564
13					5.91	4.462	3.637	3.175	2.564
14					5.90	4.461	3.636	3.174	2.564
15					5.91	4.462	3.637	3.175	2.564
16					2.95	4.461	3.636	3.174	2.564
17						4.462	3.637	3.175	2.564
18						4.461	3.636	3.174	2.564
19						4.462	3.637	3.175	2.564
20						4.461	3.636	3.174	2.564
21						2.231	3.637	3.175	2.564
22							3.636	3.174	2.564
23							3.637	3.175	2.564
24							3.636	3.174	2.564
25							3.637	3.175	2.564
26							3.636	3.174	2.564
27							3.637	3.175	2.564
28							3.636	3.174	2.564
29								3.175	2.564
30								3.174	2.564
31								3.175	2.564
32								3.174	2.564
33–39									2.564

Modified Accelerated Cost Recovery System (MACRS)

Useful Items
You may want to see:

Publication

☐ **225** Farmer's Tax Guide

☐ **463** Travel, Entertainment, and Gift Expenses

☐ **544** Sales and Other Dispositions of Assets

☐ **581** Basis of Assets

☐ **583** Taxpayers Starting a Business

☐ **587** Business Use of Your Home

☐ **917** Business Use of a Car

Source: IRS

Notice that the number of recovery years is one greater than the class life of the property. This is because only a half-year of depreciation is allowed for the first year the property is placed in service (for 31.5-year property or less), regardless of when the property is placed in service during the year. This is known as the **half-year convention** and is used by most taxpayers. Complete coverage of depreciation, including all depreciation tables, is provided in Internal Revenue Service **Publication 534**.

> **NOTE** MACRS is the income tax method of depreciation; several important points should be remembered.
>
> **1.** No salvage value is used.
> **2.** The life of the asset is determined by using the recovery periods assigned to different types of property.
> **3.** A depreciation rate is usually found for each year by referring to a MACRS table of depreciation rates.

EXAMPLE **2**   **Finding the Rate of Depreciation with MACRS**

Use Table 17.1 to find the rate of depreciation given the following recovery year and recovery period.

	(a)	(b)	(c)	(d)
Recovery year	4	2	3	9
Recovery period	5 years	3 years	10 years	27.5 years

Solution

(a) 11.52%   **(b)** 44.45%   **(c)** 14.40%   **(d)** 3.637%

Objective

4   *Use the MACRS Method to Find the Amount of Depreciation.* No salvage value is subtracted from the cost of property. Under the MACRS method, the depreciation rate multiplied by the original cost determines the depreciation amount. Depreciation by the MACRS method is given by

$$d = r \times c$$

where d is the depreciation for a rate r (from Table 17.1) and an original cost c.

EXAMPLE **3**   **Finding the Amount of Depreciation with MACRS**

Village Nursery and Landscaping purchased a pickup truck. Find the amount of depreciation in the third year if the truck had a cost of $21,500.

Solution

A pickup truck has a recovery period of 5 years. From Table 17.1, the depreciation rate in the third year of recovery of 5-year property is 19.20%. Multiply this rate by the full cost of the property to determine the amount of depreciation.

$$19.20\% \times \$21,500 = \$4128$$

The amount of depreciation is $4128.

Objective

5   *Prepare a Depreciation Schedule Using the MACRS.*

EXAMPLE 4   Preparing a Depreciation Schedule with MACRS

Omaha Insurance Agency purchased desks and chairs at a cost of $24,160. Prepare a depreciation schedule using the modified accelerated cost recovery system.

Solution

No salvage value is used with MACRS. Office desks and chairs have a 7-year recovery period. The annual depreciation rates for 7-year property from Table 17.1 are as follows.

Recovery Year	Recovery Percent (Rate)
1	14.29%
2	24.49%
3	17.49%
4	12.49%
5	8.93%
6	8.92%
7	8.93%
8	4.46%

Multiply the appropriate percents by $24,160 to get the results shown in the following depreciation schedule.

Year	Computation	Amount of Depreciation	Accumulated Depreciation	Book Value
0	—	—	—	$24,160
1	(14.29% × $24,160)	$3452	$3,452	20,708
2	(24.49% × $24,160)	5917	9,369	14,791
3	(17.49% × $24,160)	4226	13,595	10,565
4	(12.49% × $24,160)	3018	16,613	7,547
5	(8.93% × $24,160)	2157	18,770	5,390
6	(8.92% × $24,160)	2155	20,925	3,235
7	(8.93% × $24,160)	2157	23,082	1,078
8	(4.46% × $24,160)	1078	24,160	0

The MACRS method of depreciation allows a rapid rate of investment recovery and at the same time results in a less complicated computation. By eliminating the necessity of estimating the life of an asset and the need for using a salvage value, the tables provide a more direct method of calculating depreciation.

17.5	Exercises

Use Table 17.1 to find the recovery percent (rate) given the following recovery year and recovery period.

	Recovery year	Recovery period				Recovery year	Recovery period	
1.	3	5 years	19.2%	**2.**	2	3 years	44.45%
3.	4	10 years	11.52%	**4.**	1	7 years	14.29%
5.	1	5 years	20%	**6.**	2	20 years	7.219%
7.	14	27.5 years	3.636%	**8.**	10	31.5 years	3.174%
9.	6	5 years	5.76%	**10.**	4	27.5 years	3.636%
11.	14	39 years	2.564%	**12.**	4	31.5 years	3.175%

Find the first-year's depreciation for each of the following using the MACRS method of depreciation. Round to the nearest dollar.

13. Cost: $12,250
      Recovery period: 7 years $1751

14. Cost: $8790
      Recovery period: 5 years $1758

15. Cost: $9680
      Recovery period: 3 years $3226

16. Cost: $72,300
      Recovery period: 20 years $2711

17. Cost: $48,000
      Recovery period: 10 years $4800

18. Cost: $786,400
      Recovery period: 31.5 years $12,480

Find the book value at the end of the first year for each of the following using the MACRS method of depreciation. Round to the nearest dollar.

19. Cost: $9380
      Recovery period: 3 years $6254

20. Cost: $32,750
      Recovery period: 10 years $29,475

21. Cost: $18,800
      Recovery period: 10 years $16,920

22. Cost: $137,000
      Recovery period: 27.5 years $134,509

Find the book value at the end of 3 years for each of the following using the MACRS method of depreciation. Round to the nearest dollar.

23. Cost: $9570
      Recovery period: 5 years $2756

24. Cost: $6500
      Recovery period: 3 years $482

25. Cost: $87,300
      Recovery period: 27.5 years $79,364

26. Cost: $390,800
      Recovery period: 31.5 years $359,782

27. The same business asset may be depreciated using two or more different methods. Explain why a business would do this. (See Objective 1.)

28. After learning about MACRS, what three features stand out to you as being unique to this method? (See Objective 3.)

Solve the following application problems. Use Table 17.1. Round to the nearest dollar.

29. **RACE HORSE** Rocking Horse Ranch purchased a race horse for $10,980. Prepare a depreciation schedule using the MACRS method of depreciation (3-year property).

Year	Computation	Amount of Depreciation	Accumulated Depreciation	Book Value
0	—	—	—	$10,980
1	(33.33% × $10,980)	$3660	$3660	$7320
2	(44.45% × $10,980)	4881	8541	2439
3	(14.81% × $10,980)	1626	10,167	813
4	(7.41% × $10,980)	813*	10,980	0

*Due to rounding in prior years

30. **COMPANY VEHICLES** Village Nursery and Landscaping purchased a pickup truck at a cost of $21,500. Prepare a depreciation schedule using the MACRS method of depreciation (5-year property).

Year	Computation	Amount of Depreciation	Accumulated Depreciation	Book Value
0	—	—	—	$21,500
1	(20% × $21,500)	$4300	$4,300	$17,200
2	(32% × $21,500)	$6880	$11,180	$10,320
3	(19.2% × $21,500)	$4128	$15,308	$6,192
4	(11.52% × $21,500)	$2477	$17,785	$3,715
5	(11.52% × $21,500)	$2477	$20,262	$1,238
6	(5.76% × $21,500)	$1238	$21,500	$0

31. **OIL DRILLING** Prospect Drilling spent $122,700 to purchase a pump to circulate fluids when drilling for oil and natural gas. Given that is it a 10-year property and subject to the MACRS method of depreciation, find the book values at the end of each year. Book values: $110,430; $88,344; $70,675; $56,540; $45,227; $36,184; $28,147; $20,110; $12,061; $4024; $0

32. **RESIDENTIAL RENTAL PROPERTY** Andy Kirkpatrick purchased some nonresidential rental real estate before May 12, 1993, for $415,000, not including land. Prepare a depreciation schedule for the first 10 years using the MACRS method of depreciation (31.5-year property). Book values: $408,414; $395,238; $382,062; $368,886; $355,710; $342,534; $329,358; $316,182; $303,006; $289,834

33. **CORPORATE COMPUTERS** Beacon Engineering spent $285,000 for high-end workstations and associated network equipment. Find the book value at the end of the third year using the MACRS method of depreciation. $82,080

34. **DENTAL OFFICE FURNITURE** Harry Tepper, DDS, purchased new office furniture for the reception area of his dental office at a cost of $27,400. Find the book value at the end of the fifth year using the MACRS method of depreciation. $6113

35. **OFFICE BUILDING** Brailey Bookkeeping purchased an office building. The value of the building was $480,000, not including the land. Find the amount of depreciation for each of the first 5 years using the MACRS method of depreciation (39-year property). year 1: $12,326; years 2–5: $12,307

36. **INDEPENDENT BOOKSTORE** Maretha Roseborough, owner of the Barnstormer Bookstore, bought a building to use for her business. The cost of the building was $220,000, not including land. Find the amount of depreciation for each of the first 5 years using the MACRS method of depreciation (39-year property). year 1: $5650; years 2–5: $5641

CHAPTER TERMS

Review the following terms to test your understanding of the chapter. For each term you do not know, refer to the page number found next to that term.

200% method [p. 649]
accelerated cost recovery system (ACRS) [p. 668]
accelerated depreciation [p. 648]
accumulated depreciation [pp. 642, 643]
book value [pp. 642, 643]
cost [p. 642]
declining-balance method [p. 648]

depreciable amount [p. 643]
depreciation [p. 641]
depreciation fraction [p. 654]
depreciation schedule [p. 645]
double-declining-balance method [p. 649]
half-year convention [p. 671]

income tax method [p. 668]
modified accelerated cost recovery system (MACRS) [p. 668]
no salvage value [pp. 642, 643, 644]
partial-year depreciation [p. 663]
Publication 534 [p. 671]
recovery classes [p. 669]
recovery periods [p. 669]

residual value [p. 642]
salvage value [p. 642]
scrap value [p. 642]
straight-line method [p. 643]
sum-of-the-years'-digits method [p. 654]
tangible assets [p. 642]
units-of-production method [p. 661]
useful life [p. 642]

CONCEPTS	EXAMPLES
17.1 Straight-line method of depreciation The depreciation is the same each year. Use the formula $$d = \frac{c-s}{n}$$ with c = cost, s = salvage value, and n = life (in years).	Cost, \$5000; scrap value, \$1000; life of 8 years; find the annual amount of depreciation. $$d = \frac{\$5000 - \$1000}{8} = \frac{\$4000}{8} = \$500$$
17.1 Book value Book value is the value remaining at the end of the year. Book value = cost − accumulated depreciation	Cost, \$4000; scrap value, \$1000; life of 3 years; find the book value at the end of the first year. $$d = \frac{\$4000 - \$1000}{3} = \frac{\$3000}{3} = \$1000$$ Book value = \$4000 − \$1000 = \$3000
17.2 Declining-balance rate First, find the straight-line rate; then adjust it as follows. 200%: Multiply by 02. 150%: Multiply by $1\frac{1}{2}$. 125%: Multiply by $1\frac{1}{4}$.	Life of an asset is 10 years. Find the double-declining-balance (200%) rate. $$10 \text{ years} = 10\% \left(\frac{1}{10}\right) \text{ straight line}$$ $$2 \times 10\% = 20\%$$
17.2 Double-declining-balance depreciation method First, find the double-declining-balance rate; then use the formula $$d = r \times b$$ where b is total cost in the first year and the declining balance in the following years.	Cost, \$1400; life of 5 years; find the depreciation in years 1 and 2 (2 × 20% [straight-line rate] = 40%.) Year 1: Depreciation = 40% × \$1400 = \$560 Book value = \$1400 − \$560 = \$840 Year 2: Depreciation = 40% × \$840 = \$336

17.3 Sum-of-years'-digits depreciation fraction

Add the years' digits together to get the denominator. The numerator is the number of years of life remaining at the beginning of the year. The denominator shortcut is as follows.

$$\text{Sum of the years' digits} = \frac{n(n + 1)}{2}$$

Useful life is 4 years; find the depreciation fraction for each year.

$$1 + 2 + 3 + 4 = 10$$

Year	Depreciation Fraction
1	$\frac{4}{10}$
2	$\frac{3}{10}$
3	$\frac{2}{10}$
4	$\frac{1}{10}$

17.3 Sum-of-years'-digits depreciation method

First find the depreciation fraction, and then use the formula.

$$d = r \times (c - s)$$

Cost, $2500; salvage value, $400; life of 6 years; find depreciation in year 1.

$$\text{Depreciation fraction} = \frac{6}{21}$$

$$d = \frac{6}{21} \times (\$2500 - \$400)$$

$$= \frac{6}{21} \times \$2100 = \$600$$

17.4 Units-of-production depreciation amount

Use the following formula.

$$\text{Depreciation per unit} = \frac{\text{depreciable amount}}{\text{units of life}}$$

Cost, $10,000; salvage value, $2500; useful life of 15,000 units; find depreciation per unit.

$$\frac{\text{Depreciation}}{\text{per unit}} = \frac{\$7500 \text{ depreciable amount}}{15,000 \text{ units of life}} = \$0.50$$

17.4 Units-of-production depreciation method

Multiply the number of units (hours) of production by the depreciation per unit (per hour).

Depreciation = number of units (hours)
    × depreciation per unit (hour)

In the preceding example: the first year's production is 3800 units. Find depreciation in year 1.

$$3800 \times \$0.50 = \$1900$$

17.4 Partial-year depreciation

If an asset is purchased during the year, take only a fraction of the year's depreciation.

Depreciable amount, $4500; life, 5 years; date purchased, June 7. Find first partial-year depreciation by the straight-line method.

$$7 \text{ months} = \frac{7}{12} \text{ year}$$

$$\frac{\$4500}{5} \times \frac{7}{12} = \$525$$

17.5 Modified accelerated cost recovery system (MACRS)

Established in 1986 for federal income tax. No salvage value. Recovery periods are:

3-year	5-year	7-year
10-year	15-year	20-year
27.5-year	31.5-year	39-year

Find the proper rate from the table and then multiply by the cost to find depreciation.

Use Table 17.1 to find the recovery period column at the top of the table and the recovery year in the left-hand column. Cost: $4850; recovery period 5 years; recovery year, 3; find the depreciation.

Find 5-year recovery period column at top of Table 17.1, and recovery year 3 in leftmost column; rate is 19.20%.

$$d = 19.20\% \times \$4850 = \$931.20$$

CHAPTER 17 | Review Exercises

The answer section includes answers to all Review Exercises.

Find the annual straight-line and double-declining-balance rates (percents) of depreciation and the sum-of-the-years'-digits fractions in the first year for each of the following estimated lives. [17.2–17.3]

1. 5 years   20%; 40%; $\frac{5}{15}$
2. 6 years $16\frac{2}{3}\%$; $33\frac{1}{3}\%$; $\frac{6}{21}$
3. 4 years   25%; 50%; $\frac{4}{10}$
4. 10 years   10%; 20%; $\frac{10}{55}$
5. 20 years   5%; 10%; $\frac{20}{210}$
6. 8 years $12\frac{1}{2}\%$; 25%; $\frac{8}{36}$

Use Table 17.1 to find the recovery percent (rate) given the following recovery year and recovery period. [17.5]

	Recovery Year	Recovery Period			Recovery Year	Recovery Period	
7.	4	5-year	11.52%	8.	1	3-year	33.33%
9.	8	20-year	4.522%	10.	3	7-year	17.49%
11.	20	39-year	2.564%	12.	20	31.5-year	3.174%

Solve the following application problems. Round to the nearest dollar if necessary.

13. Cloverdale Creamery purchased an ice cream machine at a cost of $12,400. The machine has an estimated life of 10 years and a scrap value of $3000. Use the straight-line method of depreciation to find the annual depreciation. **[17.1]** $940

14. The water filtration system at Jackson Micro Brew costs $296,000, has an estimated life of 20 years, and an estimated scrap value of $48,000. Use the straight-line method of depreciation to find the book value of the machinery at the end of 10 years. **[17.1]** $172,000

15. Sunset Swimming Pools purchased a dump truck for $38,000. If the estimated life of the dump truck is 8 years, find the book value at the end of 2 years using the double-declining-balance method of depreciation. **[17.2]** $21,375

16. Star Bushing Company bought three drill presses from a Belgian firm at a total cost of $18,500. The estimated life of the drill presses is 5 years, and there is no scrap value. Find the depreciation in the first year using the double-declining-balance method of depreciation. **[17.2]** $7400

17. The Feather River Youth Camp purchased a diesel generator for $8250. Use the sum-of-the-years'-digits method of depreciation to determine the amount of depreciation to be taken during *each of the 4 years* on the diesel generator that has a 4-year life and scrap value of $1500. **[17.3]**   year 1: $2700; year 2: $2025; year 3: $1350; year 4: $675

18. Murray's Delicatessen purchased a new display case for $7375. It has an estimated life of 10 years and a salvage value of $500. Use the sum-of-the-years'-digits method of depreciation to find the book value at the end of the third year. **[17.3]** $4000

19. A grape press costs $11,000, has a scrap value of $2500, and an estimated life of 5000 hours. Use the units-of-production method to find the depreciation for a year in which the machine was in operation 900 hours. **[17.4]** $1530

20. Table Fresh Foods purchased a machine to package their presliced garden salads. The machine costs $20,100, has an estimated life of 30,000 hours, and has a salvage value of $1500. Use the units-of-production method of depreciation to find (a) the annual amount of depreciation and (b) the book value at the end of each year, given the following use information: year 1: 7800 hours; year 2: 4300 hours; year 3: 4850 hours; year 4: 7600 hours. **[17.4]** (a) $4836; $2666; $3007; $4712 (b) $15,264; $12,598; $9591; $4879

21. The Fashion Express purchased new clothing racks at a cost of $22,400. Using the straight-line method of depreciation, a 5-year life, and a scrap value of $3500, find the accumulated depreciation at the end of the fourth year. **[17.1]** $15,120

22. Using the sum-of-the-years'-digits method of depreciation, find the amount of depreciation to be charged off each year on a tour bus purchased by Bayside Tours. The bus has a cost of $85,000, an estimated life of 5 years, and a scrap value of $13,000. **[17.3]** $24,000; $19,200; $14,400; $9600; $4800

23. A recycled glass crusher costs $48,000, has an estimated life of 5 years, and has a scrap value of $4500. If the straight-line method of depreciation is used and the system is purchased on September 10, find the first partial-year depreciation. **[17.4]** $2900

24. A parking lot is resurfaced on June 1 at a cost of $9720. The estimated life is 8 years and there is no scrap value. Use the sum-of-the-years'-digits method to find the first partial-year depreciation and the following full-year's depreciation. **[17.4]** $1260; $2003

25. Instant Copy Service purchased a new copy system at a cost of $28,400 on June 19. The estimated life of the system is 10 years and the salvage value is $6000. Use the double-declining-balance method of depreciation to find the first partial-year depreciation and the following full-year's depreciation. **[17.4]** $2840; $5112

26. Karl Schmidt, owner of Toy Train Hobby, has added paging and intercom features to the communication systems of his four stores at a cost of $2800 per store. The estimated life of the systems is 10 years, with no expected salvage value. Using the sum-of-the-years'-digits method of depreciation, find the total book value of all the systems at the end of the third year. **[17.3]** $5702

27. A book printer purchased an automatic composer at a cost of $15,000. If the estimated life of the composer is 8 years, find the book value at the end of 4 years, using the double-declining-balance method of depreciation. Assume no scrap value. **[17.2]** $4746

28. Reef Fisheries purchased a commercial fishing boat for $222,375. The life of the boat is estimated to be 10 years and the scrap value is $45,000. Use the sum-of-the-years'-digits method of depreciation to find the book value of the fishing boat at the end of the fourth year. **[17.3]** $112,725

29. King's Table bought new dining room tables at a cost of $14,750. If the estimated life of the tables is 8 years, at which time they will be worthless, and the double-declining-balance method of depreciation is used, find the book value at the end of the third year. **[17.2]** $6222

30. A private road costs $56,000 and has a 15-year recovery period. Find the depreciation in the third year using the MACRS method of depreciation. **[17.5]** $4788

31. Kathy Woodward purchased a new refrigeration system (7-year property) for her flower shop at a cost of $8100. Find the amount of depreciation for each of the first 5 years using the MACRS method of depreciation. **[17.5]** $1157; $1984; $1417; $1012; $723

32. The Rice Growers Cooperative paid $2,800,000 to build a new rice-drying plant. The recovery period is 39 years. Use the MACRS method of depreciation to find the book value of the rice-drying plant at the end of the fifth year. **[17.5]** $2,440,928

33. The UPS Store purchased a new copy machine at a cost of $9480. Use the straight-line method of depreciation to find the amount of depreciation that should be charged off each year if the equipment has an estimated life of 4 years and a scrap value of $1500. **[17.1]** $1995

34. The Music Circus has just installed new seating at a total cost of $228,000. The estimated life of the seating is 10 years, there is no salvage value, and the double-declining-balance method of depreciation is used. Find the depreciation in the first year. **[17.1]** $45,600

CHAPTER 17	Business Application Case #1
	Comparing Depreciation Methods

Trader Joe's purchased freezer cases at a cost of $285,000. The estimated life of the freezer cases is 5 years, at which time they will have no salvage value. The company would like to compare allowable depreciation methods and decides to prepare depreciation schedules for the fixtures using the straight-line, double-declining-balance, and the sum-of-the-years'-digits methods of depreciation. Using these depreciation schedules, find the answer to these questions for Trader Joe's.

(a) What is the book value at the end of 3 years using the straight-line depreciation method? $114,000

(b) Using the double-declining-balance method of depreciation, what is the book value at the end of the third year? $61,560

(c) With the sum-of-the-year's-digits method of depreciation, what is the accumulated depreciation at the end of 3 years? $228,000

(d) What amount of depreciation will be taken in year 4 with each of the methods? $57,000 straight-line; $24,624 double-declining balance; $38,000 sum-of-the-years'-digits

CHAPTER 17	Business Application Case #2
	Effect of Depreciation on Corporate Taxes

The top accountant at Baja Oil Sands Operations wants to examine the effect of depreciation on income taxes for the next 10 years at the firm. The firm spends $28,400,000 for a variety of equipment for its oil-sands mining operation in Alberta, Canada. It has no salvage value at the end of its useful life. Based on research, the accountant determines that in this particular situation, it is possible for the equipment to fall either into the 5-year or the 7-year property MACRS definition, depending on several factors. The tax savings for one year is the amount of depreciation multiplied by the corporate tax rate of 40%, which includes federal and state taxes. Complete the following table.

Year	5-year MACRS	Depreciation	Tax Savings	7-year MACRS	Depreciation	Tax Savings
1	20.00	$5,680,000	$2,272,000	14.29	$4,058,360	$1,623,344
2	32.00	$9,088,000	$3,635,200	24.49	$6,955,160	$2,782,064
3	19.20	$5,452,800	$2,181,120	17.49	$4,967,160	$1,986,864
4	11.52	$3,271,680	$1,308,672	12.49	$3,547,160	$1,418,864
5	11.52	$3,271,680	$1,308,672	8.93	$2,536,120	$1,014,448
6	5.76	$1,635,840	$654,336	8.92	$2,533,280	$1,013,312
7	0	$0	$0	8.93	$2,536,120	$1,014,448
8	0	$0	$0	4.46	$1,266,640	$506,656
9	0	$0	$0	0	$0	$0
10	0	$0	$0	0	$0	$0

Since the total depreciation and the tax rate is the same either way, the total tax savings is the same. However, the 5-year MACRS results in quicker tax savings but no tax savings at all after year 6. Management should make sure that the appropriate category of MACRS is used. If either can be used in this particular situation, then management can choose the option that is best for the firm.

javier brosch / Fotolia.com

Financial Statements and Ratios

The financial crisis that began in 2008 had a huge effect on most businesses around the world. For example, Figure 18.1 shows annual sales of new cars and light trucks in the United States. Vehicle sales climbed to a record high of 17.8 million vehicles in 2000 and remained close to that through 2006. Sales began to fall off in 2007 but then collapsed during 2008 through 2010. The loss of nearly 40% of annual sales in such a short time resulted in very difficult issues for managers. Only companies with strong financial statements and management were able to withstand the collapse in sales without great difficulty. Firms such as General Motors and Chrysler required help from the government. As sales shrank, companies throughout the world laid off employees and unemployment levels rose to high levels.

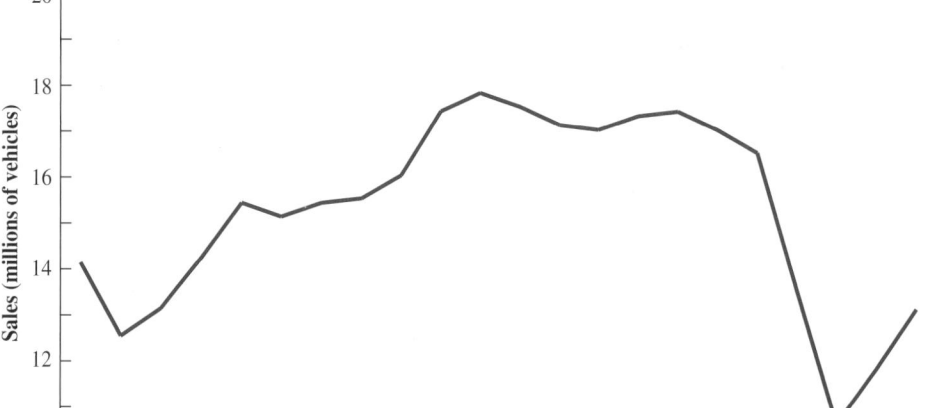

Source: Bureau of Economic Analysis.

Figure 18.1

▶ STOP&THINK

Even in normal times, it is very difficult to make an accurate forecast of future demand. What is the effect if managers in a global supply chain such as automobile manufacturing make a forecast of demand that is too high? Too low? Using only the data in Figure 18.1, what is your best guess for sales for the next year? Would you predict sales to return to the levels of 2007? Why or why not?

Business owners and managers must keep careful records of the expenses and income of their business. They need these records to help them manage the business, to inform other owners of current operations, to provide required information to lenders from whom they wish to borrow money, and for tax purposes.

Accountants keep track of income and expenses. They are concerned with issues such as meeting payroll, paying suppliers on time, and estimating and paying taxes, as well as estimating and handling revenues. This chapter covers some of the tools used by managers, accountants, lenders, and investors when looking at the financial health of a firm.

18.1	**The Income Statement**

OBJECTIVES

1 *Learn the terms used with income statements.*

2 *Understand the income statement of Apple Inc.*

3 *Complete an income statement.*

In this chapter, we look at the financial statements of Apple Inc., which has given the world the Mcintosh computer, iPod, iPhone, iPad, iTunes, and Apple Apps (applications). Apple has about 50,000 employees, but that does not include those building products for Apple in its global supply chain. Shares of the firm trade on the exchange under the symbol AAPL.

Objective

1 *Learn the Terms Used with Income Statements.* An **income statement** is used to summarize all income and expenses for a company for a given period of time such as a month, a quarter, or a year. Here are some important definitions related to financial statements.

> **Gross sales**, or **total revenue**, is the total amount of money received from customers.
> **Returns** are returns made by customers (usually used by smaller companies and not large ones).
> **Net sales** is the value of goods and services bought and kept by customers.
>
> $$\text{Net sales} = \text{gross sales} - \text{returns}$$
>
> **Cost of goods sold** is the amount paid by the firm for the items sold to customers.
> **Gross profit**, or **gross profit on sales**, is the money left over after a firm pays for the cost of goods it sells.
>
> $$\text{Gross profit} = \text{net sales} - \text{cost of goods sold}$$
>
> **Operating expenses**, or **overhead**, is the firm's cost to run the business.
> **Net income before taxes** is the amount earned by the firm before income taxes are paid.
>
> $$\text{Net income before taxes} = \text{gross profit} - \text{operating expenses}$$
>
> **Net income**, or **net income after taxes**, is the income remaining after income taxes have been paid.
>
> $$\text{Net income} = \text{net income before taxes} - \text{income taxes}$$

Banks do not wish to lend money to firms that may not be able to repay their loans. As a result, a bank will usually want to see all of the values identified in this section so far, in addition to other data, before making a loan to a firm. The values introduced here are typically included in an income statement, which we will now examine.

Objective

2

Understand the Income Statement of Apple Inc. A portion of Apple's 2010 financial statement is shown in Example 1. Rather than using a **calendar year** of January 1 to December 31 for reporting financial results, Apple uses a **fiscal year** that begins and ends in September. In this chapter, we will look at the financial statements for 2010, or for the fiscal year that ended on September 25, 2010.

> **EXAMPLE 1 Finding Net Income**
>
> In fiscal year 2010, Apple had gross sales and other income of about $65,225,000,000. (a) Write this number using words. Since the numbers are large, they are rounded to the nearest million dollars throughout the chapter. (b) Look carefully at the income statement and identify the net income.

Solution

(a) $65,225,000,000 = sixty-five billion, two hundred twenty-five million dollars

(b)

APPLE INC.
FISCAL YEAR ENDING SEPTEMBER 25, 2010
(in millions of dollars)

Total revenue	$65,225
Cost of goods sold	−39,541
Gross profit	25,684
Operating expenses and other	− 7,144
Net income before taxes	18,540
Income taxes	− 4,527
Net income after taxes	$14,013

In 2010, Apple paid about $4.5 billion in income taxes and had an after-tax net income (profit) of just over $14 billion. Check the numbers as follows.

Cost of goods sold	$39,541
Operating expenses and other	7,144
Income taxes	4,527
Net income after taxes	+14,013
Total revenue	$65,225

Apple did much better than many other companies during 2010 since its high-quality tech products had a great appeal to customers. It also sold products worldwide, so it had a large potential market.

The value of a company's stock is based on *financial results* and *perceived opportunities in the near future*. As a publicly held corporation, Apple must publish both quarterly and annual financial results and make them widely available. Generally, a firm's stock price rises when the company is doing well and the economy looks good. Similarly, stock prices tend to fall when the company is doing poorly and/or the economy is not healthy. You can obtain financial information about Apple from many financial Web sites or from the company's Web pages.

Objective

3   *Complete an Income Statement.* Example 1 gives the value for the cost of goods sold, whereas this amount would normally need to be calculated. The cost of goods sold can be found using the formula below. **Initial inventory** is the at-cost value of all goods on hand for sale at the beginning of the period, and **ending inventory** is the at-cost value of all goods on hand for sale at the end of the period.

> Initial (or beginning) inventory
>
> + cost of goods purchased during time period
>
> + freight
>
> − ending inventory
>
> Cost of goods sold

EXAMPLE 2   **Preparing an Income Statement**

One quarter, Atchinson's Smart Phones had gross sales of $159,000 with returns of $9000. Inventory at the beginning of the quarter was $47,000. A total of $104,000 worth of goods was purchased during the quarter, with freight on the goods totaling $2000. Inventory at the end of the quarter was $56,000. Wages paid to employees totaled $18,000. Rent was $9000, advertising was $1000, utilities totaled $2000, and taxes on inventory and payroll totaled $4000. Miscellaneous expenses totaled $6000 and corporate income taxes were $500. Complete an income statement for the store.

Solution

Go through the steps that follow, which refer to the income statement in Figure 18.2.

Working Through an Income Statement

STEP 1   Enter gross sales and sales returns. Subtract sales returns from gross sales to find net sales. Net sales in this example were $150,000.

STEP 2   Enter the cost of goods purchased and the freight. Add these two numbers.

STEP 3   Add the inventory at the beginning of the quarter and the total cost of goods purchased to find total of goods available for sale.

STEP 4   Subtract the inventory at the end of the quarter from the result of Step 3. This gives the cost of goods sold.

STEP 5   Subtract the cost of goods sold from net sales, which were found in Step 1. The result is the gross profit.

STEP 6   Enter all expenses and add them to get the total expenses.

STEP 7   Subtract the total expenses from the gross profit to find the net income before taxes.

STEP 8   Subtract income taxes from net income before taxes to find net income after taxes.

NOTE   Be sure to check the results of your income statement by adding the cost of goods sold, expenses, and net income before taxes. This total should equal net sales.

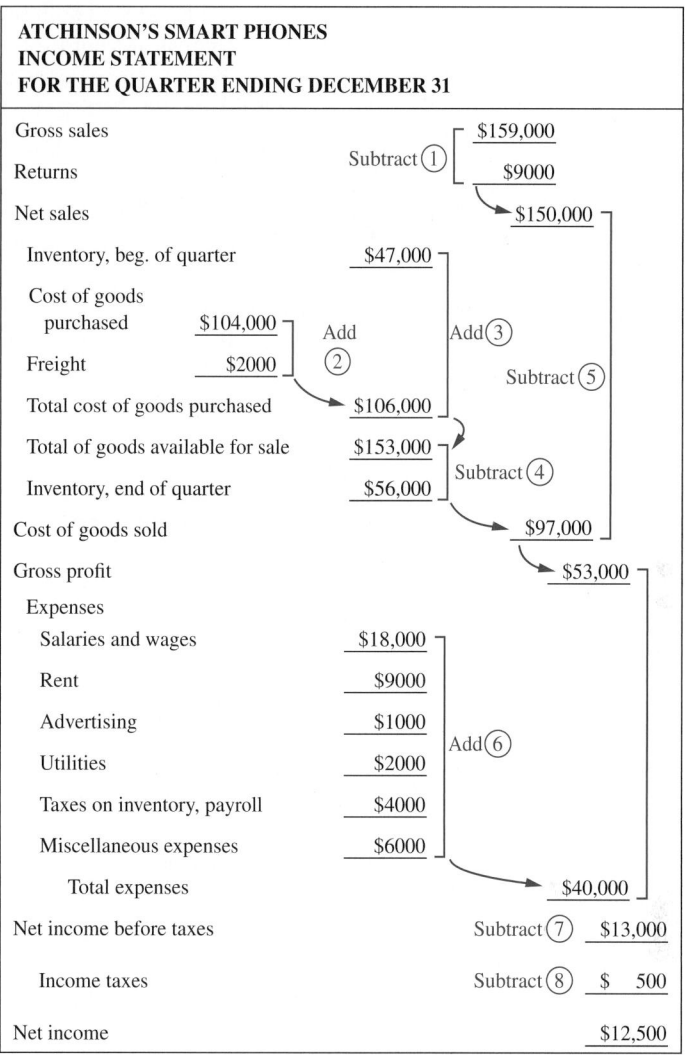

Figure 18.2

Find (a) the gross profit, (b) the net income before taxes, and (c) the net income after taxes for each firm.

1. **BIKE STORE** Janis Jacobs opened a bike store in the mall 3 years ago. Last year, the cost of goods sold was $367,200, operating expenses were $228,300, income taxes were $22,700, gross sales were $685,900, and returns were $2350. (a) $316,350 (b) $88,050 (c) $65,350

2. **CIGAR STORE** A cigar store in Ohio had net sales of $289,300, operating expenses of $68,200, cost of goods sold of $165,000, and paid $9900 in income taxes. (a) $124,300; (b) $56,100; (c) $46,200

Find the cost of goods sold in Exercises 3 and 4.

3. **VIDEO GAMES** The inventory at Yarborough Video Games, Inc. on January 1 was $263,400. Purchases during the year were $343,500, freight was $4800, and inventory at the end of the year was $287,500. $324,200

4. **SCUBA & BIKE** Jill Starkley enjoys both scuba diving and bike riding, so she opened a retail store selling equipment for both sports. Inventory was $385,200 on January 1 and $287,700 on December 31. She paid freight of $6250 during the year on purchases of $427,900. $531,650

5. **BURGLAR ALARMS** StopTheft Alarms had gross sales of $284,000 last quarter with returns of $6000. The inventory at the beginning of the quarter was $58,000. A total of $142,000 worth of goods was purchased during the quarter with freight charges of $3000. The inventory at the end of the quarter was $69,000. Wages and salaries were $19,400, rent was $6000, advertising was $2000, utilities paid by the company were $1800, taxes on inventory and payroll totaled $3000, miscellaneous expenses were $4000, and corporate income taxes were $14,650. Complete the income tax statement.

STOPTHEFT ALARMS
INCOME STATEMENT
QUARTER ENDING DECEMBER 31

Gross sales		$284,000
Returns		$6000
Net sales		$278,000
Inventory, beg. of quarter	$58,000	
Cost of goods		
purchased	$142,000	
Freight	$3000	
Total cost of goods purchased	$145,000	
Total of goods available for sale	$203,000	
Inventory, end of quarter	$69,000	
Cost of goods sold		$134,000
Gross profit		$144,000
Expenses		
Salaries and wages	$19,400	
Rent	$6000	
Advertising	$2000	
Utilities	$1800	
Taxes on inventory, payroll	$3000	
Miscellaneous expenses	$4000	
Total expenses		$36,200
Net income before taxes		$107,800
Income taxes		$14,650
Net income		$93,150

6. **DENTAL SUPPLY** New England Dental Supply is a regional wholesaler with gross sales last year of $2,215,000. Returns totaled $26,000. Inventory on January 1 was $215,000. Goods purchased during the year totaled $1,123,000. Freight was $4000. Inventory on December 31 was $265,000. Salaries and wages were $154,000, rent was $59,000, advertising was $11,000, utilities were $12,000, taxes on inventory and payroll totaled $10,000, and miscellaneous expenses were $9000. In addition, taxes for the year amounted to $287,400. Complete the following income statement for the firm.

NEW ENGLAND DENTAL SUPPLY
INCOME STATEMENT
YEAR ENDING DECEMBER 31

Gross sales			$2,215,000
Returns			$26,000
Net sales			$2,189,000
Inventory, January 1		$215,000	
Cost of goods purchased	$1,123,000		
Freight	$4000		
Total cost of goods purchased		$1,127,000	
Total of goods available for sale		$1,342,000	
Inventory, December 31		$265,000	
Cost of goods sold			$1,077,000
Gross profit			$1,112,000
Expenses			
Salaries and wages		$154,000	
Rent		$59,000	
Advertising		$11,000	
Utilities		$12,000	
Taxes on inventory, payroll		$10,000	
Miscellaneous expenses		$9000	
Total expenses			$255,000
Net income before taxes			$857,000
Income taxes			$287,400
Net income			$569,600

7. INCOME STATEMENT FOR SELF-EMPLOYED Kathy Gilmore is self-employed as a computer consultant. She sells her services to customers and has no inventory, no returns, no freight, and no cost of goods sold. Gross sales were $170,500, salaries and wages were $63,000, rent was $28,000, advertising was $12,000, utilities were $4000, taxes on payroll were $3800, and miscellaneous office expenses were $9400. Complete the income statement for this firm given that income taxes were $6800.

KATHY GILMORE, CONSULTANT
INCOME STATEMENT
FOR THE YEAR ENDING DECEMBER 31

Gross sales			$170,500
Returns			0
Net sales			$170,500
Inventory, January 1		0	
Cost of goods purchased	0		
Freight	0		
Total cost of goods purchased		0	
Total of goods available for sale		0	
Inventory, December 31		0	
Cost of goods sold			0
Gross profit			$170,500
Expenses			
Salaries and wages		$63,000	
Rent		$28,000	
Advertising		$12,000	
Utilities		$4000	
Taxes on inventory, payroll		$3800	
Miscellaneous expenses		$9400	
Total expenses			$120,200
Net income before taxes			$50,300
Income taxes			$6800
Net income			$43,500

8. What are the different factors that control gross profit? Is it important for management to continue to watch their gross profit? Why? (See Objective 1.)

 9. List the items on a family's income statement that a bank would need to look at when thinking of lending you money for a new automobile. (See Objective 2.)

 10. Name several companies that compete with General Motors.

 11. Explain why a lender might like to see an income statement before making a loan. (See Objective 1.)

 12. (a) Discuss the purpose of an income statement. (b) Outline the basic structure of an income statement. (See Objective 2.)

18.2 Analyzing the Income Statement

OBJECTIVES

1 *Compare income statements using vertical analysis.*

2 *Calculate percents of net sales.*

3 *Compare an income statement with published charts.*

4 *Prepare a horizontal analysis.*

By going through the steps presented in the previous section, a firm can find its net income for a given period of time. A question that might be asked is "What happened to each part of the sales dollar?" The first step toward answering this question is to *list each of the important items* on the income statement as a percent of net sales in a process called a **vertical analysis** of the income statement.

Objective

1 *Compare Income Statements Using Vertical Analysis.* A vertical analysis of an income statement is another application of the fundamental formula for percent from **Chapter 3**, $P = RB$. Since a percent is needed, the formula must be solved for the rate R as follows. In a vertical analysis, each item is found as a percent of net sales.

$$\left(R = \frac{P}{B}\right) \quad \text{or} \quad \left(R = \frac{\text{particular item}}{\text{net sales}}\right)$$

For example, use data from the 2010 income statement for Apple on page 683 to find the following:

$$\text{Percent cost of goods sold} = \frac{\$39,541}{\$65,225} = 60.6\% \quad \text{Rounded}$$

In 2010, Apple spent 60.6% of total annual revenue to pay its suppliers for the cost of goods that Apple sold. Much of this money went to pay the many employees of the suppliers. Although the cost of goods sold at Apple is relatively high, that is not true for all companies. For example, Microsoft Corporation writes computer software and sells it worldwide. Microsoft has a very low cost of goods sold since the firm uses very little inventory.

EXAMPLE **1** **Doing a Vertical Analysis**

Do a vertical analysis of the 2009 and 2010 income statements for Apple. Show your work in a **comparative income statement** table.

APPLE INC.
FISCAL YEAR ENDING SEPTEMBER 25
(in millions of dollars)

	2009	2010
Total revenue	$42,905	$65,225
Cost of goods sold	− 25,683	− 39,541
Gross profit	17,222	25,684
Operating expenses and other	− 5,156	− 7,144
Net income before taxes	12,066	18,540
Income taxes	− 3,831	− 4,527
Net income after taxes	$ 8,235	$14,013

Solution

Calculate each value in the 2009 column as a percent of 2009 revenue and round to the nearest tenth of a percent. Then do the same for 2010.

	Comparative Income Statement	
	2009	**2010**
Cost of goods sold	$\dfrac{\$25,683}{\$42,905} = 59.9\%$	$\dfrac{\$39,541}{\$65,225} = 60.6\%$
Gross profit	$\dfrac{\$17,222}{\$42,905} = 40.1\%$	$\dfrac{\$25,684}{\$65,225} = 39.4\%$
Operating expenses and other	$\dfrac{\$5,156}{\$42,905} = 12.0\%$	$\dfrac{\$7,144}{\$65,225} = 11.0\%$
Net income before taxes	$\dfrac{\$12,066}{\$42,905} = 28.1\%$	$\dfrac{\$18,540}{\$65,225} = 28.4\%$
Income taxes	$\dfrac{\$3,831}{\$42,905} = 8.9\%$	$\dfrac{\$4,527}{\$65,225} = 6.9\%$
Net income after taxes	$\dfrac{\$8,235}{\$42,905} = 19.2\%$	$\dfrac{\$14,013}{\$65,225} = 21.5\%$

Notice that the percents are fairly consistent from 2009 to 2010. The size of Apple and the fact that it sells globally help it maintain relatively consistent figures from year to year. A slightly higher cost of goods sold in 2010 (60.6%) versus 2009 (59.9%) caused gross profit to fall slightly. This may not seem like much, but small trends are important to watch. Perhaps this is a sign that the cost of goods produced will continue to increase, which would, in time, affect profits. However, in this situation, management reduced both operating expenses and income taxes to end up with a higher net income after taxes in 2010 (21.5%), which is better than that in 2009 (19.2%).

By the way, Apple's net income after taxes of 21.5% is higher than many other companies. For example, the net income after tax ratio for Wal-mart in 2010 was only 3.9%, far lower than Apple.

Objective

2 *Calculate Percents of Net Sales.* The formula given in the previous section for checking income statements is just as valid for percents as for dollar amounts.

$$\begin{array}{c}\text{Cost of} \\ \text{goods sold}\end{array} + \begin{array}{c}\text{Operating} \\ \text{expenses}\end{array} + \text{Income taxes} + \text{Net income after taxes} = \text{Net sales}$$

Use the information in Example 1 to verify this is true for the 2010 Apple Inc. data. Notice that net sales is the same as total revenue.

$$60.6\% + 11.0\% + 6.9\% + 21.5\% = 100.0\%$$

These figures may not always add to exactly 100% due to rounding. The next example shows how to find these percentages when there are returns.

EXAMPLE **2** **Finding Percents of Net Sales**

Write each of the following items as a percent of net sales. The salaries and wages for this firm are low because it is a small start-up business and the owner is currently not taking any income out of the business.

Gross sales	$209,000	Salaries and wages	$11,000
Returns	$9000	Rent	$6000
Cost of goods sold	$145,000	Advertising	$11,000

Solution

Use the formula for net sales, with gross sales = $209,000 and returns = $9000.

$$\text{Net sales} = \text{gross sales} - \text{returns}$$
$$= \$209,000 - \$9000 = \$200,000$$

Now find all the desired percents.

$$\text{Percent gross sales} = \frac{\$209,000}{\$200,000} = 104.5\%$$

NOTE This percent is more than 100% because returns are included in it but not in net sales.

$$\text{Percent returns} = \frac{\$9000}{\$200,000} = 4.5\%$$

$$\text{Percent cost of goods sold} = \frac{\$145,000}{\$200,000} = 72.5\%$$

$$\text{Percent salaries and wages} = \frac{\$11,000}{\$200,000} = 5.5\%$$

$$\text{Percent rent} = \frac{\$6000}{\$200,000} = 3\%$$

$$\text{Percent advertising} = \frac{\$11,000}{\$200,000} = 5.5\%$$

Objective

3   *Compare an Income Statement with Published Charts.* Once the percent of net sales for each item on the income statement has been found, they can be compared to the percents for similar businesses. To do this, consult published charts that have the required data. One such chart is shown in Table 18.1. These charts are compiled by averaging statistics from many similar firms.

Table 18.1 TYPICAL PERCENTS

Type of Business	Cost of Goods	Gross Profit	Total Operating Expenses*	Net Income	Wages	Rent	Advertising
Supermarkets	82.7%	17.3%	13.9%	3.4%	6.5%	0.8%	1.0%
Men's and women's apparel	67.0%	33.0%	21.2%	11.8%	8.0%	2.5%	1.9%
Women's apparel	64.8%	35.2%	23.4%	11.7%	7.9%	4.9%	1.8%
Shoes	60.3%	39.7%	24.5%	15.2%	10.3%	4.7%	1.6%
Furniture	68.9%	31.2%	21.7%	9.6%	9.5%	1.8%	2.5%
Appliances	66.9%	33.1%	26.0%	7.2%	11.9%	2.4%	2.5%
Drugs	67.9%	32.1%	23.5%	8.6%	12.3%	2.4%	1.4%
Restaurants	48.4%	51.6%	43.7%	7.9%	26.4%	2.8%	1.4%
Service station	76.8%	23.2%	16.9%	6.3%	8.5%	2.3%	0.5%

*This column represents the total of all expenses involved in running the firm.
Total operating expenses include, but are not limited to, wages, rent, and advertising.

EXAMPLE 3 Compare Business Ratios

Gina Burton wishes to compare the business ratios of her shoe store to industry averages. Figures from her store and industry averages for shoe stores are shown below. Burton sees that her expenses are higher and her net income is lower than the industry averages. What might Ms. Burton do to decrease total expenses and increase net income?

	Cost of Goods	Gross Profit	Total Expenses	Net Income	Wages	Rent	Advertising
Burton's Shoes	58.2%	41.8%	28.3%	13.5%	11.7%	5.6%	2.8%
Shoes (from chart)	60.3%	39.7%	24.5%	15.2%	10.3%	4.7%	1.6%

Solution

Burton's wages, rent, and advertising all seem to be above the averages. If she can decrease any of these or increase total sales without increasing any of these, then her net income will improve. Perhaps she can reschedule some employees to reduce overtime or shift more work to lower-wage employees. It may be that she can try to renegotiate her rent with her landlord or purchase her own building and move the store. Perhaps she can get the same advertising exposure by changing her advertising strategy to one that costs less.

On the other hand, her store may never compare favorably with national averages. That is fine as long as she makes an adequate profit.

Objective

4   *Prepare a Horizontal Analysis.* Another way to analyze an income statement is to prepare a **horizontal analysis**. A horizontal analysis finds percents of change (either increases or decreases) between the current time period and a previous time period. This comparison can expose *unusual changes*, such as a rapid increase in expenses or decline in net sales or profits.

Do a horizontal analysis by finding the amount of change from the previous year to the current year, both in dollars and as a percent. For example, the yearly income statements of

Apple on page 689 show that total revenue increased from $42,905 (in millions) in 2009 to $65,222 (in millions) in 2010. Find the percent increase as follows.

$$\text{Percent increase in revenue} = \frac{\$65,225 - \$42,905}{\$42,905} = 52.0\% \quad \text{Rounded}$$

Sales increased a spectacular 52% from 2009 to 2010. This happened because Apple introduced several new and innovative products in 2010. Management at Apple works very hard to develop and deliver unique and high-quality products. Apple's strategy is not to be the lowest-cost supplier of products. Rather, its strategy is to develop exciting new products that will be in very high demand worldwide and to charge accordingly for the products. Figure 18.3 shows that Apple stock lagged the market for technology stocks (called NASDAQ) during 1996 through 2005, but that it has outperformed the market since 2005.

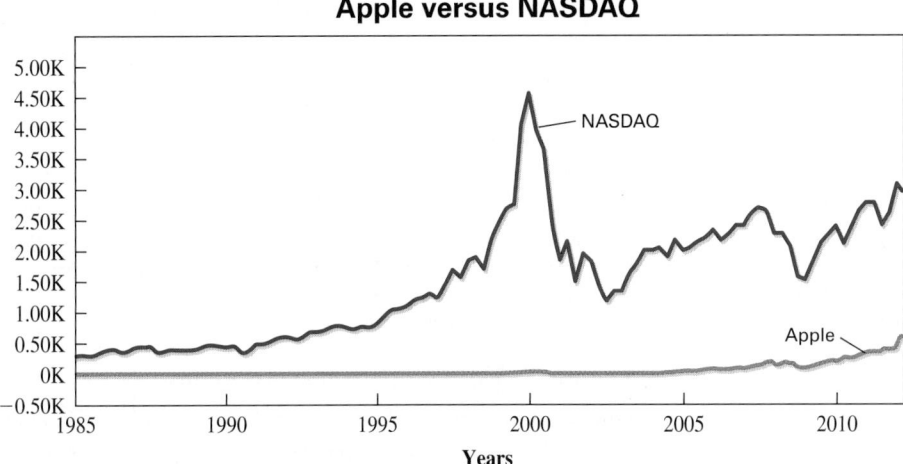

Apple versus NASDAQ

Source: www.finance.yahoo.com

Figure 18.3

EXAMPLE **4** **Doing a Horizontal Analysis**

Do a horizontal analysis for the 2009 and 2010 Apple income statements using the data given in Example 1.

Solution

Find the increase by subtracting the 2009 figure from the 2010 figure. Then divide by the 2009 figure to find the percent increase (or decrease) to the nearest tenth.

APPLE INC.
FISCAL YEAR ENDING IN SEPTEMBER
(in millions of dollars)

	2009	2010	Increase	Percent
Total revenue	$42,905	$65,225	$22,320	52.0%
Gross profit	$17,222	$25,684	$ 8,462	49.1%
Net income before taxes	$12,066	$18,540	$ 6,474	53.7%
Net income after taxes	$ 8,235	$14,013	$ 5,778	70.2%

Apple did very well in 2010. Each of these figures went up by at least 49%, which is a very rapid growth rate, especially for a large company. In particular, net income after taxes increased by an impressive 70.2%. The only question is whether management can maintain this rapid growth in the coming years.

Here are some of the things that management at Apple is doing to increase revenue and decrease costs.

1. Trying to increase sales throughout the world
2. Working to understand what customers want
3. Discontinuing products that do not sell well
4. Reducing costs everywhere possible
5. Shifting purchasing to countries that offer lower costs

NOTE During the past 40 years, many manufacturing jobs, as well as technical and professional jobs, were moved from the United States to other countries to decrease labor costs. However, recently there are signs that at least some of these jobs are being moved back to the United States. Education is a good way to help protect you and your family from job displacement—never stop learning.

18.2	Exercises

Prepare a vertical analysis for each of the following firms. Round percents to the nearest tenth of a percent.

1. **SCUBA SHOPPE** Reef Scuba, Inc. had net sales of $439,000, operating expenses of $143,180, and a cost of goods sold of $198,400.   32.6%; 45.2%

2. **WOMEN'S FASHIONS** In the third year of business, Jarita's Fashion Shoppe had operating expenses of $198,400, a cost of goods sold of $287,104, and net sales of $589,250.   33.7%; 48.7%

The following charts show some figures from the income statements of several companies. In each case, prepare a vertical analysis by expressing each item as a percent of net sales. Then write in the appropriate average percent from the table in the book. Round to the nearest tenth of a percent.

3. **CAPITAL DISTRICT APPLIANCES**

	Amount	Percent	Industry Percent from Table 18.1
Net sales	$900,000	100.0%	100.0%
Cost of goods sold	617,000	68.6%	66.9%
Gross profit	283,000	31.4%	33.1%
Wages	108,900	12.1%	11.9%
Rent	20,700	2.3%	2.4%
Advertising	27,000	3%	2.5%
Total expenses	216,000	24%	26%
Net income before taxes	67,000	7.4%	7.2%

4. ELLIS SEAFOOD RESTAURANT

	Amount	Percent	Industry Percent from Table 18.1
Net sales	$600,000	100.0%	100.0%
Cost of goods sold	280,000	46.7%	48.4%
Gross profit	320,000	53.3%	51.6%
Wages	160,000	26.7%	26.4%
Rent	15,000	2.5%	2.8%
Advertising	8000	1.3%	1.4%
Total expenses	255,000	42.5%	43.7%
Net income before taxes	65,000	10.8%	7.9%

Complete the following comparative income statement. Round percents to the nearest tenth of a percent.

5. BEST TIRES INC. COMPARATIVE INCOME STATEMENT

	This Year Amount	Percent	Last Year Amount	Percent
Gross sales	$1,856,000	100.3%	$1,692,000	100.7%
Returns	6000	0.3%	12,000	0.7%
Net sales	$1,850,000	100.0%	$1,680,000	100.0%
Cost of goods sold	1,202,000	65.0%	1,050,000	62.5%
Gross profit	648,000	35.0%	630,000	37.5%
Wages	152,000	8.2%	148,000	8.8%
Rent	82,000	4.4%	78,000	4.6%
Advertising	111,000	6.0%	122,000	7.3%
Utilities	32,000	1.7%	17,000	1.0%
Taxes on inventory, payroll	17,000	0.9%	18,000	1.1%
Miscellaneous expenses	62,000	3.4%	58,000	3.5%
Total expenses	456,000	24.6%	441,000	26.3%
Net income	$192,000	10.4%	$189,000	11.3%

Complete the following horizontal analysis for Best Tires Inc. comparative income statement given above. Round percents to the nearest tenth of a percent. Use parentheses to show that a number is negative.

6. BEST TIRES INC. COMPARATIVE INCOME STATEMENT

	This Year	Last Year	Increase (Decrease) Amount	Percent
Gross sales	$1,856,000	$1,692,000	$164,000	9.7%
Returns	6000	12,000	(6000)	(50.0%)
Net sales	1,850,000	1,680,000	170,000	10.1%
Cost of goods sold	1,202,000	1,050,000	152,000	14.5%
Gross profit	648,000	630,000	18,000	2.9%
Wages	152,000	148,000	4000	2.7%
Rent	82,000	78,000	4000	5.1%
Advertising	111,000	122,000	(11,000)	(9.0%)
Utilities	32,000	17,000	15,000	88.2%
Taxes on inventory, payroll	17,000	18,000	(1000)	(5.6%)
Miscellaneous expenses	62,000	58,000	4000	6.9%
Net income	192,000	189,000	3000	1.6%

The following tables give the percents for various items from the income statements of firms in various businesses. Complete these tables by including the appropriate percents from Table 18.1. Identify any areas that might require attention by management. Also list suggestions for improving any problem area.

Type of Store	Cost of Goods	Gross Profit	Total Operating Expenses	Net Income	Wages	Rent	Advertising
7. Supermarkets	84.5%	15.5%	14.4%	1.1%	6.4%	2.1%	0.9%
	82.7%	17.3%	13.9%	3.4%	6.5%	0.8%	1.0%

Net income is too low.

8. Shoes	60.5%	39.5%	24.3%	15.2%	10.4%	4.8%	1.5%
	60.3%	39.7%	24.5%	15.2%	10.3%	4.7%	1.6%

No major problems

9. Drug store	71.2%	28.8%	26.5%	2.3%	12.9%	5.3%	2.0%
	67.9%	32.1%	23.5%	8.6%	12.3%	2.4%	1.4%

Cost of goods and operating expenses are both high, resulting in a small net income.

10. Restaurant	57.8%	42.2%	38.6%	3.6%	28.1%	2.4%	1.0%
	48.4%	51.6%	43.7%	7.9%	26.4%	2.8%	1.4%

Net income is too low. Cost of goods and wages are too high.

 11. Compare a vertical analysis to a horizontal analysis. What are the strengths of each? (See Objectives 1 and 4.)

 12. Explain the purpose of comparing percent of net sales on an income statement to percents for similar businesses. (See Objective 2.)

 13. The average net income before taxes for supermarkets is 3.4%. Go to the supermarket where you normally shop and list 10 items that you normally buy and the price of each. Total these and find 3.4% of this total. Approximately what is the net income for the store for selling these 10 items?

 14. Why would a lender want to use both vertical and horizontal analyses before making a long-term loan to a firm? (See **Sections 18.1** and **18.2**.)

18.3   The Balance Sheet

OBJECTIVES

1 *Identify the terms used with balance sheets.*

2 *Prepare a balance sheet.*

An income statement summarizes the financial affairs of a business firm for a given period of time, such as a year. On the other hand, a **balance sheet** describes the financial condition of a firm *at one point in time*, such as the last day of a year. A balance sheet shows the worth of a business at a particular time by listing its **assets**, which are the things it owns, such as property, equipment, and money owed to the business, as well as its **liabilities**, which are amounts owed by the business to others. The difference between these two amounts gives the **owners' equity** in the business.

Objective

1 *Identify the Terms Used with Balance Sheets.* Both assets and liabilities are divided into two categories, **long-term** and **current (short-term)**. Long-term refers to assets or liabilities with a life in the firm of more than a year. Short-term applies to assets or liabilities that the company does not expect to have in one year.

ASSETS

Current assets: cash or items that can be converted into cash within a short period of time, such as 1 year

> *Cash:* cash in checking and savings accounts
> *Marketable securities:* stocks, bonds, and other securities that can quickly be converted to cash
> *Accounts receivable:* funds owed by customers of the firm
> *Notes receivable:* value of all notes owed to the firm
> *Inventory:* cost of merchandise that the firm has for sale

Plant and equipment: assets that are expected to be used for more than 1 year (also called **fixed assets** or **plant assets**)

> *Land:* book value of any land owned by the firm
> *Buildings:* book value of any building(s) owned by the firm
> *Equipment:* book value of equipment, store fixtures, furniture, and similar items owned by the firm

---

LIABILITIES

Current liabilities: items that must be paid by the firm within a short period of time, usually 1 year

> *Accounts payable:* amounts that must be paid to other firms
> *Notes payable:* value of all short-term notes owed by the firm

Long-term liabilities: items that will be paid after 1 year

> *Mortgages payable:* total due on all mortgages
> *Long-term notes payable:* total of all long-term notes

The difference between the total of all assets and the total of all liabilities is called the **owners' equity**, which is also referred to as **net worth** or, for a corporation, **stockholders' equity**. The relationship between owners' equity, assets, and liabilities is shown in the fundamental formula below.

$$\text{Owners' equity} = \text{assets} - \text{liabilities}$$
$$\text{or}$$
$$\text{Assets} = \text{liabilities} + \text{owners' equity}$$

Objective

2   *Prepare a Balance Sheet.* Now that all the terms have been defined, a balance sheet can be prepared.

EXAMPLE **1**   **Preparing a Balance Sheet**

Farmers Market lists its current cash assets as $8000. Notes receivable total $11,000, accounts receivable total $15,000, and inventory is $51,000. Plant assets include land worth $48,000, buildings worth $110,000, and fixtures worth $18,000. Current liabilities include notes payable of $28,000 and accounts payable of $26,000. Mortgages total $62,800 and long-term notes payable total $24,000. Owners' equity is $120,200. Complete a balance sheet for the market, and use the fundamental formula for accounting to find owners' equity.

Solution

To prepare a balance sheet, go through the following steps. Refer to the balance sheet in Figure 18.4.

STEP 1   Enter all current assets. On the balance sheet cash is $8000, notes receivable are $11,000, accounts receivable are $15,000, and inventory is $51,000.

STEP 2   Add the current assets. The total in the example is $85,000.

STEP 3   Enter all plant assets. In the example, land is $48,000, buildings are $110,000, and fixtures are $18,000.

STEP 4   Add the plant assets of Step 3. In the example, the total is $176,000.

STEP 5   Add the results from Steps 2 and 4. This gives the total value of all assets owned by the firm. Total assets in the example are $261,000.

STEP 6   Enter all current liabilities. In the example, notes payable are $28,000 and accounts payable are $26,000.

STEP 7   Add all current liabilities. The sum in the example is $54,000.

STEP 8   Enter long-term liabilities. In the example, mortgages total $62,800 and long-term notes payable total $24,000.

STEP 9   Add all long-term liabilities. The sum in the example is $86,800.

STEP 10   Add the results of Steps 7 and 9. This gives the total of all liabilities owed by the firm. The total of the liabilities in the example is $140,800.

STEP 11   Enter owners' equity. In the example, owners' equity is $120,200.

STEP 12   Add owners' equity to total liabilities to find $261,000.

STEP 13   Use the fundamental formula of accounting:

$$\text{Total assets} = \text{total liabilities} + \text{owners' equity}$$

Total liabilities are $140,800, owners' equity is $120,200, and total assets are $261,000. Check to make sure no mistake has been made.

$$\$140,800 + \$120,200 = \$261,000$$

So, it is correct.

NOTE   Always make sure that the total assets equal *total liabilities plus owners' equity.*

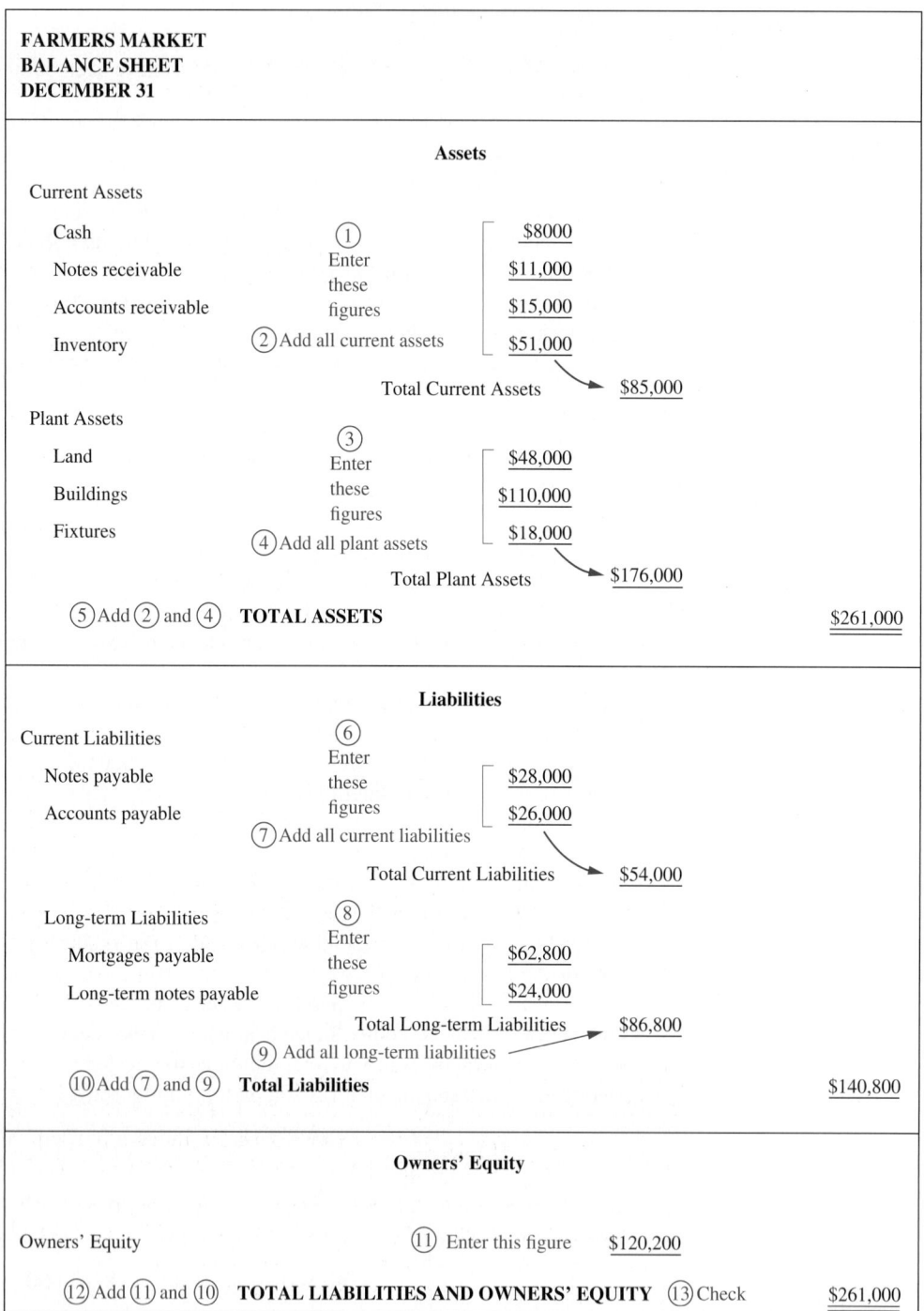

Figure 18.4

EXAMPLE 2 **Preparing a Balance Sheet**

Apple's assets in millions of dollars at the end of business on September 25, 2010, were as follows: cash and cash equivalents, $25,620; accounts receivable, $11,560; inventory and other, $4498; property and equipment, $4768; and equity and other assets, $28,737.

The firm's liabilities in millions of dollars on the same date were: accounts payable, $17,738; other current liabilities, $2984; long-term debt, $0, and short-term debt and other, $6670. Complete the balance sheet and find stockholders' equity.

Solution

APPLE INC.
FISCAL YEAR ENDING SEPTEMBER 25, 2010
(in millions of dollars)

Current Assets		
Cash and cash equivalents	$25,620	
Accounts receivable	11,560	
Inventory and other	4,498	
Total current assets	$41,678	Sum of all current assets
Other Assets		
Property and equipment	$4,768	
Equity and other assets	28,737	
Total assets	$75,183	Sum of current assets **and other assets**
Current Liabilities		
Accounts payable	$17,738	
Other current liabilities	2,984	
Total current liabilities	$20,722	Sum of current liabilities
Other Liabilities		
Long-term debt	$0	
Short-term debt and other	6,670	
Total liabilities	$27,392	Sum of current liabilities **and other liabilities**
Stockholders' equity:	$47,791	Total assets minus total liabilities
Total liabilities and equity:	$75,183	

A balance sheet shows assets and liabilities at one instant in time. For example, the data above applied only to September 25, 2010, and not to any other day. Apple has millions of transactions every day, and its balance sheet changes accordingly—essentially, it changes every day. At the end of business on September 25, 2010, Apple had $25,620,000,000 in cash and cash equivalents and no long-term debt. The company must be doing reasonably well to have that much cash and yet have no long-term debt. The short-term debt and other was only $6,670,000,000, which was quite a bit less than the cash held. It was also holding $4,498,000,000 in inventory and other assets. That is a lot of inventory. We will analyze the balance sheet in the next section.

18.3	**Exercises**

Complete the balance sheets for the following business firms.

1. **GROCERY CHAIN** Brookshire's Grocery (all figures in millions): fixtures, $28; buildings, $290; land, $466; cash, $273; notes receivable, $312; accounts receivable, $264; inventory, $180; notes payable, $312; mortgages payable, $212; accounts payable, $63; long-term notes payable, $55.

BROOKSHIRE'S GROCERY
BALANCE SHEET FOR DECEMBER 31 (in millions)

Assets			
Current Assets			
Cash	$273		
Notes receivable	$312		
Accounts receivable	$264		
Inventory	$180		
Total current assets		$1029	
Plant Assets			
Land	$466		
Buildings	$290		
Fixtures	$28		
Total plant assets		$784	
Total Assets			$1813

Liabilities			
Current Liabilities			
Notes payable	$312		
Accounts payable	$63		
Total current liabilities		$375	
Long-term Liabilities			
Mortgages payable	$212		
Long-term notes payable	$55		
Total long-term liabilities		$267	
Total Liabilities			$642

Owners' Equity		
Owners' equity	$1171	
Total Liabilities and Owners' Equity		$1813

2. **MUFFLERS** Atlas Mufflers Inc. has land valued at $87,500. Its accounts payable total $492,300; notes receivable are $26,000; accounts receivable are $378,200; cash is $148,000; buildings are $219,300; notes payable are $37,800; long-term notes payable total $187,400; mortgages total $263,300; inventory is $496,800; and fixtures are $168,200. Use the fundamental formula of accounting to find owners' equity.

ATLAS MUFFLERS, INC.
BALANCE SHEET FOR DECEMBER 31

Assets		
Current Assets		
Cash	$148,000	
Notes receivable	$26,000	
Accounts receivable	$378,200	
Inventory	$496,800	
Total current assets		$1,049,000
Plant Assets		
Land	$87,500	
Buildings	$219,300	
Fixtures	$168,200	
Total plant assets		$475,000
Total Assets		$1,524,000

ATLAS MUFFLERS, INC.
BALANCE SHEET FOR DECEMBER 31

	Liabilities		
Current Liabilities			
Notes payable	$37,800		
Accounts payable	$492,300		
Total current liabilities		$530,100	
Long-term Liabilities			
Mortgages payable	$263,300		
Long-term notes payable	$187,400		
Total long-term liabilities		$450,700	
Total Liabilities			$980,800
	Owners' Equity		
Owners' Equity	$543,200		
Total Liabilities and Owners' Equity			$1,524,000

3. Compare a balance sheet to an income statement. What are the similarities and the differences? How is each used? (See **Sections 18.1** and **18.3**.)

4. Explain how the fundamental formula for accounting is used to check a balance sheet. (See Objective 1.)

5. Prepare a balance sheet for your own family or for your parents.

6. List several reasons why a family needs to have some cash. List several reasons why a corporation needs to have some cash.

18.4   Analyzing the Balance Sheet; Financial Ratios

OBJECTIVES

1 *Compare balance sheets by vertical analysis.*

2 *Prepare a horizontal analysis.*

3 *Find the current ratio.*

4 *Find the acid-test ratio.*

5 *Find the ratio of net income after taxes to average owners' equity.*

6 *Find the accounts receivable turnover.*

7 *Find the average age of accounts receivable.*

8 *Find the debt-to-equity ratio.*

Objective

1 *Compare Balance Sheets by Vertical Analysis.* A balance sheet can be analyzed in much the same way as an income statement. In a **vertical analysis**, each item on the balance sheet is expressed as a percent of total assets. A **comparative balance sheet** shows the vertical analysis for two different years. You may want to look at a firm's comparative balance sheet before buying their stock or before accepting a job offer.

EXAMPLE | 1 | **Comparing Balance Sheets**

Do a vertical analysis for both the 2009 and 2010 balance sheets for Apple by calculating each value as a percent of the total assets for that year. Round percents to the nearest tenth. Then compare the percents to identify any significant changes that may have occurred.

Solution

APPLE INC.
FISCAL YEAR ENDING SEPTEMBER
(in millions of dollars)

	2009		2010	
	Amount	**Percent**	**Amount**	**Percent**
Current Assets				
Cash and cash equivalents	$23,464	49.4%[a]	$25,620	34.1%
Accounts receivable	6,192	13.0%	11,560	15.4%
Inventory and other	1,899	4.0%	4,498	6.0%
Total current assets	$31,555	66.4%	$41,678	55.4%[b]
Other Assets				
Property and equipment	$2,954	6.2%	$4,768	6.3%
Equity and other assets	12,992	27.4%	28,737	38.2%
Total assets	$47,501	100.0%	$75,183	100.0%
Current Liabilities	**Amount**	**Percent**	**Amount**	**Percent**
Accounts payable	$9,453	19.9%	$17,738	23.6%
Other current liabilities	2,053	4.3%	2,984	4.0%
Total current liabilities	$11,506	24.2%	$20,722	27.6%
Other Liabilities				
Long-term debt	$0	0.0%	$0	0.0%
Short-term debt and other	4,355	9.2%	6,670	8.9%
Total liabilities	$15,861	33.4%	$27,392	36.4%
Stockholders' Equity:	$31,640	66.6%	$47,791	63.6%
Total Liabilities and Owner's Equity	$47,501	100.0%	$75,183	100.0%

[a]The percent 49.4% is found by dividing cash and cash equivalents of $23,464 by total assets of $47,501 and rounding to the nearest tenth.

[b]Percents in column do not add exactly due to rounding.

Cash and cash equivalents increased strongly from $31,555 million to $41,678 million—Apple added about $10 billion dollars to its cash and cash equivalents in 1 year! Investors, bankers, and managers want firms to maintain sufficient current assets for emergencies and also for operating funds. Current liabilities also increased significantly from $11,506 in millions to $20,722 in millions, which is a trend that investors do not want to see. However, it seems to be justified in this situation by the firm's growth. Apple is a conservatively managed company, as indicated by its large cash position, no long-term debt, and rapidly growing total assets, as well as stockholders' equity.

Objective

2 *Prepare a Horizontal Analysis.* Perform a **horizontal analysis** by finding the change, both in dollars and in percent, for each item on the balance sheet from one year to the next. As before, always use the *previous year* as a base when finding the percents.

EXAMPLE **2** **Doing a Horizontal Analysis**

Apple's cash and cash equivalents increased from $23,464 in millions to $25,620 in millions.

$$\text{Percent increase} = \frac{\$25,620 - \$23,464}{\$23,464} = 9.2\%$$

The firm seemed to have a healthy increase in cash and cash equivalents. Complete a horizontal analysis of the current assets portion of Apple's balance sheet to see what else may have happened.

Solution

APPLE INC.
FISCAL YEAR ENDING SEPTEMBER
(in millions of dollars)

			Increase (Decrease)	
	2009	**2010**	**Amount**	**Percent**
Current Assets				
Cash and cash equivalents	$23,464	$25,620	$2,156	9.2%
Accounts receivable	6,192	11,560	5,368	86.7%
Inventory and other	1,899	4,498	2,599	136.9%
Total Current Assets	$31,555	$41,678	$10,123	32.1%

The data show a rapid increase in both accounts receivable, and inventory and other. Investors and creditors would want to know why both of these grew so rapidly. The economy may be getting worse, competition may be increasing in some product areas, causing inventory to grow, or some companies may be having financial problems, resulting in slower payments to Apple. Of course, Apple's revenue grew by 52% from 2009 to 2010. As revenue grows, one would expect accounts receivable and inventory to increase, so the extremely rapid growth may explain the increase in both accounts receivable and inventory and other. But these two items bear watching.

Objective

3 *Find the Current Ratio.* The **current ratio**, also known as **banker's ratio**, is found by dividing current assets by current liabilities.

$$\text{Curent ratio} = \frac{\text{current assets}}{\text{current liabilities}}$$

EXAMPLE **3** **Finding the Current Ratio**

The 2010 balance sheet for Apple shows current assets of $41,678 and current liabilities of $20,722. Find the current ratio.

Solution

$$\text{Current ratio} = \frac{\$41,678}{\$20,722} = 2.0 \quad \text{Rounded}$$

The ratio is often expressed as 2.0 to 1, or as 2.0:1.

Lending institutions look carefully at the current ratio and other financial information before making a loan. A common rule of thumb, not necessarily applicable to all firms, is that the current ratio should be at least 1:1. A firm with a current ratio significantly lower may have an increased risk of financial problems. At 2.0, Apple's current ratio is far higher than 1:1, indicating financial strength.

One disadvantage of the current ratio is that inventory is included in current assets. In a period of financial difficulty, a firm might have trouble disposing of the inventory at a reasonable price. Some accountants feel that the "acid test" for a firm's financial health is to consider only **liquid assets**: assets that are either cash or that can be converted to cash quickly, such as securities and accounts and notes receivable.

Objective

4 *Find the Acid-Test Ratio.* The **acid-test ratio**, also called the **quick ratio**, is defined as follows.

$$\text{Acid-test ratio} = \frac{\text{liquid assets}}{\text{current liabilities}}$$

NOTE As a general rule, the acid-test ratio should be at least 1 to 1, with the idea that liquid assets are at least enough to cover current liabilities.

EXAMPLE 4 **Finding the Acid-Test Ratio**

Find the acid-test ratio for Apple for 2010.

Solution

Liquid assets are cash and short-term investments plus accounts receivable. Inventory is not considered a liquid asset since it may be outdated and difficult to sell.

$$\text{Liquid assets} = \text{current assets} - \text{inventory}$$
$$= \$41{,}678 - \$4498 = \$37{,}180$$

$$\text{Acid-test ratio} = \frac{\text{liquid assets}}{\text{current liabilities}}$$

$$= \frac{\$37{,}180}{\$20{,}722} = 1.8 \quad \text{Rounded}$$

The ratio is 1.8:1, which is well above 1:1. This is another indication of how strong Apple was financially in 2010.

Objective

5 *Find the Ratio of Net Income After Taxes to Average Owners' Equity.* A company with a large amount of capital invested should have a higher net income than a company that has only a relatively small amount invested. To check on this, accountants often find the **ratio of net income after taxes to average owners' equity**. The average owners' equity is found by adding the owners' equity at the beginning and end of the year and dividing by 2.

$$\begin{array}{c} \text{Average} \\ \text{owners' equity} \end{array} = \frac{\begin{array}{c}\text{owners' equity} \\ \text{at beginning}\end{array} + \begin{array}{c}\text{owners' equity} \\ \text{at end}\end{array}}{2}$$

Then the ratio of net income after taxes to average owners' equity is found as follows.

$$\begin{array}{c} \text{Ratio of net income} \\ \text{after taxes to average} = \\ \text{owners' equity} \end{array} \frac{\text{net income after taxes}}{\text{average owners' equity}}$$

NOTE The ratio of net income after taxes to average owners' equity is also called "return on equity."

EXAMPLE **5**   **Finding the Ratio of Net Income After Taxes**

Find the 2010 ratio of net income after taxes to average owners' equity for Apple.

Solution

As seen in the balance sheet, stockholders' equity increased from $31,640 million at the end of 2009 to $47,791 million at the end of 2010.

$$\text{Average owners' equity} = \frac{\$31,640 + \$47,791}{2} = \$39,715.5 \,(\text{in millions})$$

Use the net income after taxes from the 2010 income statement in Section 18.1 to find the following.

$$\frac{\text{Ratio of net income after taxes}}{\text{to average owners' equity}} = \frac{\$14,013}{\$39,715.5} = 0.353, \text{ or } 35.3\% \quad \text{Rounded}$$

The ratio of net income after taxes to average owners' equity should be higher than the interest rate paid on savings accounts or government bonds. Otherwise, the capital represented by those assets should be deposited in bank accounts or bonds, which have lower risk. The ratio for Apple of 35.3% is much better than yields from savings accounts or bonds and is highly satisfactory.

NOTE The ratio of net income after taxes to average owners' equity is the only ratio of the three we have looked at that requires you to look at both the income statement and the balance sheet.

Objective

6   *Find the Accounts Receivable Turnover.* The accounts receivable of a firm represent credit sales—goods sold on credit and later billed to the customer. The **accounts receivable turnover** is an indication of how fast the firm is collecting its bills. If this ratio *starts to decline*, then the firm may well need to be more aggressive in collecting its receivables from customers. By collecting receivables promptly, the firm will need to borrow less money, thus cutting its interest charges.

To find the accounts receivable turnover ratio, first find the average accounts receivable.

$$\frac{\text{Average accounts}}{\text{receivable}} = \frac{\begin{array}{c}\text{accounts receivable} \\ \text{at beginning}\end{array} + \begin{array}{c}\text{accounts receivable} \\ \text{at end}\end{array}}{2}$$

Then,

$$\frac{\text{Accounts receivable}}{\text{turnover}} = \frac{\text{net sales}}{\text{average accounts receivable}}$$

EXAMPLE 6 **Finding the Accounts Receivable Turnover**

Find the accounts receivable turnover for Apple for 2010.

Solution

The balance sheet shows that accounts receivable for Apple at the beginning and end of 2010 were, respectively, $6192 and $11,560, in millions of dollars.

$$\text{Average accounts receivable} = \frac{\$6,192 + \$11,560}{2} = \$8876 \,(\text{in millions})$$

From the 2010 income statement, net sales (total revenue) was $65,225, in millions.

$$\text{Accounts receivable turnover} = \frac{\$65,225}{\$8,876} = 7.3 \quad \text{Rounded}$$

The ratio indicates that Apple is turning over its accounts receivable about 7.3 times each year, or about once every 7 weeks on average $(52 \div 7.3 = 7)$. It is generally best to evaluate this number by comparing it to the same number from a competing firm.

Objective

7 *Find the Average Age of Accounts Receivable.* As mentioned, a firm must collect its accounts receivable promptly to minimize its own need to borrow money. To tell how well accounts are being collected, the firm can find the **average age of accounts receivable**, or the average number of days needed to collect its receivables. This is found by this formula.

$$\frac{\text{Average age of}}{\text{accounts receivable}} = \frac{365}{\text{accounts receivable turnover}}$$

EXAMPLE 7 **Finding the Average Age of Accounts Receivable**

Find the average age of accounts receivable for Apple during 2010.

Solution

Divide 365 by the accounts receivable turnover found in Example 6.

$$\text{Average age of accounts receivable} = \frac{365}{7.3} = 50 \text{ days} \quad \text{Rounded}$$

On average, it takes Apple about 50 days to be paid on an accounts receivable. Certainly, anything less than 60 days is considered very good.

Objective

8 *Find the Debt-to-Equity Ratio.* Companies borrow money to expand and take advantage of business opportunities. This is fine as long as total debt *does not* become excessive. One common measure used to see if debt is reasonable is the **debt-to-equity ratio**, which is the ratio of all liabilities to all owners' equity.

$$\text{Debt-to-equity ratio} = \frac{\text{current liabilities} + \text{long-term liabilities}}{\text{owners' equity}}$$

EXAMPLE **8** **Finding the Debt-to-Equity Ratio**

Find the debt-to-equity ratio for Apple at the end of 2010.

Solution

From the balance sheet, owners' equity was $47,791 in millions.

$$\text{Current liabilities} + \text{long-term debt} = \$20,722 + \$0$$
$$= \$20,722\,(\text{in millions})$$

$$\text{Debt-to-equity ratio} = \frac{\$20,722}{\$47,791} = 0.4 \quad \text{Rounded}$$

Acceptable levels for the debt-to-equity ratio vary greatly by industry, depending on how rapidly a firm can turn inventory into cash. A company that can quickly turn inventory into cash is said to be liquid. Generally, firms with smaller debt-to-equity ratios are safer in the event of financial problems or a downturn in the economy. However, firms that manage debt well often generate larger profits. You can think of money as an asset that needs to be managed very well. In fact, managers at the best firms spend a good deal of time trying to efficiently manage the firm's financial resources.

Apple is in a very different business than, say, ExxonMobil. As a result, it does not make sense to compare the financial ratios for Apple to those of ExxonMobil. Rather, a better way is to compare the ratios against a competing firm. Some would argue that there is no real competitor to Apple, due to the uniqueness of the company. However, Hewlett-Packard does compete with Apple, at least on the sale of computers. So, perhaps we can gain a better understanding if we compare the ratios of these two firms.

The current ratio, acid-test ratio, and debt-to-equity ratios for Hewlett-Packard Co. (Figure 18.5) are all within an acceptable range. However, these ratios show that Apple has less debt and more cash than Hewlett-Packard, meaning that it is more conservatively positioned financially. The ratios involving accounts receivables are similar for the two companies, although Apple has slightly better performance. So, you have an example of two financially strong and successful companies, but one may be slightly stronger than the other.

	Financial Ratios for 2010	
	Apple Inc.	**Hewlett-Packard Co.**
Current ratio	2.0	1.1
Acid-test ratio	1.8	1.1
Ratio of net income after taxes to average owners' equity	0.353	0.216
Accounts receivable turnover	7.3	6.2
Average age of accounts receivables	50 days	58.9 days
Debt-to-equity ratio	0.4	1.4

Figure 18.5

These ratios give investors a place to begin when analyzing a company. More work would be needed before a serious investor or lender would invest in either company.

18.4	**Exercises**

Complete the following.

1. OFFICE SUPPLY   Complete this balance sheet using vertical analysis. Round to the nearest tenth of a percent.

OTERO OFFICE SUPPLY
COMPARATIVE BALANCE SHEET (in thousands)

	This Year		Last Year	
	Amount	**Percent**	**Amount**	**Percent**
Assets				
Current Assets				
Cash	$52,000	13%	$42,000	13.1%
Notes receivable	$8000	2%	$6000	1.9%
Accounts receivable	$148,000	37%	$120,000	37.5%
Inventory	$153,000	38.3%	$120,000	37.5%
Total current assets	$361,000	90.3%	$288,000	90%
Plant Assets				
Land	$10,000	2.5%	$8000	2.5%
Buildings	$14,000	3.5%	$11,000	3.4%
Fixtures	$15,000	3.8%	$13,000	4.1%
Total plant assets	$39,000	9.8%	$32,000	10%
Total Assets	$400,000	100.0%	$320,000	100.0%
Liabilities				
Current Liabilities				
Accounts payable	$3000	0.8%	$4000	1.3%
Notes payable	$201,000	50.3%	$152,000	47.5%
Total current liabilities	$204,000	51%	$156,000	48.8%
Long-term Liabilities				
Mortgages payable	$20,000	5%	$16,000	5%
Long-term notes payable	$58,000	14.5%	$42,000	13.1%
Total long-term liabilities	$78,000	19.5%	$58,000	18.1%
Total Liabilities	$282,000	70.5%	$214,000	66.9%
Owners' Equity	$118,000	29.5%	$106,000	33.1%
Total Liabilities and Owners' Equity	$400,000	100.0%	$320,000	100.0%

2. OFFICE SUPPLY   Complete the horizontal analysis for a portion of the balance sheet for Otero Office Supply.

OTERO OFFICE SUPPLY
HORIZONTAL ANALYSIS (in thousands)

	This Year	Last Year	Increase (Decrease)	
			Amount	**Percent**
Assets				
Current Assets				
Cash	$52,000	$42,000	$10,000	23.8%
Notes receivable	$8000	$6000	$2000	33.3%
Accounts receivable	$148,000	$120,000	$28,000	23.3%
Inventory	$153,000	$120,000	$33,000	27.5%
Total current assets	$361,000	$288,000	$73,000	25.3%

OTERO OFFICE SUPPLY
HORIZONTAL ANALYSIS (in thousands)

	This Year	Last Year	Increase (Decrease) Amount	Increase (Decrease) Percent
Plant Assets				
Land	$10,000	$8000	$2000	25%
Buildings	$14,000	$11,000	$3000	27.3%
Fixtures	$15,000	$13,000	$2000	15.4%
Total plant assets	$39,000	$32,000	$7000	21.9%
Total Assets	$400,000	$320,000	$80,000	25%

In Exercises 3–6, find (a) the current ratio and (b) the acid-test ratio. Round each ratio to the nearest hundredth. (c) Do the ratios suggest that the company is financially healthy using the guidelines given in the text?

3. **OTERO OFFICE SUPPLY**   Use data from Exercises 1 and 2.   (a) 1.77 (b) 1.02 (c) Yes

4. **MUSIC STORE**   Virginia Music has current assets of $216,750, current liabilities of $213,000, cash of $25,400, notes and accounts receivable of $42,500, and an inventory of mostly electric pianos and various electronic equipment valued at $148,850.   (a) 1.02 (b) 0.32 (c) No, acid-test ratio is too low.

5. **OXYGEN SUPPLY**   BlueTex Oxygen Supply has current assets of $2,234,000, current liabilities of $840,000, total cash of $339,000, notes and accounts receivable of $1,215,000, and an inventory of $680,000.   (a) 2.66 (b) 1.85 (c) Yes, ratios are okay.

6. **MOVIES**   Aktron Movies has current liabilities of $356,000, cash of $32,800, notes and accounts receivable of $248,500, and an inventory valued at $82,400.   (a) 1.02 (b) 0.79 (c) No, acid-test ratio is too low.

A portion of a comparative balance sheet is shown below. First complete the chart, then find the current ratio and the acid-test ratio for the indicated year. Round each ratio to the nearest hundredth.

7. This year   2.13; 1.27

8. Last year   2.52; 1.56

All amounts are in thousands	This Year Amount	This Year Percent	Last Year Amount	Last Year Percent
Current Assets				
Cash	$12,000	15%	$15,000	20%
Notes receivable	4000	5%	6000	8%
Accounts receivable	22,000	27.5%	18,000	24%
Inventory	26,000	32.5%	24,000	32%
Total current assets	64,000	80.0%	63,000	84.0%
Total plant and equipment	16,000	20%	12,000	16%
Total Assets	80,000	100.0%	75,000	100.0%
Total Current Liabilities	$30,000	37.5%	$25,000	33.3%

Find the debt-to-equity ratio for each of the following firms. Round to the nearest hundredth.

9. **OTERO OFFICE SUPPLY**   Use data from Exercise 1 for this year.   2.39

10. **VIRGINIA MUSIC**   Use data from Exercise 4; owners' equity of $265,000 and long-term liabilities of $174,300.   1.46

11. **BLUETEX OXYGEN** Use data from Exercise 5 along with owners' equity of $2,800,000 and long-term debt of $3,045,000.   1.39

12. **AKTRON MOVIES** Use data from Exercise 6 along with owners' equity of $380,000 and no long-term debt.   0.94

 13. To the manager of a firm, explain the meaning of an increase in the age of accounts receivable. (See Objective 2.)

14. List three ratios that can be used to analyze a balance sheet and the purpose of each ratio.

Find the ratio of net income after taxes to average owners' equity for the following firms. Round to the nearest tenth of a percent.

15. **INTERNATIONAL AIRLINE** The stockholders' equity in TNA Airline, a small start-up international airline that uses small airplanes to move freight to and from Mexico, is $845,000 at the beginning of the year and $928,500 at the end of the year. Net income after taxes for the year was $54,400.   6.1%

16. **PIPELINE COMPANY** TransCanada Pipe is an international company that does business both in Canada and in the United States. In thousands of dollars, owners' equity at the beginning of the year was $48,340 and $62,842 at the end of the year. Net income after taxes for the year was $6838.   12.3%

Find the accounts receivable turnover rate and the average age of the accounts receivable for the following firms. Round each rate to the nearest tenth.

17. **CAMEROONIAN TOBACCO** Accounts receivable at the beginning of the year of $139,000; accounts receivable at the end of the year of $284,500; and net sales of $1,805,000.   8.5 times; 42.9 days

18. **PLATES AND PLANTS** Accounts receivable at the beginning of the year of $110,000; accounts receivable at the end of the year of $80,000; and net sales of $875,000.   9.2 times; 39.7 days

 19. Explain why the acid-test ratio is a better measure of the financial health of a firm than the current ratio. (See Objectives 3 and 4.)

 20. Explain why increased risk requires a higher return on investment. (See Objective 8.)

CHAPTER TERMS

Review the following terms to test your understanding of the chapter. For any terms you do not know, refer to the page number found next to that term.

accountant [p. 682]
accounts receivable turnover [p. 705]
acid-test ratio [p. 704]
assets [p. 695]
average age of accounts receivable [p. 706]
balance sheet [p. 695]
banker's ratio [p. 703]
calendar year [p. 683]
comparative balance sheet [p. 701]
comparative income statement [p. 689]
cost of goods sold [p. 682]

current assets [p. 696]
current liabilities [p. 696]
current ratio [p. 703]
debt-to-equity ratio [p. 706]
ending inventory [p. 684]
fiscal year [p. 683]
fixed assets [p. 696]
gross profit [p. 682]
gross profit on sales [p. 682]
horizontal analysis [pp. 691, 702]
income statement [p. 682]
initial inventory [p. 684]
liabilities [p. 695]

liquid assets [p. 704]
long-term assets [p. 696]
long-term liabilities [p. 696]
net income [p. 682]
net income after taxes [p. 682]
net income before taxes [p. 682]
net sales [p. 682]
net worth [p. 696]
operating expenses [p. 682]
overhead [p. 682]
owners' equity [pp. 695, 696]

plant and equipment [p. 696]
plant assets [p. 696]
quick ratio [p. 704]
ratio of net income after taxes to average owners' equity [p. 704]
returns [p. 682]
short-term assets/liabilities [p. 696]
stockholders' equity [p. 696]
total revenue [p. 682]
vertical analysis [pp. 688, 701]

CONCEPTS

EXAMPLES

18.1 Gross profit, net income before taxes, and net income after taxes

Gross profit = net sales − cost of goods sold

Net income before taxes = gross profit − operating expenses

Net income after taxes = net income before taxes − income taxes

September: cost of goods sold, $156,000; operating expenses, $35,000; net sales, $210,000; taxes, $4000. Find gross profit, net income both before and after taxes.

Gross profit = $210,000 − $156,000 = $54,000

$$\text{Net income before taxes} = \$54,000 - \$35,000$$
$$= \$19,000$$

Net income after taxes = $19,000 − $4000 = $15,000

18.2 Finding the percent of net sales of individual items

Subtract returns from gross sales to determine net sales. Then divide the value of an item by net sales to obtain percent of net sales.

Express the following items for Capitol Appliance as percents of net sales: gross sales, $340,000; returns, $15,000; cost of goods sold, $210,000; wages, $19,000; gross profit. Round percents to the nearest tenth.

Net sales = $340,000 − $15,000 = $325,000

Gross profit = $325,000 − $210,000 = $115,000

$$\text{Percent gross sales} = \frac{\$340,000}{\$325,000} = 104.6\%$$

$$\text{Percent returns} = \frac{\$15,000}{\$325,000} = 4.6\%$$

$$\text{Percent cost of goods sold} = \frac{\$210,000}{\$325,000} = 64.6\%$$

$$\text{Percent wages} = \frac{\$19,000}{\$325,000} = 5.8\%$$

$$\text{Percent gross profit} = \frac{\$115,000}{\$325,000} = 35.4\%$$

Comparing income statements to published charts

In one chart, list the percents of net sales for each item from a published chart and a particular company.

Prepare a vertical analysis of Monica's Shoe Store.

Cost of Goods	Gross Profit	Wages	
65%	35%	6.4%	Monica's Shoe Store
60.3%	39.7%	10.3%	From chart

Her cost of goods is high, gross profit is low, and wages are low.

18.2 **Preparing a horizontal analysis**

List last year's and this year's values for each item. Then calculate the amount of the increase or decrease for each item and express it as a percent of the previous year.

The results of a horizontal analysis of the portion of a business is given. Calculate the percent of increase or decrease in each item.

	This Year	Last Year	Increase (Decrease) Amount	Percent
Gross sales	$735,000	$700,000	$35,000	5%
Returns	5000	10,000	(5000)	(50%)
Net sales	730,000	690,000	40,000	5.8%
Cost of goods sold	530,000	540,000	(10,000)	(1.9%)
Gross profit	200,000	150,000	50,000	33.3%

18.3 **Fundamental formula for accounting**

$$\text{Assets} = \text{liabilities} + \text{owners' equity}$$

or

$$\text{Assets} - \text{liabilities} = \text{owners' equity}$$

Stemco Tubing has assets of $842,300 and liabilities of $625,100. Find the owners' equity.

$$\$842,300 - \$625,100 = \$217,200$$

18.4 **Current ratio; acid-test ratio; ratio of net income after taxes to the average owners' equity**

$$\frac{\text{Current}}{\text{ratio}} = \frac{\text{current assets}}{\text{current liabilities}}$$

$$\frac{\text{Acid-test}}{\text{ratio}} = \frac{\text{liquid assets}}{\text{current liabilities}}$$

$$\text{Ratio} = \frac{\text{net income after taxes}}{\text{average owners' equity}}$$

The Circle Towne Agency has current assets of $250,000, current liabilities of $110,000, cash of $45,000, and accounts receivable of $80,000. The agency had owners' equity of $140,000 at the beginning of the year, and $180,000 at the end of the year. The net income after taxes was $25,000. Calculate the following ratios.

$$\frac{\text{Current}}{\text{ratio}} = \frac{\$250,000}{\$110,000} = 2.27$$

$$\frac{\text{Acid-test}}{\text{ratio}} = \frac{\$45,000 + \$80,000}{\$110,000} = 1.14 \quad \text{Rounded}$$

$$\frac{\text{Average owners' equity}}{} = \frac{\$140,000 + \$180,000}{2}$$

$$= \$160,000$$

Ratio of net income after taxes to average owners' equity:

$$\frac{\$25,000}{\$160,000} = 0.156{:}1$$

Accounts receivable turnover

$$= \frac{\text{net sales}}{\text{average accounts receivable}}$$

Average age of accounts receivable

Average age of accounts receivable

$$= \frac{365}{\text{accounts receivable turnover}}$$

Debt-to-equity ratio

Debt-to-equity ratio

$$= \frac{\begin{array}{cc}\text{current} & \text{long-term} \\ \text{liabilities} + \text{liabilities}\end{array}}{\text{owners' equity}}$$

A firm has net sales of $793,750; accounts receivable of $50,000 at the beginning of the year, $75,000 at the end of the year; current liabilities of $15,000; long-term liabilities of $10,000; and owners' equity of $80,000. Find the accounts receivable turnover, the average age of accounts receivable, and the debt-to-equity ratio.

Average accounts receivable

$$= \frac{\$50,000 + \$75,000}{2} = \$62,500$$

$$\text{Accounts receivable turnover} = \frac{\$793,750}{\$62,500} = 12.7$$

$$\text{Average age of accounts receivable} = \frac{365}{12.7} = 28.7 \text{ days}$$

$$\text{Debt-to-equity ratio} = \frac{\$15,000 + \$10,000}{\$80,000} = 0.31$$

CHAPTER 18	Review Exercises

The answer section includes answers to all Review Exercises.

Find the gross profit and net income before taxes for the following. **[18.1]**

	Cost of Goods	Operating Expenses	Net Sales	
1.	$124,800	$89,200	$312,200	$187,400; $98,200
2.	$379,520	$124,800	$643,250	$263,730; $138,930
3.	$300,900	$98,400	$442,500	$141,600; $43,200
4.	$606,520	$212,300	$842,400	$235,880; $23,580

Find the cost of goods sold for each of the following. **[18.1]**

	Initial Inventory	Cost of Goods Purchased	Freight	Final Inventory	
5.	$215,400	$422,000	$26,300	$247,100	$416,600
6.	$125,400	$94,300	$8200	$101,400	$126,500
7.	$84,000	$52,400	$4300	$98,000	$42,700
8.	$184,200	$245,000	$18,300	$165,400	$282,100

Find the net income after taxes for each. Then find the ratio of net income after taxes to average owners' equity. **[18.1]**

9. A surgeon has revenues of $660,500; no inventory and thus no cost of goods sold; total expenses of $412,900; average owners' equity of $340,000; and taxes of $58,800. $188,800; 0.56

10. One quarter, Beck Floors had net sales of $894,200; cost of goods sold of $462,800; expenses of $304,100; average owners' equity of $389,700; and taxes of $36,700. $90,600; 0.23

Complete the accompanying income statements for the following firms. [18.1]

11. Lori has her own boutique and is the sole employee. It had gross sales of $175,000 last quarter, with returns of $8000. The inventory on January 1 was $44,000. A total of $126,000 worth of goods was purchased with freight of $2000. The inventory on December 31 was $52,000. Salaries and wages were $9000, rent was $4000, advertising was $1500, utilities were $1000, taxes on inventory and payroll totaled $2000, and miscellaneous expenses totaled $3000.

LORI'S BOUTIQUE
INCOME STATEMENT
FOR THE QUARTER ENDING DECEMBER 31

Gross sales		$175,000
Returns		$8000
Net sales		$167,000
Inventory, January 1	$44,000	
Cost of goods		
purchased	$126,000	
Freight	$2000	
Total cost of goods purchased	$128,000	
Total of goods available for sale	$172,000	
Inventory, December 31	$52,000	
Cost of goods sold		$120,000
Gross profit		$47,000
Expenses		
Salaries and wages	$9000	
Rent	$4000	
Advertising	$1500	
Utilities	$1000	
Taxes on inventory, payroll	$2000	
Miscellaneous expenses	$3000	
Total expenses		$20,500
Net income before taxes		$26,500

12. The Guitar Warehouse had gross sales of $2,215,000 with returns of $26,000. The inventory on January 1 was $215,000. A total of $1,123,000 worth of goods was purchased with freight of $4000. The inventory on December 31 was $265,000. Salaries and wages were $154,000, rent was $59,000, advertising was $11,000, utilities were $12,000, taxes on inventory and payroll totaled $10,000, and miscellaneous expenses totaled $9000. Income taxes for the year were $242,300.

THE GUITAR WAREHOUSE
INCOME STATEMENT
FOR THE YEAR ENDING DECEMBER 31

Gross sales		$2,215,000
Returns		$26,000
Net sales		$2,189,000
Inventory, January 1	$215,000	
Cost of goods		
purchased	$1,123,000	
Freight	$4000	
Total cost of goods purchased	$1,127,000	
Total of goods available for sale	$1,342,000	
Inventory, December 31	$265,000	
Cost of goods sold		$1,077,000

THE GUITAR WAREHOUSE
INCOME STATEMENT
FOR THE YEAR ENDING DECEMBER 31

Gross profit		$1,112,000
Expenses		
Salaries and wages	$154,000	
Rent	$59,000	
Advertising	$11,000	
Utilities	$12,000	
Taxes on inventory, payroll	$10,000	
Miscellaneous expenses	$9000	
Total expenses		$255,000
Net income before taxes		$857,000
Income taxes		$242,300
Net income		$614,700

Prepare a vertical analysis for the following firms. Round to the nearest tenth of a percent. **[18.2]**

	Cost of Goods Sold	Operating Expenses	Net Sales	
13.	$485,800	$104,300	$812,200	59.8%; 12.8%
14.	$813,200	$387,100	$1,329,400	61.2%; 29.1%

Complete the following chart. Express each item as a percent of net sales and then write in the appropriate average percent from Table 18.1. Round each percent to the nearest tenth of a percent. **[18.2]**

15.

JALISCO MEXICAN FOODS (3RD QUARTER)

	Amount	Percent	Percent from Table 18.1
Net sales	$300,000	100%	100%
Cost of goods sold	$125,000	41.7%	48.4%
Gross profit	$175,000	58.3%	51.6%
Wages	$72,000	24.0%	26.4%
Rent	$12,000	4.0%	2.8%
Advertising	$5700	1.9%	1.4%
Total expenses	$123,000	41.0%	43.7%
Net income	$52,000	17.3%	7.9%

Complete the following balance sheet. **[18.3]**

16. Gaskets, Inc. manufactures gaskets for gasoline engines. It has been under intense financial pressure recently due to foreign competition. The firm has notes payable of $410,000; accounts receivable of $460,000; cash of $240,000; long-term notes payable of $194,000; buildings worth $260,000; inventory of $225,000; fixtures worth $48,000; notes receivable of $180,000; land worth $180,000; accounts payable of $882,000; and mortgages payable of $220,000. Use the fundamental formula of accounting to find owners' equity.

GASKETS, INC.
BALANCE SHEET FOR DECEMBER 31

Assets		
Current Assets		
Cash	$240,000	
Notes receivable	$180,000	
Accounts receivable	$460,000	
Inventory	$225,000	
Total current assets		$1,105,000

GASKETS, INC.
BALANCE SHEET FOR DECEMBER 31

Plant Assets			
Land	$180,000		
Buildings	$260,000		
Fixtures	$48,000		
Total plant assets			
Total Assets		$488,000	$1,593,000

Liabilities			
Current Liabilities			
Notes payable	$410,000		
Accounts payable	$882,000		
Total current liabilities		$1,292,000	
Long-term Liabilities			
Mortgages payable	$220,000		
Long-term notes payable	$194,000		
Total long-term liabilities		$414,000	
Total Liabilities			$1,706,000

Owners' equity			
Owners' equity	($113,000)		
Total liabilities and owners' equity			$1,593,000

Calculate the current ratio, acid-test ratio, and debt-to-equity ratio for the following. Round to the nearest hundredth. **[18.4]**

	Current Assets	Current Liabilities	Long-Term Liabilities	Owners' Equity	Liquid Assets	
17.	$342,000	$260,000	$140,000	$225,000	$120,000	1.32; 0.46; 1.78
18.	$95,000	$115,000	$85,000	$48,000	$5000	0.83; 0.04; 4.17
19.	$160,000	$205,000	$0	$185,000	$145,000	0.78; 0.71; 1.11

Find the accounts receivable turnover rate and the average age of the accounts receivable in the following firms. Round to the nearest tenth. **[18.4]**

20. Accounts receivable at beginning of year $875,400   5.0; 73 days
Accounts receivable at end of year $962,300
Net sales $4,612,000

21. Accounts receivable at beginning of year $126,800   8.6; 42.4 days
Accounts receivable at end of year $92,400
Net sales $942,500

22. Complete the following comparative balance sheet. Round to the nearest tenth of a percent. **[18.4]**

	This Year		Last Year	
	Amount	Percent	Amount	Percent
Current Assets				
Cash	$28,000	18.8%	$22,000	21.1%
Notes receivable	$12,000	8.1%	$15,000	14.4%
Accounts receivable	$39,000	26.2%	$31,500	30.1%
Inventory	$22,000	14.8%	$20,000	19.1%
Total current assets	$101,000	67.8%	$88,500	84.7%
Total plant and equipment	$48,000	32.2%	$16,000	15.3%
Total Assets	$149,000	100.0%	$104,500	100.0%
Total current liabilities	$38,000	25.5%	$36,000	34.4%

BUSINESS APPLICATION CASE #1   **717**

CHAPTER 18	Business Application Case #1
	Borrowing from a Bank

Tom Walker wants to expand his small bicycle shop and has gone to a bank for a $180,000 loan. The commercial loan officer asks Walker for his most recent income statement and balance sheets based on the following data.

Gross sales	$272,500	Salaries and wages	$97,500
Returns	$12,500	Rent	$12,000
Inventory on January 1	$44,000	Advertising	$2000
Cost of goods purchased	$75,000	Utilities	$3000
Freight	$8000	Taxes on inventory, payroll	$7000
Inventory on December 31	$26,000	Miscellaneous expenses	$4500
		Income taxes	$4320

(a) Prepare an income statement.

WALKER BICYCLE SHOP
INCOME STATEMENT
YEAR ENDING DECEMBER 31

Gross sales		$272,500	
Returns		$12,500	
Net sales		$260,000	
Inventory, January 1		$44,000	
Cost of goods purchased	$75,000		
Freight	$8000		
Total cost of goods purchased		$83,000	
Total of goods available for sale		$127,000	
Inventory, December 31		$26,000	
Cost of goods sold			$101,000
Gross profit			$159,000
Expenses			
Salaries and wages		$97,500	
Rent		$12,000	
Advertising		$2000	
Utilities		$3000	
Taxes on inventory, payroll		$7000	
Miscellaneous expenses		$4500	
Total expenses			$126,000
Net income before taxes			$33,000
Income taxes			$4320
Net income after taxes			$28,680

(b) Express the following items as a percent of net sales. Round to tenths of a percent.

Gross sales	104.8%	Salaries and wages	37.5%
Returns	4.8%	Rent	4.6%
Cost of goods sold	38.8%	Utilities	1.2%

(c) After the year is completed, Walker has $62,000 in cash, $2500 in notes receivable, $8200 in accounts receivable, and $26,000 in inventory. He has land valued at $39,500, buildings valued at $98,400, and fixtures worth $13,500. He also has $4500 in notes payable and $27,000 in accounts payable, mortgages for $68,000, long-term notes payable of $8000, and owners' equity of $142,600. Prepare a balance sheet.

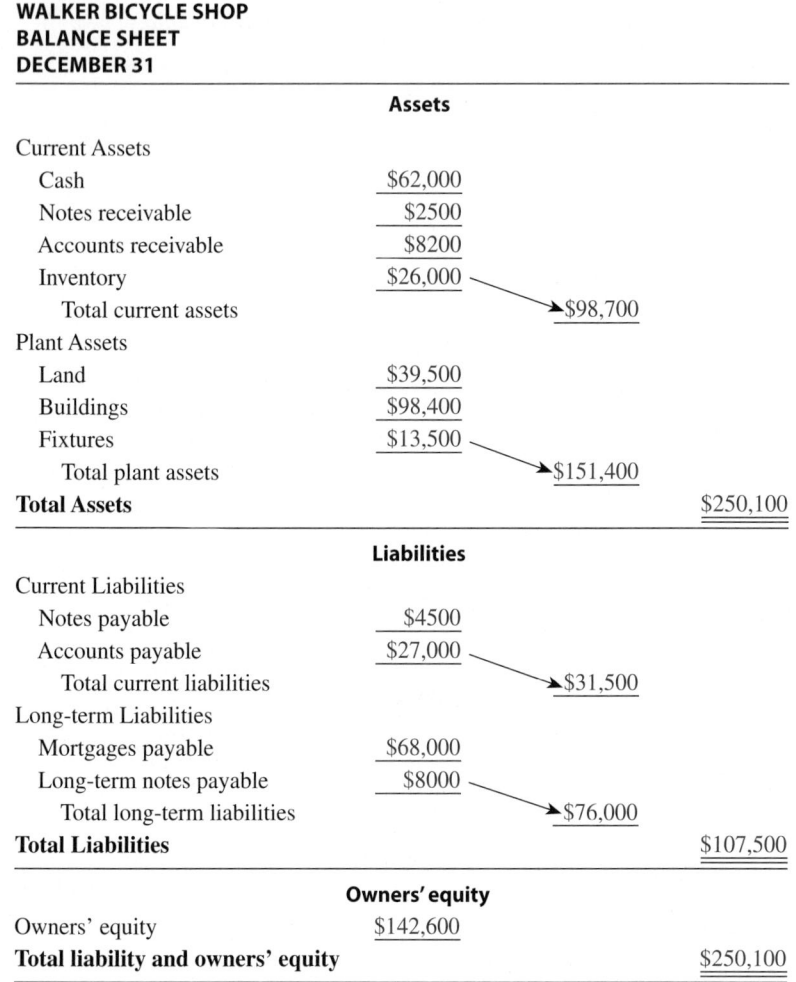

WALKER BICYCLE SHOP
BALANCE SHEET
DECEMBER 31

Assets

Current Assets
Cash	$62,000	
Notes receivable	$2500	
Accounts receivable	$8200	
Inventory	$26,000	
Total current assets		$98,700

Plant Assets
Land	$39,500	
Buildings	$98,400	
Fixtures	$13,500	
Total plant assets		$151,400
Total Assets		$250,100

Liabilities

Current Liabilities
Notes payable	$4500	
Accounts payable	$27,000	
Total current liabilities		$31,500

Long-term Liabilities
Mortgages payable	$68,000	
Long-term notes payable	$8000	
Total long-term liabilities		$76,000
Total Liabilities		$107,500

Owners' equity

Owners' equity	$142,600	
Total liability and owners' equity		$250,100

(d) Find the current ratio and the acid-test ratio for Walker's business. Round to nearest hundredth.   3.13; 2.31

(e) If you were the commercial loan officer, would you approve Walker's requested loan? Why or why not?   Probably not, profits are too small. Any small problem could result in an inability to repay the loan.

CHAPTER 18	Business Application Case #2
	Analyzing Financial Statements

First, choose one large, publicly held company that you are familiar with, such as Apple, eBay, Nike, Microsoft, Toyota, Target, Best Buy, etc. Go to any of the financial Web sites (e.g., finance.yahoo.com) or to the company's home page on the Web and find the income statement and balance sheet for the two most recent years. Then find all of the following values: current ratio, acid-test ratio, ratio of net income after taxes to average owners' equity, accounts receivable turnover, average age of accounts receivable, and debt-to-equity ratio. Based on everything you know about the company, including personal experience, is the company doing well? If so, do you expect it to continue to do well in the future? Answers will vary.

javier brosch / Fotolia.com

Distribution of Profit, Stocks, and Bonds

Businesses usually distribute some or all of their profits to the owners. The way in which profits are distributed depends on the type of company. For example, an individual who owns a small business, such as a hair salon, a small restaurant, or a small retail store, often operates the business as a **sole proprietorship**. In a sole proprietorship, there is no division between personal and company assets and the profits or losses pass directly through, to the owner. Both personal assets of the owner as well as business assets can be **attached** to pay debts in a sole proprietorship.

A **partnership** is a business formed by two or more people and is common for somewhat larger businesses such as a chain of two small retail stores or the ownership of a 50-unit apartment house. Unless they have a prior agreement, profits in a partnership are divided equally among the partners. Partners are jointly and severally liable for partnership debts. This means that the lender to the partnership can recover the entire indebtedness from any of the partners. So be very careful about going into a partnership with someone! You may end up having to pay off all of the debts. **Silent partners** invest money but are usually not directly involved in the day-to-day operations of the partnership. A **limited partnership** is one in which some partners invest money and then do not participate in the running of the business. Unlike in a regular partnership, a limited partner's loss is limited to the amount invested.

Because of the lack of protection for personal assets in regular partnerships, most larger businesses are set up as **corporations**. The people investing money in a corporation have **limited liability** and can lose no more than they have invested in the corporation. Another advantage of a corporation is that its structure and the laws make it relatively simple to have many different owners. Large companies sometimes incorporate in states or countries that have particularly favorable laws for them, such as the state of Delaware or the country of Antilles. However, most smaller firms incorporate in the state where they do most of their business and where their offices are located.

Figure 19.1 shows U.S. wages and corporate profits as a percent of **gross domestic product (GDP)**. GDP is one measure of the total economic activity in a country. Notice that wages have fallen from over 50% of GDP during 1950 through 1975 to less than 45% of GDP today. During the past 5 years in particular, corporate profits have risen to over 10% of GDP. Effectively, wages have not kept up with the increase in corporate profits during the last few years.

▶ STOP & THINK

Figure 19.1 really talks about the piece of the total income that goes for wages and also for corporate profits. Do you think corporations make too little or too much profit, or do you have enough information to make a decision? Explain. Are wages high enough? What would happen if corporate profits were somehow smaller and wages were higher? Remember, we live in a global world, so you have to consider the effects worldwide.

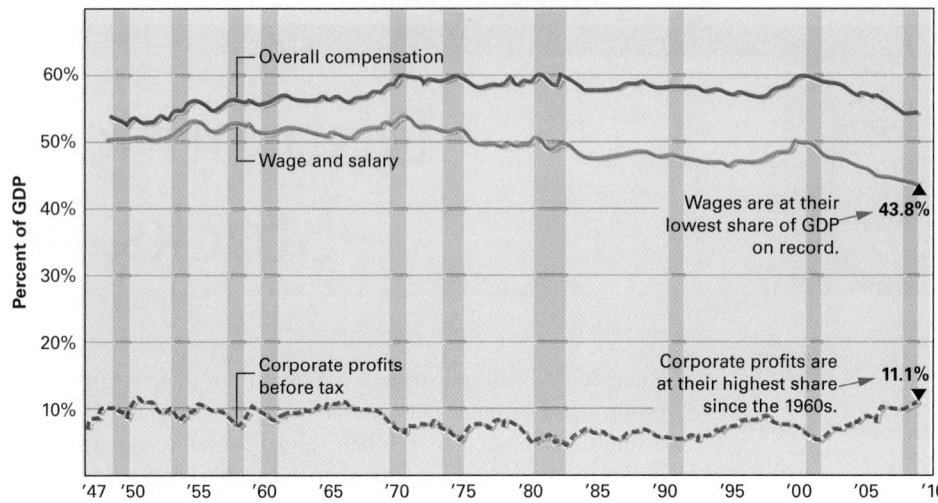

Employee Compensation and Corporate Profits as Share of GDP

Shaded areas show recessions

Source: Dept. of Commerce; Economic Policy Institute.

Figure 19.1

19.1 | Distribution of Profits in a Corporation

OBJECTIVES

1 *Compare preferred and common stocks.*

2 *Distribute profits to shareholders and calculate dividend per share.*

3 *Find earnings per share.*

A corporation is set up with money, or **capital**, raised by selling shares of **stock**. A share of stock represents partial ownership in a corporation. If 1 million shares of stock are sold to establish a new firm, the owner of one share is a **stockholder** who owns 1/1,000,000 of the corporation. A **publicly held corporation** is one whose stock is registered to trade in public stock markets such as the New York Stock Exchange. Stock ownership can be indicated by a **stock certificate**, as shown in Figure 19.2. Publicly held corporations must disclose their operating results to the public regularly. Managers must be careful that their employees do not participate in **insider trading**, or buying and selling stock on information that employees have but that has not yet been made available to the public. Managers also must be careful not to make significant misstatements in the information they release to the public since doing so can result in fines or imprisonment.

Corporations are required to hold an **annual meeting** that is open to all shareholders of the company. At this meeting, the management of the firm is open to questions from stockholders. The stockholders also elect a **board of directors**—a group of people who represent the stockholders. The board of directors hires the **executive officers** of the corporation, such as the president and vice presidents. The board of directors also typically authorizes the distribution of some of the profits in the form of dividends. Dividends are covered in more detail later in this section.

Objective

1 *Compare Preferred and Common Stocks.* Corporations of all sizes need money to operate and grow. Without growth, they will not hire additional employees and may even lay workers off. Corporations can raise money by selling ownership in the company by selling stock, as discussed in **Section 19.2**. Or, they can borrow money from banks or other investors or sell

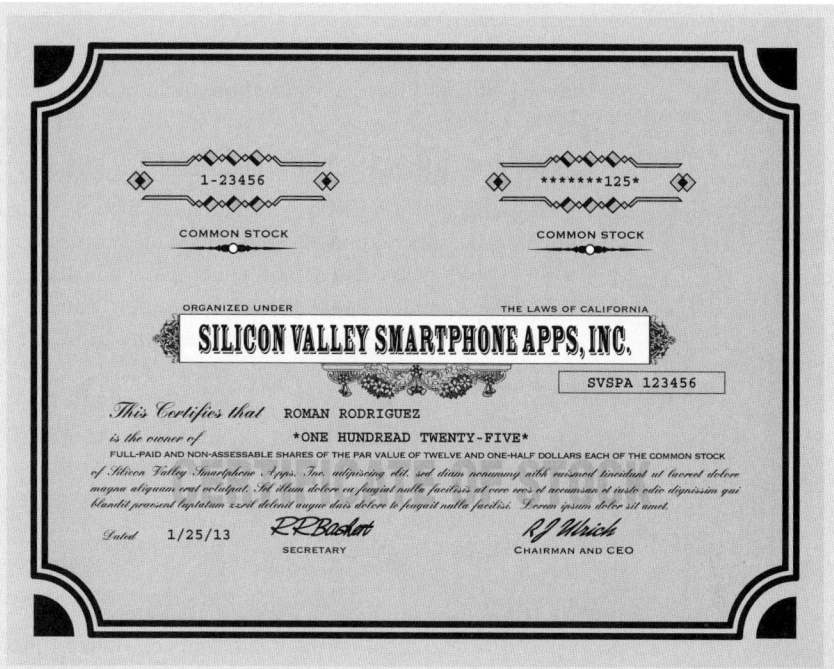

Figure 19.2

bonds, as discussed in **Section 19.3**. Most stock issued by corporations is **common stock**, which has no guarantees. In the event of bankruptcy, common stockholders receive nothing until bankruptcy attorneys, debtors, and preferred shareholders are paid in full. However, common stockholders vote at the annual shareholder meeting, so they have some control over some of the issues faced by the corporation.

Some corporations also issue **preferred stock**, which has the following advantages over common stock:

Advantages of Preferred Stock

- Dividends on preferred stock are paid before any dividends are paid on common stock.
- In the event of bankruptcy, owners of preferred stocks are paid before common stockholders receive anything. Preferred shareholders receive nothing until all debts of the corporation have been paid.
- Each share has a **par value**—the face value of the stock, which is used to calculate the dividend.
- Each share has a stated **dividend**, usually given as a percent of par value.

Holders of preferred stock are usually not allowed to vote at the annual meetings of the corporation. Also, most preferred stock is **nonparticipating**, meaning that the corporation will never pay dividends above the stated rate. However, holders of **participating** preferred stock could share in the successes of the corporation by an increase in the dividend.

Sometimes, preferred stock is given additional features to make it more attractive to potential buyers. For example, the stock may be **cumulative preferred stock**, which means that any dividends not paid in the past must be paid before common stockholders receive any money. The stock might also be **convertible preferred stock**, which means that one share is convertible into a stated number of shares of common stock at some future date.

Objective

2 *Distribute Profits to Shareholders and Calculate Dividend per Share.* The next examples show how the profits of a corporation might be distributed.

EXAMPLE **1** **Calculating Dividend per Share**

Last year, Thornton Electronics had a net income after taxes of $1,200,000. The board of directors decides to reinvest $500,000 in the business and distribute the remaining $700,000 to stockholders as dividends. The company has 40,000 shares of $100 par value, 4% preferred stock, and 350,000 shares of common stock. Find (a) the amount per share paid to holders of preferred stock and (b) the amount per share given to holders of common stock.

Solution

(a) Each share of preferred stock has a par value of $100 and pays a dividend of 4%. The dividend per share is

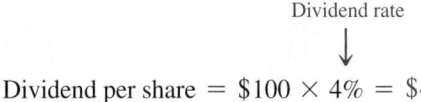

$$\text{Dividend per share} = \$100 \times 4\% = \$4$$

A dividend of $4 must be paid for each share of preferred stock. Since there are 40,000 shares of preferred, a total of

$$\$4 \times 40,000 = \$160,000$$

will be paid to owners of preferred shares.

(b) A total of $700,000 is available for stockholders, with $160,000 going to the owners of preferred shares, leaving

$$
\begin{array}{ll}
\$700,000 & \text{Total} \\
-\ \ 160,000 & \text{Preferred} \\
\hline
\$540,000 &
\end{array}
$$

available for the common stockholders. There are 350,000 shares of common stock outstanding, with each share being paid a dividend of

$$\frac{\$540,000}{350,000} = \$1.54 \text{ per share} \quad \text{Rounded}$$

EXAMPLE **2** **Finding Cumulative Dividends**

Due to excessive debt, Alamo Energy paid no dividend last year. The company did much better this year and the board of directors has set aside $175,000 for the payment of dividends. The company has 12,500 outstanding shares of cumulative preferred stock having par value of $50, with an 8% dividend. The company also has 40,000 shares of common stock. What dividend will be paid to the owners of each type of stock?

Solution

The dividend per share of preferred stock follows.

$$\text{Dividend rate}$$
$$\downarrow$$
$$\$50 \text{ par value} \times 8\% = \$4$$

Dividends have not been paid for 2 years (last year and this year), so each share of preferred stock must be paid

$$\$4 \text{ per share} \times 2 \text{ years} = \$8$$

before any dividends can be paid to holders of common stock. Since there are 12,500 shares of cumulative preferred stock outstanding, a total of

$$\$8 \times 12{,}500 = \$100{,}000$$

must be paid to the owners of the preferred stock. This leaves

$$\begin{array}{rl} \$175{,}000 & \text{Total} \\ - \ \ 100{,}000 & \text{Preferred} \\ \hline \$75{,}000 & \end{array}$$

to be divided among owners of common stock. Since there are 40,000 shares of common stock, each share will be paid a dividend of

$$\frac{\$75{,}000}{40{,}000} = \$1.88 \quad \text{Rounded}$$

NOTE In Example 2, the dividend for owners of preferred stock was paid for each of the last 2 years before any common stock dividends were paid.

Objective

3 *Find Earnings per Share.* One way to measure the financial success of a corporation is by finding the **earnings per share** made by the corporation. Earnings per share is found with the following formula.

$$\text{Earnings per share} = \frac{\text{net income} - \text{dividends on preferred}}{\text{number of shares of common outstanding}}$$

EXAMPLE 3   Finding Earnings per Share

Adam Nguyen started an import business as a sole proprietorship with an investment of $380,000. He then took on a partner who remains with the company as part owner. A few years later, they incorporated under the name of Asia Imports, Inc. The founding owners gave stock to three key employees so that they too will share in the success of the firm and therefore be motivated to stay and work harder.

(a) Asia Imports Inc. had a net income of $420,000 last year after paying salaries and taxes. It had 500,000 shares of common stock outstanding and no preferred stock. Find the earnings per share.

$$\text{Earnings per share} = \frac{\$420{,}000 - \$0}{500{,}000 \text{ shares}} = \$0.84 \text{ per share}$$

(b) This year, the company issued preferred stock and paid $85,000 in dividends to preferred shareholders out of a net income of $544,000 after salaries and taxes. There are still 500,000 shares of common stock. Find the earnings per share for this year.

$$\text{Earnings per share} = \frac{\$544{,}000 - \$85{,}000}{500{,}000 \text{ shares}} = \$0.92 \text{ per share} \quad \text{Rounded}$$

(c) Find Mr. Nguyen's total dividend this year if he owns 300,000 shares of common stock and one-fourth of the preferred stock.

$$\text{Total dividend} = \text{dividend from common stock} + \text{dividend from preferred stock}$$

$$= 300{,}000 \times \$0.92 \qquad + \qquad \left(\frac{1}{4} \times \$85{,}000 \right)$$

$$= \$297{,}250$$

(d) Find Mr. Nguyen's total dividends in a bad year with no profits, no dividends on common stock, and only a $10,000 dividend to preferred shareholders.

$$\text{Total dividend} = \frac{1}{4} \times \$10{,}000 = \$2500$$

19.1 Exercises

Find the dividend that will be paid for each share of preferred stock and common stock.

	Common Stock (in shares)	Preferred Stock (in shares)	Total Dividends	
1.	80,000	None	$0	$0; $0
2.	200,000	None	$16,000	$0; $0.08
3.	175,000	50,000, $10 par value, 3%	$40,000	$0.30; $0.14
4.	200,000	30,000, $5 par value, 5%	$80,000	$0.25; $0.36
5.	1,000,000	100,000, $1000 par value, 2%	$2,000,000	$20; $0
6.	500,000	40,000, $50 par value, 3%	$44,800	No dividends paid since $60,000 needed to pay dividends on preferred

Solve the following application problems. Round percents to the nearest tenth and money to the nearest cent.

7. **ANIMAL HOSPITAL**   Reeves Animal Hospital had a net income of $320,000 last year. If $280,000 was reinvested in an expansion of the business and the remainder was paid in dividends, what is the dividend per share on the 400,000 shares of common stock outstanding? $0.10

8. **TUGBOAT COMPANY**   Fleet Operations Inc. had a net income of $1,480,000 last year. The board of directors decided to purchase another tugboat for $850,000 and pay the remainder of the profits out as dividends. Find the dividend per share given 504,000 common shares of stock outstanding. $1.25

9. **FASHION GOODS**   Junior Fashions operates three separate retail stores in the San Francisco Bay area. It has 250,000 shares of common stock and 15,000 shares of preferred stock with a $100 par value at $6\frac{1}{2}\%$. Find the dividend per share for both preferred and common stock if the total dividend is $280,000. $6.50; $0.73

10. **MOVING COMPANY**   A moving company affiliated with North American Van Lines has 200,000 shares of common stock and 8000 shares of preferred stock with a par value of $100 per share at 7%. Find the dividend per share for both preferred and common stock if the board of directors allocates $165,000 for dividends. $7.00; $0.55

11. **PAPER PRODUCTS COMPANY**   Northern Maine Paper Products has sold 25,000 shares of $40 par value, 4% preferred stock to help remodel its mill. It already had 300,000 shares of common stock. Find the dividend per share if the total profit is $850,000 and 35% was distributed to shareholders. $1.60; $0.86

12. **DENTAL SUPPLIES**   To help him start up a dental supply company, James Madison sold to investors 230,000 shares of common stock and 10,000 shares of preferred stock with a par value of $100 at 4%. Find the dividend per share for both types of shares if 60% of the $148,000 in profits is distributed to shareholders. $4; $0.21

13. **COMPUTER CONSULTING**   A company has decided to pay no dividend for 3 years and, instead, reinvest the profits in expansion. During the fourth year, the board decides to pay a dividend of $2,675,000. Find the dividend per share if the company has outstanding 20,000 cumulative preferred shares of $100 par value at 5% and 450,000 common shares. $20; $5.06

14. **RUBBER GOODS COMPANY**   To pay for a new factory, Wilson Rubber Goods has paid no dividend for 2 years. Now, at the end of the third year, a dividend of $1,200,000 was declared. Find the dividend per share if the company has 10,000 cumulative preferred shares outstanding of $100 par value at 10% and 400,000 common shares. $30; $2.25

15. **STETSON HATS**   A manufacturer of Stetson hats reported an after-tax net income of $400,000. The firm had 120,000 common shares and no preferred shares. Find the earnings per share. $3.33

16. **WASHERS AND DRYERS**   A large retailer of appliances had 750,000 common shares and no preferred shares. In a year with $2,350,000 in net income, find the earnings per share. $3.13

17. **FAR EAST IMPORTS**   Eastern Manufacturing, Inc., operates two factories in Thailand that produce goods shipped to Asia, Australia, Europe, and the United States. The firm has 4,500,000 shares of common stock and 100,000 shares of preferred stock outstanding with a $100 par value at 6%. Last year, the company had a net income of $1,235,000 with $600,000 paid to preferred shareholders and the remainder paid to common stock shareholders. Find the earnings per share of common stock. $0.14

18. **FRUIT DISTRIBUTOR**   Florida Fruit Inc. has 50,000 shares of preferred stock outstanding with a $50 par value at 7%. It also had 4,000,000 shares of common stock outstanding. This year, the company has a net income of $138,000 with all of it going to shareholders. Find the earnings per share of common stock. $0

19. **EARNINGS PER SHARE**   Arckat has 250,000 shares of common stock and 40,000 shares of preferred stock ($50 par, 4%) outstanding. Net income last year and this year were, respectively, $680,000 and $765,000. The board of directors disbursed 40% of net income as dividends in both years. Find the dividend per share of common stock (a) last year and (b) this year. (c) Find the percent increase in the *earnings per share* of this year over last year.   (a) $0.77 (b) $0.90 (c) 14.2%

20. **RECORDING STUDIO**   Rhythm Recording Studio has 60,000 shares of $1000 par value, 4% preferred stock. It also has 2,000,000 shares of common stock outstanding. This year the company increased its net income by 20% over last year's $4,300,000. In both years the board of directors authorized the payment of 60% of net income for payment of dividends. Find the dividend per share of common stock for (a) last year and (b) this year. (c) Find the percent increase in *earnings per share* of this year over last year.   (a) $0.09 (b) $0.35 (c) 45.3%

21. **PAVING COMPANY**   Bill Baker owns a paving company with 1,000,000 shares of common stock. He wishes to help provide for his six grandchildren, so he establishes 20,000 shares of preferred stock with a $100 par value, 8%, and donates the preferred stock to a trust for his grandchildren. Given a year with a net income of $620,000 and a payment of 30% of net income for dividends, find the dividend to be paid on behalf of *each* grandchild. $26,666.67 each since there are sufficient dividends

22. **PAVING COMPANY**   In Exercise 21, find the dividend to be paid on behalf of *each* grandchild if net income is $85,000 and 30% of net income is used for dividends. $4250 each

23. Explain the difference between common stock and preferred stock. (See Objective 1.)

24. List several reasons why a corporation would issue preferred stock in addition to common stock. (See Objective 1.)

19.2	**Buying Stock**

OBJECTIVES

1 *Know the basics of stock ownership.*

2 *Read stock tables.*

3 *Find the commission for buying or selling stocks.*

4 *Find the total to purchase or sell stock.*

5 *Find the current yield on a stock.*

6 *Find the PE ratio of a stock.*

7 *Define the common stock indices.*

8 *Define a mutual fund.*

Objective

1 *Know the Basics of Stock Ownership.* Buying stock in a corporation makes the stockholder a *part owner* of the corporation. In return for the money a person invests in stock, he or she shares in any profits the company makes. Hopefully, the company will do well and prosper. If this happens, many other people will want the company's stock, and they will be willing to pay a good price for its shares. If this happens, the stockholders may share in profits through dividends and then sell their stock at a profit.

On the other hand, if the company does not do well, then fewer people will want its stock and the price will fall. The price of the shares of most large, publicly held firms is set by supply and demand at institutions called **stock exchanges**. The largest stock exchange is the New York Stock Exchange, located on Wall Street in New York City. Many foreign countries, including Japan, Taiwan, England, China, Canada, and Mexico, have their own stock exchanges. Figure 19.3 was taken from *Barron's* online newspaper (online.barrons.com) published by Dow Jones & Co. This newspaper lists prices for many stocks and bonds as well as mutual funds.

52-Wk High	Low	Name	Tick Sym	Vol. 100s	Yld	P/E	Close	Div. Amt.	52-Wk High	Low	Name	Tick Sym	Vol. 100s	Yld	P/E	Close	Div. Amt.
27.73	10.34	Aeroposvtale	ARO	277230	...	5	10.71	...	21.06	8.45	BarnesNoble	BKS	90556	...	dd	9.98	.25
46.01	26.42	Aetna	AET	215616	.4	8	35.48	.15	25.85	14.95	♣BarnesGp	B	18438	1.6	18	19.71	.08
113.00	63.32	AffilMangr	AMG	50201	...	30	77.10	...	55.74	42.50	♣BarckGld	ABX	432474	.9	16	50.78	.12
55.33	26.68	Agilent Tch	A	323337	...	12	31.08	...	37.79	7.03	BscEngySvs	BAS	58809	...	dd	19.62	...
88.20	54.19	♣AgnicoEgl	AEM	119729	1.0	31	65.57	.16	62.50	42.47	BaxterInt	BAX	219100	2.4	15	51.64	.31
29.25	19.50	AgreeRlty	ADC	2390	7.6	20	20.99	.40	61.96	31.14	BaytexEnergy g	BTE	18190	...	42	47.23	.20
99.14	64.53	♣Agrium	AGU	72411	.1	16	76.64	.055	6.23	1.52	BeazerHm	BZH	149451	...	dd	1.58	...
29.94	19.87	AirLease	AL	7165	...	...	21.15	...	89.75	68.07	BectonDksn	BDX	83030	2.1	15	76.92	.41
98.00	72.81	AirProduct	APD	90840	3.1	15	75.24	.58	40.41	21.53	Belden	BDC	21505	.7	20	27.10	.05
13.82	7.75	Aircastle	AYR	52486	4.7	10	10.70	.125	9.27	4.69	♣Belo	BLC	60880	...	8	5.08	.05
71.28	58.00	Airgas	ARG	54941	...	20	59.59	.29	34.40	28.06	♣Bernis	BMS	46063	3.4	14	28.60	.24
29.27	18.68	AlamoGp	ALG	2063	1.1	11	20.91	.06	20.24	12.28	BenchmkElec	BHE	27488	...	10	12.52	...
70.61	43.89	AlaskaAir	ALK	18726	...	6	53.33	...	33.26	26.05	Berkley	WRB	52000	1.1	10	28.81	.08
28.08	17.44	AlbanyInt	AIN	15498	2.8	12	18.63	.13	131463	100265	BerkHathwy A	BRK/A	z3228	...	16	102600	...
71.79	38.75	Albemarle	ALB	112347	1.4	12	46.31	.165	87.65	66.51	BerkHathwy B	BRK/B	370324	...	13	68.33	...
6.63	2.46	AlcatelLucentADS	ALU	f13335	...	56	3.33	...	61.17	26.47	BerryPete A	BRY	44461	.7	cc	44.28	.075
18.47	9.92	Alcoa	AA	f12439	1.1	16	11.21	.03	45.63	23.25	BestBuy	BBY	351694	2.7	8	24.06	.16
41.18	21.67	Alere	ALR	71303	...	dd	23.20	...	44.44	27.82	BigLots	BIG	51450	...	11	30.09	...
55.50	32.48	Alex&Bldwn	ALEX	9947	3.4	27	37.36	.315	464.77	265.15	BiglariHldgs	BH	z48882	...	13	320.08	...
454.00	297.21	Alexanders	ALX	z21182	3.1	28	389.00	3.00	52.13	32.06	BillBarrett	BBG	49966	...	29	45.16	...

Source: BARRON'S: THE DOW JONES BUSINESS AND FINANCIAL WEEKLY Copyright 2011 by DOW JONES & COMPANY, INC. Reproduced with permission of DOW JONES & COMPANY, INC. in the format Textbook and Other book via Copyright Clearance Center.

Figure 19.3

There is almost unlimited advice about which stocks to buy. However, studies have shown that very few investors consistently make better-than-average returns on their investments. Many professionals suggest either that you purchase the stocks of companies that you know very well or that you purchase mutual funds that hold the stocks of many different companies. Mutual funds are discussed later in this section.

Objective

2 *Read Stock Tables.* Daily stock prices can easily be found on the World Wide Web, but some newspapers also print daily stock prices for at least some stocks. The format of the information given varies from one source of information to another, but we will be using the format used by *Barron's*, as shown in Figure 19.3.

> **NOTE** Historically, fractions were used for stock prices but that changed in 2001 and decimal numbers are now used.

EXAMPLE 1 Reading the Stock Table

Roman Rodriguez has been studying stocks. He particularly likes music and computers, so one of his favorite retail stores is Best Buy. Since he knows Best Buy from personal experience, he is interested in buying stock in the company. Analyze the following information on Best Buy taken from Figure 19.3.

| 52 week | | | | | | | | Dividend |
High	Low	Stock	Sym	Vol (100s)	Yld%	P/E	Close	Latest
45.63	23.25	Best Buy	BBY	351694	2.7	8	24.06	0.16

Solution

(a) The highest price the stock sold for during the past year was $45.63 per share.
(b) The lowest price the stock sold for during the past year was $23.25 per share.
(c) The company name is shown as Best Buy, but it refers to Best Buy Co., Inc.
(d) The stock trades under the symbol BBY on the New York Stock Exchange.
(e) The number of shares traded that day was $351694 \times 100 = 35{,}169{,}400$ shares.
(f) The dividend yield was 2.7% per year based on the close price of the stock.
(g) The ratio of the close price for the day to company earnings was 8.
(h) The close price for the stock that day was $24.06 per share.
(i) The latest quarterly dividend was $0.16 per share.

If the quarterly dividend continues at $0.16 per share, then the annual dividend will be 4 times that amount, or $0.64.

EXAMPLE 2 Finding the Cost to Buy Stock

Ignoring commissions, first find (a) Roman Rodriguez's combined cost to purchase 100 shares of Best Buy (BBY) at the close for the day and 200 shares of Barnes and Noble (BKS) at the close for the day. Then find (b) the combined dividend these shares would pay for a quarter. Finally, find (c) the annual dividend and the annual percent return on investment to the nearest tenth of a percent (annual dividend ÷ total cost). Does that rate compare favorably with interest paid on a certificate of deposit?

Solution

(a) Cost 100 shares BBY $= 100 \times \$24.06 = \$2406$
     Cost 200 shares of BKS $= 200 \times \ \$9.98 = \underline{\$1996}$
                        Total cost $= \$4402$

(b) Add quarterly dividends from the two companies.

From 100 shares of BBY = 100 × $0.16 = $16.00

From 200 shares of BKS = 200 × $0.25 = $50.00

Total quarterly dividend = $66.00

(c) Annual dividend = 4 × $66 = $264

$$\text{Return on investment} = \frac{\$264}{\$4402} = 6.0\% \quad \text{Rounded}$$

The rate of 6.0% is much higher than current rates paid by banks as well as the normal dividend rates of 1% to 4% paid by many firms. The reason the dividend rate is so high is the very high dividend from Barnes and Noble. Since this dividend is very high and the stock price has fallen precipitously recently, investors apparently believe that the dividend will be cut in the near future.

Objective

3

Find the Commission for Buying or Selling Stocks. Many individuals do not **trade** (buy and sell) the stocks of individual companies although they may invest in stocks using mutual funds in a retirement plan. However, even individuals who do buy the stock of individual companies cannot buy or sell stock directly. Rather, they buy and sell through an intermediary called a **broker**, who is licensed to trade stock on an exchange. The primary responsibility for enforcing federal securities laws and regulating the securities industry, the electronic securities markets, and the stock and options exchanges is the **Securities and Exchange Commission (SEC)**. So, brokers are carefully monitored by the SEC.

There are several different kinds of brokers. Years ago, most people used a regular **stockbroker** at a firm such as Merrill Lynch, which charged perhaps 1% of the total amount as a **commission** to buy or sell stock. Merrill Lynch now specializes in financial advising for wealthier individuals. The introduction of the World Wide Web in 1993 changed things as new firms called **discount brokers**, or **online brokers**, sprang up; these firms allowed individuals to buy and sell individual stock cheaply using the Internet. These firms tended to offer far less counseling and guidance, but charged a low, fixed price of, say, $7.95 to buy or sell the stock of a company no matter how many shares were bought or sold. Today, most people who buy and sell the stock of individual companies do so using an online broker such as Schwab, E*Trade, or Fidelity.

Shares are usually traded in multiples of 100 shares called **round lots**. An **odd lot** refers to the purchase of fewer than 100 shares at one time. For example, someone buying 300 shares of Microsoft is buying in round lots, although someone selling 50 shares of Apple Inc. is selling an odd lot. It makes no difference to individuals using online brokers whether they buy and sell in round lots or odd lots.

Objective

4

Find the Total to Purchase or Sell Stock. The next two examples show the total cost of purchasing stock and the total revenue from selling stock using a discount broker that charges a fixed fee of $7.95 per transaction.

EXAMPLE **3** **Finding the Total Cost of a Stock Purchase**

Jerita Beacon used an online broker to purchase 100 shares of Target Corporation at $50.73. Find the total cost if the online broker charges a commission of $7.95.

Solution

Cost of stock: 100 shares × $50.73 per share = $5073.00

Commission: + 7.95

Total cost $5080.95

EXAMPLE **4** **Finding the Total Cost of a Stock Sale**

Jerita Beacon (Example 3) sold the 100 shares of Target Corporation 1 year later for $52.15 per share. Find (a) the amount received after a commission to sale them of $7.95, (b) her profit, not including any dividend received during the year, and (c) the return on investment, not including any dividend received.

Solution

(a) Sale of stock: 100 shares $\times$ $52.15 per share = $5215.00
    Commission: $-\ \ \ \ 7.95$
                              Total received $5207.05

(b) Received when stock sold: $5207.05
    Paid when stock purchased: -5080.95
                         Profit $ \ 126.10

(c) She made a profit of $126.10 in 1 year on an investment of $5080.05.

$$\text{Return on investment} = \frac{\$126.10}{\$5080.05} = 2.5\% \quad \text{Rounded}$$

Her return on investment was 2.5% for the year, not including dividends received.

NOTE   Discount brokers usually just charge a specific fee, no matter how many shares are bought or sold.

Objective

5   *Find the Current Yield on a Stock.* There is no certain way of choosing stocks that will go up in price. However, two **stock ratios** that people commonly look at before buying shares of a company are the **current yield** and the **price-earnings ratio**.

Although current yield is shown in the stock tables as Yld %, we show how to find it here since you may not always have the tables available. It is used to compare the dividends paid by stocks selling at different prices. The result is commonly rounded to the nearest tenth of a percent.

$$\text{Current yield} = \frac{\text{annual dividend per share}}{\text{closing price per share}}$$

EXAMPLE **5** **Finding the Current Yield**

Use the information in Figure 19.3 to find the current yield for (a) Best Buy (BBY) and (b) Aetna (AET) rounded to the nearest tenth of a percent. (*Hint:* Multiply the quarterly dividend in the table by 4 to find the annual dividend.)

Solution

(a) **Best Buy**

$$\text{Annual dividend} = 4 \times 0.16 = \$0.64$$

$$\text{Current yield} = \frac{\text{annual dividend}}{\text{close price}} = \frac{\$0.64}{\$24.06} = 2.7\%$$

(b) **Aetna**

$$\text{Annual dividend} = 4 \times 0.15 = \$0.60$$

$$\text{Current yield} = \frac{\text{annual dividend}}{\text{close price}} = \frac{\$0.60}{\$35.48} = 1.7\%$$

> **NOTE** A company may not pay a dividend because of the following:
> **1.** it is going through difficult financial times;
> **2.** it needs the funds that would be paid out for research and development; or
> **3.** it may be growing rapidly and needs the money to finance its growth.

Objective

6 *Find the PE Ratio of a Stock.* Another number that some people use to help decide which stock to buy is the **price-earnings ratio**, also called the **PE ratio**. It is often rounded to the nearest whole number.

$$\text{PE ratio} = \frac{\text{closing price per share}}{\text{annual net income per share}}$$

EXAMPLE **6** **Finding the PE Ratio**

Find the price-earnings ratio for each of the following. Round to the nearest whole number.

(a) Wal-Mart Stores with a close price of $52.99 and annual earnings of $4.70.
(b) ExxonMobil with a close price of $72.56 and annual earnings of $7.60.

Solution

(a) Wal-Mart Stores PE ratio $= \dfrac{\$52.99}{\$4.70} = 11$ Rounded

(b) ExxonMobil PE ratio $= \dfrac{\$72.56}{\$7.60} = 10$ Rounded

---

A company that grows more rapidly should have significantly higher earnings in the future. As a result, investors are willing to pay more for rapidly growing firms, resulting in higher PE ratios. A low PE ratio may simply indicate that investors see a poor future for the company. It is best to compare the PE ratios of similar firms such as the giant retailers Wal-Mart Stores and Target Corporation. It does not make sense to compare the PE ratio of Target Corporation to ExxonMobil, since they are in very different industries.

Objective

7 *Define the Common Stock Indices.* Several stock indices are used to identify trends in the market. The most common are the Dow Jones Industrial Average, the NASDAQ Composite Index, and Standard and Poor's 500.

> **Dow Jones Industrial Average**—based on 30 of the largest and most widely owned companies in the United States and is no longer limited to "industrial" companies
> **NASDAQ Composite Index**—computed from over 3000 international technology and growth companies
> **Standard and Poor's 500**, or **S&P 500**—based on the price of 500 large companies that trade on stock exchanges in the United States

Figure 19.4 shows all three indices for the past 5 years. All three indices peaked in late 2007 and then fell sharply near the end of 2008 as the serious recession began. The financial headlines in late 2008 were very negative—scary, actually. Was it time to sell stock? Apparently not! An investor who sold stock in late 2008 and stayed out of the market missed the rapid increase of stock prices during 2009–2010. A far better strategy than selling in late 2008 was to simply hold stock and wait for the eventual recovery in prices.

Major Stock Indicies

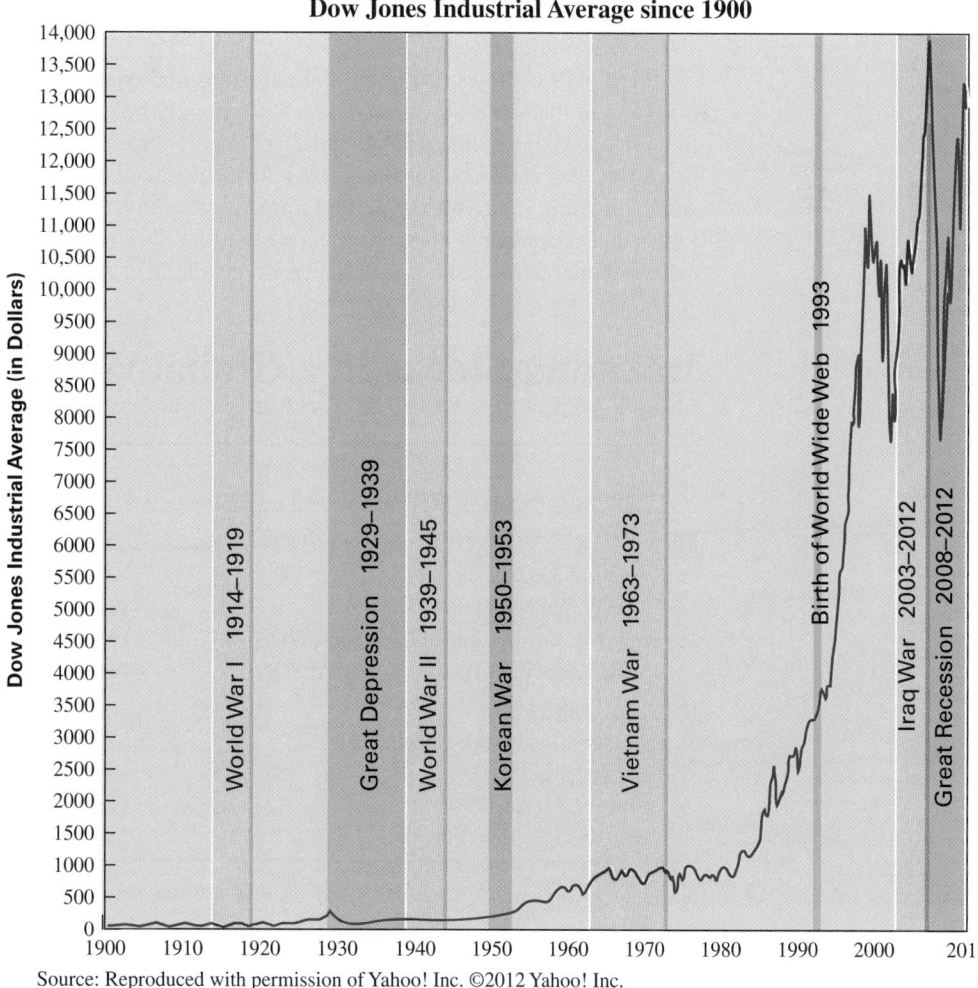

Source: Reproduced with permission of Yahoo! Inc. ©2012 Yahoo! Inc.

Figure 19.4

The Dow Jones Industrial Average has been widely used for over 100 years, as shown in Figure 19.5. The Great Depression of 1929–1939 devastated many firms, investors, and families. Stock prices collapsed. It became difficult to borrow, and many companies fired employees and declared bankruptcy. The entire world was mired in the depression until the

Dow Jones Industrial Average since 1900

Source: Reproduced with permission of Yahoo! Inc. ©2012 Yahoo! Inc.

Figure 19.5

war-related activities of World War II helped bring the world out of it. Stock prices did not recover until the 1950s. In spite of the Great Depression and the financial crisis beginning in 2008, it is important to note that the overall trend has clearly been up over the past 100 years.

Objective

8 *Define a Mutual Fund.* Ownership of shares in a single company *can be risky*—the company may suffer poor financial results, causing the stock price to fall. This risk can be reduced by simultaneously investing in the stocks of several different companies. One way of doing this is to invest with a mutual fund that buys stocks. A **mutual fund** that invests in stocks receives investment funds from many different investors and uses the money to purchase stock in several different companies.

Another way to diversify and control the risk of losing money is to invest in **exchange traded funds (ETFs)**. An ETF holds stocks, bonds, or futures contracts and trades throughout the day at the same price as the underlying assets. Most mutual funds are actively managed with managers constantly assessing what to own, when to buy, and when to sell. Originally, ETFs were not actively managed, but simply bought and held specific financial assets. However, some ETFs are also actively managed, such as those tracking futures contracts on commodities and a few others, too.

> **NOTE** Historically, stocks have generally resulted in a better return on investment than savings accounts, certificates of deposit, or bonds. Most financial planners agree that stocks should be a part of any long-range investment plan.

Figure 19.6 shows that some mutual funds and exchange traded funds *specialize* by investing in the stocks *of different types* of publicly held companies. They may specialize in large-cap (large companies), small-cap (small companies), overseas (global), or specific industries (real estate, oil, banking, etc.). Many financial planners say that *the first fund* you should invest in is an **index fund** that tracks a broad index such as Standard and Poor's 500. Funds that specialize in companies in one industry such as biotechnology or funds that specialize in international stock are usually more volatile or risky.

Investing Stocks in a Global World

Invest in a few of these funds and quickly create a diversified portfolio.

Fund	Invests in	Price	One-year Return
Mutual Funds			
Vanguard 500 Index (VFINX)	Large U.S. firms	$107.36	10.7%
Fidelity Contrafund (FCNTX)	Intl. value stocks	$64.33	14.9%
Dodge & Cox Diversified International (DODFX)	Large int. firms	$31.27	4.2%
Amer. Funds Euro-Pacific Growth (AEPGX)	Europe & Asia	$37.30	4.2%
Exchange Traded Funds			
Vanguard Total Stock Market (VTI)	Large U.S. firms	$59.57	10.3%
iShares Russell 1000 Growth (IWF)	Large U.S. firms	$53.88	14.6%
iShares S&P 500 (IVV)	Large U.S. firms	$116.77	10.2%
MSCI EAFE Index (EFA)	Large int. firms	$51.60	4.2%

Source: Reproduced with permission of Yahoo! Inc. ©2012 Yahoo! Inc.

Figure 19.6

Notice that the 1-year returns on all the funds in Figure 19.6 were positive, with several being over 10%. Although not always true, markets today have a tendency to move together. Most markets fell sharply during late 2008 and early 2009; then most of them moved strongly upward in the remainder of 2009–2011. The markets moving up and down without ceasing causes the value of many retirement accounts to move up and down. This is frustrating to an individual saving for retirement. You should expect the value of any investment in stocks to fluctuate. The real issue is what your investments are worth when you sell, not what are they worth every week or month as you hold them.

EXAMPLE **7**   **Comparing Investment Alternatives**

Cynthia Peck wants to know whether she should invest her retirement funds in certificates of deposit or in a mutual fund containing stock. Assume payments of $2000 per year for 30 years. Find the future value assuming (a) a certificate of deposit paying 4% compounded annually and (b) a mutual fund containing stocks that has returned 8% per year. (c) Then compare the two future values.

Solution

(a) Use 4% per year and 30 years in the Amount of Annuity column in **Appendix C** to find 56.08493775.

$$\text{Future value} = \$2000 \times 56.08493775 = \$112{,}169.88$$

(b) Use 8% per year and 30 years in the Amount of Annuity column in **Appendix C** to find 113.28321111.

$$\text{Future value} = \$2000 \times 113.28321111 = \$226{,}566.42$$

(c) Difference = $226,566.42 − $112,169.88 = $114,396.54

The mutual fund with stocks results in a much higher value in 30 years. However, neither the return on the CDs nor the mutual fund is guaranteed. Stocks may do better or worse than a bank CD in any year, but stocks have historically done much better over long periods of time than bank CDs.

NOTE   Some people feel they have lost money when stocks go down. Actually, for anyone making regular investments towards a long-term payoff, *it is good for stock prices to fall.* This allows them to buy more shares with the same amount of dollars. Studies have shown that regular investing is the best method for long-term investors.

19.2	**Exercises**

Find the following using the stock table in Figure 19.3.

1. Close price for the day for Aeropostale (ARO) $10.71

2. Close price for the day for Big Lots (BIG) $30.09

3. Low price for the year for Alcoa $9.92

4. Low price for the year for Barack Gold (ABX) $42.50

5. Latest quarterly dividend for Bill Barrett (BBG) $0

6. Latest quarterly dividend for Belden (BDC) $0.05

7. High price for the year for Alere (ALR) $41.18

8. High price for the year for Air Lease (AL) $29.94

9. Annual dividend yield for Beazer Homes (BZH)   0%

10. Annual dividend yield for Best Buy (BBY)   2.7%

11. PE ratio for Baxter Int (BAX)   15

12. PE ratio for Aircastle (AYR)   10

13. Daily volume for Benchmark Elec. (BHE)   2,748,800 shares

14. Daily volume for Albermarle (ALB)   11,234,700 shares

15. Annual dividend yield for Berry Pete A (BRY)   0.7%

16. Annual dividend yield for Alamo Gap (ALG)   1.1%

17. Close price for the day for Berhskire Hathway A (BRK/A) $102.600

18. Close price for the day for Alaska Air (ALK) $53.33

Find the total cost of the following stock purchases assuming a commission of $7.95.

19. 300 shares at $47.52 $14,263.95

20. 100 shares at $20.45 $2052.95

21. 50 shares at $90.78 $4546.95

22. 200 shares at $17.40 $3487.95

23. 250 shares at $34.98 $8752.95

24. 700 shares at $40.69 $28,490.95

Find the amount received by sellers of the following stock, assuming a commission of $7.95.

25. 200 shares at $17.65 $3522.05

26. 100 shares at $48.32 $4824.05

27. 150 shares at $84.50 $12,667.05

28. 300 shares at $19.42 $5818.05

29. 800 shares at $32.63 $26,096.05

30. 400 shares at $112.27 $44,900.05

Find the current yield for the following stocks. Round to the nearest tenth of a percent.

Stock	Price per Share	Annual Dividend per Share	
31. Coca-Cola	$68.68	$1.88	2.7%
32. Chevron	$96.30	$3.12	3.2%
33. Wal-Mart	$53.00	$1.46	2.8%
34. Nike	$84.97	$1.24	1.5%
35. Microsoft	$24.64	$0.64	2.6%
36. Apple	$373.00	$0	0%

Find the PE ratio for the following. Round to the nearest whole number.

Stock	Price per Share	Net Income per Share	
37. Toyota	$71.57	$1.82	39
38. Home Depot	$34.29	$2.22	15
39. Google	$521.07	$18.80	28
40. Best Buy	$24.85	$3.10	8

Solve each of the following application problems. Assume the cost of buying or selling the stock of each company has a commission of $7.95. Exercises 47 and 48 require concepts from Chapter 15.

41. **STOCK PURCHASE**   Triston Bates purchased 200 shares of Microsoft at $28.17 and 300 shares of General Electric at $24.12. Find the total cost. $12,885.90

42. **STOCK PURCHASE**   Theresa Tabor purchased 200 shares of Coca-Cola at $68.68 and 100 shares of Wal-Mart for $53.95. Find the total cost. $19,146.90

43. **STOCK TRADING**   Leslie Toombs purchased 250 shares of Chevron at $90.42 and later sold the stock for $98.47 per share. Find her profit, ignoring dividends. $1996.60

44. **STOCK TRADING**   Jenny O'Neill purchased 340 shares of Google at $482.61 and later sold the stock for $573.88 per share. Find her profit, ignoring any dividends. $31,015.90

45. Explain current yield and the PE ratio. Why might investors be interested in these numbers? (See Objectives 5 and 6.)

46. List four advantages of mutual funds. Name any particular mutual fund(s) that you have read or heard about. (See Objective 8.)

47. **TWO INVESTMENT ALTERNATIVES**   Toni Chavez is comparing two different investment alternatives for his $1200 semiannual contribution to a retirement plan. Plan A uses an investment currently yielding 5% compounded semiannually. Plan B uses a global stock mutual fund with Merrill Lynch that has historically yielded 8% compounded semiannually. Find the amount of an annuity after 25 years of (a) plan A and (b) plan B. (c) Find the difference between the two. (See **Section 15.1**.)   (a) $116,981.22 (b) $183,200.50 (c) $66,219.28

48. **RETIREMENT ACCOUNT INVESTMENT**   Laurie Zimms is trying to decide whether she should place her quarterly $2000 retirement account investment in a bond fund yielding 6% compounded quarterly or in a stock fund that has historically yielded 10% compounded quarterly. Find the amount of an annuity after 12 years using (a) the bond fund and (b) the stock fund. (c) Find the difference between the two. (See **Section 15.1**.)   (a) $139,130.44 (b) $181,719.16 (c) $42,588.72

49. Use Figure 19.5 to estimate the length of the Great Depression.   10 years

50. Use Figure 19.5 to identify the year the Dow Jones Industrial Index was at 2000 and the year it reached its peak of about 14,000.   1988 and 2007

19.3	**Bonds**

OBJECTIVES

1 *Know the basics of bonds.*

2 *Read bond tables.*

3 *Find the cost of bonds, including commission.*

4 *Find the present value of a bond.*

5 *Understand how mutual funds containing bonds can be used for monthly income.*

Businesses need money to invest and to pay operating expenses. They can obtain funds by selling stock, by borrowing short-term from banks, insurance companies, or investment firms, or by borrowing long-term using bonds. Stockholders are part owners of a corporation and share in profits and losses. Banks, investment firms, insurance companies, and individuals that lend money to firms are creditors of the corporation and not owners. Creditors expect to be paid back with interest, but they do not expect to own part of the future profits and do not receive dividends.

1 *Know the Basics of Bonds.* For longer-term borrowing of, say, 5 years or more, corporations often borrow money by selling bonds to the public. A **bond** is a contractual *promise to repay the borrowed money at a specific date in the future*. The issuers of most bonds also agree to pay interest each year at a rate specified on the bond. For example, the owner of a bond that originally sold for a **face value** of $1000 with a 7.5% yield will receive interest of $75 each year and also receive a return of the $1000 at a specified date in the future. Most corporate bonds have a face value of $1000.

On the other hand, a corporation issuing a **zero-coupon bond** pays all interest at the maturity date (in the future) of the bond and does not pay interest each year. An example is a zero-coupon bond purchased for $600 in 2009 with no annual payment, and a payment of $1000 in 2016. This bond costs $600 but returns a future value of $1000 in 7 years, which results in a **yield-to-maturity** of 7.57% per year.

National governments, states and provinces, and some cities also issue bonds. Bonds issued by a state or local governmental authority are called **municipal bonds**. Bonds issued by a corporation are called **corporate bonds**. One advantage of municipal bonds is that the income from these bonds is usually *not* subject to federal income taxes, although it may be subject to a state income tax.

Treasury Inflation-Protected Securities (TIPS) are U.S. government bonds that are essentially a mixture of the two types of bonds discussed. TIPS pay a constant interest rate each year. In addition, the principal is adjusted up or down depending on the amount of inflation or deflation. TIPS protect a lender against rapid increases in inflation.

2 *Read Bond Tables.* The **face value**, or **par value**, of a bond is *the original amount of money borrowed by a company*. Most corporations issue bonds with a par value of $1000. Suppose that a bond's owner needs money before the **maturity date** of the bond. In that event, the bond can be quickly sold through a bond dealer such as Merrill Lynch. However, the price of the bond is not determined by its initial price, but rather *by market conditions at the time of the sale.*

Market *interest rates fluctuate widely* from year to year, yet each bond pays exactly the same dollar amount of interest each year. If interest rates rise, investors will pay less for a bond because they want the new, higher interest yield. If interest rates fall, investors will pay more for a bond because they will still earn a favorable yield. As a result, the price of a bond fluctuates in the opposite direction of interest rates. A bond may have a face value of $1000, but it often trades at a different value than $1000, as shown in Example 1.

EXAMPLE 1 Working with the Bond Table

Brandy Barrett was in an automobile accident that put her in the hospital for 3 weeks and required months of rehabilitation. The other driver was at fault and his insurance company paid Barrett the liability limits on his policy of $50,000. Barrett needs monthly income and is thinking about investing the insurance proceeds in Wal-Mart bonds that pay interest each year, but that are due in 2041. Data on this bond is taken from the information from *Barron's* in Figure 19.7.

Company (Ticker)	Coupon	Maturity	Last Price	Last Yield	EST $VOL (000'S)
Wal-Mart Stores (WMT)	5.625	Apr 15, 2041	115.596	4.650	242,225

Solution

(a) The coupon rate of 5.625 means that annual interest payments are 5.625% of the original face value of $1000, or $56.25.

(b) The bond matures on April 15, 2041, at which time the principal of $1000 must be repaid.

(c) The last price (close price) of the bond for the day was 115.596, or 115.596% of $1000, which is $1155.96.

(d) The last yield means that the yield-to-maturity of the bond, based on its current price, is 4.650%.

(e) The estimated dollar volume means that 242,225 × $1000 = $242,225,000 of these bonds sold today.

EXAMPLE 2 **Using the Bond Table**

Find the annual interest and close price for each bond.

(a) Citigroup (C) maturing in 2020
(b) International Business Machines (IBM) maturing in 2016
(c) Walt Disney Co. (DIS) maturing in 2016

Solution

The annual interest is the coupon rate times the face value of $1000.

Company	Annual Interest	Close Price
Citigroup	5.375% of $1000 = $53.75	106.732% of $1000 = $1067.32
International Business Machines	1.950% of $1000 = $19.50	101.409% of $1000 = $1014.09
Walt Disney Co.	1.350% of $1000 = $13.50	98.917% of $1000 = $989.17

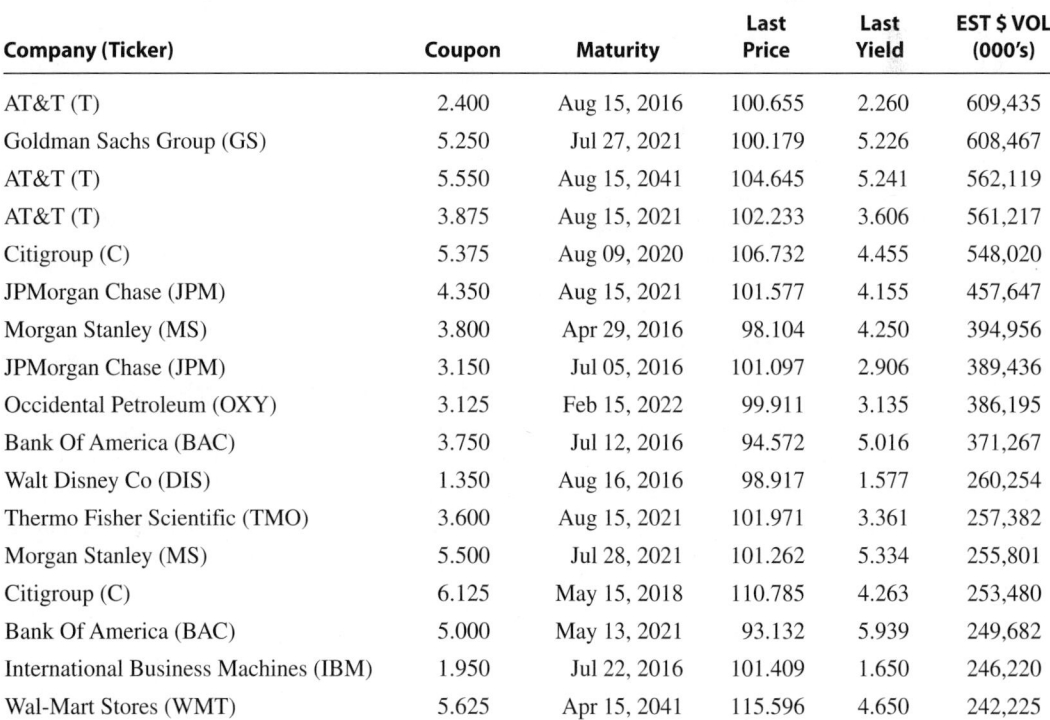

Company (Ticker)	Coupon	Maturity	Last Price	Last Yield	EST $ VOL (000's)
AT&T (T)	2.400	Aug 15, 2016	100.655	2.260	609,435
Goldman Sachs Group (GS)	5.250	Jul 27, 2021	100.179	5.226	608,467
AT&T (T)	5.550	Aug 15, 2041	104.645	5.241	562,119
AT&T (T)	3.875	Aug 15, 2021	102.233	3.606	561,217
Citigroup (C)	5.375	Aug 09, 2020	106.732	4.455	548,020
JPMorgan Chase (JPM)	4.350	Aug 15, 2021	101.577	4.155	457,647
Morgan Stanley (MS)	3.800	Apr 29, 2016	98.104	4.250	394,956
JPMorgan Chase (JPM)	3.150	Jul 05, 2016	101.097	2.906	389,436
Occidental Petroleum (OXY)	3.125	Feb 15, 2022	99.911	3.135	386,195
Bank Of America (BAC)	3.750	Jul 12, 2016	94.572	5.016	371,267
Walt Disney Co (DIS)	1.350	Aug 16, 2016	98.917	1.577	260,254
Thermo Fisher Scientific (TMO)	3.600	Aug 15, 2021	101.971	3.361	257,382
Morgan Stanley (MS)	5.500	Jul 28, 2021	101.262	5.334	255,801
Citigroup (C)	6.125	May 15, 2018	110.785	4.263	253,480
Bank Of America (BAC)	5.000	May 13, 2021	93.132	5.939	249,682
International Business Machines (IBM)	1.950	Jul 22, 2016	101.409	1.650	246,220
Wal-Mart Stores (WMT)	5.625	Apr 15, 2041	115.596	4.650	242,225

Source: BARRON'S: THE DOW JONES BUSINESS AND FINANCIAL WEEKLY Copyright 2011 by DOW JONES & COMPANY, INC. Reproduced with permission of DOW JONES & COMPANY, INC. in the format Textbook and Other book via Copyright Clearance Center.

Figure 19.7

Objective

3 *Find the Cost of Bonds, Including Commission.* Similar to stocks, bonds can be bought through stockbrokers or online brokers. The commission charged on bond sales varies significantly depending both on the broker and the size of the order. The commission on a smaller order is often about $5 per bond.

EXAMPLE 3   Finding the Cost to Buy Bonds and the Annual Interest

The sales charge on an order for 25 Morgan Stanley 2021 bonds is $5 per bond. Find (a) the total purchase price at the close for the day, (b) annual interest paid by the corporation, and (c) the effective rate of interest earned the first year to the nearest tenth of a percent.

Solution

From Figure 19.7, the close price is 101.262% of $1000, or $1012.62. The coupon rate used to find annual interest is 5.50%.

(a) Total cost = 25 bonds × ($1012.62 + $5 commission per bond)

= $25,440.50

(b) Annual interest = 25 bonds × $1000 face value × 5.50%

= $1375

(c) Effective rate for the year = annual interest ÷ total cost

= $1375   ÷ $25,440.50

= 5.4%

NOTE   The effective interest rate is not the same as the last yield. The last yield takes into consideration the cost of the bond, the maturity value of the bond, the time to maturity, and all interest payments.

EXAMPLE 4   Find the Net Amount from the Sale of Bonds

Find the amount received from the sale of 30 Occidental Petroleum bonds sold at the close, if the commission is $5 per bond.

Solution

Sale price = 30 × 99.911% of $1000

= 30 × 0.99911 × $1000

= $29,973.30

Net amount = sale price − commission of $5 × 30 bonds

= $29,973.30 − $150

= $29,823.30

Bonds are a debt, since they indicate that a corporation owes money to its bondholders. As such, *bondholders have first claim,* after bankruptcy lawyers, taxing authorities, and wage earners, on the assets of the corporation if it goes into bankruptcy. Stockholders have the last claim. Even so, bonds may pay off only a few cents on the dollar in the event of bankruptcy. Bondholders have lost substantial amounts in recent bankruptcies. Some investors like to buy the bonds of bankrupt and troubled companies. Such **junk bonds**, or high-yield securities, have been known to pay off handsomely when and if a company regains its financial health. Junk bonds are usually very risky and best left for professional investors.

Objective

4   *Find the Present Value of a Bond.* Interestingly, the value of a bond can be calculated based on the future cash flows given the **market interest rate**. The owner of a bond receives interest during the life of the bond and then also receives the face amount of the bond at maturity. Therefore, the value of the bond today (the present value) is found by adding these two present values.

Present value of interest payments during the life of the bond	+	Present value of face amout to be paid at maturity of the bond	=	Value of bond today

---

EXAMPLE 5   **Finding the Present Value of a Bond**

On April 15, 2011, Wal-Mart Stores had a bond with a face value of $1000 that matures on April 15, 2041. The coupon rate is 5.625%. Estimate the present value if the market interest rate is 5%. Assume that the interest payments are made at the end of each year.

Solution

First find the present value of the annual interest payments and also of the $1000 maturity value of the bond to be paid on April 15, 2041. Use the concepts of Section 15.2 to find the present value of the interest payments, which are $56.25 (5.625% of $1000) at the end of each year for 30 years (from 2011 to 2041).

PV of interest payments $= R \cdot a_{\overline{n}|i}$

$= \$56.25 \times 15.37245103$ Value from column D of the 5% interest table in Appendix C.

$= \$864.70$

Now use the concepts of Section 14.4 to find the present value of the $1000 face amount to be paid to the holder of the bond on April 15, 2041, or in 30 years.

$$P = \frac{M}{(1 + i)^n} = \frac{\$1000}{(1 + 0.05)^{30}} = \$231.38$$

The value of the bond today is the sum of these two values.

PV of interest payments:	$864.70
PV of face amount:	+ 231.38
Value of bond:	$1096.08

So, the bond has a market value of $1096.08 on the day these calculations were done. Notice that this is close to the last price of the bond in Figure 19.7, which is $1155.96. The two numbers differ slightly since the market interest rate was not exactly 5% at the time.

NOTE   The market interest rate in Example 5 changes very frequently. It depends on the financial strength of the company issuing the bond and also on general economic conditions.

Objective

5 *Understand How Mutual Funds Containing Bonds Can Be Used for Monthly Income.* A mutual fund can invest everything in stocks, everything in bonds, or part in stocks and part in bonds. Stock prices can be quite volatile, so financial planners recommend stock investments for people *who have a longer time horizon* over which to accumulate funds. Many planners recommend that *people invest in both stocks and bonds* during their lifetimes. Stocks may be a better investment *when investors are young* since stocks have tended to have a higher return. Bonds may be a better investment *for investors close to retirement* since there is less risk of losing principal in bonds and bonds pay regular interest.

EXAMPLE **6** **Using a Bond Fund for Income**

Brandy Barrett from Example 1 is undergoing rehabilitation and needs safety of principal. She also needs regular interest payments to help with medical expenses. She decides to place the $50,000 received from the insurance company in a mutual fund containing bonds. It is a no-load mutual fund, meaning that no commission is paid. (a) Find her annual income if the fund yields 6.5% per year. (b) How much would Barrett need to invest in the fund to earn $10,000 per year?

Solution

(a) Use the formula for simple interest: $I = PRT$.

$$\text{Interest} = \$50,000 \times 0.065 \times 1 = \$3250$$

(b) Again use the formula for simple interest, but now the principal (P) is unknown. Divide both sides of $I = PRT$ by RT to find the following form of the equation.

$$\text{Principal} = P = \frac{I}{RT} = \frac{\$10,000}{0.065 \times 1} = \$153,846.15$$

19.3	**Exercises**

Use Figure 19.7 to find the following information for International Business Machine bonds maturing in 2016. (See Examples 1–2.)

1. Close price per bond $1014.09
2. Maturity date   July 22, 2016
3. Coupon rate   1.950%
4. Annual interest $19.50
5. Yield to maturity (Yield %)   1.650%
6. Price to buy 40 bonds at the last price if commission is $5 per bond $40,763.60

Use Figure 19.7 to find the cost for the following purchases at the last price if the commission is $4 per bond.

Bond	Maturity	Number Purchased	
7. Bank of America (BAC)	May 13, 2021	30	$28,059.60
8. Occidental Petroleum (OXY)	Feb 15, 2022	80	$80,248.80
9. Goldman Sachs Group (GS)	July 27, 2021	100	$100,579
10. Walt Disney (DIS)	Aug 16, 2016	500	$496,585
11. Morgan Stanley (MS)	Apr 29, 2016	100	$98,504
12. JPMorgan Chase (JPM)	Aug 15, 2021	200	$203,954
13. Wal-Mart Stores (WMT)	Apr 15, 2041	50	$57,998
14. AT&T (T)	Aug 15, 2021	70	$71,843.10

15. Explain the purpose of bonds. (See Objective 1.)

16. Explain the differences between common stock, preferred stock, and bonds. (See **Sections 19.1** and **19.3.**)

Solve these application problems using bond prices from Figure 19.7. Unless stated otherwise, assume a commission of $5 per bond.

17. BOND PURCHASE   Anita Fields purchased 50 International Business Machine bonds at the close. Find the total cost and annual interest. $50,954.50; $975

18. BOND PURCHASE   Mary Dunlap bought 25 Wal-Mart Stores bonds since she shops there and knows the store. Find the total cost and annual interest. $29,024; $1406.25

19. BOND PURCHASE   A mutual fund manager purchased 2000 bonds of Morgan Stanley that mature on July 28, 2021 at a commission of $0.15 per bond. Find the total cost and annual interest. $2,025,540; $110,000

20. BOND PURCHASE   A hedge fund manager purchased 5000 bonds of Thermo Fisher Scientific that mature on August 15, 2021, at a commission of $0.15 per bond. Find the total cost and annual interest. $5,099,300; $180,000

21. CARE OF MENTALLY ILL   On behalf of a mentally ill son, Kitty Wysong purchased 30 bonds each of Walt Disney Co. and Goldman Sachs, (a) Find the total cost if the commission is $3 per bond. Then find (b) the annual interest and (c) the effective interest rate for the first year.   (a) $59,908.80 (b) $1980 (c) 3.3%

22. ALZHEIMER'S DISEASE   On behalf of her mother, Karen Becker purchased 50 Occidental Petroleum bonds and 50 JP Morgan Chase bonds maturing in 2021 and paid a commission of $3 per bond. Find (a) the total cost, (b) the annual interest, and (c) the effective interest rate for the first year.   (a) $101,044 (b) $3737.50 (c) 3.7%

23. INTEREST   A wealthy couple places $100,000 in a municipal bond fund that allows them to reduce their taxes. Find their tax-free income from this investment if the fund earns 2.8% per year. $2800

24. ANNUAL INTEREST   Helmut Schmidt places all $150,000 of his retirement funds in a mutual fund containing corporate bonds. Find his annual interest if the fund earns 8% per year. $12,000

25. INCOME FROM A DIVORCE   Bill and Jane Fickland recently divorced. As a part of the divorce settlement, Mr. Fickland agrees to pay Ms. Fickland $7000 per year for several years. Find the amount that must be invested in a mutual fund containing bonds that is expected to yield 4.1% annually, to generate the needed income. $170,731.71

26. LAWSUIT AWARD   Joan Klein lost a lawsuit to Milton Freeman. As a result, she must make annual payments of $28,500 to Freeman for several years. Find the amount that must be invested in a mutual fund containing bonds that is expected to yield 7.8% annually to generate the needed income. $365,384.62

27. VALUE OF A BOND   A corporate bond with a face value of $1000 matures in 22 years and pays $72.50 in annual interest. Find the present value if the market interest rate is 6%. $1150.52

28. VALUE OF A BOND   A bond issued by Apple Inc. has a face value of $1000 and matures in 12 years. It pays $65 in annual interest. Find the present value if the market interest rate is 5.5%. $1086.18

19.4   Distribution of Profits and Losses in a Partnership

OBJECTIVES

1 *Divide profits by equal shares.*

2 *Divide profits by agreed ratio.*

3 *Divide profits by original investment.*

4 *Divide profits by salary and agreed ratio.*

5 *Divide profits by interest on investment and agreed ratio.*

In a partnership, a business is owned by two or more people. The partners may have invested equal amounts of money to start the business, or one may have invested money while another invested specialized knowledge. The partners must agree on the relative amounts of money and time that will be invested in the business. They must also agree on the method by which any profits will be distributed. This section considers the various methods by which partnership profits may be distributed.

Objective

1 *Divide Profits by Equal Shares.* The partners may simply agree to share all profits and losses equally. In fact, if there is no formal agreement stating the terms under which profits are to be divided, most states require that profits be divided equally.

> **EXAMPLE** **1** **Dividing Profits by Equal Shares**
>
> Three partners open a menswear store. Each agrees to put up one-third of the investment funds needed and to work 40 hours per week in the business for no salary at first. They also agree to split profits equally. In a year with $96,000 in profits, each partner would get
>
> $$\frac{1}{3} \times \$96,000 = \$32,000$$

Objective

2 *Divide Profits by Agreed Ratio.* Partners may agree to divide the profits using some given rule. For example, two partners might agree that profits will be divided so that 60% goes to one partner and 40% to the other. Profit divisions are sometimes given as a ratio; this division could be written 60 : 40, or in a reduced form, 3 : 2, with profits said to be divided in an **agreed ratio.**

> **EXAMPLE** **2** **Dividing Profits by Agreed Ratio**
>
> Aaron Ortego and Gary Wayne purchase the Ter Marche Apartments in New Orleans, Louisiana, and agree to split profits in the ratio of 1 : 3. How would profits of $18,000 be divided?
>
> **Solution**
>
> The ratio 1 : 3 says that profits will be divided into $1 + 3 = 4$ equal shares. Ortego gets 1 and Wayne gets 3 of the equal shares.
>
> $$\$18,000 \div 4 = \$4500$$
>
> | | | |
> |---|---|---|
> | Ortego's share: | $\$4500 \times 1 =$ | $\$\ 4,500$ |
> | Wayne's share: | $\$4500 \times 3 =$ | $\underline{\$13,500}$ |
> | Total: | | $18,000$ |

Objective

3 *Divide Profits by Original Investment.* A common way of dividing the profits is on the basis of the **original investments** made by each partner. The fraction of the total original investment supplied by each partner is used to find the fraction of the profit that each partner receives.

EXAMPLE 3	**Dividing Profits by Original Investment**

Bob Huffman and Gary White form a partnership to drill a shallow well for oil. Huffman contributes $160,000 and White contributes $80,000. They sign an agreement that says that each partner will lose the money each invested if they drill a dry hole and that any profits will be distributed based on the original investment. If they discover an oil field and sell it for $600,000, find the share received by each.

Solution

The total amount contributed to start the venture was

$$\$160{,}000 + \$80{,}000 = \$240{,}000$$

Of this total,

$$\text{Huffman contributed} = \frac{\$160{,}000}{\$240{,}000} = \frac{2}{3}$$

$$\text{White contributed} = \frac{\$80{,}000}{\$240{,}000} = \frac{1}{3}$$

So profits are distributed as follows.

$$\text{Profits to Huffman} = \frac{2}{3} \times \$600{,}000 = \$400{,}000$$

$$\text{Profits to White} = \frac{1}{3} \times \$600{,}000 = \$200{,}000$$

If the two men lost their investments by drilling dry holes, then Huffman would have lost $160,000 and White would have lost $80,000.

NOTE   Each partner's fraction or percent of the total investment must be determined before the profit distribution is calculated.

EXAMPLE 4	**Dividing Losses by Original Investment**

Suppose the oil company in Example 3 had a loss of $40,000 the first year. Find the share of the loss that each partner must pay.

Solution

Just as partners share profits, they may be called on to share losses. In this case, Huffman must pay $\frac{2}{3}$ of the loss, or

$$\frac{2}{3} \times \$40{,}000 = (\$26{,}666.67)$$

Losses are usually indicated with parentheses.

and White must pay $\frac{1}{3}$ of the loss.

$$\frac{1}{3} \times \$40{,}000 = (\$13{,}333.33)$$

Objective

4   *Divide Profits by Salary and Agreed Ratio.* Sometimes one partner contributes money to get a business started, while a second partner contributes money and also operates the business on a daily basis. In such a case, the partner operating the business may be paid a salary out of profits, with any additional profits divided in some agreed-upon ratio, which is called dividing profits by **salary and agreed ratio.**

EXAMPLE **5**   **Dividing Profits by Salary and Original Investment**

Ben Walker has managed a restaurant for 8 years and would like to open his own restaurant, but he does not have enough money. He finally decides to form a partnership with Herma Gonzalez to open a restaurant that will be managed by Walker at a guaranteed first-year salary of $18,000 in addition to his part of any profits. Walker invests $20,000 and Gonzalez invests $60,000. They agree to divide any profits based on the original investment. Find the amount each partner would receive from a first-year profit of $70,000.

Solution

The first $18,000 is used for Walker's salary.

$$\begin{array}{ll} \$70,000 & \text{Profit} \\ -\quad 18,000 & \text{Salary} \\ \hline \$52,000 & \text{Profit to be divided} \end{array}$$

Walker would also receive

$$\frac{1}{4} \times \$52,000 = \$13,000$$

and Gonzalez would receive

$$\frac{3}{4} \times \$52,000 = \$39,000$$

Thus, Walker receives $18,000 + \$13,000 = \$31,000$ and Gonzalez receives $39,000.

Objective

5   *Divide Profits by Interest on Investment and Agreed Ratio.* Sometimes one partner will put up a large share of the money necessary to start a firm, while other partners may actually operate the firm. In such a case, an agreement to divide profits by **interest on investment and agreed ratio** may be reached by which the partner putting up the money gets interest on the investment before any further division of profits.

EXAMPLE **6**   **Dividing Profits by Interest and Agreed Ratio**

Laura Cameron, Jay Davis, and Donna Friedman opened a tool rental business. Cameron contributed $250,000 to the opening of the business, which will be operated by Davis and Friedman. The partners agree that Cameron will first receive a 10% return on her investment before any further division of profits. Additional profits will be divided in the ratio $1:2:2$. Find the amount that each partner would receive from a profit of $75,000.

Solution

Cameron is first paid a 10% return on her investment of $250,000. This amounts to

$$\$250,000 \times 10\% = \$250,000 \times 0.10 = \$25,000$$

This leaves an additional

$75,000   Total profit
$-$ 25,000   Amount to Cameron
$50,000

to be divided. The additional profit of $50,000 is to be divided in the ratio 1 : 2 : 2, respectively. First divide this amount into $1 + 2 + 2 = 5$ equal shares. Cameron gets 1 of these 5 shares, or

$$\frac{1}{5} \times \$50,000 = \$10,000$$

Davis and Friedman each get 2 of the 5 shares or

$$\frac{2}{5} \times \$50,000 = \$20,000$$

In summary, Cameron gets the following amount.

$25,000   Return on investment
$+$ 10,000   Share of profit
$35,000   Total

Davis and Friedman each receive $20,000.

NOTE   The return on investment is paid first and then the remaining profit is divided among the partners.

EXAMPLE **7**   **Distribute Losses by Agreed Ratios**

Suppose the tool rental business in Example 6 had a profit of only $15,000. What would be the distribution of this amount?

Solution

The partners agreed to give Cameron a 10% return, or $25,000. The profits were only $15,000, leaving a loss of $10,000.

$25,000
$-$ 15,000
($10,000)

This loss of $10,000 will be shared in the ratio 1 : 2 : 2, just as were the profits. Cameron's share of the loss is

$$\frac{1}{5} \times \$10,000 = (\$2000)$$

while the share of both Davis and Friedman is

Losses are shown in parentheses.

$$\frac{2}{5} \times \$10,000 = (\$4000)$$

Cameron gets $25,000, minus her share of the loss.

$25,000   Due to Cameron
$-$ 2,000   Her share of loss
$23,000   Actually received by Cameron

Davis and Friedman must each *contribute* $4000 toward the loss. The $23,000 that Cameron actually receives is made up as follows.

$15,000	Profit
4,000	From Davis
+ 4,000	From Friedman
$23,000	Total to Cameron

NOTE Cameron does absorb her share of the loss by accepting $23,000 instead of the $25,000 return on investment initially agreed upon.

19.4 | Exercises

Divide the following profits. Round all answers to the nearest dollar.

	Partners	Investment	Method	Profits	
1.	1	$40,000	Equal shares	$58,000	$29,000 each
	2	$40,000			
2.	1	$20,000	Ratio 1 : 3 : 4	$120,000	$15,000 for 1;
	2	$50,000			$45,000 for 2;
	3	$50,000			$60,000 for 3
3.	1	$80,000	Ratio of investment	$92,000	$73,600 for 1;
	2	$20,000			$18,400 for 2
4.	1	$20,000	$22,000 salary to partner 3;	$72,000	$18,750 for 1;
	2	$20,000	balance divided 3 : 3 : 2		$18,750 for 2;
	3	$5,000			$34,500 for 3
5.	1	$40,000	12% return to partner 1;	$25,000	$16,920 for 1;
	2	$10,000	balance in ratio 3 : 2		$8080 for 2
6.	1	$40,000	10% return to partner 2;	$111,000	$28,000 for 1;
	2	$60,000	balance in ratio of		$48,000 for 2;
	3	$50,000	investment		$35,000 for 3
7.	1	$20,000	$10,000 salary to partner 1;	$22,000	$10,000 for 1;
	2	$15,000	$12,000 salary to partner 2;		$12,000 for 2;
	3	$40,000	balance in ratio of investment		$0 for 3
8.	1	$40,000	$20,000 salary to partner 3;	$133,000	$34,000 for 1;
	2	$40,000	10% return to partners 1		$34,000 for 2;
	3	$5,000	and 2; balance divided		$35,000 for 3;
	4	$35,000	2 : 2 : 1 : 2		$30,000 for 4

Solve the following application problems.

9. CLOWN SCHOOL Twin brothers became circus performers and finally decided to open a school to train clowns with the idea of sharing any profits or losses equally. Find the amount each receives given a quarterly profit of $78,300. $39,150

10. SURGEONS A firm with five surgeons has agreed to split the profits equally. Find the profit to each if the firm has a profit of $1,400,000 one year. $280,000 each

11. **MEXICAN RESTAURANT** Three brothers from Guadalajara invest $10,000, $20,000, and $20,000, respectively, to start up a Mexican restaurant. Find the share that each receives if profit the first year is $93,600 and profits are divided in the ratio of the original investments. $18,720; $37,440; $37,440

12. **BLOOD WORK** Two doctors established a lab in Mexico City to do blood work, such as testing for the HIV virus or tuberculosis. Dr. Rodriguez contributed 850,000 pesos and Dr. Pacas contributed 1,200,000 pesos to found the company. Find the distribution of 1,350,000 pesos of profit if profits are divided in the ratio of the original investments. Round to the nearest peso. Rodriguez: 559,756 pesos; Pacas: 790,244 pesos

13. **INTERNATIONAL TRADE** Three international trade brokers combine their businesses into one company and agree to divide profits in the ratio 2 : 4 : 4. Find the distribution of a profit of $220,000. $44,000; $88,000; $88,000

14. **INTERNATIONAL TRADE** Suppose the partners in Exercise 13 have a loss of $84,000. How much of the loss would be paid by each? $16,800 by 1; $33,600 by 2; $33,600 by 3

15. **TRAVEL AGENCY** Mary Finch and Pete Renz have started a new travel agency. Finch will run the agency. She gets a $15,000 salary, with any additional profits distributed in the ratio 1 : 4. Find the distribution of a profit of $57,000. $23,400 for Finch; $33,600 for Renz

16. **TOY STORE** June Thomas, Ben Walker, and his sister Sara Walker start a toy store to be managed by Thomas at a salary of $20,000 per year. They agree that any additional profits will be divided in the ratio of 1 : 3 : 2. Find the distribution of a profit of $86,000. Thomas—$31,000; Ben Walker—$33,000; Sara Walker—$22,000

17. **HARDWARE STORE** Bob Coker has invested $80,000 in a new hardware store. His partner, Will Toms, will actually run the store. The partners agree that Coker will get a 10% return on his investment, with any additional profits divided in the ratio 1 : 3. Find the distribution of a profit of (a) $60,000 and (b) $6000. (a) $21,000 for Coker; $39,000 for Toms (b) $7500 for Coker; $1500 from Toms to Coker

18. **ELECTRONICS** Wilma Dickson has invested $350,000 in a small electronics plant, to be run by her partner, John Ardery. They agree that she will receive a 10% return on her investment and that any additional profits will be divided in the ratio 2 : 3. Distribute a profit of (a) $90,000 and (b) $30,000. (a) $57,000 to Dickson, $33,000 to Ardery (b) $3000 from Ardery to Dickson; $33,000 to Dickson

19. **PARTNERSHIP** Three partners invest $15,000, $25,000, and $30,000 in a business. The partners agree that partner 1 will receive a 10% return on investment, with partner 2 receiving a salary of $12,000. Any additional profits will be divided in the ratio of the original investments. Divide a profit of $110,000. $22,179 to 1; $46,464 to 2; $41,357 to 3

20. **WHOLESALE PLUMBING** A wholesale plumbing business has three partners. Partner 1 invested $50,000 in the business and is given a 10% return on investment. Partner 2 invested $75,000 and earns a 6% return on investment plus a salary of $21,000. Partner 3 invested $100,000 and earns a 12% return on investment. Any additional profits are distributed in the ratio 2 : 1 : 2. Divide a profit of $180,000. $60,000 to 1; $53,000 to 2; $67,000 to 3

21. State the approach used to divide profits among three partners if partner 1 gets a fixed salary and the remaining profits are divided according to a ratio of 2 : 3 : 2. (See Objective 4.)

22. Explain the difference between the distribution of profits and losses in a partnership versus those in a corporation. (See **Sections 19.1** and **19.4**.)

19.5	**Distribution of Overhead**

OBJECTIVES

1 *Allocate overhead by floor space.*

2 *Allocate overhead by sales.*

3 *Allocate overhead by number of employees.*

Businesses have many expenses. For example, grocery stores tend to have profit margins of less than 3%, meaning that over 97% of the cost of items you buy at a grocery store is generally used to pay expenses. Firms must pay the following: salaries, rent, utilities, suppliers, insurance, taxes, and so on. **Overhead** refers to those expenses of a business that are *not directly attributable* to the production or sale of goods. For a grocery store, overhead would include rent, utilities, insurance premiums, taxes, and the salaries of corporate managers. It would *not include* payments made to suppliers of grocery items.

Managers must continually determine if each line of business is profitable. In order to do so, overhead must be allocated (divided) among the various products or lines of business within a company. This is one area of **cost accounting**. Various methods are used to divide overhead and the choice often depends on industry practice. The **allocation of overhead** is usually done by forming a ratio of each product or department to the entire firm. There are several ways to form this ratio.

Objective

1 *Allocate Overhead by Floor Space.* Overhead can be allocated to departments according to the **floor space** used by each department of the company.

EXAMPLE **1** **Allocating Overhead by Floor Space**

Clover Printing has three departments, with floor space as shown.

Department	Floor Space
Magazine printing	5,000 square feet
Book printing	3,000 square feet
Catalog printing	2,000 square feet
Total:	10,000 square feet

Allocate an overhead of $275,000.

Solution

The magazine printing department has a floor space of 5000 square feet out of a total of 10,000 square feet. Therefore, this department is allocated

$$\frac{5000}{10,000} = \frac{1}{2}$$

of the overhead, or

$$\frac{1}{2} \times \$275,000 = \$137,500$$

When finding the expenses of this department, the company accountants would assign an overhead expense of $137,500 for the department.

The book printing department uses

$$\frac{3000}{10,000} = \frac{3}{10}$$

of the floor space and so would be allocated $\frac{3}{10}$ of the overhead, or

$$\frac{3}{10} \times \$275{,}000 = \$82{,}500$$

Finally, catalog printing would be allocated

$$\frac{2000}{10{,}000} = \frac{1}{5}$$

of the overhead, or

$$\frac{1}{5} \times \$275{,}000 = \$55{,}000$$

NOTE Check your answer by adding the individual departmental allocations. This sum should equal the total overhead.

Objective

2   *Allocate Overhead by Sales.* It is common to allocate overhead according to the **sales** of each department or product, as shown in the next example.

EXAMPLE **2**   **Allocating Overhead by Sales Value**

A European firm owns a clothing manufacturing company in India that exports to the United States. It has these departments and sales figures.

Product Line	Production	Average Sale Price
Men's clothes	5,800 units	$42
Women's clothes	10,930 units	$54
Children's clothes	8,400 units	$38

Allocate an overhead of $186,000 by sales volume and round to the nearest dollar.

Solution

First complete the following table.

Product Line	Production		Average Sale Price		Sales Volume
Men's clothes	5,800	$\times$	$42	=	$243,600
Women's clothes	10,930	$\times$	$54	=	$590,220
Children's clothes	8,400	$\times$	$38	=	$319,200
				Total:	$1,153,020

Now allocate overhead based on sales volume and round to the nearest dollar.
  Overhead to:

$$\text{Men's clothes} = \frac{\$243{,}600}{\$1{,}153{,}020} \times \$186{,}000 = \$39{,}296$$

$$\text{Women's clothes} = \frac{\$590{,}220}{\$1{,}153{,}020} \times \$186{,}000 = \$95{,}212$$

$$\text{Children's clothes} = \frac{\$319{,}200}{\$1{,}153{,}020} \times \$186{,}000 = \$51{,}492$$

Note that the three values total $186,000.

Objective

3 *Allocate Overhead by Number of Employees.* Overhead can also be allocated by the **number of employees** associated with a department or product.

EXAMPLE 3 **Allocating Overhead by Number of Employees**

A local insurance agency has a building overhead-related charge of $80,000. Allocate this overhead expense based on the number of employees.

Solution

Allocate this expense based on a ratio of the number of employees in the department to the total number of employees.

Department	Number of Employees	Ratio of Employees	Overhead of Department
Commercial	5	$\frac{5}{8}$	$\frac{5}{8} \times \$80,000 = \$50,000$
Personal	2	$\frac{2}{8}$	$\frac{2}{8} \times \$80,000 = \$20,000$
Life	1	$\frac{1}{8}$	$\frac{1}{8} \times \$80,000 = \underline{\$10,000}$
Total:	8		$\$80,000$

19.5	**Exercises**

Allocate overhead as indicated. Round to the nearest dollar.

1.

Department	Floor Space
1	4000 square feet
2	8000 square feet
3	10,000 square feet

Overhead: $330,000

$60,000; $120,000; $150,000

2.

Department	Floor Space
A	8000 square feet
B	14,000 square feet
C	10,000 square feet

Overhead: $288,000

$72,000; $126,000; $90,000

3.

Department	Floor Space
1	2400 square feet
2	3600 square feet
3	4000 square feet
4	6000 square feet

Overhead: $120,000

$18,000; $27,000; $30,000; $45,000

4.

Department	Floor Space
1	4200 square feet
2	13,500 square feet
3	21,800 square feet
4	3600 square feet

$40,928; $131,555; $212,436; $35,081

Overhead: $420,000

5.

Product	Number Produced	Average Sale Price
M	15,000	$8.00
N	20,000	$3.50
P	35,000	$2.00

$64,615; $37,692; $37,692

Overhead: $140,000

6.

Product	Number Produced	Average Sale Price
X	5000	$20
Y	8000	$25
Z	4000	$50

$12,500; $25,000; $25,000

Overhead: $62,500

7.

Product	Number Produced	Average Sale Price
1	140	$100
2	2000	$15
3	150	$20
4	1000	$22

$9739; $20,870; $2087; $15,304

Overhead: $48,000

8.

Product	Number Produced	Average Sale Price
1	150	$6
2	200	$12
3	75	$3
4	125	$8

$19,890; $53,039; $4972; $22,099

Overhead: $100,000

9.

Department	Number of Employees
X	110
Y	60
Z	80

$572,000; $312,000; $416,000

Overhead: $1,300,000

10.

Department	Number of Employees
J	10
K	70
L	20

$90,000; $630,000; $180,000

Overhead: $900,000

11.

Department	Number of Employees
1	25
2	30
3	35
4	15

$190,476; $228,571; $266,667; $114,286

Overhead: $800,000

12.

Department	Number of Employees
1	90
2	20
3	50
4	40

$162,000; $36,000; $90,000; $72,000

Overhead: $360,000

13. AUTO PARTS STORE   Dayton Auto Parts allocates its $360,000 overhead based on the floor space used by each department. Allocate the overhead for the following departments.

Department	Floor Space
Hoses	2000 square feet
Radiators	8000 square feet
Water pumps	6000 square feet
Fuel pumps	9000 square feet
Gaskets	1000 square feet
Filters	4000 square feet

$24,000; $96,000;
$72,000; $108,000;
$12,000; $48,000

14. OFFICE SUPPLIES   Savon Office and School Supplies wishes to allocate its $110,000 overhead among its various departments based on floor space. Allocate the overhead for the following departments.

Department	Floor Space
Pens, pencils	750 square feet
Copy machine paper	600 square feet
Copy machines	1000 square feet
Office furniture	1500 square feet
Filing cabinets	500 square feet
Calculators	650 square feet

$16,500; $13,200;
$22,000; $33,000;
$11,000, $14,300

15. LUMBER PRODUCTION   Boght Lumber wishes to allocate 1 month's overhead of $68,000 according to sales based on bundles. Allocate overhead for the following products.

Product	Number of Bundles Produced	Average Sale Price
Construction 2 × 4s	150	$200
Plywood	200	$400
Veneers	100	$600
Wood chips	500	$75
Furniture wood	300	$150

$8079; $21,545;
$16,158; $10,099;
$12,119

16. **MEAT DISTRIBUTOR**   The manager of Jason's Meats needs to allocate the $8732 in weekly overhead based on sales of packaged units. Allocate overhead for the following products.

Product	Number Produced	Average Sale Price	
Beef	10	$800	
Lamb	7	$300	
Pork	5	$750	$3200; $840;
Chicken	14	$120	$1500; $672;
Sausage	12	$150	$720; $1800
Luncheon meats	15	$300	

17. **TEA COMPANY**   Boston Teas has a weekly overhead of $6000 that it wishes to allocate based on the number of employees per department. Use the following chart.

Department	Number of Employees	
Office	6	
Marketing	8	$720; $960; $3360; $960
Distribution	28	
Accounting	8	

18. **HARDWARE STORE**   Allocate overhead of $247,100 among departments according to the number of employees.

Department	Number of Employees	
Paint	4	
Lumber	7	$32,947; $57,657;
Appliances	4	$32,947; $49,420;
Plumbing	6	$74,130
All other	9	

19. Define the term *overhead*. List at least three expenses that would be included in overhead. Explain why a manager needs to allocate overhead. (See Objective 1.)

20. Compare and contrast the three ways of allocating overhead that were discussed in this section. Give circumstances under which each of the three might be appropriate. (See Objectives 1–3.)

CHAPTER TERMS

Review the following terms to test your understanding of the chapter. For any terms you do not know, refer to the page number found next to that term.

agreed ratio [p. 742]
allocation of overhead [p. 748]
annual meeting [p. 720]
attached [p. 719]
board of directors [p. 720]
bond [p. 736]
broker [p. 728]
capital [p. 720]
commission [p. 728]
common stock [p. 721]
convertible preferred stock [p. 721]
corporate bonds [p. 736]
corporations [p. 719]
cost accounting [p. 748]
cumulative preferred stock [p. 721]
current yield [p. 729]
discount broker [p. 728]
dividend [p. 721]

Dow Jones Industrial Average [p. 730]
earnings per share [p. 723]
exchange traded fund (ETF) [p. 732]
executive officers [p. 720]
face value [p. 736]
floor space [p. 748]
gross domestic product GDP [p. 719]
index fund [p. 732]
insider trading [p. 720]
interest on investment and agreed ratio [p. 744]
junk bond [p. 739]
limited liability [p. 719]
limited partnership [p. 719]
market interest rate [p. 739]
maturity date [p. 736]
municipal bond [p. 736]
mutual fund [p. 732]

NASDAQ Composite Index [p. 730]
nonparticipating [p. 721]
number of employees [p. 750]
odd lot [p. 728]
online brokers [p. 728]
original investments [p. 742]
overhead [p. 748]
par value [p. 736]
participating [p. 721]
partnership [p. 719]
preferred stock [p. 721]
present value of a bond [p. 000]
price-earnings ratio (PE ratio) [p. 730]
publicly held corporation [p. 720]
round lot [p. 728]

salary and agreed ratio [p. 744]
Securities and Exchange Commission (SEC) [p. 728]
silent partner [p. 719]
sole proprietorship [p. 719]
Standard and Poor's 500 (S&P 500) [p. 730]
stock [p. 720]
stockbroker [p. 728]
stock certificate [p. 720]
stock exchange [p. 726]
stockholder [p. 720]
stock ratios [p. 729]
trade [p. 728]
Treasury Inflation-Protected Securities (TIPS) [p. 736]
yield-to-maturity [p. 736]
zero-coupon bond [p. 736]

CONCEPTS

19.1 Determining the amounts paid to holders of preferred and common stock

To find total paid to owners of preferred stock, multiply par value by dividend rate to obtain dividend per share, then multiply by number of shares.

To find the dividend paid to owners of common stock, subtract total paid to owners of preferred stock from total available to stockholders, then divide by number of shares of common stock.

19.1 Finding earnings per share

Subtract dividends on preferred stock from net income, then divide by the number of shares of common stock outstanding.

EXAMPLES

A company distributes $750,000 to stockholders. It has 15,000 shares of $100 par value 4% preferred stock and 150,000 shares of common stock. Find (a) amount paid to holders of preferred stock and (b) amount per share to holders of common stock.

(a) Dividend per share $= \$100 \times 0.04 = \$4$

Total to preferred stockholders $= \$4 \times 15,000$
$$= \$60,000$$

(b) Dividend to common

$$= \frac{\$750,000 - \$60,000}{150,000} = \$4.60$$

A company made $500,000 last year. The company has 750,000 shares of common stock outstanding and paid $75,000 to owners of preferred stock. Find the earnings per share.

$$EPS = \frac{\$500,000 - \$75,000}{750,000}$$

$$= \$0.57 \qquad \text{Rounded}$$

19.2 Reading the stock table

Locate the stock involved and determine the various quantities required.

Use Figure 19.3 to find the following information for Albemarle (ALB).

| 52 week | | | | | | | | Dividend |
High	Low	Stock	Sym	Vol (100s)	Yld %	P/E	Close	Latest
71.79	38.75	Albemarle	ALB	112347	1.4	12	46.31	.165
↑	↑		↑	↑	↑	↑	↑	↑
High for the year	Low for the year		Symbol	Volume for day	Dividend yield	Price-to-earnings ratio	Close for day	Latest quarterly dividend

19.2 Selling shares of a stock

Find the basic price of the stock from Figure 19.3. Subtract the broker's commission.

Find the amount received by a person selling 300 shares of a stock at $45.82 if the commission is $7.95.

$$\text{Sale price} = 300 \times \$45.82 = \$13,746$$

$$
\begin{array}{ll}
\$13,746.00 & \text{Sale Price} \\
- \quad \$7.95 & \text{Commission} \\
\hline
\$13,738.05 &
\end{array}
$$

19.2 Finding the current yield on a stock

$$\text{Current yield} = \frac{\text{annual dividend}}{\text{current price}}$$

Find the current yield of a stock if the purchase price is $65.42 per share and the annual dividend is $1.44.

$$\text{Current yield} = \frac{\$1.44}{\$65.42} = 2.2\%$$

19.2 Finding the price-to-earnings ratio (PE ratio)

To find the price-to-earnings ratio, use the formula

$$\text{PE ratio} = \frac{\text{price per share}}{\text{annual net income per share}}$$

Price per share, $42.50; annual net income per share, $2.75.

$$\text{PE ratio} = \frac{\$42.50}{\$2.75} = 15.45$$

19.2 Reading the Bond Table

Locate the bond table and determine the various quantities required.

Use Figure 19.7 to find the following information for a AT&T (T) bond maturing in 2041.

Company	Coupon	Maturity	Last	Yield %	EST $ VOL (000's)
AT&T	5.550	August 15, 2041	104.645	5.241	562,119
↑	↑	↑	↑	↑	
Company	Interest rate on $1000 face value	Maturity date	Last price for day	Yield to maturity	

19.3 Determining the cost of purchasing bonds

Locate the bond in Figure 19.7, then multiply the price of the bond by 1000 and the number of bonds purchased. Then, add the commission.

Find the cost, including sales charges of $5 per bond, of 30 Citigroup 2020 bonds selling at the last price of the day.

$$\text{Price of 1 bond} = 106.732\% \text{ of } \$1000$$
$$= \$1067.32$$
$$(30 \times \$1067.32) + (30 \times \$5) = \$32{,}169.60$$

19.3 Determining the amount received from the sale of bonds

Locate the bond in the table, then multiply the price of the bond by 1000 and the number of bonds sold. Then subtract the commission.

Find the amount received from the sale of 20 Supervalu bonds selling at 96.108 if the commission is $5 per bond.

$$\text{Price of 1 bond} = 96.108\% \text{ of } \$1000$$
$$= \$961.08$$
$$(20 \times \$961.08) - (20 \times \$5) = \$19{,}121.60$$

19.3 Finding the annual income from a mutual fund containing bonds

Multiply the amount invested in the fund by the yield rate.

Find the annual income from $120,000 invested in a bond fund yielding $7\frac{1}{2}\%$.

$$\$120{,}000 \times 0.075 = \$9000$$

19.3 Finding the present value of a bond

Use the market interest rate to find

1. Present value of interest payments
2. Present value of $1000 face amount

Add the present values.

A corporate bond has a face value of $1000 and matures in 18 years. The annual interest payment is $58.75 and the market interest rate is 5%. Find the present value of the bond.

$$\text{PV interest payments} = \$58.75 \times a_{\overline{n}|i}; n = 18,$$
$$i = 0.05$$
$$= \$58.75 \times 11.68958690$$
$$= \$686.76$$

$$\text{PV face} = \frac{M}{(1 + i)^n} = \frac{\$1000}{(1 + 0.05)^{18}}$$
$$= \$415.52$$

Now add the two present values.

$$\begin{array}{r} \$686.76 \\ + \$415.52 \\ \hline \$1102.28 \quad \text{Value of bond} \end{array}$$

19.4 Dividing profits in a partnership

Use one of the following methods to determine each partner's ratio of the profits.

1. Equal shares
2. Agreed ratio
3. Original investment
4. Salary and agreed ratio
5. Interest on investment and agreed ratio
6. Multiply total profits by each partner's ratio

Divide profits of $75,000 among three investors by the *original investment* if each partner invests the following amount.

Partner	Investment
1	$12,000
2	$15,000
3	$18,000

$$\text{Total initial investment} = \$12,000 + \$15,000$$
$$+ \$18,000 = \$45,000$$

Ratios for each partner:

1. $\dfrac{12,000}{45,000} = \dfrac{4}{15}$

2. $\dfrac{15,000}{45,000} = \dfrac{1}{3}$

3. $\dfrac{18,000}{45,000} = \dfrac{2}{5}$

Profit for each partner:

1. $\dfrac{4}{15}(\$75,000) = \$20,000$

2. $\dfrac{1}{3}(\$75,000) = \$25,000$

3. $\dfrac{2}{5}(\$75,000) = \$30,000$

19.5 Allocating overhead by floor space

First, find the total floor space. Then, determine the fraction of total floor space each department occupies. Multiply the fraction by the amount of overhead to be allocated.

Department	Floor Space
Printing	40,000 sq.ft
Cutting	25,000 sq.ft
Binding	55,000 sq.ft

Allocate $3,300,000 overhead.

$$\text{Printing: } \frac{40,000}{120,000} \times \$3,300,000 = \$1,100,000$$

$$\text{Cutting: } \frac{25,000}{120,000} \times \$3,300,000 = \$687,500$$

$$\text{Binding: } \frac{55,000}{120,000} \times \$3,300,000 = \$1,512,500$$

19.5 Allocating overhead by sales

Determine the fraction of total sales for each department. Multiply this fraction by the amount of overhead to be allocated.

Product	Number Produced	Average Sales Price
A	5000	$12
B	8000	$5
C	10,000	$10

Allocate $60,000 overhead.

$$\text{Total value} = (5000)(\$12) + (8000)(\$5) \\ + (10,000)(\$10)$$
$$= \$200,000$$

$$A: \frac{(5000)(\$12)}{\$200,000} \times \$60,000 = \$18,000$$

$$B: \frac{(8000)(\$5)}{\$200,000} \times \$60,000 = \$12,000$$

$$C: \frac{(10,000)(\$10)}{\$200,000} \times \$60,000 = \$30,000$$

19.5 Allocating overhead by number of employees

Find the fraction of total employees in each department and multiply the fraction by the overhead to be allocated.

Dept.	Number of Employees
A	40
B	20

Allocate $180,000 overhead.

$$A: \frac{40}{40 + 20} \times \$180,000 = \$120,000$$

$$B: \frac{20}{40 + 20} \times \$180,000 = \$60,000$$

CHAPTER 19 | Review Exercises

The answer section includes answers to all Review Exercises.

Find the amount per share paid to holders of (a) preferred stock and (b) common stock. [19.1]

	Net Income	Reinvested Funds	Par Value	Rate	Number of Shares of Preferred Stock	Number of Shares of Common Stock	
1.	$460,000	$317,000	$50	$6\frac{1}{2}\%$	8000	180,000	**(a)** $3.25 **(b)** $0.65
2.	$2,375,000	$750,000	$150	4%	15,000	200,000	**(a)** $6 **(b)** $7.68
3.	$2,640,000	$425,000	$125	7%	22,750	750,000	**(a)** $8.75 **(b)** $2.69

Find the earnings per share. Round to the nearest cent. [19.1]

	Net Income	Dividends on Preferred Stock	Number of Shares of Common Stock	
4.	$127,500	$0	82,000	$1.55
5.	$1,425,000	$675,000	275,000	$2.73
6.	$2,750,000	$900,000	500,000	$3.70

Use Figure 19.3 to find each of the following. Round money answers to the nearest penny. [19.2]

7. 52-week low for Aetna (AET) $26.42

8. Volume for Berkley (WRB)   5,200,000

9. Close price for Aeropostale (ARO) $10.71

10. Quarterly dividend for BaxterInt (BAX) $0.31

11. 52-week low for BerkHathwy A (BRKA) $100,265

12. Annual yield for BigLots (BIG)   0%

13. PE Ratio for BarckGld (ABX)   16

14. Close for Bemis (BMS) $28.60

15. 52-week low for Agrium (AGU) $64.53

Find the cost of the stock purchase. Ignore any broker's fees. [19.2]

	Stock	Number of Shares	Transaction	
16.	Alcoa (AA)	100	52-week low	$992
17.	Best Buy (BBY)	250	Close	$6015
18.	Alexanders	400	Close	$155,600

Find the cost of the stock purchase. Assume a broker's fee of $7.95. [19.2]

19. 200 shares at $43.37 $8681.95

20. 450 shares at $52.12 $23,461.95

Find the amount received from the sale of stock. Assume a commission of $7.95. [19.2]

21. 100 shares at $30.85 $3077.05

22. 180 shares at $47.25 $8497.05

Find the current yield for each stock. Round to the nearest tenth of a percent. [19.2]

23. Intel at $16.80 per share and a dividend of $0.56   3.3%

24. Target at $41.80 per share and a dividend of $0.64   1.5%

Find the PE ratio of the following. Round all answers to the nearest whole number. [19.2]

25. Apple at $601.32 per share with a net income of $41.04   15

26. British Petroleum at $53.79 per share with a net income of $9.73   6

Use Figure 19.7 to find the following for Occidental Petroleum bonds due in 2022. [19.3]

27. Last price $999.11

28. Maturity date   February 15, 2022

29. Annual coupon rate   3.125%

30. Yield to maturity   3.135%

31. Volume $386,195,000

32. Cost of 10 bonds if no commission is paid $9991.10

Find the total cost including the commission of $5 per bond, if purchased at the last price of the day. [19.3]

Bond	Number Purchased	
33. Wal-Mart Stores	30	$34,828.80
34. JPMorgan Chase (2016)	25	$25,399.25

In Exercises 35–37, divide the profits among the partners based on the indicated method. Round all answers to the nearest dollar. [19.4]

	Partners	Investment	Method	Profits	
35.	1	$8500	Equal shares	$72,000	$24,000 to each
	2	$7000			
	3	$10,500			
36.	1	$16,000	Ratio 2 : 3	$120,000	$48,000 to 1; $72,000 to 2
	2	$25,000			
37.	1	$9000	Ratio of	$90,000	$38,571 to 1; $51,429 to 2
	2	$12,000	investment		

In Exercises 38–40, allocate the overhead to each department of the company. Round to the nearest dollar. [19.5]

38.

Department	Floor Space	
A	3000 square feet	
B	5000 square feet	$25,000; $41,667; $33,333
C	4000 square feet	

Overhead: $100,000

39.

Product	Number Produced	Average Sale Price	
1	8000	$12	
2	40,000	$6	$23,256; $58,140; $43,605
3	20,000	$9	

Overhead: $125,000

40.

Department	Number of Employees	
A	70	
B	55	$258,696; $203,261; $166,304; $221,739
C	45	
D	60	

Overhead: $850,000

Solve each of the following application problems. [19.3]

41. Ralph Toombs invested his retirement funds of $225,000 in a bond fund currently paying $8\frac{1}{4}\%$. Find his annual income. $18,562.50

42. George and Wanda Joyce invested their life's savings of $320,000 in a bond fund. If the fund charged them a 1% sales commission, find the annual income if the fund is currently paying 7.5%. $23,760

43. A corporate bond with a face value of $1000 matures in 8 years. The coupon rate is 4.50%. Find the present value of the bond if the market interest rate is 6%. $906.85

44. A corporate bond matures in 25 years. It has a coupon rate of 6.25% and a maturity value of $1000. Find the present value of the bond if the market interest rate is 6.5% for similar firms. $969.51

CHAPTER 19	Business Application Case #1
	Investing Proceeds from Selling a House

Miranda Waters just sold a house and has decided to use some of the funds to purchase 200 shares of Best Buy at the close price and 10 Walt Disney Co. bonds maturing in 2016. Use Figures 19.3 and 19.7 as needed to find the following.

(a) Total cost given a commission on stock of $7.95 per execution and $5 per bond purchased $14,761.65

(b) Total of annual dividend plus interest (*Hint:* Multiply dividend in the table by 4 to get the annual dividend.) $263

(c) Effective interest rate to the nearest tenth of a percent   1.8%

CHAPTER 19	Business Application Case #2
	Investing for Employees

Becky and Joe Rooter own their own small company. They have a retirement plan called a SEP IRA for all employees of the company. It is at Charles Schwab Corporation (www.schwab.com), where they can buy stocks or bonds within the SEP IRA. The Rooters have invested all previous funds in a very conservatively managed growth and income mutual fund containing both stocks and bonds. The $192,380 already in the fund before this quarterly contribution currently pays 4.2% per year, including dividends and interest.

The overall market is down sharply and a financial advisor has advised them to invest a portion of any new contributions in the stocks of a few of the best international companies. After careful consideration, the Rooters decided to buy 100 shares of each of the following international companies.

Company	Country	Close Price	Dividend	PE Ratio
Sony	Japan	$20.32	$0.30	11
Toyota	Japan	$62.58	$0.95	14
Siemens	Germany	$99.52	$2.70	14

(a) Find the total cost to buy the stock, including a commission of $7.95 per company. $18,265.85

(b) Find the *annual dividend earned* and effective rate of interest to the nearest tenth. $395; 2.2%

(c) The Rooters also purchased 10 International Business Machines Corporation bonds maturing in July 2016 at the close price for the day. Use Figure 19.7 to find the cost if the brokerage commission is $5 per bond. $10,190.90

(d) Find the annual interest paid on the bonds. $195

(e) Find the total annual interest and dividends from all sources. $8669.96

PART 5	Cumulative Review: Chapters 17–19

Solve the following application problems.

1. Wild Oats Grocery purchased new store fixtures at a cost of $24,200. The estimated life of the fixtures is 4 years and the salvage value is estimated to be $3000. If straight-line depreciation, find (a) the annual rate of depreciation, (b) the annual amount of depreciation, and (c) the book value at the end of the *second* year. **[17.1]**   (a) 25% (b) $5300 (c) $13,600

2. The owner of an Arco gas station purchased a new gasoline pump at a cost of $32,800. The pump is expected to have a useful life of 10 years but will then have no salvage value. Find (a) the first year's annual depreciation and (b) the second year's annual depreciation using the 200% declining-balance method. **[17.2]**   (a) $6560 (b) $5248

3. To control the rate at which the bananas ripen, Wholesale Bananas, Inc. bought a new walk-in cooler for $12,820. It is estimated to have a salvage value of $400 after 8 years. Find the first and second year's depreciation using the sum-of-the-years'-digits method. Then find the book value at the end of the second year. **[17.3]** $2760; $2415; $7645

4. A robotic welding system costing $42,250 is expected to operate for 11,500 hours and to then have a salvage value of $2000. Use the units-of-production method to find the depreciation for the first year if the system is operated 12 hours per day for all 365 days of the year. Then find the book value at the end of the first year. **[17.4]** $15,330; $26,920

5. An automobile manufacturing company bought a die for a stamping press for $115,800 to stamp out automobile fenders and placed it in service on April 1. The salvage value after an expected useful life of 5 years is $3800. Find the first year's partial depreciation using (a) the straight-line method, (b) the double-declining-balance method, and (c) the sum-of-the-years'-digits method. **[17.4]**   (a) $16,800 (b) $34,740 (c) $28,000

6. Find the recovery period under MACRS for (a) a tugboat, (b) a delivery van, (c) a 4-year-old race horse, (d) a 32-unit apartment house, and (e) a couch for the waiting room in a dentist's office. **[17.5]**   (a) 10 years (b) 5 years (c) 3 years (d) 27.5 years (e) 7 years

7. Atlas Moving and Storage purchased a tractor unit for moving people's household goods long distances. The cost of the truck was $96,000. Prepare a depreciation schedule using the MACRS method of depreciation. **[17.5]**

Year	Computation	Amount of Depreciation	Accumulated Depreciation	Book Value
0	—	—	—	$96,000
1	33.33% of $96,000	$31,996.80	$31,996.80	$64,003.20
2	44.45% of $96,000	$42,672.00	$74,668.80	$21,331.20
3	14.81% of $96,000	$14,217.60	$88,886.40	$7,113.60
4	7.41% of $96,000	$7,113.60	$96,000.00	$0.00

8. The Fashion Shoppe had gross sales of $240,800 with returns of $4300. Inventory at the beginning of the quarter was $48,300 and by the end of the quarter inventory was $41,500. A total of $102,000 worth of goods was purchased last quarter and freight charges were $2900. Wages were $32,400, rent was $15,000, advertising was $2200, utilities were $3100, and taxes on inventory and payroll totaled $6100. Miscellaneous expenses totaled $8900 and income taxes were $11,400. Complete an income statement for the company. **[18.1]**

The Fashion Shoppe	Income Statement	Quarter Ending March 31		
Gross sales			$240,800	
Returns			$4300	
Net sales			$236,500	
Inventory, January 1		$48,300		
Cost of goods purchased	$102,000			
Freight	$2900			
Total cost of goods purchased		$104,900		
Total of goods available for sale		$153,200		
Inventory, December 31		$41,500		
Cost of goods sold			$111,700	
Gross profit				$124,800
Expenses				
Salaries and wages		$32,400		
Rent		$15,000		
Advertising		$2200		
Utilities		$3100		
Taxes on inventory, payroll		$6100		
Miscellaneous expenses		$8900		
Total expenses				$67,700
Net income before taxes				$57,100
Income taxes				$11,400
Net income				$45,700

9. Analyze the income statement of Exercise 8 by finding cost of goods sold, gross profit, net income before taxes, and net income as a percent of net sales. Round to the nearest tenth of a percent. **[18.2]**   47.2%, 52.8%, 24.1%, 19.3%

10. The Fashion Shoppe (see Exercise 8) has $28,400 cash, $8400 in notes receivable, $3800 in accounts receivable, and inventory of $41,500. It does not own the land or building that it uses, but fixtures have an estimated value of $12,200. The company has notes payable of $4800 and accounts payable of $32,500 but has neither mortgages nor long-term notes payable. Complete a balance sheet for this company. **[18.3]**

The Fashion Shoppe	**Balance Sheet For December 31**		
Assets			
Current Assets			
Cash	$28,400		
Notes receivable	$8400		
Accounts receivable	$3800		
Inventory	$41,500		
Total current assets		$82,100	
Plant Assets			
Land	$0		
Buildings	$0		
Fixtures	$12,200		
Total plant assets		$12,200	
Total Assets			$94,300
Liabilities			
Current Liabilities			
Notes payable	$4800		
Accounts payable	$32,500		
Total current liabilities		$37,300	
Long-term Liabilities			
Mortgages payable	$0		
Long-term notes payable	$0		
Total long-term liabilities		$0	
Total Liabilities			$37,300
Owners' Equity			
Owner's equity		$57,000	
Total Liabilities and Owners' Equity			$94,300

11. Find the current ratio, acid-test ratio, and ratio of net income after taxes to average owners' equity, assuming owners' equity 1 year previous to the balance sheet of Exercise 10 was $42,800 and using the income statement from Exercise 8. **[18.4]**   2.20; 1.09; 0.92

12. Noel Saturn owns 50 shares of preferred stock with a par value of $80 and a dividend of 5%. Find his total dividend payment. **[19.1]** $200

13. Jackson Brewery paid no dividend last year but has set aside $80,750 for the payment of dividends this year. It has 10,000 shares of cumulative preferred stock outstanding with a par value of $60 and a 6% dividend. Find this year's dividend per share of common stock given 25,000 shares of common stock outstanding. **[19.1]** $0.35

14. ABC Inc. was incorporated in 1990 and now has 200,000 shares of common stock outstanding. Given a net income of $85,000 and preferred dividends of $8000, find the earnings per share of common stock. **[19.1]** $0.385 per share

15. Elizabeth Neault bought 200 shares of Intel at $23.22 per share and 100 shares of Toyota at $75.12 per share. Find the total cost if the broker charged a commission of $30. **[19.2]** $12,186

16. A publicly held company that writes computer software had net income this year of $2.06 per share and paid a dividend this year of $0.40 per share. Given a stock price of $62.50, find (a) the current yield and (b) the PE ratio. **[19.2]** **(a)** 0.6% (rounded) **(b)** 30 (rounded)

17. Antonio Pondillo sold 200 shares of stock at $47.70 per share and paid a commission of $12.95. Find the amount he received after expenses of the sale. **[19.2]** $9527.05

18. Use Figure 19.3 on page 726 to find the quarterly dividend yield and price-to-earnings ratio for Aetna (symbol AET). **[19.2]** $0.15; 8

19. Use Figure 19.7 on page 737 to find the last price and yield to maturity for the day for Wal-Mart Stores bonds. **[19.3]** $1155.96 ; 4.650%

20. Use Figure 19.6 on page 732 to find the current price and two-year return for Fidelity Contrafund. **[19.2]** $64.33; 14.9%

21. Find the cost of purchasing 25 bonds selling at $97.25 assuming a commission of $5 per bond. **[19.3]** $24,437.50

22. Find the net proceeds after a $5 commission per bond from the sale of 40 bonds at a market price of $92.375. **[19.3]** $36,750

23. Two partners invested $40,000 and $60,000, respectively, in a business venture. If there was a profit of $48,000, find the distribution of profit to the two partners using (a) equal shares, (b) an agreed ratio of 3 : 1, and (c) the original investment. **[19.4]** **(a)** $24,000 to each **(b)** $36,000 to partner 1; $12,000 to partner 2 **(c)** $19,200 to partner 1; $28,800 to partner 2

24. Alan Padgett and Gina Harden own a retail business that Harden manages at a salary of $28,000. Originally, Padgett invested $60,000 and Harden invested $20,000 to start the business. Find the amount each partner would receive from a profit of $85,000 if they agree to divide profits based on their original investment. **[19.4]** Padgett—$42,750; Harden—$42,250

25. Allocate an overhead of $340,000 by floor space. **[19.5]**

Department	Floor Space	
Machining	30,000 square feet	
Stamping	15,000 square feet	
Assembly	35,000 square feet	$127,500; $63,750; $148,750
Total:	80,000 square feet	

26. Allocate an overhead of $180,000 by number of employees. **[19.5]**

Department	Number of Employees	
A	20	
B	12	
C	18	$72,000; $43,200; $64,800
	Total: 50	

27. Allocate an overhead of $140,000 by sales value. **[19.5]**

Product	Number Produced	Value of Each	
1	12,800	$25	
2	14,200	$15	$78,734.62; $52,407.73;
3	180	$200	$8857.64

28. A corporate bond with a face value of $1000 matures in 13 years. The coupon rate is 5.125%. Find the present value of the bond if the market interest rate is 5.5%. **[19.3]** $965.81

29. A corporate bond matures in 16 years. It has a coupon rate of 6.125% and a maturity value of $1000. Find the present value of the bond if the market interest rate is 5% for similar firms. **[19.3]** $1121.92

javier brosch / Fotolia.com

Calculator Basics

Calculators are among the more popular inventions of the last four decades. Each year better calculators are developed and costs drop. The first all-transistor desktop calculator was introduced to the market in 1966. It weighed 55 pounds, cost $2500, and was slow. Today, these same calculations are performed quite well on a calculator costing less than $10. And today's $100 pocket calculators have more ability to calculate than some of the early computers.

Many colleges allow students to use calculators in business mathematics courses. Some courses require calculator use. Although you can still purchase a basic four-function calculator, you're probably better off spending $10 to $20 on either a **basic** or a **financial calculator**. These calculators allow you to do a lot more than the basic four-function calculators. A **graphing calculator** allows you to graph functions and visualize data; however, it is beyond the scope of this text.

In **Section A.1**, we discuss a basic calculator, including percent key, reciprocal key, exponent keys, square root key, memory function, order of operations, and parentheses keys. In **Section A.2**, we discuss the financial calculator with its associated financial keys.

A.1   Basic Calculators

OBJECTIVES

1 *Learn the basic calculator keys.*

2 *Understand the* $\boxed{C}$ *,* $\boxed{CE}$ *, and* $\boxed{ON/C}$ *keys.*

3 *Understand the floating decimal point.*

4 *Use the* $\boxed{\%}$ *and* $\boxed{1/x}$ *keys.*

5 *Use the* $\boxed{y^x}$ *,* $\boxed{e^x}$ *, and* $\boxed{\sqrt{x}}$ *keys.*

6 *Use the* $\boxed{a^b/_c}$ *key.*

7 *Solve problems with negative numbers.*

8 *Use the calculator memory function.*

9 *Solve chain calculations using order of operations.*

10 *Use the parentheses keys.*

11 *Use the calculator for problem solution.*

NOTE The various calculator models differ significantly. *Use the instruction booklet that came with your calculator* for specifics about your calculator.

Objective

1 *Learn the Basic Calculator Keys.* Most calculators use **algebraic logic**. Some problems can be solved by entering number and function keys in the same order as you would solve a problem by hand, but many others require a knowledge of the order of operations when entering the problem. Order of operations are discussed in Objective 9 of this appendix.

EXAMPLE 1 **Using the Basic Keys**

(a) $12 + 25$ **(b)** $456 \div 24$

Solution

(a) The problem $12 + 25$ is entered as

$$12 \;\boxed{+}\; 25 \;\boxed{=}$$

and 37 appears as the answer.

(b) Enter $456 \div 24$ as

$$456 \;\boxed{\div}\; 24 \;\boxed{=}$$

and 19 appears as the answer.

Objective

2 *Understand the* $\boxed{\text{C}}$, $\boxed{\text{CE}}$, *and* $\boxed{\text{ON/C}}$ *Keys.* All calculators have a $\boxed{\text{C}}$ key. Pressing this key erases everything in most calculators and prepares them for a new problem. Some calculators have a $\boxed{\text{CE}}$ key. Pressing this key erases only the number displayed, thus allowing for correction of a mistake without having to start the problem over. Many calculators combine the $\boxed{\text{C}}$ key and the $\boxed{\text{CE}}$ key and use an $\boxed{\text{ON/C}}$ key. This key is used both to turn the calculator on and to erase the calculator display. If $\boxed{\text{ON/C}}$ is pressed after the $\boxed{=}$ or after one of the operation keys $\boxed{+}$, $\boxed{-}$, $\boxed{\times}$, or $\boxed{\div}$, everything in the calculator is erased. If the wrong operation key is pressed, simply press the correct key and the error is corrected. For example, in 7 $\boxed{+}$ $\boxed{-}$ 3 $\boxed{=}$ 4 pressing the $\boxed{-}$ key cancels out the previous $\boxed{+}$ key entry.

> **NOTE** Be sure to look at the directions that come with your calculator in terms of clearing the memory since keys and the operational sequence vary from calculator to calculator.

Objective

3 *Understand the Floating Decimal Point.* Calculators have a **floating decimal**, which locates the decimal point in the final result.

EXAMPLE 2 **Calculating with Decimal Numbers**

A contractor purchased 55.75 square yards of vinyl floor covering at a cost of $18.99 per square yard. Find her total cost.

Solution

Proceed as follows.

$$55.75 \boxed{\times} 18.99 \boxed{=} 1058.6925$$

The decimal point is automatically placed in the answer. Since money answers are usually rounded to the nearest cent, the answer is $1058.69.

EXAMPLE 3 **Placing the Decimal Point in Money Answers**

Add $21.38 and $1.22.

Solution

$$21.38 \boxed{+} 1.22 \boxed{=} 22.6$$

The final 0 is left off. Remember that the problem deals with dollars and cents, so write the answer as $22.60.

Objective

4 *Use the* ⎡%⎤ *and* ⎡1/x⎤ *Keys.* The ⎡%⎤ key moves the decimal point two places to the left when used following multiplication or division.

EXAMPLE 4 Using the ⎡%⎤ Key

Find 8% of $4205.

Solution

$$4205 \boxed{\times} 8 \boxed{\%} \boxed{=} 336.4 = \$336.40$$

The ⎡1/x⎤ key replaces a number with the reciprocal of that number.

EXAMPLE 5 Using the ⎡1/x⎤ Key

Find the multiplicative inverse, or reciprocal, of 40.

Solution

$$40 \boxed{1/x} \ 0.025$$

Objective

5 *Use the* ⎡y^x⎤ , ⎡e^x⎤ , *and* ⎡$\sqrt{x}$⎤ *Keys.* The product of 3 × 3 can be written as follows.

$$3^2$$

The **exponent** (2 in this case) shows how many times the **base** (3 in this case) is multiplied by itself. The ⎡y^x⎤ key raises a base to a power. Be sure to enter the base first followed by the exponent.

EXAMPLE 6 Using the ⎡y^x⎤ and ⎡e^x⎤ Keys

Note that *e* is a constant that is found on most calculators. It is approximately 2.71828, which is the same thing as e^1.
   Solve the following: (a) 5^3 and (b) e^2.

Solution

(a)

$$5 \boxed{y^x} 3 \boxed{=} 125$$

(b) In this case, the number *e* on your calculator is the base. Raise it to the second power by first entering the exponent 2 and then using the ⎡e^x⎤ key.

$$2 \boxed{e^x} \ 7.389 \quad \text{Rounded}$$

Since $3^2 = 9$, the number 3 is called the **square root** of 9. The symbol $\sqrt{}$ is used to write the square root of a number.

$$\sqrt{9} = 3$$

EXAMPLE 7 Using the $\boxed{\sqrt{x}}$ Key

Find each square root.

(a) $\sqrt{144}$ **(b)** $\sqrt{20}$

Solution

(a) Using the calculator, enter

$$144 \boxed{\sqrt{x}}$$

and 12 appears in the display. The square root of 144 is 12.

(b) The square root of 20 is

$$20 \boxed{\sqrt{x}} \; 4.472136$$

which may be rounded to the desired place.

Objective

6 *Use the* $\boxed{a^b/_c}$ *Key.* Many calculators have an $\boxed{a^b/_c}$ key that can be used for problems containing fractions and mixed numbers. A mixed number is a number with both a whole number and a fraction, such as $7\frac{3}{4}$ which equals $7 + \frac{3}{4}$. The rules for adding, subtracting, multiplying, and dividing both fractions and mixed numbers are given in **Chapter 1**. Here, we simply show how these operations are done on a calculator.

EXAMPLE 8 Using the $\boxed{a^b/_c}$ Key with Fractions

Solve the following.

(a) $\dfrac{6}{11} + \dfrac{3}{4}$ **(b)** $\dfrac{3}{8} \div \dfrac{5}{6}$

Solution

(a) $6 \boxed{a^b/_c} \; 11 \boxed{+} \; 3 \boxed{a^b/_c} \; 4 \boxed{=} \; 1\dfrac{13}{44}$

(b) $3 \boxed{a^b/_c} \; 8 \boxed{\div} \; 5 \boxed{a^b/_c} \; 6 \boxed{=} \; \dfrac{9}{20}$

NOTE The calculator automatically reduces fractions for you.

EXAMPLE 9   Using the $a\frac{b}{c}$ Key

Solve the following.

(a) $4\dfrac{7}{8} \div 3\dfrac{4}{7}$ (b) $\dfrac{5}{3} \div 27.5$ (c) $65.3 \times 6\dfrac{3}{4}$

Solution

(a) $4\;\boxed{a\tfrac{b}{c}}\;7\;\boxed{a\tfrac{b}{c}}\;8\;\boxed{\div}\;3\;\boxed{a\tfrac{b}{c}}\;4\;\boxed{a\tfrac{b}{c}}\;7\;\boxed{=}\;1\dfrac{73}{200}$

(b) $5\;\boxed{a\tfrac{b}{c}}\;3\;\boxed{\div}\;27.5\;\boxed{=}\;0.060606061$

(c) $65.3\;\boxed{\times}\;6\;\boxed{a\tfrac{b}{c}}\;3\;\boxed{a\tfrac{b}{c}}\;4\;\boxed{=}\;440.775$

Objective

7 *Solve Problems with Negative Numbers.* There are several calculations in business that result in a **negative number**, or **deficit amount**.

EXAMPLE 10   Working with Negative Numbers

The amount in the advertising account last month was $4800, while $5200 was actually spent. Find the balance remaining in the advertising account.

Solution

Enter the numbers in the calculator.

$$4800\;\boxed{-}\;5200\;\boxed{=}\;-400$$

The minus sign in front of the 400 indicates that there is a deficit, or negative amount. This value can be written as $-$$400 or as ($400), which indicates a negative amount. Some calculators place the minus after the number, as 400$-$.

Negative numbers may be entered into the calculator by using the $\boxed{-}$ before entering the number. For example, if $3000 is now added to the advertising account in Example 10, the new balance is calculated as follows.

$$\boxed{-}\;400\;\boxed{+}\;3000\;\boxed{=}\;2600$$

The new account balance is $2600.

The $\boxed{+/-}$ key can be used to change the sign of a number that has already been entered. For example, 520 $\boxed{+/-}$ changes $+520$ to -520.

Objective

8 *Use the Calculator Memory Function.* Many calculators feature **memory keys**, which are used to store intermediate steps in a calculation. On some calculators, a key labeled $\boxed{M}$

or $\boxed{\text{STO}}$ is used to store the numbers in the display, with $\boxed{\text{MR}}$ or $\boxed{\text{RCL}}$ used to recall the numbers from memory. Other calculators have $\boxed{\text{M+}}$ and $\boxed{\text{M−}}$ keys. The $\boxed{\text{M+}}$ key adds the number displayed to the number already in memory. For example, if the memory contains the number 0 at the beginning of a problem, and the calculator display contains the number 29.4, then pushing $\boxed{\text{M+}}$ will cause 29.4 to be stored in the memory (the result of adding 0 and 29.4). If 57.8 is then entered into the display, pushing $\boxed{\text{M+}}$ will cause

$$29.4 + 57.8 = 87.2$$

to be stored. If 11.9 is then entered into the display and $\boxed{\text{M−}}$ is pushed, the memory will contain the difference of 75.3.

$$87.2 - 11.9 = 75.3$$

The $\boxed{\text{MR}}$ key is used to recall the number in memory as needed, with $\boxed{\text{MC}}$ used to clear the memory.

Basic calculators typically have one or more storage registers in which to store numbers. These memory keys are usually labeled as $\boxed{\text{STO}}$ for store and $\boxed{\text{RCL}}$ for recall. For example, 32.5 can be stored in register 1 by

$$32.5 \boxed{\text{STO}} 1$$

or it can be stored in memory register 2 by 32.5 $\boxed{\text{STO}}$ 2, and so forth. Values are retrieved from a particular memory register by using the $\boxed{\text{RCL}}$ key followed by the number of the register. For example, $\boxed{\text{RCL}}$ 2 recalls the contents of memory register 2.

With a basic calculator, a number stays in memory until it is replaced by another number or until the memory is cleared. The contents of the memory are saved *even when the calculator is turned off.*

NOTE Always clear the memory before beginning work on a new problem. This is the only way to make sure there are no numbers remaining from the previous problem. Clear the memory by pressing 0 followed by $\boxed{\text{STO}}$ followed by the register number.

EXAMPLE **11** **Using the Memory Registers**

An elevator repairperson counted the number of people entering an elevator and also measured the weight of each group of people. Find the average weight per person.

Solution

First, find the weight of all three groups and store in memory register 1.

$$839 \boxed{+} 1184 \boxed{+} 640 \boxed{=} 2663 \boxed{\text{STO}} 1$$

Then find the total number of people and store in register 2.

$$6 \boxed{+} 8 \boxed{+} 4 \boxed{=} 18 \boxed{\text{STO}} 2$$

Finally, divide the contents of memory register 1 by the 18 people.

$$\boxed{\text{RCL}} 1 \boxed{÷} \boxed{\text{RCL}} 2 \boxed{=} 147.94444 \text{ pounds}$$

This value can be rounded as needed.

Number of People	Total Weight
6	839 pounds
8	1184 pounds
4	640 pounds

Objective

9   *Solve Chain Calculations Using Order of Operations.* Long calculations involving several operations (adding, subtracting, multiplying, and dividing) must be done in a specific sequence called the **order of operations** and are called **chain calculations**. The logic of the following order of operations is built into most calculators and can help us work problems without having to store a lot of intermediate values.

Solving Chain Calculations

STEP 1 Do all operations inside parentheses first.

STEP 2 Simplify any expressions with exponents (powers) and find any square roots.

STEP 3 Multiply and divide from left to right.

STEP 4 Add and subtract from left to right.

EXAMPLE 12   Using the Order of Operations

Solve the following.

(a) $3 + 7 \times 9\frac{3}{4}$ **(b)** $42.1 \times 5 - 90 \div 4$ **(c)** $6.75^2 \times 9 - 7$

Solution

The calculator automatically keeps track of the order of operations for us.

(a) The order of operations tells us to multiply before doing the addition in the problem.

$$3 \boxed{+} 7 \boxed{\times} 9 \boxed{a\%} 3 \boxed{a\%} 4 \boxed{=} 71\frac{1}{4}$$

(b) The order of operations tells us to multiply, then divide, and only then subtract.

$$42.1 \boxed{\times} 5 \boxed{-} 90 \boxed{\div} 4 \boxed{=} 188$$

(c) The order of operations tells us to square 6.75 first, then multiply, and finally subtract.

$$6.75 \boxed{y^x} 2 \boxed{\times} 9 \boxed{-} 7 \boxed{=} 403.0625$$

NOTE Basic calculators keep track of the order of operations for us. All we have to do is enter the problem correctly into the calculator and the calculator does the rest. However, the basic four-function calculator is not programmed to observe the order of operations and can be used only if you enter numbers in the proper order. If you do not get the answer above with your calculator, try using parentheses, as shown next.

Objective

10   *Use the Parentheses Keys.* The parentheses keys can be used to help establish the order of operations in a more complex chain calculation. For example, $\dfrac{4}{5 + 7}$ can be written as $\dfrac{4}{(5 + 7)}$, which can be solved as

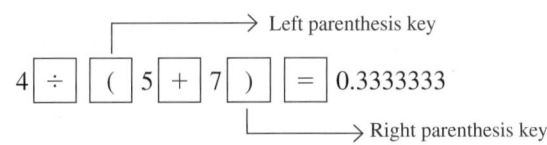

Left parenthesis key

$$4 \boxed{\div} \boxed{(} 5 \boxed{+} 7 \boxed{)} \boxed{=} 0.3333333$$

Right parenthesis key

EXAMPLE 13 Using Parentheses

Solve the following problem.

$$\frac{16 \div 2.5}{39.2 - 29.8 \times 0.6}$$

Solution

Think of this problem as follows.

$$\frac{(16 \div 2.5)}{(39.2 - 29.8 \times 0.6)}$$

Using parentheses to set off the numerator and denominator will help you minimize errors.

(16 ÷ 2.5) ÷ (39.2 − 29.8 × 0.6) = 0.3001876

Objective

11 *Use the Calculator for Problem Solution.*

EXAMPLE 14 Finding Sale Price

A necklace with an original price of $560 is on sale at 10% off. Find the sale price.

Solution

If the discount from the original price is 10%, then the sale price is 100% − 10% of the original price.

560 × (100 − 10) % = 504

On some calculators the following keystrokes will also work.

560 − 10 % = 504

EXAMPLE 15 Applying Calculator Use to Problem Solving

After a good-sized down payment, a home buyer borrows $86,400 at 10% for 30 years. The monthly payment on the loan is $8.78 per $1000 borrowed. Annual taxes are $2780, and fire insurance is $670 a year. Find the total monthly payment including taxes and insurance.

Solution

The monthly payment is the *sum* of the monthly payment on the loan plus monthly taxes plus monthly fire insurance costs. The monthly payment on the loan is the number of thousands in the loan (86.4) times the monthly payment per $1000 borrowed ($8.78).

→Monthly taxes

86400 ÷ 1000 × 8.78 + 2780 ÷ 12 + 670 ÷ 12 = $1046.09   Rounded

→Monthly fire insurance

The monthly payment is $1046.09.

A.1	**Exercises**

Solve the following problems on a calculator. Round each answer to the nearest hundredth.

1.
$$\begin{array}{r} 384.92 \\ 407.61 \\ 351.14 \\ + \ 27.93 \end{array}$$ 1771.60

2.
$$\begin{array}{r} 85.76 \\ 21.94 \\ + \ 39.89 \end{array}$$ 147.59

3.
$$\begin{array}{r} 6,850 \\ 321 \\ + \ 4,207 \end{array}$$ 11,378

4.
$$\begin{array}{r} 781.42 \\ 304.59 \\ + \ 261.35 \end{array}$$ 1347.36

5.
$$\begin{array}{r} 4270.41 \\ - \ 365.09 \end{array}$$ 3905.32

6.
$$\begin{array}{r} 3000.07 \\ - \ 48.12 \end{array}$$ 2951.95

7.
$$\begin{array}{r} 384.96 \\ - \times 129.72 \end{array}$$ 255.24

8. $36.84 - 12.17$ 24.67

9.
$$\begin{array}{r} 365 \\ \times \ 43 \end{array}$$ 15,695

10.
$$\begin{array}{r} 27.51 \\ \times \ 1.18 \end{array}$$ 32.46

11. 3.7×8.4 31.08

12. 62.5×81 5062.5

13. $\dfrac{375.4}{10.6}$ 35.42

14. $\dfrac{9625}{400}$ 24.06

15. $96.7 \div 3.5$ 27.63

16. $103.7 \div 0.35$ 296.29

Solve the following chain calculations. Round each answer to the nearest hundredth.

17. $\dfrac{9 \times 9}{2 \times 5}$ 8.1

18. $\dfrac{15 \times 8 \times 3}{11 \times 7 \times 4}$ 1.17

19. $\dfrac{87 \times 24 \times 47.2}{13.6 \times 12.8}$ 566.14

20. $\dfrac{2 \times (3 + 4)}{6 + 10}$ 0.88

21. $\dfrac{2 \times 3 + 4}{6 + 10}$ 0.63

22. $\dfrac{4200 \times 0.12 \times 90}{365}$ 124.27

23. $\dfrac{640 - 0.6 \times 12}{17.5 + 3.2}$ 30.57

24. $\dfrac{16 \times 18 - 0.4 \div 2}{95.4 \times 3 - 0.8}$ 1.01

25. $\dfrac{14^2 - 3.6 \times 6}{95.2 \div 0.5}$ 0.92

26. $\dfrac{9^2 + 3.8 \div 2}{14 + 7.5}$ 3.86

27. e^2 7.39

28. $9^2 \cdot e^{2.5}$ 986.78

29. $175 \div e^1$ 64.38

30. $15e^{1.2}$ 49.80

Solve the following problems. Reduce any fractions to lowest terms or round to the nearest hundredth.

31. $7\dfrac{5}{8} \div \left(1 + \dfrac{3}{8}\right)$ $5\frac{6}{11}$

32. $\left(5\frac{1}{4}\right)^2 \times 3.65$ 100.60

33. $\left(\dfrac{3}{4} \div \dfrac{5}{8}\right)^3 \div 3\dfrac{1}{2}$ 0.49

34. $\sqrt{6} \times \dfrac{3^2 + 2\frac{1}{2}}{7 \times \frac{5}{6}}$ 4.83

35. Describe in your own words the order of operations to be used when solving chain calculations. (See Objective 9.)

36. Explain how the parentheses keys are used when solving chain calculations. (See Objective 9.)

Solve the following application problems on a calculator. Round each answer to the nearest cent.

37. A sporting goods store bought 15 pairs of skis at an average cost of $187 per pair, 30 parkas at an average cost of $128 each, and 10 mountain bikes at an average cost of $163 each. Find the total cost. $8275

38. Ben Thompson fishes for halibut off the coast of Alaska. His daily catches over the past few days were 263.5 pounds, 122.7 pounds, 82.4 pounds, and 90.8 pounds. Find the average catch per day by adding the values and dividing the sum by 4.   139.85 pounds

39. Jessica Rodriguez owns a company that installs sprinkler systems. She has three crews made up of 3, 3, and 4 individuals, respectively. One of the workers in each crew is a crew chief who is paid $15.75 per hour. The others in each crew are paid $8.40 per hour. Find payroll for a week in which the first two crews worked 32 hours each and the third crew worked 40 hours. $3721.20

40. Ben James is a college professor whose travel expenses to a conference are paid. His round-trip flight to Phoenix was $295, a shuttle to the conference in Sedona, Arizona, was $65, the conference fee was $320, and he spent 2 nights at a hotel for $154.13 per night. Find the total cost. $988.26

41. In Virginia City, the sales tax is 6.5%. Find the tax on each of the following items: (a) a new car costing $17,908.43 and (b) an office word processor costing $1463.58. (a) $1164.05 (b) $95.13

42. Marja Strutz bought a used commercial fishing boat equipped for sardine fishing at a cost of $78,250. Additional safety equipment was needed at a cost of $4820, and sales tax of $7\frac{1}{4}\%$ was due on the boat and safety equipment. In addition she was charged a licensing fee of $1135 and a Coast Guard registration fee of $428. Strutz will pay $\frac{1}{3}$ of the total cost as a down payment and will borrow the balance. How much will she borrow? $60,437.05

43. Elizabeth Daigle purchased a home for $154,000. She paid $16,000 down and agreed to 30 years with payments of $1036.75 per month. Find the difference between the down payment plus all payments and the price of the home. $235,230

44. Linda Smelt purchased a 22-unit apartment house for $620,000. She made a down payment of $150,000, which she had inherited from her parents, and agreed to make monthly payments of $5050 for 15 years. By how much does the sum of her down payment and all monthly payments exceed the original purchase price? $439,000

45. Ben Hurd wishes to open a small repair shop but has only $32,400 in cash. He estimates that he will need $15,000 for equipment, $2800 for the first month's rent on a building, and about $28,000 operating expenses until the business is profitable. How much additional funding does he need? $13,400

46. Koplan Kitchens wishes to expand its retail store. In order to do so, it must first purchase the $26,000 vacant lot next door. The company then anticipates $120,000 in construction costs plus an additional $28,500 for additional inventory. It has $50,000 in cash and must borrow the balance from a bank. How much must the company borrow? $124,500

A.2	**Financial Calculators**

OBJECTIVES

1 *Learn the basic conventions used with cash flows.*

2 *Learn the basic financial calculator keys.*

3 *Understand which keys to use for a particular problem.*

4 *Use the financial calculator to solve financial problems.*

Financial calculators have added features that allow you to make certain compound interest calculations quickly and accurately. These calculators are commonly used by people in business. Financial calculators differ greatly from one another. *Be sure to use the booklet that came with your financial calculator* for specific information about your calculator.

1 *Learn the Basic Conventions Used with Cash Flows.* Many financial calculators are based on logic that separates cash received by an individual or a company from cash paid out by the same individual or company using + and − signs. *Cash received is given a + sign, and cash paid out is given a − sign.*

Inflows of cash to a person or firm are ***positive***. Outflows of cash from the same person or firm are ***negative***. For example, suppose you put $100 per month into an investment for 10 years and then take out the balance of $23,000 at the end of 10 years. The $100 payment each month *is shown as a negative number*, since cash is leaving you. But the $23,000 received in 10 years *is shown as a positive number*, since cash flows to you at that time. We will use this convention throughout this text even though some financial calculators differ.

2 *Learn the Basic Financial Calculator Keys.* Financial calculators have special functions that allow the user to solve financial problems involving time, interest rates, and money. Many of the compound interest problems presented in this text can be solved using a financial calculator rather than using tables as shown in the text. Most financial calculators have financial keys similar to those shown below.

These keys represent the following functions:

n	The number of compounding periods
i	The interest rate *per compounding period*
PV	**Present value:** the value in *today's* dollars
PMT	The amount of a **level payment** (e.g., $625 per month); this is used for annuity-type problems.
FV	**Future value:** the value at *some future date*

> **NOTE** Different financial calculators look and work somewhat differently from one another. *Look at the instruction booklet* that came with your calculator to determine how the keys are used with your particular calculator.

You will also find that different financial calculators will sometimes give slightly different answers to the same problems because of rounding.

3 *Understand Which Keys to Use for a Particular Problem.* Most simple financial problems require only four of the five financial keys described above. Both the number of compounding periods n and the interest rate per compounding period i are needed for each financial problem—these two keys will always be used. Which two of the remaining three financial keys (PV , PMT , and FV) are used depends on the particular problem. Using the convention described above, one of these monetary values will be negative and one will be positive. *The process of solving a financial problem is to enter values for the three variables that are known, then press the key for the unknown, fourth variable.*

For example, if you wish to know the future value of a series of known, equal payments, enter the specific values for $\boxed{n}$, $\boxed{i}$, and $\boxed{\text{PMT}}$. Then press $\boxed{\text{FV}}$ for the result. Or, if you wish to know how long it will take for an investment to grow to some specific value at a given interest rate, enter values for $\boxed{\text{PV}}$, $\boxed{i}$, and $\boxed{\text{FV}}$. Then press $\boxed{n}$ to find the required number of compounding periods.

> **NOTE** Be sure to enter a cash inflow as a positive number and a cash outflow as a negative number. Also be sure to clear all values from the memory of your calculator before working a problem.

Objective

4 *Use the Financial Calculator to Solve Financial Problems.*

EXAMPLE **1** **Given *n*, *i*, and PV, Find FV**

Mr. Willis invests $1000 in a fund containing bonds that pays 8% compounded quarterly. Find the future value in $1\frac{1}{2}$ years.

Solution

The present value of $1000 (a cash outflow entered as a negative number) is compounded at 2% per quarter (8% ÷ 4 = 2%) for 6 quarters ($1\frac{1}{2} \times 4 = 6$). Enter values for $\boxed{\text{PV}}$, $\boxed{i}$, and $\boxed{n}$.

$$-1000 \;\boxed{\text{PV}}\; 2 \;\boxed{i}\; 6 \;\boxed{n}$$

Then press $\boxed{\text{FV}}$ to find the compound amount at the end of 6 quarters.

$$\boxed{\text{FV}} \; 1126.16$$

which is the future value.

EXAMPLE **2** **Given *n*, *i*, and PMT, Find FV**

Joan Jones plans to invest $100 at the end of each month in a mutual fund that she believes will grow at 9% per year compounded monthly. Find the future value in 20 years.

Solution

She makes 240 payments (12 × 20 = 240) of $100 each (cash outflows entered as a negative number) into an account earning 0.75% per month (9% ÷ 12 = 0.75%).

Enter values for $\boxed{n}$, $\boxed{\text{PMT}}$, and $\boxed{i}$.

$$240 \;\boxed{n}\; -100 \;\boxed{\text{PMT}}\; 0.75 \;\boxed{i}$$

Press $\boxed{\text{FV}}$ to find the future value.

$$\boxed{\text{FV}} \; 66{,}788.69$$

the future value is $66,788.69.

> **NOTE**   The order in which data are entered into the calculator does not matter. Just remember to *press the financial key for the unknown value last.*

Any one of the four values used to solve a particular financial problem can be unknown. Look at the next three examples in which the number of compounding periods $\boxed{n}$, the payment amount $\boxed{\text{PMT}}$, and the interest rate per compounding period $\boxed{i}$, respectively, are unknown.

EXAMPLE **3**   **Given *i*, PMT, and FV, Find *n***

Mr. Trebor needs $140,000 for a new farm tractor. He can invest $8000 at the end of each month in an account paying 6% per year compounded monthly. How many monthly payments are needed?

Solution

The $8000 monthly payment (cash outflow) will grow at 0.5% per compounding period (6% ÷ 12 = 0.5%) until a future value of $140,000 (cash inflow at a future date) is accumulated. Enter values for $\boxed{\text{PMT}}$, $\boxed{i}$, and $\boxed{\text{FV}}$.

$$-8000 \boxed{\text{PMT}} \; 0.5 \boxed{i} \; 140000 \boxed{\text{FV}}$$

Press $\boxed{n}$ to determine the number of payments.

$$\boxed{n} \; 17 \text{ monthly payments of \$8000 each}$$

Actually, 17 payments of $8000 each in an account earning 0.5% per month will grow to slightly more than $140,000:

$$-8000 \boxed{\text{PMT}} \; 0.5 \boxed{i} \; 17 \boxed{n}$$

Press $\boxed{\text{FV}}$ to determine the future value.

$$\boxed{\text{FV}} \; 141578.41$$

which is the future value.

The 17th payment would need to be only

$$\$8000 - (\$141{,}578.41 - \$140{,}000) = \$6421.59$$

in order to accumulate exactly $140,000.

EXAMPLE **4**   **Given *n*, *i*, and FV, Find PMT**

Jane Abel wishes to have $1,000,000 at her retirement in 40 years. Find the payment she must make at the end of each quarter into an account earning 8% compounded quarterly to attain her goal.

Solution

Abel makes 160 payments ($40 \times 4 = 160$) into an account earning 2% per quarter ($8\% \div 4 = 2\%$) until a future value of $1,000,000 (cash inflow at a future date) is accumulated. Enter values for $\boxed{n}$, $\boxed{i}$, and $\boxed{\text{FV}}$.

$$160\,\boxed{n}\,2\,\boxed{i}\,1000000\,\boxed{\text{FV}}$$

Press $\boxed{\text{PMT}}$ for the quarterly payment:

$$\boxed{\text{PMT}}\;-878.35$$

which is the required quarterly payment of cash. Hence, 160 payments of $878.35 at the end of each quarter in an account earning 8% compounded quarterly will grow to $1,000,000.

EXAMPLE ▉5▉   Given *n*, PV, and FV, Find *i*

Tom Fernandez bought 200 shares of stock in an oil company at $33.50 per share. Exactly 3 years later he sold the stock at $41.25 per share. Find the annual interest rate, rounded to the nearest tenth of a percent, that Fernandez earned on this investment, assuming the company paid no dividends.

Solution

In 3 years, the per share price increased from a present value of $33.50 to a future value of $41.25. The purchase of the stock is a cash outflow and the eventual sale of the stock is a cash inflow. It is not necessary to multiply the stock price by the number of shares. The interest rate indicating the return on the investment is the same whether 1 share or 200 shares are used. Enter values for $\boxed{n}$, $\boxed{\text{PV}}$, and $\boxed{\text{FV}}$.

$$3\,\boxed{n}\,-33.50\,\boxed{\text{PV}}\,41.25\,\boxed{\text{FV}}$$

Press $\boxed{i}$ for the annual interest rate:

$$\boxed{i}\;7.18\%$$

or about 7.2% per year. Fernandez's return on his original investment compounded at 7.2% per year.

Interest rates can have a great influence on both individuals and businesses. Individuals borrow for homes, cars, and other personal items, whereas firms borrow to buy real estate, expand operations, or cover operating expenses. A small difference in interest rates can make a large difference in costs over time, as shown in the next example.

EXAMPLE ▉6▉   Compare Monthly House Payments

Layne and Leticia Hare wish to refinance the remaining $62,000 debt on their home for 30 years. Find the monthly payment at interest rates of (a) 5% and (b) 7%. Show (c) the monthly savings at the lower rate and (d) the total savings in monthly payments over the 30 years.

Solution

(a) Enter a present value of $62,000 (cash inflow) with 360 compounding periods ($30 \times 12 = 360$) and a rate of 0.4166667% per month ($5\% \div 12 = 0.4166667$, rounded) and press $\boxed{\text{PMT}}$ to find the monthly payment.

$$62000 \; \boxed{\text{PV}} \; 360 \; \boxed{n} \; 0.4166667 \; \boxed{i}$$

$\boxed{\text{PMT}}$ -331.45 is the monthly payment at 5% per year, rounded to the nearest cent.

(b) Enter the values again using the new interest rate of 0.5833333% ($7\% \div 12 = 0.5833333\%$).

$$62000 \; \boxed{\text{PV}} \; 360 \; \boxed{n} \; 0.5833333 \; \boxed{i}$$

$\boxed{\text{PMT}}$ -410.10 is the monthly payment at 7% per year, again, rounded to the nearest cent.

(c) The difference in the monthly payments is

$$\$410.10 - \$331.45 = \$78.65$$

(d) The total difference saved over 30 years ($30 \times 12 = 360$ payments) is

$$\$78.65 \times 360 \text{ payments} = \$28{,}314$$

The lower interest rate will result in a savings of $28,314 over 30 years.

EXAMPLE **7** **Retirement Planning**

Courtney and Nathan Wright plan to retire in 25 years and feel that they will need $3500 per month beyond what Social Security will pay. They plan on needing the additional income for 20 years.

(a) Find the amount needed at retirement to fund the monthly retirement payments, assuming the annuity earns 9% compounded monthly while payments are being made.
(b) Find the amount of the quarterly payment they must make for the next 25 years to accumulate the necessary funds, assuming earnings of 6% compounded quarterly during the accumulation period.

Solution

(a) The accumulated funds at the end of 25 years is, at their retirement, a present value that must generate a cash inflow to the Wrights of $3500 per month for 240 months ($20 \times 12 = 240$), assuming earnings of 0.75% per month ($9\% \div 12 = 0.75\%$).
Enter values for $\boxed{n}$, $\boxed{i}$, and $\boxed{\text{PMT}}$.

$$240 \; \boxed{n} \; 0.75 \; \boxed{i} \; 3500 \; \boxed{\text{PMT}}$$

Press $\boxed{\text{PV}}$ to find the amount needed at the end of 25 years.

$$\boxed{\text{PV}} \; -389007.34$$

is the amount they must accumulate.

(b) The Wrights have 25 years of quarterly payments (100 payments that are cash out-flows) in an account earning 1.5% per quarter (6% ÷ 4 = 1.5%) to accumulate a future value of $389,007.34. The question is one of what quarterly payment is required.

Enter values for $\boxed{n}$, $\boxed{i}$, and $\boxed{FV}$.

$$100 \; \boxed{n} \; 1.5 \; \boxed{i} \; 389007.34 \; \boxed{FV}$$

Press $\boxed{PMT}$ to find the quarterly payment needed:

$$\boxed{PMT} \; {-}1700.18$$

is the required quarterly payment.

Thus, the Wrights must make 100 end-of-quarter deposits of $1700.18 each into an account earning 1.5% per quarter. They will then receive 20 years of payments of $3500 per month, assuming 9% per year during the time that payments are made.

A.2	**Exercises**

Solve the following problems for the missing quantity using a financial calculator. Round dollar answers to the nearest hundredth, interest rates to the nearest hundredth of a percent, and number of compounding periods to the nearest whole number. Assume that any payments are made at the end of the period.

	n	i	PV	PMT	FV
1.	10	8%	$3500	—	$7556.24
2.	8	1.5%	$6400	—	$7209.55
3.	10	3%	$8929.13	—	$12,000
4.	16	4%	$4378.05	—	$8200
5.	7	8%	—	$300	$2676.84
6.	25	2%	—	$1000	$32,030.30
7.	30	1.5%	—	$319.67	$12,000
8.	50	0.75%	—	$4718.99	$285,000
9.	360	1%	$83,500	$858.89	—
10.	180	0.5%	$125,000	$1054.82	—
11.	24	4%	$85,383	$5600	—
12.	73	2%	$3822	$100	—

Solve the following application problems. Round to the nearest cent.

13. Tremaine Walker received $2000 as a Christmas bonus. He placed the funds in a 4-year certificate of deposit earning 6% compounded quarterly. Find the future value. $2537.97

14. Junella Ruiz decides to begin saving at a young age. She has $60 per month taken out of her paycheck and automatically deposited in an account containing technology stocks that she hopes will grow at 1% per month. Find the future value in 15, 30, and 45 years. $29,974.81; $209,697.85; $1,287,281.58

15. After making a down payment, Mr. and Mrs. Thrash borrowed $128,400 on a 30-year home loan at 6% per year. Find the monthly payment. $765.99

16. Terrance Walker wishes to have $20,000 in 10 years when his son begins college. What payment must he make at the end of each quarter in an investment earning 6% compounded quarterly? $368.54

17. The *Daily Gazette* needs $340,000 for new printing presses. It can invest $12,000 per month in bonds paying 0.6% per month. Find the number of payments that must be paid before reaching the goal. Round to the nearest whole number.   27

18. Mr. and Mrs. Peters wish to build their dream home and must borrow $248,500 on a 30-year mortgage to do so. Find the highest acceptable annual interest rate, to the nearest tenth of a percent, if they cannot afford a monthly payment above $1825.   8%

19. A farmer purchases a farm costing $345,000, with 25% down and quarterly payments at 8% per year for 10 years. Find the payment. $9458.80

20. A technical school purchases 25 classroom computers with projection systems at a cost of $2300 each. It pays 20% down and finances the balance at 0.8% per month for 3 years. Find the monthly payment. $1475.67

APPENDIX TERMS

Review the following terms to test your understanding of the appendix. For any terms you do not know, refer to the page number found next to the term.

algebraic logic [p. 766]	deficit amount [p. 770]	future value [p. 776]	negative number [p. 770]
base [p. 768]	exponent [p. 768]	graphing calculator [p. 765]	order of operations [p. 772]
calculator [p. 765]	financial calculator [p. 765]	level payment [p. 776]	present value [p. 776]
chain calculations [p. 772]	floating decimal [p. 767]	memory keys [p. 770]	square root [p. 769]

javier brosch / Fotolia.com

The Metric System

Today, the **metric system** is used just about everywhere in the world. In the United States, many industries are switching over to this improved system. The metric system is being taught in elementary schools, and it may eventually replace the current system.

A table on the English system is included here to refresh your memory. Notice that the time relationships are the same in the English and metric systems.

Length	Weight
1 foot (ft) = 12 inches (in.)	1 pound (lb) = 16 ounces (oz)
1 yard (yd) = 3 feet (ft)	1 ton (T) = 2000 pounds (lb)
1 mile (mi) = 5280 feet (ft)	

Capacity	Time
1 cup (c) = 8 fluid ounces	1 week (wk) = 7 days
1 pint (pt) = 2 cup (c)	1 day = 24 hours (h)
1 quart (qt) = 2 pints (pt)	1 hour (hr) = 60 minutes (min)
1 gallon (gal) = 4 quarts (qt)	1 minute (min) = 60 seconds (s)

OBJECTIVES

1 *Learn the metric system.*

2 *Learn how to convert from one system to the other.*

Objective

1   *Learn the Metric System.* The basic unit of length in the metric system is the **meter**. A meter is a little longer than a yard. For shorter lengths, the units **centimeter** and **millimeter** are used. The prefix "centi" means hundredth, so 1 centimeter is one-hundredth of a meter. Thus

$$100 \text{ centimeters} = 1 \text{ meter}$$

The prefix "milli" means thousandth, so 1 millimeter means one-thousandth of a meter. Thus

$$1000 \text{ millimeters} = 1 \text{ meter}$$

Meter is abbreviated m, centimeter is cm, and millimeter is mm.

Convert from centimeters to millimeters to meters by moving the decimal point, as shown in the following example.

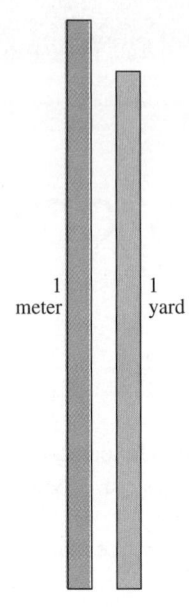

1 meter | 1 yard

1 yard is 36 inches
1 meter is about 39.37 inches

Recall the basic metric units for length, volume, weight, and temperature

Prefixes in the Metric System
deca = 10 times
kilo = 1000 times
deci = $\frac{1}{10}$ times
centi = $\frac{1}{100}$ times
milli = $\frac{1}{1000}$ times

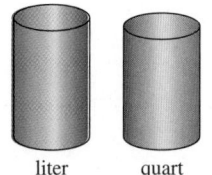

liter   quart

A liter equals about 1.06 quarts

kilogram   pound

A kilogram equals about 2.2 pounds.

EXAMPLE 1 **Converting Length Measurements**

(a) 6.4 m to cm   (b) 0.98 m to mm   (c) 34 cm to m

Solution

(a) A centimeter is a small unit of measure (a centimeter is about $\frac{1}{2}$ of the diameter of a penny) and a meter is a large unit (a little over 3 feet), so many centimeters make a meter. *Multiply* by 100 to convert meters to centimeters.

$$6.4 \text{ m} = 6.4 \times 100 = 640 \text{ cm}$$

(b) Multiply by 1000 to convert meters to millimeters.

$$0.98 \text{ m} = 0.98 \times 1000 = 980 \text{ mm}$$

(c) A meter is a large unit of measure, and a centimeter is a smaller unit, so 34 cm is less than a meter. Thus, *divide* by 100 to convert centimeters to meters.

$$34 \text{ cm} = \frac{34}{100} = 0.34 \text{ m}$$

Long distances are measured in **kilometer** (km) units. The prefix "kilo" means one thousand. Thus,

$$1 \text{ kilometer} = 1000 \text{ meters}$$

Since a meter is about a yard, 1000 meters is about 1000 yards, or 3000 feet. Therefore, 1 kilometer is about 3000 feet. One mile is 5280 feet, so 1 kilometer is about 3000/5280 of a mile. Divide 3000 by 5280 to find that 1 kilometer is about 0.6 miles.

The basic unit of volume in the metric system is the **liter** (L), which is a little more than a quart. You may have noticed that Coca-Cola is often sold in 2-liter plastic bottles. Again the prefixes "milli" and "centi" are used. Thus,

$$1 \text{ liter} = 100 \text{ centiliters}$$
$$1 \text{ liter} = 1000 \text{ milliliters}$$

Milliliter (mL) and **centiliter** (cL) are such small volumes that they find their main uses in science. In particular, drug dosages are often expressed in milliliters.

Weight is measured in **grams** (g). A nickel weighs about 5 grams. **Milligrams** (mg; one-thousandth of a gram) and **centigrams** (cg; one-hundredth of a gram) are so small that they are used mainly in science. A more common measure is the **kilogram** (kg), which is 1000 grams. A kilogram weighs about 2.2 pounds.

$$1000 \text{ grams} = 1 \text{ kilogram}$$

EXAMPLE 2 **Converting Weight and Volume Measurements**

(a) 650 g to kg   (b) 9.4 L to cL   (c) 4350 mg to g

Solution

(a) A gram is a small unit, and a kilogram is a large unit. Thus, *divide* by 1000 to convert grams to kilograms.

$$650 \text{ g} = \frac{650}{1000} = 0.65 \text{ kg}$$

(b) *Multiply* by 100 to convert liters to centiliters.

$$9.4 \text{ L} = 9.4 \times 100 = 940 \text{ cL}$$

(c) *Divide* by 1000 to convert milligrams to grams.

$$4350 \text{ mg} = \frac{4350}{1000} = 4.35 \text{ g}$$

Objective

2   *Learn How to Convert from One System to the Other.* Eventually, everyone may think in the metric system as easily as in the **English system** of feet, quarts, pounds, and so on. However, during the period of changeover from the English system to the metric system, most people will find it necessary to convert from one system to the other. Approximate conversion can be made with the aid of Table B.1.

Table B.1 ENGLISH–METRIC CONVERSION TABLE (approximate)

From Metric	To English	Multiply By	From English	To Metric	Multiply By
Meters	Yards	1.09	Yards	Meters	0.914
Meters	Feet	3.28	Feet	Meters	0.305
Meters	Inches	39.37	Inches	Meters	0.0254
Kilometers	Miles	0.62	Miles	Kilometers	1.609
Grams	Pounds	0.00220	Pounds	Grams	454
Kilograms	Pounds	2.20	Pounds	Kilograms	0.454
Liters	Quarts	1.06	Quarts	Liters	0.946
Liters	Gallons	0.264	Gallons	Liters	3.785

EXAMPLE 3   Convert the Following Measurements

(a) 15 meters to yards   **(b)** 39 yards to meters   **(c)** 47 meters to inches
(d) 87 kilometers to miles   **(e)** 598 miles to kilometers   **(f)** 12 quarts to liters

Solution

(a) Look at Table B.1 for the meters-to-yards conversion, and find the number 1.09. Multiply 15 meters by 1.09.

$$15 \times 1.09 = 16.35 \text{ yards}$$

(b) Read the yards-to-meters row of Table B.1. The number 0.914 appears. Multiply 39 yards by 0.914.

$$39 \times 0.914 = 35.646 \text{ meters}$$

(c) 47 meters $= 47 \times 39.37 = 1850.39$ inches

(d) 87 kilometers $= 87 \times 0.62 = 53.94$ miles

(e) 598 miles $= 598 \times 1.609 = 962.182$ kilometers

(f) 12 quarts $= 12 \times 0.946 = 11.352$ liters

EXAMPLE **4** Solving a Proportion

At a depth of 16.5 feet under the water, a diver experiences additional pressure of 0.5 atmosphere. Estimate the additional pressure in atmospheres experienced by a submersible that is 400 feet under the water.

Solution

Set up a proportion with 16.5 feet to 0.5 atmosphere (atm) equal to 400 feet to an unknown number of atmospheres, which we represent with the variable x. Then solve the equation.

$$\frac{16.5 \text{ feet}}{0.5 \text{ atm}} = \frac{400 \text{ feet}}{x}$$

$$16.5 \times x = 400 \times 0.5 \quad \text{Cross multiply.}$$

$$x = \frac{400 \times 0.5}{16.5} \quad \text{Divide both sides by 16.5.}$$

$$x = 12.1 \text{ atmospheres of additional pressure} \quad \text{Rounded}$$

°F °C

Temperature in the metric system is measured in degrees **Celsius** (abbreviated C). Using the Fahrenheit system, water freezes at 32°F and boils at 212°F. In the Celsius scale, water freezes at 0°C and boils at 100°C. This is more sensible than degrees **Fahrenheit** (abbreviated F) in use now, in which a mixture of salt and water freezes at 0°F, and 100°F represents the temperature inside Gabriel Fahrenheit's mouth.

Converting from Fahrenheit to Celsius

Step 1	Subtract 32 from the degrees Fahrenheit.
Step 2	Multiply by 5.
Step 3	Divide by 9.

These steps can be expressed by the following formula.

$$C = \frac{5(F - 32)}{9}$$

EXAMPLE **5** Convert 68° Fahrenheit to Celsius

Solution

Use the steps above.

Step 1 Subtract 32. $68 - 32 = 36$

Step 2 Multiply by 5. $36 \times 5 = 180$

Step 3 Divide by 9. $\frac{180}{9} = 20$

Thus, 68°F = 20°C.

Converting from Celsius to Fahrenheit

Step 1	Multiply degrees Celsius by 9.
Step 2	Divide by 5.
Step 3	Add 32.

These steps can be expressed by the following formula.

$$F = \frac{9 \times C}{5} + 32$$

EXAMPLE **6** **Convert 11° Celsius to Fahrenheit**

Solution

Use the steps above.

Step 1 Multiply by 9. $9 \times 11 = 99$
Step 2 Divide by 5. $99 \div 5 = 19.8$
Step 3 Add 32. $19.8 + 32 = 51.8°F$

Thus, $11°C = 51.8°F$.

B.1   **Exercises**

Convert the following measurements.

1. 68 cm to m   0.68 m
2. 934 mm to m   0.934 m
3. 4.7 m to mm   4700 mm
4. 7.43 m to cm   743 cm
5. 8.9 kg to g   8900 g
6. 4.32 kg to g   4320 g
7. 39 cL to L   0.39 L
8. 469 cL to L   4.69 L
9. 46,000 g to kg   46 kg
10. 35,800 g to kg   35.8 kg
11. 0.976 kg to g   976 g
12. 0.137 kg to g   137 g

Convert the following measurements. Round to the nearest hundredth.

13. 36 m to yards   39.24 yards
14. 76.2 m to yards   83.06 yards
15. 55 yards to m   50.27 m
16. 89.3 yards to m   81.62 m
17. 4.7 m to feet   15.42 feet
18. 1.92 m to feet   6.30 feet
19. 3.6 feet to m   1.10 m
20. 12.8 feet to m   3.90 m
21. 496 km to miles   307.52 miles
22. 138 km to miles   85.56 miles
23. 768 miles to km   1235.71 km
24. 1042 miles to km   1676.58 km
25. 683 g to pounds   1.50 pounds
26. 1792 g to pounds   3.94 pounds
27. 4.1 pounds to g   1861.4 g
28. 12.9 pounds to g   5856.60 g
29. 38.9 kg to pounds   85.58 pounds
30. 40.3 kg to pounds   88.66 pounds

Work the following application problems. Round to the nearest hundredth.

31. One nickel weighs 5 grams. How many nickels are in 1 kilogram of nickels?   200
32. Seawater contains about 3.5 grams of salt per 1000 milliliters of water. How many grams of salt would 5 liters of seawater contain?   17.5 g
33. Helium weighs about 0.0002 grams per milliliter. A balloon contains 3 liters of helium. How much would the helium weigh?   0.6 g
34. About 1500 grams of sugar can be dissolved in a liter of warm water. How much sugar could be dissolved in 1 milliliter of warm water?   1.5 g
35. Find your height in centimeters.   Answers will vary.
36. Find your height in meters.   Answers will vary.

Convert the following Fahrenheit temperatures to Celsius. Round to the nearest degree.

37. 104°F   40°C   **38.** 86°F   30°C   **39.** 536°F   280°C

40. 464°F   240°C   **41.** 98°F   37°C   **42.** 114°F   46°C

Convert the following Celsius temperatures to Fahrenheit. Round to the nearest degree.

43. 35°C   95°F   **44.** 100°C   212°F   **45.** 10°C   50°F

46. 25°C   77°F   **47.** 135°C   275°F   **48.** 215°C   419°F

In most cases today, medical measurements are given in the metric system. In the following problems, a doctor's prescription is given. Some of these are for reasonable amounts of medicine, and some are not. Decide which you think must not be correct.

49. 1940 grams of Kaopectate after each meal   Unreasonable

50. 76.8 centiliters of cough syrup every 2 hours   Unreasonable

51. 94.3 milliliters of antibiotic every 6 hours   Reasonable

52. 1.4 kilograms of vitamins every 3 hours   Unreasonable

53. Apply a bandage 5 centimeters square as needed   Reasonable

54. Soak your feet in 3 milligrams of Epsom salts per 4 liters of water   Unreasonable

APPENDIX TERMS

Review the following terms to test your understanding of the appendix. For any terms you do not know, refer to the page number found next to the term.

Celsius (C) [p. 786]	English system [p. 785]	kilometer [p. 784]	milligram [p. 784]
centiliter [p. 784]	Fahrenheit (F) [p. 786]	liter [p. 784]	milliliter [p. 784]
centimeter [p. 783]	gram [p. 784]	meter [p. 783]	millimeter [p. 783]
centigram [p. 784]	kilogram [p. 784]	metric system [p. 783]	

javier brosch / Fotolia.com

Interest Tables

Rate $\frac{1}{3}$%	A Compound Interest	B Present Value	C Amount of Annuity	D Present Value of Annuity	E Sinking Fund	F Amortization
n	$(1 + i)^n$	$\dfrac{1}{(1 + i)^n}$	$s_{\overline{n}\rceil i}$	$a_{\overline{n}\rceil i}$	$\dfrac{1}{s_{\overline{n}\rceil i}}$	$\dfrac{1}{a_{\overline{n}\rceil i}}$
1	1.00333333	0.99667774	1.00000000	0.99667774	1.00000000	1.00333333
2	1.00667778	0.99336652	2.00333333	1.99004426	0.49916805	0.50250139
3	1.01003337	0.99006630	3.01001111	2.98011056	0.33222469	0.33555802
4	1.01340015	0.98677704	4.02004448	3.96688760	0.24875347	0.25208680
5	1.01677815	0.98349871	5.03344463	4.95038631	0.19867110	0.20200444
6	1.02016741	0.98023127	6.05022278	5.93061759	0.16528317	0.16861650
7	1.02356797	0.97697469	7.07039019	6.90759228	0.14143491	0.14476824
8	1.02697986	0.97372893	8.09395816	7.88132121	0.12354895	0.12688228
9	1.03040313	0.97049395	9.12093802	8.85181516	0.10963785	0.11297118
10	1.03383780	0.96726972	10.15134114	9.81908487	0.09850915	0.10184248
11	1.03728393	0.96405620	11.18517895	10.78314107	0.08940402	0.09273736
12	1.04074154	0.96085335	12.22246288	11.74399442	0.08181657	0.08514990
13	1.04421068	0.95766115	13.26320442	12.70165557	0.07539656	0.07872989
14	1.04769138	0.95447955	14.30741510	13.65613512	0.06989383	0.07322716
15	1.05118369	0.95130852	15.35510648	14.60744364	0.06512491	0.06845825
16	1.05468763	0.94814803	16.40629017	15.55559167	0.06095223	0.06428557
17	1.05820326	0.94499803	17.46097781	16.50058970	0.05727056	0.06060389
18	1.06173060	0.94185851	18.51918107	17.44244821	0.05399807	0.05733140
19	1.06526971	0.93872941	19.58091167	18.38117762	0.05107015	0.05440348
20	1.06882060	0.93561071	20.64618137	19.31678832	0.04843511	0.05176844
21	1.07238334	0.93250236	21.71500198	20.24929069	0.04605111	0.04938445
22	1.07595795	0.92940435	22.78738532	21.17869504	0.04388393	0.04721726
23	1.07954448	0.92631663	23.86334327	22.10501167	0.04190528	0.04523861
24	1.08314296	0.92323916	24.94288775	23.02825083	0.04009159	0.04342492
25	1.08675344	0.92017192	26.02603071	23.94842275	0.03842307	0.04175640
26	1.09037595	0.91711487	27.11278414	24.86553763	0.03688297	0.04021630
27	1.09401053	0.91406798	28.20316009	25.77960561	0.03545702	0.03879035
28	1.09765724	0.91103121	29.29717062	26.69063682	0.03413299	0.03746632
29	1.10131609	0.90800453	30.39482786	27.59864135	0.03290033	0.03623367
30	1.10498715	0.90498790	31.49614395	28.50362925	0.03174992	0.03508325
31	1.10867044	0.90198130	32.60113110	29.40561055	0.03067378	0.03400712
32	1.11236601	0.89898468	33.70980154	30.30459523	0.02966496	0.03299830
33	1.11607389	0.89599802	34.82216754	31.20059325	0.02871734	0.03205067
34	1.11979414	0.89302128	35.93824143	32.09361454	0.02782551	0.03115885
35	1.12352679	0.89005444	37.05803557	32.98366898	0.02698470	0.03031803
36	1.12727187	0.88709745	38.18156236	33.87076642	0.02619065	0.02952399
37	1.13102945	0.88415028	39.30883423	34.75491670	0.02543957	0.02877291
38	1.13479955	0.88121290	40.43986368	35.63612960	0.02472808	0.02806141
39	1.13858221	0.87828528	41.57466322	36.51441488	0.02405311	0.02738644
40	1.14237748	0.87536739	42.71324543	37.38978228	0.02341194	0.02674527
41	1.14618541	0.87245920	43.85562292	38.26224147	0.02280209	0.02613543
42	1.15000603	0.86956066	45.00180833	39.13180213	0.02222133	0.02555466
43	1.15383938	0.86667175	46.15181436	39.99847389	0.02166762	0.02500095
44	1.15768551	0.86379245	47.30565374	40.86226633	0.02113912	0.02447246
45	1.16154446	0.86092270	48.46333925	41.72318903	0.02063415	0.02396749
46	1.16541628	0.85806249	49.62488371	42.58125153	0.02015118	0.02348451
47	1.16930100	0.85521179	50.79029999	43.43646332	0.01968880	0.02302213
48	1.17319867	0.85237055	51.95960099	44.28883387	0.01924572	0.02257905
49	1.17710933	0.84953876	53.13279966	45.13837263	0.01882077	0.02215410
50	1.18103303	0.84671637	54.30990899	45.98508900	0.01841285	0.02174618

Rate $\frac{5}{12}$%	A Compound Interest	B Present Value	C Amount of Annuity	D Present Value of Annuity	E Sinking Fund	F Amortization
n	$(1 + i)^n$	$\dfrac{1}{(1 + i)^n}$	$s_{\overline{n}\vert i}$	$a_{\overline{n}\vert i}$	$\dfrac{1}{s_{\overline{n}\vert i}}$	$\dfrac{1}{a_{\overline{n}\vert i}}$
1	1.00416667	0.99585062	1.00000000	0.99585062	1.00000000	1.00416667
2	1.00835069	0.99171846	2.00416667	1.98756908	0.49896050	0.50312717
3	1.01255216	0.98760345	3.01251736	2.97517253	0.33194829	0.33611496
4	1.01677112	0.98350551	4.02506952	3.95867804	0.24844291	0.25260958
5	1.02100767	0.97942457	5.01484064	4.93810261	0.19834026	0.20250693
6	1.02526187	0.97536057	6.06284831	5.91346318	0.16493898	0.16910564
7	1.02953379	0.97131343	7.08811018	6.88477661	0.14108133	0.14524800
8	1.03382352	0.96728308	8.11764397	7.85205970	0.12318845	0.12735512
9	1.03813111	0.96326946	9.15146749	8.81532916	0.10927209	0.11343876
10	1.04245666	0.95927249	10.18959860	9.77460165	0.09813929	0.10230596
11	1.04680023	0.95529211	11.23205526	10.72989376	0.08903090	0.09319757
12	1.05116190	0.95132824	12.27885549	11.68122200	0.08144082	0.08560748
13	1.05554174	0.94738082	13.33001739	12.62860283	0.07501866	0.07918532
14	1.05993983	0.94344978	14.38555913	13.57205261	0.06951416	0.07368082
15	1.06435625	0.93953505	15.44549896	14.51158766	0.06474378	0.06891045
16	1.06879106	0.93563657	16.50985520	15.44722422	0.06056988	0.06473655
17	1.07324436	0.93175426	17.57864627	16.37897848	0.05688720	0.06105387
18	1.07771621	0.92788806	18.65189063	17.30686654	0.05361387	0.05778053
19	1.08220670	0.92403790	19.72960684	18.23090443	0.05068525	0.05485191
20	1.08671589	0.92020372	20.81181353	19.15110815	0.04804963	0.05221630
21	1.09124387	0.91638544	21.89852942	20.06749359	0.04566517	0.04983183
22	1.09579072	0.91258301	22.98977330	20.98007661	0.04349760	0.04766427
23	1.10035652	0.90879636	24.08556402	21.88887297	0.04151865	0.04568531
24	1.10494134	0.90502542	25.18592053	22.79389839	0.03970472	0.04387139
25	1.10954526	0.90127013	26.29086187	23.69516853	0.03803603	0.04220270
26	1.11416836	0.89753042	27.40040713	24.59269895	0.03649581	0.04066247
27	1.11881073	0.89380623	28.51457549	25.48650517	0.03506978	0.03923645
28	1.12347244	0.89009749	29.63338622	26.37660266	0.03374572	0.03791239
29	1.12815358	0.88640414	30.75685866	27.26300680	0.03251307	0.03667974
30	1.13285422	0.88272611	31.88501224	28.14573291	0.03136270	0.03552936
31	1.13757444	0.87906335	33.01786646	29.02479626	0.03028663	0.03445330
32	1.14231434	0.87541578	34.15544090	29.90021205	0.02927791	0.03344458
33	1.14707398	0.87178335	35.29775524	30.77199540	0.02833041	0.03249708
34	1.15185346	0.86816599	36.44482922	31.64016139	0.02743873	0.03160540
35	1.15665284	0.86456365	37.59668268	32.50472504	0.02659809	0.03076476
36	1.16147223	0.86097624	38.75333552	33.36570128	0.02580423	0.02997090
37	1.16631170	0.85740373	39.91480775	34.22310501	0.02505336	0.02922003
38	1.17117133	0.85384604	41.08111945	35.07695105	0.02434208	0.02850875
39	1.17605121	0.85030311	42.25229078	35.92725416	0.02366736	0.02783402
40	1.18095142	0.84677488	43.42834199	36.77402904	0.02302644	0.02719310
41	1.18587206	0.84326129	44.60929342	37.61729033	0.02241685	0.02658352
42	1.19081319	0.83976228	45.79516547	38.45705261	0.02183637	0.02600303
43	1.19577491	0.83627779	46.98597866	39.29333040	0.02128295	0.02544961
44	1.20075731	0.83280776	48.18175357	40.12613816	0.02075474	0.02492141
45	1.20576046	0.82935212	49.38251088	40.95549028	0.02025008	0.02441675
46	1.21078446	0.82591083	50.58827134	41.78140111	0.01976743	0.02393409
47	1.21582940	0.82248381	51.79905581	42.60388492	0.01930537	0.02347204
48	1.22089536	0.81907102	53.01488521	43.42295594	0.01886263	0.02302929
49	1.22598242	0.81567238	54.23578056	44.23862832	0.01843801	0.02260468
50	1.23109068	0.81228785	55.46176298	45.05091617	0.01803044	0.02219711

Rate $\frac{1}{2}$%	A Compound Interest	B Present Value	C Amount of Annuity	D Present Value of Annuity	E Sinking Fund	F Amortization
n	$(1 + i)^n$	$\dfrac{1}{(1 + i)^n}$	$s_{\overline{n}|i}$	$a_{\overline{n}|i}$	$\dfrac{1}{s_{\overline{n}|i}}$	$\dfrac{1}{a_{\overline{n}|i}}$
1	1.00500000	0.99502488	1.00000000	0.99502488	1.00000000	1.00500000
2	1.01002500	0.99007450	2.00500000	1.98509938	0.49875312	0.50375312
3	1.01507513	0.98514876	3.01502500	2.97024814	0.33167221	0.33667221
4	1.02015050	0.98024752	4.03010012	3.95049566	0.24813279	0.25313279
5	1.02525125	0.97537067	5.05025063	4.92586633	0.19800997	0.20300997
6	1.03037751	0.97051808	6.07550188	5.89638441	0.16459546	0.16959546
7	1.03552940	0.96568963	7.10587939	6.86207404	0.14072854	0.14572854
8	1.04070704	0.96088520	8.14140879	7.82295924	0.12282886	0.12782886
9	1.04591058	0.95610468	9.18211583	8.77906392	0.10890736	0.11390736
10	1.05114013	0.95134794	10.22802641	9.73041186	0.09777057	0.10277057
11	1.05639583	0.94661487	11.27916654	10.67702673	0.08865903	0.09365903
12	1.06167781	0.94190534	12.33556237	11.61893207	0.08106643	0.08606643
13	1.06698620	0.93721924	13.39724018	12.55615131	0.07464224	0.07964224
14	1.07232113	0.93255646	14.46422639	13.48870777	0.06913609	0.07413609
15	1.07768274	0.92791688	15.53654752	14.41662465	0.06436436	0.06936436
16	1.08307115	0.92330037	16.61423026	15.33992502	0.06018937	0.06518937
17	1.08848651	0.91870684	17.69730141	16.25863186	0.05650579	0.06150579
18	1.09392894	0.91413616	18.78578791	17.17276802	0.05323173	0.05823173
19	1.09939858	0.90958822	19.87971685	18.08235624	0.05030253	0.05530253
20	1.10489558	0.90506290	20.97911544	18.98741915	0.04766645	0.05266645
21	1.11042006	0.90056010	22.08401101	19.88797925	0.04528163	0.05028163
22	1.11597216	0.89607971	23.19443107	20.78405896	0.04311380	0.04811380
23	1.12155202	0.89162160	24.31040322	21.67568055	0.04113465	0.04613465
24	1.12715978	0.88718567	25.43195524	22.56286622	0.03932061	0.04432061
25	1.13279558	0.88277181	26.55911502	23.44563803	0.03765186	0.04265186
26	1.13845955	0.87837991	27.69191059	24.32401794	0.03611163	0.04111163
27	1.14415185	0.87400986	28.83037015	25.19802780	0.03468565	0.03968565
28	1.14987261	0.86966155	29.97452200	26.06768936	0.03336167	0.03836167
29	1.15562197	0.86533488	31.12439461	26.93302423	0.03212914	0.03712914
30	1.16140008	0.86102973	32.28001658	27.79405397	0.03097892	0.03597892
31	1.16720708	0.85674600	33.44141666	28.65079997	0.02990304	0.03490304
32	1.17304312	0.85248358	34.60862375	29.50328355	0.02889453	0.03389453
33	1.17890833	0.84824237	35.78166686	30.35152592	0.02794727	0.03294727
34	1.18480288	0.84402226	36.96057520	31.19554818	0.02705586	0.03205586
35	1.19072689	0.83982314	38.14537807	32.03537132	0.02621550	0.03121550
36	1.19668052	0.83564492	39.33610496	32.87101624	0.02542194	0.03042194
37	1.20266393	0.83148748	40.53278549	33.70250372	0.02467133	0.02967139
38	1.20867725	0.82735073	41.73544942	34.52985445	0.02396045	0.02896045
39	1.21472063	0.82323455	42.94412666	35.35308900	0.02328607	0.02828607
40	1.22079424	0.81913886	44.15884730	36.17222786	0.02264552	0.02764552
41	1.22689821	0.81506354	45.37964153	36.98729141	0.02203631	0.02703631
42	1.23303270	0.81100850	46.60653974	37.79829991	0.02145622	0.02645622
43	1.23919786	0.80697363	47.83957244	38.60527354	0.02090320	0.02590320
44	1.24539385	0.80295884	49.07877030	39.40823238	0.02037541	0.02537541
45	1.25162082	0.79896402	50.32416415	40.20719640	0.01987117	0.02487117
46	1.25787892	0.79498907	51.57578497	41.00218547	0.01938894	0.02438894
47	1.26416832	0.79103390	52.83366390	41.79321937	0.01892733	0.02392733
48	1.27048916	0.78709841	54.09783222	42.58031778	0.01848503	0.02348503
49	1.27684161	0.78318250	55.36832138	43.36350028	0.01806087	0.02306087
50	1.28322581	0.77928607	56.64516299	44.14278635	0.01765376	0.02265376

Rate $\frac{3}{4}$%	A Compound Interest	B Present Value	C Amount of Annuity	D Present Value of Annuity	E Sinking Fund	F Amortization
n	$(1 + i)^n$	$\dfrac{1}{(1 + i)^n}$	$s_{\overline{n}|i}$	$a_{\overline{n}|i}$	$\dfrac{1}{s_{\overline{n}|i}}$	$\dfrac{1}{a_{\overline{n}|i}}$
1	1.00750000	0.99255583	1.00000000	0.99255583	1.00000000	1.00750000
2	1.01505625	0.98516708	2.00750000	1.97772291	0.49813200	0.50563200
3	1.02266917	0.97783333	3.02255625	2.95555624	0.33084579	0.33834579
4	1.03033919	0.97055417	4.04522542	3.92611041	0.24720501	0.25470501
5	1.03806673	0.96332920	5.07556461	4.88943961	0.19702242	0.20452242
6	1.04585224	0.95615802	6.11363135	5.84559763	0.16356891	0.17106891
7	1.05369613	0.94904022	7.15948358	6.79463785	0.13967488	0.14717488
8	1.06159885	0.94197540	8.21317971	7.73661325	0.12175552	0.12925552
9	1.06956084	0.93496318	9.27477856	8.67157642	0.10781929	0.11531929
10	1.07758255	0.92800315	10.34433940	9.59957958	0.09667123	0.10417123
11	1.08566441	0.92109494	11.42192194	10.52067452	0.08755094	0.09505094
12	1.09380690	0.91423815	12.50758636	11.43491267	0.07995148	0.08745148
13	1.10201045	0.90743241	13.60139325	12.34234508	0.07352188	0.08102188
14	1.11027553	0.90067733	14.70340370	13.24302242	0.06801146	0.07551146
15	1.11860259	0.89397254	15.81367923	14.13699495	0.06323639	0.07073639
16	1.12699211	0.88731766	16.93228183	15.02431261	0.05905879	0.06655879
17	1.13544455	0.88071231	18.05927394	15.90502492	0.05537321	0.06287321
18	1.14396039	0.87415614	19.19471849	16.77918107	0.05209766	0.05959766
19	1.15254009	0.86764878	20.33867888	17.64682984	0.04916740	0.05666740
20	1.16118414	0.86118985	21.49121897	18.50801969	0.04653063	0.05403063
21	1.16989302	0.85477901	22.65240312	19.36279870	0.04414543	0.05164543
22	1.17866722	0.84841589	23.82229614	20.21121459	0.04197748	0.04947748
23	1.18750723	0.84210014	25.00096336	21.05331473	0.03999846	0.04749846
24	1.19641353	0.83583140	26.18847059	21.88914614	0.03818474	0.04568474
25	1.20538663	0.82960933	27.38488412	22.71875547	0.03651650	0.04401650
26	1.21442703	0.82343358	28.59027075	23.54218905	0.03497693	0.04247693
27	1.22353523	0.81730380	29.80469778	24.35949286	0.03355176	0.04105176
28	1.23271175	0.81121966	31.02823301	25.17071251	0.03222871	0.03972871
29	1.24195709	0.80518080	32.26094476	25.97589331	0.03099723	0.03849723
30	1.25127176	0.79918690	33.50290184	26.77508021	0.02984816	0.03734816
31	1.26065630	0.79323762	34.75417361	27.56831783	0.02877352	0.03627352
32	1.27011122	0.78733262	36.01482991	28.35565045	0.02776634	0.03526634
33	1.27963706	0.78147158	37.28494113	29.13712203	0.02682048	0.03432048
34	1.28923434	0.77565418	38.56457819	29.91277621	0.02593053	0.03343053
35	1.29890359	0.76988008	39.85381253	30.68265629	0.02509170	0.03259170
36	1.30864537	0.76414896	41.15271612	31.44680525	0.02429973	0.03179973
37	1.31846021	0.75846051	42.46136149	32.20526576	0.02355082	0.03105082
38	1.32834866	0.75281440	43.77982170	32.95808016	0.02284157	0.03034157
39	1.33831128	0.74721032	45.10817037	33.70529048	0.02216893	0.02966893
40	1.34834861	0.74164796	46.44648164	34.44693844	0.02153016	0.02903016
41	1.35846123	0.73612701	47.79483026	35.18306545	0.02092276	0.02842276
42	1.36864969	0.73064716	49.15329148	35.91371260	0.02034452	0.02784452
43	1.37891456	0.72520809	50.52194117	36.63892070	0.01979338	0.02729338
44	1.38925642	0.71980952	51.90085573	37.35873022	0.01926751	0.02676751
45	1.39967584	0.71445114	53.29011215	38.07318136	0.01876521	0.02626521
46	1.41017341	0.70913264	54.68978799	38.78231401	0.01828495	0.02578495
47	1.42074971	0.70385374	56.09996140	39.48616775	0.01782532	0.02532532
48	1.43140533	0.69861414	57.52071111	40.18478189	0.01738504	0.02488504
49	1.44214087	0.69341353	58.95211644	40.87819542	0.01696292	0.02446292
50	1.45295693	0.68825165	60.39425732	41.56644707	0.01655787	0.02405787

Rate $\frac{5}{6}$%	A Compound Interest	B Present Value	C Amount of Annuity	D Present Value of Annuity	E Sinking Fund	F Amortization
n	$(1 + i)^n$	$\dfrac{1}{(1 + i)^n}$	$s_{\overline{n}\rvert i}$	$a_{\overline{n}\rvert i}$	$\dfrac{1}{s_{\overline{n}\rvert i}}$	$\dfrac{1}{a_{\overline{n}\rvert i}}$
1	1.00833333	0.99173554	1.00000000	0.99173554	1.00000000	1.00833333
2	1.01673611	0.98353938	2.00833333	1.97527491	0.49792531	0.50625864
3	1.02520891	0.97541095	3.02506944	2.95068586	0.33057092	0.33890426
4	1.03375232	0.96734970	4.05027836	3.91803557	0.24689661	0.25522994
5	1.04236692	0.95935508	5.08403068	4.87739065	0.19669433	0.20502766
6	1.05105331	0.95142652	6.12639760	5.82881717	0.16322806	0.17156139
7	1.05981209	0.94356349	7.17745091	6.77238066	0.13932523	0.14765856
8	1.06864386	0.93576545	8.23726300	7.70814611	0.12139955	0.12973288
9	1.07754922	0.92803185	9.30590686	8.63617796	0.10745863	0.11579196
10	1.08652880	0.92036217	10.38345608	9.55654013	0.09630705	0.10464038
11	1.09558321	0.91275587	11.46998489	10.46929600	0.08718407	0.09551741
12	1.10471307	0.90521243	12.56556809	11.37450843	0.07958255	0.08791589
13	1.11391901	0.89773134	13.67028116	12.27223976	0.07315138	0.08148472
14	1.12320167	0.89031207	14.78420017	13.16255183	0.06763978	0.07597311
15	1.13256168	0.88295412	15.90740184	14.04550595	0.06286382	0.07119715
16	1.14199970	0.87565698	17.03996352	14.92116292	0.05868557	0.06701890
17	1.15151636	0.86842014	18.18196322	15.78958306	0.05499956	0.06333289
18	1.16111233	0.86124312	19.33347958	16.65082618	0.05172375	0.06005708
19	1.17078827	0.85412540	20.49459191	17.50495158	0.04879336	0.05712669
20	1.18054483	0.84706652	21.66538017	18.35201810	0.04615659	0.05448992
21	1.19038271	0.84006597	22.84592501	19.19208406	0.04377148	0.05210482
22	1.20030256	0.83312327	24.03630772	20.02520734	0.04160373	0.04993706
23	1.21030509	0.82623796	25.23661028	20.85144529	0.03962497	0.04795831
24	1.22039096	0.81940954	26.44691537	21.67085483	0.03781159	0.04614493
25	1.23056089	0.81263756	27.66730633	22.48349240	0.03614374	0.04447708
26	1.24081556	0.80592155	28.89786721	23.28941395	0.03460463	0.04293796
27	1.25115569	0.79926104	30.13868277	24.08867499	0.03317995	0.04151328
28	1.26158199	0.79265558	31.38983846	24.88133057	0.03185744	0.04019078
29	1.27209517	0.78610471	32.65142045	25.66743527	0.03062654	0.03895987
30	1.28269596	0.77960797	33.92351562	26.44704325	0.02947808	0.03781141
31	1.29338510	0.77316493	35.20621158	27.22020818	0.02840408	0.03673741
32	1.30416331	0.76677514	36.49959668	27.98698332	0.02739756	0.03573090
33	1.31503133	0.76043815	37.80375999	28.74742147	0.02645240	0.03478573
34	1.35298993	0.75415354	39.11879132	29.50157501	0.02556316	0.03389650
35	1.33703984	0.74792087	40.44478125	30.24949588	0.02472507	0.03305840
36	1.34818184	0.74173970	41.78182109	30.99123559	0.02393385	0.03226719
37	1.35941669	0.73560962	43.13000293	31.72684521	0.02318572	0.03151905
38	1.37074516	0.72953020	44.48941962	32.45637541	0.02247725	0.03081059
39	1.38216804	0.72350103	45.86016479	33.17987644	0.02180542	0.03013875
40	1.39368611	0.71752168	47.24233283	33.89739813	0.02116746	0.02950079
41	1.40530016	0.71159175	48.63601893	34.60898988	0.02056089	0.02889423
42	1.41701099	0.70571083	50.04131909	35.31470070	0.01998349	0.02831682
43	1.42881942	0.69987851	51.45833008	36.01457921	0.01943320	0.02776653
44	1.44072625	0.69409439	52.88714950	36.70867360	0.01890818	0.02724152
45	1.45273230	0.68835807	54.32787575	37.39703167	0.01840676	0.02674009
46	1.46483840	0.68266916	55.78060805	38.07970083	0.01792738	0.02626071
47	1.47704539	0.67702727	57.24544645	38.75672809	0.01746864	0.02580197
48	1.48935410	0.67143200	58.72249183	39.42816009	0.01702925	0.02536258
49	1.50176538	0.66588297	60.21184593	40.09404307	0.01660803	0.02494136
50	1.51428009	0.66037981	61.71361131	40.75442288	0.01620388	0.02453721

Rate 1%	A Compound Interest	B Present Value	C Amount of Annuity	D Present Value of Annuity	E Sinking Fund	F Amortization
n	$(1 + i)^n$	$\dfrac{1}{(1 + i)^n}$	$s_{\overline{n}\vert i}$	$a_{\overline{n}\vert i}$	$\dfrac{1}{s_{\overline{n}\vert i}}$	$\dfrac{1}{a_{\overline{n}\vert i}}$
1	1.01000000	0.99009901	1.00000000	0.99009901	1.00000000	1.01000000
2	1.02010000	0.98029605	2.01000000	1.97039506	0.49751244	0.50751244
3	1.03030100	0.97059015	3.03010000	2.94098521	0.33002211	0.34002211
4	1.04060401	0.96098034	4.06040100	3.90196555	0.24628109	0.25628109
5	1.05101005	0.95146569	5.10100501	4.85343124	0.19603980	0.20603980
6	1.06152015	0.94204524	6.15201506	5.79547647	0.16254837	0.17254837
7	1.07213535	0.93271805	7.21353521	6.72819453	0.13862828	0.14862828
8	1.08285671	0.92348322	8.28567056	7.65167775	0.12069029	0.13069029
9	1.09368527	0.91433982	9.36852727	8.56601758	0.10674036	0.11674036
10	1.10462213	0.90528695	10.46221254	9.47130453	0.09558208	0.10558208
11	1.11566835	0.89632372	11.56683467	10.36762825	0.08645408	0.09645408
12	1.12682503	0.88744923	12.68250301	11.25507747	0.07884879	0.08884879
13	1.13809328	0.87866260	13.80932804	12.13374007	0.07241482	0.08241482
14	1.14947421	0.86996297	14.94742132	13.00370304	0.06690117	0.07690117
15	1.16096896	0.86134947	16.09689554	13.86505252	0.06212378	0.07212378
16	1.17257864	0.85282126	17.25786449	14.71787378	0.05794460	0.06794460
17	1.18430443	0.84437749	18.43044314	15.56225127	0.05425806	0.06425806
18	1.19614748	0.83601731	19.61474757	16.39826858	0.05098205	0.06098205
19	1.20810895	0.82773992	20.81089504	17.22600850	0.04805175	0.05805175
20	1.22019004	0.81954447	22.01900399	18.04555297	0.04541531	0.05541531
21	1.23239194	0.81143017	23.23919403	18.85698313	0.04303075	0.05303075
22	1.24471586	0.80339621	24.47158598	19.66037934	0.04086372	0.05086372
23	1.25716302	0.79544179	25.71630183	20.45582113	0.03888584	0.04888584
24	1.26973465	0.78756613	26.97346485	21.24338726	0.03707347	0.04707347
25	1.28243200	0.77976844	28.24319950	22.02315570	0.03540675	0.04540675
26	1.29525631	0.77204796	29.52563150	22.79520366	0.03386888	0.04386888
27	1.30820888	0.76440392	30.82088781	23.55960759	0.03244553	0.04244553
28	1.32129097	0.75683557	32.12909669	24.31644316	0.03112444	0.04112444
29	1.33450388	0.74934215	33.45038766	25.06578530	0.02989502	0.03989502
30	1.34784892	0.74192292	34.78489153	25.80770822	0.02874811	0.03874811
31	1.36132740	0.73457715	36.13274045	26.54228537	0.02767573	0.03767573
32	1.37494068	0.72730411	37.49406785	27.26958947	0.02667089	0.03667089
33	1.38869009	0.72010307	38.86900853	27.98969255	0.02575744	0.03572744
34	1.40257699	0.71297334	40.25769862	28.70266589	0.02483997	0.03483997
35	1.41660276	0.70591420	41.66027560	29.40853009	0.02400368	0.03400368
36	1.43076878	0.69892495	43.07687836	30.10750504	0.02321431	0.03321431
37	1.44507647	0.69200490	44.05764714	30.79950994	0.02246805	0.03246805
38	1.45952724	0.68515337	45.95272361	31.48466330	0.02176150	0.03176150
39	1.47412251	0.67836967	47.41225085	32.16303298	0.02109160	0.03109160
40	1.48886373	0.67165314	48.88637336	32.83468611	0.02045560	0.03045560
41	1.50375237	0.66500311	50.37523709	33.49968922	0.01985102	0.02985102
42	1.51878989	0.65841892	51.87898946	34.15810814	0.01927563	0.02927563
43	1.53397779	0.65189992	53.39777936	34.81000806	0.01872737	0.02872737
44	1.54931757	0.64544546	54.93175715	35.45545352	0.01820441	0.02820441
45	1.56481075	0.63905492	56.48107472	36.09450844	0.01770505	0.02770505
46	1.58045885	0.63272764	58.04588547	36.72723608	0.01722775	0.02722775
47	1.59626344	0.62646301	59.62634432	37.35369909	0.01677111	0.02677111
48	1.61222608	0.62026041	61.22260777	37.97395949	0.01633384	0.02633384
49	1.62834834	0.61411921	62.83483385	38.58807871	0.01591474	0.02591474
50	1.64463182	0.60803882	64.46318218	39.19611753	0.01551273	0.02551273

	A	B	C	D	E	F
Rate $1\frac{1}{4}$%	Compound Interest	Present Value	Amount of Annuity	Present Value of Annuity	Sinking Fund	Amortization
n	$(1 + i)^n$	$\dfrac{1}{(1 + i)^n}$	$s_{\overline{n}|i}$	$a_{\overline{n}|i}$	$\dfrac{1}{s_{\overline{n}|i}}$	$\dfrac{1}{a_{\overline{n}|i}}$
1	1.01250000	0.98765432	1.00000000	0.98765432	1.00000000	1.01250000
2	1.02515625	0.97546106	2.01250000	1.96311538	0.49689441	0.50939441
3	1.03797070	0.96341833	3.03765625	2.92653371	0.32920117	0.34170117
4	1.05094534	0.95152428	4.07562695	3.87805798	0.24536102	0.25786102
5	1.06408215	0.93977706	5.12657229	4.81783504	0.19506211	0.20756211
6	1.07738318	0.92817488	6.19065444	5.74600992	0.16153381	0.17403381
7	1.09085047	0.91671593	7.26803762	6.66272585	0.13758872	0.15008872
8	1.10448610	0.90539845	8.35888809	7.56812429	0.11963314	0.13213314
9	1.11829218	0.89422069	9.46337420	8.46234498	0.10567055	0.11817055
10	1.13227083	0.88318093	10.58166637	9.34552591	0.09450307	0.10700307
11	1.14642422	0.87227746	11.71393720	10.21780337	0.08536839	0.09786839
12	1.16075452	0.86150860	12.86036142	11.07931197	0.07775831	0.09025831
13	1.17526395	0.85087269	14.02111594	11.93018466	0.07132100	0.08382100
14	1.18995475	0.84036809	15.19637988	12.77055275	0.06580515	0.07830515
15	1.20482918	0.82999318	16.38633463	13.60054592	0.06102646	0.07352646
16	1.21988955	0.81974635	17.59116382	14.42029227	0.05684672	0.06934672
17	1.23513817	0.80962602	18.81105336	15.22991829	0.05316023	0.06566023
18	1.25057739	0.79963064	20.04619153	16.02954893	0.04988479	0.06238479
19	1.26620961	0.78975866	21.29676893	16.81930759	0.04695548	0.05945548
20	1.28203723	0.78000855	22.56297854	17.59931613	0.04432039	0.05682039
21	1.29806270	0.77037881	23.84501577	18.36969495	0.04193749	0.05443749
22	1.31428848	0.76086796	25.14307847	19.13056291	0.03977238	0.05227238
23	1.33071709	0.75147453	26.45736695	19.88203744	0.03779666	0.05029666
24	1.34735105	0.74219707	27.78808403	20.62423451	0.03598665	0.04848665
25	1.36419294	0.73303414	29.13543508	21.35726865	0.03432247	0.04682247
26	1.38124535	0.72398434	30.49962802	22.08125299	0.03278729	0.04528729
27	1.39851092	0.71504626	31.88087337	22.79629925	0.03136677	0.04386677
28	1.41599230	0.70621853	33.27938429	23.50251778	0.03004863	0.04254863
29	1.43369221	0.69749978	34.69537659	24.20001756	0.02882228	0.04132228
30	1.45161336	0.68888867	36.12906880	24.88890623	0.02767854	0.04017854
31	1.46975853	0.68038387	37.58068216	25.56929010	0.02660942	0.03910942
32	1.48813051	0.67198407	39.05044069	26.24127418	0.02560791	0.03810791
33	1.50673214	0.66368797	40.53857120	26.90496215	0.02466786	0.03716786
34	1.52556629	0.65549429	42.04530334	27.56045644	0.02378387	0.03628387
35	1.54463587	0.64740177	43.57086963	28.20785822	0.02295111	0.03545111
36	1.56394382	0.63940916	45.11550550	28.84726737	0.02216533	0.03466533
37	1.58349312	0.63151522	46.67944932	29.47878259	0.02142270	0.03392270
38	1.60328678	0.62371873	48.26294243	30.10250133	0.02071983	0.03321983
39	1.62332787	0.61601850	49.86622921	30.71851983	0.02005365	0.03255365
40	1.64361946	0.60841334	51.48955708	31.32693316	0.01942141	0.03192141
41	1.66416471	0.60090206	53.13317654	31.92783522	0.01882063	0.03132063
42	1.68496677	0.59348352	54.79734125	32.52131874	0.01824906	0.03074906
43	1.70602885	0.58615656	56.48230801	33.10747530	0.01770466	0.03020466
44	1.72735421	0.57892006	58.18833687	33.68639536	0.01718557	0.02968557
45	1.74894614	0.57177290	59.91569108	34.25816825	0.01669012	0.02919012
46	1.77080797	0.56471397	61.66463721	34.82288222	0.01621675	0.02871675
47	1.79294306	0.55774219	63.43544518	35.38064224	0.01576406	0.02826406
48	1.81535485	0.55085649	65.22838824	35.93148091	0.01533075	0.02783075
49	1.83804679	0.54405579	67.04374310	36.47553670	0.01491563	0.02741563
50	1.86102237	0.53733905	68.88178989	37.01287575	0.01451763	0.02701763

Rate $1\frac{1}{2}$%	A Compound Interest	B Present Value	C Amount of Annuity	D Present Value of Annuity	E Sinking Fund	F Amortization
n	$(1 + i)^n$	$\dfrac{1}{(1 + i)^n}$	$s_{\overline{n}|i}$	$a_{\overline{n}|i}$	$\dfrac{1}{s_{\overline{n}|i}}$	$\dfrac{1}{a_{\overline{n}|i}}$
1	1.01500000	0.98522167	1.00000000	0.98522167	1.00000000	1.01500000
2	1.03022500	0.97066175	2.01500000	1.95588342	0.49627792	0.51127792
3	1.04567838	0.95631699	3.04522500	2.91220042	0.32838296	0.34338296
4	1.06136355	0.94218423	4.09090337	3.85438465	0.24444479	0.25944479
5	1.07728400	0.92826033	5.15226693	4.78264497	0.19408932	0.20908932
6	1.09344326	0.91454219	6.22955093	5.69718717	0.16052521	0.17552521
7	1.10984491	0.90102679	7.32299419	6.59821396	0.13655616	0.15155616
8	1.12649259	0.88771112	8.43283911	7.48592508	0.11858402	0.13358402
9	1.14338998	0.87459224	9.55933169	8.36051732	0.10460982	0.11960982
10	1.16054083	0.86166723	10.70272167	9.22218455	0.09343418	0.10843418
11	1.17794894	0.84893323	11.86326249	10.07111779	0.08429384	0.09929384
12	1.19561817	0.83638742	13.04121143	10.90750521	0.07667999	0.09167999
13	1.21355244	0.82402702	14.23682960	11.73153222	0.07024036	0.08524036
14	1.23175573	0.81184928	15.45038205	12.54338150	0.06472332	0.07972332
15	1.25023207	0.79985150	16.68213778	13.34323301	0.05994436	0.07494436
16	1.26898555	0.78803104	17.93236984	14.13126405	0.05576508	0.07076508
17	1.28802033	0.77638526	19.20135539	14.90764931	0.05207966	0.06707966
18	1.30734064	0.76491159	20.48937572	15.67256089	0.04880578	0.06380578
19	1.32695075	0.75360747	21.79671636	16.42616837	0.04587847	0.06087847
20	1.34685501	0.74247042	23.12366710	17.16863879	0.04324574	0.05824574
21	1.36705783	0.73149795	24.47052211	17.90013673	0.04086550	0.05586550
22	1.38756370	0.72068763	25.83757994	18.62082437	0.03870332	0.05370332
23	1.40837715	0.71003708	27.22514364	19.33086145	0.03673075	0.05173075
24	1.42950281	0.69954392	28.63352080	20.03040537	0.03492410	0.04992410
25	1.45094535	0.68920583	30.06302361	20.71961120	0.03326345	0.04826345
26	1.47270953	0.67902052	31.51396896	21.39863172	0.03173196	0.04673196
27	1.49480018	0.66898574	32.98667850	22.06761746	0.03031527	0.04531527
28	1.51722218	0.65909925	34.48147867	22.72671671	0.02900108	0.04400108
29	1.53998051	0.64935887	35.99870085	23.37607558	0.02777878	0.04277878
30	1.56308022	0.63976243	37.53868137	24.01583801	0.02663919	0.04163919
31	1.58652642	0.63030781	39.10176159	24.64614582	0.02557430	0.04057430
32	1.61032432	0.62099292	40.68828801	25.26713874	0.02457710	0.03957710
33	1.63447918	0.61181568	42.29861233	25.87895442	0.02364144	0.03864144
34	1.65899637	0.60277407	43.93309152	26.48172849	0.02276189	0.03776189
35	1.68388132	0.59386608	45.59208789	27.07559458	0.02193363	0.03693363
36	1.70913954	0.58508974	47.27596921	27.66068431	0.02115240	0.03615240
37	1.73477663	0.57644309	48.98510874	28.23712740	0.02041437	0.03541437
38	1.76079828	0.56792423	50.71988538	28.80505163	0.01971613	0.03471613
39	1.78721025	0.55953126	52.48068366	29.36458288	0.01905463	0.03405463
40	1.81401841	0.55126232	54.26789391	29.91584520	0.01842710	0.03342710
41	1.84122868	0.54311559	56.08191232	30.45896079	0.01783106	0.03283106
42	1.86884712	0.53508925	57.92314100	30.99405004	0.01726426	0.03226426
43	1.89687982	0.52718153	59.79198812	31.52123157	0.01672465	0.03172465
44	1.92533302	0.51939067	61.68886794	32.04062223	0.01621038	0.03121038
45	1.95421301	0.51171494	63.61420096	32.55233718	0.01571976	0.03071976
46	1.98352621	0.50415265	65.56841398	33.05648983	0.01525125	0.03025125
47	2.01327910	0.49670212	67.55194018	33.55319195	0.01480342	0.02980342
48	2.04347829	0.48936170	69.56521929	34.04255365	0.01437500	0.02937500
49	2.07413046	0.48212975	71.60869758	34.52468339	0.01396478	0.02896478
50	2.10524242	0.47500468	73.68282804	34.99968807	0.01357168	0.02857168

Rate $1\frac{3}{4}$%	A Compound Interest	B Present Value	C Amount of Annuity	D Present Value of Annuity	E Sinking Fund	F Amortization
n	$(1 + i)^n$	$\dfrac{1}{(1 + i)^n}$	$s_{\overline{n}|i}$	$a_{\overline{n}|i}$	$\dfrac{1}{s_{\overline{n}|i}}$	$\dfrac{1}{a_{\overline{n}|i}}$
1	1.01750000	0.98280098	1.00000000	0.98280098	1.00000000	1.01750000
2	1.03530625	0.96589777	2.01750000	1.94869875	0.49566295	0.51316295
3	1.05342411	0.94928528	3.05280625	2.89798403	0.32756746	0.34506746
4	1.07185903	0.93295851	4.10623036	3.83094254	0.24353237	0.26103237
5	1.09061656	0.91691254	5.17808939	4.74785508	0.19312142	0.21062142
6	1.10970235	0.90114254	6.26870596	5.64899762	0.15952256	0.17702256
7	1.12912215	0.88564378	7.37840831	6.53464139	0.13553059	0.15303059
8	1.14888178	0.87041157	8.50753045	7.40505297	0.11754292	0.13504292
9	1.16898721	0.85544135	9.65641224	8.26049432	0.10355813	0.12105813
10	1.18944449	0.84072860	10.82539945	9.10122291	0.09237534	0.10987534
11	1.21025977	0.82626889	12.01484394	9.92749181	0.08323038	0.10073038
12	1.23143931	0.81205788	13.22510371	10.73954969	0.07561377	0.09311377
13	1.25298950	0.79809128	14.45654303	11.53764097	0.06917283	0.08667283
14	1.27491682	0.78436490	15.70953253	12.32200587	0.06365562	0.08115562
15	1.29722786	0.77087459	16.98444935	13.09288046	0.05887739	0.07637739
16	1.31992935	0.75761631	18.28167721	13.85049677	0.05469958	0.07219958
17	1.34302811	0.74458605	19.60160656	14.59508282	0.05101623	0.06851623
18	1.36653111	0.73177990	20.94463468	15.32686272	0.04774492	0.06524492
19	1.39044540	0.71919401	22.31116578	16.04605673	0.04482061	0.06232061
20	1.41477820	0.70682458	23.70161119	16.75288130	0.04219122	0.05969122
21	1.43953681	0.69466789	25.11638938	17.44754919	0.03981464	0.05731464
22	1.46472871	0.68272028	26.55592620	18.13026948	0.03765638	0.05515638
23	1.49036146	0.67097817	28.02065490	18.80124764	0.03568796	0.05318796
24	1.51644279	0.65943800	29.51101637	19.46068565	0.03388565	0.05138565
25	1.54298054	0.64809632	31.02745915	20.10878196	0.03222952	0.04972952
26	1.56998269	0.63694970	32.57043969	20.74573166	0.03070269	0.04820269
27	1.59745739	0.62599479	34.14042238	21.37172644	0.02929079	0.04679079
28	1.62541290	0.61522829	35.73787977	21.98695474	0.02798151	0.04548151
29	1.65385762	0.60464697	37.36329267	22.59160171	0.02676424	0.04426424
30	1.68280013	0.59424764	39.01715029	23.18584934	0.02562975	0.04312975
31	1.71224913	0.58402716	40.69995042	23.76987650	0.02457005	0.04207005
32	1.74221349	0.57398247	42.41219955	24.34385897	0.02357812	0.04107812
33	1.77270223	0.56411053	44.15441305	24.90796951	0.02264779	0.04014779
34	1.80372452	0.55440839	45.92711527	25.46237789	0.02177363	0.03927363
35	1.83528970	0.54487311	47.73083979	26.00725100	0.02095082	0.03845082
36	1.86740727	0.53550183	49.56612949	26.54275283	0.02017507	0.03767507
37	1.90008689	0.52629172	51.43353675	27.06904455	0.01944257	0.03694257
38	1.93333841	0.51724002	53.33362365	27.58628457	0.01874990	0.03624990
39	1.96717184	0.50834400	55.26696206	28.09462857	0.01809399	0.03559399
40	2.00159734	0.49960098	57.23413390	28.59422955	0.01747209	0.03497209
41	2.03662530	0.49100834	59.23573124	29.08523789	0.01688170	0.03438170
42	2.07226624	0.48256348	61.27235654	29.56780136	0.01632057	0.03382057
43	2.10853090	0.47426386	63.34462278	30.04206522	0.01578666	0.03328666
44	2.14543019	0.46610699	65.45315367	30.50817221	0.01527810	0.03277810
45	2.18297522	0.45809040	67.59858386	30.96626261	0.01479321	0.03229321
46	2.22117728	0.45021170	69.78155908	31.41647431	0.01433043	0.03183043
47	2.26004789	0.44246850	72.00273637	31.85894281	0.01388836	0.03138836
48	2.29959872	0.43485848	74.26278425	32.29380129	0.01346569	0.03096569
49	2.33984170	0.42737934	76.56238298	32.72118063	0.01306124	0.03056124
50	2.38078893	0.42002883	78.90222468	33.14120946	0.01267391	0.03017391

Rate 2%	A Compound Interest	B Present Value	C Amount of Annuity	D Present Value of Annuity	E Sinking Fund	F Amortization
n	$(1 + i)^n$	$\dfrac{1}{(1 + i)^n}$	$s_{\overline{n}\vert i}$	$a_{\overline{n}\vert i}$	$\dfrac{1}{s_{\overline{n}\vert i}}$	$\dfrac{1}{a_{\overline{n}\vert i}}$
1	1.02000000	0.98039216	1.00000000	0.98039216	1.00000000	1.02000000
2	1.04040000	0.96116878	2.02000000	1.94156094	0.49504950	0.51504950
3	1.06120800	0.94232233	3.06040000	2.88388327	0.32675467	0.34675467
4	1.08243216	0.92384543	4.12160800	3.80772870	0.24262375	0.26262375
5	1.10408080	0.90573081	5.20404016	4.71345951	0.19215839	0.21215839
6	1.12616242	0.88797138	6.30812096	5.60143089	0.15852581	0.17852581
7	1.14868567	0.87056018	7.43428338	6.47199107	0.13451196	0.15451196
8	1.17165938	0.85349037	8.58296905	7.32548144	0.11650980	0.13650980
9	1.19509257	0.83675527	9.75462843	8.16223671	0.10251544	0.12251544
10	1.21899442	0.82034830	10.94972100	8.98258501	0.09132653	0.11132653
11	1.24337431	0.80426304	12.16871542	9.78684805	0.08217794	0.10217794
12	1.26824179	0.78849318	13.41208973	10.57534122	0.07455960	0.09455960
13	1.29360663	0.77303253	14.68033152	11.34837375	0.06811835	0.08811835
14	1.31947876	0.75787502	15.97393815	12.10624877	0.06260197	0.08260197
15	1.34586834	0.74301473	17.29341692	12.84926350	0.05782547	0.07782547
16	1.37278571	0.72844581	18.63928525	13.57770931	0.05365013	0.07365013
17	1.40024142	0.71416256	20.01207096	14.29187188	0.04996984	0.06996984
18	1.42824625	0.70015937	21.41231238	14.99203125	0.04670210	0.06670210
19	1.45681117	0.68643076	22.84055863	15.67846201	0.04378177	0.06378177
20	1.48594740	0.67297133	24.29736980	16.35143334	0.04115672	0.06115672
21	1.51566634	0.65977582	25.78331719	17.01120916	0.03878477	0.05878477
22	1.54597967	0.64683904	27.29898354	17.65804820	0.03663140	0.05663140
23	1.57689926	0.63415592	28.84496321	18.29220412	0.03466810	0.05466810
24	1.60843725	0.62172149	30.42186247	18.91392560	0.03287110	0.05287110
25	1.64060599	0.60953087	32.03029972	19.52345647	0.03122044	0.05122044
26	1.67341811	0.59757928	33.67090572	20.12103576	0.02969923	0.04969923
27	1.70688648	0.58586204	35.34432383	20.70689780	0.02829309	0.04829309
28	1.74102421	0.57437455	37.05121031	21.28127236	0.02698967	0.04698967
29	1.77584469	0.56311231	38.79223451	21.84438466	0.02577836	0.04577836
30	1.81136158	0.55207089	40.56807921	22.39645555	0.02464992	0.04464992
31	1.84758882	0.54124597	42.37944079	22.93770152	0.02359635	0.04359635
32	1.88454059	0.53063330	44.22702961	23.46833482	0.02261061	0.04261061
33	1.92223140	0.52022873	46.11157020	23.98856355	0.02168653	0.04168653
34	1.96067603	0.51002817	48.03380160	24.49859172	0.02081867	0.04081867
35	1.99988955	0.50002761	49.99447763	24.99861933	0.02000221	0.04000221
36	2.03988734	0.49022315	51.99436719	25.48884248	0.01923285	0.03923285
37	2.08068509	0.48061093	54.03425453	25.96945341	0.01850678	0.03850678
38	2.12229879	0.47118719	56.11493962	26.44064060	0.01782057	0.03782057
39	2.16474477	0.46194822	58.23723841	26.90258883	0.01717114	0.03717114
40	2.20803966	0.45289042	60.40198318	27.35547924	0.01655575	0.03655575
41	2.25220046	0.44401021	62.61002284	27.79948945	0.01597188	0.03597188
42	2.29724447	0.43530413	64.86222330	28.23479358	0.01541729	0.03541729
43	2.34318936	0.42676875	67.15946777	28.66156233	0.01488993	0.03488993
44	2.39005314	0.41840074	69.50265712	29.07996307	0.01438794	0.03438794
45	2.43785421	0.41019680	71.89271027	29.49015987	0.01390962	0.03390962
46	2.48661129	0.40215373	74.33056447	29.89231360	0.01345342	0.03345342
47	2.53634352	0.39426836	76.81717576	30.28658196	0.01301792	0.03301792
48	2.58707039	0.38653761	79.35351927	30.67311957	0.01260184	0.03260184
49	2.63881179	0.37895844	81.94058966	31.05207801	0.01220396	0.03220396
50	2.69158803	0.37152788	84.57940145	31.42360589	0.01182321	0.03182321

Rate $2\frac{1}{2}$%	A Compound Interest	B Present Value	C Amount of Annuity	D Present Value of Annuity	E Sinking Fund	F Amortization
n	$(1 + i)^n$	$\dfrac{1}{(1 + i)^n}$	$s_{\overline{n}|i}$	$a_{\overline{n}|i}$	$\dfrac{1}{s_{\overline{n}|i}}$	$\dfrac{1}{a_{\overline{n}|i}}$
1	1.02500000	0.97560976	1.00000000	0.97560976	1.00000000	1.02500000
2	1.05062500	0.95181440	2.02500000	1.92742415	0.49382716	0.51882716
3	1.07689063	0.92859941	3.07562500	2.85602356	0.32513717	0.35013717
4	1.10381289	0.90595064	4.15251562	3.76197421	0.24081788	0.26581788
5	1.13140821	0.88385429	5.25632852	4.64582850	0.19024686	0.21524686
6	1.15969342	0.86229687	6.38773673	5.50812536	0.15654997	0.18154997
7	1.18868575	0.84126524	7.54753015	6.34939060	0.13249543	0.15749543
8	1.21840290	0.82074657	8.73611590	7.17013717	0.11446735	0.13946735
9	1.24886297	0.80072836	9.95451880	7.97086553	0.10045689	0.12545689
10	1.28008454	0.78119840	11.20338177	8.75206393	0.08925876	0.11425876
11	1.31208666	0.76214478	12.48346631	9.51420871	0.08010596	0.10510596
12	1.34488882	0.74355589	13.79555297	10.25776460	0.07248713	0.09748713
13	1.37851104	0.72542038	15.14044179	10.98318497	0.06604827	0.09104827
14	1.41297382	0.70772720	16.51895284	11.69091217	0.06053652	0.08553652
15	1.44829817	0.69046556	17.93192666	12.38137773	0.05576646	0.08076646
16	1.48450562	0.67362493	19.38022483	13.05500266	0.05159899	0.07659899
17	1.52161826	0.65719506	20.86473045	13.71219772	0.04792777	0.07292777
18	1.55965872	0.64116591	22.38634871	14.35336363	0.04467008	0.06967008
19	1.59865019	0.62552772	23.94600743	14.97889134	0.04176062	0.06676062
20	1.63861644	0.61027094	25.54465761	15.58916229	0.03914713	0.06414713
21	1.67958185	0.59538629	27.18327405	16.18454857	0.03678733	0.06178733
22	1.72157140	0.58086467	28.86285590	16.76541324	0.03464661	0.05964661
23	1.76461068	0.56669724	30.58442730	17.33211048	0.03269638	0.05769638
24	1.80872595	0.55287535	32.34903798	17.88498583	0.03091282	0.05591282
25	1.85394410	0.53939059	34.15776393	18.42437642	0.02927592	0.05427592
26	1.90029270	0.52623472	36.01170803	18.95061114	0.02776875	0.05276875
27	1.94780002	0.51339973	37.91200073	19.46401087	0.02637687	0.05137687
28	1.99649502	0.50087778	39.85980075	19.96488866	0.02508793	0.05008793
29	2.04640739	0.48866125	41.85629577	20.45354991	0.02389127	0.04889127
30	2.09756758	0.47674269	43.90270316	20.93029259	0.02277764	0.04777764
31	2.15000677	0.46511481	46.00027074	21.39540741	0.02173900	0.04673900
32	2.20375694	0.45377055	48.15027751	21.84917796	0.02076831	0.04576831
33	2.25885086	0.44270298	50.35403445	22.29188094	0.01985938	0.04485938
34	2.31532213	0.43190534	52.61288531	22.72378628	0.01900675	0.04400675
35	2.37320519	0.42137107	54.92820744	23.14515734	0.01820558	0.04320558
36	2.43253532	0.41109372	57.30141263	23.55625107	0.01745158	0.04245158
37	2.49334870	0.40106705	59.73394794	23.95731812	0.01674090	0.04174090
38	2.55568242	0.39128492	62.22729664	24.34860304	0.01607012	0.04107012
39	2.61957448	0.38174139	64.78297906	24.73034443	0.01543615	0.04043615
40	2.68506384	0.37243062	67.40255354	25.10277505	0.01483623	0.03983623
41	2.75219043	0.36334695	70.08761737	25.46612200	0.01426786	0.03926786
42	2.82099520	0.35448483	72.83980781	25.82060683	0.01372876	0.03872876
43	2.89152008	0.34583886	75.66080300	26.16644569	0.01321688	0.03821688
44	2.96380808	0.33740376	78.55232308	26.50384945	0.01273037	0.03773037
45	3.03790328	0.32917440	81.51613116	26.83302386	0.01226751	0.03726751
46	3.11385086	0.32114576	84.55403443	27.15416962	0.01182676	0.03682676
47	3.19169713	0.31331294	87.66788530	27.46748255	0.01140669	0.03640669
48	3.27148956	0.30567116	90.85958243	27.77315371	0.01100599	0.03600599
49	3.35327680	0.29821576	94.13107199	28.07136947	0.01062348	0.03562348
50	3.43710872	0.29094221	97.48434879	28.36231168	0.01025806	0.03525806

Rate 3%	A Compound Interest	B Present Value	C Amount of Annuity	D Present Value of Annuity	E Sinking Fund	F Amortization
n	$(1 + i)^n$	$\dfrac{1}{(1 + i)^n}$	$s_{\overline{n}\rvert i}$	$a_{\overline{n}\rvert i}$	$\dfrac{1}{s_{\overline{n}\rvert i}}$	$\dfrac{1}{a_{\overline{n}\rvert i}}$
1	1.03000000	0.97087379	1.00000000	0.97087379	1.00000000	1.03000000
2	1.06090000	0.94259591	2.03000000	1.91346970	0.49261084	0.52261084
3	1.09272700	0.91514166	3.09090000	2.82861135	0.32353036	0.35353036
4	1.12550881	0.88848705	4.18362700	3.71709840	0.23902705	0.26902705
5	1.15927407	0.86260878	5.30913581	4.57970719	0.18835457	0.21835457
6	1.19405230	0.83748426	6.46840988	5.41719144	0.15459750	0.18459750
7	1.22987387	0.81309151	7.66246218	6.23028296	0.13050635	0.16050635
8	1.26677008	0.78940923	8.89233605	7.01969219	0.11245639	0.14245639
9	1.30477318	0.76641673	10.15910613	7.78610892	0.09843386	0.12843386
10	1.34391638	0.74409391	11.46387931	8.53020284	0.08723051	0.11723051
11	1.38423387	0.72242128	12.80779569	9.25262411	0.07807745	0.10807745
12	1.42576089	0.70137988	14.19202956	9.95400399	0.07046209	0.10046209
13	1.46853371	0.68095134	15.61779045	10.63495533	0.06402954	0.09402954
14	1.51258972	0.66111781	17.08632416	11.29607314	0.05852634	0.08852634
15	1.55796742	0.64186195	18.59891389	11.93793509	0.05376658	0.08376658
16	1.60470644	0.62316694	20.15688130	12.56110203	0.04961085	0.07961085
17	1.65284763	0.60501645	21.76158774	13.16611847	0.04595253	0.07595253
18	1.70243306	0.58739461	23.41443537	13.75351308	0.04270870	0.07270870
19	1.75350605	0.57028603	25.11686844	14.32379911	0.03981388	0.06981388
20	1.80611123	0.55367575	26.87037449	14.87747486	0.03721571	0.06721571
21	1.86029457	0.53754928	28.67648572	15.41502414	0.03487178	0.06487178
22	1.91610341	0.52189250	30.53678030	15.93691664	0.03274739	0.06274739
23	1.97358651	0.50669175	32.45288370	16.44360839	0.03081390	0.06081390
24	2.03279411	0.49193374	34.42647022	16.93554212	0.02904742	0.05904742
25	2.09377793	0.47760557	36.45926432	17.41314769	0.02742787	0.05742787
26	2.15659127	0.46369473	38.55304225	17.87684242	0.02593829	0.05593829
27	2.22128901	0.45018906	40.70963352	18.32703147	0.02456421	0.05456421
28	2.28792768	0.43707675	42.93092252	18.76410823	0.02329323	0.05329323
29	2.35656551	0.42434636	45.21885020	19.18845459	0.02211467	0.05211467
30	2.42726247	0.41198676	47.57541571	19.60044135	0.02101926	0.05101926
31	2.50008035	0.39998715	50.00267818	20.00042849	0.01999893	0.04999893
32	2.57508276	0.38833703	52.50275852	20.38876553	0.01904662	0.04904662
33	2.65233524	0.37702625	55.07784128	20.76579178	0.01815612	0.04815612
34	2.73190530	0.36604490	57.73017652	21.13183668	0.01732196	0.04732196
35	2.81386245	0.35538340	60.46208181	21.48722007	0.01653929	0.04653929
36	2.89827833	0.34503243	63.27594427	21.83225250	0.01580379	0.04580379
37	2.98522668	0.33498294	66.17422259	22.16723544	0.01511162	0.04511162
38	3.07478348	0.32522615	69.15944927	22.49246159	0.01445934	0.04445934
39	3.16702698	0.31575355	72.23423275	22.80821513	0.01384385	0.04384385
40	3.26203779	0.30655684	75.40125973	23.11477197	0.01326238	0.04326238
41	3.35989893	0.29762800	78.66329753	23.41239997	0.01271241	0.04271241
42	3.46069589	0.28895922	82.02319645	23.70135920	0.01219167	0.04219167
43	3.56451677	0.28054294	85.48389234	23.98190213	0.01169811	0.04169811
44	3.67145227	0.27237178	89.04840911	24.25427392	0.01122985	0.04122985
45	3.78159584	0.26443862	92.71986139	24.51871254	0.01078518	0.04078518
46	3.89504372	0.25673653	96.50145723	24.77544907	0.01036254	0.04036254
47	4.01189503	0.24925876	100.39650095	25.02470783	0.00996051	0.03996051
48	4.13225188	0.24199880	104.40839598	25.26670664	0.00957777	0.03957777
49	4.25621944	0.23495029	108.54064785	25.50165693	0.00921314	0.03921314
50	4.38390602	0.22810708	112.79686729	25.72976401	0.00886549	0.03886549

Rate $3\frac{1}{2}$%	A Compound Interest	B Present Value	C Amount of Annuity	D Present Value of Annuity	E Sinking Fund	F Amortization
n	$(1 + i)^n$	$\dfrac{1}{(1 + i)^n}$	$s_{\overline{n}|i}$	$a_{\overline{n}|i}$	$\dfrac{1}{s_{\overline{n}|i}}$	$\dfrac{1}{a_{\overline{n}|i}}$
1	1.03500000	0.96618357	1.00000000	0.96618357	1.00000000	1.03500000
2	1.07122500	0.93351070	2.03500000	1.89969428	0.49140049	0.52640049
3	1.10871788	0.90194271	3.10622500	2.80163698	0.32193418	0.35693418
4	1.14752300	0.87144223	4.21494287	3.67307921	0.23725114	0.27225114
5	1.18768631	0.84197317	5.36246588	4.51505238	0.18648137	0.22148137
6	1.22925533	0.81350064	6.55015218	5.32855302	0.15266821	0.18766821
7	1.27227926	0.78599096	7.77940751	6.11454398	0.12854449	0.16354449
8	1.31680904	0.75941156	9.05168677	6.87395554	0.11047665	0.14547665
9	1.36289735	0.73373097	10.36849581	7.60768651	0.09644601	0.13144601
10	1.41059876	0.70891881	11.73139316	8.31660532	0.08524137	0.12024137
11	1.45996972	0.68494571	13.14199192	9.00155104	0.07609197	0.11109197
12	1.51106866	0.66178330	14.60196164	9.66333433	0.06848395	0.10348395
13	1.56395606	0.63940415	16.11303030	10.30273849	0.06206157	0.09706157
14	1.61869452	0.61778179	17.67698636	10.92052028	0.05657073	0.09157073
15	1.67534883	0.59689062	19.29568088	11.51741090	0.05182507	0.08682507
16	1.73398604	0.57670591	20.97102971	12.09411681	0.04768483	0.08268483
17	1.79467555	0.55720378	22.70501575	12.65132059	0.04404313	0.07904313
18	1.85748920	0.53836114	24.49969130	13.18968173	0.04081684	0.07581684
19	1.92250132	0.52015569	26.35718050	13.70983742	0.03794033	0.07294033
20	1.98978886	0.50256588	28.27968181	14.21240330	0.03536108	0.07036108
21	2.05943147	0.48557090	30.26947068	14.69797420	0.03303659	0.06803659
22	2.13151158	0.46915063	32.32890215	15.16712484	0.03093207	0.06593207
23	2.20611448	0.45328563	34.46041373	15.62041047	0.02901880	0.06401880
24	2.28332849	0.43795713	36.66652821	16.05836760	0.02727283	0.06227283
25	2.36324498	0.42314699	38.94985669	16.48151459	0.02567404	0.06067404
26	2.44595856	0.40883767	41.31310168	16.89035226	0.02420540	0.05920540
27	2.53156711	0.39501224	43.75906024	17.28536451	0.02285241	0.05785241
28	2.62017196	0.38165434	46.29062734	17.66701885	0.02160265	0.05660265
29	2.71187798	0.36874815	48.91079930	18.03576700	0.02044538	0.05544538
30	2.80679370	0.35627841	51.62267728	18.39204541	0.01937133	0.05437133
31	2.90503148	0.34423035	54.42947098	18.73627576	0.01837240	0.05337240
32	3.00670759	0.33258971	57.33450247	19.06886547	0.01744150	0.05244150
33	3.11194235	0.32134271	60.34121005	19.39020818	0.01657242	0.05157242
34	3.22086033	0.31047605	63.45315240	19.70068423	0.01575966	0.05075966
35	3.33359045	0.29997686	66.67401274	20.00066110	0.01499835	0.04999835
36	3.45026611	0.28983272	70.00760318	20.29049381	0.01428416	0.04928416
37	3.57102543	0.28003161	73.45786930	20.57052542	0.01361325	0.04861325
38	3.69601132	0.27056194	77.02889472	20.84108736	0.01298214	0.04798214
39	3.82537171	0.26141250	80.72490604	21.10249987	0.01238775	0.04738775
40	3.95925972	0.25257247	84.55027775	21.35507234	0.01182728	0.04682728
41	4.09783381	0.24403137	88.50953747	21.59910371	0.01129822	0.04629822
42	4.24125799	0.23577910	92.60737128	21.83488281	0.01079828	0.04579828
43	4.38970202	0.22780590	96.84862928	22.06268870	0.01032539	0.04532539
44	4.54334160	0.22010231	101.23833130	22.28279102	0.00987768	0.04487768
45	4.70235855	0.21265924	105.78167290	22.49545026	0.00945343	0.04445343
46	4.86694110	0.20546787	110.48403145	22.70091813	0.00905108	0.04405108
47	5.03728404	0.19851968	115.35097255	22.89943780	0.00866919	0.04366919
48	5.21358898	0.19180645	120.38825659	23.09124425	0.00830646	0.04330646
49	5.39606459	0.18532024	125.60184557	23.27656450	0.00796167	0.04296167
50	5.58492686	0.17905337	130.99791016	23.45561787	0.00763371	0.04263371

Rate $3\frac{3}{4}$%	A Compound Interest	B Present Value	C Amount of Annuity	D Present Value of Annuity	E Sinking Fund	F Amortization
n	$(1 + i)^n$	$\dfrac{1}{(1 + i)^n}$	$s_{\overline{n}|i}$	$a_{\overline{n}|i}$	$\dfrac{1}{s_{\overline{n}|i}}$	$\dfrac{1}{a_{\overline{n}|i}}$
1	1.03750000	0.96385542	1.00000000	0.96385542	1.00000000	1.03750000
2	1.07640625	0.92901727	2.03750000	1.89287270	0.49079755	0.52829755
3	1.11677148	0.89543834	3.11390625	2.78831103	0.32114005	0.35864005
4	1.15865042	0.86307310	4.23067773	3.65138413	0.23636875	0.27386875
5	1.20209981	0.83187768	5.38932815	4.48326181	0.18555189	0.22305189
6	1.24717855	0.80180981	6.59142796	5.28507162	0.15171219	0.18921219
7	1.29394774	0.77282874	7.83860650	6.05790036	0.12757370	0.16507370
8	1.34247078	0.74489517	9.13255425	6.80279553	0.10949839	0.14699839
9	1.39281344	0.71797125	10.47502503	7.52076677	0.09546517	0.13296517
10	1.44504394	0.69202048	11.86783847	8.21278725	0.08426134	0.12176134
11	1.49923309	0.66700769	13.31288241	8.87979494	0.07511521	0.11261521
12	1.55545433	0.64289898	14.81211550	9.52269392	0.06751230	0.10501230
13	1.61378387	0.61966167	16.36756983	10.14235558	0.06109642	0.09859642
14	1.67430076	0.59726426	17.98135370	10.73961984	0.05561317	0.09311317
15	1.73708704	0.57567639	19.65565447	11.31529623	0.05087595	0.08837595
16	1.80222781	0.55486881	21.39274151	11.87016504	0.04674483	0.08424483
17	1.86981135	0.53481331	23.19496932	12.40497835	0.04311280	0.08061280
18	1.93992927	0.51548271	25.06478067	12.92046106	0.03989662	0.07739662
19	2.01267662	0.49685080	27.00470994	13.41731187	0.03703058	0.07453058
20	2.08815200	0.47889234	29.01738656	13.89620421	0.03446210	0.07196210
21	2.16645770	0.46158298	31.10553856	14.35778719	0.03214862	0.06964862
22	2.24769986	0.44489926	33.27199626	14.80268645	0.03005531	0.06755531
23	2.33198860	0.42881856	35.51969612	15.23150501	0.02815339	0.06565339
24	2.41943818	0.41331910	37.85168472	15.64482411	0.02641890	0.06391890
25	2.51016711	0.39837985	40.27112290	16.04320396	0.02483169	0.06233169
26	2.60429838	0.38398058	42.78129001	16.42718454	0.02337470	0.06087470
27	2.70195956	0.37010176	45.38558838	16.79728630	0.02203343	0.05953343
28	2.80328305	0.35672459	48.08754794	17.15401089	0.02079540	0.05829540
29	2.90840616	0.34383093	50.89083099	17.49784183	0.01964991	0.05714991
30	3.01747139	0.33140331	53.79923715	17.82924513	0.01858762	0.05608762
31	3.13062657	0.31942487	56.81670855	18.14867001	0.01760046	0.05510046
32	3.24802507	0.30787940	59.94733512	18.45654941	0.01668131	0.05418131
33	3.36982601	0.29675123	63.19536019	18.75330063	0.01582395	0.05332395
34	3.49619448	0.28602528	66.56518619	19.03932591	0.01502287	0.05252287
35	3.62730178	0.27568702	70.06138067	19.31501293	0.01427320	0.05177320
36	3.76332559	0.26572242	73.68868245	19.58073535	0.01357060	0.05107060
37	3.90445030	0.25611800	77.45200804	19.83685335	0.01291122	0.05041122
38	4.05086719	0.24686072	81.35645834	20.08371407	0.01229159	0.04979159
39	4.20277471	0.23793805	85.40732553	20.32165212	0.01170860	0.04920860
40	4.36037876	0.22933788	89.61010024	20.55098999	0.01115946	0.04865946
41	4.52389296	0.22104855	93.97047900	20.77203855	0.01064164	0.04814164
42	4.69353895	0.21305885	98.49437196	20.98509739	0.01015286	0.04765286
43	4.86954666	0.20535793	103.18791091	21.19045532	0.00969106	0.04719106
44	5.05215466	0.19793535	108.05745757	21.38839067	0.00925434	0.04675434
45	5.24161046	0.19078106	113.10961223	21.57917173	0.00884098	0.04634098
46	5.43817085	0.18388536	118.35122269	21.76305709	0.00844943	0.04594943
47	5.64210226	0.17723890	123.78939354	21.94029599	0.00807824	0.04557824
48	5.85368109	0.17083268	129.43149579	22.11112866	0.00772609	0.04522609
49	6.07319413	0.16465800	135.28517689	22.27578666	0.00739179	0.04489179
50	6.30093891	0.15870651	141.35837102	22.43449317	0.00707422	0.04457422

Rate 4%	A Compound Interest	B Present Value	C Amount of Annuity	D Present Value of Annuity	E Sinking Fund	F Amortization
n	$(1 + i)^n$	$\dfrac{1}{(1 + i)^n}$	$s_{\overline{n}\mid i}$	$a_{\overline{n}\mid i}$	$\dfrac{1}{s_{\overline{n}\mid i}}$	$\dfrac{1}{a_{\overline{n}\mid i}}$
1	1.04000000	0.96153846	1.00000000	0.96153846	1.00000000	1.04000000
2	1.08160000	0.92455621	2.04000000	1.88609467	0.49019608	0.53019608
3	1.12486400	0.88899636	3.12160000	2.77509103	0.32034854	0.36034854
4	1.16985856	0.85480419	4.24646400	3.62989522	0.23549005	0.27549005
5	1.21665290	0.82192711	5.41632256	4.45182233	0.18462711	0.22462711
6	1.26531902	0.79031453	6.63297546	5.24213686	0.15076190	0.19076190
7	1.31593178	0.75991781	7.89829448	6.00205467	0.12660961	0.16660961
8	1.36856905	0.73069021	9.21422626	6.73274487	0.10852783	0.14852783
9	1.42331181	0.70258674	10.58279531	7.43533161	0.09449299	0.13449299
10	1.48024428	0.67556417	12.00610712	8.11089578	0.08329094	0.12329094
11	1.53945406	0.64958093	13.48635141	8.76047671	0.07414904	0.11414904
12	1.60103222	0.62459705	15.02580546	9.38507376	0.06655217	0.10655217
13	1.66507351	0.60057409	16.62683768	9.98564785	0.06014373	0.10014373
14	1.73167645	0.57747508	18.29191119	10.56312293	0.05466897	0.09466897
15	1.80094351	0.55526450	20.02358764	11.11838743	0.04994110	0.08994110
16	1.87298125	0.53390818	21.82453114	11.65229561	0.04582000	0.08582000
17	1.94790050	0.51337325	23.69751239	12.16566885	0.04219852	0.08219852
18	2.02581652	0.49362812	25.64541288	12.65929697	0.03899333	0.07899333
19	2.10684918	0.47464242	27.67122940	13.13393940	0.03613862	0.07613862
20	2.19112314	0.45638695	29.77807858	13.59032634	0.03358175	0.07358175
21	2.27876807	0.43883360	31.96920172	14.02915995	0.03128011	0.07128011
22	2.36991879	0.42195539	34.24796979	14.45111533	0.02919881	0.06919881
23	2.46471554	0.40572633	36.61788858	14.85684167	0.02730906	0.06730906
24	2.56330416	0.39012147	39.08260412	15.24696314	0.02558683	0.06558683
25	2.66583633	0.37511680	41.64590829	15.62207994	0.02401196	0.06401196
26	2.77246978	0.36068923	44.31174462	15.98276918	0.02256738	0.06256738
27	2.88336858	0.34681657	47.08421440	16.32958575	0.02123854	0.06123854
28	2.99870332	0.33347747	49.96758298	16.66306322	0.02001298	0.06001298
29	3.11865145	0.32065141	52.96628630	16.98371463	0.01887993	0.05887993
30	3.24339751	0.30831867	56.08493775	17.29203330	0.01783010	0.05783010
31	3.37313341	0.29646026	59.32833526	17.58849356	0.01685535	0.05685535
32	3.50805875	0.28505794	62.70146867	17.87355150	0.01594859	0.05594859
33	3.64838110	0.27409417	66.20952742	18.14764567	0.01510357	0.05510357
34	3.79431634	0.26355209	69.85790851	18.41119776	0.01431477	0.05431477
35	3.94608899	0.25341547	73.65222486	18.66461323	0.01357732	0.05357732
36	4.10393255	0.24366872	77.59831385	18.90828195	0.01288688	0.05288688
37	4.26808986	0.23429685	81.70224640	19.14257880	0.01223957	0.05223957
38	4.43881345	0.22528543	85.97033626	19.36786423	0.01163192	0.05163192
39	4.61636599	0.21662061	90.40914971	19.58448484	0.01106083	0.05106083
40	4.80102063	0.20828904	95.02551570	19.79277388	0.01052349	0.05052349
41	4.99306145	0.20027793	99.82653633	19.99305181	0.01001738	0.05001738
42	5.19278391	0.19257493	104.81959778	20.18562674	0.00954020	0.04954020
43	5.40049527	0.18516820	110.01238169	20.37079494	0.00908989	0.04908989
44	5.61651508	0.17804635	115.41287696	20.54884129	0.00866454	0.04866454
45	5.84117568	0.17119841	121.02939204	20.72003970	0.00826246	0.04826246
46	6.07482271	0.16461386	126.87056772	20.88465356	0.00788205	0.04788205
47	6.31781562	0.15828256	132.94539043	21.04293612	0.00752189	0.04752189
48	6.57052824	0.15219476	139.26320604	21.19513088	0.00718065	0.04718065
49	6.83334937	0.14634112	145.83373429	21.34147200	0.00685712	0.04685712
50	7.10668335	0.14071262	152.66708366	21.48218462	0.00655020	0.04655020

Rate $4\frac{1}{2}$%	A Compound Interest	B Present Value	C Amount of Annuity	D Present Value of Annuity	E Sinking Fund	F Amortization
n	$(1 + i)^n$	$\dfrac{1}{(1 + i)^n}$	$s_{\overline{n}|i}$	$a_{\overline{n}|i}$	$\dfrac{1}{s_{\overline{n}|i}}$	$\dfrac{1}{a_{\overline{n}|i}}$
1	1.04500000	0.95693780	1.00000000	0.95693780	1.00000000	1.04500000
2	1.09202500	0.91572995	2.04500000	1.87266775	0.48899756	0.53399756
3	1.14116613	0.87629660	3.13702500	2.74896435	0.31877336	0.36377336
4	1.19251860	0.83856134	4.27819112	3.58752570	0.23374365	0.27874365
5	1.24618194	0.80245105	5.47070973	4.38997674	0.18279164	0.22779164
6	1.30226012	0.76789574	6.71689166	5.15787248	0.14887839	0.19387839
7	1.36086183	0.73482846	8.01915179	5.89270094	0.12470147	0.16970147
8	1.42210061	0.70318513	9.38001362	6.59588607	0.10660965	0.15160965
9	1.48609514	0.67290443	10.80211423	7.26879050	0.09257447	0.13757447
10	1.55296942	0.64392768	12.28820937	7.91271818	0.08137882	0.12637882
11	1.62285305	0.61619874	13.84117879	8.52891692	0.07224818	0.11724818
12	1.69588143	0.58966386	15.46403184	9.11858078	0.06466619	0.10966619
13	1.77219610	0.56427164	17.15991327	9.68285242	0.05827535	0.10327535
14	1.85194492	0.53997286	18.93210937	10.22282528	0.05282032	0.09782032
15	1.93528244	0.51672044	20.78405429	10.73954573	0.04811381	0.09311381
16	2.02237015	0.49446932	22.71933673	11.23401505	0.04401537	0.08901537
17	2.11337681	0.47317639	24.74170689	11.70719143	0.04041758	0.08541758
18	2.20847877	0.45280037	26.85508370	12.15999180	0.03723690	0.08223690
19	2.30786031	0.43330179	29.06356246	12.59329359	0.03440734	0.07940734
20	2.41171402	0.41464286	31.37142277	13.00793645	0.03187614	0.07687614
21	2.52024116	0.39678743	33.78313680	13.40472388	0.02960057	0.07460057
22	2.63365201	0.37970089	36.30337795	13.78442476	0.02754565	0.07254565
23	2.75216635	0.36335013	38.93702996	14.14777489	0.02568249	0.07068249
24	2.87601383	0.34770347	41.68919631	14.49547837	0.02398703	0.06898703
25	3.00543446	0.33273060	44.56521015	14.82820896	0.02243903	0.06743903
26	3.14067901	0.31840248	47.57064460	15.14661145	0.02102137	0.06602137
27	3.28200956	0.30469137	50.71132361	15.45130282	0.01971946	0.06471946
28	3.42969999	0.29157069	53.99333317	15.74287351	0.01852081	0.06352081
29	3.58403649	0.27901502	57.42303316	16.02188853	0.01741461	0.06241461
30	3.74531813	0.26700002	61.00706966	16.28888854	0.01639154	0.06139154
31	3.91385745	0.25550241	64.75238779	16.54439095	0.01544345	0.06044345
32	4.08998104	0.24449991	68.66624524	16.78889086	0.01456320	0.05956320
33	4.27403018	0.23397121	72.75622628	17.02286207	0.01374453	0.05874453
34	4.46636154	0.22389589	77.03025646	17.24675796	0.01298191	0.05798191
35	4.66734781	0.21425444	81.49661800	17.46101240	0.01227045	0.05727045
36	4.87737846	0.20502817	86.16396581	17.66604058	0.01160578	0.05660578
37	5.09686049	0.19619921	91.04134427	17.86223979	0.01098402	0.05598402
38	5.32621921	0.18775044	96.13820476	18.04999023	0.01040169	0.05540169
39	5.56589908	0.17966549	101.46442398	18.22965572	0.00985567	0.05485567
40	5.81636454	0.17192870	107.03032306	18.40158442	0.00934315	0.05434315
41	6.07810094	0.16452507	112.84668760	18.56610949	0.00886158	0.05386158
42	6.35161548	0.15744026	118.92478854	18.72354975	0.00840868	0.05340868
43	6.63743818	0.15066054	125.27640402	18.87421029	0.00798235	0.05298235
44	6.93612290	0.14417276	131.91384220	19.01838305	0.00758071	0.05258071
45	7.24824843	0.13796437	138.84996510	19.15634742	0.00720202	0.05220202
46	7.57441961	0.13202332	146.09821353	19.28837074	0.00684471	0.05184471
47	7.91526849	0.12633810	153.67263314	19.41470884	0.00650734	0.05150734
48	8.27145557	0.12089771	161.58790163	19.53560654	0.00618858	0.05118858
49	8.64367107	0.11569158	169.85935720	19.65129813	0.00588722	0.05088722
50	9.03263627	0.11070965	178.50302828	19.76200778	0.00560215	0.05060215

Rate 5% n	A Compound Interest $(1 + i)^n$	B Present Value $\dfrac{1}{(1 + i)^n}$	C Amount of Annuity $s_{\overline{n}\mid i}$	D Present Value of Annuity $a_{\overline{n}\mid i}$	E Sinking Fund $\dfrac{1}{s_{\overline{n}\mid i}}$	F Amortization $\dfrac{1}{a_{\overline{n}\mid i}}$
1	1.05000000	0.95238095	1.00000000	0.95238095	1.00000000	1.05000000
2	1.10250000	0.90702948	2.05000000	1.85941043	0.48780488	0.53780488
3	1.15762500	0.86383760	3.15250000	2.72324803	0.31720856	0.36720856
4	1.21550625	0.82270247	4.31012500	3.54595050	0.23201183	0.28201183
5	1.27628156	0.78352617	5.52563125	4.32947667	0.18097480	0.23097480
6	1.34009564	0.74621540	6.80191281	5.07569207	0.14701747	0.19701747
7	1.40710042	0.71068133	8.14200845	5.78637340	0.12281982	0.17281982
8	1.47745544	0.67683936	9.54910888	6.46321276	0.10472181	0.15472181
9	1.55132822	0.64460892	11.02656432	7.10782168	0.09069008	0.14069008
10	1.62889463	0.61391325	12.57789254	7.72173493	0.07950457	0.12950457
11	1.71033936	0.58467929	14.20678716	8.30641422	0.07038889	0.12038889
12	1.79585633	0.55683742	15.91712652	8.86325164	0.06282541	0.11282541
13	1.88564914	0.53032135	17.71298285	9.39357299	0.05645577	0.10645577
14	1.97993160	0.50506795	19.59863199	9.89864094	0.05102397	0.10102397
15	2.07892818	0.48101710	21.57856359	10.37965804	0.04634229	0.09634229
16	2.18287459	0.45811152	23.65749177	10.83776956	0.04226991	0.09226991
17	2.29201832	0.43629669	25.84036636	11.27406625	0.03869914	0.08869914
18	2.40661923	0.41552065	28.13238467	11.68958690	0.03554622	0.08554622
19	2.52695020	0.39573396	30.53900391	12.08532086	0.03274501	0.08274501
20	2.65329771	0.37688948	33.06595410	12.46221034	0.03024259	0.08024259
21	2.78596259	0.35894236	35.71925181	12.82115271	0.02799611	0.07799611
22	2.92526072	0.34184987	38.50521440	13.16300258	0.02597051	0.07597051
23	3.07152376	0.32557131	41.43047512	13.48857388	0.02413682	0.07413682
24	3.22509994	0.31006791	44.50199887	13.79864179	0.02247090	0.07247090
25	3.38635494	0.29530277	47.72709882	14.09394457	0.02095246	0.07095246
26	3.55567269	0.28124073	51.11345376	14.37518530	0.01956432	0.06956432
27	3.73345632	0.26784832	54.66912645	14.64303362	0.01829186	0.06829186
28	3.92012914	0.25509364	58.40258277	14.89812726	0.01712253	0.06712253
29	4.11613560	0.24294632	62.32271191	15.14107358	0.01604551	0.06604551
30	4.32194238	0.23137745	66.43884750	15.37245103	0.01505144	0.06505144
31	4.53803949	0.22035947	70.76078988	15.59281050	0.01413212	0.06413212
32	4.76494147	0.20986617	75.29882937	15.80267667	0.01328042	0.06328042
33	5.00318854	0.19978254	80.06377084	16.00254921	0.01249004	0.06249004
34	5.25334797	0.19035480	85.06695938	16.19290401	0.01175545	0.06175545
35	5.51601537	0.18129029	90.32030735	16.37419429	0.01107171	0.06107171
36	5.79181614	0.17265741	95.83632272	16.54685171	0.01043446	0.06043446
37	6.08140694	0.16443563	101.62813886	16.71128734	0.00983979	0.05983979
38	6.38547729	0.15660536	107.70954580	16.86789271	0.00928423	0.05928423
39	6.70475115	0.14914797	114.09502309	17.01704067	0.00876462	0.05876462
40	7.03998871	0.14204568	120.79977424	17.15908635	0.00827816	0.05827816
41	7.39198815	0.13528160	127.83976295	17.29436796	0.00782229	0.05782229
42	7.76158756	0.12883962	135.23175110	17.42320758	0.00739471	0.05739471
43	8.14966693	0.12270440	142.99333866	17.54591198	0.00699333	0.05699333
44	8.55715028	0.11686133	151.14300559	17.66277331	0.00661625	0.05661625
45	8.98500779	0.11129651	159.70015587	17.77406982	0.00626173	0.05626173
46	9.43425818	0.10599668	168.68516366	17.88006650	0.00592820	0.05592820
47	9.90597109	0.10094921	178.11942185	17.98101571	0.00561421	0.05561421
48	10.40126965	0.09614211	188.02539294	18.07715782	0.00531843	0.05531843
49	10.92133313	0.09156391	198.42666259	18.16872173	0.00503965	0.05503965
50	11.46739979	0.08720373	209.34799572	18.25592546	0.00477674	0.05477674

Rate $5\frac{1}{2}$%	A Compound Interest	B Present Value	C Amount of Annuity	D Present Value of Annuity	E Sinking Fund	F Amortization
n	$(1 + i)^n$	$\dfrac{1}{(1 + i)^n}$	$s_{\overline{n}|i}$	$a_{\overline{n}|i}$	$\dfrac{1}{s_{\overline{n}|i}}$	$\dfrac{1}{a_{\overline{n}|i}}$
1	1.05500000	0.94786730	1.00000000	0.94786730	1.00000000	1.05500000
2	1.11302500	0.89845242	2.05500000	1.84631971	0.48661800	0.54161800
3	1.17424138	0.85161366	3.16802500	2.69793338	0.31565407	0.37065407
4	1.23882465	0.80721674	4.34226637	3.50515012	0.23029449	0.28529449
5	1.30696001	0.76513435	5.58109103	4.27028448	0.17917644	0.23417644
6	1.37884281	0.72524583	6.88805103	4.99553031	0.14517895	0.20017895
7	1.45467916	0.68743681	8.26689384	5.68296712	0.12096442	0.17596442
8	1.53468651	0.65159887	9.72157300	6.33456599	0.10286401	0.15786401
9	1.61909427	0.61762926	11.25625951	6.95219525	0.08883946	0.14383946
10	1.70814446	0.58543058	12.87535379	7.53762583	0.07766777	0.13266777
11	1.80209240	0.55491050	14.58349825	8.09253633	0.06857065	0.12357065
12	1.90120749	0.52598152	16.38559065	8.61851785	0.06102923	0.11602923
13	2.00577390	0.49856068	18.28679814	9.11707853	0.05468426	0.10968426
14	2.11609146	0.47256937	20.29257203	9.58964790	0.04927912	0.10427912
15	2.23247649	0.44793305	22.40866350	10.03758094	0.04462560	0.09962560
16	2.35526270	0.42458109	24.64113999	10.46216203	0.04058254	0.09558254
17	2.48480215	0.40244653	26.99640269	10.86460856	0.03704197	0.09204197
18	2.62146627	0.38146590	29.48120483	11.24607447	0.03391992	0.08891992
19	2.76564691	0.36157906	32.10267110	11.60765352	0.03115006	0.08615006
20	2.91775749	0.34272896	34.86831801	11.95038248	0.02867933	0.08367933
21	3.07823415	0.32486158	37.78607550	12.27524406	0.02646478	0.08146478
22	3.24753703	0.30792567	40.86430965	12.58316973	0.02447123	0.07947123
23	3.42615157	0.29187267	44.11184669	12.87504239	0.02266965	0.07766965
24	3.61458990	0.27665656	47.53799825	13.15169895	0.02103580	0.07603580
25	3.81339235	0.26223370	51.15258816	13.41393266	0.01954935	0.07454935
26	4.02312893	0.24856275	54.96598051	13.66249541	0.01819307	0.07319307
27	4.24440102	0.23560450	58.98910943	13.89809991	0.01695228	0.07195228
28	4.47784307	0.22332181	63.23351045	14.12142172	0.01581440	0.07081440
29	4.72412444	0.21167944	67.71135353	14.33310116	0.01476857	0.06976857
30	4.98395129	0.20064402	72.43547797	14.53374517	0.01380539	0.06880539
31	5.25806861	0.19018390	77.41942926	14.72392907	0.01291665	0.06791665
32	5.54726238	0.18026910	82.67749787	14.90419817	0.01209519	0.06709519
33	5.85236181	0.17087119	88.22476025	15.07506936	0.01133469	0.06633469
34	6.17424171	0.16196321	94.07712207	15.23703257	0.01062958	0.06562958
35	6.51382501	0.15351963	100.25136378	15.39055220	0.00997493	0.06497493
36	6.87208538	0.14551624	106.76518879	15.53606843	0.00936635	0.06436635
37	7.25005008	0.13793008	113.63727417	15.67399851	0.00879993	0.06379993
38	7.64880283	0.13073941	120.88732425	15.80473793	0.00827217	0.06327217
39	8.06948699	0.12392362	128.53612708	15.92866154	0.00777991	0.06277991
40	8.51330877	0.11746314	136.60561407	16.04612469	0.00732034	0.06232034
41	8.98154076	0.11133947	145.11892285	16.15746416	0.00689090	0.06189090
42	9.47552550	0.10553504	154.10046360	16.26299920	0.00648927	0.06148927
43	9.99667940	0.10003322	163.57598910	16.36303242	0.00611337	0.06111337
44	10.54649677	0.09481822	173.57266850	16.45785063	0.00576128	0.06076128
45	11.12655409	0.08987509	184.11916527	16.54772572	0.00543127	0.06043127
46	11.73851456	0.08518965	195.24571936	16.63291537	0.00512175	0.06012175
47	12.38413287	0.08074849	206.98423392	16.71366386	0.00483129	0.05983129
48	13.06526017	0.07653885	219.36836679	16.79020271	0.00455854	0.05955854
49	13.78384948	0.07254867	232.43362696	16.86275139	0.00430230	0.05930230
50	14.54196120	0.06876652	246.21747645	16.93151790	0.00406145	0.05906145

Rate 6% n	A Compound Interest $(1 + i)^n$	B Present Value $\dfrac{1}{(1 + i)^n}$	C Amount of Annuity $s_{\overline{n}\rvert i}$	D Present Value of Annuity $a_{\overline{n}\rvert i}$	E Sinking Fund $\dfrac{1}{s_{\overline{n}\rvert i}}$	F Amortization $\dfrac{1}{a_{\overline{n}\rvert i}}$
1	1.06000000	0.94339623	1.00000000	0.94339623	1.00000000	1.06000000
2	1.12360000	0.88999644	2.06000000	1.83339267	0.48543689	0.54543689
3	1.19101600	0.83961928	3.18360000	2.67301195	0.31410981	0.37410981
4	1.26247696	0.79209366	4.37461600	3.46510561	0.22859149	0.28859149
5	1.33822558	0.74725817	5.63709296	4.21236379	0.17739640	0.23739640
6	1.41851911	0.70496054	6.97531854	4.91732433	0.14336263	0.20336263
7	1.50363026	0.66505711	8.39383765	5.58238144	0.11913502	0.17913502
8	1.59384807	0.62741237	9.89746791	6.20979381	0.10103594	0.16103594
9	1.68947896	0.59189846	11.49131598	6.80169227	0.08702224	0.14702224
10	1.79084770	0.55839478	13.18079494	7.36008705	0.07586796	0.13586796
11	1.89829856	0.52678753	14.97164264	7.88687458	0.06679294	0.12679294
12	2.01219647	0.49696936	16.86994120	8.38384394	0.05927703	0.11927703
13	2.13292826	0.46883902	18.88213767	8.85268296	0.05296011	0.11296011
14	2.26090396	0.44230096	21.01506593	9.29498393	0.04758491	0.10758491
15	2.39655819	0.41726506	23.27596988	9.71224899	0.04296276	0.10296276
16	2.54035168	0.39364628	25.67252808	10.10589527	0.03895214	0.09895214
17	2.69277279	0.37136442	28.21287976	10.47725969	0.03544480	0.09544480
18	2.85433915	0.35034379	30.90565255	10.82760348	0.03235654	0.09235654
19	3.02559950	0.33051301	33.75999170	11.15811649	0.02962086	0.08962086
20	3.20713547	0.31180473	36.78559120	11.46992122	0.02718456	0.08718456
21	3.39956360	0.29415540	39.99272668	11.76407662	0.02500455	0.08500455
22	3.60353742	0.27750510	43.39229028	12.04158172	0.02304557	0.08304557
23	3.81974966	0.26179726	46.99582769	12.30337898	0.02127848	0.08127848
24	4.04893464	0.24697855	50.81557735	12.55035753	0.01967900	0.07967900
25	4.29187072	0.23299863	54.86451200	12.78335616	0.01822672	0.07822672
26	4.54938296	0.21981003	59.15638272	13.00316619	0.01690435	0.07690435
27	4.82234594	0.20736795	63.70576568	13.21053414	0.01569717	0.07569717
28	5.11168670	0.19563014	68.52811162	13.40616428	0.01459255	0.07459255
29	5.41838790	0.18455674	73.63979832	13.59072102	0.01357961	0.07357961
30	5.74349117	0.17411013	79.05818622	13.76483115	0.01264891	0.07264891
31	6.08810064	0.16425484	84.80167739	13.92908599	0.01179222	0.07179222
32	6.45338668	0.15495740	90.88977803	14.08404339	0.01100234	0.07100234
33	6.84058988	0.14618622	97.34316471	14.23022961	0.01027293	0.07027293
34	7.25102528	0.13791153	104.18375460	14.36814114	0.00959843	0.06959843
35	7.68608679	0.13010522	111.43477987	14.49824636	0.00897386	0.06897386
36	8.14725200	0.12274077	119.12086666	14.62098713	0.00839483	0.06839483
37	8.63608712	0.11579318	127.26811866	14.73678031	0.00785743	0.06785743
38	9.15425235	0.10923885	135.90420578	14.84601916	0.00735812	0.06735812
39	9.70350749	0.10305552	145.05845813	14.94907468	0.00689377	0.06689377
40	10.28571794	0.09722219	154.76196562	15.04629687	0.00646154	0.06646154
41	10.90286101	0.09171905	165.04768356	15.13801592	0.00605886	0.06605886
42	11.55703267	0.08652740	175.95054457	15.22454332	0.00568342	0.06568342
43	12.25045463	0.08162962	187.50757724	15.30617294	0.00533312	0.06533312
44	12.98548191	0.07700908	199.75803188	15.38318202	0.00500606	0.06500606
45	13.76461083	0.07265007	212.74351379	15.45583209	0.00470050	0.06470050
46	14.59048748	0.06853781	226.50812462	15.52436990	0.00441485	0.06441485
47	15.46591673	0.06465831	241.09861210	15.58902821	0.00414768	0.06414768
48	16.39387173	0.06099840	256.56452882	15.65002661	0.00389765	0.06389765
49	17.37750403	0.05754566	272.95840055	15.70757227	0.00366356	0.06366356
50	18.42015427	0.05428836	290.33590458	15.76186064	0.00344429	0.06344429

Rate $6\frac{1}{2}$%	A Compound Interest	B Present Value	C Amount of Annuity	D Present Value of Annuity	E Sinking Fund	F Amortization
n	$(1 + i)^n$	$\dfrac{1}{(1 + i)^n}$	$s_{\overline{n}\|i}$	$a_{\overline{n}\|i}$	$\dfrac{1}{s_{\overline{n}\|i}}$	$\dfrac{1}{a_{\overline{n}\|i}}$
1	1.06500000	0.93896714	1.00000000	0.93896714	1.00000000	1.06500000
2	1.13422500	0.88165928	2.06500000	1.82062642	0.48426150	0.54926150
3	1.20794963	0.82784909	3.19922500	2.64847551	0.31257570	0.37757570
4	1.28646635	0.77732309	4.40717462	3.42579860	0.22690274	0.29190274
5	1.37008666	0.72988084	5.69364098	4.15567944	0.17563454	0.24063454
6	1.45914230	0.68533412	7.06372764	4.84101356	0.14156831	0.20656831
7	1.55398655	0.64350621	8.52286994	5.48451977	0.11733137	0.18233137
8	1.65499567	0.60423119	10.07685648	6.08875096	0.09923730	0.16423730
9	1.76257039	0.56735323	11.73185215	6.65610419	0.08523803	0.15023803
10	1.87713747	0.53272604	13.49442254	7.18883022	0.07410469	0.13910469
11	1.99915140	0.50021224	15.37156001	7.68904246	0.06505521	0.13005521
12	2.12909624	0.46968285	17.37071141	8.15872532	0.05756817	0.12256817
13	2.26748750	0.44101676	19.49980765	8.59974208	0.05128256	0.11628256
14	2.41487418	0.41410025	21.76729515	9.01384233	0.04594048	0.11094048
15	2.57184101	0.38882652	24.18216933	9.40266885	0.04135278	0.10635278
16	2.73901067	0.36509533	26.75401034	9.76776418	0.03737757	0.10237757
17	2.91704637	0.34281251	29.49302101	10.11057670	0.03390633	0.09890633
18	3.10655438	0.32188969	32.41006738	10.43246638	0.03085461	0.09585461
19	3.30858691	0.30224384	35.51672176	10.73471022	0.02815575	0.09315575
20	3.52364506	0.28379703	38.82530867	11.01850725	0.02575640	0.09075640
21	3.75268199	0.26647608	42.34895373	11.28498333	0.02361333	0.08861333
22	3.99660632	0.25021228	46.10163573	11.53519562	0.02169120	0.08669120
23	4.25638573	0.23494111	50.09824205	11.77013673	0.01996078	0.08496078
24	4.53305081	0.22060198	54.35462778	11.99073871	0.01839770	0.08339770
25	4.82769911	0.20713801	58.88767859	12.19787673	0.01698148	0.08198148
26	5.14149955	0.19449579	63.71537769	12.39237251	0.01569480	0.08069480
27	5.47569702	0.18262515	68.85687725	12.57499766	0.01452288	0.07952288
28	5.83161733	0.17147902	74.33257427	12.74647668	0.01345305	0.07845305
29	6.21067245	0.16101316	80.16419159	12.90748984	0.01247440	0.07747440
30	6.61436616	0.15118607	86.37486405	13.05867591	0.01157744	0.07657744
31	7.04429996	0.14195875	92.98923021	13.20063465	0.01075393	0.07575393
32	7.50217946	0.13329460	100.03353017	13.33392925	0.00999665	0.07499665
33	7.98982113	0.12515925	107.53570963	13.45908850	0.00929924	0.07429924
34	8.50915950	0.11752042	115.52553076	13.57660892	0.00865610	0.07365610
35	9.06225487	0.11034781	124.03469026	13.68695673	0.00806226	0.07306226
36	9.65130143	0.10361297	133.09694513	13.79056970	0.00751332	0.07251332
37	10.27863603	0.09728917	142.74824656	13.88785887	0.00700534	0.07200534
38	10.94674737	0.09135134	153.02688259	13.97921021	0.00653480	0.07153480
39	11.65828595	0.08577590	163.97362996	14.06498611	0.00609854	0.07109854
40	12.41607453	0.08054075	175.63191590	14.14552687	0.00569373	0.07069373
41	13.22311938	0.07562512	188.04799044	14.22115199	0.00531779	0.07031779
42	14.08262214	0.07100950	201.27110981	14.29216149	0.00496842	0.06996842
43	14.99799258	0.06667559	215.35373195	14.35883708	0.00464352	0.06964352
44	15.97286209	0.06260619	230.35172453	14.42144327	0.00434119	0.06934119
45	17.01109813	0.05878515	246.32458662	14.48022842	0.00405968	0.06905968
46	18.11681951	0.05519733	263.33568475	14.53542575	0.00379743	0.06879743
47	19.29441278	0.05182848	281.45250426	14.58725422	0.00355300	0.06855300
48	20.54854961	0.04866524	300.74691704	14.63591946	0.00332505	0.06832505
49	21.88420533	0.04569506	321.29546665	14.68161451	0.00311240	0.06811240
50	23.30667868	0.04290616	343.17967198	14.72452067	0.00291393	0.06791393

Rate 7%	A Compound Interest	B Present Value	C Amount of Annuity	D Present Value of Annuity	E Sinking Fund	F Amortization
n	$(1 + i)^n$	$\dfrac{1}{(1 + i)^n}$	$s_{\overline{n}\mid i}$	$a_{\overline{n}\mid i}$	$\dfrac{1}{s_{\overline{n}\mid i}}$	$\dfrac{1}{a_{\overline{n}\mid i}}$
1	1.07000000	0.93457944	1.00000000	0.93457944	1.00000000	1.07000000
2	1.14490000	0.87343873	2.07000000	1.80801817	0.48309179	0.55309179
3	1.22504300	0.81629788	3.21490000	2.62431604	0.31105167	0.38105167
4	1.31079601	0.76289521	4.43994300	3.38721126	0.22522812	0.29522812
5	1.40255173	0.71298618	5.75073901	4.10019744	0.17389069	0.24389069
6	1.50073035	0.66634222	7.15329074	4.76653966	0.13979580	0.20979580
7	1.60578148	0.62274974	8.65402109	5.38928940	0.11555322	0.18555322
8	1.71818618	0.58200910	10.25980257	5.97129851	0.09746776	0.16746776
9	1.83845921	0.54393374	11.97798875	6.51523225	0.08348647	0.15348647
10	1.96715136	0.50834929	13.81644796	7.02358154	0.07237750	0.14237750
11	2.10485195	0.47509280	15.78359932	7.49867434	0.06335690	0.13335690
12	2.25219159	0.44401196	17.88845127	7.94268630	0.05590199	0.12590199
13	2.40984500	0.41496445	20.14064286	8.35765074	0.04965085	0.11965085
14	2.57853415	0.38781724	22.55048786	8.74546799	0.04434494	0.11434494
15	2.75903154	0.36244602	25.12902201	9.10791401	0.03979462	0.10979462
16	2.95216375	0.33873460	27.88805355	9.44664860	0.03585765	0.10585765
17	3.15881521	0.31657439	30.84021730	9.76322299	0.03242519	0.10242519
18	3.37993228	0.29586392	33.99903251	10.05908691	0.02941260	0.09941260
19	3.61652754	0.27650833	37.37896479	10.33559524	0.02675301	0.09675301
20	3.86968446	0.25841900	40.99549232	10.59401425	0.02439293	0.09439293
21	4.14056237	0.24151309	44.86517678	10.83552733	0.02228900	0.09228900
22	4.43040174	0.22571317	49.00573916	11.06124050	0.02040577	0.09040577
23	4.74052986	0.21094688	53.43614090	11.27218738	0.01871393	0.08871393
24	5.07236695	0.19714662	58.17667076	11.46933400	0.01718902	0.08718902
25	5.42743264	0.18424918	63.24903772	11.65358318	0.01581052	0.08581052
26	5.80735292	0.17219549	68.67647036	11.82577867	0.01456103	0.08456103
27	6.21386763	0.16093037	74.48382328	11.98670904	0.01342573	0.08342573
28	6.64883836	0.15040221	80.69769091	12.13711125	0.01239193	0.08239193
29	7.11425705	0.14056282	87.34652927	12.27767407	0.01144865	0.08144865
30	7.61225504	0.13136712	94.46078632	12.40904118	0.01058640	0.08058640
31	8.14511290	0.12277301	102.07304137	12.53181419	0.00979691	0.07979691
32	8.71527080	0.11474113	110.21815426	12.64655532	0.00907292	0.07907292
33	9.32533975	0.10723470	118.93342506	12.75379002	0.00840807	0.07840807
34	9.97811354	0.10021934	128.25876481	12.85400936	0.00779674	0.07779674
35	10.67658148	0.09366294	138.23687835	12.94767230	0.00723396	0.07723396
36	11.42394219	0.08753546	148.91345984	13.03520776	0.00671531	0.07671531
37	12.22361814	0.08180884	160.33740202	13.11701660	0.00623685	0.07623685
38	13.07927141	0.07645686	172.56102017	13.19347345	0.00579505	0.07579505
39	13.99482041	0.07145501	185.64029158	13.26492846	0.00538676	0.07538676
40	14.97445784	0.06678038	199.63511199	13.33170884	0.00500914	0.07500914
41	16.02266989	0.06241157	214.60956983	13.39412041	0.00465962	0.07465962
42	17.14425678	0.05832857	230.63223972	13.45244898	0.00433591	0.07433591
43	18.34435475	0.05451268	247.77649650	13.50696167	0.00403590	0.07403590
44	19.62845959	0.05094643	266.12085125	13.55790810	0.00375769	0.07375769
45	21.00245176	0.04761349	285.74931084	13.60552159	0.00349957	0.07349957
46	22.47262338	0.04449859	306.75176260	13.65002018	0.00325996	0.07325996
47	24.04570702	0.04158747	329.22438598	13.69160764	0.00303744	0.07303744
48	25.72890651	0.03886679	353.27009300	13.73047443	0.00283070	0.07283070
49	27.52992997	0.03632410	378.99899951	13.76679853	0.00263853	0.07263853
50	29.45702506	0.03394776	406.52892947	13.80074629	0.00245985	0.07245985

Rate $7\frac{1}{2}$%	A Compound Interest	B Present Value	C Amount of Annuity	D Present Value of Annuity	E Sinking Fund	F Amortization
n	$(1 + i)^n$	$\dfrac{1}{(1 + i)^n}$	$s_{\overline{n}\vert i}$	$a_{\overline{n}\vert i}$	$\dfrac{1}{s_{\overline{n}\vert i}}$	$\dfrac{1}{a_{\overline{n}\vert i}}$
1	1.07500000	0.93023256	1.00000000	0.93023256	1.00000000	1.07500000
2	1.15562500	0.86533261	2.07500000	1.79556517	0.48192771	0.55692771
3	1.24229688	0.80496057	3.23062500	2.60052574	0.30953763	0.38453763
4	1.33546914	0.74880053	4.47292187	3.34932627	0.22356751	0.29856751
5	1.43562933	0.69655863	5.80839102	4.04588490	0.17216472	0.24716472
6	1.54330153	0.64796152	7.24402034	4.69384642	0.13804489	0.21304489
7	1.65904914	0.60275490	8.78732187	5.29660132	0.11380032	0.18880032
8	1.78347783	0.56070223	10.44637101	5.85730355	0.09572702	0.17072702
9	1.91723866	0.52158347	12.22984883	6.37888703	0.08176716	0.15676716
10	2.06103156	0.48519393	14.14708750	6.86408096	0.07068593	0.14568593
11	2.21560893	0.45134319	16.20811906	7.31542415	0.06169747	0.13669747
12	2.38177960	0.41985413	18.42372799	7.73527827	0.05427783	0.12927783
13	2.56041307	0.39056198	20.80550759	8.12584026	0.04806420	0.12306420
14	2.75244405	0.36331347	23.36592066	8.48915373	0.04279737	0.11779737
15	2.95887735	0.33796602	26.11836470	8.82711975	0.03828724	0.11328724
16	3.18079315	0.31438699	29.07724206	9.14150674	0.03439116	0.10939116
17	3.41935264	0.29245302	32.25803521	9.43395976	0.03100003	0.10600003
18	3.67580409	0.27204932	35.67738785	9.70600908	0.02802896	0.10302896
19	3.95148940	0.25306913	39.35319194	9.95907821	0.02541090	0.10041090
20	4.24785110	0.23541315	43.30468134	10.19449136	0.02309219	0.09809219
21	4.56643993	0.21898897	47.55253244	10.41348033	0.02102937	0.09602937
22	4.90892293	0.20371067	52.11897237	10.61719101	0.01918687	0.09418687
23	5.27709215	0.18949830	57.02789530	10.80668931	0.01753528	0.09253528
24	5.67287406	0.17627749	62.30498744	10.98296680	0.01605008	0.09105008
25	6.09833961	0.16397906	67.97786150	11.14694586	0.01471067	0.08971067
26	6.55571508	0.15253866	74.07620112	11.29948452	0.01349961	0.08849961
27	7.04739371	0.14189643	80.63191620	11.44138095	0.01240204	0.08740204
28	7.57594824	0.13199668	87.67930991	11.57337763	0.01140520	0.08640520
29	8.14414436	0.12278761	95.25525816	11.69616524	0.01049811	0.08549811
30	8.75495519	0.11422103	103.39940252	11.81038627	0.00967124	0.08467124
31	9.41157683	0.10625212	112.15435771	11.91663839	0.00891628	0.08391628
32	10.11744509	0.09883918	121.56593454	12.01547757	0.00822599	0.08322599
33	10.87625347	0.09194343	131.68337963	12.10742099	0.00759397	0.08259397
34	11.69197248	0.08552877	142.55963310	12.19294976	0.00701461	0.08201461
35	12.56887042	0.07956164	154.25160558	12.27251141	0.00648291	0.08148291
36	13.51153570	0.07401083	166.82047600	12.34652224	0.00599447	0.08099447
37	14.52490088	0.06884729	180.33201170	12.41536952	0.00554533	0.08054533
38	15.61426844	0.06404399	194.85691258	12.47941351	0.00513197	0.08013197
39	16.78533858	0.05957580	210.47118102	12.53898931	0.00475124	0.07975124
40	18.04423897	0.05541935	227.25651960	12.59440866	0.00440031	0.07940031
41	19.39755689	0.05155288	245.30075857	12.64596155	0.00407663	0.07907663
42	20.85237366	0.04795617	264.69831546	12.69391772	0.00377789	0.07877789
43	22.41630168	0.04461039	285.55068912	12.73852811	0.00350201	0.07850201
44	24.09752431	0.04149804	307.96699080	12.78002615	0.00324710	0.07824710
45	25.90483863	0.03860283	332.06451511	12.81862898	0.00301146	0.07801146
46	27.84770153	0.03590961	357.96935375	12.85453858	0.00279354	0.07779354
47	29.93627915	0.03340428	385.81705528	12.88794287	0.00259190	0.07759190
48	32.18150008	0.03107375	415.75333442	12.91901662	0.00240527	0.07740527
49	34.59511259	0.02890582	447.93483451	12.94792244	0.00223247	0.07723247
50	37.18974603	0.02688913	482.52994709	12.97481157	0.00207241	0.07707241

Rate 8%	A Compound Interest	B Present Value	C Amount of Annuity	D Present Value of Annuity	E Sinking Fund	F Amortization
n	$(1 + i)^n$	$\dfrac{1}{(1 + i)^n}$	$s_{\overline{n}\,i}$	$a_{\overline{n}\,i}$	$\dfrac{1}{s_{\overline{n}\,i}}$	$\dfrac{1}{a_{\overline{n}\,i}}$
1	1.08000000	0.92592593	1.00000000	0.92592593	1.00000000	1.08000000
2	1.16640000	0.85733882	2.08000000	1.78326475	0.48076923	0.56076923
3	1.25971200	0.79383224	3.24640000	2.57709699	0.30803351	0.38803351
4	1.36048896	0.73502985	4.50611200	3.31212684	0.22192080	0.30192080
5	1.46932808	0.68058320	5.86660096	3.99271004	0.17045645	0.25045645
6	1.58687432	0.63016963	7.33592904	4.62287966	0.13631539	0.21631539
7	1.71382427	0.58349040	8.92280336	5.20637006	0.11207240	0.19207240
8	1.85093021	0.54026888	10.63662763	5.74663894	0.09401476	0.17401476
9	1.99900463	0.50024897	12.48755784	6.24688791	0.08007971	0.16007971
10	2.15892500	0.46319349	14.48656247	6.71008140	0.06902949	0.14902949
11	2.33163900	0.42888286	16.64548746	7.13896426	0.06007634	0.14007634
12	2.51817012	0.39711376	18.97712646	7.53607802	0.05269502	0.13269502
13	2.71962373	0.36769792	21.49529658	7.90377594	0.04652181	0.12652181
14	2.93719362	0.34046104	24.21492030	8.24423698	0.04129685	0.12129685
15	3.17216911	0.31524170	27.15211393	8.55947869	0.03682954	0.11682954
16	3.42594264	0.29189047	30.32428304	8.85136916	0.03297687	0.11297687
17	3.70001805	0.27026895	33.75022569	9.12163811	0.02962943	0.10962943
18	3.99601950	0.25024903	37.45024374	9.37188714	0.02670210	0.10670210
19	4.31570106	0.23171206	41.44626324	9.60359920	0.02412763	0.10412763
20	4.66095714	0.21454821	45.76196430	9.81814741	0.02185221	0.10185221
21	5.03383372	0.19865575	50.42292144	10.01680316	0.01983225	0.09983225
22	5.43654041	0.18394051	55.45675516	10.20074366	0.01803207	0.09803207
23	5.87146365	0.17031528	60.89329557	10.37105895	0.01642217	0.09642217
24	6.34118074	0.15769934	66.76475922	10.52875828	0.01497796	0.09497796
25	6.84847520	0.14601790	73.10593995	10.67477619	0.01367878	0.09367878
26	7.39635321	0.13520176	79.95441515	10.80997795	0.01250713	0.09250713
27	7.98806147	0.12518682	87.35076836	10.93516477	0.01144810	0.09144810
28	8.62710639	0.11591372	95.33882983	11.05107849	0.01048891	0.09048891
29	9.31727490	0.10732752	103.96593622	11.15840601	0.00961854	0.08961854
30	10.06265689	0.09937733	113.28321111	11.25778334	0.00882743	0.08882743
31	10.86766944	0.09201605	123.34586800	11.34979939	0.00810728	0.08810728
32	11.73708300	0.08520005	134.21353744	11.43499944	0.00745081	0.08745081
33	12.67604964	0.07888893	145.95062044	11.51388837	0.00685163	0.08685163
34	13.69013361	0.07304531	158.62667007	11.58693367	0.00630411	0.08630411
35	14.78534429	0.06763454	172.31680368	11.65456822	0.00580326	0.08580326
36	15.96817184	0.06262458	187.10214797	11.71719279	0.00534467	0.08534467
37	17.24562558	0.05798572	203.07031981	11.77517851	0.00492440	0.08492440
38	18.62527563	0.05369048	220.31594540	11.82886899	0.00453894	0.08453894
39	20.11529768	0.04971341	238.94122103	11.87858240	0.00418513	0.08418513
40	21.72452150	0.04603093	259.05651871	11.92461333	0.00386016	0.08386016
41	23.46248322	0.04262123	280.78104021	11.96723457	0.00356149	0.08356149
42	25.33948187	0.03946411	304.24352342	12.00669867	0.00328684	0.08328684
43	27.36664042	0.03654084	329.58300530	12.04323951	0.00303414	0.08303414
44	29.55597166	0.03383411	356.94964572	12.07707362	0.00280152	0.08280152
45	31.92044939	0.03132788	386.50561738	12.10840150	0.00258728	0.08258728
46	34.47408534	0.02900730	418.42606677	12.13740880	0.00238991	0.08238991
47	37.23201217	0.02685861	452.90015211	12.16426741	0.00220799	0.08220799
48	40.21057314	0.02486908	490.13216428	12.18913649	0.00204027	0.08204027
49	43.42741899	0.02302693	530.34273742	12.21216341	0.00188557	0.08188557
50	46.90161251	0.02132123	573.77015642	12.23348464	0.00174286	0.08174286

Rate 9%	A Compound Interest	B Present Value	C Amount of Annuity	D Present Value of Annuity	E Sinking Fund	F Amortization
n	$(1 + i)^n$	$\dfrac{1}{(1 + i)^n}$	$s_{\overline{n}\vert i}$	$a_{\overline{n}\vert i}$	$\dfrac{1}{s_{\overline{n}\vert i}}$	$\dfrac{1}{a_{\overline{n}\vert i}}$
1	1.09000000	0.91743119	1.00000000	0.91743119	1.00000000	1.09000000
2	1.18810000	0.84167999	2.09000000	1.75911119	0.47846890	0.56846890
3	1.29502900	0.77218348	3.27810000	2.53129467	0.30505476	0.39505476
4	1.41158161	0.70842521	4.57312900	3.23971988	0.21866866	0.30866866
5	1.53862395	0.64993139	5.98471061	3.88965126	0.16709246	0.25709246
6	1.67710011	0.59626733	7.52333456	4.48591859	0.13291978	0.22291978
7	1.82803912	0.54703424	9.20043468	5.03295284	0.10869052	0.19869052
8	1.99256264	0.50186628	11.02847380	5.53481911	0.09067438	0.18067438
9	2.17189328	0.46042778	13.02103644	5.99524689	0.07679880	0.16679880
10	2.36736367	0.42241081	15.19292972	6.41765770	0.06582009	0.15582009
11	2.58042641	0.38753285	17.56029339	6.80519055	0.05694666	0.14694666
12	2.81266478	0.35553473	20.14071980	7.16072528	0.04965066	0.13965066
13	3.06580461	0.32617865	22.95338458	7.48690392	0.04356656	0.13356656
14	3.34172703	0.29924647	26.01918919	7.78615039	0.03843317	0.12843317
15	3.64248246	0.27453804	29.36091622	8.06068843	0.03405888	0.12405888
16	3.97030588	0.25186976	33.00339868	8.31255819	0.03029991	0.12029991
17	4.32763341	0.23107318	36.97370456	8.54363137	0.02704625	0.11704625
18	4.71712042	0.21199374	41.30133797	8.75562511	0.02421229	0.11421229
19	5.14166125	0.19448967	46.01845839	8.95011478	0.02173041	0.11173041
20	5.60441077	0.17843089	51.16011964	9.12854567	0.01954648	0.10954648
21	6.10880774	0.16369806	56.76453041	9.29224373	0.01761663	0.10761663
22	6.65860043	0.15018171	62.87333815	9.44242544	0.01590499	0.10590499
23	7.25787447	0.13778139	69.53193858	9.58020683	0.01438188	0.10438188
24	7.91108317	0.12640494	76.78981305	9.70661177	0.01302256	0.10302256
25	8.62308066	0.11596784	84.70089623	9.82257960	0.01180625	0.10180625
26	9.39915792	0.10639251	93.32397689	9.92897211	0.01071536	0.10071536
27	10.24508213	0.09760781	102.72313481	10.02657992	0.00973491	0.09973491
28	11.16713952	0.08954845	112.96821694	10.11612837	0.00885205	0.09885205
29	12.17218208	0.08215454	124.13535646	10.19828291	0.00805572	0.09805572
30	13.26767847	0.07537114	136.30753855	10.27365404	0.00733635	0.09733635
31	14.46176953	0.06914783	149.57521702	10.34280187	0.00668560	0.09668560
32	15.76332879	0.06343838	164.03698655	10.40624025	0.00609619	0.09609619
33	17.18202838	0.05820035	179.80031534	10.46444060	0.00556173	0.09556173
34	18.72841093	0.05339481	196.98234372	10.51783541	0.00507660	0.09507660
35	20.41396792	0.04898607	215.71075465	10.56682148	0.00463584	0.09463584
36	22.25122503	0.04494135	236.12472257	10.61176282	0.00423505	0.09423505
37	24.25383528	0.04123059	258.37594760	10.65299342	0.00387033	0.09387033
38	26.43668046	0.03782623	282.62978288	10.69081965	0.00353820	0.09353820
39	28.81598170	0.03470296	309.06646334	10.72552261	0.00323555	0.09323555
40	31.40942005	0.03183758	337.88244504	10.75736020	0.00295961	0.09295961
41	34.23626789	0.02920879	369.29186510	10.78656899	0.00270789	0.09270789
42	37.31753197	0.02679706	403.52813296	10.81336604	0.00247814	0.09247814
43	40.67610984	0.02458446	440.84566492	10.83795050	0.00226837	0.09226837
44	44.33695973	0.02255455	481.52177477	10.86050504	0.00207675	0.09207675
45	48.32728610	0.02069224	525.85873450	10.88119729	0.00190165	0.09190165
46	52.67674185	0.01898371	574.18602060	10.90018100	0.00174160	0.09174160
47	57.41764862	0.01741625	626.86276245	10.91759725	0.00159525	0.09159525
48	62.58523700	0.01597821	684.28041107	10.93357546	0.00146139	0.09146139
49	68.21790833	0.01465891	746.86564807	10.94823436	0.00133893	0.09133893
50	74.35752008	0.01344854	815.08355640	10.96168290	0.00122687	0.09122687

Rate 10%	A Compound Interest	B Present Value	C Amount of Annuity	D Present Value of Annuity	E Sinking Fund	F Amortization
n	$(1 + i)^n$	$\dfrac{1}{(1 + i)^n}$	$s_{\overline{n}\,i}$	$a_{\overline{n}\,i}$	$\dfrac{1}{s_{\overline{n}\,i}}$	$\dfrac{1}{a_{\overline{n}\,i}}$
1	1.10000000	0.90909091	1.00000000	0.90909091	1.00000000	1.10000000
2	1.21000000	0.82644628	2.10000000	1.73553719	0.47619048	0.57619048
3	1.33100000	0.75131480	3.31000000	2.48685199	0.30211480	0.40211480
4	1.46410000	0.68301346	4.64100000	3.16986545	0.21547080	0.31547080
5	1.61051000	0.62092132	6.10510000	3.79078677	0.16379748	0.26379748
6	1.77156100	0.56447393	7.71561000	4.35526070	0.12960738	0.22960738
7	1.94871710	0.51315812	9.48717100	4.86841882	0.10540550	0.20540550
8	2.14358881	0.46650738	11.43588810	5.33492620	0.08744402	0.18744402
9	2.35794769	0.42409762	13.57947691	5.75902382	0.07364054	0.17364054
10	2.59374246	0.38554329	15.93742460	6.14456711	0.06274539	0.16274539
11	2.85311671	0.35049390	18.53116706	6.49506101	0.05396314	0.15396314
12	3.13842838	0.31863082	21.38428377	6.81369182	0.04676332	0.14676332
13	3.45227121	0.28966438	24.52271214	7.10335620	0.04077852	0.14077852
14	3.79749834	0.26333125	27.97498336	7.36668746	0.03574622	0.13574622
15	4.17724817	0.23939205	31.77248169	7.60607951	0.03147378	0.13147378
16	4.59497299	0.21762914	35.94972986	7.82370864	0.02781662	0.12781662
17	5.05447028	0.19784467	40.54470285	8.02155331	0.02466413	0.12466413
18	5.55991731	0.17985879	45.59917313	8.20141210	0.02193022	0.12193022
19	6.11590904	0.16350799	51.15909045	8.36492009	0.01954687	0.11954687
20	6.72749995	0.14864363	57.27499949	8.51356372	0.01745962	0.11745962
21	7.40024994	0.13513057	64.00249944	8.64869429	0.01562439	0.11562439
22	8.14027494	0.12284597	71.40274939	8.77154026	0.04100506	0.11400506
23	8.95430243	0.11167816	79.54302433	8.88321842	0.01257181	0.11257181
24	9.84973268	0.10152560	88.49732676	8.98474402	0.01129978	0.11129978
25	10.83470594	0.09229600	98.34705943	9.07704002	0.01016807	0.11016807
26	11.91817654	0.08390545	109.18176538	9.16094547	0.00915904	0.10915904
27	13.10999419	0.07627768	121.09994191	9.23722316	0.00825764	0.10825764
28	14.42099361	0.06934335	134.20993611	9.30656651	0.00745101	0.10745101
29	15.86309297	0.06303941	148.63092972	9.36960591	0.00672807	0.10672807
30	17.44940227	0.05730855	164.49402269	9.42691447	0.00607925	0.10607925
31	19.19434250	0.05209868	181.94342496	9.47901315	0.00549621	0.10549621
32	21.11377675	0.04736244	201.13776745	9.52637559	0.00497172	0.10497172
33	23.22515442	0.04305676	222.25154420	9.56943236	0.00449941	0.10449941
34	25.54766986	0.03914251	245.47669862	9.60857487	0.00407371	0.10407371
35	28.10243685	0.03558410	271.02436848	9.64415897	0.00368971	0.10368971
36	30.91268053	0.03234918	299.12680533	9.67650816	0.00334306	0.10334306
37	34.00394859	0.02940835	330.03948586	9.70591651	0.00302994	0.10302994
38	37.40434344	0.02673486	364.04343445	9.73265137	0.00274692	0.10274692
39	41.14477779	0.02430442	401.44777789	9.75695579	0.00249098	0.10249098
40	45.25925557	0.02209493	442.59255568	9.77905072	0.00225941	0.10225941
41	49.78518112	0.02008630	487.85181125	9.79913702	0.00204980	0.10204980
42	54.76369924	0.01826027	537.63699237	9.81739729	0.00185999	0.10185999
43	60.24006916	0.01660025	592.40069161	9.83399753	0.00168805	0.10168805
44	66.26407608	0.01509113	652.64076077	9.84908867	0.00153224	0.10153224
45	72.89048369	0.01371921	718.90483685	9.86280788	0.00139100	0.10139100
46	80.17953205	0.01247201	791.79532054	9.87527989	0.00126295	0.10126295
47	88.19748526	0.01133819	871.97485259	9.88661808	0.00114682	0.10114682
48	97.01723378	0.01030745	960.17233785	9.89692553	0.00104148	0.10104148
49	106.71895716	0.00937041	1057.18957163	9.90629594	0.00094590	0.10094590
50	117.39085288	0.00851855	1163.90852880	9.91481449	0.00085917	0.10085917

Rate 11%	A Compound Interest	B Present Value	C Amount of Annuity	D Present Value of Annuity	E Sinking Fund	F Amortization
n	$(1 + i)^n$	$\dfrac{1}{(1 + i)^n}$	$s_{\overline{n}\rvert i}$	$a_{\overline{n}\rvert i}$	$\dfrac{1}{s_{\overline{n}\rvert i}}$	$\dfrac{1}{a_{\overline{n}\rvert i}}$
1	1.11000000	0.90090090	1.00000000	0.90090090	1.00000000	1.11000000
2	1.23210000	0.81162243	2.11000000	1.71252333	0.47393365	0.58393365
3	1.36763100	0.73119138	3.34210000	2.44371472	0.29921307	0.40921307
4	1.51807041	0.65873097	4.70973100	3.10244569	0.21232635	0.32232635
5	1.68505816	0.59345133	6.22780141	3.69589702	0.16057031	0.27057031
6	1.87041455	0.53464084	7.91285957	4.23053785	0.12637656	0.23637656
7	2.07616015	0.48165841	9.78327412	4.71219626	0.10221527	0.21221527
8	2.30453777	0.43392650	11.85943427	5.14612276	0.08432105	0.19432105
9	2.55803692	0.39092477	14.16397204	5.53704753	0.07060166	0.18060166
10	2.83942099	0.35218448	16.72200896	5.88923201	0.05980143	0.16980143
11	3.15175729	0.31728331	19.56142995	6.20651533	0.05112101	0.16112101
12	3.49845060	0.28584082	22.71318724	6.49235615	0.04402729	0.15402729
13	3.88328016	0.25751426	26.21163784	6.74987040	0.03815099	0.14815099
14	4.31044098	0.23199482	30.09491800	6.98186523	0.03322820	0.14322820
15	4.78458949	0.20900435	34.40535898	7.19086958	0.02906524	0.13906524
16	5.31089433	0.18829220	39.18994847	7.37916178	0.02551675	0.13551675
17	5.89509271	0.16963262	44.50084281	7.54879440	0.02247148	0.13247148
18	6.54355291	0.15282218	50.39593551	7.70161657	0.01984287	0.12984287
19	7.26334373	0.13767764	56.93948842	7.83929421	0.01756250	0.12756250
20	8.06231154	0.12403391	64.20283215	7.96332812	0.01557564	0.12557564
21	8.94916581	0.11174226	72.26514368	8.07507038	0.01383793	0.12383793
22	9.93357404	0.10066870	81.21430949	8.17573908	0.01231310	0.12231310
23	11.02626719	0.09069252	91.14788353	8.26643160	0.01097118	0.12097118
24	12.23915658	0.08170498	102.17415072	8.34813658	0.00978721	0.11978721
25	13.58546380	0.07360809	114.41330730	8.42174466	0.00874024	0.11874024
26	15.07986482	0.06631359	127.99877110	8.48805826	0.00781258	0.11781258
27	16.73864995	0.05974197	143.07863592	8.54780023	0.00698916	0.11698916
28	18.57990145	0.05382160	159.81728587	8.60162183	0.00625715	0.11625715
29	20.62369061	0.04848793	178.39718732	8.65010976	0.00560547	0.11560547
30	22.89229657	0.04368282	199.02087793	8.69379257	0.00502460	0.11502460
31	25.41044919	0.03935389	221.91317450	8.73314646	0.00450627	0.11450627
32	28.20559861	0.03545395	247.32362369	8.76860042	0.00404329	0.11404329
33	31.30821445	0.03194050	275.52922230	8.80054092	0.00362938	0.11362938
34	34.75211804	0.02877522	306.83743675	8.82931614	0.00325905	0.11325905
35	38.57485103	0.02592363	341.58955480	8.85523977	0.00292749	0.11292749
36	42.81808464	0.02335462	380.16440582	8.87859438	0.00263044	0.11263044
37	47.52807395	0.02104020	422.98249046	8.89963458	0.00236416	0.11236416
38	52.75616209	0.01895513	470.51056441	8.91858971	0.00212535	0.11212535
39	58.55933991	0.01707670	523.26672650	8.93566641	0.00191107	0.11191107
40	65.00086731	0.01538441	581.82606641	8.95105082	0.00171873	0.11171873
41	72.15096271	0.01385983	646.82693372	8.96491065	0.00154601	0.11154601
42	80.08756861	0.01248633	718.97789643	8.97739698	0.00139086	0.11139086
43	88.89720115	0.01124895	799.06546504	8.98864593	0.00125146	0.11125146
44	98.67589328	0.01013419	887.96266619	8.99878011	0.00112617	0.11112617
45	109.53024154	0.00912990	986.63855947	9.00791001	0.00101354	0.11101354
46	121.57856811	0.00822513	1096.16880101	9.01613515	0.00091227	0.11091227
47	134.95221060	0.00741003	1217.74736912	9.02354518	0.00082119	0.11082119
48	149.79695377	0.00667570	1352.69957973	9.03022088	0.00073926	0.11073926
49	166.27461868	0.00601415	1502.49653350	9.03623503	0.00066556	0.11066556
50	184.56482674	0.00541815	1668.77115218	9.04165318	0.00059924	0.11059924

Rate 12%	A Compound Interest	B Present Value	C Amount of Annuity	D Present Value of Annuity	E Sinking Fund	F Amortization
n	$(1 + i)^n$	$\dfrac{1}{(1 + i)^n}$	$s_{\overline{n}\rvert i}$	$a_{\overline{n}\rvert i}$	$\dfrac{1}{s_{\overline{n}\rvert i}}$	$\dfrac{1}{a_{\overline{n}\rvert i}}$
1	1.12000000	0.89285714	1.00000000	0.89285714	1.00000000	1.12000000
2	1.25440000	0.79719388	2.12000000	1.69005102	0.47169811	0.59169811
3	1.40492800	0.71178025	3.37440000	2.40183127	0.29634898	0.41634898
4	1.57351936	0.63551808	4.77932800	3.03734935	0.20923444	0.32923444
5	1.76234168	0.56742686	6.35284736	3.60477620	0.15740973	0.27740973
6	1.97382269	0.50663112	8.11518904	4.11140732	0.12322572	0.24322572
7	2.21068141	0.45234922	10.08901173	4.56375654	0.09911774	0.21911774
8	2.47596318	0.40388323	12.29969314	4.96763977	0.08130284	0.20130284
9	2.77307876	0.36061002	14.77565631	5.32824979	0.06767889	0.18767889
10	3.10584821	0.32197324	17.54873507	5.65022303	0.05698416	0.17698416
11	3.47854999	0.28747610	20.65458328	5.93769913	0.04841540	0.16841540
12	3.89597599	0.25667509	24.13313327	6.19437423	0.04143681	0.16143681
13	4.36349311	0.22917419	28.02910926	6.42354842	0.03567720	0.15567720
14	4.88711229	0.20461981	32.39260238	6.62816823	0.03087125	0.15087125
15	5.47356576	0.18269626	37.27971466	6.81086449	0.02682424	0.14682424
16	6.13039365	0.16312166	42.75328042	6.97398615	0.02339002	0.14339002
17	6.86604098	0.14564434	48.88367407	7.11963049	0.02045673	0.14045673
18	7.68996580	0.13003959	55.74971496	7.24967008	0.01793731	0.13793731
19	8.61276169	0.11610678	63.43968075	7.36577686	0.01576300	0.13576300
20	9.64629309	0.10366677	72.05244244	7.46944362	0.01387878	0.13387878
21	10.80384826	0.09255961	81.69873554	7.56200324	0.01224009	0.13224009
22	12.10031006	0.08264251	92.50258380	7.64464575	0.01081051	0.13081051
23	13.55234726	0.07378796	104.60289386	7.71843370	0.00955996	0.12955996
24	15.17862893	0.06588210	118.15524112	7.78431581	0.00846344	0.12846344
25	17.00006441	0.05882331	133.33387006	7.84313911	0.00749997	0.12749997
26	19.04007214	0.05252081	150.33393446	7.89565992	0.00665186	0.12665186
27	21.32488079	0.04689358	169.37400660	7.94255350	0.00590409	0.12590409
28	23.88386649	0.04186927	190.69888739	7.98442277	0.00524387	0.12524387
29	26.74993047	0.03738327	214.58275388	8.02180604	0.00466021	0.12466021
30	29.95992212	0.03337792	241.33268434	8.05518397	0.00414366	0.12414366
31	33.55511278	0.02980172	271.29260646	8.08498569	0.00368606	0.12368606
32	37.58172631	0.02660868	304.84771924	8.11159436	0.00328033	0.12328033
33	42.09153347	0.02375775	342.42944555	8.13535211	0.00292031	0.12292031
34	47.14251748	0.02121227	384.52097901	8.15656438	0.00260064	0.12260064
35	52.79961958	0.01893953	431.66349649	8.17550391	0.00231662	0.12231662
36	59.13557393	0.01691029	484.46311607	8.19241421	0.00206414	0.12206414
37	66.23184280	0.01509848	543.59869000	8.20751269	0.00183959	0.12183959
38	74.17966394	0.01348078	609.83053280	8.22099347	0.00163980	0.12163980
39	83.08122361	0.01203641	684.01019674	8.23302988	0.00146197	0.12146197
40	93.05097044	0.01074680	767.09142034	8.24377668	0.00130363	0.12130363
41	104.21708689	0.00959536	860.14239079	8.25337204	0.00116260	0.12116260
42	116.72313732	0.00856728	964.35947768	8.26193932	0.00103696	0.12103696
43	130.72991380	0.00764936	1081.08261500	8.26958868	0.00092500	0.12092500
44	146.41750346	0.00682978	1211.81252880	8.27641846	0.00082521	0.12082521
45	163.98760387	0.00609802	1358.23003226	8.28251648	0.00073625	0.12073625
46	183.66611634	0.00544466	1522.21763613	8.28796115	0.00065694	0.12065694
47	205.70605030	0.00486131	1705.88375247	8.29282245	0.00058621	0.12058621
48	230.39077633	0.00434045	1911.58980276	8.29716290	0.00052312	0.12052312
49	258.03766949	0.00387540	2142.98057909	8.30103831	0.00046686	0.12046686
50	289.00218983	0.00346018	2400.01824858	8.30449849	0.00041666	0.12041666

Rate 13%	A Compound Interest	B Present Value	C Amount of Annuity	D Present Value of Annuity	E Sinking Fund	F Amortization
n	$(1 + i)^n$	$\dfrac{1}{(1 + i)^n}$	$s_{\overline{n}\vert i}$	$a_{\overline{n}\vert i}$	$\dfrac{1}{s_{\overline{n}\vert i}}$	$\dfrac{1}{a_{\overline{n}\vert i}}$
1	1.13000000	0.88495575	1.00000000	0.88495575	1.00000000	1.13000000
2	1.27690000	0.78314668	2.13000000	1.66810244	0.46948357	0.59948357
3	1.44289700	0.69305016	3.40690000	2.36115260	0.29352197	0.42352197
4	1.63047361	0.61331873	4.84979700	2.97447133	0.20619420	0.33619420
5	1.84243518	0.54275994	6.48027061	3.51723126	0.15431454	0.28431454
6	2.08195175	0.48031853	8.32270579	3.99754979	0.12015323	0.25015323
7	2.35260548	0.42506064	10.40465754	4.42261043	0.09611080	0.22611080
8	2.65844419	0.37615986	12.75726302	4.79877029	0.07838672	0.20838672
9	3.00404194	0.33288483	15.41570722	5.13165513	0.06486890	0.19486890
10	3.39456739	0.29458835	18.41974915	5.42624348	0.05428956	0.18428956
11	3.83586115	0.26069765	21.81431654	5.68694113	0.04584145	0.17584145
12	4.33452310	0.23070589	25.65017769	5.91764702	0.03898608	0.16898608
13	4.89801110	0.20416450	29.98470079	6.12181152	0.03335034	0.16335034
14	5.53475255	0.18067655	34.88271190	6.30248807	0.02866750	0.15866750
15	6.25427038	0.15989075	40.41746444	6.46237882	0.02474178	0.15474178
16	7.06732553	0.14149624	46.67173482	6.60387506	0.02142624	0.15142624
17	7.98607785	0.12521791	53.73906035	6.72909298	0.01860844	0.14860844
18	9.02426797	0.11081231	61.72513819	6.83990529	0.01620085	0.14620085
19	10.19742280	0.09806399	70.74940616	6.93796928	0.01413439	0.14413439
20	11.52308776	0.08678229	80.94682896	7.02475158	0.01235379	0.14235379
21	13.02108917	0.07679849	92.46991672	7.10155007	0.01081433	0.14081433
22	14.71383077	0.06796327	105.49100590	7.16951334	0.00947948	0.13947948
23	16.62662877	0.06014448	120.20483667	7.22965782	0.00831913	0.13831913
24	18.78809051	0.05322521	136.83146543	7.28288303	0.00730826	0.13730826
25	21.23054227	0.04710195	155.61955594	7.32998498	0.00642593	0.13642593
26	23.99051277	0.04168314	176.85009821	7.37166812	0.00565451	0.13565451
27	27.10927943	0.03688774	200.84061098	7.40855586	0.00497907	0.13497907
28	30.63348575	0.03264402	227.94989040	7.44119988	0.00438693	0.13438693
29	34.61583890	0.02888851	258.58337616	7.47008839	0.00386722	0.13386722
30	39.11589796	0.02556505	293.19921506	7.49565344	0.00341065	0.13341065
31	44.20096469	0.02262394	332.31511301	7.51827738	0.00300919	0.13300919
32	49.94709010	0.02002119	376.51607771	7.53829857	0.00265593	0.13265593
33	56.44021181	0.01771786	426.46316781	7.55601643	0.00234487	0.13234487
34	63.77743935	0.01567953	482.90337962	7.57169596	0.00207081	0.13207081
35	72.06850647	0.01387569	546.68081897	7.58557164	0.00182922	0.13182922
36	81.43741231	0.01227937	618.74932544	7.59785101	0.00161616	0.13161616
37	92.02427591	0.01086670	700.18673775	7.60871771	0.00142819	0.13142819
38	103.98743178	0.00961655	792.21101365	7.61833426	0.00126229	0.13126229
39	117.50579791	0.00851022	896.19844543	7.62684447	0.00111582	0.13111582
40	132.78155163	0.00753117	1013.70424333	7.63437564	0.00098648	0.13098648
41	150.04315335	0.00666475	1146.48579497	7.64104039	0.00087223	0.13087223
42	169.54876328	0.00589801	1296.52894831	7.64693840	0.00077129	0.13077129
43	191.59010251	0.00521948	1466.07771159	7.65215787	0.00068209	0.13068209
44	216.49681583	0.00461901	1657.66781410	7.65677688	0.00060326	0.13060326
45	244.64140189	0.00408762	1874.16462994	7.66086450	0.00053357	0.13053357
46	276.44478414	0.00361736	2118.80603183	7.66448185	0.00047196	0.13047196
47	312.38260608	0.00320120	2395.25081596	7.66768306	0.00041749	0.13041749
48	352.99234487	0.00283292	2707.63342204	7.67051598	0.00036933	0.13036933
49	398.88134970	0.00250701	3060.62576691	7.67302299	0.00032673	0.13032673
50	450.73592516	0.00221859	3459.50711660	7.67524158	0.00028906	0.13028906

Calendar and Important Formulas

THE NUMBER OF EACH OF THE DAYS OF THE YEAR*

Number of Days	Jan.	Feb.	Mar.	Apr.	May	June	July	Aug.	Sept.	Oct.	Nov.	Dec.	Number of Days
1	1	32	60	91	121	152	182	213	244	274	305	335	1
2	2	33	61	92	122	153	183	214	245	275	306	336	2
3	3	34	62	93	123	154	184	215	246	276	307	337	3
4	4	35	63	94	124	155	185	216	247	277	308	338	4
5	5	36	64	95	125	156	186	217	248	278	309	339	5
6	6	37	65	96	126	157	187	218	249	279	310	340	6
7	7	38	66	97	127	158	188	219	250	280	311	341	7
8	8	39	67	98	128	159	189	220	251	281	312	342	8
9	9	40	68	99	129	160	190	221	252	282	313	343	9
10	10	41	69	100	130	161	191	222	253	283	314	344	10
11	11	42	70	101	131	162	192	223	254	284	315	345	11
12	12	43	71	102	132	163	193	224	255	285	316	346	12
13	13	44	72	103	133	164	194	225	256	286	317	347	13
14	14	45	73	104	134	165	195	226	257	287	318	348	14
15	15	46	74	105	135	166	196	227	258	288	319	349	15
16	16	47	75	106	136	167	197	228	259	289	320	350	16
17	17	48	76	107	137	168	198	229	260	290	321	351	17
18	18	49	77	108	138	169	199	230	261	291	322	352	18
19	19	50	78	109	139	170	200	231	262	292	323	353	19
20	20	51	79	110	140	171	201	232	263	293	324	354	20
21	21	52	80	111	141	172	202	233	264	294	325	355	21
22	22	53	81	112	142	173	203	234	265	295	326	356	22
23	23	54	82	113	143	174	204	235	266	296	327	357	23
24	24	55	83	114	144	175	205	236	267	297	328	358	24
25	25	56	84	115	145	176	206	237	268	298	329	359	25
26	26	57	85	116	146	177	207	238	269	299	330	360	26
27	27	58	86	117	147	178	208	239	270	300	331	361	27
28	28	59	87	118	148	179	209	240	271	301	332	362	28
29	29		88	119	149	180	210	241	272	302	333	363	29
30	30		89	120	150	181	211	242	273	303	334	364	30
31	31		90		151		212	243		304		365	31

*Add 1 to each date after February 29 for a leap year.

Percent Formula	Part $=$ base $\times$ rate or $P = B \times R$ or $P = BR$
Markup Formula	Cost $+$ markup $=$ selling price or $C + M = S$
Converting Markup Percent on Cost to Selling Price	$\dfrac{\% \text{ of markup on}}{\text{selling price}} = \dfrac{\% \text{ of markup on cost}}{100\% \ + \ \% \text{ of markup on cost}}$ or, if M_c represents markup on cost and M_s represents markup on selling price, $$M_s = \dfrac{M_c}{1 \ + \ M_c}$$
Converting Markup Percent on Selling Price to Cost	$\dfrac{\% \text{ of markup on}}{\text{cost}} = \dfrac{\% \text{ of markup on selling price}}{100\% \ - \ \% \text{ of markup on selling price}}$ or, if M_c represents markup on cost and M_s represents markup on selling price, $$M_c = \dfrac{M_s}{1 \ - \ M_s}$$
Stock Turnover	$\text{Turnover at retail} = \dfrac{\text{retail sales}}{\text{average inventory at retail}}$ $\text{Turnover at cost} = \dfrac{\text{cost of goods sold}}{\text{average inventory at cost}}$
Simple Interest	The *simple interest*, I, on a principal of P dollars at a rate of interest R per year for T years is given by $$I = PRT$$

Number of Days in Each Month	31 Days		30 Days	28 Days
	January	August	April	February
	March	October	June	(29 days in leap year)
	May	December	September	
	July		November	

Types of Interest	The method for forming the *time fraction* used for T in the formula $I = PRT$ is summarized as follows.
	    The *numerator* is the *exact number* of days in a loan period.
	    The *denominator* is one of the following:
	        Exact interest assumes 365 days in a year and uses 365 as a denominator.
	        Ordinary, or *banker's interest*, assumes 360 days in a year and uses 360 as a denominator.

Interest, Principal, Rate, and Time Formulas	Interest	$I = PRT$	Time	Time in years $= \dfrac{I}{PR}$

Interest $\quad I = PRT \qquad$ Time $\quad$ Time in years $= \dfrac{I}{PR}$

Principal $\quad P = \dfrac{I}{RT} \qquad\qquad$ Time in days $= \dfrac{I}{PR} \times 360$

Rate $\quad R = \dfrac{I}{PT}$

Maturity Value

The *maturity value*, M, of a principal of P dollars at a rate of interest R for T years is either

$$M = P + I$$

or, since $I = PRT$,

$$M = P(1 + RT)$$

Present Value at Simple Interest

The *present value at simple interest*, P, of a future value M at a rate of interest R for a time T is

$$P = \frac{M}{1 + RT}$$

Simple Interest and Simple Discount

Variables Used for Simple Interest	Variables Used for Simple Discount
$I = $ Interest	$B = $ Discount
$P = $ Principal (Face value)	$P = $ Proceeds
$R = $ Rate of interest	$D = $ Discount rate
$T = $ Time in years, or Fraction of a year	$T = $ Time in years, or Fraction of a year
$M = $ Maturity value	$M = $ Maturity value

	Simple Interest	Simple Discount
Face value	Stated on note, or $P = \dfrac{M}{1 + RT}$	Same as maturity value, or $M = \dfrac{P}{1 - DT}$
Interest charge	$I = PRT$	$B = M \cdot D \cdot T$
Maturity value	$M = P + I$ or $M = P(1 + RT)$	Same as face value, or $M = \dfrac{P}{1 - DT}$
Amount received by borrower	Face value or principal	Proceeds: $P = M - B$ or $P = M(1 - DT)$
Identifying phrases	Interest at a certain rate Maturity value greater than face value	Discounted at a certain rate Proceeds Maturity value equal to face value
Annual interest rate	Same as stated rate, R	Greater than stated rate, D

Comparing Simple Interest and Simple Discount Rates	The simple interest rate R and the simple discount rate D are calculated by the formulas $$R = \frac{D}{1 - DT} \quad \text{and} \quad D = \frac{R}{1 + RT}$$ where T is time in years.
Compound Interest	If P dollars are deposited at a rate of interest i per period for n periods, then the *compound amount M*, or the final amount on deposit, is $$M = P(1 + i)^n$$ The interest earned I is $$I = M - P$$ (Use column A of the interest table.)
Present Value at Compound Interest	The *present value P* of the future amount M at an interest rate of i per period for n periods is $$P = \frac{M}{(1 + i)^n} \qquad \text{(Use column B of the interest table.)}$$
Unearned Interest	The *unearned interest* is given by $U = F\left(\dfrac{N}{P}\right)\left(\dfrac{1 + N}{1 + P}\right)$ where: U = unearned interest N = number of payments remaining F = finance charge P = total number of payments
Annuities, Sinking Funds, and Amortization	**Lump Sums.** A lump sum is deposited today; to find the *compound amount* in the future, use the formula $M = P(1 + i)^n$ and column A of the interest table in Appendix C.

To find the lump sum that is the *present value* today of a known amount in the future, use $P = \dfrac{M}{(1 + i)^n}$ and column B.

Making Periodic Payments. To find the *amount of an annuity* when periodic payments are made for a fixed period of time, use $S = R \cdot s_{\overline{n}|i}$ and column C.

To find the amount that could be deposited today that would be equivalent to a series of periodic payments, find the *present value of an annuity* by using the formula $A = R \cdot a_{\overline{n}|i}$ and column D.

Find Periodic Payments. To find the periodic payment that must be made to produce some fixed total in the future, use the formula for a *sinking fund*,

$$R = S\left(\frac{1}{s_{\overline{n}|i}}\right)$$

and column E.

The periodic payment that will pay off, or amortize, a loan is given by

$$R = A\left(\frac{1}{a_{\overline{n}|i}}\right)$$

and column F.

Answers to Selected Exercises

Chapter 1

Section 1.1 (page 5)

1. 382 miles   **3.** 467 passengers   **5.** 1.7 billion tons   **7.** 2477 pounds   **9.** 23,993,000 small and midsize businesses   **11.** 328,500 veterans   **13.** $750   **15.** $20,961   **17.** 20 seats   **19.** 35.2 hours   **21.** 65.5 million shares   **23.** 26 coins   **25. (a)** 0.43 inch **(b)** 4.3 inches   **27. (a)** 180.6 hours **(b)** $18.00   **29.** $14,790

Section 1.2 (page 16)

1. $\frac{11}{8}$ **3.** $\frac{17}{4}$ **5.** $\frac{183}{8}$ **7.** $\frac{101}{8}$ **9.** $\frac{1}{2}$ **11.** $\frac{8}{15}$ **13.** $\frac{5}{8}$ **15.** $\frac{4}{5}$ **17.** $\frac{11}{12}$ **19.** $\frac{8}{15}$ **21.** $3\frac{1}{2}$ **23.** $3\frac{4}{5}$ **25.** $1\frac{3}{11}$ **27.** $1\frac{2}{5}$ **29.** $1\frac{15}{16}$ **31.** $2\frac{17}{32}$ **35.** $\frac{3}{5}$ **37.** $\frac{17}{20}$ **39.** $1\frac{7}{60}$ **41.** $\frac{19}{22}$ **43.** $1\frac{23}{36}$ **45.** $2\frac{5}{24}$ **47.** $97\frac{4}{5}$ **49.** $80\frac{3}{4}$ **51.** $53\frac{17}{24}$ **53.** 187   **55.** $\frac{1}{2}$ **57.** $\frac{1}{2}$ **59.** $\frac{17}{48}$ **61.** $\frac{1}{3}$ **63.** $4\frac{3}{8}$ **65.** $3\frac{11}{24}$ **67.** $9\frac{1}{24}$ **69.** $6\frac{1}{4}$ **75.** $\frac{31}{40}$ inch   **77.** $4\frac{3}{8}$ miles   **79.** $\frac{3}{16}$ inch   **81.** $22\frac{1}{2}$ hours   **83.** $1\frac{5}{8}$ cubic yards   **85.** $19\frac{5}{6}$ cases   **87.** $9\frac{1}{6}$ hours   **89.** $104\frac{5}{8}$ feet

Section 1.3 (page 27)

1. $\frac{5}{12}$ **3.** $\frac{99}{160}$ **5.** $4\frac{1}{2}$ **7.** 69   **9.** $4\frac{7}{12}$ **11.** 90   **13.** $\frac{1}{2}$ **15.** $\frac{3}{4}$ **17.** $1\frac{1}{2}$ **19.** $\frac{2}{3}$ **21.** $3\frac{1}{3}$ **23.** $4\frac{4}{5}$ **27.** $12   **29.** $25.50   **31.** $15.75   **33.** $\frac{4}{5}$ **35.** $\frac{6}{25}$ **37.** $\frac{73}{100}$ **39.** $\frac{7}{8}$ **41.** $\frac{3}{80}$ **43.** $\frac{3}{16}$ **45.** 3.5; 3.52   **47.** 0.1; 0.08   **49.** 8.6; 8.64   **51.** 59.0; 58.96   **53.** 23.0; 23.05   **55.** 39.5; 39.50   **57.** 0.75   **59.** 0.375   **61.** 0.167   **63.** 0.813   **65.** 0.32   **67.** 0.010   **69.** 0.625   **71.** 0.833   **77.** 36 yards   **79.** 88 dispensers   **81.** 12 homes   **83.** $21\frac{7}{8}$ ounces   **85.** 471 gallons   **87.** 60 trips   **89.** $2632\frac{1}{2}$ inches

Chapter 1 Review Exercises (page 33)

1. $\frac{3}{5}$ **2.** $\frac{1}{2}$ **3.** $\frac{1}{3}$ **4.** $\frac{1}{2}$ **5.** $\frac{9}{10}$ **6.** $\frac{7}{11}$ **7.** $\frac{1}{50}$ **8.** $\frac{3}{8}$ **9.** $8\frac{1}{8}$ **10.** $4\frac{2}{3}$ **11.** $1\frac{7}{12}$ **12.** $7\frac{6}{7}$ **13.** $2\frac{2}{3}$ **14.** $8\frac{1}{6}$ **15.** $8\frac{1}{16}$ **16.** $3\frac{1}{32}$ **17.** $1\frac{5}{24}$ **18.** $\frac{7}{8}$ **19.** $\frac{8}{21}$ **20.** $\frac{1}{12}$ **21.** $71\frac{5}{6}$ **22.** $91\frac{5}{6}$ **23.** $4\frac{1}{4}$ **24.** $81\frac{1}{4}$ **25.** $4843   **26.** 14,454 gallons saved   **27.** $22\frac{1}{2}$ hours   **28.** $35\frac{7}{8}$ gallons   **29.** $319\frac{1}{2}$ ft.   **30.** $54\frac{11}{24}$ lb.   **31.** $\frac{5}{12}$ **32.** $\frac{7}{40}$ **33.** $\frac{1}{2}$ **34.** 16   **35.** $\frac{2}{3}$ **36.** $2\frac{2}{9}$ **37.** $20\frac{5}{6}$ **38.** $6\frac{1}{6}$ **39.** $2998   **40.** 3.6 million shares   **41.** $42\frac{1}{2}$ acres   **42.** 2480 anchors   **43.** 36 pull cords   **44.** $140,550   **45.** $\frac{1}{4}$ **46.** $\frac{5}{8}$ **47.** $\frac{93}{100}$ **48.** $\frac{1}{200}$ **49.** 68.4; 68.43   **50.** 975.5; 975.54   **51.** 0.4; 0.35   **52.** 8.0; 8.03   **53.** 7.0; 6.97   **54.** 0.4; 0.43   **55.** 1.0; 0.96   **56.** 71.2; 71.25   **57.** 0.625   **58.** 0.75   **59.** 0.833   **60.** 0.438

Chapter 1 Business Application Case #1 (page 34)

(a) $432,000   **(b)** $\frac{5}{12}, \frac{1}{4}, \frac{1}{12}, \frac{1}{16}, \frac{1}{16}, \frac{1}{8}$ **(c)**

Pie chart: Miscellaneous $\frac{1}{8}$; Insurance $\frac{1}{16}$; Advertising $\frac{1}{16}$; Utilities $\frac{1}{12}$; Rent $\frac{1}{4}$; Salaries $\frac{5}{12}$

Chapter 1 Business Application Case #2 (page 35)

1. 1 foot $3\frac{5}{8}$ inches
2. 290 shares
3. Answers will vary.
4. Answers will vary.

Chapter 2

Section 2.1 (page 44)

1. 42   **3.** 305   **5.** 46   **7.** 4.2   **9.** 12   **11.** 2
13. 3   **15.** 2.2   **17.** 0.8   **19.** 400   **21.** 294
23. 7   **25.** 12   **27.** 25   **29.** $\frac{5}{6}$ **31.** $\frac{5}{36}$ **33.** 4   **35.** $11\frac{4}{7}$ **37.** 4.65   **39.** $1\frac{5}{24}$ **41.** $\frac{2}{3}$ **43.** 1   **45.** 3.5   **47.** 13   **49.** 2   **51.** 5
53. 7   **55.** 10   **57.** $\frac{16}{19}$ **59.** $\frac{2}{3}$ **61.** $1\frac{1}{6}$ **63.** 2.1   **65.** 0.8

Section 2.2 (page 49)

1. $27 + x$ **3.** $22 + x$ **5.** $x - 4$ **7.** $x - 3\frac{1}{2}$ **9.** $3x$ **11.** $\frac{3}{5}x$ **13.** $\frac{9}{x}$ **15.** $\frac{16}{x}$ **17.** $2.1(4 + x)$ **19.** $7(x - 3)$ **21.** $12y$
23. $472 - x$ **25.** $73 - x$ **27.** $\frac{22,210}{x}$ **29.** $21 - x$ **31.** 13   **33.** 1.5   **35.** 1   **37.** $1\frac{3}{7}$ **39.** 59 stereos   **41.** 207   **43.** $20,500
45. 42 deluxe; 63 economy   **47.** $14,440 announcers; $18,050 all other employees   **49.** office space $30,000; retail stores $105,000
51. 3 new; 19 experienced   **53.** 81 Altimas; 39 Sentras

Section 2.3 (page 55)

1. $586.50 **3.** $10,080 **5.** $16.50 **7.** 14 **9.** 2250 **11.** 151.2 **13.** $749.86 **15.** 7.5 **17.** 7 **19.** 24,000 **21.** $\frac{A}{W}$ **23.** $\frac{nRT}{P}$ **25.** $\frac{M}{(1+i)^n}$ **27.** $\frac{(A-P)}{P}$ **29.** $\frac{(M-P)}{MT}$ **31.** $\frac{2A}{(b+B)}$ **33.** $2.40 **35.** $93.80 **37.** (a) $427 (b) $502.50 **39.** $236 million **41.** $3.40 **43.** $644,400 **45.** $390 **47.** 0.13, or 13% **49.** 4 years **51.** $4000 **53.** $4500

Section 2.4 (page 62)

1. $\frac{9}{32}$ **3.** $\frac{27}{1}$ **5.** $\frac{4}{3}$ **7.** $\frac{3750}{1}$ **9.** $\frac{225}{1}$ **11.** $\frac{8}{5}$ **13.** $\frac{1}{6}$ **15.** $\frac{4}{15}$ **17.** $\frac{9}{2}$ **19.** T **21.** F **23.** F **25.** F **27.** F **29.** F **31.** T **33.** T **35.** F **37.** T **39.** 7 **41.** 72 **43.** 105 **45.** $3\frac{1}{2}$ **47.** 24 **49.** 8 **53.** 1575 tickets **55.** $516,000 **57.** $360 **59.** 372 red sports models **61.** 1020 miles **63.** $713,211.20 **65.** $128,000 **67.** 350 miles **69.** 3,500,000 cubic meters **71.** U.S. $254.44

Section 2.5 (page 69)

1. p^2 **3.** r^3 **5.** x^4 **7.** 49 **9.** 1 **11.** 1 **13.** $t^4 g^4$ **15.** 9^4 **17.** $\frac{3^2}{4^2}$ **19.** $x^2 y^2$ **21.** 5 **23.** 83 **25.** 66 **27.** 20 **29.** 5625 **31.** 1 **33.** 161 **35.** 21 **37.** 553.2 **39.** 54.2 **41.** $53,928 **43.** $5834.43

Chapter 2 Review Exercises (page 73)

1. 51 **2.** 50.7 **3.** 16.3 **4.** $5\frac{1}{4}$ **5.** 252 **6.** 136 **7.** 56 **8.** $13\frac{1}{2}$ **9.** 7 **10.** $1\frac{2}{3}$ **11.** 21 **12.** 3.6 **13.** $94x$ **14.** $\frac{1}{2}x$ **15.** $6x + x$ **16.** $5x - 11$ **17.** $3x + 7$ **18.** $92.35 **19.** $3000 **20.** $108 water; $432 phone **21.** 76 **22.** 70 child; 30 adult **23.** $P = $4000 **24.** $P = $3250 **25.** $P = $8200 (rounded) **26.** $\frac{I}{PT}$ **27.** $\frac{M-P}{PR}$ **28.** $\frac{B}{R}$ **29.** $\frac{34}{1}$ **30.** $\frac{18}{1}$ **31.** $\frac{20}{1}$ **32.** $\frac{12}{5}$ **33.** $\frac{8}{3}$ **34.** 3 **35.** $6\frac{3}{4}$ **36.** $4\frac{1}{2}$ **37.** 165 **38.** 24 **39.** 4293 bass **40.** 4734 pounds per square inch (rounded) **41.** 6624 pounds **42.** 105 **43.** $112,008 **44.** $139.50 **45.** y^3 **46.** 5^2 **47.** 9^4 **48.** 3.1^2 **49.** $\frac{1}{8}$ **50.** 1 **51.** 102 **52.** Undefined **53.** 7^5 **54.** r^6 **55.** $s^4 t^4$ **56.** $\frac{z^2}{y^2}$ **57.** 43 **58.** 27 **59.** Undefined **60.** 11 **61.** 1931 **62.** 324 **63.** $680,296 **64.** $449,941.56

Chapter 2 Business Application Case #1 (page 75)

(a) $12,570 (b) $\frac{3}{10}$ (c) $\left(\frac{3}{10} \cdot \$24.80 \cdot N\right) - \$12,570$ or $7.44N - \$12,570$ (d) 1690 books (e) The owner would probably receive a lower salary (f) 2496 books

Chapter 2 Business Application Case #2 (page 76)

(a) $806,452 (b) $806,452 $\cdot (31,000 + N)$ (c) $30 billion (d) Answers will vary.

Chapter 3

Section 3.1 (page 82)

1. 20% **3.** 72% **5.** 140% **7.** 37.5% **9.** 462.5% **11.** 0.25% **13.** 0.15% **15.** 345% **17.** 25% **19.** 10% **21.** 2% **23.** 37.5% **25.** 12.5% **27.** 0.5% **29.** 87.5% **31.** 6% **33.** 0.65 **35.** 0.75 **37.** 0.006 **39.** 0.0025 **41.** 3.15 **43.** 2.006 **45.** 5.406 **47.** 0.0007 **53.** 0.5; 50% **55.** $\frac{3}{20}$; 0.15 **57.** $\frac{1}{4}$; 25% **59.** 6.125; 612.5% **61.** $7\frac{1}{4}$; 725% **63.** $\frac{1}{400}$; 0.25% **65.** $0.33\overline{3}$; $33\frac{1}{3}$% **67.** $\frac{3}{400}$; 0.0075 **69.** $\frac{1}{8}$; 0.125 **71.** $2\frac{1}{2}$; 250% **73.** $10\frac{767}{2000}$; 10.3835 **75.** 4.375; 437.5% **77.** $\frac{27}{400}$; 0.0675 **79.** $8\frac{4}{5}$; 880% **81.** $\frac{1}{400}$; 0.0025

Section 3.2 (page 89)

1. 16 bicycles **3.** $244.35 **5.** 4.8 feet **7.** 10,185 miles **9.** 182 homes **11.** 148.444 yds **13.** $5366.65 **15.** $6.50 **19.** 264 adults **21.** $645.42 **23.** 2024 shoppers **25.** 206 scientists **27.** (a) 37.5% (b) 16.5 million female workers **29.** 3.78 million office workers **31.** 2156 products **33.** $135 million **35.** $51,844.20 **37.** $2098.80 **39.** $205.29 **41.** $119.93

Section 3.3 (page 94)

1. 1060 **3.** 187.5 **5.** 1000 **7.** 4800 **9.** 22,000 **11.** 20,000 **13.** $90,320 **15.** 1750 **17.** 312,500 **19.** 65,400 **21.** 40,000 **25.** 5022 juniors and seniors **27.** 7761 students **29.** $3800 **31.** 1055 people (rounded) **33.** $65.1 billion **35.** $185,500

Section 3.3 Supplementary Exercises (page 95)

1. 16 ounces (rounded) **3.** $288,150 **5.** 478,175 Mustangs **7.** $93.9 million **9.** $39,000 **11.** 836 drivers **13.** $61.4 million

Section 3.4 (page 101)

1. 10 **3.** 125 **5.** 28.3 **7.** 9.3 **9.** 4.1 **11.** 5.9 **13.** 102.5 **15.** 17.6 **17.** 27.8 **21.** 5.6% **23.** 2% **25.** 8.7% **27.** 9.1% **29.** 20%

Section 3.4 Supplementary Exercises (page 102)

1. 300 doctors   **3.** 40%   **5.** 16,910 hotels   **7.** 2,900,844 injuries   **9.** $396.05   **11. (a)** 30% **(b)** 70%   **13.** $134 sale price
15. 2.98%   **17.** 12.5%   **19.** 5.5%   **21.** 960 candy bars   **23.** $4473   **25.** 23.6%   **27.** 1.1 billion   **29.** 36%

Section 3.5 (page 110)

1. $375   **3.** $27.91   **5.** $25   **7.** $854.50   **11.** $173,534   **13. (a)** $1900 **(b)** $152   **15.** $2.3 billion   **17.** $19,100
19. $236,160   **21.** $78,854   **23.** $3864   **25.** 145.24 million (rounded)   **27.** 51.2 million   **29.** 34,741 students
31. 695 deaths   **33.** 361,461 phones

Chapter 3 Review Exercises (page 114)

1. 150 members   **2.** 24 vans   **3.** 1100 shippers   **4.** 2.5%   **5.** $3.75   **6.** $\frac{6}{25}$ **7.** 960 loads   **8.** $\frac{7}{8}$ **9.** 8.5%   **10.** $\frac{1}{200}$
11. $5185; $25,315   **12.** 224,000 units   **13.** 6.22 million   **14.** 21.43 million people   **15. (a)** 35% **(b)** $28,560   **16.** 71.2%
17. $350   **18.** 1200 backpacks   **19.** 2.8%   **20.** 21.4 million   **21.** 75%   **22.** 12.5 ounces   **23.** 97,757 copies   **24.** $39,840
25. 48.7%   **26.** 1.2%   **27.** 314,395,000 people   **28.** $1.365 billion   **29.** 1900%   **30.** 6.0%   **31.** 1.1%   **32.** 1,800,000 tourists
33. $140.8 million   **34.** 148,507 units   **35.** $11.90 per hour   **36.** 97 units

Chapter 3 Business Application Case #1 (page 116)

77.3%; $248.08; $67.54; 21.3%; 118.8%; 20.8%; $55.30; $23.27; $26.25; $52.68

Chapter 3 Business Application Case #2 (page 117)

(a) $271,095   **(b)** $504,000   **(c)** 7.1%   **(d)** Answers will vary.   **(e)** Answers will vary.

Chapter 4

Section 4.1 (page 126)

1. 17.7%   **3.** 3.91 times as much in investments as in banks   **5.** It has increased.   **7.** 4   **9.** 6   **11.** 5
13.

15. 23   **17.** 7   **21. (a)** Almost 1 acre **(b)** Almost $3\frac{7}{8}$ acres **(c)** 2 mph **(d)** 99 inches
23. Computer Skills Evaluation

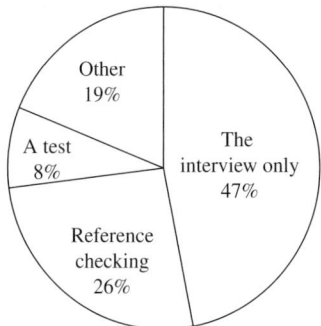

25. (a) 14% **(b)** 8% to 13% **(c)** 2% to $6\frac{1}{2}$% **(d)** Up; down

27.

Percent Increase in Average College Tuition and Fees from 2010–11 to 2011–12

Private, nonprofit 4-year colleges — 4.5%
Public 4-year colleges (in-state students) — 8.3%
Community colleges — 8.7%

Section 4.2 (page 141)

1. Interest earned, Total investment **3.** Profit, Sales **5.** Weight of calf, Age of calf **7.** Profit, Sales and total expenses

9.

Water Height at Monitoring Station on Indus River

11.

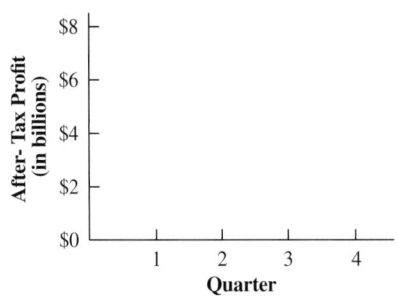

Quarterly Profit at Apple Inc.

13.

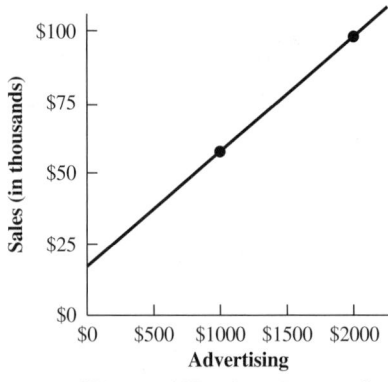

Sales based on Advertising

15. $P = +25N - +275$, where $P = $ profit and $N = $ number tutored in a month

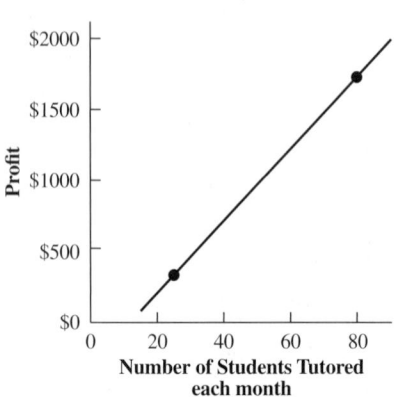

Monthly Profit

17. Tigard's profit per yard is $+40 - +7 = +33$ per yard. He has no other costs.
$P = +33N$ where $P = $ profit per week and $N = $ number of yards mowed per week

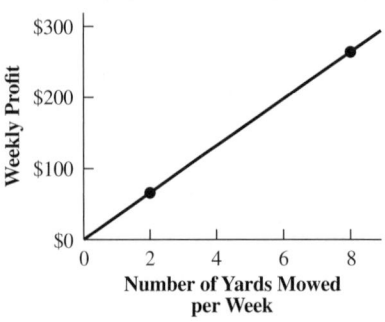

Weekly Profit Based on Number of Yards Mowed

19.

Monthly Costs at Computer Shoppe

Section 4.3 (page 151)

1. 228   **3.** 3689.6   **5.** 73 pounds   **7.** $1300   **9.** 10.3 inches   **11.** 39.4   **13.** 167.2   **17.** $31,000   **19.** 1.62   **21.** 76.3   **23.** 105.8
25. 68%   **27.** 55 inches

Section 4.4 (page 157)

1. 32   **3.** 88   **5.** 0.83   **7.** 60   **9.** none   **11.** 4 and 6   **15.** 81.2 feet; 82 feet   **19.** 115.1; 114.5; 114.5   **21.** Mean $3.66; Median $3.69
23. 3.01 pounds; probably so

Section 4.5 (page 164)

1. 18; 1.9   **3.** 21; 1.6   **5.** 55.9; 3.1   **7.** 43   **9.** 388   **13.** 100   **15.** 136   **17.** 27   **19.** 190   **21.** 50%   **23.** 95%   **25.** 50%   **27.** 16%
29. 95%   **31.** $\frac{1}{2}$%   **33.** 84%   **35.** 97.5%   **37.** 84%   **39.** 97.5%   **41.** 68%   **43.** 3 swimmers

Section 4.6 (page 168)

1. 302.2   **3.** 42   **5.** 340   **7.** $220.10   **9.** $196.60   **11.** $417.40   **13.** $135,000   **15.** $635.27   **17.** Medical costs

Chapter 4 Review Exercises (page 176)

1. 1; 3; 10; 3; 2; 1   **2.** 6
3.

Weekly Gasoline Sales

4. 72°; 10%; 108°; 108°; 36°
5.

6. 60%

7.

Temperature Scales

8.

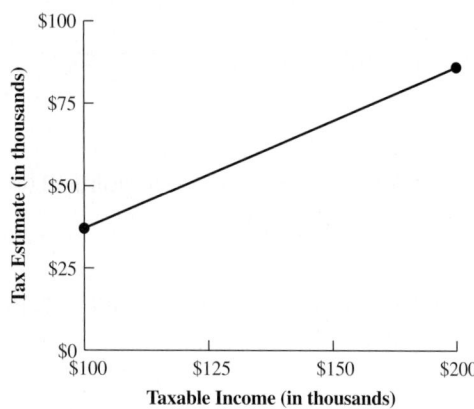

Estimate of Total Tax for Jolicka's

9.

Profit

10.

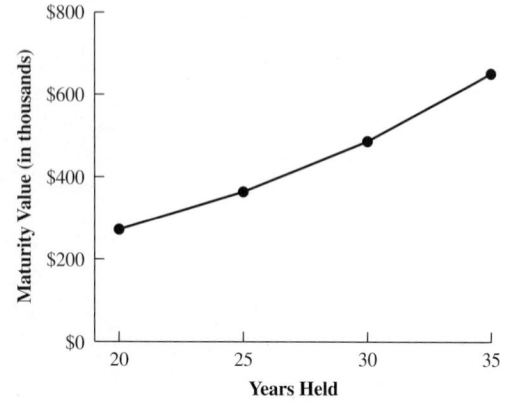

Maturity Value versus Years Investment Held

11. 23.4; 20; no mode   **12.** 85.6; 85; 82   **13.** 20.3; 20.5; 21   **14.** 43.3; 44; 44   **15.** 6.9; 7; 7   **16.** 2.4; 2.4; 2.4   **17.** 26.1
18. 34.8   **19.** 8; 3   **20.** 74.5; 74.5   **21.** 67; 22.77   **22.** 13; 4.05   **23.** 21; 7.21   **24.** 42; 14.88   **25.** 143.6
26. 164.0   **27.** 52.8   **28.** 162.2   **29.** $46,489   **30.** 84%
31. Since the mean ± 2 standard deviations includes 95% of the area, the price range that corresponds to a 95% chance of finding an acceptable automobile is $9412 $\pm$ $1520, or between $7892 and $10,932

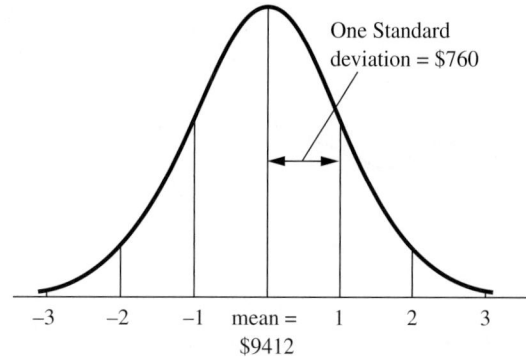

32. Sales are relatively flat

33.

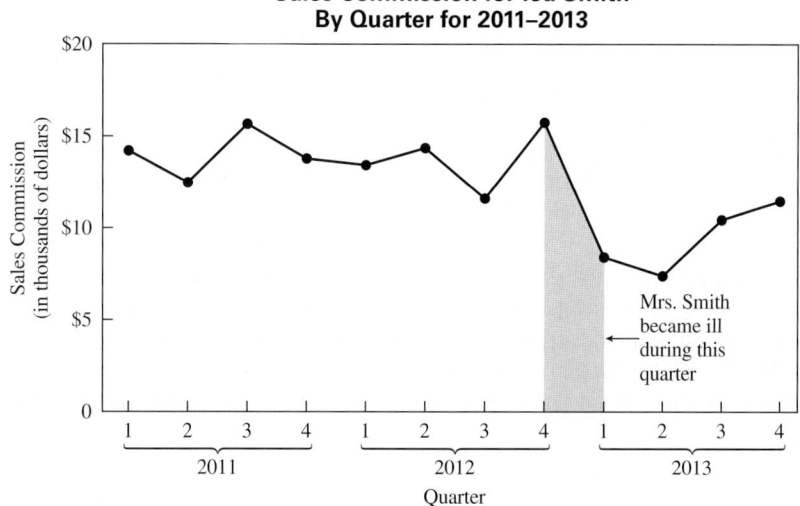

Mrs. Smith's illness affected Mr. Smith's work

34. 2.54; 2.31   **35.** 273.8   **36. (a)** Mean = $4741; median = $4825; mode = $5000 **(b)** Standard deviation = 1786.4 (rounded)

Chapter 4 Business Application Case #1 (page 181)
(a) Midland: 18.8, 18.5, no mode
    Lockhart: 8.5, 9.4, 10.2

(b)

Monthly Sales at Oil and Gas Services Company

(c) Sales grew rapidly in Midland, and are also growing in Lockhart.
(d) Sales have grown more rapidly in Midland. Pat Farmer has worked in Midland for several years and knows a lot of people. She does not know as many people in Lockhart.

Chapter 4 Business Application Case #2 (page 182)

(a) Income taxes paid: mean = $6.98 billion; median = $7.1 billion
Profit: mean = $13.64 billion; median = $13.4 billion
(b) $34.9, 68.2; $103.1; 33.9%
(c) Sales have a clear upward trend, indicating that Wal-Mart Stores continues to grow even though the company is the largest retailer in the world.

Net Sales at Wal-Mart Stores, Inc.

Part 1 Cumulative Review: Chapters 1–4 (page 183)

1. $60 per month   **2.** $20,961   **3.** $31,658.27   **4.** 24 payments   **5.** $\frac{8}{9}$ **6.** $\frac{65}{8}$ **7.** $7\frac{2}{15}$ **8.** $4\frac{5}{12}$ **9.** $13\frac{13}{24}$ **10.** $1\frac{3}{4}$ **11.** 3
12. $2\frac{2}{9}$ **13.** $42\frac{1}{2}$ acres   **14.** $22\frac{1}{2}$ hours   **15.** 130 feet   **16.** $\frac{1}{12}$ of the total   **17.** $\frac{7}{20}$ **18.** 0.667   **19.** 78.57   **20.** 4732.49   **21.** 62.7
22. 215.675   **23.** 26   **24.** 85.4   **25.** 112   **26.** 12   **27.** $\frac{3}{4}x$ **28.** $5x + x$ **29.** $8x - 8$ **30.** $6x + 5$ **31.** $T = 3$ **32.** $P = 1850
33. $\frac{5}{1}$ **34.** $\frac{7}{5}$ **35.** 9   **36.** $35\frac{1}{5}$ **37.** 525 students   **38.** $154,000   **39.** t^3 **40.** 17^2 **41.** 400   **42.** 1   **43.** $\frac{r^2}{t^2}$ **44.** $s^3 t^3$ **45.** 9^2
46. T^8 **47.** 23   **48.** 0   **49.** 21   **50.** 117   **51.** 62.5%   **52.** 0.0025   **53.** 450 prospects   **54.** $107.20   **55.** 25%   **56.** 150%
57. 13.1%   **58.** 21,888 people   **59.** 58,484 students   **60.** $16,760   **61.** 90,000%   **62.** 16.7% (rounded)   **63. (a)** 1990 − $3.25; 2010 − $7.25; 123.1%; **(b)** 1990 − $5.75; 2010 − $7.00; 21.7%; **(c)** Peaked in 1968; peaked at $10 per hour; 30% decline; **(d)** The purchasing power of the minimun-wage worker has continued to fall since 1968. In other words, those working for minimum wage are worse off today than in 1968.
64.

Price of a Gallon of Regular Gasoline

65.

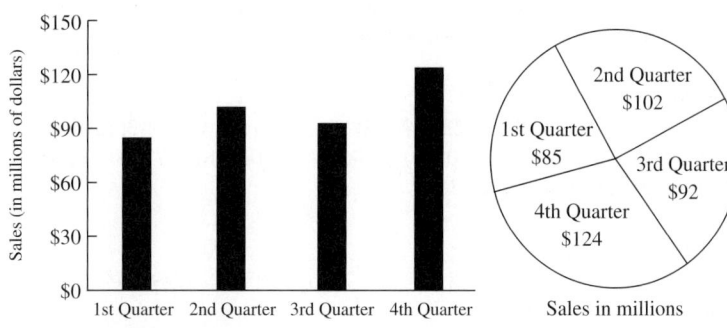

Benson's Medical Supplies

66.

Irrigated Field

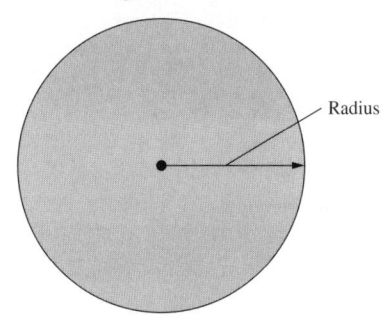

Area of a Circle Based on Radius

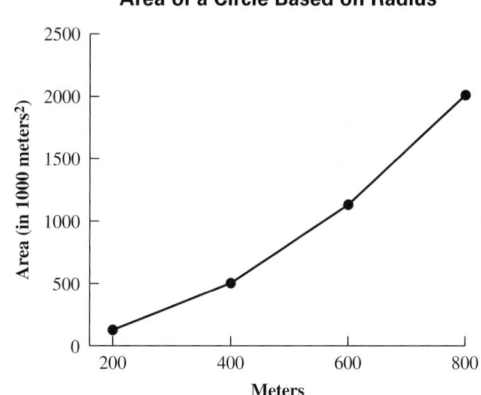

67. 2.69   **68.** 75; 13; 5.2   **69.** 47.5%
70.

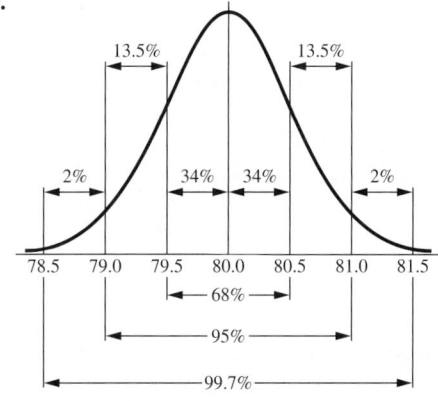

71. 57   **72.** $602

Chapter 5

Section 5.1 (page 198)

1. $14.20   **3.** $0   **5.** $17.10   **7.** $13.10
9.

857		
Mar. 8 _____ 20 ____		
Amount $380.71		
To Patty Demko		
For Tutoring		
Bal. Bro't. For'd.	3971	28
Am't. Deposited	79	26
Total	4050	54
Am't. this Check	380	71
Balance For'd.	3669	83

11.

735		
Dec. 4 _____ 20 ____		
Amount $37.52		
To Paul's Pools		
For Chemicals		
Bal. Bro't. For'd.	1126	73
Am't. Deposited		
Total	1126	73
Am't. this Check	37	52
Balance For'd.	1089	21

17.

5312		
Oct. 10 20 ____		
Amount $39.12		
To County Clerk		
For License		
Bal. Bro't. For'd.	5972	89
Am't. Deposited	752	18
	23	32
Total	6748	39
Am't. this Check	39	12
Balance For'd.	6709	27

19. 1379.41; 1230.41; 1348.14; 1278.34; 1608.20; 2026.50; 1916.74; 1302.62; 1270.44; 1791.39   **21.** 3709.32; 3590.92; 3877.24; 3797.24; 2811.02; 2435.52; 3637.34; 2901.66; 2677.72; 3175.73; 3097.49

Section 5.2 (page 205)

1. (a) $2419.76 **(b)** $203.86 **(c)** $2215.90 **(d)** $66.48 **(e)** $2149.42   **3. (a)** $1591.44 **(b)** $189.39 **(c)** $1402.05 **(d)** $56.08 **(e)** $1345.97   **5. (a)** $1064.72 **(b)** $72.83 **(c)** $991.89 **(d)** $29.76 **(e)** $962.13

Section 5.3 (page 214)

1. $5095.47   **3.** $7690.62   **5.** $18,314.72   **7.** $6967.88   **9.** $7498.20 **11.** $4496.01   **17.** $5657.67

Chapter 5 Review Exercises (page 219)

1. $15.90   **2.** $19   **3.** $10.20   **4.** 9517.70   **5.** 9831.34   **6.** 19,415.20   **7.** $1064.72   **8.** $72.83   **9.** $991.89   **10.** $19.84 **11.** $972.05   **12.** $6043.16   **13.** $8992.02   **14.** $1267.21

Chapter 5 Business Application Case #1 (page 221)

(a) $8178.46 gross profit   **(b)** $7974 credit   **(c)** $9810.36 total of checks outstanding   **(d)** $4882.58 deposits not recorded **(e)** $7274.56 balance

Chapter 5 Business Application Case #2 (page 222)

1. $7.40   **2. (a)** $2570 **(b)** $2531.45   **3.** Answers will vary.   **4.** Answers will vary.

Chapter 6

Section 6.1 (page 232)

1. 40; 0; $12.15   **3.** 38.75; 0; $11.70   **5.** 40; 5.25; $17.22   **7.** $324; $0; $324   **9.** $302.25; $0; $302.25   **11.** $459.20; $90.41; $549.61   **13.** $13.20; $347.60; $0; $347.60   **15.** $21.60; $576; $97.20; $673.20   **17.** $13.77; $367.20; $58.52; $425.72   **19.** 51; 11; $3.70; $377.40; $40.70; $418.10   **21.** 50.25; 10.25; $4.30; $432.15; $44.08; $476.23   **23.** 50.25; 10.25; $5.10; $512.55; $52.28; $564.83   **25.** 35; 6; $14.25; $332.50; $85.50; $418.00   **27.** 39.5; 3.75; $17.10; $450.30; $64.13; $514.43   **29.** 39.75; 3.5; $15.30; $405.45; $53.55; $459.00   **33.** $496; $537.33; $1074.67; $12,896   **35.** $426; $923; $1846; $22,152   **37.** $501.92; $1003.85; $2175; $26,100   **39.** $618.46; $1236.92; $1340; $32,160   **41.** $830; $1660; $1798.33; $3596.67   **43.** $832   **45.** $487.70 **47.** $703.08   **49.** $436.80   **51.** $678.90   **53.** $1127   **55.** $925.16   **57. (a)** $1260 biweekly **(b)** $1365 semimonthly **(c)** $2730 monthly **(d)** $32,760 annually

Section 6.2 (page 239)

1. $208.16   **3.** $421.65   **5.** $1941.75   **7.** $433.37   **9.** $1405   **11.** $688.40   **13.** $748   **15.** $2136   **19.** $5030; $201.20; $491.20   **21.** $4085; $245.10; $745.10   **23.** $19,530; $585.90; $585.90   **25.** $2897; $144.85; $454.85   **27.** $916.20 **29.** $5646   **31. (a)** $2495 **(b)** $1695   **33.** $874.27

Section 6.3 (page 245)

1. 652; $378.16   **3.** 451; $338.25   **5.** 665; $452.20   **7.** 588; $270.48   **9.** 670; $522.60   **11.** $190.00   **13.** $230.24 **15.** $421.75   **17.** $260.19   **19.** $284.65   **21.** $297   **23.** $274.80   **25.** $439.52   **27.** $503.80   **29.** $322.57   **31.** $340.73 **35.** $844   **37.** $777.75   **39.** $648.40

Section 6.4 (page 251)

1. $20.13; $4.71   **3.** $28.72; $6.72   **5.** $52.99; $12.39   **7.** $67.35; $15.75   **9.** $261.55   **11.** $39.66   **13.** $28.46   **15.** $368.80; $76.07; $444.87; $27.58; $6.45; $4.45   **17.** $412; $61.80; $473.80; $29.38; $6.87; $4.74   **19.** $327.20; $61.35; $388.55; $24.09; $5.63; $3.89   **21.** $700; $177.19; $877.19; $54.39; $12.72; $8.77   **23. (a)** $24.07 **(b)** $5.63   **25. (a)** $95.67 **(b)** $22.38 **(c)** $15.43   **27.** $7221.60; $1688.92   **29.** $4317.33; $1009.70   **31.** $3328.61; $778.46

Section 6.5 (page 262)

1. $163   **3.** $49   **5.** $83   **7.** $31   **9.** $21   **11.** $73   **13.** $21.15   **15.** $5.49   **17.** $88.58   **19.** $35.73, $8.36, $13.97, $518.22 **21.** $155.78, $36.43, $268.98, $2051.34   **23.** $141.16, $33.01, $187.35, $1915.31   **25.** $122.21, $28.58, $72.11, $1748.16 **27.** $168.02, $39.30, $401.47, $2101.21   **29.** $110.76, $25.90, $346.24, $1303.54   **31.** $114.84, $26.86, $123.65, $1586.85 **35.** $752.60   **37.** $573.84   **39.** $3778.09

Section 6.6 (page 267)

1. $2392.04 **3.** $2671.70 **5.** $2162.14 **7.** $9558.80 **9.** $1570.26 **11.** $13,129.72 **13.** $12,831.18 **15.** $17,914.01
19. $3355 **21.** $2791.98 **23. (a)** $1120 **(b)** $67.20 **25. (a)** $1600 **(b)** $96

Chapter 6 Review Exercises (page 272)

1. 40; 8.5; $482.14 **2.** 40; 8; $442 **3.** 38.25; 0; $415.01 **4.** 40; 17.25; $803.68 **5.** $821.60; $890.07; $1780.13; $21,361.60
6. $530; $1148.33; $2296.67; $27,560 **7.** $346.15; $692.31; $750; $1500 **8.** $403.85; $807.69; $1750; $21,000 **9.** $760
10. $427.50 **11.** $3641.12 **12.** $3374.55 **13.** $532.10 **14.** $134 **15.** $3525 **16.** $465 **17.** $600 **18.** $265.02
19. (a) $576.60 **(b)** $134.85 **20. (a)** $477.40 **(b)** $134.85 **21.** $42 **22.** $45 **23.** $175 **24.** $45 **25.** $35 **26.** $21
27. $1484.69 **28.** $564.92 **29.** $809.42 **30.** $1946.18 **31.** $9386.32 **32. (a)** $31.90 **(b)** $7.46 **(c)** $5.14 **33. (a)** $110.98
(b) $38.43 **34.** $5451.25 **35. (a)** $4810.61 **(b)** $1125.06 **36. (a)** $3424.70 **(b)** $800.94 **37. (a)** $913 **(b)** $54.78 **38. (a)** $2140
(b) $128.40

Chapter 6 Business Application Case #1 (page 275)

(a) $740 **(b)** $333 **(c)** $1073 **(d)** $66.53 **(e)** $15.56 **(f)** $148.08 **(g)** $10.73 **(h)** $37.56 **(i)** $220 **(j)** $574.54

Chapter 6 Business Application Case #2 (page 276)

(a) 25.5 million; 54 million; 111.8% increase **(b)** FICA, $1029.20; Medicare, $240.70

Chapter 7

Section 7.1 (page 282)

1. $2.29; $8.38; $86.87 **3.** $2.15; $1.43; $51.28 **5.** $7.43; $30.36; $186.29 **7.** $57.55; $98.66; $978.39 **9.** $1837.50; $504;
$31,741.50 **11.** $160; $169.60 **13.** $157.50; $163.80 **15.** $330; $351.45 **17.** $1276.80; $1340.64 **19.** $102.20; $5.11
21. $520.30; $31.22 **23.** $19.76; $0.84 **25.** $315; $18.90 **27.** $2753.05; $192.71 **31. (a)** $7.19 **(b)** $13.18 **(c)** $140.17
33. $258.53 **35.** $699 **37.** $54,899.64 **39. (a)** $149.48 **(b)** $12.70 too high **41.** $2688 **43.** $16,500

Section 7.2 (page 289)

1. $136,480 **3.** $60,830 **5.** $325,125 **7.** 5.6% **9.** 3.7% **11.** 3% **13. (a)** 2.8% **(b)** $2.80 **(c)** $28 **15. (a)** $2.41
(b) $24.10 **(c)** 24.1 **17. (a)** 7.08% **(b)** $70.80 **(c)** 70.8 **21.** $5861.60 **23.** $47,498.22 **25.** $4464 **27.** 5.8% **29.** $6273
31. $5.25 **33.** $236,800 **35.** 3.4% **37.** $13,817.55 **39.** $200,925 **41. (a)** The second county **(b)** $300.96 **43.** 2.5%
45. $2500

Section 7.3 (page 304)

1. $23,131 **3.** $21,710 **5.** $39,031 **7.** $22,900; $3010 **9.** $16,051; $1605.10 **11.** $41,100; $5315 **13.** $15,750; $1937.50
15. $49,220; $8430 **17.** $46,713; $6445.75 **19.** $808.70 tax refund **21.** $645.56 tax refund **23.** $3293 tax due
27. $79,146; $12,036.50 **29.** $69,800; $13,575 **31.** $67,680; $11,687.50; **33.** $101,028; $17,507

Chapter 7 Review Exercises (page 308)

1. $51.13; $85.22; $988.50 **2.** $6.89; $9.48; $102.52 **3.** $825; $1342; $18,667 **4.** $24.22; $52.16; $422.34 **5.** $1134 **6.** $284
7. $261.33 **8.** $327.15 **9.** $422 **10.** $125 **11.** $277.68 **12.** $159.68 **13.** 4.06%; $40.60; 40.6 **14.** 2.7%; $2.70; $27
15. $1.27; $12.70; 12.7 **16.** 1.95%; $1.95; 19.5 **17.** $13,632 **18.** $18.50 **19.** $46,500 **20.** 2.8% **21.** $96,200 **22.** $2797.20
23. $28,915; $3912.25 **24.** $58,528; $7929.20 **25.** $45,470; $5970.50 **26.** $100,660; $19,932.50 **27.** 2.2% **28.** $194.88
29. $39,124.50 **30.** $71,620; $10,155 **31.** $19,140; $2263.50 **32.** $42,844; $5576.60 **33.** $1519.30 tax refund
34. $196.55 tax refund **35.** $1631.86 tax due **36.** $1379.90 tax refund

Chapter 7 Business Application Case #1 (page 310)

(a) Anderson: $3,143,664; Bentonville: $3,488,706 **(b)** Anderson: $785,916; Bentonville: $697,741.20 **(c)** Anderson: $25,149.31;
Bentonville: $52,330.59 **(d)** Anderson: $3,395,157.10; Bentonville: $4,012,011.90 **(e)** Anderson

Chapter 7 Business Application Case #2 (page 311)

(a) $1718.25 **(b)** $3757.56 **(c)** $4016.25 **(d)** $31,640 **(e)** $3896 **(f)** $800.03 **(g)** $14,188.09 **(h)** $25.2% rounded

Chapter 8

Section 8.1 (page 321)

1. $4707 **3.** $3158 **5.** $9299 **7.** $8648 **9.** $432.40 **11.** $3985.20 **13.** $828.85 **15.** $243 **17. (a)** $2010 **(b)** $670
19. (a) $2552.08 **(b)** $1822.92 **21. (a)** $2654 **(b)** $2654 **23.** $19,850 **25.** $92,201.90 **27.** $36,500 **29.** $12,554.95

31. A: $60,000; B: $20,000 **33.** 1: $292,500; 2: $260,000; 3: $97,500 **35. (a)** $300,000 **(b)** A: $175,000, B: $125,000 **(c)** $60,000 **37. (a)** $12,500 **(b)** 1: $7500; 2: $5000 **(c)** $7500 **39.** $18,804 **41.** $1084 **43.** $1057.50 **45.** $930 **47. (a)** $1112.50 **(b)** $1557.50 **49. (a)** $1134 **(b)** $810 **53. (a)** $19,936.71 **(b)** $2563.29 **55. (a)** $30,681.82 **(b)** $14,318.18 **59.** A: $274,000 B: $182,667 C: $91,333 **61. (a)** $375,000 **(b)** A: $281,250; B: $93,750 **63. (a)** $75,000 **(b)** 1: $41,667; 2: $20,833; 3: $12,500

Section 8.2 (page 332)

1. $931 **3.** $932 **5.** $609 **7.** $970 **9.** $748 **11.** $810 **15.** $1223.25 **17.** $655 **19. (a)** $25,000 **(b)** $11,500 **21. (a)** $1628 **(b)** $6936 **(c)** $100,000 **(d)** $15,250 **23. (a)** $60,000 **(b)** $20,250

Section 8.3 (page 343)

1. $952.50; $485.78; $247.65; $86.49 **3.** $849.10; $433.04; $220.77; $77.10 **5.** $516.80; $263.57; $134.37; $46.93 **7.** $297; $151.47; $77.22; $26.97 **9.** $531; $270.81; $138.06; $48.21 **11.** $1836.10; $936.41; $477.39; $166.72 **13.** $3175; $1619.25; $825.50; $288.29 **17.** $15,500 **19.** $30,000 **21.** $196,800 **23.** 23 yr. 315 days **25.** $289 **27.** 18 years **29.** $160.20 **31. (a)** $384 **(b)** $50,000 **33.** $592.62 **35.** $110.41 **37. (a)** $444.72 **(b)** $226.72 **(c)** $79.18 **(d)** $889.44; $906.88; $950.16 **39. (a)** $5660 **(b)** $11,580 **(c)** 23 yr. 315 days **41.** $149,500 **43. (a)** $211.50 **(b)** approx. 20 years **(c)** $115.75 **(d)** $109.50 **45. (a)** $345.50 **(b)** 18 yr. **(c)** $297 **(d)** $286.50

Chapter 8 Review Exercises (page 349)

1. $4630 **2.** $3510 **3.** $434 **4.** $1028 **5.** $1152.45 **6.** $323.40 **7.** $222.90 **8.** $1007.30 **9. (a)** $1312.50 **(b)** $1837.50 **10. (a)** $1481.25 **(b)** $493.75 **11. (a)** $1230 **(b)** $246 **12. (a)** $464 **(b)** $2320 **13.** $39,473.68 **14.** $72,689.19 **15.** $2731.66 **16.** $35,707.69 **17.** $796 **18.** $1086.55 **19.** $1183 **20.** $902 **21.** $2281.30 **22.** $246 **23.** $133.50 **24.** $192 **25.** A: $36,000; B: $21,600; C: $14,400 **26. (a)** $125,762 **(b)** 1: $80,030; 2: $45,732 **27. (a)** $25,000 **(b)** $13,400 **28. (a)** $15,000 **(b)** $0 **29. (a)** $40,000 **(b)** $36,800 **30. (a)** $494.70 **(b)** $252.20 **(c)** $88.08 **(d)** $989.40; $1008.80; $1056.96 **31.** $67,500 **32. (a)** $11,320 **(b)** $23,160 **(c)** 23 yr. 315 days **33. (a)** $552.80 **(b)** about 12 yr. **(c)** $475.20 **(d)** $392.80 **34. (a)** $231.20 **(b)** about 18 yr. **(c)** $185.20 **(d)** $179.60

Chapter 8 Business Application Case #1 (page 351)

(a) $39,940.40 **(b)** $370.39 **(c)** $40,310.79 **(d)** $1389.21

Chapter 8 Business Application Case #2 (page 351)

(a) $2796.96 **(b)** P. Russo: $129, $1457, $340.75, $1926.75; E. Martin: $492, $2777.60, $649.60, $3919.20; T. Hicks: $984, $3596, $841, $5421 **(c)** $140,363.91

Part 2 Cumulative Review: Chapters 5–8 (page 352–353)

1. $1014.40 **2.** $208.15 **3.** $806.25 **4.** $18.14 **5.** $788.11 **6.** $17,984.04 **7.** $595.20 **8. (a)** $2710 **(b)** $1510 **9.** $679.43 **10. (a)** $102.58 **(b)** $23.99 **(c)** $16.54 **11.** $871.02 **12.** $4359.38 **13.** $272 **14. (a)** $2.68% **(b)** $26.80 **(c)** 26.8 **15. (a)** $4.62 **(b)** $46.20 **(c)** 46.2 **16.** $37,389.93 **17.** $211,910; $47,404.30 **18.** $1330.56 **19. (a)** $150,000 **(b)** A: $83,333; B: $41,667; C: $25,000 **20.** $879 **21. (a)** $6090 **(b)** $25,000 **(c)** $50,000 **(d)** $125,050 **22. (a)** $1662.09 **(b)** $847.34 **(c)** $295.92 **(d)** $3324.18; $3389.36; $3551.04

Chapter 9

Section 9.1 (page 362)

1. foot **3.** sack **5.** great gross **7.** case **9.** drum **11.** cost per thousand **13.** gallon **15.** cash on delivery **17.** $226.80; $37.80; $126.36; $848.96; $3610.36; $4850.28; $4887.73 **21.** 0.72 **23.** 0.48 **25.** 0.54 **27.** 0.4025 **29.** 0.532 **31.** 0.342 **33.** $267.52 **35.** $7.01 **37.** $7.14 **39.** $4919.67 **41.** $11.81 **43.** $640 **49.** $242.99 **51. (a)** 20/15 **(b)** $12.24 **53.** $16,416 **55.** $2.14 for each music player **57.** $189 **59. (a)** $274.02 **(b)** $18.27

Section 9.2 (page 369)

1. 0.72; 28% **3.** 0.5525; 44.75% **5.** 0.64; 36% **7.** 0.576; 42.4% **9.** 0.675; 32.5% **11.** 0.75; 25% **13.** 0.648; 35.2% **15.** 0.243; 75.7% **17.** 0.45; 55% **19.** 0.7; 30% **21.** 0.5184; 48.16% **23.** 0.5054; 49.46% **27.** $720 **29.** $700 **31.** $1920 **33. (a)** $25.89 **(b)** $28.76 **(c)** $2.87 **35.** $740 **37. (a)** $544.32 **(b)** $604.80 **(c)** $60.48 **39.** 25.0% **41.** $3857.14 **43.** 5.0%

Section 9.3 (page 375)

1. Oct. 18; Nov. 7 **3.** Mar. 25; Mar. 30 **5.** Sept. 21; Nov. 10 **7.** Jan. 24; Mar. 15 **9.** Jan. 20; Mar. 6 **11.** $3.03; $160.90 **13.** $0; $101.28 **15.** $14.48; $747.66 **17.** $0; $659.50 **19.** $29.15; $607.03 **23.** $1990.59 **25.** $674.42 **27.** $1571.62 **29.** $2511.13 **31.** $2021.32 **33. (a)** April 24; May 4; May 14 **(b)** June 3 **35. (a)** April 25 **(b)** May 5 **37.** $3547.50 **39.** $3106.60

Section 9.4 (page 381)

1. Mar. 10; Mar. 30 **3.** Sept. 18; Oct. 8 **5.** Dec. 22; Jan. 11 **7.** Aug. 10; Aug. 30 **9.** Aug. 24; Sep. 13 **11.** $20.47; $661.81
13. $0; $194.04 **15.** $59.20; $2900.80 **17.** $168.80; $4051.20 **19.** $0.25; $12.13 **21.** $97.52; $3153.08 **23.** $68.33; $1639.85
27. $1900; $1250 **29.** $720; $1030 **31.** $100; $60 **35. (a)** Sept. 15 **(b)** Oct. 5 **37. (a)** Dec. 23 **(b)** Jan. 12 **39. (a)** July 10
(b) July 30 **41. (a)** Dec. 13 **(b)** $2334.93 **43. (a)** May 4 **(b)** $9469.61 **45. (a)** $1000 **(b)** $920 **47.** $1495.58 **49.** $93.02
51. (a) $306.12 **(b)** $220.68 **53. (a)** $597.94 **(b)** $522.21 **55. (a)** $489.13 **(b)** $183.17

Chapter 9 Review Exercises (page 388)

1. $345.60 **2.** $195.62 **3.** $1828.18 **4.** $826.20 **5. (a)** 0.6375 **(b)** 36.25% **6. (a)** 0.576 **(b)** 42.4% **7. (a)** 0.54 **(b)** 46%
8. (a) 0.4536 **(b)** 54.64% **9.** $502.08 **10.** $1545.21 **11.** $537.09 **12.** $2262.11 **13.** Mar. 15; April 4 **14.** May 30; June 19
15. Jan. 10; Jan. 30 **16.** Dec. 19; Jan. 8 **17.** $38.41; $1318.17 **18.** $28.37; $917.23 **19.** $35.02; $907.66 **20.** $44.21; $2166.39
21. $306.12; $353.88 **22.** $2597.94; $2712.06 **23.** $505.05; $354.95 **24.** $2113.40; $1736.60 **25. (a)** $394.40 **(b)** $386.51
(c) $398.06 **26. (a)** Builders Supply **(b)** $1.91 **27.** $48,450 **28.** 10% **29.** $1779.95 **30.** $218.74 **31. (a)** April 15 **(b)** $821.24
32. (a) $1875 **(b)** $3405 **(c)** $75

Chapter 9 Business Application Case #1 (page 390)

(a) $17,750.66 **(b)** October 15 **(c)** November 4 **(d)** $17,966.52 **(e)** $10,309.28; $8189.76

Chapter 9 Business Application Case #2 (page 390)

(a) Trident, Inc., $135,193; Shanghai Industries, $148,024 **(b)** Trident, Inc.; Savings = $12,831 **(c)** Answers will vary.

Chapter 10

Section 10.1 (page 397)

1. $4.96; $17.36 **3.** 50%; $35.25 **5.** $39.80; 25.1% **7.** $67.50; 20% **9.** $118; 56.2% **11.** $133.65; $628.65 **15.** $102.22
17. $13.73 **19.** $3609.60 **21.** 59.1% **23. (a)** $95.96 **(b)** 25% **(c)** 125% **25. (a)** 132% **(b)** $97.02 **(c)** $23.52 **27. (a)** $70
(b) 27.2% **(c)** $19.04 **29.** $214,171 **31.** $6.63

Section 10.2 (page 404)

1. $7; $28 **3.** $131.48; $243.48 **5.** $37.20; $55.80 **7.** $46.36; $24.96 **9.** $77.82; 35.2% **11.** $230; $287.50 **13.** $8.46; $22.26;
61.3% **15.** $750; $1050; 28.6% **17.** $357.52; 22% **19.** 25% **21.** 35.1% **23.** 33.3% **25.** 66.7% **29.** $48.98 **31.** $386.75
33. $119 **35. (a)** $4.50 **(b)** $2.88 **(c)** 64% **37.** 26.5% **39. (a)** 72% **(b)** $259.99 **(c)** $72.80 **41. (a)** $0.72 **(b)** 100%
43. (a) $13,680 **(b)** $6080 **(c)** 44.4% **(d)** 80% **45. (a)** $472 **(b)** 150% **47. (a)** 43.8% **(b)** 30.4% **49. (a)** $64.80 **(b)** 25.9%
51. (a) $24.90 **(b)** 12.5% **(c)** 14.2%

Section 10.3 (page 411)

1. $1.11 **3.** $3.13 **5.** $9 **7.** $1.65 **9.** 24; $8.94 **11.** 18; $22 **13.** 76; $3.75 **15.** 1900; $16.58 **17.** 160; 40; $3.41 **19.** 34; 6;
$78.53 **21.** 108; 36; $4.17 **23.** 700; 300; $4.71 **27.** $75.88 **29.** $78.75 **31.** $30 **33.** $308.75 **35.** $177.78 **37.** $24.13

Section 10.3 Supplementary Exercises (page 413)

1. $22.35 **3.** 19.1% **5.** $6.98 **7.** $125.50 **9. (a)** 76% **(b)** $179.99 **(c)** $43.20 **11.** $0.65

Chapter 10 Review Exercises (page 416)

1. $6.40; $38.40 **2.** $24.60; $30.75 **3.** $147; 50% **4.** $45.90; 42.5% **5.** $18.08; $90.40 **6.** $105; 25% **7.** $34.70; $52.05
8. 38.5%; $460.20 **9.** $1920; $2400; 25% **10.** $64.50; 100%; 50% **11.** $8; 46%; 31.5% **12.** $474.28; $948.56; 50%
13. $22.08; 50%; $33\frac{1}{3}$% **14.** $150.16; $525.56; 28.6% **15.** 25% **16.** 50% **17.** 18.1% **18.** $16\frac{2}{3}$% **19.** $1.25 **20.** $32.50
21. $13.59 **22.** $17.04 **23.** 135; 15; $6.67 **24.** 72; 18; $2.38 **25.** 216; 72; $8.27 **26.** 700; 300; $4.71 **27.** $34.31
28. $632 **29.** 40% **30. (a)** $37.99 **(b)** 19.0% **(c)** 23.5% **31. (a)** $19,050.25 **(b)** 47% **32.** $6 **33. (a)** 20% **(b)** 25% **34.** $12.35

Chapter 10 Business Application Case #1 (page 417)

(a) $16,116.41 **(b)** $20,127 **(c)** $4010.59 **(d)** 20% **(e)** 25%

Chapter 10 Business Application Case #2 (page 418)

(a) 5.2% **(b)** $373,375.60 **(c)** 63.4% **(d)** 38.8%

Chapter 11

Section 11.1 (page 426)

1. 25%; $645   **3.** 45%; $13.86   **5.** $6.50; $1.30   **7.** $2.70; $1.62   **9.** $21.75; $21.75   **11.** $857; 20%   **13.** $60; $10; none
15. $16; $22; $6   **17.** $385; $250; $60   **19.** $29; $10; $39   **23.** $239   **25.** 18%   **27.** $298 operating loss   **29. (a)** $63.62
(b) $40.75 **(c)** 27%   **31. (a)** $256.50 **(b)** 11%

Section 11.2 (page 431)

1. $11,680   **3.** $22,673   **5.** $24,500   **7.** 2.81; 2.83   **9.** 7.94; 7.98   **11.** 10.25; 10.25   **13.** 4.66; 4.69   **17.** $49,717.15
19. 5.43   **21.** 4.84   **23.** 39.46   **25.** 4.17

Section 11.3 (page 439)

1. $827   **3.** $560   **5. (a)** $18,200 **(b)** $19,500 **(c)** $17,000   **7. (a)** $2352 **(b)** $2385 **(c)** $2313   **9.** $1770   **11. (a)** $48 **(b)** $50
(c) $51   **13. (a)** $1251 **(b)** $1430 **(c)** $1040   **15. (a)** $6144 **(b)** $6784 **(c)** $5500   **17.** $130,600   **19.** $30,641

Chapter 11 Review Exercises (page 445)

1. $28.80; $67.20   **2.** $15; $5   **3.** $5.40; $2.70   **4.** 25%; $585   **5.** $48; $66   **6.** $100; $7; none   **7.** $100; $70; $8   **8.** $6.25;
$0.75; none   **9.** $41,051   **10.** $348,468   **11.** $76,411.80   **12.** $32,859.80   **13.** 5.73; 5.76   **14.** 7.94; 7.98   **15.** 4.66; 4.69
16. 4.56; 4.63   **17.** $556   **18.** $1242   **19.** $3640   **20.** $6017   **21.** 28%   **22. (a)** $78.40 **(b)** 7%   **23.** $32,568   **24.** 10.77
25. 12.64   **26. (a)** $6489 **(b)** $5887.50 **(c)** $6675   **27.** $115,000   **28.** $75,600

Chapter 11 Business Application Case #1 (page 447)

(a) $187.50   **(b)** $3093.75   **(c)** $562.50   **(d)** $0

Chapter 11 Business Application Case #2 (page 447)

(a) Small boats, 27.2%; Mid-sized boats, 34.8%; Parts, 60%; Misc, 50.9%   **(b)** Total Cost, $271,890; Original Selling Price,
$370,820; 36.4%   **(c)** $283,677.30   **(d)** 4.3%

Part 3 Cumulative Review: Chapters 9–11 (page 448)

1. $201.60   **2.** $240.47   **3.** 0.72; 28%   **4.** 0.64; 36%   **5.** 0.532; 46.8%   **6.** 0.27; 73%   **7.** $14.81; $762.57   **8.** $34.97; $839.25
9. $113.65; $3745.73   **10.** $93.85; $4598.65   **11.** $288.14; 100%; 50%   **12.** $114.66; $152.88; 25%   **13.** 700 pr.; 300 pr.; $2.36
14. 135; 15; $20   **15.** $48; $66; $18   **16.** $50; $35; $4   **17.** $64,877   **18.** $211,981   **19.** 5.73 at retail; 5.76 at cost   **20.** 4.66 at
retail; 4.69 at cost   **21. (a)** $1533.44 **(b)** $1916.80 **(c)** $383.36   **22.** $3506.44   **23.** $730   **24.** 20%   **25. (a)** $124.99 **(b)** 25%
(c) $33\frac{1}{3}$%   **26.** 28%   **27. (a)** $131.10 operating loss **(b)** $45.60 absolute loss   **28.** $65,139 average inventory   **29.** $12,978
weighted-average method   **30. (a)** $11,775 FIFO **(b)** $13,350 LIFO

Chapter 12

Section 12.1 (page 456)

1. $850   **3.** $785.33   **5.** $1340.63   **7.** $644.90   **9.** $3821.17   **11.** $500   **13.** $4062.50   **15.** 7%   **17.** 14   **19.** 1.5 years
21. $4200   **23.** 11 months   **25.** 8%   **27.** $146.25   **29.** $1,525,000   **31.** 8 months   **33.** 1.25%   **37.** $170.67   **39.** 11.1%
41. $21.27   **43.** $1660

Section 12.2 (page 463)

1. 209 days   **3.** 36 days   **5.** 196 days   **7.** October 12   **9.** March 10   **11.** April 11   **13.** $450   **15.** $3281.25   **17.** $336.46
19. $13,155.04   **21.** $104.11   **23.** $115.56   **25.** $114.68   **27.** $314.07   **31.** $912.55   **33.** $2092.54   **35.** $3234   **37.** $18,229.17
39. (a) $532.60 **(b)** $540 **(c)** $7.40   **41. (a)** $9057.53 **(b)** $9183.33 **(c)** $125.80   **43.** $175.80   **45.** First Bank; $9.34

Section 12.3 (page 470)

1. $637.50; $9137.50   **3.** $191.72; $5991.72   **5.** $1080; $9720   **7.** $133.33; $4933.33   **9.** 70; $8733.78   **11.** $10\frac{1}{2}$%; $14,490
13. $16,400; $717.50   **15.** $14,800; 180   **17.** $126; 180   **19.** $42,459.44; 15%   **21.** $490; $12,490   **23.** 140 days; $512.36
25. $1200; 12%   **27.** $59,315.59; $5684.41

Section 12.4 (page 478)

1. $4932   **3.** $11,462.50   **5.** $4529.22   **7.** $2400   **9.** $8400   **11.** $8700   **15.** $6,755,576.39   **17.** $1,412,062.50   **19.** $78,333.34
21. $7104.85   **23.** $5501.25   **25.** $397.50 loss   **27.** $17,400 in 150 days

Chapter 12 Review Exercises (page 484)

1. $840 **2.** $840 **3.** $8710 **4.** $2400 **5.** 9% **6.** 7.5% **7.** 9 months **8.** 30 months **9.** 114 days **10.** 115 days
11. $258.90 **12.** $336.58 **13.** $222.51 **14.** $867.95 **15.** $43.17 **16.** $3241.33 **17.** $12,199.80 **18.** $6181.82 **19.** 7%
20. $8\frac{1}{4}$% **21.** 40 days **22.** 90 days **23.** $6270 **24.** $7272.60 **25.** $12,000 **26.** $6500 **27.** 9% **28.** 12% **29.** $6418.15
30. $11,612.90 **31.** $8093.75 **32.** $19,550.56 **33.** $8096.89 **34.** $15,598.34 **35.** $84.38 **36.** $19,297.50 **37.** 250 days
38. $3600 **39.** 9.5% **40.** 17.3%; no **41.** 322 days **42.** $9127.31 **43.** $19,528.16 **44.** $11,948.33 **45.** $852 gain
46. $2811 loss

Chapter 12 Business Application Case #1 (page 486)

September 3, $600, $12,600; July 16, $186, $6386; January 25 of the following year, $971.11, $19,371.11; Totals: $1757.11,
$38,357.11

Chapter 12 Business Application Case #2 (page 486)

(a)

	Interest	Maturity Value
Shanghai Bank	$558,080	$13,358,080
Bacon Funds	$1,228,800	$14,028,800
Jidlaka Investments	$707,093.33	$13,507,093.33

(b) The loan from Jidlaka Investments is only for 1 more month than the one from Shanghai Bank but the interest rate is quite a bit higher. So that does not appear to be a good choice. The loan from Shanghai Bank looks best unless Navistar Shipping needs the longer term of 12 months from Bacon Funds.

Chapter 13

Section 13.1 (page 495)

1. Helen Spence **3.** Leta Clendenen **5.** 90 days **7.** January 25 **9.** September 20 **11.** June 30 **13.** March 17 **15.** April 23
17. November 9; $6225 **19.** June 10; $5354.17 **21.** $8400 **23.** 120 days **25.** 11% **27.** $12,954 **31.** **(a)** April 25
(b) $19,396.67 **33.** **(a)** November 15 **(b)** $90,206.25 **35.** $284,289.28 **37.** **(a)** April 7 **(b)** $28,400 **39.** 90 days **41.** 8%
43. $2004

Section 13.2 (page 504)

1. $103.50; $4496.50 **3.** $779.17; $7720.83 **5.** $42; $8358 **7.** April 13; $8143.33 **9.** February 17; $11,430
11. 8/3; $1140; $22,860 **13.** 11%; $13,740 **15.** $7200; 6%; 2/10 **17.** $220; $5780 **19.** 120 days **21.** 7.2%
23. $3329.48 **25.** $7358; 9.0% **27.** $415,891.80; 4.3% **29.** **(a)** $24,812,500 **(b)** $25,000,000 **(c)** $187,500 **(d)** 3.02%

Section 13.3 (page 509)

1. 9.28% **3.** 11.15% **5.** 8.22% **7.** 8.27% **9.** 11.18% **11.** 9.73% **15.** 13% simple interest **17.** $22.98
19. First Financial; $193.33

Section 13.4 (page 514)

1. 83 days **3.** 59 days **5.** $7981.33 **7.** $14,100 **9.** 61 days; $73.30; $3531.70 **11.** 68 days; $159.98; $6897.85 **13.** 81 days;
$286.50; $10,324.61 **15.** **(a)** 93 days **(b)** $274.48 **(c)** $8579.69 **17.** **(a)** $719.77 **(b)** $18,473.98 **19.** **(a)** $22,950 **(b)** $23,340
(c) $390 **21.** **(a)** $33,093.33 **(b)** $35,202.22 **(c)** $2108.89 **23.** **(a)** $95,200 **(b)** $1923.08 **(c)** $98,076.92 **(d)** 4.91%

Chapter 13 Review Exercises (page 519)

1. $462.78; $10,262.78 **2.** $10\frac{1}{2}$%; 3078.75 **3.** 240 days; $8640 **4.** $14,500; $15,170.63 **5.** May 8; $12,360 **6.** January 5; $6325
7. $480; $17,520 **8.** $1365; $24,635 **9.** **(a)** 99 days **(b)** $410.85 **(c)** $12,039.15 **10.** **(a)** 50 days **(b)** $146.92
(c) $8668.29 **11.** 11.53% **12.** 9.40% **13.** 11.32% **14.** $24,642.36 **15.** $547.61 **16.** 9% **17.** 180 days **18.** 200 days
19. 10.75% **20.** 11%; 10.71% **21.** 8.45% **22.** $13,874.39 **23.** 150 days **24.** $2216.67 **25.** 15.9% **26.** $18,400
27. $8318.53 **28.** 170 days **29.** $1900; $23,100 **30.** $36,000 **31.** $24,366.67 **32.** $15,750.67 **33.** $85,420.83 **34.** $38,000
35. $11,279.51 **36.** 12.66%; 8.98%

Chapter 13 Business Application Case #1 (page 521)

(a) $1,037,500; Interest to be paid to the Chinese investment house:
$I = \$80,000,000 \times 0.05 \times \frac{180}{360} = \$2,000,000$
Interest from the Canadian firm:
$I = \$38,000,000 \times 0.07 \times \frac{180}{360} = \$1,330,000$
Interest from the British contractor:
$B = \$27,500,000 \times 0.082 \times \frac{180}{360} = \$1,127,500$
Interest from the Louisiana company:
$B = \$14,500,000 \times 0.08 \times \frac{180}{360} = \$580,000$

Interest received by Bank of America:	$1,330,000
	1,125,500
	+ 580,000
	$3,037,500

Interest received by Bank of America:	$3,037,500
Interest paid by Bank of America:	−$2,000,000
Difference:	$1,037,500

(b) $78,292,500

Loan	Amount loaned out
First	$38,000,000
Second $27,500,000 − $1,127,500 =	$26,372,500
Third $14,500,000 − $580,000 =	$13,920,000
Total loaned out	$78,292,500

(c) 2.65%

Chapter 13 Business Application Case #2 (page 522)

(a) Bank U.S., $19,419,889.50, $204,419,889.50; Japan FundCo, $18,130,000.00, $203,130,000.00; Niacin Strong, $21,473,214.29, $206,473,214.29. The best loan is the one with the lowest total interest for the one-year loan, or the loan offered by Japan FundCo.
(b) The most expensive loan is the one offered by Niacin Strong. Difference in interest = $3,343,214.29

Chapter 14

Section 14.1 (page 531)

1. $15,116.54; $3116.54 **3.** $6626.92; $626.92 **5.** $21,724.52 **7.** $17,024.33 **9.** $6032.76 **11.** $5755.82 **13.** $300; $338.23; $38.23 **15.** $3163.37; $3775.92; $612.55 **17.** 8.24% **19.** 9.38% **21.** (a) $5978.09 (b) $5983.40 **23.** (a) $2624.77 (b) $2667.70 (c) $2689.86 (d) $2704.89 (e) $2400 **25.** $12,043.41 **27.** (a) $11,248.64; $11,268.25 (b) $19.61 **29.** $577,152.52 **31.** 6.09%; 5.12%; the first option **33.** $18,119.24 **35.** $12,250.08 **39.** $587.92 **41.** $85,280.20

Section 14.2 (page 542)

1. $38.16 **3.** $35.62 **5.** $7267.81 **7.** $2992.00 **9.** $5637.43 **11.** $17,271.15 **13.** $4673.06 **15.** $867.50 **19.** $5845.41 **21.** (a) $118.49 (b) $11,638.49 **23.** $0 **25.** $175.61 **27.** $9019.97; $1019.97 **29.** $19,053.58; $853.58 **31.** $7033.42; $233.42 **33.** $13,069.46; $269.46 **35.** (a) $901,988.58 (b) $101,988.58 **37.** 7% compounded semiannually; $5726.58

Section 14.3 (page 547)

1. 3 **3.** 3 **5.** 6% **7.** 8% **11.** about $2\frac{1}{2}$ years **13.** (a) $14,347.42 (b) $16,162.26 **15.** 10% **17.** 3 years **19.** 28 years **21.** 20 years **23.** 35 years **25.** $40,224.31 **27.** $8219.12 **29.** $21,247.04

Section 14.4 (page 552)

1. $3810.39; $989.61 **3.** $9077.95; $3122.05 **5.** $7543.32; $956.68 **9.** $7129.86; $2870.14 **11.** $8401.69 **13.** $7987.04 **15.** $3800 in 5 years **17.** $38,288.45; $31,409.86 **19.** $23,520; $18,534.49 **21.** (a) $26,620 (b) $20,989.69

Chapter 14 Review Exercises (page 557)

1. $18,093.36; $5693.36 **2.** $8867.39; $1867.39 **3.** $27,454.28; $4954.28 **4.** $23,758.73; $5758.73 **5.** $11,261.45; $2261.45 **6.** $14,576.65; $2576.65 **7.** 7.19% **8.** 8.24% **9.** 4.04% **10.** 9.38% **11.** $24.29 **12.** $24.21 **13.** $22.68 **14.** $3523.23 **15.** $7248.84 **16.** $9648.39 **17.** $4647.29 **18.** $7328.66 **19.** $12,213.89 **20.** $22,058.47; $9458.47 **21.** $5809.17; $809.17 **22.** 6% **23.** 10% **24.** $9896.09 **25.** 3 **26.** $3\frac{1}{2}$ **27.** $12,178.08; $2121.92 **28.** $3551.89; $448.11 **29.** $3661.63; $2338.37 **30.** $2361.30; $638.70 **31.** $4120.01 **32.** $5238.54 **33.** $2983.58; $983.58 **34.** $5399.30; $1399.30 **35.** $49,699.68 **36.** (a) $15,173.40 (b) $13,481.37 **37.** 4 years **38.** approximately 12 years

Chapter 14 Business Application Case #1 (page 559)

(a) $4,053,386; $3,016,100   **(b)** $2,539,386; $1,889,542   **(c)** $2,798,302; $2,082,199   **(d)** $2,539,386; $1,889,542; $2,798,302; $2,082,199; $4,053,386; $3,016,100

Chapter 14 Business Application Case #2 (page 559)

(a) $47,504,179.84   **(b)** $2,495,820.16   **(c)** $1,949,730.72

Chapter 15

Section 15.1 (page 571)

1. 18.59891389   **3.** 15.19292972   **5.** $58,248.89; $34,448.89   **7.** $73,105.94; $48,105.94   **9.** $67,410.39; $22,610.39
11. $46,016.57; $7616.57   **13.** $13,475.82; $3875.82   **15.** $138,997.66; $33,733.66   **17.** $11,320.10   **19.** $13,673.64
21. $16,577.77   **23.** $36,895.94   **25.** $57,782.55   **27.** $59,794.96   **29.** $122,676.78   **31.** $263,879.29   **35.** $24,687.62; $4687.62
37. $5303.43; $1703.43   **39.** $1413.72   **41.** $952.33   **43.** 28 quarterly payments; $15,516.67   **45.** 37 monthly payments;
$35,030.62   **47.** $7188.27   **49. (a)** $17,256.21 **(b)** $2856.21   **51.** $34,186.78; $14,706.78   **53.** 31 months; $4075.14
55. (a) $15,100.50 **(b)** $13,566.97

Section 15.2 (page 578)

1. 8.82711975   **3.** 6.81086449   **5.** $16,004.78   **7.** $11,901.98   **9.** $6540.57   **13.** $839,255.24   **15.** $239,326.76   **17.** $12,675.75;
$4124.25   **19. (a)** $253,691.00 **(b)** $209,764.50   **21. (a)** $48,879.75 **(b)** No   **23.** $93,636.35   **25.** $51,000 down and $8000 per year
27. $335,000 today   **29.** $28,847.04   **31.** $27,050.13

Section 15.3 (page 583)

1. 0.05427783   **3.** 0.00295961   **5.** $1957.50   **7.** $576.19   **11. (a)** $106,747.76 **(b)** $699.22   **13. (a)** $305,866.11 **(b)** $2003.48
15. (a) $274,802.78 **(b)** $151,183.32   **17.** $9572.45   **19.** $404,143.76; $766,849.92   **21.** $17,047.28; $443,229.18; $443,229.18;
$213,090.95; $35,458.33; $691,778.46; $691,778.46; $213,090.98; $55,342.28; $960,211.72   **23. (a)** $604,910.16 **(b)** $437,596.64

Chapter 15 Review Exercises (page 588)

1. $69,152.45   **2.** $34,426.47   **3.** $113,736.00   **4.** $49,153.29   **5.** $163,383.42   **6.** $97,457.37   **7.** $20,114.46; $2514.46
8. $134,489.45; $21,989.45   **9.** $38,253.24   **10.** $5948.27   **11.** $8055.06   **12.** $5094.30   **13.** $11,298.18   **14.** $1332.74
15. $22,217.87   **16.** $623.89   **17.** $80,627.53   **18.** 31 years   **19.** $6427.17   **20.** $20,891.12   **21.** $25,723.79   **22.** $2676.72
23. $32,625.58   **24.** $98,713.33   **25. (a)** $886,898.80 **(b)** $713,918.56   **26.** $21,866.87; $21,886.87; $1968.02; $45,701.76;
$45,701.76; $21,866.87; $4113.16; $71,681.79; $71,681.79; $21,866.85; $6451.36; $100,000.00

Chapter 15 Business Application Case #1 (page 590)

(a) $517,204.85   **(b)** $53,046.70   **(c)** $520,820.32   **(d)** Almost, but not quite

Chapter 15 Business Application Case #2 (page 590)

(a) $6,165,389.97   **(b)** $15,134,610.03   **(c)** $2,658,160.27

Chapter 16

Section 16.1 (page 599)

1. $10.03   **3.** $4.87   **5.** $132.64; $1.99; $133.80   **7.** $2764.63; $41.47; $2881.75   **9.** $938.73; $14.08; $857.83   **11.** $681.52;
$10.22; $769.01   **13. (a)** $42.01 **(b)** $28 **(c)** $14.01   **15. (a)** $72.76 **(b)** $38.80 **(c)** $33.96   **21.** $276

Section 16.2 (page 607)

1. $20,896.40; $3496.40   **3.** $180; $30   **5.** $1200; $120   **7.** 12.50%   **9.** 10.25%   **11.** 11.25%   **15.** 12.00%   **17.** 11.00%
19. (a) 732,212.32 pesos **(b)** 13.75%   **21. (a)** $209,239.80 **(b)** 12.00%

Section 16.3 (page 614)

1. $5130.57; $130.57   **3.** $3754.46; $254.46   **5.** $4333.78; $333.78   **7.** $385.52   **9.** $21.90   **11.** $139.81   **17. (a)** $6569.44
(b) $131,569.44   **19.** $148.50   **21. (a)** $51.82   **(b)** $490.58   **23.** $41,176.11; $1876.11   **25. (a)** 66 days   **(b)** $11,564.31

Section 16.4 (page 619)

1. 0.11328724   **3.** 0.10334306   **5.** $1153.61   **7.** $404.73   **9.** $4185.25   **11.** $161.95   **13.** $152.64; $695.04   **15.** $321.92;
$3452.16   **17.** $15,987.97; $147,663.16

19.

Payment Number	Amount of Payment	Interest for Period	Portion to Principal	Principal at End of Period
0	—	—	—	$4000.00
1	$1207.68	$320.00	$887.68	3112.32
2	1207.68	248.99	958.69	2153.63
3	1207.68	172.29	1035.39	1118.24
4	1207.70	89.46	1118.24	0

21.

Payment Number	Amount of Payment	Interest for Period	Portion to Principal	Principal at End of Period
0	—	—	—	$14,500.00
1	$374.77	$132.92	$241.85	14,258.15
2	374.77	130.70	244.07	14,014.08
3	374.77	128.46	246.31	13,767.77
4	374.77	126.20	248.57	13,519.20
5	374.77	123.93	250.84	13,268.36

25.

Payment Number	Amount of Payment	Interest for Period	Portion to Principal	Principal at End of Period
0	—	—	—	$8000.00
1	$576.99	$80.00	$496.99	7503.01
2	576.99	75.03	501.96	7001.05
3	576.99	70.01	506.98	6494.07
⋮	⋮	⋮	⋮	⋮
14	576.99	11.37	565.62	571.28
15	576.99	5.71	571.28	0

Section 16.5 (page 628)

1. $651.70   **3.** $1367.28   **5.** $1728.25   **9.** $928.17   **11.** $1451.93   **13.** $1281.64   **15.** Yes, they are qualified. The payment would be $1434.58.

17.

Payment Number	Total Payment	Interest Payment	Principal Payment	Balance of Principal
0	—	—	—	$212,000.00
1	$1908	$1590.00	$318.00	$211,682.00
2	$1908	$1587.62	$320.38	$211,361.62

19. (a) $951.38 **(b)** $719.46 **(c)** $86,268.70   **21.** $122,000   **25.** $134,852; $134,656.91; $134,460.84; $134,263.79; $134,065.76; $133,866.74; $134,852; $134,256.91, $133,658.84; $133,057.78; $132,453.72; $131,846.64

Chapter 16 Review Exercises (page 635)

1. $126.95   **2.** $40.51   **3.** $14.18   **4.** $552.56; $8.29; $551.80   **5.** $216.51; $3.25; $203.40   **6.** $2700; $2915.14; $215.14
7. $4600; $5040; $440   **8.** $8000; $9600; $1600   **9.** 13%   **10.** 10.00%   **11.** 12.75%   **12.** 11.5%   **13.** $10,876.33; $476.33
14. $7309.87; $309.87   **15.** $915.66; $115.66   **16.** $4641.89; $141.89   **17.** $3638.63   **18.** $2395.83   **19.** $795.42
20. $392.89   **21.** $442.51; $1220.24   **22.** $339.80; $2271.60   **23.** $219.72; $1546.56   **24.** $574.16; $2224.80   **25.** $858.60
26. $807.65   **27.** $956   **28.** $1377.09   **29. (a)** $2788.22 **(b)** $173.22   **30.** $171.85; $2.58   **31.** $18,756.32; 10.50%
32. $2822.98   **33.** $1400.03   **34. (a)** $1397.02 **(b)** $360,284.80   **35. (a)** 60 days **(b)** $8100.82

Chapter 16 Business Application Case #1 (page 637)

(a) $495.08; $420.06; $978.51; $149.46; $2043.11   **(b)** $2043.11; $215.00; $120.00; $295; $2673.11   **(c)** $392.37; $285.64; $695.83; $149.46; $187.00; $120.00; $295.00; $2125.30   **(d)** $547.81

Chapter 16 Business Application Case #2 (page 638)

(a) $1647.59 (b) $501.33 (c) $4380.78 (d) $6028.37 (e) $524.96 (f) $281,000 (g) $22,888.89; 41 months

Part 4 Cumulative Review: Chapters 12–16 (page 639)

1. $150 **2.** $417.64 **3.** $2400.17 **4.** $12,449.83 **5.** 9.7% **6.** 13.5% **7.** 80 days **8.** 150 days **9.** $270; $8730 **10.** $33.18; $841.82 **11.** 10.3% **12.** 11.3% **13.** $1947.90 **14.** $7599.42 **15.** $12,686.07; $86.07 **16.** $7562.10; $62.10 **17.** $583.49; $416.51 **18.** $12,182.15; $6817.85 **19.** $9214.23 **20.** $31,123.18 **21.** $13,367.28 **22.** $639,160.10 **23.** $403.46 **24.** $112.90 **25.** $10,129.08 **26.** $10,823.31 **27.** (a) $12,106.67 (b) $106.67 **28.** (a) $416.67 (b) $14,583.33 **29.** $7993.14 **30.** $94 **31.** (a) $94.91 (b) $50.62 (c) $44.29 **32.** (a) $12,340 (b) $1840 (c) $9500 (d) 12% **33.** $2343.75 **34.** $9.828 million (rounded) **35.** (a) $10,344.44 (b) $20,869.57 **36.** $469.22 **37.** $20.01 **38.** No, the monthly payment would be $1527.68

Chapter 17

Section 17.1 (page 646)

1. 20% **3.** 12.5% **5.** 5% **7.** $6\frac{2}{3}$% **9.** 1.25% **11.** 2% **13.** $450 **15.** $16,020 **17.** $840 **19.** $2850 **21.** $5000 **23.** $2775 **25.** $73,000

29.

Year	Computation	Amount of Depreciation	Accumulated Depreciation	Book Value
0	—	—	—	$12,000
1	$\left(33\frac{1}{3}\% \times \$9000\right)$	$3000	$3000	$9000
2	$\left(33\frac{1}{3}\% \times \$9000\right)$	$3000	$6000	$6000
3	$\left(33\frac{1}{3}\% \times \$9000\right)$	$3000	$9000	$3000

31. Book values: $8200; $7000; $5800; $4600; $3400; $2200 **33.** (a) $55,000 depreciation (b) $1,025,000 book value **35.** (a) $2527 depreciation (b) $20,211 book value **37.** (a) 20% (b) $3726 (c) $16,104

Section 17.2 (page 652)

1. 40% **3.** 25% **5.** $13\frac{1}{3}$% **7.** 20% **9.** $33\frac{1}{3}$% **11.** 4% **13.** $3600 **15.** $5000 **17.** $1900 **19.** $3360 **21.** $1215 **23.** $6834 **25.** $750

29.

Year	Computation	Amount of Depreciation	Accumulated Depreciation	Book Value
0	—	—	—	$14,400
1	(50% × $14,400)	$7200	$7200	$7200
2	(50% × $7200)	$3600	$10,800	$3600
3	(50% × $3600)	$1800	$12,600	$1800
4	—	$1800*	$14,400	$0

*To depreciate to $0 scrap value

31. Book values: $19,125; $14,344; $10,758; $8068; $6051; $4538; $3500; $3500 **33.** $1153 **35.** $8476 **37.** (a) 25% (b) $1450 (c) $4425 (d) $1375

Section 17.3 (page 659)

1. $\frac{4}{10}$ **3.** $\frac{6}{21}$ **5.** $\frac{7}{28}$ **7.** $\frac{10}{55}$ **9.** $1640 **11.** $10,000 **13.** $600 **15.** $7700 **17.** $2700 **19.** $890 **21.** $2400 **25.**

Year	Computation	Amount of Depreciation	Accumulated Depreciation	Book Value
0	—	—	—	$10,800
1	$\left(\frac{6}{21} \times \$8400\right)$	$2400	$2400	$8400
2	$\left(\frac{5}{21} \times \$8400\right)$	$2000	$4400	$6400
3	$\left(\frac{4}{21} \times \$8400\right)$	$1600	$6000	$4800
4	$\left(\frac{3}{21} \times \$8400\right)$	$1200	$7200	$3600
5	$\left(\frac{2}{21} \times \$8400\right)$	$800	$8000	$2800
6	$\left(\frac{1}{21} \times \$8400\right)$	$400	$8400	$2400

27. Book values: $2100; $1600; $1200; $900; $700; $600   **29.** $9300   **31.** $24,584   **33. (a)** $7200 **(b)** $6000   **35. (a)** $\frac{8}{36}$
(b) $2360 **(c)** $10,620 **(d)** $4750

Section 17.4 (page 666)

1. $0.35   **3.** $0.029   **5.** $68.75   **7.** $30   **9.** $17,940   **11.** $17,280   **13.** $2775   **15.** $6960   **19.** $1313; $2250   **21.** $1667; $1833
23. $450; $825   **25.** $900; $1088
27.

Year	Computation	Amount of Depreciation	Accumulated Depreciation	Book Value
0	—	—	—	$6800
1	(1350 × $1.26)	$1701	$1701	$5099
2	(1820 × $1.26)	$2293	$3994	$2806
3	(730 × $1.26)	$920	$4914	$1886
4	(1100 × $1.26)	$1386	$6300	$500

29. $26,350   **31.** $3650; $14,600   **33.** $450; $1620   **35.** $2775; $5365

Section 17.5 (page 673)

1. 19.2%   **3.** 11.52%   **5.** 20%   **7.** 3.636%   **9.** 5.76%   **11.** 2.564%   **13.** $1751   **15.** $3226   **17.** $4800   **19.** $6254
21. $16,920   **23.** $2756   **25.** $79,364
29.

Year	Computation	Amount of Depreciation	Accumulated Depreciation	Book Value
0	—	—	—	$10,980
1	(33.33% × $10,980)	$3660	$3660	$7320
2	(44.45% × $10,980)	$4881	$8541	$2439
3	(14.81% × $10,980)	$1626	$10,167	$813
4	(7.41% × $10,980)	$813*	$10,980	$0

*Due to rounding in prior years

31. Book values: $110,430; $88,344; $70,675; $56,540; $45,227; $36,184; $28,147; $20,110; $12,061; $4024; $0
33. $82,080   **35.** year 1: $12,326; years 2–5: $12,307

Chapter 17 Review Exercises (page 677)

1. 20%; 40%; $\frac{5}{15}$ **2.** $16\frac{2}{3}$%; $33\frac{1}{3}$%; $\frac{6}{21}$ **3.** 25%; 50%; $\frac{4}{10}$ **4.** 10%; 20%; $\frac{10}{55}$ **5.** 5%; 10%; $\frac{20}{210}$ **6.** $12\frac{1}{2}$%; 25%; $\frac{8}{36}$ **7.** 11.52%
8. 33.33%   **9.** 4.522%   **10.** 17.49%   **11.** 2.564%   **12.** 3.174%   **13.** $940   **14.** $172,000   **15.** $21,375   **16.** $7400   **17.** year
1: $2700; year 2: $2025; year 3: $1350; year 4: $675   **18.** $4000   **19.** $1530   **20. (a)** $4836; $2666; $3007; $4712 **(b)** $15,264;
$12,598; $9591; $4879   **21.** $15,120   **22.** $24,000; $19,200; $14,400; $9600; $4800   **23.** $2900   **24.** $1260; $2003
25. $2840; $5112   **26.** $5702   **27.** $4746   **28.** $112,725   **29.** $6222   **30.** $4788   **31.** $1157; $1984; $1417; $1012; $723
32. $2,440,928   **33.** $1995   **34.** $45,600

Chapter 17 Business Application Case #1 (page 679)

(a) $114,000   **(b)** $61,560   **(c)** $228,000   **(d)** $57,000 straight-line; $24,624 double-declining balance; $38,000 sum-of-the-years'-digits

Chapter 17 Business Application Case #2 (page 679)

Year	5-year MACRS	Depreciation	Tax Savings	7-year MACRS	Depreciation	Tax Savings
1	20.00	$5,680,000	$2,272,000	14.29	$4,058,360	$1,623,344
2	32.00	$9,088,000	$3,635,200	24.49	$6,955,160	$2,782,064
3	19.20	$5,452,800	$2,181,120	17.49	$4,967,160	$1,986,864
4	11.52	$3,271,680	$1,308,672	12.49	$3,547,160	$1,418,864
5	11.52	$3,271,680	$1,308,672	8.93	$2,536,120	$1,014,448
6	5.76	$1,635,840	$654,336	8.92	$2,533,280	$1,013,312
7	0	$0	$0	8.93	$2,536,120	$1,014,448
8	0	$0	$0	4.46	$1,266,640	$506,656
9	0	$0	$0	0	$0	$0
10	0	$0	$0	0	$0	$0

Chapter 18

Section 18.1 (page 685)

1. (a) $316,350   **(b)** $88,050   **(c)** $65,350   **3.** $324,200

5.

STOPTHEFT ALARMS
INCOME STATEMENT
QUARTER ENDING DECEMBER 31

Gross sales		$284,000
Returns		$6000
Net sales		$278,000
Inventory, beg. of quarter	$58,000	
Cost of goods		
purchased $142,000		
Freight $3,000		
Total cost of goods purchased	$145,000	
Total of goods available for sale	$203,000	
Inventory, end of quarter	$69,000	
Cost of goods sold		$134,000
Gross profit		$144,000
Expenses		
Salaries and wages	$19,400	
Rent	$6000	
Advertising	$2000	
Utilities	$1800	
Taxes on inventory, payroll	$3000	
Miscellaneous expenses	$4000	
Total expenses		$36,200
Net income before taxes		$107,800
Income taxes		$14,650
Net income		$93,150

7.

KATHY GILMORE, CONSULTANT
INCOME STATEMENT
FOR THE YEAR ENDING DECEMBER 31

Gross sales		$170,500
Returns		0
Net sales		$170,500
Inventory, January 1	0	
Cost of goods purchased	0	
Freight	0	
Total cost of goods purchased	0	
Total of goods available for sale	0	
Inventory, December 31	0	
Cost of goods sold		0
Gross profit		$170,500
Expenses		
Salaries and wages	$63,000	
Rent	$28,000	
Advertising	$12,000	
Utilities	$4000	
Taxes on inventory, payroll	$3800	
Miscellaneous expenses	$9400	
Total expenses		$120,200
Net income before taxes		$50,300
Income taxes		$6800
Net income		$43,500

Section 18.2 (page 693)

1. 32.6%; 45.2%

3.

CAPITAL DISTRICT APPLIANCES

	Amount	Percent	Percent from Table 18.1
Net sales	$900,000	100.0%	100.0%
Cost of goods sold	617,000	68.6%	66.9%
Gross profit	283,000	31.4%	33.1%
Wages	108,900	12.1%	11.9%
Rent	20,700	2.3%	2.4%
Advertising	27,000	3%	2.5%
Total expenses	216,000	24%	26%
Net income before taxes	67,000	7.4%	7.2%

5.

BEST TIRES INC.
COMPARATIVE INCOME STATEMENT

	This Year		Last Year	
	Amount	Percent	Amount	Percent
Gross sales	$1,856,000	100.3%	$1,692,000	100.7%
Returns	6000	0.3%	12,000	0.7%
Net sales	1,850,000	100.0%	1,680,000	100.0%
Cost of goods sold	1,202,000	65.0%	1,050,000	62.5%
Gross profit	648,000	35.0%	630,000	37.5%
Wages	152,000	8.2%	148,000	8.8%
Rent	82,000	4.4%	78,000	4.6%
Advertising	111,000	6.0%	122,000	7.3%
Utilities	32,000	1.7%	17,000	1.0%
Taxes on inventory, payroll	17,000	0.9%	18,000	1.1%
Miscellaneous expenses	62,000	3.4%	58,000	3.5%
Total expenses	456,000	24.6%	441,000	26.3%
Net income	192,000	10.4%	189,000	11.3%

7. 82.7%; 17.3%; 13.9%; 3.4%; 6.5%; 0.8%; 1.0%; Net income is low.   **9.** 67.9%; 32.1%; 23.5%; 8.6%; 12.3%; 2.4%; 1.4%; Cost of goods and operating expenses are both high, resulting in a small net income.

Section 18.3 (page 699)

1.

BROOKSHIRE'S GROCERY
BALANCE SHEET FOR DECEMBER 31 (IN MILLIONS)

	Assets	
Current Assets		
Cash	$273	
Notes receivable	$312	
Accounts receivable	$264	
Inventory	$180	
Total Current Assets		$1029
Plant Assets		
Land	$466	
Buildings	$290	
Fixtures	$28	
Total Plant Assets		$784
Total assets		$1813

BROOKSHIRE'S GROCERY
BALANCE SHEET FOR DECEMBER 31 (IN MILLIONS)

Liabilities

Current Liabilities			
Notes payable	$312		
Accounts payable	$63		
Total Current Liabilities		$375	
Long-term Liabilities			
Mortgages payable	$212		
Long-term notes payable	$55		
Total Long-term Liabilities		$267	
Total liabilities			$642

Owners' Equity

Owners' equity	$1171		
Total Liabilities and Owners' Equity			$1813

Section 18.4 (page 708)

1.

OTERO OFFICE SUPPLY
COMPARATIVE BALANCE SHEET

	This Year		Last Year	
	Amount	**Percent**	**Amount**	**Percent**
Assets				
Current Assets				
Cash	$52,000	13%	$42,000	13.1%
Notes receivable	$8000	2%	$6000	1.9%
Accounts receivable	$148,000	37%	$120,000	37.5%
Inventory	$153,000	38.3%	$120,000	37.5%
Total Current Assets	$361,000	90.3%	$288,000	90%
Plant Assets				
Land	$10,000	2.5%	$8000	2.5%
Buildings	$14,000	3.5%	$11,000	3.4%
Fixtures	$15,000	3.8%	$13,000	4.1%
Total Plant Assets	$39,000	9.8%	$32,000	10%
Total Assets	$400,000	100.0%	$320,000	100.0%
Liabilities				
Current Liabilities				
Accounts payable	$3000	0.8%	$4000	1.3%
Notes payable	$201,000	50.3%	$152,000	47.5%
Total Current Liabilities	$204,000	51%	$156,000	48.8%
Long-term Liabilities				
Mortgages payable	$20,000	5%	$16,000	5%
Long-term notes payable	$58,000	14.5%	$42,000	13.1%
Total Long-term Liabilities	$78,000	19.5%	$58,000	18.1%
Total Liabilities	$282,000	70.5%	$214,000	66.9%
Owners' Equity	$118,000	29.5%	$106,000	33.1%
Total Liabilities and Owners' Equity	$400,000	100.0%	$320,000	100.0%

3. (a) 1.77   **(b)** 1.02   **(c)** Yes.   **5. (a)** 2.66   **(b)** 1.85   **(c)** Yes, ratios are okay.   **7.** 2.13; 1.27   **9.** 2.39   **11.** 1.39
15. 6.1%   **17.** 8.5 times; 42.9 days

Chapter 18 Review Exercises (page 713)
1. $187,400; $98,200 **2.** $263,730; $138,930 **3.** $141,600; $43,200 **4.** $235,880; $23,580 **5.** $416,600 **6.** $126,500
7. $42,700 **8.** $282,100 **9.** $188,800; 0.56 **10.** $90,600; 0.23

11.

LORI'S BOUTIQUE
INCOME STATEMENT FOR
THE YEAR ENDING DECEMBER 31

Gross sales		$175,000
Returns		$8000
Net sales		$167,000
Inventory, January 1	$44,000	
Cost of goods purchased	$126,000	
Freight	$2000	
Total cost of goods purchased	$128,000	
Total of goods available for sale	$172,000	
Inventory, December 31	$52,000	
Cost of goods sold		$120,000
Gross profit		$47,000
Expenses		
Salaries and wages	$9000	
Rent	$4000	
Advertising	$1500	
Utilities	$1000	
Taxes on inventory, payroll	$2000	
Miscellaneous expenses	$3000	
Total expenses		$20,500
Net income before taxes		$26,500

12.

THE GUITAR WAREHOUSE
INCOME STATEMENT
FOR THE YEAR ENDING DECEMBER 31

Gross sales		$2,215,000
Returns		$26,000
Net sales		$2,189,000
Inventory, January 1	$215,000	
Cost of goods purchased	$1,123,000	
Freight	$4000	
Total cost of goods purchased	$1,127,000	
Total of goods available for sale	$1,342,000	
Inventory, December 31	$265,000	
Cost of goods sold		$1,077,000
Gross profit		$1,112,000
Expenses		
Salaries and wages	$154,000	
Rent	$59,000	
Advertising	$11,000	
Utilities	$12,000	
Taxes on inventory, payroll	$10,000	
Miscellaneous expenses	$9000	
Total expenses		$255,000
Net income before taxes		$857,000
Income taxes		$242,300
Net income		$614,700

13. 59.8%; 12.8%   **14.** 61.2%; 29.1%

15.

JALISCO MEXICAN FOODS (3RD QUARTER)

	Amount	Percent	Percent from Table 18.1
Net sales	$300,000	100%	100%
Cost of goods sold	$125,000	41.7%	48.4%
Gross profit	$175,000	58.3%	51.6%
Wages	$72,000	24.0%	26.4%
Rent	$12,000	4.0%	2.8%
Advertising	$5700	1.9%	1.4%
Total expenses	$123,000	41.0%	43.7%
Net income	$52,000	17.3%	7.9%

16.

GASKETS INC.
BALANCE SHEET FOR DECEMBER 31

Assets			
Current Assets			
Cash	$240,000		
Notes receivable	$180,000		
Accounts receivable	$460,000		
Inventory	$225,000		
Total Current Assets		$1,105,000	
Plant Assets			
Land	$180,000		
Buildings	$260,000		
Fixtures	$48,000		
Total Plant Assets		$488,000	
Total Assets			$1,593,000
Liabilities			
Current Liabilities			
Notes payable	$410,000		
Accounts payable	$882,000		
Total Current Liabilities		$1,292,000	
Long-term Liabilities			
Mortgages payable	$220,000		
Long-term notes payable	$194,000		
Total Long-Term Liabilities		$414,000	
Total Liabilities			$1,706,000
Owners' equity			
Owners' equity	($113,000)		
Total liabilities and owners' equity			$1,593,000

17. 1.32; 0.46; 1.78   **18.** 0.83; 0.04; 4.17   **19.** 0.78; 0.71; 1.11   **20.** 5.0; 73 days   **21.** 8.6; 42.4 days

22.

	This Year		Last Year	
	Amount	Percent	Amount	Percent
Current Assets				
Cash	$28,000	18.8%	$22,000	21.1%
Notes receivable	$12,000	8.1%	$15,000	14.4%
Accounts receivable	$39,000	26.2%	$31,500	30.1%
Inventory	$22,000	14.8%	$20,000	19.1%
Total Current Assets	$101,000	67.8%	$88,500	84.7%
Total Plant and Equipment	$48,000	32.2%	$16,000	15.3%
Total Assets	$149,000	100.0%	$104,500	100.0%
Total current liabilities	$38,000	25.5%	$36,000	34.4%

Chapter 18 Business Application Case #1 (page 717)

(a)
WALKER BICYCLE SHOP
INCOME STATEMENT
YEAR ENDING DECEMBER 31

Gross sales			$272,500
Returns			$12,500
Net sales			$260,000
Inventory, January 1		$44,000	
Cost of goods purchased	$75,000		
Freight	$8000		
Total cost of goods purchased		$83,000	
Total of goods available for sale		$127,000	
Inventory, December 31		$26,000	
Cost of goods sold			$101,000
Gross profit			$159,000
Expenses			
Salaries and wages		$97,500	
Rent		$12,000	
Advertising		$2000	
Utilities		$3000	
Taxes on inventory, payroll		$7000	
Miscellaneous expenses		$4500	
Total expenses			$126,000
Net income before taxes			$33,000
Income taxes			$4320
Net income after taxes			$28,680

(b) 104.8%; 37.5%; 4.8%; 4.6%; 38.8%; 1.2%

(c)
WALKER BICYCLE SHOP
BALANCE SHEET
DECEMBER 31

Assets		
Current Assets		
Cash	$62,000	
Notes receivable	$2500	
Accounts receivable	$8200	
Inventory	$26,000	
Total Current Assets		$98,700
Plant Assets		
Land	$39,500	
Buildings	$98,400	
Fixtures	$13,500	
Total Plant Assets		$151,400
Total Assets		$250,100

Liabilities		
Current Liabilities		
Notes payable	$4500	
Accounts payable	$27,000	
Total Current Liabilities		$31,500
Long-term Liabilities		
Mortgages payable	$68,000	
Long-term notes payable	$8000	
Total Long-term Liabilities		$76,000
Total Liabilities		$107,500

Owners' Equity		
Owners' equity	$142,600	
Total liability and owners' equity		$250,100

(d) 3.13; 2.31 **(e)** Probably not, profits are too small. Any small problem could result in an inability to repay the loan.

Chapter 18 Business Application Case #2 (page 718)

Answers will vary.

Chapter 19

Section 19.1 (page 724)

1. $0; $0   **3.** $0.30; $0.14   **5.** $20; $0   **7.** $0.10   **9.** $6.50; $0.73   **11.** $1.60; $0.86   **13.** $20; $5.06   **15.** $3.33   **17.** $0.14
19. (a) $0.77 **(b)** $0.90 **(c)** 14.2%   **21.** $26,666.67 each since there are sufficient dividends

Section 19.2 (page 733)

1. $10.71   **3.** $9.92   **5.** $0   **7.** $41.18   **9.** 0%   **11.** 15   **13.** 2,748,800 shares   **15.** 0.7%   **17.** $102.600   **19.** $14,263,95
21. $4546.95   **23.** $8752.95   **25.** $3522.05   **27.** $12,667.05   **29.** $26,096.05   **31.** 2.7%   **33.** 2.8%   **35.** 2.6%   **37.** 39
39. 28   **41.** $12,885.90   **43.** $1996.60   **47. (a)** $116,981.22 **(b)** $183,200.50 **(c)** $66,219.28   **49.** 10 years

Section 19.3 (page 740)

1. $1014.09   **3.** 1.950%   **5.** 1.650%   **7.** $28,059.60   **9.** $100,579   **11.** $98,504   **13.** $57,998   **17.** $50,954.50; $975
19. $2,025,540; $110,000   **21. (a)** $59,908.80 **(b)** $1980 **(c)** 3.3%   **23.** $2800   **25.** $170,731.71   **27.** $1150.52

Section 19.4 (page 746)

1. $29,000 each   **3.** $73,600 for 1; $18,400 for 2   **5.** $16,920 for 1; $8080 for 2   **7.** $10,000 for 1; $12,000 for 2; $0 for 3
9. $39,150   **11.** $18,720; $37,440; $37,440   **13.** $44,000; $88,000; $88,000   **15.** $23,400 for Finch; $33,600 for Renz
17. (a) $21,000 for Coker; $39,000 for Toms **(b)** $7500 for Coker; $1500 by Toms to Coker   **19.** $22,179 to 1; $46,464 to 2; $41,357 to 3

Section 19.5 (page 750)

1. $60,000; $120,000; $150,000   **3.** $18,000; $27,000; $30,000; $45,000   **5.** $64,615; $37,692; $37,692   **7.** $9739; $20,870;
$2087; $15,304   **9.** $572,000; $312,000; $416,000   **11.** $190,476; $228,571; $266,667; $114,286   **13.** $24,000; $96,000; $72,000;
$108,000; $12,000; $48,000   **15.** $8079; $21,545; $16,158; $10,099; $12,119   **17.** $720; $960; $3360; $960

Chapter 19 Review Exercises (page 758)

1. (a) $3.25 **(b)** $0.65   **2. (a)** $6 **(b)** $7.68   **3. (a)** $8.75 **(b)** $2.69   **4.** $1.55   **5.** $2.73   **6.** $3.70   **7.** $26.42   **8.** 5,200,000
9. $10.71   **10.** $0.31   **11.** $100,265   **12.** 0%   **13.** 16   **14.** $28.60   **15.** $64.53   **16.** $992   **17.** $6015   **18.** $155,600
19. $8681.95   **20.** $23,461.95   **21.** $3077.05   **22.** $8497.05   **23.** 3.3%   **24.** 1.5%   **25.** 15   **26.** 6   **27.** $999.11
28. February 15, 2022   **29.** 3.125%   **30.** 3.135%   **31.** $386,195,000   **32.** $9991.10   **33.** $34,828.80   **34.** $25,399.25
35. $24,000 to each   **36.** $48,000 to 1; $72,000 to 2   **37.** $38,571 to 1; $51,429 to 2   **38.** $25,000; $41,667; $33,333
39. $23,256; $58,140; $43,605   **40.** $258,696; $203,261; $166,304; $221,739   **41.** $18,562.50   **42.** $23,760   **43.** $906.85
44. $969.51

Chapter 19 Business Application Case #1 (page 761)

(a) $14,761.65   **(b)** $263   **(c)** 1.8%

Chapter 19 Business Application Case #2 (page 761)

(a) $18,265.85   **(b)** $395; 2.2%   **(c)** $10,190.90   **(d)** $195   **(e)** $8669.96

Part 5 Cumulative Review: Chapters 17–19 (page 761)

1. (a) 25% **(b)** $5300 **(c)** $13,600   **2. (a)** $6560 **(b)** $5248   **3.** $2760; $2415; $7645   **4.** $15,330; $26,920
5. (a) $16,800 **(b)** $34,740 **(c)** $28,000   **6. (a)** 10 years **(b)** 5 years **(c)** 3 years **(d)** 27.5 years **(e)** 7 years
7.

Year	Computation	Amount of Depreciation	Accumulated Depreciation	Book Value
0	—	—	—	$96,000
1	33.33% of $96,000	$31,996.80	$31,996.80	$64,003.20
2	44.45% of $96,000	$42.672.00	$74,668.80	$21,331.20
3	14.81% of $96,000	$14,217.60	$88.886.40	$7,113.60
4	7.41% of $96,000	$7,113.60	$96,000.00	$0.00

8.

THE FASHION SHOPPE	INCOME STATEMENT	QUARTER ENDING DECEMBER 31		
Gross sales			$240,800	
Returns			$4300	
Net sales			$236,500	
Inventory, January 1		$48,300		
Cost of goods purchased	$102,000			
Freight	$2900			
Total cost of goods purchased		$104,900		
Total of goods available for sale		$153,200		
Inventory, December 31		$41,500		
Cost of goods sold			$111,700	
Gross profit				$124,800
Expenses				
Salaries and wages		$32,400		
Rent		$15,000		
Advertising		$2200		
Utilities		$3100		
Taxes on inventory, payroll		$6100		
Miscellaneous expenses		$8900		
Total expenses				$67,700
Net income before taxes				$57,100
Income taxes				$11,400
Net income				$45,700

9. 47.2%, 52.8%, 24.1%, 19.3%

10.

THE FASHION SHOPPE	BALANCE SHEET FOR DECEMBER 31		
Assets			
Current assets			
Cash	$28,400		
Notes receivable	$8400		
Accounts receivable	$3800		
Inventory	$41,500		
Total current assets		$82,100	
Plant assets			
Land	$0		
Buildings	$0		
Fixtures	$12,200		
Total plant assets		$12,200	
Total Assets			$94,300
Liabilities			
Current liabilities			
Notes payable	$4800		
Accounts payable	$32,500		
Total current liabilities		$37,300	
Long-term liabilities			
Mortgages payable	$0		
Long-term notes payable	$0		
Total long-term liabilities		$0	
Total Liabilities			$37,300
Owners' Equity			
Owner's equity		$57,000	
Total Liabilities and Owners' Equity			$94,300

11. 2.20; 1.09; 0.92   **12.** $200   **13.** $0.35   **14.** $0.385 per share   **15.** $12,186   **16. (a)** 0.6% (rounded) **(b)** 30 (rounded)
17. $9527.05   **18.** 0.15%; 8   **19.** $1155.96; 4.650%   **20.** $64.33; 14.9%   **21.** $24,437.50   **22.** $36,750   **23. (a)** $24,000 to each
(b) $36,000 to partner 1; $12,000 to partner 2 **(c)** $19,200 to partner 1; $28,800 to partner 2   **24.** Padgett—$42,750; Harden—$42,250
25. $127,500; $63,750; $148,750   **26.** $72,000; $43,200; $64,800   **27.** $78,734.62; $52,407.73; $8857.64   **28.** $965.81   **29.** $1121.92

Appendix A

Section A.1 (page 774)

1. 1771.60   **3.** 11,378   **5.** 3905.32   **7.** 255.24   **9.** 15,695   **11.** 31.08   **13.** 35.42   **15.** 27.63   **17.** 8.1   **19.** 566.14   **21.** 0.63
23. 30.57   **25.** 0.92   **27.** 7.39   **29.** 64.38   **31.** $5\frac{6}{11}$ **33.** 0.49   **37.** $8275   **39.** $3721.20   **41. (a)** $1164.05 **(b)** $95.13
43. $235,230   **45.** $13,400

Section A.2 (page 781)

1. $7556.24   **3.** $8929.13   **5.** $2676.84   **7.** 1.5%   **9.** $858.89   **11.** 24   **13.** $2537.97   **15.** $942.15   **17.** 26   **19.** $9458.80

Appendix B

Section B.1 (page 787)

1. 0.68 m   **3.** 4700 mm   **5.** 8900 g   **7.** 0.39 L   **9.** 46 g   **11.** 976 g   **13.** 39.24 yards   **15.** 50.27 m   **17.** 15.42 feet   **19.** 1.10 m
21. 307.52 miles   **23.** 1235.71 km   **25.** 1.50 pounds   **27.** 1861.4 g   **29.** 85.58 pounds   **31.** 200   **33.** 0.6 g   **35.** Answers will vary.
37. 40°C   **39.** 280°C   **41.** 37°C   **43.** 95°F   **45.** 50°F   **47.** 275°F   **49.** Unreasonable   **51.** Reasonable   **53.** Reasonable

Glossary

For further information on any of these terms, see the index.

1040EZ This form is used by some single individuals when filing their income tax returns.

1099 forms These forms show miscellaneous income received such as stock dividends or interest income.

absolute or **gross loss** The loss resulting when the selling price is less than the cost.

accelerated cost recovery system (ACRS) The method of depreciation required on all federal income tax returns for property acquired after January 1, 1981 and before 1986.

accelerated depreciation Depreciation that has a rate greater than a straight-line rate of depreciation. For example, declining balance, sum-of-the-years'-digits, or ACRS.

accelerated mortgages Home mortgages that are paid off faster than the typical 30 years for most home mortgages.

accidental death benefit Coverage which pays an additional death benefit if the insured dies as the result of an accident.

accountant A professional who keeps track of costs, depreciation, revenues, etc. both to help managers make decisions and also to report to various agencies such as the Internal Revenue Service.

accounts payable Funds owed by a firm that must be paid within a short period of time such as a year or less.

accounts receivable Funds owed to a firm, by customers, that must be paid within a short period of time such as a year or less.

accounts receivable turnover Net sales divided by average accounts receivable.

accumulated depreciation A running balance or total of the depreciation to date on an asset.

acid-test ratio The ratio of current assets and current liabilities. Also called quick ratio.

actual selling price *See* reduced price.

actuary A person who determines insurance premiums.

addition rule The same value can be added to both sides of an equation.

adjustable-rate mortgage (ARM) A mortgage on a house in which the interest rate is adjusted periodically.

adjusted bank balance This number represents the current checking account balance.

adjusted gross income (AGI) The sum total of all income received from wages, salaries, interest, and dividends less any adjustments to income such as sick pay and moving expenses.

adult operator A driver of a motor vehicle over a certain age, usually 25 years of age or older.

agreed ratio Partners of a business divide the profits using some rule. These profit divisions are sometimes given as a ratio.

algebraic logic The logic used by most electronic calculators.

allocation of overhead Dividing the overhead among the various products or lines of business of a company.

allowances *See* withholding allowances.

amortization schedule A table showing the equal payment necessary to pay off a loan for a specific amount of money including interest, for a specific amount of time. Also called a repayment schedule.

amortization table *See* amortization schedule.

amortized When principal and interest are paid by a sequence of equal payments (on a loan).

amount financed The amount borrowed or financed.

amount of an annuity The sum of the compound amounts of all the periodic payments into an annuity, compounded to the end of the term.

annual meeting A meeting open to all owners of stock where the management of the firm is open to questions from stockholders and where the board of directors is elected.

annual percentage rate A rate of interest that must be stated for each loan, by federal regulation. This annual percentage rate is designed to help consumers compare interest rates. This is the true or effective rate of interest.

annuity Periodic payments of a given, fixed amount of money.

annuity certain An annuity with a fixed beginning date and a fixed ending date.

annuity due An annuity with payments made at the beginning of a time period.

anticipation The seller's offer of interest for early payment of an invoice, in addition to a cash discount.

APR *See* annual percentage rate.

AS OF An invoice which is postdated "AS OF" a future date.

assessed The procedure whereby a local official, called the assessor, makes an estimate of the fair market value of property.

assessed valuation The value for property tax purposes set by the tax assessor on a piece of property.

assessment rate A certain percent used in an area to determine assessed valuation.

assets Items of value owned by a firm.

ATM cards Many people now carry automatic teller machine cards, which results in a debit to their account when they obtain cash from an ATM machine or when they make a purchase.

attached A seizure of property by court order.

automated teller machine (ATM) A machine allowing 24-hour banking.

average *See* mean.

average age of accounts receivable One year (365 days) divided by accounts receivable turnover rate.

average daily balance A method of calculating the balance owed on a revolving charge account. With this method, the balance on the account is found at the end of each day in the month and the total is divided by the number of days in the month.

average inventory Determined by dividing the sum of all inventories taken by the number of times inventory was taken.

axis A horizontal or vertical line along the edge of a graph that usually has a scale with units of measurement.

bad check A check that is not honored because there are insufficient funds in the checking account.

balance brought forward The amount left in a checking account after previous checks written have been subtracted; the current balance.

balance forward *See* balance brought forward.

balance sheet A summary of the financial condition of a firm at one point in time.

balanced Agreement reached between the bank statement amount and the depositor's checkbook balance.

bank statement A list of all charges and deposits made against and to a checking account, usually sent out monthly by the bank.

bank statement balance This is the checking account balance appearing on the front of the bank statement.

banker's interest *See* ordinary interest.

banker's ratio *See* current ratio.

bar graph A graph that uses bars to show data.

base In the number 3^2, the number 3 is the base. *See* exponent. The starting point or reference point or that to which something is being compared.

base year A previous year against which something is being compared.

basic percent equation Rate $\times$ Base $=$ Part, or $R \times B = P$.

bell-shaped curve This refers to the normal probability distribution function which is a symmetric curve often used to describe data.

beneficiary The person receiving insurance benefits upon the occurrence of a certain event.

bimodal A set of data in which two numbers occur equally often.

blank endorsement The endorsement of a check with a signature alone.

board of directors A group of people who represent the stockholders.

bodily injury insurance Another name for liability insurance.

bond A promise by a corporation or government to pay a certain fixed amount of money at a certain time in the future.

book value The cost of an asset minus any depreciation to date.

borrow Taking a number from one column of numbers in a problem in order to make a larger number in the column to which the borrowed number is added.

bounced check A check is said to be bounced when there are insufficient funds in the account on which the check was written.

break-even point The cost of an item plus the operating expenses associated with the item. Above this amount a profit is made; below it, a loss is incurred.

breaking even This occurs when the reduced price at which at item is sold just covers cost plus operating expenses.

brick-to-click banks Refers to the trend from banking in a building (brick) to banking over the Internet (clicking the mouse).

broker An intermediary who helps the seller and buyer complete a transaction. Brokers include real estate brokers and stock brokers.

budget deficit A budget deficit occurs when a governmental entity spends more than they take in through taxes and other revenues.

budget surplus A budget surplus occurs when a governmental entity takes in more money than they spend.

business checking account The type of checking account used by businesses.

business owner's package policy A business insurance policy insuring many additional perils beyond fire.

calendar year A year starting on January 1 and ending on December 31. Although most individuals file income taxes based on calendar year information, many firms do not, using a fiscal year instead.

canceled check A check is canceled after credit has been received for the amount of the check by the depositor's bank.

cancellation A process used to simplify multiplication and division of fractions using a modification of the method of writing fractions in lowest terms.

cancellation rate Another name for short-term rate.

cap The maximum interest rate on an ARM loan.

capital The amount of money originally invested in a firm.

carrier The insurance company. Also known as the insurer.

cash discount A discount offered by the seller allowing the buyer to take a discount if payment is made within a specified period of time.

cash settlement option Life insurance benefits that are paid in cash.

cash value The value in cash remaining after a policy holder has canceled or borrowed against a life insurance policy.

cashier's check A check written by the financial institution itself and having the full faith and backing of the institution.

certificate of deposit Money placed in a time deposit account.

chain calculation A long sequence of calculations.

chain discount A discount: involving two or more individual discounts.

Chapter 7 bankruptcy Results in the liquidation of the borrower's assets with funds used to pay creditors.

Chapter 11 bankruptcy Requires borrowers to enter into a repayment plan and make payments until debt has been repaid.

charge account An account that allows an individual to charge purchases at a specific store.

chargeback A fee charged to a production employee for a rejected item of production.

Check 21 A federal law known as the 21st Century Act. It allows financial institutions to take electronic photos of all canceled checks and then destroy the originals.

check register A single-page record of checks written and deposits made to a checking account.

checks outstanding Checks written that have not reached and cleared the bank as of the statement date.

check stub A stub attached to the check and retained for keeping a record of checks written.

circle graph A circle broken up into various parts, based on percentages of 360°.

class frequency The frequency of values for each class.

class mark The midpoint of an interval.

classes The intervals of a frequency distribution.

COD A shipping term meaning *cash on delivery.*

coefficient A number multiplied by a variable.

coinsurance clause A fire insurance clause that places part of the risk of fire loss upon the insured.

collateral Goods pledged as security for a loan—in the event that a loan is not paid off, the collateral can be seized by the lender and sold to pay the debt.

collision insurance A form of automobile insurance that pays for repairs to the insured's car in case of an accident.

commission A fee paid to an employee for transacting a piece of business or performing a service. A charge for buying or selling stock.

common denominator A number that all the denominators of a fraction problem divide into evenly.

common stock Ordinary stock not sharing the privileges of preferred stock and showing ownership in corporation.

companion or **spouse insurance** Lets the insured add a companion or spouse to a policy, resulting in both being insured.

comparative balance sheet A balance sheet used to compare the assets and liabilities of a firm at two different periods.

comparative income statement Preparation of a vertical analysis for two or more years in order to compare income or expense items for each year analyzed.

comparative line graph One graph that shows how several different things relate.

compensatory time (comp time) Time off given an employee to compensate for overtime previously worked.

complement The number that must be added to a given discount to get 1, or 100%.

compound amount The final amount, both principal and interest, after money is deposited at compound interest.

compound interest Interest computed on both principal and interest.

compounded daily Interest paid for every day that money is on deposit in a savings account.

comprehensive insurance A form of automobile insurance that pays for damage to the insured's car caused by fire, theft, vandalism, and so on.

consolidate loans Several smaller loans can sometimes be consolidated, or brought together into one larger loan, in order to reduce payments or gain more favorable terms.

consolidated A consolidated statement is one that includes the financial results of all subsidiaries of a company.

consumer The ultimate user of a product or service, the public.

Consumer Price Index (CPI) A monthly publication by the federal government showing the change in the cost of living.

contingent annuity An annuity with a variable beginning or ending date.

continuous compounding An account offering continuous compounding features interest compounded every instant.

conversion formulas These formulas allow one to convert from percent markup on cost to percent markup on selling price or from percent markup on selling price to percent markup on cost.

convertible preferred stock One share is convertible into a stated number of shares of common stock at some date.

corporate bond A bond issued by a corporation.

corporation A form of business organization offering limited liability to shareholders—no more money may be lost than has been invested.

cosign For instance, young people who want a credit card often need a working adult to cosign to get the card. The cosignor will be liable for any unpaid debts of anyone for whom the person cosigns.

cost The price paid to a supplier after trade and cash discounts have been taken. This price includes transportation and insurance charges. The amount paid for a depreciable asset. This is the amount used to determine depreciation.

cost accounting A detailed look at the costs of material, labor, and overhead underlying a product or a production process.

cost of goods sold The amount paid by a firm for the goods it sold during the time period covered by an income statement.

country club billing A type of billing received on revolving charge plans in which actual carbon copies of charges are returned.

credit cards Cards that allow an individual to make charges at several different businesses such as retail stores and restaurants.

credit limit The limit on the amount an individual can charge.

creditor *See* lender.

credit union share draft account A credit union account that may be used as a checking account.

cross products In the proportion $\frac{a}{b} = \frac{c}{d}$, the cross products are ad and bc.

cumulative preferred stock Stock requiring that any dividends not paid in the past must be paid before common stockholders receive any dividends.

current assets Cash or items that can be converted into cash within a given period of time, such as a year.

current balance *See* adjusted bank balance.

current (short-term) liabilities Those items that must be paid by a firm within a given period of time, such as a year.

current ratio The quotient of current assets and current liabilities. Also called banker's ratio.

current yield The annual dividend per share of stock divided by the current price per share.

daily overtime Some companies pay overtime on all hours over 8 that are worked in one day.

debit card A bank card used at a point of sale terminal. The amount of the purchase is instantly subtracted from the customer's account and credit is given to the seller's account.

debtor The person or firm borrowing money.

debt-to-equity ratio All liabilities divided by owner's equity.

decimal A number written with a decimal point, such as 4.3 or 7.22.

decimal equivalent of a fraction The decimal fraction that is equal to a proper fraction. For example, $\frac{1}{2} = 0.5, \frac{3}{8} = 0.375$.

decimal number A fraction with a denominator that is a power of 10, which is written with a decimal point, such as 4.3 or 7.22.

decimal point The starting point in the decimal system (.).

declining-balance depreciation An accelerated depreciation method.

declining-balance method A method of depreciation using a declining balance rate.

(200%) declining-balance method An accelerated method of depreciation using twice, or 200%, of the straight-line rate. Also called double-declining-balance method.

(150%) declining-balance method An accelerated method of depreciation using one and one-half, or 150%, of the straight-line rate.

(125%) declining-balance method An accelerated method of depreciation using one and one-fourth, or 125%, of the straight-line rate.

decrease problem Often called a difference problem; the part equals the base minus some portion of the base. Usually the base must be found.

decreasing term insurance A form of life insurance in which the insured pays a fixed premium until age 60 or 65 with the amount of life insurance decreasing periodically.

deductible The amount of the deductible is paid by the insured with the balance of the loss being paid by the insurance company.

deductions Amounts that are subtracted from the gross earnings of an employee to arrive at the amount of money the employee actually receives as net pay.

deferred payment price The cash price of an item, plus any finance charge.

deficit number *See* negative number.

denominator The number below the line in a fraction. For example, in the fraction $\frac{7}{9}$, 9 is the denominator.

dependent variable One whose value *depends on* the value of a different variable.

deposit in transit A deposit that has been made but that has not yet been posted by the bank, so it is not shown in the current balance.

deposit slip (deposit ticket) The form used for making a bank savings or checking account deposit.

depreciable amount The amount to be depreciated over the life of the asset.

depreciation A method used to spread the value of an asset over the several years of its life.

depreciation fraction The fraction used with sum-of-the-years'-digits depreciation. The numerator is the year and the denominator is the sum of the years of life of the asset.

depreciation schedule A schedule or table showing the depreciation rate, amount of depreciation, book value, and accumulated depreciation for each year of an asset's life.

destination The city or town where goods or merchandise are being shipped.

developed world The developed world refers to the more economically developed countries such as Germany, France, the United Kingdom, and the U.S., among others.

differential-piece plan A pay rate designed to pay a greater amount for each unit of production as the number of units produced is increased.

diability insurance This type of insurance covers individuals who become disabled.

direct deposit An arrangement by which an entity such as a business electronically deposits funds into an account of, say, an employee.

direct payment Direct payments are payments made directly into a checking account. For example, the government makes Social Security payments to seniors using direct payments.

discount An amount subtracted from the price of a product or service that helps the buyer purchase at a lower cost and increase profits. The amount of interest charged on a note. Also called a bank discount.

discount broker A stockbroker who charges less than full price for buying and selling stocks.

discount fee A bank collects a discount fee on credit-card deposits from the merchant.

discount note A note where interest is deducted in advance.

discount period The period of time in the discounting process.

discounting a note The holder of a note sometimes sells the note to a bank before its maturity date. This gives cash to the holder earlier than otherwise.

dispersion Spread of data.

distributive property A property of algebra that says a number on the outside of the parentheses should be multiplied times each term inside the parentheses.

distributors Firms that buy in bulk and then distribute goods to various retail outlets.

dividends Money paid by a company to the holders of a stock.

divisibility rules These rules allow us to quickly determine if a number is evenly divisible by 2, 3, 4, 5, 6, 8, 9, and/or 10.

docking Same meaning as chargeback.

dollars per $100 Property tax rates are sometimes stated in dollars per $100 of appraised value.

dollars per $1000 Property tax rates are sometimes stated in dollars per $1000 of appriased value.

double-declining-balance method *See* (200%) declining-balance method.

double time Twice the regular hourly rate. A premium often paid for working holidays and Sunday.

Dow Jones Industrial Average A commonly quoted average of the stock prices of 30 large industrial, publicly held corporations.

down payment An amount paid when an item is bought.

draw An amount paid by an employer to salespeople at regular intervals. This is often paid against future income.

drawing account An account from which a salesperson can receive payment against future commissions.

duplicate statement A duplicate of a checking account statement issued by the bank.

early withdrawal penalty A fine or amount of money charged by the lending institution for withdrawal of money earlier than the time agreed upon by the depositor and the institution. These penalties apply only to interest, not to principal.

earnings per share The difference of the net income of a corporation and any dividends on preferred shares, divided by the number of common shares outstanding.

e-commerce The buying and selling of products over the Internet or other network system.

effective annual yield *See* effective rate of interest.

effective rate of interest The simple interest rate corresponding to a given discount rate. Also called true rate of interest. The actual percent of interest earned during a year.

electronic banking The use of electronic technology in banking. Such services as direct deposits, ATM cards, debit cards, and home and business banking are all a part of electronic banking.

electronic commerce People and companies can now purchase products and pay bills electronically using the Internet.

Electronic Federal Tax Payment System (EFTPS) This system allows taxpayers to make tax payments electronically.

electronic funds transfer Many companies choose to move money electronically using computer networks, rather than using checks that are mailed.

electronic payment The payment of a bill using the Internet.

Employer's Quarterly Federal Tax Return The form (Form 941) is sent to the IRS along with quarterly payments of FICA and withholding tax.

ending inventory The value at cost of inventory at the end of a period.

end-of-month dating (EOM) In cash discounts, the time period beginning at the end of the month the invoice is dated. Proximo and prox. have the same meaning.

endowment policy A form of life insurance guaranteeing the payment of a fixed amount of money to a given individual whether or not the insured person lives.

equal shares Partners in a business share all profits equally.

equation A statement that says two expressions are equal.

equivalent cash price A single amount today equal to the present value of an annuity.

escrow account An account maintained by real estate lenders and used to pay taxes and insurance. Also called an impound account.

exact interest Simple interest calculated using 365 days in a year.

Exchange Traded Fund (ETF) An ETF holds stocks and bonds and trades at about the same price as the underlying assets throughout the day. These have become very popular investment vehicles.

excise tax A tax charged on specific items that are purchased. Tobacco, alcoholic beverages, and gasoline have an excise tax.

executive officers President, vice president, and so on, of a corporation.

exponent In the number 3^2 the small number 2 is the exponent. It says to multiply 3 by itself. A number that tells how many times a number is used in a product. For example, $3^2 = 3 \times 3 = 9$.

expression Here are three examples of expressions: $7, 8.5x, 6y - 9$.

extended term insurance The nonforfeiture option that gives the insured term insurance for a fixed number of years and days.

extension total On an invoice, the product of the number of items times the unit price.

extra dating (extra, ex., or x) Extra time allowed in determining the net payment date of a cash discount.

Exchange Traded Fund (ETF) An ETF holds stocks and bonds and trades at about the same price as the underlying assets throughout the day. These have become very popular investment vehicles.

face value The amount shown on the face of a note. *See* par value.

face value of the policy The amount of an insurance policy.

factor A person who buys accounts receivable of a firm (accounts receivable represent money owed to the firm).

factoring The term for when a business sells part of its accounts receivable to a financial institution.

Fair Labor Standards Act A federal law setting work conditions and standards of employee treatment.

fair market value The price for which a piece of property could reasonably be expected to be sold in the market.

FAS (free alongside ship) Free alongside the ship on the loading dock with all freight charges to that point paid by the shipper.

Federal Deposit Insurance Corporation (FDIC) This branch of the government insures funds at members' banks. It protects small investors from losses when a member bank goes out of business.

Federal Insurance Contributions Act (FICA) A federal act requiring that a specified amount of money be collected from the paycheck of almost all nongovernmental employees, which is used by the federal government to pay pensions, survivors benefits, and disability.

Federal Savings and Loan Insurance Corporation (FSLIC) This branch of the government insures funds at member savings and loan associations. It protects small investors from losses.

Federal Tax Deposit Coupon (Form 8109) Employers use this form when depositing taxes due to the IRS.

Federal Truth in Lending Act (Regulation Z) An act passed in 1969 that requires that all interest rates be given as comparable percents.

Federal Unemployment Tax Act (FUTA) A federal act covering unemployment insurance.

finance charges Charges paid to obtain credit.

financial calculator A calculator that includes common business applications such as present value, future value, payments, and interest rates.

first-in, first-out method (FIFO) Inventory valuation method following the flow of goods, first-in, first-out.

fiscal year Many firms use a fiscal year which starts and ends on dates other than January 1 and December 31. They file their income taxes and report financial results based on their fiscal year.

fixed-amount annuity A settlement option that pays a fixed amount per month to life insurance beneficiaries.

fixed assets *See* plant and equipment assets.

fixed-period annuity A settlement option for life insurance beneficiaries paying a sum of money for a fixed period of time.

fixed-rate loan A home loan made at a fixed rate of interest for a fixed period of time.

flat-fee checking account Some banks offer checking accounts that charge a flat fee each month for a checking account and perhaps an ATM card, debit card, and credit card.

float In finance, float refers to the time between the actual deposit of a sum of money and the time at which those funds are credited to an account.

floating decimal point A feature on electronic calculators that locates the decimal point in the answer.

floor space Overhead is sometimes allocated among lines of business based on the amount of floor space used by each line.

FOB (free on board) Free on board shipping point means that the buyer pays for shipping. Free on board destination means that the seller pays for shipping.

Form 1040A Many people use this form when filling out their income tax returns.

formula A rule showing how quantities are related.

formula for base In a percent problem, the base is the part divided by the rate.

formula for rate In a percent problem, the rate is the part divided by the base.

fraction Used to indicate a part of a whole. For example, $\frac{3}{4}$ means that the whole is divided into 4 parts and we are considering 3 of them.

frequency distribution table A table showing the number of times one or more events occur.

fringe benefits Companies often provide benefits other than a paycheck, including child care or medical insurance.

future amount The future amount, also called future value, is the amount of money an investment grows to at a future date.

future value The amount an investment grows to at some future date.

global supply chain A supply chain with at least some of the suppliers in other countries.

graph A visual presentation of numeric data.

graphing calculator A calculator that allows functions to be graphed.

gross domestic product (GDP) GDP is one measure of the total of income and output for a country. Economists and journalists constantly refer to GDP.

gross earnings The total amount of money earned by an employee before any deductions are taken.

gross loss *See* absolute loss.

gross profit The difference between the amount received from customers for goods and what the firm paid for the goods.

gross-profit method A method used to estimate inventory value at cost that utilizes cost amounts.

gross sales The total amount of money received from customers for the goods or services sold by the firm.

group insurance plan An insurance plan that includes a group of people employed by the same company or belonging to the same organization.

grouped data Items combined into groups (taken from a table) to simplify information for more immediate comprehension.

guaranteed conversion privilege This provision allows the insured to convert term insurance to ordinary or variable life insurance without physical examination.

half-year convention Under MACRS, property placed in service or disposed of is allowed one-half year of depreciation.

head of household A filing status on an income tax return for an unmarried person who provides a home for others, such as a dependent child or children or parent(s) of the taxpayer.

home banking A system that allows the customer to do banking from the home or business using the Internet.

homeowner's policy A policy for homeowners providing fire, theft, and vandalism protection.

horizontal analysis Prepared by finding the amount of any change from last year to current year, both in dollars and as a percent.

hourly wage A rate of pay expressed as so much per hour. *See* time rate.

hundredths Refers to the number of parts out of one hundred.

I Bond A bond issued by the federal government that pays a low fixed interest rate plus a rate based on inflation.

identity theft The theft of enough information about a person so that charges can be made fraudulently on behalf of the thief. Identity theft is becoming somewhat common.

IMMA *See* insured money market accounts.

impound account *See* escrow account.

improper fraction A fraction with a numerator larger than or equal to the denominator. For example, $\frac{7}{5}$ is an improper fraction; $\frac{1}{9}$ is not.

incentive rate A payment system based on the amount of work completed.

income statement A summary of all the income and expenses involved in running a business for a given period of time.

income tax withholding Federal income tax withheld from gross earnings by the employer.

increase problem Often called an amount problem; the part equals the base plus some portion of the base, resulting in a new value. Usually the base must be found.

independent variable One whose value *does not depend on* the value of another variable.

indicator words These words help indicate to us whether addition, subtraction, multiplication, or division is used in solving the problem.

individual retirement account (IRA) An account that permits an individual to establish a retirement plan and to deduct any contributions to the account.

inflation The increase over time in the price levels of goods and services.

initial inventory The value at cost of inventory at the beginning of a period.

insider trading An illegal practice in which someone trades the stocks and/or bonds of publicly held corporations using information that has not been released to the public.

inspection Sometimes we can quickly find a common denominator by inspecting the denominators of two or three fractions.

installment loan A loan paid off in a series of equal payments made at equal periods of time. Car loans are examples of installment loans.

insufficient funds (NSF) Not enough funds in a checking account for the bank to honor the check.

insured A person or business that has purchased insurance. Also known as the policyholder.

insured money market accounts (IMMAs) Accounts that are insured up to a certain maximum by the federal government and that offer a higher rate than passbook accounts.

insurer The insurance company.

intangible assets These are assets of a company that are not physical and include something like the good name and reputation of a company.

interest A charge paid for borrowing money or a fee received for lending money.

interest-in-advance note *See* simple discount note.

interest on investment and agreed ratio Sometimes one partner will put up a large share of money to start a firm, while other partners operate it. The partner putting up the larger share of money gets interest on the investment before any further division of profits.

interest paying accounts Some checking accounts receive interest based on the amount in the account.

interest rate spread The difference between the interest rate charged on loans and interest rate paid on deposits.

Internal Revenue Service (IRS) The IRS is the branch of the United States Government that is responsible for collecting the taxes due to the government.

inventory The value of all goods on hand for sale.

inventory turnover The number of times each year that the average inventory is sold; also called stock turnover.

inventory turns *See* turns.

inventory valuation Determining the value of merchandise in stock. Four common methods are specific identification, weighted average cost, FIFO, and LIFO.

invoice A document that helps businesses keep track of sales and purchases.

invoice total The total amount owed on an invoice.

IRA *See* individual retirement account.

irregulars Items that are blemished or have flaws and must be sold at a reduced price.

itemized billing A method of credit-card billing in which purchases are listed, along with payments, with no actual receipts returned to the user.

itemized deductions A taxpayer can itemize certain expenses, such as interest and taxes on a home and cash donations, among others, and deduct from income before calculating taxes.

junk bonds Bonds of bankrupt or troubled companies.

last-in, first-out method (LIFO) Inventory valuation method following the flow of goods, last-in, first-out.

late fees Fees charged by lenders for late payments.

least common denominator The smallest whole number that all the denominators of two or more fractions evenly divide into.

left side In the equation $4x = 28$, the left side is $4x$.

lender The person or firm making the loan.

liabilities Expenses that must be paid by a firm.

liability or **bodily injury insurance** Coverage that provides protection from suit by an injured party.

like fractions Two fractions that have the same denominator.

like terms Algebraic terms that have the same variables raised to the same power.

limited liability No more money can be lost than has been invested.

limited partnership A partnership with partners who have limited liability and no management authority.

limited-payment life insurance A form of life insurance in which premiums are paid for only a certain fixed number of years.

line graph A graph that uses a line to show data.

linear equation An equation that does not have any variables raised to a power (such as x^2) or multiplied by another variable (such $x \cdot y$).

liquid assets Cash or items that can be converted to cash quickly.

liquidity A firm is liquid if it has the ability to pay its bills as they come due.

list price The suggested retail price or final consumer price given by the manufacturer or supplier.

loan repayment table A table used to decide on the payment that will amortize a loan.

long-term liabilities Those items that will be paid after one year.

lowest terms A fraction is written in lowest terms when no number except the number 1 divides evenly into both the numerator and denominator of the fraction.

lump sum Benefits from a retirement plan can be paid all at once in a lump sum.

luxury tax A name sometimes given to excise tax.

maintenance charge per month A flat charge for maintaining a checking account.

maker The person borrowing the money on a note.

manufacturer The assembler of component parts or finished products.

margin *See* gross profit.

marital status A married individual pays less income tax than does a single person with the same income.

markdown A reduction from the original selling price. It may be expressed as a dollar amount or as a percent of the original selling price.

marketable securities Stocks, bonds, and other securities that can be converted quickly to cash.

marketing channels The path or steps that goods take from manufacturer to consumer.

market interest rate An interest rate set by the market.

markup (margin or **gross profit)** The difference between the cost and the selling price.

markup conversion formula A formula used to convert markup from one base to the other base.

markup equivalents A markup of 20% on selling price is equivalent to a markup of 25% on cost.

markup formula The formula used when working with markup. Cost + Markup = Selling price.

markup on cost Markup that is calculated as a percent of cost.

markup on selling price Markup that is calculated as a percent of selling price.

markup with spoilage The calculation of markup including deduction for spoiled or unsaleable merchandise.

MasterCard A credit-card plan.

mathematics of buying The mathematics involving trade and cash discounts.

maturity date The date a loan is due.

maturity value The total amount, principal and interest, that must be repaid when a loan is paid off. It equals face value plus interest.

mean The sum of numbers divided by the number of numbers.

measure of central tendency A number that tries to estimate the middle of a set of data. Measures of central tendency include the mean, median, and mode.

median The middle number in an ordered array.

medical and dental expenses Medical and dental expenses in excess of a certain percent of an individual's adjusted gross income may be deducted.

medical insurance Insurance providing medical protection in the event of accident or injury.

Medicare tax Part of the Social Security tax (FICA) until 1991. Since 1991 Medicare tax has been collected separately.

memory keys A feature on electronic calculators that allows answers to be stored for future use and recalled.

merchant batch header ticket A form used to deposit credit-card sales in a business checking account.

method of prime numbers The least common denominator of two or more fractions can be found using this method.

metric system A system of measurement established by a group of scientists after the French Revolution of 1789.

middlemen Those along the marketing channels, such as wholesalers, brokers, and retailers.

mill A mill is one-tenth of a cent or one-thousandth of a dollar.

minimum wage The federal government and some states define a minimum wage to be paid. It does not apply to managers or salaried employees, but to hourly employees.

miscellaneous deductions In some cases, deductions such as union dues, qualified education expenses, income tax preparation fees, etc. may be deducted from income before calculating income taxes.

mixed number The sum of a fraction and a whole number. For example, $1\frac{1}{5}$ or $2\frac{5}{9}$ are mixed numbers.

mobile payments The use of a mobile phone (cell phone) to make payments.

mode The most common number in a list of numbers.

modified accelerated cost recovery system (MACRS) The Tax Reform Act of 1986 replaces the ACRS with the MACRS.

money market A money market is a short-term investment account that pays a small amount of interest but allows money to be quickly withdrawn without penalty.

money order An instrument that is purchased and used in place of cash. It is usually preferred over a personal or business check.

mortality table A table showing statistics on life expectancy, survival, and death rates.

multiple carriers More than one insurance company sharing an insurable risk.

multiplication rule Both sides of an equation can be multiplied by the same number.

municipal bond A bond issued by a municipality such as a city or school district.

mutual company An insurance company owned by the policy-holders, who receive a dividend.

mutual fund Typically receives money from many different small investors and reinvests the funds in stocks and/or bonds.

negative number (deficit number) A number that is less than zero; a negative balance or deficit; for example, $-\$800$ or ($800).

net cost The cost or price after allowable discounts have been taken.

net cost equivalent, or **percent paid** The decimal number derived from the product of the complements of the trade discounts. This number may be multiplied by the list price to find the net cost (price).

net income Net income before taxes minus taxes.

net income after taxes *See* net income.

net income before taxes Gross sales minus Returns minus Cost of goods sold minus Operating expenses.

net pay The amount of money actually received by an employee after deductions are taken from gross pay.

net price The net price is the list price minus the trade discount minus the cash discount.

net profit (or **net earnings**) The difference between gross margin and expenses. After the cost of goods and operating expenses are subtracted from total sales, the remainder is net profit.

net sales The value of goods bought by customers after subtracting goods returned.

net worth Same as owners' equity.

no-fault insurance Motor vehicle insurance that pays directly to the insured no matter who causes the accident.

nominal rate *See* stated rate.

noncustomer check cashing A service that allows an individual who is not a bank customer to cash a check upon payment of a fee.

nonforfeiture options Options available to the insured when canceling the insurance policy.

nonlinear equations An equation whose graph is not a straight line. An equation is nonlinear if it includes an exponent or if any variable is multiplied by another variable.

nonparticipating A form of stock that will never pay dividends above the stated rate.

nonparticipating policy This is an insurance policy sold by a stock company. If the company prospers, the stockholders, not the policyholders, receive a dividend.

nonsmokers discount A discount given to nonsmokers because they are better insurance risks.

nonsufficient funds (NSF) Not enough funds in a checking account for the bank to honor the check.

normal curve The bell-shaped curve commonly used in statistics.

notary service A service that provides notarization, which is required on certain business documents and transfers.

NOW account This account uses a "Negotiable Order of Withdrawal," which works and looks like a check.

numerator The number above the line in a fraction. For example, in the fraction $\frac{5}{8}$, 5 is the numerator.

odd lot Fewer than 100 shares of stock.

offshore Refers to moving work out of the country. The main advantage of offshoring would be the substantially lower wages paid in many countries such as Mexico or China.

online brokers Online brokers allow you to buy or sell stock through them using the Internet.

open-end credit An account that is not paid off in a fixed period of time; MasterCard and Visa accounts are examples of open-end credit.

operating expenses (or **overhead**) Expenses of operating a business. Wages, salaries, rent, utilities, and advertising are examples of operating expenses.

operating loss The loss resulting when the selling price is less than the break-even point.

order of operations The rules determining which calculations must be done first in chain calculations.

ordered array An arrangement of a list of numbers from smallest to largest.

ordinary annuity An annuity with payments made at the end of a given period of time.

ordinary dating method A method for calculating the discount date and the net payment date. Days are counted from the date of the invoice.

ordinary interest Simple interest calculated assuming 360 days in a year. Also called banker's interest.

ordinary life insurance (whole-life insurance, straight life insurance) A form of life insurance in which the insured pays a constant premium until death or retirement, whichever occurs sooner. Upon retirement, monthly payments are made by the company to the insured until the death of the insured.

origin The point of a coordinate system at which all coordinate axes meet.

original investment Partners divide profits of a business on the basis of original investments by each partner.

overdraft This occurs when a customer writes a check for which there are insufficient funds in the account.

overdraft protection The bank service of honoring checks written on an account that has insufficient funds.

overhead *See* operating expenses.

override A commission received by a sales supervisor or department head based on total sales of the sales group or department.

over the limit fees Many lenders charge a fee in the event the debt exceeds the amount authorized by the issuer of the card.

overtime The number of hours worked by an employee in excess of 40 hours per week, or 8 hours per day.

overtime premium method Payment of overtime as a premium. All hours worked are paid at regular rate. Overtime hours are paid at $\frac{1}{2}$ rate. Gross earnings are the sum of these.

owners' equity The difference between assets and liabilities. Also called proprietorship or net worth.

paid-up insurance A nonforfeiture option that provides paid-up insurance of a certain amount.

par value The amount printed on a stock certificate; usually the price at which a share of stock is first offered to the public.

part The result of multiplying the base times the rate.

partial payment A payment that is less than the total owed on an invoice; a cash discount may be earned.

partial-year depreciation The amount of depreciation that is determined for the asset during a period of less than one year.

participating A type of stock that could be affected by an increase in the dividend.

participating policy The type of life insurance policy issued by a mutual insurance company.

partnership A business formed by two or more people.

passbook account A bank account used for day-in and day-out deposits of money. These accounts usually have the lowest interest rates of any accounts but have no penalties when money is withdrawn.

pay period The time period for which an employee is paid.

payee The person who loans the money and will receive payment on a note.

payer *See* maker.

payment period The time between the payments of an annuity.

payments for life A life insurance settlement option that pays an annuity for life.

payments for life with a guaranteed number of years A life insurance settlement option that pays a certain amount per month for the life of the insured but guarantees a certain length of time in the event that the insured dies before this guaranteed time period.

payroll ledger A chart showing all payroll information.

PE ratio *See* price-earnings ratio.

peak oil Refers to the idea that world oil production may peak and then decline.

per debit charge A charge per check. Usually continues regardless of the number of checks written.

percent A percent is one hundredth. For example, 2 percent means 2 parts of a hundred.

percent formula The basic percent formula is $P = B \times R$, or Part $=$ Base $\times$ Rate.

percent key The electronic calculator key $\boxed{\%}$ that moves the decimal point two places to the left when used following multiplication or division.

percent or **rate of markdown** The markdown expressed as a percent of original price.

percent or **rate of markup** The markup expressed as a percent of original price.

percentage method of withholding Used to determine federal withholding tax. This method does not require the several pages of tables needed with the wage bracket method.

peril insurance Insurance that pays upon a loss by the insured.

period of compounding Amount of time between the addition of interest to a deposit or loan.

periodic inventory A physical inventory taken at regular intervals.

periodic payments A series of payments made at regular intervals in time.

perpetual inventory A continuous inventory system normally utilizing a computer.

personal checking account The type of checking account used by individuals.

personal exemption Each taxpayer currently gets a deduction for each dependent, including the taxpayer.

personal identification number (PIN) A special code that must be entered when using an ATM card or a debit card.

personal income tax A type of tax charged by states and the federal government to individuals. The tax is based on income.

personal property Property other than real estate, such as furnishings, appliances, cars, trucks, clothing, boats, and money.

physical inventory An actual physical count of each item in stock at a given time.

pie chart A chart in the shape of a pie that is used to show data.

piecework rate A method of pay by which an employee receives so much money per item completed.

PIN A personal identification number is needed in addition to an ATM card in order to make a cash withdrawal.

plant assets *See* plant and equipment assets.

plant and equipment assets Items owned by a firm that will not be converted to cash within a year. Also called fixed assets or plant assets.

point of sale This refers to the point in a store where the sale is actually made—commonly at a cash register where scanners are used to record the items purchased.

policy A contract between an insured and an insurance company.

policy fee An annual fee charged by insurance companies to cover the cost of processing the policy.

policyholder A person or business that has purchased insurance. Also known as the insured.

population The entire group being studied.

postdating Dating in the future; on an invoice, **"AS OF"** dating.

preferred stock Stock that pays dividends before common stockholders receive any dividends.

premium The amount of money charged for an insurance policy.

premium factor A factor used to convert annual premiums to either semiannual, quarterly, or monthly premiums of an insurance policy.

premium payment An additional payment for extra service.

premium rate A higher amount of pay given for additional hours worked or additional units produced.

prepaid card A card that allows purchases. The amount of money that has been prepaid to the company sponsoring the card is stored magnetically on the card and reduced at every use.

present value An amount that can be invested today to produce a given amount in the future.

present value of an annuity (1) The lump sum that can be deposited today that will amount to the same final total as would the periodic payment of an annuity. (2) A lump sum that could be deposited today so that equal periodic withdrawals could be made.

present value of a bond The value that a bond is worth today. The present value is based on the present value of all future cash flows (interest payments) from the bond.

price-earnings ratio (PE ratio) The price per share of stock divided by the firm's annual earnings per share of the stock.

price relative The quotient of the current price and the price in some past year with the quotient multiplied by 100.

prime number A number divisible without remainder only by itself or 1 (such as 7 or 13).

prime rate The interest rate at which large, financially secure corporations borrow money.

principal An amount of money either borrowed, loaned, or deposited. The initial amount of money deposited.

proceeds The amount of money the borrower receives after subtracting the discount from the face value of a note.

processing (check) A check given to a merchant is processed by being deposited with the merchant's bank, where it is then routed to a Federal Reserve bank and then to the payer's bank.

profit margin The profit margin refers to the (usually) small portion of the total revenues earned by a firm that actually goes to profit. For example, many grocery stores have profit margins of about 3%, meaning that only 3% of their total sales end up as profit.

promissory note A document in which one person agrees to pay money to another person, a certain amount of time in the future, and at a certain rate of interest.

proper fraction A fraction in which the numerator is smaller than the denominator. For example, $\frac{2}{3}$ is a proper fraction; $\frac{9}{5}$ is not.

property damage insurance A type of automobile insurance that pays for damages caused to the property of others.

property tax rate The tax rate applied to the assessed value of property.

proportion A proportion says that two ratios are equal.

proprietorship *See* owners' equity.

prox. *See* proximo dating.

proximo dating In cash discounts, the time period beginning at the end of the month the invoice is dated. End-of-month dating (EOM) and "prox." have the same meaning.

Publication 534 The Internal Revenue Service publication that gives a complete coverage of depreciation.

publicly held corporation A company owned by the public, rather than by one or a very few individuals.

purchase invoice The invoice or document received by the purchaser of goods or services from the seller.

quick ratio *See* acid-test ratio.

quota bonus system A plan that pays a bonus to an employee after reaching a quota.

range The difference between the largest value and the smallest value in a set of numbers.

rate A number followed by "%" or "percent."

rate of commission Many people in sales are paid based on a commission or percent of sales.

rate of interest The percent of interest charged for one year.

ratio A quotient of two quantities.

ratio of net income after taxes to average owners' equity Net income divided by average owners' equity.

raw data A set of data before analysis.

real estate Real property such as land and buildings.

real property All land, buildings, and other improvements attached to the land.

receipt-of-goods dating (ROG) In cash discounts, time is counted from the date that goods are received.

reciprocal The result of interchanging the numerator and denominator of a fraction.

reconciliation The process of checking a bank statement against the depositor's own personal records.

recourse Merchants sometimes sell debts that are owed them. If the person owing the money is unavailable and the bank buying the debt has recourse to the merchant—the merchant is liable for the debt.

recovery class The class into which property is placed under MACRS (3-, 5-, 7- 10-, 15-, 20-, 27.5-, 31.5-, or 39-year class).

recovery period The number of years over which the cost of an asset is recovered using the MACRS.

rediscounting The process in which one financial institution discounts a note at a second institution.

reduced net profit This occurs when a markdown decreases the selling price to a point that is still above the break-even point.

reduced price The selling price after subtracting the markdown; also called sale price and actual selling price.

Regulation DD A federal law requiring that interest paid on funds in savings accounts be paid based on the exact number of days.

Regulation Z *See* Federal Truth in Lending Act.

repayment schedule *See* amortization schedule.

repeating decimal A decimal that repeats one or more digits without ending. A bar is often placed over the repeating digit(s). For example, $.333\overline{3}$ and $.16\overline{16}$ are both repeating decimals.

replacement cost The amount of money it would take to construct a building should it be completely destroyed by fire for example.

repossess The act by a lender of taking back ownership of an item when payments have not been made.

Request for Earnings and Benefit Estimate Statement This form is used by individuals when checking with the Social Security Administration to see if they have the correct information on the individuals' previous Social Security contributions.

residual value *See* salvage value.

restricted endorsement Endorsement of a check so that only the person or company given the check may cash it.

retail method A method used to estimate inventory value at cost that utilizes both cost and retail amounts.

retail price The price at which merchandise is offered for sale to the public.

retailer A firm that sells directly to the consumer.

returned check A check that has been deposited but returned to the bank due to nonsufficient funds (NSF) is said to be returned.

returned-deposit item The return to the bank of an item that has been deposited, due to any number of irregularities.

returned goods Merchandise returned due to incorrect shipment or damage.

returns The total value of all goods returned by customers.

revolving charge account *See* open-end credit.

right side In the equation $4x = 28$, the right side is 28.

ROG *See* receipt-of-goods dating.

Roth IRA Contributions to this type of IRA are not deductible when made, but funds in the IRA grow tax-free and eventual withdrawals are also tax-free.

round lot Multiple of 100 shares of stock.

rounded decimals Decimals reduced to a number with fewer decimals.

Rule of 78 A method of calculating interest charges that need not be paid because the loan was paid off earlier than planned.

rules for divisibility Rules that help determine whether a number is evenly divisible by another number.

salary A fixed amount of money per pay period.

salary and agreed ratio Same as agreed ratio, except that a salary may be allowed to one partner or the other in addition to the profit division.

salary plus commission A commission is paid as a premium in addition to salary.

sale price *See* reduced price.

sales invoice The invoice or document retained by the seller of goods or services, a copy of which is sent to the purchaser.

sales quota An expected level of production. A premium may be paid for surpassing quota.

sales tax A tax placed on sales to the final consumer. The tax is collected by the state, county, or local government.

sales value Value of sales for each department of a company.

salvage value or **scrap value** The value of an asset at the end of its useful life. For depreciation purposes, this is often an estimate.

sample A portion of the entire population being studied.

savings account *See* passbook account.

scale Markings indicating units of measurement on the axis of a graph.

Schedule 1 (Form 1040) This is the basic form used for reporting interest dividend income.

scientific calculator A calculator that includes common math operations used in science, including the grouping of operations using parentheses.

SDI (State Disability Insurance) deduction The deduction for a state disability insurance program.

Securities and Exchange Commission (SEC) The SEC is an organization within the U.S. government that is responsible for enforcing laws related to securities and regulating that industry.

self-employed individuals Individuals who work for themselves instead of for the government or a company owned by someone else.

selling price The price at which merchandise is offered for sale to the public. The cost of an item plus its markup.

series discount *See* chain discount.

settlement options Methods of receiving life insurance benefits in addition to a cash payment.

shift differential A premium paid for working a less desirable shift, such as swing shift or graveyard shift.

shipping point The location from which merchandise is shipped by the seller to the buyer.

short-term or **cancellation rate** A rate used when charging for short-term policies and the refunds given when policies are canceled by the policyholder.

silent partner A partner who invests in a partnership but takes no part in running it.

similar terms *See* like terms.

simple annuity An annuity with payment dates matching the compounding period.

simple discount note A note whose interest is deducted in advance from the face value, with only the difference given to the borrower.

simple interest Interest computed only on the principal.

simple interest notes Notes on which interest is found by formulas for simple interest.

single discount A discount expressed as a single percent and not as a series or chain discount.

single discount equivalent to a series discount A series or chain discount that is expressed as a single discount.

sinking fund A fund set up to receive equal periodic payments in order to pay off an obligation at some fixed time in the future.

sliding-scale commission A graduated commission plan giving a higher rate to top-producing salespeople.

smart card A card on which is stored information such as identification, authentification, and data storage that can involve dollar amounts.

SMP The abbreviation for a special multiperils policy. This policy gives additional insurance coverage to businesses. *See* business owner's package policy.

Social Security *See* Federal Insurance Contributions Act (FICA).

sole proprietorship A business owned by one person.

solution A number that can replace a variable in an equation and result in a true statement.

special endorsement An endorsement to a specific payee.

specific-identification method Inventory valuation method that identifies the cost of each individual item.

split-shift premium A premium paid for working a split shift. For example, an employee who is on 4 hours, off 4 hours, and then on 4 hours.

spoilage Merchandise that becomes unsaleable. Usually considered when calculating markup.

square root The square root ($\sqrt{}$) of a number is a number that when multiplied by itself equals that number. The square root of 9, $\sqrt{9}$, is 3, since $3 \times 3 = 9$.

square root key The electronic calculator key $\boxed{\sqrt{}}$ that calculates the square root of the number on the calculator.

Stafford loan Government loans that can be subsidized—they are frequently used by students.

Standard and Poor's 500 (S&P 500) This is an index that reflects the combined prices of the stocks of 500 of the largest and best companies in the U.S. It is often used as one measure of how well the stock market is doing.

standard deduction A deduction used to reduce taxable income for taxpayers who do not itemize their deductions.

standard deviation A measurement of the dispersion of a set of data.

state income tax Some states levy a state income tax on income.

state unemployment insurance (SUTA) Many states have unemployment insurance to help those who have become unemployed.

state withholding State income tax withheld from gross earnings by the employer.

stated rate The rate of interest quoted by a bank; also called the nominal rate.

statistics Data and/or the analysis of data.

stock A share of stock represents partial ownership of a corporation.

stock certificates Documentation of stock ownership.

stock company An insurance company owned by stockholders. No dividend is paid to policyholders.

stock exchange A place or mechanism at or through which stocks can be bought and sold.

stock fund There are many mutual funds that own stocks.

stock ratio Numbers used to compare stocks—typically the current yield and the PE ratio.

stock turnover *See* inventory turnover.

stockbroker A person who buys and sells stock for the public.

stockholders The owners of a corporation.

stockholders' equity The difference between a corporation's assets and liabilities.

stop-payment order A request that the bank not pay on a check previously written.

straight commission A fixed amount or percent for each unit of work. Earnings are based on performance alone.

straight life insurance Another name for ordinary or whole-life insurance.

straight-line depreciation A depreciation method whereby depreciation is spread evenly over the life of the asset.

subsidiary A company controlled by another company or corporation.

substitution Replacing the variable in an equation by the solution; substitution is used to check a solution.

suicide clause A clause that excludes suicide as an insurable cause of death (usually for the first two years of the policy).

sum-of-the-balances method *See* Rule of 78.

sum-of-the-years'-digits method An accelerated depreciation method using a depreciation fraction.

suppliers Firms from whom companies buy products.

supply chain Retailers and manufacturers depend on their supply chain to keep goods coming to them.

T-account form This is a method for reconciling a bank statement in which the bank statement balance is on the left and the checkbook balance is on the right side.

T-bills *See* U.S. Treasury bills.

tangible assets These are physical assets such as machinery, trucks, and buildings.

tax deduction Any expense that the IRS will allow a taxpayer to subtract from adjusted gross income.

tax rate schedule A schedule that shows the individual tax rates for tax filing status.

taxable income Adjusted gross income, minus exemptions, minus deductions.

taxes Individuals and companies pay many types of taxes, including sales tax, income tax, and property tax, among others.

telephone transfer The transfer of funds with a verbal request over the telephone.

term A single letter, a single number, or the product of a number and a letter.

term insurance A form of insurance providing protection for a fixed length of time.

term of an annuity The time from the beginning of the first payment into an annuity until the end of the last payment.

term of the note The length of time until a note is due.

territorial ratings Insurance companies use territorial ratings to adjust for the fact that automobile accidents occur more often in certain territories than in others.

texting A means of communicating with customers.

third world country Third world refers to countries that are underdeveloped and include countries such as Ethiopia and Mexico.

time The number of years or fraction of a year for which the loan is made.

time-and-a-half rate Many employees are paid $1\frac{1}{2}$ times the normal rate of pay for any hours worked in excess of 40 hours per week or 8 hours per day.

time card A card that is helpful in preparing the payroll. The time card includes such information as the dates of the pay period, the employee's name, and the number of hours worked.

time deposit account A savings account in which the depositor agrees to leave money for a certain period of time.

time rates Earnings based on hours worked, not work accomplished.

time value of money, or **value of money** The average interest rate for which money is loaned at a given time.

total installment cost Find the total installment cost by multiplying the amount of each payment on a loan and the number of payments; then add any down payment.

total invoice amount The sum of all the extension totals on an invoice.

total revenue Total revenue from all sources.

trade As referred to in this book, buying and selling stock or bonds.

trade discount The discount offered to businesses. This discount is expressed either as a single discount (such as 25%) or a series discount (such as 20/10) and is subtracted from the list price.

traditional banking The use of paper checks and check registers to record deposits and checks.

transaction costs Transaction costs refer to the costs of making a transaction. For example, it costs banks to handle each check (a transaction).

transaction register A single-page record of checks written, deposits made, and other transactions made to a checking account.

transfer tax A tax charged by some cities and states on the purchase or sale of stock.

Treasury bills *See* U.S. Treasury bills.

Treasury-bill fund Some funds invest most of their assets in Treasury bills.

Treasury Inflation-Protected Securities (TIPS) TIPS refer to government bonds that pay a stated interest in addition to additional interest to offset inflation. Many believe that they are a good way to save during a time when inflation is increasing.

true rate of interest *See* effective rate of interest.

turnover at cost Found by the following formula.

$$\frac{\text{Cost of goods sold}}{\text{Amount of inventory at cost}}$$

turnover at retail Found by the following formula.

$$\frac{\text{Retail sales}}{\text{Average inventory at retail}}$$

turns Inventory turns refer to how many times a year a company turns over its inventory and is one of the measures of the efficiency with which the firm manages its inventory.

underinsured motorist insurance Insurance coverage that covers the insured when involved in an accident with a driver who is underinsured. Coverage for bodily injury above the amounts of insurance carried by the underinsured driver.

underwriter An insurance company employee who determines the risk factors involved in the occurrence of various insurable losses. This helps determine the insurance premium.

unearned interest The amount of interest not owed when a loan is paid off early.

unemployment insurance tax A tax paid by employers. The money is used to pay unemployment benefits to qualified unemployed workers.

uniform product codes (UPC) Bar codes found on each product in most stores; used for efficient inventory control by stores. It also provides greater accuracy and perhaps faster service to the customer.

uninsured motorist insurance Insurance coverage that covers the insured when involved in an accident with a driver who is not insured.

unit price The cost of each unit on an invoice.

units-of-production method A depreciation method using the units produced to determine depreciation allowance.

units shipped The number of units shipped.

United States Rule A method of handling partial loan pay-offs; any payment is first applied to the interest owed on the loan, with any balance then used to reduce the principal amount of the loan.

universal life insurance Allows the insured to vary the amount of premium and type of protection depending on changing insurance needs.

unlike fractions Fractions having different denominators.

unpaid balance The balance outstanding on a revolving charge account at the end of a billing period.

unpaid balance method A method of calculating the finance charge on a revolving charge account by using the balance at the end of the previous month.

unsaleable items Merchandise that cannot be sold. Usually considered when calculating markup.

useful life The estimated life of an asset. The IRS gives guidelines of useful life for depreciation purposes.

U.S. Treasury bills A loan of money to the United States government. Treasury bills (or T-bills) are a very safe way to invest money.

variability The spread in the values in a set of data. For example, the height of students in a sixth grade class has variability (or variation) since not all students are the same height.

variable A letter that represents a number.

variable commission A rate of commission that depends on the total amount of the sales, with the rate increasing as sales increase.

variable life insurance Provides life insurance protection and allows the insured to select investment funds to invest the balance of the premium.

variable interest rate loan A home loan made at an interest rate that varies with market conditions.

variance The square of the standard deviation.

vertical analysis The process of listing each of the important items on an income statement as a percent of total net sales or each item on a balance sheet as a percent of total assets.

virtual bank A virtual bank is one that can be accessed over the Internet but may not have a lobby that a customer can walk into to make a transaction.

Visa A credit-card plan.

W–2 form The wage and tax statement given to the employee each year by the employer.

wage bracket method of withholding Used to determine federal withholding tax. This method requires several pages of tables.

waiver of premium clause Allows insurance to continue without payment of premium when the insured becomes disabled.

weighted-average method Inventory valuation method where the cost of all purchases during a time period is divided by the number of units purchased.

weighted mean A mean calculated by using weights so that each number is multiplied by its frequency.

whole-life insurance (ordinary or straight life insurance) A form of life insurance in which the insured pays a constant premium until death or retirement, whichever occurs sooner. Upon retirement, monthly payments are made by the company to the insured until the death of the insured.

wholesaler The middleman; purchases from manufacturers or other wholesalers and sells to retailers.

wire transfer The instant electronic transfer of funds from one account to another.

withholding allowances These allowances, for employees, their spouses, and dependents, determine the amount of withholding tax taken from gross earnings.

worker's compensation insurance Insurance that provides payments to an employee who is unable to work due to a job-related injury or illness.

x-axis The horizontal axis, used for the *independent variable*.

y-axis The vertical axis, used for the *dependent variable*.

y-intercept The point at which the line intersects the *y-axis*.

youthful operator A driver of a motor vehicle under a certain age, usually 25 years of age or younger.

zero-coupon bond A bond that does not pay annual interest, rather it only pays the face value of the bond at maturity.

Index